# FOOTBALL CARD

## PRICE GUIDE
### 1994

W0007445

*Other* **CONFIDENT COLLECTOR** *Titles*
*by Allan Kaye and Michael McKeever*
*from Avon Books*

BASEBALL CARD PRICE GUIDE 1994

*Coming Soon*

BASKETBALL CARD PRICE GUIDE 1994
HOCKEY CARD PRICE GUIDE 1994

# FOOTBALL CARD

## PRICE GUIDE
## 1994

## ALLAN KAYE
### AND
## MICHAEL McKEEVER

*The* CONFIDENT COLLECTOR™

AVON BOOKS ◆ NEW YORK

THE CONFIDENT COLLECTOR: FOOTBALL CARD PRICE GUIDE (1994) is an original publication of Avon Books. This work has never before appeared in book form.

AVON BOOKS
A division of
The Hearst Corporation
1350 Avenue of the Americas
New York, New York 10019

Copyright © 1993 by Michael McKeever
Cover art: Clifford Spohn
*The Confident Collector* and its logo are trademarked properties of Avon Books.
Published by arrangement with the author
Library of Congress Catalog Card Number: 93-90224
ISBN: 0-380-77237-X

First Avon Books Printing: September 1993

AVON TRADEMARK REG. U.S. PAT. OFF. AND IN OTHER COUNTRIES, MARCA REGISTRADA, HECHO EN U.S.A.

Printed in the U.S.A.

OPM 10 9 8 7 6 5 4 3 2 1

**Important Notice:** All of the information, including valuations, in this book has been compiled from the most reliable sources, and every effort has been made to eliminate errors and questionable data. Nevertheless, the possibility of error always exists in a work of such immense scope. The publisher and the author will not be held responsible for losses which may occur in the purchase, sale, or other transaction of property because of information contained herein. Readers who feel they have discovered errors are invited to *write* the authors in care of Avon Books, so that the errors may be corrected in subsequent editions.

# TABLE OF CONTENTS

# Acknowledgements

This book would not have been possible without the contributions of dozens of people whose imput and expertise in the areas of card evaluations, research and technical support have significantly enhanced this edition. We sincerely appreciate their efforts and want to thank each of them for their time, dedication and hard work.

Betty and Jonathan Abraham, Cape Coral Cards; Darren Adams, West Coast SportsCards; Michael Balser, Classic Games; Bill Baron, NFL Properties; Bill Boake, Hall Of Fame Cards; Tim Boyle, Lesnik Public Relations; Rich Bradley, The Upper Deck Company; Scott Bradshaw, Centerfield; John Brenner; Joie Casey, Field Of Dreams; Ken Cicalo, Vivid Graphics; Lou Costanza, Champion Sports; Mike Cramer; Pacific Trading Cards; Dick DeCourcy; Georgia Music & Sports; Larry Dluhy, Sports Collectibles of Houston; Doug Drotman, National Media Group; Chris Eberheart; Joe Esposito, B & E Collectibles; Eddie Fisher, Batter's Box; Larry Fritsch, Larry Fritsch Cards; Richard Galasso, Home Plate Collectibles; Steve Galletta, Touchdown Cards; Tony Galovich, American Card Exchange; Richard Gelman, Card Collector's Company; Dawn Marie Giargiari, Graphic Designer; Selina Gonzalez George, Pro Set; Dick Gilkeson; Bill Goepner, San Diego Sports Collectibles; Laurie Goldstein, Action Packed; Dean Golombeski, Score; David Greenhill, New York Card Company; Wayne Grove, First Base Sports Nostalgia; Bill Goodwin, St. Louis Baseball Cards; Walter Hall, Hall's Nostalgia; Eric Handler, Lapin Public Relations; Don Harrison, The Tenth Inning; Bill Henderson (King Of The Commons); Eric Herskind, Pro Set; Neil Hoppenworth; Peter Hughes, NFL Properties; Bob Ibach, Lesnik Public Relations; Toby Johnson; Donn Jennings, Donn Jennings Cards; Bill Karaman; Bill Kennedy, No Gum Just Cards; Tim Kilbane, Ron Klasnick, JW International; Rick Kohl, The Strike Zone; David Kohler, SportsCards Plus; Chuck LaPaglia, The SportsCard Report Radio Show; Don Lepore; Alan Lewis, Collectors Edge; Lew Lipset; Kay Longmire, O-Pee-Chee of Canada; Greg Manning; Jane McKeever; Katherine McKeever; Jim Mayfield; Blake Meyer, Lone Star SportsCards; Chuck Miller; The SportsCard Report Radio Show; Mike Miller; Dick Millerd; Richard Morris; Steve Myland; Vince Nauss, Leaf/Donruss; Donovan Niemi; Joe Pasternack, Card Collectors Company; Frank and Steve Pemper, Ball Four Cards; Jack and Patti Petruzzelli, 59 Innings; Warren Power; Andy Rapoza; Peter Reeves (Our computer guru); Gavin Riley; Alan "Mr. Mint" Rosen; Steve Rotman, Rotman Productions; Murray Rubenfeld, The SportsCard Report Radio Show; Robert Rusnak; Ben Runyan; Kevin Savage; The Sports Gallery; Duke and Smokey Scheinman, Smokey's Baseball Cards; Michelle Serrio; Ira H. Silverman, Silverman, Warren/Kremer, Inc. Eric Slutsky, Edelman Public Relations Worldwide; Nigel Spill, Oldies And Goodies; Jim Stevens; Ted Taylor; Fleer Corp.; Bud Tompkins, Minnesota Connection; Joe Valle, Cardboard Dreams; Eddie Vidal; Tom Wall; Virginia Webster; Bill Wesslund, Portland SportsCards; Chris Widmaier, Silverman, Warren/Kremer, Inc. Katherine Wilkins, Del Mar Broadcasting and Publishing; Dean Winskill, Argyle SportsCards; Matt Wozniak, Julie Yolles, Star Pics; and Kit Young. We especially want to thank our Editor, Dorothy Harris and all of the staff at Avon Books.

# Introduction

Over the past several years football card collecting has surged in popularity and footballl card prices have soared in value. When we first started collecting cards there was only one company, Topps. When we published our first hobby magazine there were only three card companies, Donruss, Fleer and Topps. Today more than a dozen companies manufacture cards on a annual basis and collecting has grown from a passive, fun-filled hobby to a huge industry with investment grade cards selling for hundreds, even thousands of dollars.

The purpose of this edition is to provide you with an accurate, up-to-date listing of football card values. These prices don't reflect our opinions but are the result of extensive research throughout the marketplace. The prices listed in this volume are actual retail prices obtained by monitoring retail sports card shops, card shows, memorabilia conventions and auctions, hobby publications and mail order catalogues. The card values were then entered in the book just prior to the press run.

We have also tried to make this edition as easy to use as possible. Since rookie cards are among the most popular in the hobby, and are usually a player's most valuable card, we've provided rookie card designations for thousands of players. Look for the (R) symbol next to the player's name.

Since bonus cards and limited edition inserts are among the hottest cards in the hobby we have provided a checklist and values for these special cards following the regular checklist for the set in which they were issued.

Finally, we have provided a complete card grading and conditioning guide to help you analyze the condition of your collection and a glossary with definitions to help you better understand the terminology of the hobby.

Over the past decade card collecting and sports memorabilia has grown from a cottage industry to a $5 billion a year business. It is estimated that 20 million people actively participate in what has become the most popular hobby in America. We sincerely hope this edition will enhance your enjoyment of the hobby and will serve as your official reference guide to the exciting world of football cards.

# Glossary Of Terms

**AFC-**American Football Conference

**AFL-**American Football League

**AP-** All-Pro. Cards with the AP designation are usually part of a subset and mean the player was chosen for his league's All-Star team the previous year.

**AW-**Award Winners. Cards that are usually part of a subset that honors a player's achievements from the previous season.

**BC-**Bonus card. Cards that are not part of a regular set but are often issued in conjunction with the set. Bonus cards are often issued in limited quantities and randomly inserted into selected wax or foil packs.

**CL-**Checklist. Cards that contain a numerical list of all the cards in a set.

**Commons-**Applies to the typical card in a set. A card that is not in demand. Most cards in any particular set are commons and have no significant value above the listing for all the common cards in a set.

**COR-**A card that's been reissued with corrections after an error was discovered on the original.

**DP-**Draft Pick

**DT-**Dream Team. The title of a popular subset produced by Score.

**ER-**Error Card. Signifies that an error exists on a baseball card. Covers such mistakes as misspelling, erroneous statistics or biographical information, wrong photograph or other graphics. The card has no significant value unless a corrected card is issued creating a variation. (See Variation)

**HL-**Highlight Cards. These cards appear in various sets, primarily Topps, as part of subsets that depict selected players who are honored for special achievements.

**HOF-**Hall of Famer.

**IA-**In-Action Cards. Usually appears as part of a subset and features an action photo of a player that differs from the player's regular card in the set.

**INSERT-**A card that's not part of a regular edition but usually produced in conjunction with that issue. Some insert cards are produced in limited quantities and packed randomly in wax or foil backs.

**IR**-Instant Replay. Cards that are usually part of a subset depciting a player in a game-action situation on a card other that his regular card in the set.

**LL**-League Leaders. A card in a subset that depicts leaders in various passing, rushing, receiving, scoring, and kicking and categories from the previous year.

**MVP**-Most Valuable Player.

**NFC**-National Football Conference

**PB**-Pro Bowl. Usually part of a subset that honors players who made the annual NFL Pro Bowl the previous season.

**PV**-Pro Visions. A popular subset produced by Fleer

**R**-Rookie Card. Indicates the player's first appearance on a card in a regular annual baseball card set, including update, traded and rookie sets. Rookie cards are usually a player's most valuable card.

**RB**-Record Breaker. A card that's usually part of a subset that honors a player for a particular milestone or record set the previous season.

**ROY**-Rookie Of The Year.

**SB**-Super Bowl. Cards that depict players or action scenes from the previous years Super Bowl.

**SP**- Short Print. These cards were under-produced and available in lesser quantities than other cards in the same set.

**SR**-Star Rookies. A popular subset produced by Upper Deck.

**TL**-Team Leaders. The name of a popular subset or insert set.

**USFL**-United States Football League

**VAR**-Variations. This symbol means that at least two versions of the same card exist. This usually happens when an error card is corrected in future print runs and then put in circulation by the card company.

**WLAF**-World League of American Football

# Grading And Conditioning Guide

All prices quoted in this edition are retail prices, the price the card would sell for in established sports card stores. Buy prices, the price the dealer would pay for a card, range from about one-third of the price listed for common cards to one-half or more for higher valued cards. Regional interest and other factors may cause the value of a card to vary from one part of the country to another.

The values appearing in this edition are intended only to serve as an aid in evaluating your cards. They are not a solicitation to buy or sell on the part of the publisher or any other party.

**Mint (MT)**: A perfect card. Well-centered, with equal borders. Four sharp, square corners. No nicks, creases, scratches, yellowing or fading. The printing must be flawless. No miscut cards or out of register photo's. Cards with gum or wax stains cannot be considered truly mint, even when removed from brand new packs.

**Near Mint (NR MT)**: A nearly perfect card that contains a minor flaw upon close inspection. Must be well-centered and three of the four corners must be perfectly sharp. A slightly off-centered card with four perfect corners would fit this grade. No creases, scratches, yellowing or fading. Card is valued at 50% to 60% of a mint card depending on the scarcity of the card and the demand for the player.

**Excellent (EX)**: Moderate wear, corners still fairly sharp. Card borders might be off-center. No creases, scratches, gum or wax stains on front or back. Surface may show some lack of luster. Card is valued at 40% of mint.

**Very Good (VG)**: Corners rounded or showing minor wear or light creases. Loss of surface luster. All printing must be perfect. No gum or wax stains, no major creases, no writing or markings on the card. Card is valued at 30% to 40% of mint.

**Good (G)**: A well-worn card with rounded corners and a major crease. Could have a small tear, pencil, tape or glue marks on the back. Printing must be intact, but overall, the card shows excessive wear. Card is valued at 20% to 30% of mint.

**Fair (F)**: Card shows major damage such as creases that break the cardboard or pin holes along the border. Shows tape and glue marks. May have a tear or missing a bit of paper. Could have writing or other markings on the back. Card has very little value, less than 10% of mint.

**Poor (P)**: Card fronts have been defaced with pen and ink marks. Corners may be torn off or paper may be missing or ripped-off. Card may have pin holes, glue and tape marks and major cracks through the cardboard. Cards have little or no value, less than 10% of the good (G) value.

# O. J. Simpson Remembers

O. J. Simpson is a former Heisman Trophy winner and a Pro Football Hall of Famer. He was the first NFL running back to rush for more than 2,000 yards in a season and he remains a popular figure throughout the hobby.

In this exclusive interview Simpson talks about the hobby and recalls some highlights from his illustrious career.

**Q. Your 1970 rookie Topps card is priced in the $175 range. Are you surprised at its value?**

A. Yes I am. I'm shocked really at what's been happening to card collecting overall, not just football. I'm surprised that collectors put so much value into a little picture on a piece of cardboard. I remember my rookie card mainly because they had a tradition in Buffalo, when you made the team, after the final cut, the veterans would shave the heads of all the rookies. That's when Topps came by to take my picture. I was bald headed at the time and I didn't like the way I looked on that card. I'm still not too crazy about it.

**Q. Did you collect cards as a kid and did you save any of your own memorabilia from your playing days?**

A. I was a big collector of baseball cards when I was a kid. We're talking in the 1950's and 60's. My mother probably has a box of those cards stored away somewhere and they're probably worth some money today. As far as my own memorabilia is concerned, I've saved some jerseys and a couple of footballs from special occasions. I still have my jersey from the 1973 season when I rushed for 2,003 yards. I have autographs of all the members of my offensive line on it.

**Q. You were the first NFL running back to break the 2,000 yard barrier in a season. Was that your biggest thrill?**

A. Actually my biggest thrill came in college at USC when we beat UCLA and won the National Championship in 1967. I had a big fourth quarter touchdown run that cinched it. I've had a lot of thrills in football but nothing compares to a championship. Unfortunately, in Buffalo, we never won a championship so that was a disappointment. But going over 2,000 yards was exciting because I knew that no matter what happened, I would be remembered as the first guy who's ever done it. But all records are not monuments, they're great to have, but you know most of them will be broken.

**Q. Where does the Heisman Trophy rank on your list of achievements?**

A. It definately ranks at the top. I mean, it's a special award. It only goes to one player each year. Winning it puts you in a select group of players. I think there's

more pressure on the front runners today than in my day. Winning it can add a million dollars to a player's (pro) contract. Back then I didn't set out to win the Heisman Trophy. You
did the best you could game by game, then if you were still in the running as the season wound down there was a little added pressure. But media coverage of the candidates is much bigger today. The ceremony has its own television show. It's become a big event and I'm glad to be a part of it.

**Q. Your duties with NBC Sports and The NFL Today allow you to stay close to the game. Which running backs impress you the most?**

A. The guy down in Dallas, Emmitt Smith is a great running back on a great team. He has the ability to rush for 2,000 yards. Barry Sanders in Detroit is another good one. The Lions beefed up their offensive line which should help him. Barry Foster in Pittsburgh has some great moves and instincts. He could be a good one. Thurman Thomas in Buffalo may be the best all around back in football. He's a great receiver too, but he doesn't get as many rushing attempts as the others. The kid down at San Diego State, Marshall Falk, could be the next great running back if he stays healty. He's got the natural ability to become a franchise player.

**Q. You don't attend many card shows, so how do you feel about signing autographs?**

A. I've attended the Super Bowl Card Show and I've gone to the National Sports Collectors Conventions a few times. Last winter I did a show in Buffalo, but my businesses and my work with NBC keep me pretty busy. I get stopped for autographs all the time and I don't mind signing. When I was a kid I remember what it was like to be a fan. I was a fan before I became a football player.

# ACTION PACKED

## 1989 Action Packed Test Set

This 30-card set is the first ever issued by Action Packed and was designed to test-market the Action Packed concept. The cards feature embossed four-color action photos on the card fronts framed by gold borders. The horizontal card backs contain a small head shot, an Action Note and a block for an autograph. The set included 10 players each from the Chicago Bears, New York Giants and Washington Redskins.

|  |  | MINT | NR/MT |
|---|---|---|---|
| **Complete Set (30)** | | 28.00 | 18.00 |
| **Commons** | | .50 | .35 |
| | | | |
| 1 | Neal Anderson | 3.00 | 2.00 |
| 2 | Trace Armstrong | .60 | .45 |
| 3 | Kevin Butler | .50 | .35 |
| 4 | Richard Dent | .70 | .50 |
| 5 | Dennis Gentry | .50 | .35 |
| 6 | Dan Hampton (Er) (Wrong Number) | 1.00 | .70 |
| 7 | Jay Hilgenberg | .60 | .45 |
| 8 | Thomas Sanders | .50 | .35 |
| 9 | Mike Singletary | 1.00 | .70 |
| 10 | Mike Tomczak | .60 | .45 |
| 11 | Raul Allegre | .50 | .35 |
| 12 | Ottis Anderson | .80 | .60 |
| 13 | Mark Bavaro | .60 | .45 |
| 14 | Terry Kinard | .50 | .35 |
| 15 | Lionel Manuel | .50 | .35 |
| 16 | Leonard Marshall | .50 | .35 |
| 17 | Dave Meggett | 3.00 | 2.00 |
| 18 | Joe Morris | .60 | .45 |
| 19 | Phil Simms | 1.00 | .70 |
| 20 | Lawrence Taylor | 3.00 | 2.00 |
| 21 | Kelvin Bryant | .60 | .35 |
| 22 | Darrell Green | 1.75 | 1.00 |
| 23 | Dexter Manley | .50 | .35 |
| 24 | Charles Mann | .50 | .35 |
| 25 | Wilbur Marshall | .75 | .55 |
| 26 | Art Monk | 2.50 | 1.50 |
| 27 | Jamie Morris | .50 | .35 |
| 28 | Tracy Rocker | .50 | .35 |
| 29 | Mark Rypien | 10.00 | 7.50 |
| 30 | Ricky Sanders | 1.25 | .80 |

## 1990 Action Packed

This 280-card set is Action Packed's premier edition and is similar to 1989's test set. The cards measure 2-1/2" by 3-1/2" and feature embossed four-color photos on the card fronts and horizontal card backs with a small head shot, an Action Note and a block for an autograph at the bottom. Ten players from each team are included in the set and teams are listed alphabetically in the checklist. A special braille card, featuring Jim Plunkett, was issued as a limited edition insert and is listed at the end of this checklist.

|  | MINT | NR/MT |
|---|---|---|
| **Complete Set (280)** | 70.00 | 48.00 |
| **Commons** | .25 | .15 |

| # | Player | | | # | Player | | |
|---|--------|------|------|-----|--------|------|------|
| 1 | Aundray Bruce | .30 | .18 | 58 | Paul Palmer | .25 | .15 |
| 2 | Scott Case | .25 | .15 | 59 | Everson Walls | .25 | .15 |
| 3 | Tony Casillas | .35 | .20 | 60 | Steve Walsh | .35 | .20 |
| 4 | Shawn Collins | .25 | .15 | 61 | Steve Atwater | .60 | .35 |
| 5 | Marcus Cotton | .25 | .15 | 62 | Tyrone Braxton | .25 | .15 |
| 6 | Bill Fralic | .25 | .15 | 63 | John Elway | 1.25 | .80 |
| 7 | Tim Green | .25 | .15 | 64 | Bobby Humphrey | .70 | .40 |
| 8 | Chris Miller | 1.25 | .80 | 65 | Mark Jackson | .25 | .15 |
| 9 | Deion Sanders | 1.75 | 1.00 | 66 | Vance Johnson | .30 | .18 |
| 10 | John Settle | .25 | .15 | 67 | Greg Kragen | .25 | .15 |
| 11 | Cornelius Bennett | .50 | .35 | 68 | Karl Mecklenburg | .50 | .30 |
| 12 | Shane Conlan | .30 | .18 | 69 | Dennis Smith | .25 | .15 |
| 13 | Kent Hill | .25 | .15 | 70 | David Treadwell | .25 | .15 |
| 14 | Jim Kelly | 2.50 | 1.50 | 71 | Jim Arnold | .25 | .15 |
| 15 | Mark Kelso | .25 | .15 | 72 | Jerry Ball | .25 | .15 |
| 16 | Scott Norwood | .25 | .15 | 73 | Bennie Blades | .40 | .25 |
| 17 | Andre Reed | .80 | .50 | 74 | Mel Gray | .30 | .18 |
| 18 | Fred Smerlas | .25 | .15 | 75 | Richard Johnson | .25 | .15 |
| 19 | Bruce Smith | .60 | .35 | 76 | Eddie Murray | .25 | .15 |
| 20 | Thurman Thomas | 3.00 | 2.00 | 77 | Rodney Peete | .60 | .35 |
| 21 | Neal Anderson | .70 | .40 | 78 | Barry Sanders | 5.00 | 3.50 |
| 22 | Kevin Butler | .25 | .15 | 79 | Chris Spielman | .30 | .18 |
| 23 | Richard Dent | .30 | .18 | 80 | Walter Stanley | .25 | .15 |
| 24 | Dennis Gentry | .25 | .15 | 81 | Dave Brown | .25 | .15 |
| 25 | Dan Hampton | .40 | .25 | 82 | Brent Fullwood | .25 | .15 |
| 26 | Jay Hilgenberg | .30 | .18 | 83 | Tim Harris | .35 | .20 |
| 27 | Steve McMichael | .25 | .15 | 84 | Johnny Holland | .25 | .15 |
| 28 | Brad Muster | .30 | .18 | 85 | Don Majkowski | .60 | .35 |
| 29 | Mike Singletary | .60 | .35 | 86 | Tony Mandarich | .25 | .15 |
| 30 | Mike Tomczak | .25 | .15 | 87 | Mark Murphy | .25 | .15 |
| 31 | James Brooks | .35 | .20 | 88 | Brian Noble | .25 | .15 |
| 32 | Rickey Dixon (R) | .60 | .35 | 89 | Ken Ruettgers | .25 | .15 |
| 33 | Boomer Esiason | .70 | .40 | 90 | Sterling Sharpe | 1.75 | 1.00 |
| 34 | Dave Fulcher | .25 | .15 | 91 | Ray Childress | .35 | .20 |
| 35 | Rodney Holman | .30 | .18 | 92 | Ernest Givins | .60 | .35 |
| 36 | Tim Krumrie | .25 | .15 | 93 | Alonzo Highsmith | .25 | .15 |
| 37 | Tim McGee | .25 | .15 | 94 | Drew Hill | .35 | .20 |
| 38 | Anthony Munoz | .50 | .35 | 95 | Bruce Matthews | .25 | .15 |
| 39 | Reggie Williams | .25 | .15 | 96 | Bubba McDowell | .35 | .20 |
| 40 | Ickey Woods | .30 | .19 | 97 | Warren Moon | 1.50 | .90 |
| 41 | Thane Gash (R) | .50 | .30 | 98 | Mike Munchak | .25 | .15 |
| 42 | Mike Johnson | .25 | .15 | 99 | Allen Pinkett | .25 | .15 |
| 43 | Bernie Kosar | .75 | .45 | 100 | Mike Rozier | .30 | .18 |
| 44 | Reggie Langhorne | .25 | .15 | 101 | Albert Bentley | .25 | .15 |
| 45 | Clay Matthews | .25 | .15 | 102 | Duane Buckett | .25 | .15 |
| 46 | Eric Metcalf | .75 | .45 | 103 | Bill Brooks | .25 | .15 |
| 47 | Frank Minnifield | .25 | .15 | 104 | Chris Chandler | .25 | .15 |
| 48 | Ozzie Newsome | .60 | .35 | 105 | Ray Donaldson | .25 | .15 |
| 49 | Webster Slaughter | .25 | .15 | 106 | Chris Hinton | .30 | .18 |
| 50 | Felix Wright | .25 | .15 | 107 | Andre Rison | 1.25 | .80 |
| 51 | Troy Aikman | 5.00 | 3.50 | 108 | Keith Taylor | .25 | .15 |
| 52 | James Dixon (R) | .35 | .20 | 109 | Clarence Verdin | .30 | .18 |
| 53 | Michael Irvin | 2.50 | 1.50 | 110 | Fredd Young | .25 | .15 |
| 54 | Jim Jeffcoat | .25 | .15 | 111 | Deron Cherry | .30 | .18 |
| 55 | Ed Too Tall Jones | .50 | .30 | 112 | Steve DeBerg | .35 | .20 |
| 56 | Eugene Lockhart | .25 | .15 | 113 | Dino Hackett | .25 | .15 |
| 57 | Danny Noonan | .25 | .15 | 114 | Albert Lewis | .25 | .15 |

| # | Player | | |
|---|--------|------|------|
| 115 | Nick Lowery | .35 | .20 |
| 116 | Christian Okoye | .70 | .40 |
| 117 | Stephane Paige | .30 | .18 |
| 118 | Kevin Ross | .25 | .15 |
| 119 | Derrick Thomas | 1.75 | 1.00 |
| 120 | Mike Webster | .35 | .20 |
| 121 | Marcus Allen | .70 | .35 |
| 122 | Eddie Anderson | .25 | .15 |
| 123 | Steve Beuerlein | .60 | .35 |
| 124 | Tim Brown | .50 | .30 |
| 125 | Mervyn Fernandez | .35 | .20 |
| 126 | Willie Gault | .30 | .18 |
| 127 | Bob Golic | .25 | .15 |
| 128 | Bo Jackson | 1.25 | .80 |
| 129 | Howie Long | .35 | .20 |
| 130 | Greg Townsend | .30 | .18 |
| 131 | Flipper Anderson | .60 | .35 |
| 132 | Greg Bell | .25 | .15 |
| 133 | Robert Delpino | .35 | .20 |
| 134 | Henry Ellard | .30 | .18 |
| 135 | Jim Everett | 1.00 | .70 |
| 136 | Jerry Gray | .25 | .15 |
| 137 | Kevin Greene | .30 | .18 |
| 138 | Tom Newberry | .25 | .15 |
| 139 | Jackie Slater | .30 | .18 |
| 140 | Doug Smith | .25 | .15 |
| 141 | Mark Clayton | .50 | .30 |
| 142 | Jeff Cross | .25 | .15 |
| 143 | Mark Duper | .35 | .20 |
| 144 | Ferrell Edmunds | .25 | .15 |
| 145 | Jim Jenson | .25 | .15 |
| 146 | Dan Marino | 2.00 | 1.25 |
| 147 | John Offerdahl | .40 | .25 |
| 148 | Louis Oliver | .35 | .20 |
| 149 | Reggie Roby | .25 | .15 |
| 150 | Sammie Smith | .50 | .35 |
| 151 | Joey Browner | .30 | .18 |
| 152 | Anthony Carter | .60 | .35 |
| 153 | Chris Doleman | .40 | .25 |
| 154 | Steve Jordan | .25 | .15 |
| 155 | Carl Lee | .25 | .15 |
| 156 | Randall McDaniel | .25 | .15 |
| 157 | Keith Millard | .35 | .20 |
| 158 | Herschel Walker | .80 | .50 |
| 159 | Wade Wilson | .30 | .18 |
| 160 | Gary Zimmerman | .25 | .15 |
| 161 | Hart Lee Dykes | .25 | .15 |
| 162 | Irving Fryar | .35 | .20 |
| 163 | Steve Grogan | .40 | .25 |
| 164 | Maurice Hurst | .25 | .15 |
| 165 | Fred Marion | .25 | .15 |
| 166 | Stanley Morgan | .50 | .35 |
| 167 | Robert Perryman | .25 | .15 |
| 168 | John Stephens | .35 | .20 |
| 169 | Andre Tippett | .40 | .25 |
| 170 | Brent Williams | .25 | .15 |
| 171 | John Fourcade | .35 | .20 |
| 172 | Bobby Hebert | .40 | .25 |
| 173 | Dalton Hilliard | .40 | .25 |
| 174 | Rickey Jackson | .35 | .20 |
| 175 | Vaughan Johnson | .30 | .18 |
| 176 | Eric Martin | .30 | .18 |
| 177 | Robert Massey | .25 | .15 |
| 178 | Rueben Mayes | .25 | .15 |
| 179 | Sam Mills | .35 | .20 |
| 180 | Pat Swilling | .50 | .30 |
| 181 | Ottis Anderson | .40 | .25 |
| 182 | Carl Banks | .30 | .18 |
| 183 | Mark Bavaro | .30 | .18 |
| 184 | Mark Collins | .25 | .15 |
| 185 | Leonard Marshall | .25 | .15 |
| 186 | Dave Meggett | .75 | .45 |
| 187 | Gary Reasons | .25 | .15 |
| 188 | Phil Simms | .70 | .40 |
| 189 | Lawrence Taylor | 1.25 | .80 |
| 190 | Odessa Turner | .50 | .35 |
| 191 | Kyle Clifton | .25 | .15 |
| 192 | James Hasty | .25 | .15 |
| 193 | Johnny Hector | .25 | .15 |
| 194 | Jeff Lageman | .25 | .15 |
| 195 | Pat Leahy | .25 | .15 |
| 196 | Erik McMillan | .30 | .18 |
| 197 | Ken O'Brien | .35 | .20 |
| 198 | Mickey Shuler | .25 | .15 |
| 199 | Al Toon | .40 | .25 |
| 200 | Jo Jo Townsell | .25 | .15 |
| 201 | Eric Allen | .25 | .15 |
| 202 | Jerome Brown | .30 | .18 |
| 203 | Keith Byars | .30 | .18 |
| 204 | Cris Carter | .50 | .30 |
| 205 | Wes Hopkins | .25 | .15 |
| 206 | Keith Jackson | .75 | .45 |
| 207 | Seth Joyner | .30 | .18 |
| 208 | Mike Quick | .25 | .15 |
| 209 | Andre Waters | .25 | .15 |
| 210 | Reggie White | .75 | .45 |
| 211 | Rich Camarillo | .25 | .15 |
| 212 | Roy Green | .30 | .18 |
| 213 | Ken Harvey (R) | .35 | .20 |
| 214 | Gary Hogeboom | .25 | .15 |
| 215 | Tim McDonald | .25 | .15 |
| 216 | Stump Mitchell | .25 | .15 |
| 217 | Luis Sharpe | .25 | .15 |
| 218 | Val Sikahema | .25 | .15 |
| 219 | J.T. Smith | .25 | .15 |
| 220 | Ron Wolfley | .25 | .15 |
| 221 | Gary Anderson | .25 | .15 |
| 222 | Bubby Brister | .50 | .30 |
| 223 | Merril Hoge | .25 | .15 |
| 224 | Tunch Ilkin | .25 | .15 |
| 225 | Louis Lipps | .30 | .18 |
| 226 | David Little | .25 | .15 |
| 227 | Greg Lloyd | .25 | .15 |
| 228 | Dwayne Woodruff | .25 | .15 |

| 229 | Rod Woodson | .50 | .30 |
| 230 | Tim Worley | .35 | .20 |
| 231 | Marion Butts | .75 | .45 |
| 232 | Gil Byrd | .25 | .15 |
| 233 | Burt Grossman | .30 | .18 |
| 234 | Jim McMahon | .40 | .25 |
| 235 | Anthony Miller | .60 | .35 |
| 236 | Leslie O'Neal | .30 | .18 |
| 237 | Gary Plummer | .25 | .15 |
| 238 | Billy Ray Smith | .25 | .15 |
| 239 | Tim Spencer | .25 | .15 |
| 240 | Lee Williams | .25 | .15 |
| 241 | Mike Cofer | .25 | .15 |
| 242 | Roger Craig | .50 | .30 |
| 243 | Charles Haley | .30 | .18 |
| 244 | Ronnie Lott | .75 | .45 |
| 245 | Guy McIntyre | .25 | .15 |
| 246 | Joe Montana | 2.50 | 1.50 |
| 247 | Tom Rathman | .30 | .18 |
| 248 | Jerry Rice | 2.00 | 1.25 |
| 249 | John Taylor | .75 | .45 |
| 250 | Michael Walter | .25 | .15 |
| 251 | Brian Blades | .40 | .25 |
| 252 | Jacob Green | .25 | .15 |
| 253 | Dave Krieg | .50 | .30 |
| 254 | Steve Largent | 1.00 | .70 |
| 255 | Joe Nash | .25 | .15 |
| 256 | Rufus Porter | .25 | .15 |
| 257 | Eugene Robinson | .25 | .15 |
| 258 | Paul Skansi (R) | .25 | .15 |
| 259 | Curt Warner | .25 | .15 |
| 260 | John L. Williams | .35 | .20 |
| 261 | Mark Carrier (Bucs) | .50 | .30 |
| 262 | Reuben Davis | .25 | .15 |
| 263 | Harry Hamilton | .25 | .15 |
| 264 | Bruce Hill | .25 | .15 |
| 265 | Donald Igwebuike | .25 | .15 |
| 266 | Eugene Marve | .25 | .15 |
| 267 | Kevin Murphy | .25 | .15 |
| 268 | Mark Robinson | .25 | .15 |
| 269 | Lars Tate | .25 | .15 |
| 270 | Vinny Testaverde | .40 | .25 |
| 271 | Gary Clark | .75 | .45 |
| 272 | Monte Coleman | .25 | .15 |
| 273 | Darrell Green | .50 | .30 |
| 274 | Charles Mann | .25 | .15 |
| 275 | Wilber Marshall | .35 | .20 |
| 276 | Art Monk | 1.25 | .80 |
| 277 | Gerald Riggs | .30 | .18 |
| 278 | Mark Rypien | 1.75 | 1.00 |
| 279 | Ricky Sanders | .30 | .18 |
| 280 | Alvin Walton | .25 | .15 |
| xx | Jim Plunkett(Braille) | 12.00 | 8.00 |

# 1990 Action Packed Rookies

This 84-card set marks Action Packed's first update set and features prominent rookies from the 1990 NFL draft, traded players, and a few stars who were not included in the regular edition. Cards measure 2-1/2" by 3-1/2" and are similar in design to the regular set.

| | | MINT | NR/MT |
| --- | --- | --- | --- |
| Complete Set (84) | | 38.00 | 28.00 |
| Commons | | .25 | .15 |

| 1 | Jeff George (R) | 6.00 | 4.50 |
| --- | --- | --- | --- |
| 2 | Richmond Webb (R) | .60 | .35 |
| 3 | James Williams (R) | .25 | .15 |
| 4 | Tony Bennett (R) | .50 | .30 |
| 5 | Darrell Thompson (R) | .70 | .40 |
| 6 | Steve Broussard (R) | .75 | .45 |
| 7 | Rodney Hampton (R) | 3.00 | 2.00 |
| 8 | Rob Moore (R) | 2.00 | 1.25 |
| 9 | Alton Montgomery (R) | .25 | .15 |
| 10 | LeRoy Butler (R) | .25 | .15 |
| 11 | Anthony Johnson (R) | .30 | .18 |
| 12 | Scott Mitchell (R) | .30 | .18 |
| 13 | Mike Fox (R) | .30 | .18 |
| 14 | Robert Blackmon (R) | .30 | .18 |
| 15 | Blair Thomas (R) | 1.50 | .90 |
| 16 | Tony Stargell (R) | .30 | .18 |
| 17 | Peter Tom Willis (R) | .75 | .45 |
| 18 | Harold Green (R) | 1.75 | 1.00 |
| 19 | Bernard Clark (R) | .25 | .15 |
| 20 | Aaron Wallace (R) | .35 | .20 |
| 21 | Dennis Brown (R) | .25 | .15 |
| 22 | Johnny Johnson (R) | 3.00 | 2.00 |
| 23 | Chris Calloway (R) | .30 | .18 |
| 24 | Walter Wilson (R) | .25 | .15 |
| 25 | Dexter Carter (R) | .90 | .60 |

| | | | |
|---|---|---|---|
| 26 | Percy Snow (R) | .75 | .45 |
| 27 | Johnny Bailey (R) | .60 | .35 |
| 28 | Mike Bellamy (R) | .30 | .18 |
| 29 | Ben Smith (R) | .30 | .18 |
| 30 | Mark Carrier (CHI)(R) | .90 | .60 |
| 31 | James Francis (R) | .75 | .45 |
| 32 | Lamar Lathon (R) | .50 | .30 |
| 33 | Bern Brostek (R) | .25 | .15 |
| 34 | Emmitt Smith (R) | 22.00 | 16.00 |
| 35 | Andre Collins (R) | .50 | .30 |
| 36 | Alexander Wright (R) | .60 | .35 |
| 37 | Fred Barnett (R) | 1.25 | .80 |
| 38 | Junior Seau (R) | 1.25 | .80 |
| 39 | Cortez Kennedy (R) | 1.00 | .70 |
| 40 | Terry Wooden (R) | .25 | .15 |
| 41 | Eric Davis (R) | .25 | .15 |
| 42 | Fred Washington (R) | .25 | .15 |
| 43 | Reggie Cobb (R) | 1.50 | .90 |
| 44 | Andre Ware (R) | .80 | .50 |
| 45 | Anthony Smith (R) | .50 | .30 |
| 46 | Shannon Sharpe (R) | .50 | .30 |
| 47 | Harlon Barnett (R) | .25 | .15 |
| 48 | Greg McMurtry (R) | .40 | .25 |
| 49 | Stacey Simmons (R) | .35 | .20 |
| 50 | Calvin Williams (R) | .70 | .40 |
| 51 | A. Thompson (R) | .80 | .50 |
| 52 | Ricky Proehl (R) | .80 | .50 |
| 53 | Tony Jones (R) | .60 | .35 |
| 54 | Ray Agnew (R) | .30 | .18 |
| 55 | Tommy Hodson (R) | .70 | .40 |
| 56 | Ron Cox (R) | .30 | .18 |
| 57 | Leroy Hoard (R) | .70 | .40 |
| 58 | Eric Green (R) | 1.00 | .70 |
| 59 | Barry Foster (R) | 8.00 | 5.50 |
| 60 | Keith McCants (R) | .80 | .50 |
| 61 | Oliver Barnett (R) | .30 | .18 |
| 62 | Chris Warren (R) | .50 | .30 |
| 63 | Pat Terrell (R) | .30 | .18 |
| 64 | Renaldo Turnbull (R) | .30 | .18 |
| 65 | Chris Chandler | .25 | .15 |
| 66 | Everson Walls | .25 | .15 |
| 67 | Alonzo Highsmith | .25 | .15 |
| 68 | Gary Anderson | .25 | .15 |
| 69 | Fred Smerlas | .25 | .15 |
| 70 | Jim McMahon | .30 | .18 |
| 71 | Curt Warner | .25 | .15 |
| 72 | Stanley Morgan | .25 | .15 |
| 73 | Dave Waymer | .25 | .15 |
| 74 | Billy Joe Tolliver | .40 | .25 |
| 75 | Tony Eason | .25 | .15 |
| 76 | Max Montoya | .25 | .15 |
| 77 | Greg Bell | .25 | .15 |
| 78 | Dennis McKinnon | .25 | .15 |
| 79 | Raymon Clayborn | .25 | .15 |
| 80 | Broderick Thomas | .70 | .40 |
| 81 | Timm Rosenbach | .75 | .45 |
| 82 | Tim McKyer | .25 | .15 |
| 83 | Andre Rison | 1.00 | .70 |
| 84 | Randall Cunningham | 1.25 | .80 |

# 1991 Action Packed

This 280-card set features embossed full-color photos on the card fronts with a gold border that runs along the left side and across the bottom. The Action Packed logo is stamped in the upper left corner and a team helmut appears in the lower right corner. Card backs feature a small head shot, an Action Note and a blank strip at the bottom for a player's autograph. Factory sets contained special braille cards honoring league leaders. Those cards are listed at the end of this checklist beginning with #281 but are not included in the complete set price below.

| | MINT | NR/MT |
|---|---|---|
| Complete Set (280) | 68.00 | 48.00 |
| Commons | .20 | .12 |

| | | | |
|---|---|---|---|
| 1 | Steve Broussard | .50 | .30 |
| 2 | Scott Case | .20 | .12 |
| 3 | Brian Jordan | 1.00 | .70 |
| 4 | Darion Conner | .20 | .12 |
| 5 | Tim Green | .20 | .12 |
| 6 | Chris Miller | .75 | .45 |
| 7 | Andre Rison | .80 | .50 |
| 8 | Mike Rozier | .20 | .12 |
| 9 | Deion Sanders | .80 | .50 |
| 10 | Jessie Tuggle | .20 | .12 |
| 11 | Leonard Smith | .20 | .12 |
| 12 | Shane Conlan | .30 | .18 |
| 13 | Kent Hull | .20 | .12 |
| 14 | Keith McKeller | .20 | .12 |

| | | | | | | | | |
|---|---|---|---|---|---|---|---|---|
| 15 | James Lofton | .80 | .50 | 72 | Lomas Brown | .20 | .12 |
| 16 | Andre Reed | .70 | .40 | 73 | Robert Clark | .20 | .12 |
| 17 | Bruce Smith | .40 | .25 | 74 | Michael Cofer | .20 | .12 |
| 18 | Darryl Talley | .25 | .15 | 75 | Mel Gray | .20 | .12 |
| 19 | Steve Tasker | .20 | .12 | 76 | Richard Johnson | .20 | .12 |
| 20 | Thurman Thomas | 2.00 | 1.25 | 77 | Rodney Peete | .50 | .30 |
| 21 | Neal Anderson | .50 | .30 | 78 | Barry Sanders | 3.00 | 2.00 |
| 22 | Trace Armstrong | .25 | .15 | 79 | Chris Spielman | .25 | .15 |
| 23 | Mark Bortz | .20 | .12 | 80 | Andre Ware | .40 | .25 |
| 24 | Mark Carrier (Chi) | .60 | .35 | 81 | Matt Brock | .25 | .15 |
| 25 | Wendell Davis | .60 | .35 | 82 | LeRoy Butler | .20 | .12 |
| 26 | Richard Dent | .30 | .18 | 83 | Tim Harris | .25 | .15 |
| 27 | Jim Harbaugh | .50 | .30 | 84 | Perry Kemp | .20 | .12 |
| 28 | Jay Hilgenberg | .20 | .12 | 85 | Don Majkowski | .50 | .30 |
| 29 | Brad Muster | .25 | .15 | 86 | Mark Murphy | .20 | .12 |
| 30 | Mike Singletary | .40 | .25 | 87 | Brian Noble | .20 | .12 |
| 31 | Harold Green | .50 | .30 | 88 | Sterling Sharpe | .90 | .60 |
| 32 | James Brooks | .30 | .18 | 89 | Darrell Thompson | .40 | .25 |
| 33 | Eddie Brown | .30 | .18 | 90 | Ed West | .20 | .12 |
| 34 | Boomer Esiason | .60 | .35 | 91 | Ray Childress | .25 | .15 |
| 35 | James Francis | .30 | .18 | 92 | Ernest Givins | .50 | .30 |
| 36 | David Fulcher | .20 | .12 | 93 | Drew Hill | .30 | .18 |
| 37 | Rodney Holman | .20 | .12 | 94 | Haywood Jeffires | .80 | .50 |
| 38 | Tim McGee | .25 | .15 | 95 | Richard Johnson | .20 | .12 |
| 39 | Anthony Munoz | .35 | .20 | 96 | Sean Jones | .20 | .12 |
| 40 | Ickey Woods | .20 | .12 | 97 | Bruce Matthews | .20 | .12 |
| 41 | Rob Burnett | .25 | .15 | 98 | Warren Moon | 1.00 | .70 |
| 42 | Thane Gash | .20 | .12 | 99 | Mike Munchak | .25 | .15 |
| 43 | Mike Johnson | .20 | .12 | 100 | Lorenzo White | .35 | .20 |
| 44 | Brian Brennan | .20 | .12 | 101 | Albert Bentley | .20 | .12 |
| 45 | Reggie Langhorne | .20 | .12 | 102 | Duane Bickett | .20 | .12 |
| 46 | Kevin Mack | .25 | .15 | 103 | Bill Brooks | .20 | .12 |
| 47 | Clay Matthews | .20 | .12 | 104 | Jeff George | 1.00 | .70 |
| 48 | Eric Metcalf | .40 | .25 | 105 | Jon Hand | .20 | .12 |
| 49 | Anthony Pleasant | .20 | .12 | 106 | Jeff Herrod | .20 | .12 |
| 50 | Ozzie Newsome | .35 | .20 | 107 | Jessie Hester | .20 | .12 |
| 51 | Troy Aikman | 2.50 | 1.50 | 108 | Mike Prior | .20 | .12 |
| 52 | Issac Holt | .20 | .12 | 109 | Rohn Stark | .20 | .12 |
| 53 | Michael Irvin | 1.25 | .80 | 110 | Clarence Verdin | .25 | .15 |
| 54 | Jimmie Jones | .20 | .12 | 111 | Steve DeBerg | .30 | .18 |
| 55 | Eugene Lockhart | .20 | .12 | 112 | Dan Saleaumua | .20 | .12 |
| 56 | Kelvin Martin | .25 | .15 | 113 | Albert Lewis | .25 | .15 |
| 57 | Ken Norton, Jr. | .20 | .12 | 114 | Nick Lowery | .30 | .18 |
| 58 | Jay Novacek | .30 | .18 | 115 | Christian Okoye | .40 | .25 |
| 59 | Emmitt Smith | 6.50 | 4.00 | 116 | Stephone Paige | .25 | .15 |
| 60 | Daniel Stubbs | .20 | .12 | 117 | Kevin Ross | .20 | .12 |
| 61 | Steve Atwater | .50 | .30 | 118 | Dino Hackett | .20 | .12 |
| 62 | Michael Brooks | .20 | .12 | 119 | Derrick Thomas | .90 | .60 |
| 63 | John Elway | .70 | .40 | 120 | Barry Word | .80 | .50 |
| 64 | Simon Fletcher | .20 | .12 | 121 | Marcus Allen | .50 | .30 |
| 65 | Bobby Humphrey | .50 | .30 | 122 | Mervyn Fernandez | .30 | .18 |
| 66 | Mark Jackson | .25 | .15 | 123 | Willie Gault | .25 | .15 |
| 67 | Vance Johnson | .30 | .18 | 124 | Bo Jackson | 1.00 | .70 |
| 68 | Karl Mecklenburg | .30 | .18 | 125 | Terry McDaniel | .20 | .12 |
| 69 | Dennis Smith | .20 | .12 | 126 | Don Mosebar | .20 | .12 |
| 70 | Greg Kragen | .20 | .12 | 127 | Jay Schroeder | .35 | .20 |
| 71 | Jerry Ball | .20 | .12 | 128 | Greg Townsend | .25 | .15 |

| No. | Name | | |
|---|---|---|---|
| 129 | Aaron Wallace | .25 | .15 |
| 130 | Steve Wisniewski | .20 | .12 |
| 131 | Flipper Anderson | .30 | .18 |
| 132 | Henry Ellard | .25 | .15 |
| 133 | Jim Everett | .50 | .30 |
| 134 | Cleveland Gary | .35 | .20 |
| 135 | Jerry Gray | .20 | .12 |
| 136 | Kevin Green | .25 | .15 |
| 137 | Buford McGee | .20 | .12 |
| 138 | Vince Newsome | .20 | .12 |
| 139 | Jackie Slater | .25 | .15 |
| 140 | Frank Stams | .20 | .12 |
| 141 | Jeff Cross | .20 | .12 |
| 142 | Mark Duper | .40 | .25 |
| 143 | Ferrell Edmunds | .20 | .12 |
| 144 | Dan Marino | 1.25 | .80 |
| 145 | Louis Oliver | .25 | .15 |
| 146 | John Offerdahl | .25 | .15 |
| 147 | Tony Paige | .20 | .12 |
| 148 | Sammie Smith | .30 | .18 |
| 149 | Richmond Webb | .25 | .15 |
| 150 | Jarvis Williams | .20 | .12 |
| 151 | Joey Browner | .25 | .15 |
| 152 | Anthony Carter | .35 | .20 |
| 153 | Chris Doleman | .30 | .18 |
| 154 | Hassan Jones | .20 | .12 |
| 155 | Steve Jordan | .20 | .12 |
| 156 | Carl Lee | .20 | .12 |
| 157 | Randall McDaniel | .20 | .12 |
| 158 | Mike Merriweather | .20 | .12 |
| 159 | Herschel Walker | .50 | .30 |
| 160 | Wade Wilson | .30 | .18 |
| 161 | Ray Agnew | .20 | .12 |
| 162 | Bruce Armstrong | .20 | .12 |
| 163 | Marv Cook | .25 | .15 |
| 164 | Hart Lee Dykes | .25 | .15 |
| 165 | Irving Fryar | .25 | .15 |
| 166 | Tommy Hodson | .30 | .18 |
| 167 | Ronnie Lippett | .20 | .12 |
| 168 | Fred Marion | .20 | .12 |
| 169 | John Stephens | .30 | .18 |
| 170 | Brent Williams | .20 | .12 |
| 171 | Morten Andersen | .25 | .15 |
| 172 | Gene Atkin | .20 | .12 |
| 173 | Craig Heyward | .25 | .15 |
| 174 | Rickey Jackson | .25 | .15 |
| 175 | Vaughan Johnson | .25 | .15 |
| 176 | Eric Martin | .25 | .15 |
| 177 | Rueben Mayes | .25 | .15 |
| 178 | Pat Swilling | .50 | .30 |
| 179 | Renaldo Turnbull | .25 | .15 |
| 180 | Steve Walsh | .30 | .18 |
| 181 | Ottis Anderson | .35 | .20 |
| 182 | Rodney Hampton | 1.25 | .80 |
| 183 | Jeff Hostetler | .75 | .45 |
| 184 | Pepper Johnson | .25 | .15 |
| 185 | Sean Landeta | .20 | .12 |
| 186 | Dave Meggett | .60 | .35 |
| 187 | Bart Oates | .20 | .12 |
| 188 | Phil Simms | .40 | .25 |
| 189 | Lawrence Taylor | .70 | .40 |
| 190 | Reyna Thompson | .30 | .18 |
| 191 | Brad Baxter | .40 | .25 |
| 192 | Dennis Byrd | .20 | .12 |
| 193 | Kyle Clifton | .20 | .12 |
| 194 | James Hasty | .20 | .12 |
| 195 | Pat Leahy | .20 | .12 |
| 196 | Erik McMillan | .25 | .15 |
| 197 | Rob Moore | .80 | .50 |
| 198 | Ken O'Brien | .30 | .18 |
| 199 | Mark Boyer | .20 | .12 |
| 200 | Al Toon | .30 | .18 |
| 201 | Fred Barnett | .50 | .30 |
| 202 | Jerome Brown | .25 | .15 |
| 203 | Keith Byars | .25 | .15 |
| 204 | Randall Cunningham | .90 | .60 |
| 205 | Wes Hopkins | .20 | .12 |
| 206 | Keith Jackson | .40 | .25 |
| 207 | Seth Joyner | .25 | .15 |
| 208 | Heath Sherman | .35 | .20 |
| 209 | Reggie White | .50 | .30 |
| 210 | Calvin Williams | .40 | .25 |
| 211 | Roy Green | .25 | .15 |
| 212 | Ken Harvey | .20 | .12 |
| 213 | Luis Sharpe | .20 | .12 |
| 214 | Ernie Jones | .20 | .12 |
| 215 | Tim McDonald | .20 | .12 |
| 216 | Freddie Joe Nunn | .20 | .12 |
| 217 | Ricky Proehl | .25 | .15 |
| 218 | Timm Rosenbach | .50 | .30 |
| 219 | Anthony Thompson | .35 | .20 |
| 220 | Lonnie Young | .20 | .12 |
| 221 | Gary Anderson | .20 | .12 |
| 222 | Bubby Brister | .40 | .25 |
| 223 | Eric Green | .40 | .25 |
| 224 | Merril Hoge | .25 | .15 |
| 225 | Carnell Lake | .20 | .12 |
| 226 | Lous Lipps | .25 | .15 |
| 227 | David Little | .20 | .12 |
| 228 | Greg Lloyd | .20 | .12 |
| 229 | Gerald Williams | .20 | .12 |
| 230 | Rod Woodson | .40 | .25 |
| 231 | Marion Butts | .50 | .30 |
| 232 | Gil Byrd | .20 | .12 |
| 233 | Burt Grossman | .25 | .15 |
| 234 | Courtney Hall | .20 | .12 |
| 235 | Ronnie Harmon | .25 | .15 |
| 236 | Anthony Miller | .35 | .20 |
| 237 | Leslie O'Neal | .25 | .15 |
| 238 | Junior Seau | .50 | .30 |
| 239 | Billy Joe Tolliver | .30 | .18 |
| 240 | Lee Williams | .20 | .12 |
| 241 | Dexter Carter | .30 | .18 |
| 242 | Kevin Fagan | .20 | .12 |

| 243 | Charles Haley | .30 | .18 |
|---|---|---|---|
| 244 | Brent Jones | .20 | .12 |
| 245 | Ronnie Lott | .35 | .20 |
| 246 | Guy McIntyre | .20 | .12 |
| 247 | Joe Montana | 1.50 | .90 |
| 248 | Jerry Rice | 1.50 | .90 |
| 249 | John Taylor | .50 | .30 |
| 250 | Roger Craig | .40 | .25 |
| 251 | Brian Blades | .25 | .15 |
| 252 | Derrick Fenner | .40 | .25 |
| 253 | Nesby Glasgow | .20 | .12 |
| 254 | Jacob Green | .20 | .12 |
| 255 | Tommy Kane | .25 | .15 |
| 256 | Dave Krieg | .35 | .20 |
| 257 | Rufus Porter | .20 | .12 |
| 258 | Eugene Robinson | .20 | .12 |
| 259 | Cortez Kennedy | .50 | .30 |
| 260 | John L. Williams | .30 | .18 |
| 261 | Gary Anderson | .25 | .15 |
| 262 | Mark Carrier (TB) | .35 | .20 |
| 263 | Steve Christie | .20 | .12 |
| 264 | Reggie Cobb | .50 | .30 |
| 265 | Paul Gruber | .20 | .12 |
| 266 | Wayne Haddix | .25 | .15 |
| 267 | Bruce Hill | .20 | .12 |
| 268 | Keith McCants | .30 | .18 |
| 269 | Vinny Testaverde | .35 | .20 |
| 270 | Broderick Thomas | .35 | .20 |
| 271 | Earnest Byner | .30 | .18 |
| 272 | Gary Clark | .60 | .35 |
| 273 | Darrell Green | .50 | .30 |
| 274 | Jim Lachey | .25 | .15 |
| 275 | Chip Lohmiller | .20 | .12 |
| 276 | Charles Mann | .20 | .12 |
| 277 | Wilber Marshall | .25 | .15 |
| 278 | Art Monk | .75 | .45 |
| 279 | Mark Rypien | .80 | .50 |
| 280 | Alvin Walton | .20 | .12 |
| 281 | Randall Cunningham (Braille) | 2.00 | 1.25 |
| 282 | Warren Moon (Braille) | 2.00 | 1.25 |
| 283 | Barry Sanders (Braille) | 5.00 | 3.50 |
| 284 | Thurman Thomas (Braille) | 4.00 | 2.50 |
| 285 | Jerry Rice (Braille) | 4.00 | 2.50 |
| 286 | Haywood Jeffires (Braille) | 2.00 | 1.25 |
| 287 | Charles Haley (Braille) | 1.50 | .90 |
| 288 | Derrick Thomas (Braille) | 2.00 | 1.25 |
| 289 | NFC Logo | .30 | .20 |
| 290 | AFC Logo | .30 | .20 |
| ___ | Checklist | .40 | .25 |

# 1991 Action Packed 24K Gold Inserts

These limited inserts were found in Action Packed foil packs and feature 24K gold stamping on the fronts and gold borders on the backs. Cards measure 2-1/2" by 3-1/2" and the design is identical to the regular issue.

| | | MINT | NR/MT |
|---|---|---|---|
| **Complete Set (42)** | | 4,000.00 | 3,000.00 |
| **Commons** | | 28.00 | 18.00 |
| | | | |
| 1 | Andre Rison | 75.00 | 50.00 |
| 2 | Deion Sanders | 100.00 | 75.00 |
| 3 | Andre Reed | 60.00 | 35.00 |
| 4 | Bruce Smith | 50.00 | 30.00 |
| 5 | Thurman Thomas | 150.00 | 100.00 |
| 6 | Neal Anderson | 60.00 | 35.00 |
| 7 | Mark Carrier | 35.00 | 22.50 |
| 8 | Mike Singletary | 40.00 | 25.00 |
| 9 | Boomer Esiason | 75.00 | 50.00 |
| 10 | James Francis | 30.00 | 20.00 |
| 11 | Anthony Munoz | 30.00 | 20.00 |
| 12 | Troy Aikman | 200.00 | 125.00 |
| 13 | Emmitt Smith | 275.00 | 200.00 |
| 14 | John Elway | 75.00 | 50.00 |
| 15 | Bobby Humphrey | 50.00 | 30.00 |
| 16 | Barry Sanders | 200.00 | 125.00 |
| 17 | Don Majkowski | 60.00 | 35.00 |
| 18 | Sterling Sharpe | 100.00 | 75.00 |
| 19 | Warren Moon | 125.00 | 80.00 |
| 20 | Jeff George | 125.00 | 80.00 |
| 21 | Christian Okoye | 60.00 | 35.00 |
| 22 | Derrick Thomas | 80.00 | 55.00 |
| 23 | Barry Word | 60.00 | 35.00 |
| 24 | Marcus Allen | 50.00 | 30.00 |
| 25 | Bo Jackson | 150.00 | 100.00 |
| 26 | Jim Everett | 75.00 | 50.00 |
| 27 | Cleveland Gary | 28.00 | 18.00 |
| 28 | Dan Marino | 200.00 | 125.00 |
| 29 | Herschel Walker | 75.00 | 50.00 |
| 30 | Ottis Anderson | 35.00 | 22.50 |
| 31 | Rodney Hampton | 100.00 | 75.00 |
| 32 | Dave Meggett | 75.00 | 50.00 |
| 33 | Marion Butts | 60.00 | 35.00 |
| 34 | Rndl. Cunningham | 100.00 | 75.00 |
| 35 | Reggie White | 50.00 | 30.00 |

| 36 | Jerry Rice | 175.00 | 100.00 |
|---|---|---|---|
| 37 | Eric Green | 35.00 | 22.50 |
| 38 | Charles Haley | 28.00 | 18.00 |
| 39 | Ronnie Lott | 50.00 | 30.00 |
| 40 | Joe Montana | 200.00 | 125.00 |
| 41 | Vinny Testaverde | 30.00 | 20.00 |
| 42 | Gary Clark | 50.00 | 30.00 |

# 1991 Action Packed Rookies

This update set contains 84 cards including the top rookies from the 1991 NFL draft plus traded players. The cards measure 2-1/2" by 3-1/2" and are similar to the regular issue except for a small "R" in the lower right corner and a thin red border.

Card backs are horizontal and printed in red type. A bonus Emmitt Smith card was included in foil cases. That card is listed at the end of this checklist but not included in the complete set price.

| | | MINT | NR/MT |
|---|---|---|---|
| **Complete Set (84)** | | 27.00 | 18.00 |
| **Commons** | | .20 | .12 |

| 1 | Herman Moore (R) | 1.50 | .90 |
|---|---|---|---|
| 2 | Eric Turner (R) | .80 | .50 |
| 3 | Mike Croel (R) | 1.25 | .80 |
| 4 | Alfred Williams (R) | .60 | .35 |
| 5 | Stanley Richard (R) | .75 | .45 |

| 6 | Russell Maryland (R) | .90 | .60 |
|---|---|---|---|
| 7 | Pat Harlow (R) | .30 | .18 |
| 8 | Alvin Harper (R) | 1.75 | 1.00 |
| 9 | Mike Pritchard (R) | 1.25 | .80 |
| 10 | Leonard Russell (R) | 2.00 | 1.25 |
| 11 | Jarrod Bunch (R) | .70 | .40 |
| 12 | Dan McGwire (R) | 1.50 | .90 |
| 13 | Bobby Wilson (R) | .20 | .12 |
| 14 | Vinnie Clark (R) | .40 | .25 |
| 15 | Kelvin Pritchett (R) | .50 | .30 |
| 16 | Harvey Williams (R) | 1.50 | .90 |
| 17 | Stan Thomas (R) | .25 | .15 |
| 18 | Todd Marinovich (R) | 1.75 | 1.00 |
| 19 | Antone Davis (R) | .25 | .15 |
| 20 | Greg Lewis (R) | .50 | .30 |
| 21 | Brett Favre (R) | 3.00 | 2.00 |
| 22 | Wesley Carroll (R) | .80 | .50 |
| 23 | Ed McCaffrey (R) | .80 | .50 |
| 24 | Reggie Barrett (R) | .40 | .25 |
| 25 | Chris Zorich (R) | .50 | .30 |
| 26 | Kenny Walker (R) | .75 | .45 |
| 27 | Aaron Craver (R) | .35 | .20 |
| 28 | Browning Nagle | 2.50 | 1.50 |
| 29 | Nick Bell (R) | 1.50 | .90 |
| 30 | Anthony Morgan (R) | .60 | .35 |
| 31 | Jesse Campbell (R) | .25 | .15 |
| 32 | Eric Bieniemy (R) | .50 | .30 |
| 33 | Ricky Ervins (R) | 2.00 | 1.25 |
| 34 | Kanavis McGhee (R) | .30 | .18 |
| 35 | Shawn Moore (R) | .30 | .18 |
| 36 | Todd Lyght (R) | .70 | .40 |
| 37 | Eric Swann (R) | .40 | .25 |
| 38 | Henry Jones (R) | .25 | .15 |
| 39 | Ted Washington (R) | .30 | .18 |
| 40 | Charles McRae (R) | .25 | .15 |
| 41 | Randal Hill (R) | 1.00 | .70 |
| 42 | Huey Richardson (R) | .25 | .15 |
| 43 | Roman Phifer (R) | .25 | .15 |
| 44 | Ricky Watters (R) | 3.50 | 2.25 |
| 45 | Esera Tuaolo (R) | .25 | .15 |
| 46 | Michael Jackson (R) | 1.00 | .70 |
| 47 | Shawn Jefferson (R) | .75 | .45 |
| 48 | Tim Barnett (R) | .75 | .45 |
| 49 | Chuck Webb (R) | .40 | .25 |
| 50 | Moe Gardner (R) | .35 | .20 |
| 51 | Mo Lewis (R) | .35 | .20 |
| 52 | Mike Dumas (R) | .30 | .18 |
| 53 | Jon Vaughn (R) | .70 | .40 |
| 54 | J. Henderson (R) | .30 | .18 |
| 55 | Harry Colon (R) | .25 | .15 |
| 56 | David Daniels (R) | .20 | .12 |
| 57 | Phil Hansen (R) | .25 | .15 |
| 58 | Ernie Mills (R) | .70 | .40 |
| 59 | John Kasay (R) | .25 | .15 |
| 60 | Darren Lewis (R) | .75 | .45 |
| 61 | James Joseph (R) | .40 | .25 |
| 62 | Robert Wilson (R) | .25 | .15 |

| 63 | Lawrence Dawsey (R) | 1.25 | .80 |
|----|---------------------|------|-----|
| 64 | Mike Jones (R) | .25 | .15 |
| 65 | Dave McCloughan (R) | .20 | .12 |
| 66 | Erric Pegram (R) | .70 | .40 |
| 67 | Aeneas Williams (R) | .35 | .20 |
| 68 | Reggie Johnson (R) | .40 | .25 |
| 69 | Todd Scott (R) | .25 | .15 |
| 70 | James Jones (R) | .25 | .15 |
| 71 | Lamar Rogers (R) | .25 | .15 |
| 72 | Darryl Lewis (R) | .30 | .18 |
| 73 | Bryan Cox (R) | .40 | .25 |
| 74 | Leroy Thompson (R) | .25 | .15 |
| 75 | Mark Higgs (R) | 1.25 | .80 |
| 76 | John Friesz (R) | .50 | .30 |
| 77 | Tim McKyer | .20 | .12 |
| 78 | Roger Craig | .25 | .15 |
| 79 | Ronnie Lott | .25 | .15 |
| 80 | Steve Young | .80 | .50 |
| 81 | Percy Snow | .20 | .12 |
| 82 | Cornelius Bennett | .25 | .15 |
| 83 | Johnny Johnson | .35 | .20 |
| 84 | Blair Thomas | .60 | .35 |

| 15 | Dan McGwire | 125.00 | 80.00 |
|----|-------------|--------|-------|
| 16 | Bobby Wilson | 35.00 | 22.50 |
| 17 | Alfred Williams | 50.00 | 30.00 |
| 18 | Vinnie Clark | 40.00 | 25.00 |
| 19 | Kelvin Pritchett | 40.00 | 25.00 |
| 20 | Harvey Williams | 100.00 | 75.00 |
| 21 | Stan Thomas | 35.00 | 22.50 |
| 22 | Randal Hill | 75.00 | 50.00 |
| 23 | Todd Marinovich | 150.00 | 100.00 |
| 24 | Ted Washington | 40.00 | 25.00 |
| 25 | Henry Jones | 35.00 | 22.50 |
| 26 | Jarrod Bunch | 50.00 | 30.00 |

# 1992 Action Packed

# 1991 Action Packed Rookies 24K Gold Inserts

|  |  | MINT | NR/MT |
|--|--|------|-------|
| **Complete Set (26)** | | 2,500.00 | 1,650.00 |
| **Commons** | | 35.00 | 22.50 |
| 1 | Russell Maryland | 100.00 | 75.00 |
| 2 | Eric Turner | 60.00 | 35.00 |
| 3 | Mike Croel | 100.00 | 75.00 |
| 4 | Todd Lyght | 60.00 | 35.00 |
| 5 | Eric Swann | 50.00 | 30.00 |
| 6 | Charles McRae | 35.00 | 22.50 |
| 7 | Antone Davis | 35.00 | 22.50 |
| 8 | Stanley Richard | 50.00 | 30.00 |
| 9 | Herman Moore | 75.00 | 50.00 |
| 10 | Pat Harlow | 35.00 | 22.50 |
| 11 | Alvin Harper | 100.00 | 75.00 |
| 12 | Mike Pritchard | 100.00 | 75.00 |
| 13 | Leonard Russell | 150.00 | 100.00 |
| 14 | Huey Richardson | 35.00 | 22.50 |

For the third straight year Action Packed issued a 280-card set with embossed, full-color photos on the fronts. The borderless design is highlighted by thin gold and red or gold and blue lines while the player's name and position appears across the botom of the card. The flip side is horizontal with a small head shot, an Action Note and a small blank box suitable for an autograph. Cards measure 2-1/2" by 3-1/2". Eight braille cards that honor league leaders were randomly inserted into the company's foil packs. Those braille cards are listed at the end of this checklist starting with card #281 but are not included in the complete set price below.

|  |  | MINT | NR/MT |
|---|---|---|---|
| **Complete Set (280)** |  | 68.00 | 48.00 |
| **Commons** |  | .20 | .12 |
| 1 | Steve Broussard | .25 | .15 |
| 2 | Michael Haynes | .75 | .45 |
| 3 | Tim McKyer | .20 | .12 |
| 4 | Chris Miller | .60 | .35 |
| 5 | Andre Rison | .80 | .50 |
| 6 | Jessie Tuggle | .20 | .12 |
| 7 | Mike Pritchard | .75 | .45 |
| 8 | Moe Gardner | .20 | .12 |
| 9 | Brian Jordan | .50 | .30 |
| 10 | Mike Kenn/ | .20 | .12 |
|  | Chris Hinton |  |  |
| 11 | Steve Tasker | .20 | .12 |
| 12 | Cornelius Bennett | .30 | .18 |
| 13 | Shane Conlan | .25 | .15 |
| 14 | Darryl Talley | .25 | .15 |
| 15 | Thurman Thomas | 1.50 | .90 |
| 16 | James Lofton | .60 | .35 |
| 17 | Don Beebe | .20 | .12 |
| 18 | Jim Ritcher | .20 | .12 |
| 19 | Keith McKeller | .20 | .12 |
| 20 | Nate Odomes | .20 | .12 |
| 21 | Mark Carrier (Chi) | .35 | .20 |
| 22 | Wendell Davis | .30 | .18 |
| 23 | Richard Dent | .25 | .15 |
| 24 | Jim Harbaugh | .30 | .18 |
| 25 | Jay Hilgenberg | .20 | .12 |
| 26 | Steve McMichael | .20 | .12 |
| 27 | Tom Waddle | .50 | .30 |
| 28 | Neal Anderson | .30 | .18 |
| 29 | Brad Muster | .25 | .15 |
| 30 | Shaun Gayle | .20 | .12 |
| 31 | Jim Breech | .20 | .12 |
| 32 | James Brooks | .25 | .15 |
| 33 | James Francis | .25 | .15 |
| 34 | David Fulcher | .20 | .12 |
| 35 | Harold Green | .35 | .20 |
| 36 | Rodney Holman | .25 | .15 |
| 37 | Anthony Munoz | .30 | .18 |
| 38 | Tim Krumrie | .20 | .12 |
| 39 | Tim McGee | .20 | .12 |
| 40 | Eddie Brown | .25 | .15 |
| 41 | Kevin Mack | .25 | .15 |
| 42 | James Jones | .20 | .12 |
| 43 | Vince Newsome | .20 | .12 |
| 44 | Ed King | .20 | .12 |
| 45 | Eric Metcalf | .35 | .20 |
| 46 | Leroy Hoard | .25 | .15 |
| 47 | Stephen Braggs | .20 | .12 |
| 48 | Clay Matthews | .20 | .12 |
| 49 | David Brandon | .25 | .15 |
| 50 | Rob Burnett | .20 | .12 |
| 51 | Larry Brown | .20 | .12 |
| 52 | Alvin Harper | .75 | .45 |
| 53 | Michael Irvin | 1.00 | .70 |
| 54 | Ken Norton, Jr. | .20 | .12 |
| 55 | Jay Novacek | .25 | .15 |
| 56 | Emmitt Smith | 6.00 | 3.75 |
| 57 | Tony Tolbert | .20 | .12 |
| 58 | Nate Newton | .20 | .12 |
| 59 | Steve Beuerlein | .25 | .15 |
| 60 | Tony Casillas | .25 | .15 |
| 61 | Steve Atwater | .30 | .18 |
| 62 | Mike Croel | .70 | .40 |
| 63 | Gaston Green | .30 | .18 |
| 64 | Mark Jackson | .20 | .12 |
| 65 | Greg Kragen | .20 | .12 |
| 66 | Karl Mecklenburg | .25 | .15 |
| 67 | Dennis Smith | .20 | .12 |
| 68 | Steve Sewell | .20 | .12 |
| 69 | John Elway | .70 | .40 |
| 70 | Simon Fletcher | .20 | .12 |
| 71 | Mel Gray | .20 | .12 |
| 72 | Barry Sanders | 2.50 | 1.50 |
| 73 | Jerry Ball | .20 | .12 |
| 74 | Bennie Blades | .20 | .12 |
| 75 | Lomas Brown | .20 | .12 |
| 76 | Erik Kramer | .90 | .60 |
| 77 | Chris Spielman | .25 | .15 |
| 78 | Ray Crockett | .20 | .12 |
| 79 | Willie Green | .90 | .60 |
| 80 | Rodney Peete | .30 | .18 |
| 81 | Sterling Sharpe | 1.00 | .70 |
| 82 | Tony Bennett | .20 | .12 |
| 83 | Chuck Cecil | .20 | .12 |
| 84 | Perry Kemp | .20 | .12 |
| 85 | Brian Noble | .20 | .12 |
| 86 | Darrell Thompson | .25 | .15 |
| 87 | Mike Tomczak | .25 | .15 |
| 88 | Vince Workman | .35 | .20 |
| 89 | Esera Tuaolo | .35 | .20 |
| 90 | Mark Murphy | .20 | .12 |
| 91 | William Fuller | .20 | .12 |
| 92 | Ernest Givins | .40 | .25 |
| 93 | Drew Hill | .25 | .15 |
| 94 | Al Smith | .20 | .12 |
| 95 | Ray Childress | .25 | .15 |
| 96 | Haywood Jeffires | .70 | .40 |
| 97 | Cris Dishman | .20 | .12 |
| 98 | Warren Moon | .80 | .50 |
| 99 | Lamar Lathon | .25 | .15 |
| 100 | Mike Munchak/ | .25 | .15 |
|  | Bruce Matthews |  |  |
| 101 | Bill Brooks | .20 | .12 |
| 102 | Duane Bickett | .20 | .12 |
| 103 | Eugene Daniel | .20 | .12 |
| 104 | Jeff Herrod | .20 | .12 |
| 105 | Jessie Hester | .20 | .12 |
| 106 | Donnell Thompson | .20 | .12 |
| 107 | Anthony Johnson | .20 | .12 |

| | | | |
|---|---|---|---|
| 108 | Jon Hand | .20 | .12 |
| 109 | Rohn Stark | .20 | .12 |
| 110 | Clarence Verdin | .25 | .15 |
| 111 | Derrick Thomas | .75 | .45 |
| 112 | Steve DeBerg | .25 | .15 |
| 113 | Deron Cherry | .20 | .12 |
| 114 | Chris Martin | .20 | .12 |
| 115 | Christian Okoye | .30 | .18 |
| 116 | Dan Saleaumua | .20 | .12 |
| 117 | Neil Smith | .20 | .12 |
| 118 | Barry Word | .50 | .30 |
| 119 | Tim Barnett | .50 | .30 |
| 120 | Albert Lewis | .20 | .12 |
| 121 | Ronnie Lott | .25 | .15 |
| 122 | Marcus Allen | .35 | .20 |
| 123 | Todd Marinovich | 1.25 | .80 |
| 124 | Nick Bell | .80 | .50 |
| 125 | Tim Brown | .30 | .18 |
| 126 | Ethan Horton | .20 | .12 |
| 127 | Greg Townsend | .20 | .12 |
| 128 | Jeff Gossett/ | .20 | .12 |
| | Jeff Jaeger | | |
| 129 | Scott Davis | .20 | .12 |
| 130 | Steve Wisniewski/ | .20 | .12 |
| | Don Mosebar | | |
| 131 | Kevin Greene | .25 | .15 |
| 132 | Roman Phifer | .20 | .12 |
| 133 | Tony Zendejas | .20 | .12 |
| 134 | Pat Terell | .20 | .12 |
| 135 | Flipper Anderson | .30 | .18 |
| 136 | Robert Delpino | .25 | .15 |
| 137 | Jim Everett | .40 | .25 |
| 138 | Larry Kelm | .20 | .12 |
| 139 | Todd Lyght | .40 | .25 |
| 140 | Henry Ellard | .25 | .15 |
| 141 | Mark Clayton | .35 | .20 |
| 142 | Jeff Cross | .20 | .12 |
| 143 | Mark Duper | .25 | .15 |
| 144 | John Offerdahl | .25 | .15 |
| 145 | Louis Oliver | .25 | .15 |
| 146 | Pete Stoyanovich | .20 | .12 |
| 147 | Richmond Webb | .20 | .12 |
| 148 | Mark Higgs | .70 | .40 |
| 149 | Tony Paige | .20 | .12 |
| 150 | Bryan Cox | .20 | .12 |
| 151 | Anthony Carter | .30 | .18 |
| 152 | Cris Carter | .30 | .18 |
| 153 | Rich Gannon | .60 | .35 |
| 154 | Steve Jordan | .20 | .12 |
| 155 | Mike Merriweather | .20 | .12 |
| 156 | Henry Thomas | .20 | .12 |
| 157 | Herschel Walker | .40 | .25 |
| 158 | Randall McDaniel | .20 | .12 |
| 159 | Terry Allen | 1.25 | .80 |
| 160 | Joey Browner | .25 | .15 |
| 161 | Leonard Russell | 1.00 | .70 |
| 162 | Bruce Armstrong | .20 | .12 |
| 163 | Vincent Brown | .20 | .12 |
| 164 | Hugh Millen | .75 | .45 |
| 165 | Andre Tippett | .25 | .15 |
| 166 | Jon Vaughn | .40 | .25 |
| 167 | Pat Harlow | .20 | .12 |
| 168 | Marv Cook | .20 | .12 |
| 169 | Irving Fryar | .25 | .15 |
| 170 | Maurice Hurst | .20 | .12 |
| 171 | Pat Swilling | .35 | .20 |
| 172 | Vince Buck | .20 | .12 |
| 173 | Rickey Jackson | .25 | .15 |
| 174 | Sam Mills | .25 | .15 |
| 175 | Bobby Hebert | .30 | .18 |
| 176 | Vaughan Johnson | .20 | .12 |
| 177 | Floyd Turner | .20 | .12 |
| 178 | Fred McAfee | .40 | .25 |
| 179 | Morten Andersen | .25 | .15 |
| 180 | Eric Martin | .20 | .12 |
| 181 | Rodney Hampton | .80 | .50 |
| 182 | Pepper Johnson | .20 | .12 |
| 183 | Leonard Marshall | .20 | .12 |
| 184 | Stephen Baker | .20 | .12 |
| 185 | Mark Ingram | .20 | .12 |
| 186 | Dave Meggett | .40 | .25 |
| 187 | Bart Oates | .20 | .12 |
| 188 | Mark Collins | .20 | .12 |
| 189 | Myron Guyton | .20 | .12 |
| 190 | Jeff Hostetler | .60 | .35 |
| 191 | Jeff Lageman | .25 | .15 |
| 192 | Brad Baxter | .30 | .18 |
| 193 | Mo Lewis | .20 | .12 |
| 194 | Chris Burkett | .20 | .12 |
| 195 | James Hasty | .20 | .12 |
| 196 | Rob Moore | .75 | .45 |
| 197 | Kyle Clifton | .20 | .12 |
| 198 | Terance Mathis | .20 | .12 |
| 199 | Marvin Washington | .20 | .12 |
| 200 | Lonnie Young | .20 | .12 |
| 201 | Reggie White | .40 | .25 |
| 202 | Eric Allen | .20 | .12 |
| 203 | Fred Barnett | .50 | .30 |
| 204 | Keith Byars | .25 | .15 |
| 205 | Seth Joyner | .25 | .15 |
| 206 | Clyde Simmons | .30 | .18 |
| 207 | Jerome Brown | .25 | .15 |
| 208 | Wes Hopkins | .20 | .12 |
| 209 | Keith Jackson | .35 | .20 |
| 210 | Calvin Williams | .20 | .12 |
| 211 | Aeneas Williams | .20 | .12 |
| 212 | Ken Harvey | .20 | .12 |
| 213 | Ernie Jones | .20 | .12 |
| 214 | Freddie Joe Nunn | .20 | .12 |
| 215 | Rich Camarillo | .20 | .12 |
| 216 | Johnny Johnson | .35 | .20 |
| 217 | Tim McDonald | .20 | .12 |
| 218 | Eric Swann | .30 | .18 |
| 219 | Eric Hill | .20 | .12 |

| | | | |
|---|---|---|---|
| 220 | Anthony Thompson | .25 | .15 |
| 221 | Hardy Nickerson | .20 | .12 |
| 222 | Barry Foster | 1.50 | .90 |
| 223 | Louis Lipps | .25 | .15 |
| 224 | Greg Lloyd | .20 | .12 |
| 225 | Neil O'Donnell | 1.25 | .80 |
| 226 | Jerrol Williams | .20 | .12 |
| 227 | Eric Green | .30 | .18 |
| 228 | Rod Woodson | .25 | .15 |
| 229 | Carnell Lake | .20 | .12 |
| 230 | Dwight Stone | .20 | .12 |
| 231 | Mario Butts | .35 | .20 |
| 232 | John Friesz | .35 | .20 |
| 233 | Burt Grossman | .25 | .15 |
| 234 | Ronnie Harmon | .25 | .15 |
| 235 | Gil Byrd | .20 | .12 |
| 236 | Rod Bernstine | .25 | .15 |
| 237 | Courtney Hall | .20 | .12 |
| 238 | Nate Lewis | .20 | .12 |
| 239 | Joe Phillips | .20 | .12 |
| 240 | Henry Rolling | .20 | .12 |
| 241 | Keith Henderson | .25 | .15 |
| 242 | Guy McIntyre | .20 | .12 |
| 243 | Bill Romanowski | .20 | .12 |
| 244 | Don Griffin | .20 | .12 |
| 245 | Dexter Carter | .25 | .15 |
| 246 | Charles Haley | .25 | .15 |
| 247 | Brent Jones | .20 | .12 |
| 248 | John Taylor | .40 | .25 |
| 249 | Steve Young | .75 | .45 |
| 250 | Larry Roberts | .20 | .12 |
| 251 | Brian Blades | .25 | .15 |
| 252 | Jacob Green | .20 | .12 |
| 253 | John Kasay | .20 | .12 |
| 254 | Cortez Kennedy | .35 | .20 |
| 255 | Rufus Porter | .20 | .12 |
| 256 | John L. Williams | .25 | .15 |
| 257 | Tommy Kane | .20 | .12 |
| 258 | Eugene Robinson | .20 | .12 |
| 259 | Terry Wooden | .20 | .12 |
| 260 | Chris Warren | .20 | .12 |
| 261 | Lawrence Dawsey | .70 | .40 |
| 262 | Mark Carrier (TB) | .25 | .15 |
| 263 | Keith McCants | .25 | .15 |
| 264 | Jesse Solomon | .20 | .12 |
| 265 | Vinny Testaverde | .25 | .15 |
| 266 | Ricky Reynolds | .20 | .12 |
| 267 | Broderick Thomas | .25 | .15 |
| 268 | Gary Anderson | .20 | .12 |
| 269 | Reggie Cobb | .40 | .25 |
| 270 | Tony Covington | .20 | .12 |
| 271 | Darrell Green | .30 | .18 |
| 272 | Charles Mann | .20 | .12 |
| 273 | Wilber Marshall | .25 | .15 |
| 274 | Gary Clark | .40 | .25 |
| 275 | Chip Lohmiller | .20 | .12 |
| 276 | Earnest Byner | .25 | .15 |

| | | | |
|---|---|---|---|
| 277 | Jim Lachey | .25 | .15 |
| 278 | Art Monk | .60 | .35 |
| 279 | Mark Rypien | .75 | .45 |
| 280 | Mark Schlereth | .20 | .12 |
| 281 | Mark Rypien (Braille) | 1.50 | .90 |
| 282 | Warren Moon (Braille) | 1.75 | 1.00 |
| 283 | Emmitt Smith (Braille) | 7.50 | 4.50 |
| 284 | Thurman Thomas (Braille) | 3.50 | 2.00 |
| 285 | Michael Irvin (Braille) | 2.50 | 1.50 |
| 286 | Haywood Jeffires (Braille) | 1.50 | .90 |
| 287 | Pat Swilling (Braille) | .80 | .50 |
| 288 | Ronnie Lott (Braille) | 1.00 | .70 |
| 289 | NFC Logo | .30 | .18 |
| 290 | AFC Logo | .30 | .18 |

# 1992 Action Packed 24K Gold Inserts

The 42 cards in this set measure 2-1/2" by 3-1/2" and are similar in design to Action Packed's regular edition except these cards carry 24K gold stamping on the front. The limited edition cards were randomly inserted into the company's foil packs.

| | | MINT | NR/MT |
|---|---|---|---|
| Complete Set (42) | | 2,400.00 | 1,500.00 |
| Commons | | 28.00 | 18.00 |
| 1 | Michael Haynes | 75.00 | 50.00 |
| 2 | Chris Miller | 75.00 | 50.00 |
| 3 | Andre Rison | 90.00 | 65.00 |
| 4 | Cornelius Bennett | 30.00 | 20.00 |
| 5 | James Lofton | 50.00 | 30.00 |
| 6 | Thurman Thomas | 125.00 | 90.00 |
| 7 | Neal Anderson | 40.00 | 25.00 |
| 8 | Michael Irvin | 90.00 | 60.00 |
| 9 | Emmitt Smith | 225.00 | 175.00 |

| | | | |
|---|---|---|---|
| 10 | Mike Croel | 30.00 | 20.00 |
| 11 | John Elway | 80.00 | 55.00 |
| 12 | Gaston Green | 35.00 | 22.50 |
| 13 | Barry Sanders | 175.00 | 125.00 |
| 14 | Sterling Sharpe | 75.00 | 50.00 |
| 15 | Ernest Givins | 35.00 | 22.50 |
| 16 | Drew Hill | 28.00 | 18.00 |
| 17 | Haywood Jeffires | 40.00 | 25.00 |
| 18 | Warren Moon | 80.00 | 55.00 |
| 19 | Christian Okoye | 40.00 | 25.00 |
| 20 | Derrick Thomas | 60.00 | 35.00 |
| 21 | Ronnie Lott | 50.00 | 30.00 |
| 22 | Todd Marinovich | 75.00 | 50.00 |
| 23 | Henry Ellard | 28.00 | 18.00 |
| 24 | Mark Clayton | 35.00 | 22.50 |
| 25 | Herschel Walker | 60.00 | 35.00 |
| 26 | Irving Fryar | 28.00 | 18.00 |
| 27 | Leonard Russell | 80.00 | 55.00 |
| 28 | Pat Swilling | 30.00 | 20.00 |
| 29 | Rodney Hampton | 75.00 | 50.00 |
| 30 | Rob Moore | 60.00 | 35.00 |
| 31 | Seth Joyner | 28.00 | 18.00 |
| 32 | Reggie White | 40.00 | 25.00 |
| 33 | Eric Green | 30.00 | 20.00 |
| 34 | Rod Woodson | 30.00 | 20.00 |
| 35 | Marion Butts | 35.00 | 22.50 |
| 36 | Charles Haley | 28.00 | 18.00 |
| 37 | John Taylor | 50.00 | 30.00 |
| 38 | Steve Young | 60.00 | 35.00 |
| 39 | Earnest Byner | 30.00 | 20.00 |
| 40 | Gary Clark | 40.00 | 25.00 |
| 41 | Art Monk | 75.00 | 50.00 |
| 42 | Mark Rypien | 75.00 | 50.00 |

# 1992 Action Packed Rookies

This 84-card update set consists primarily of rookie selected in the 1992 NFL draft along with some veteran players who have never appeared in an Action Packed set. The card design is similar to the 1992 regular edition except for a small "R" in the top corner designating the rookie cards. Limited insert cards of Deion Sanders, printed in orange neon colors, were radnoly distributed in the company's foil packs. All cards measure 2-1/2" by 3-1/2".

| | | MINT | NR/MT |
|---|---|---|---|
| **Complete Set (84)** | | 26.00 | 16.00 |
| **Commons** | | .20 | .12 |
| | | | |
| 1 | Steve Emtman (R) | 2.50 | 1.50 |
| 2 | Quentin Coryatt (R) | 1.75 | .75 |
| 3 | Sean Gilbert (R) | .50 | .30 |
| 4 | John Fina (R) | .25 | .15 |
| 5 | Alonzo Spellman (R) | .50 | .30 |
| 6 | Amp Lee (R) | 1.50 | .90 |
| 7 | Robert Porcher (R) | .40 | .25 |
| 8 | Jason Hanson (R) | .20 | .12 |
| 9 | Ty Detmer | .35 | .20 |
| 10 | Ray Roberts (R) | .25 | .15 |
| 11 | Bob Whitfield (R) | .25 | .15 |
| 12 | Greg Skrepenak (R) | .25 | .15 |
| 13 | Vaughn Dunbar (R) | 1.75 | 1.00 |
| 14 | Siran Stacy (R) | .75 | .45 |
| 15 | Mark D'Onofrio (R) | .50 | .30 |
| 16 | Tony Sacca (R) | .80 | .50 |
| 17 | Dana Hall (R) | .60 | .35 |
| 18 | Courtney Hawkins (R) | .75 | .45 |
| 19 | Shane Collins (R) | .30 | .18 |
| 20 | Tony Smith (R) | 1.50 | .90 |
| 21 | Rod Smith (R) | .25 | .15 |
| 22 | Troy Auzenne (R) | .25 | .15 |
| 23 | David Klingler (R) | 3.50 | 2.50 |
| 24 | Darryl Williams (R) | .50 | .30 |
| 25 | Carl Pickens (R) | 1.50 | .90 |
| 26 | Ricardo McDonald (R) | .25 | .15 |
| 27 | Tommy Vardell (R) | 1.50 | .90 |
| 28 | Kevin Smith (R) | .40 | .25 |
| 29 | Rodney Culver (R) | .40 | .25 |
| 30 | Jimmy Smith (R) | .35 | .20 |
| 31 | Robert Jones (R) | .50 | .30 |
| 32 | Tommy Maddox (R) | 2.50 | 1.50 |
| 33 | Shane Dronett (R) | .25 | .15 |
| 34 | Terrell Buckley (R) | 1.25 | .80 |
| 35 | Santana Dotson (R) | .60 | .35 |
| 36 | Edgar Bennett (R) | .60 | .35 |
| 37 | Ashley Ambrose (R) | .35 | .20 |
| 38 | Dale Carter (R) | .40 | .25 |

| | | | |
|---|---|---|---|
| 39 | C. McGlockton (R) | .25 | .15 |
| 40 | Steve Israel (R) | .25 | .15 |
| 41 | Marc Boutte (R) | .25 | .15 |
| 42 | Marco Coleman (R) | .60 | .35 |
| 43 | Troy Vincent (R) | .40 | .25 |
| 44 | Mark Wheeler (R) | .25 | .15 |
| 45 | Darren Perry (R) | .30 | .18 |
| 46 | Eugene Chung (R) | .25 | .15 |
| 47 | Derek Brown (R) | .60 | .35 |
| 48 | Phillippi Sparks (R) | .25 | .15 |
| 49 | Johnny Mitchell (R) | .70 | .40 |
| 50 | Kurt Barber (R) | .25 | .15 |
| 51 | Leon Searcy (R) | .25 | .15 |
| 52 | Chris Mims (R) | .40 | .25 |
| 53 | Keith Jackson | .35 | .20 |
| 54 | Charles Haley | .20 | .12 |
| 55 | Dave Krieg | .25 | .15 |
| 56 | Dan McGwire | .77 | .45 |
| 57 | Phil Simms | .25 | .15 |
| 58 | Bobby Humphrey | .25 | .15 |
| 59 | Jerry Rice | 1.50 | .90 |
| 60 | Joe Montana | 1.25 | .80 |
| 61 | Junior Seau | .25 | .15 |
| 62 | Leslie O'Neal | .20 | .12 |
| 63 | Anthony Miller | .30 | .18 |
| 64 | Timm Rosenbach | .25 | .15 |
| 65 | Herschel Walker | .30 | .18 |
| 66 | Randal Hill | .40 | .25 |
| 67 | Randall Cunningham | .75 | .45 |
| 68 | Al Toon | .25 | .15 |
| 69 | Browning Nagle | 1.25 | .80 |
| 70 | Lawrence Taylor | .25 | .15 |
| 71 | Dan Marino | .80 | .50 |
| 72 | Eric Dickerson | .50 | .30 |
| 73 | Harvey Williams | .75 | .45 |
| 74 | Jeff George | .75 | .45 |
| 75 | Russell Maryland | .30 | .18 |
| 76 | Troy Aikman | 1.75 | 1.00 |
| 77 | Michael Dean Perry | .25 | .15 |
| 78 | Bernie Kosar | .25 | .15 |
| 79 | Boomer Esiason | .25 | .15 |
| 80 | Mike Singletary | .25 | .15 |
| 81 | Bruce Smith | .25 | .15 |
| 82 | Andre Reed | .30 | .18 |
| 83 | Jim Kelly | 1.00 | .70 |
| 84 | Deion Sanders | .50 | .30 |
| 84N | Deion Sanders Insert | 25.00 | 15.00 |

# 1993 Action Packed

The 1993 Action Packed set has been redesigned and reduced to 204-cards which includes 42 new 24k Gold Inserts. The card fronts are embossed and feature full-bleed, full color action photos. The player's last name is printed vertically on the side of the card of gold block letters. Card backs contain a head shot, stats and an Action Note. The gold inserts consist of 18-Quarterback Club members (QB), 12-Moving Targets (MT) and 12-1,000 yard rushers (RB). Those inserts are listed at the end of this checklist. All cards measure 2-1/2" by 3-1/2".

| | MINT | NR/MT |
|---|---|---|
| Complete Set (162) | 60.00 | 38.00 |
| Commons (1-162) | .15 | .10 |
| Complete Gold (42) | 2,150.00 | 1,350.00 |
| Common Gold | 25.00 | 15.00 |

| | | | |
|---|---|---|---|
| 1 | Michael Haynes | .75 | .40 |
| 2 | Chris Miller | .35 | .20 |
| 3 | Andre Rison | .50 | .30 |
| 4 | Jim Kelly | .80 | .50 |
| 5 | Andre Reed | .35 | .20 |
| 6 | Thurman Thomas | 1.25 | .70 |
| 7 | Jim Harbaugh | .25 | .15 |
| 8 | Harold Green | .60 | .35 |
| 9 | David Klingler | 2.00 | 1.25 |
| 10 | Bernie Kosar | .25 | .15 |
| 11 | Troy Aikman | 3.00 | 1.75 |
| 12 | Michael Irvin | 1.00 | .60 |
| 13 | Emmitt Smith | 6.00 | 3.50 |
| 14 | John Elway | .75 | .40 |
| 15 | Barry Sanders | 2.50 | 1.50 |
| 16 | Brett Favre | 1.50 | .80 |
| 17 | Sterling Sharpe | 1.00 | .60 |
| 18 | Ernest Givens | .50 | .30 |
| 19 | Haywood Jeffires | .75 | .45 |

| 20 | Warren Moon | .75 | .40 |
|----|-------------|-----|-----|
| 21 | Lorenzo White | .50 | .30 |
| 22 | Jeff George | .50 | .30 |
| 23 | Joe Montana | .80 | .50 |
| 24 | Jim Everett | .25 | .15 |
| 25 | Cleveland Gary | .20 | .12 |
| 26 | Dan Marino | .80 | .50 |
| 27 | Terry Allen | 1.25 | .70 |
| 28 | Rodney Hampton | 1.00 | .60 |
| 29 | Phil Simms | .25 | .15 |
| 30 | Fred Barnett | .50 | .30 |
| 31 | Randall Cunningham | .75 | .40 |
| 32 | Gary Clark | .30 | .18 |
| 33 | Barry Foster | 1.75 | 1.00 |
| 34 | Neil O'Donnell | 1.25 | .70 |
| 35 | Stan Humphries | 1.50 | .80 |
| 36 | Anthony Miller | .30 | .18 |
| 37 | Jerry Rice | .75 | .40 |
| 38 | Ricky Watters | 1.75 | 1.00 |
| 39 | Steve Young | .80 | .50 |
| 40 | Chris Warren | .25 | .15 |
| 41 | Reggie Cobb | .50 | .30 |
| 42 | Mark Rypien | .40 | .25 |
| 43 | Deion Sanders | .75 | .40 |
| 44 | Henry Jones | .15 | .10 |
| 45 | Bruce Smith | .25 | .15 |
| 46 | Richard Dent | .20 | .12 |
| 47 | Tommy Vardell | .60 | .35 |
| 48 | Charles Haley | .20 | .12 |
| 49 | Ken Norton | .20 | .12 |
| 50 | Jay Novacek | .35 | .20 |
| 51 | Simon Fletcher | .15 | .10 |
| 52 | Pat Swilling | .20 | .12 |
| 53 | Tony Bennett | .20 | .12 |
| 54 | Reggie White | .25 | .15 |
| 55 | Ray Childress | .20 | .12 |
| 56 | Quentin Coryatt | .90 | .50 |
| 57 | Steve Emtman | 1.00 | .60 |
| 58 | Derrick Thomas | .40 | .25 |
| 59 | James Lofton | .25 | .15 |
| 60 | Marco Coleman | .90 | .50 |
| 61 | Bryan Cox | .20 | .12 |
| 62 | Troy Vincent | .30 | .18 |
| 63 | Chris Doleman | .20 | .12 |
| 64 | Audray McMillian | .15 | .10 |
| 65 | Vaughn Dunbar | .80 | .50 |
| 66 | Rickey Jackson | .15 | .10 |
| 67 | Lawrence Taylor | .30 | .18 |
| 68 | Ronnie Lott | .30 | .18 |
| 69 | Rob Moore | .25 | .15 |
| 70 | Browning Nagle | 1.00 | .60 |
| 71 | Eric Allen | .15 | .10 |
| 72 | Tim Harris | .15 | .10 |
| 73 | Clyde Simmons | .15 | .10 |
| 74 | Steve Beuerlein | .60 | .35 |
| 75 | Randal Hill | .40 | .25 |
| 76 | Darren Perry | .15 | .10 |
| 77 | Rod Woodson | .20 | .12 |
| 78 | Marion Butts | .25 | .15 |
| 79 | Leslie O'Neal | .20 | .12 |
| 80 | Junior Seau | .40 | .25 |
| 81 | Cortez Kennedy | .40 | .25 |
| 82 | Santana Dotson | .50 | .30 |
| 83 | Earnest Byner | .20 | .12 |
| 84 | Charles Mann | .15 | .10 |
| 85 | Pierce Holt | .15 | .10 |
| 86 | Mike Pritchard | .50 | .30 |
| 87 | Cornelius Bennett | .20 | .12 |
| 88 | Neal Anderson | .25 | .15 |
| 89 | Carl Pickens | .75 | .40 |
| 90 | Eric Metcalf | .20 | .12 |
| 91 | Michael Dean Perry | .20 | .12 |
| 92 | Alvin Harper | .75 | .40 |
| 93 | Robert Jones | .35 | .20 |
| 94 | Steve Atwater | .20 | .12 |
| 95 | Rod Bernstine | .25 | .15 |
| 96 | Herman Moore | .75 | .40 |
| 97 | Chris Spielman | .15 | .10 |
| 98 | Terrell Buckley | .60 | .35 |
| 99 | Dale Carter | .60 | .35 |
| 100 | Neil Smith | .20 | .12 |
| 101 | Tim Brown | .25 | .15 |
| 102 | Gaston Green | .20 | .12 |
| 103 | Howie Long | .15 | .10 |
| 104 | Todd Marinovich | .40 | .25 |
| 105 | Anthony Smith | .15 | .10 |
| 106 | Willie Anderson | .25 | .15 |
| 107 | Henry Ellard | .25 | .15 |
| 108 | Mark Higgs | .35 | .20 |
| 109 | Keith Jackson | .35 | .20 |
| 110 | Irving Fryar | .20 | .12 |
| 111 | Cris Carter | .25 | .15 |
| 112 | Leonard Russell | .35 | .20 |
| 113 | Wayne Martin | .15 | .10 |
| 114 | Mark Jackson | .20 | .12 |
| 115 | Dave Meggett | .20 | .12 |
| 116 | Brad Baxter | .20 | .12 |
| 117 | Boomer Esiason | .25 | .15 |
| 118 | Johnny Johnson | .20 | .12 |
| 119 | Seth Joyner | .15 | .10 |
| 120 | Kevin Greene | .15 | .10 |
| 121 | Ronnie Harmon | .25 | .15 |
| 122 | Chris Mims | .30 | .18 |
| 123 | Amp Lee | .75 | .40 |
| 124 | Tim McDonald | .15 | .10 |
| 125 | Darrell Green | .20 | .12 |
| 126 | Art Monk | .30 | .18 |
| 127 | Tony Smith | .25 | .15 |
| 128 | Bill Brooks | .20 | .12 |
| 129 | Kenneth Davis | .25 | .15 |
| 130 | Donnell Woolford | .15 | .10 |
| 131 | Derrick Fenner | .20 | .12 |
| 132 | Michael Jackson | .25 | .15 |
| 133 | Michael Brooks | .15 | .10 |

| | | | |
|---|---|---:|---:|
| 134 | Al Smith | .15 | .10 |
| 135 | Curtis Duncan | .20 | .12 |
| 136 | Rodney Culver | .20 | .12 |
| 137 | Harvey Williams | .25 | .15 |
| 138 | Terry McDaniel | .15 | .10 |
| 139 | Eric Dickerson | .25 | .15 |
| 140 | Sean Gilbert | .25 | .15 |
| 141 | Shane Conlan | .15 | .10 |
| 142 | Todd Scott | .15 | .10 |
| 143 | Jim McMahon | .20 | .12 |
| 144 | Vincent Brown | .15 | .10 |
| 145 | Andre Tippett | .15 | .10 |
| 146 | Jon Vaughn | .20 | .12 |
| 147 | Marv Cook | .20 | .12 |
| 148 | Morten Andersen | .20 | .12 |
| 149 | Sam Mills | .15 | .10 |
| 150 | Mark Collins | .20 | .12 |
| 151 | Heath Sherman | .20 | .12 |
| 152 | Herschel Walker | .25 | .15 |
| 153 | Johnny Bailey | .20 | .12 |
| 154 | Greg Lloyd | .15 | .10 |
| 155 | Gill Byrd | .15 | .10 |
| 156 | Brent Jones | .20 | .12 |
| 157 | Rufus Porter | .15 | .10 |
| 158 | Eugene Robinson | .15 | .10 |
| 159 | Broderick Thomas | .15 | .10 |
| 160 | Lawrence Dawsey | .35 | .20 |
| 161 | Anthony Munoz | .15 | .10 |
| 162 | Wilber Marshall | .15 | .10 |
| QB1 | Troy Aikman | 175.00 | 100.00 |
| QB2 | R.Cunningham | 60.00 | 38.00 |
| QB3 | John Elway | 75.00 | 45.00 |
| QB4 | Jim Everett | 35.00 | 22.00 |
| QB5 | Brett Favre | 100.00 | 65.00 |
| QB6 | Jim Harbaugh | 35.00 | 22.00 |
| QB7 | Jeff Hostetler | 30.00 | 18.00 |
| QB8 | Jim Kelly | 60.00 | 38.00 |
| QB9 | David Klingler | 125.00 | 75.00 |
| QB10 | Bernie Kosar | 30.00 | 18.00 |
| QB11 | Dan Marino | 100.00 | 65.00 |
| QB12 | Chris Miller | 30.00 | 18.00 |
| QB13 | Boomer Esiason | 35.00 | 22.00 |
| QB14 | Warren Moon | 60.00 | 38.00 |
| QB15 | Neil O'Donnell | 50.00 | 30.00 |
| QB16 | Mark Rypien | 35.00 | 22.00 |
| QB17 | Phil Simms | 30.00 | 18.00 |
| QB18 | Steve Young | 80.00 | 50.00 |
| MT1 | Fred Barnett | 40.00 | 25.00 |
| MT2 | Gary Clark | 40.00 | 25.00 |
| MT3 | Mark Clayton | 30.00 | 18.00 |
| MT4 | Ernest Givens | 30.00 | 18.00 |
| MT5 | Michael Haynes | 50.00 | 30.00 |
| MT6 | Michael Irvin | 90.00 | 60.00 |
| MT7 | Haywood Jeffires | 40.00 | 25.00 |
| MT8 | Anthony Miller | 40.00 | 25.00 |
| MT9 | Andre Reed | 40.00 | 25.00 |
| MT10 | Jerry Rice | 100.00 | 65.00 |
| MT11 | Andre Rison | 40.00 | 25.00 |
| MT12 | Sterling Sharpe | 65.00 | 42.00 |
| RB1 | Terry Allen | 40.00 | 25.00 |
| RB2 | Reggie Cobb | 35.00 | 20.00 |
| RB3 | Barry Foster | 80.00 | 50.00 |
| RB4 | Cleveland Gary | 25.00 | 15.00 |
| RB5 | Harold Green | 40.00 | 25.00 |
| RB6 | Rodney Hampton | 50.00 | 30.00 |
| RB7 | Barry Sanders | 125.00 | 75.00 |
| RB8 | Emmitt Smith | 200.00 | 125.00 |
| RB9 | Thurman Thomas | 100.00 | 65.00 |
| RB10 | Chris Warren | 25.00 | 15.00 |
| RB11 | Ricky Watters | 80.00 | 50.00 |
| RB12 | Lorenzo White | 35.00 | 20.00 |

# ALL WORLD NFL

## 1992 All World NFL

    This 300-card set is the first NFL edition produced by All World Sports. Card fronts feature full color action photos printed on a glossy stock. An American flag design is printed across the top of the card. Key subsets include Legends in the Making (L) (1-10), Rookies (R) (11-60) and Greats of the Game (G) (266-300). Joe Namath and Jim Brown are also honored with special 5-card subsets. All cards measure 2-1/2" by 3-1/2".

|  |  | MINT | NR/MT |
|---|---|---|---|
| **Complete Set (300)** | | 20.00 | 14.00 |
| **Commons** | | .05 | .02 |
| 1 | Emmitt Smith (L) | .80 | .50 |
| 2 | Thurman Thomas (L) | .25 | .15 |
| 3 | Deion Sanders (L) | .12 | .07 |
| 4 | R. Cunningham (L) | .10 | .06 |
| 5 | Michael Irvin (L) | .15 | .10 |
| 6 | Bruce Smith (L) | .08 | .05 |
| 7 | Jeff George (L) | .15 | .10 |
| 8 | Derrick Thomas (L) | .12 | .07 |
| 9 | Andre Rison (L) | .12 | .07 |
| 10 | Troy Aikman (L) | .20 | .12 |
| 11 | Quentin Coryatt (R) | .60 | .35 |
| 12 | Carl Pickens (R) | .70 | .40 |
| 13 | Steve Emtman (R) | .80 | .50 |
| 14 | Derek Brown (R) | .25 | .15 |
| 15 | Desmond Howard (R) | 2.75 | 1.75 |
| 16 | Troy Vincent (R) | .15 | .10 |
| 17 | David Klingler (R) | 1.50 | .90 |

| # | Player | | |
|---|---|---|---|
| 18 | Vaughn Dunbar (R) | .60 | .35 |
| 19 | Terrell Buckley (R) | .50 | .30 |
| 20 | Jimmy Smith (R) | .12 | .07 |
| 21 | Marquez Pope (R) | .10 | .06 |
| 22 | Kurt Barber (R) | .08 | .05 |
| 23 | Robert Harris (R) | .08 | .05 |
| 24 | Tony Sacca (R) | .15 | .10 |
| 25 | Alonzo Spellman (R) | .12 | .07 |
| 26 | Shane Collins (R) | .12 | .07 |
| 27 | Chris Mims (R) | .25 | .15 |
| 28 | Siran Stacy (R) | .20 | .12 |
| 29 | Edgar Bennett (R) | .50 | .30 |
| 30 | Sean Gilbert (R) | .15 | .10 |
| 31 | Eugene Chung (R) | .08 | .05 |
| 32 | Levon Kirkland (R) | .10 | .06 |
| 33 | Chuck Smith (R) | .08 | .05 |
| 34 | C. McGlockton (R) | .12 | .07 |
| 35 | Ashley Ambrose (R) | .12 | .07 |
| 36 | Phillippi Sparks (R) | .10 | .06 |
| 37 | Darryl Williams (R) | .20 | .12 |
| 38 | Tracy Scroggins (R) | .08 | .05 |
| 39 | Mike Gaddis (R) | .12 | .07 |
| 40 | Tony Brooks (R) | .15 | .10 |
| 41 | Steve Israel (R) | .10 | .06 |
| 42 | Patrick Rowe (R) | .20 | .12 |
| 43 | Shane Dronett (R) | .15 | .10 |
| 44 | Mike Pawlawski (R) | .12 | .07 |
| 45 | Dale Carter (R) | .20 | .12 |
| 46 | Tyji Armstrong (R) | .08 | .05 |
| 47 | Kevin Smith (R) | .15 | .10 |
| 48 | Courtney Hawkins (R) | .25 | .15 |
| 49 | Marco Coleman (R) | .25 | .15 |
| 50 | Tommy Vardell (R) | .75 | .45 |
| 51 | Ray Ethridge (R) | .12 | .07 |
| 52 | Robert Porcher (R) | .10 | .06 |
| 53 | Todd Collins (R) | .08 | .05 |
| 54 | Robert Jones (R) | .15 | .10 |
| 55 | Tommy Maddox (R) | 1.50 | .90 |
| 56 | Dana Hall (R) | .12 | .07 |
| 57 | Leon Searcy (R) | .08 | .05 |
| 58 | Robert Brooks (R) | .12 | .07 |
| 59 | Darren Woodsen (R) | .08 | .05 |
| 60 | Jeremy Lincoln (R) | .08 | .05 |
| 61 | Sean Jones | .05 | .02 |
| 62 | Howie Long | .07 | .04 |
| 63 | Rich Gannon | .20 | .12 |
| 64 | Keith Byars | .07 | .04 |
| 65 | John Taylor | .15 | .10 |
| 66 | Burt Grossman | .07 | .04 |
| 67 | Chris Hinton | .05 | .02 |
| 68 | Brad Muster | .08 | .05 |
| 69 | Cris Dishman | .07 | .04 |
| 70 | Russell Maryland | .15 | .10 |
| 71 | Harvey Williams | .25 | .15 |
| 72 | Broderick Thomas | .12 | .07 |
| 73 | Louis Lipps | .07 | .04 |
| 74 | Erik Kramer | .25 | .15 |
| 75 | David Fulcher | .05 | .02 |
| 76 | Andre Tippett | .07 | .04 |
| 77 | Timm Rosenbach | .12 | .07 |
| 78 | Mark Rypien | .20 | .12 |
| 79 | James Lofton | .15 | .10 |
| 80 | Dan Saleaumua | .05 | .02 |
| 81 | John L. Williams | .07 | .04 |
| 82 | Kevin Fagan | .05 | .02 |
| 83 | Willie Anderson | .08 | .05 |
| 84 | Michael Dean Perry | .12 | .07 |
| 85 | Mark Higgs | .15 | .10 |
| 86 | Pat Swilling | .15 | .10 |
| 87 | Pierce Holt | .05 | .02 |
| 88 | John Elway | .20 | .12 |
| 89 | Billy Brooks | .05 | .02 |
| 90 | Rob Moore | .15 | .10 |
| 91 | Junior Seau | .15 | .10 |
| 92 | Wendell Davis | .10 | .06 |
| 93 | Brian Noble | .05 | .02 |
| 94 | Ernest Givins | .08 | .05 |
| 95 | Phil Simms | .12 | .07 |
| 96 | Eric Dickerson | .20 | .12 |
| 97 | Bennie Blades | .07 | .04 |
| 98 | Gary Anderson | .05 | .02 |
| 99 | Erric Pegram | .10 | .06 |
| 100 | Hart Lee Dykes | .07 | .04 |
| 101 | Charles Haley | .07 | .04 |
| 102 | Bruce Smith | .10 | .06 |
| 103 | Nick Lowery | .07 | .04 |
| 104 | Webster Slaughter | .07 | .04 |
| 105 | Ray Childress | .07 | .04 |
| 106 | Gene Atkins | .05 | .02 |
| 107 | Bruce Armstrong | .05 | .02 |
| 108 | Anthony Miller | .12 | .07 |
| 109 | Eric Thomas | .05 | .02 |
| 110 | Greg Townsend | .07 | .04 |
| 111 | Anthony Carter | .07 | .04 |
| 112 | James Hasty | .05 | .02 |
| 113 | Chris Miller | .20 | .12 |
| 114 | Sammie Smith | .10 | .06 |
| 115 | Bubby Brister | .10 | .06 |
| 116 | Mark Clayton | .10 | .06 |
| 117 | Richard Johnson | .05 | .02 |
| 118 | Bernie Kosar | .15 | .10 |
| 119 | Lionel Washington | .05 | .02 |
| 120 | Gary Clark | .12 | .07 |
| 121 | Anthony Munoz | .08 | .05 |
| 122 | Brent Jones | .07 | .04 |
| 123 | Thurman Thomas | .30 | .18 |
| 124 | Lee Williams | .05 | .02 |
| 125 | Jessie Hester | .05 | .02 |
| 126 | Andre Ware | .12 | .07 |
| 127 | Patrick Hunter | .05 | .02 |
| 128 | Erik Howard | .05 | .02 |
| 129 | Keith Jackson | .12 | .07 |
| 130 | Troy Aikman | .40 | .25 |
| 131 | Mike Singletary | .12 | .07 |

| # | Name | | |
|---|------|---|---|
| 132 | Carnell Lake | .05 | .02 |
| 133 | Jeff Hostetler | .20 | .12 |
| 134 | Alonzo Highsmith | .05 | .02 |
| 135 | Vaughn Johnson | .07 | .04 |
| 136 | Louis Oliver | .07 | .04 |
| 137 | Mel Gray | .05 | .02 |
| 138 | Al Toon | .08 | .05 |
| 139 | Bubba McDowell | .05 | .02 |
| 140 | Ronnie Lott | .15 | .10 |
| 141 | Deion Sanders | .15 | .10 |
| 142 | Jim Harbaugh | .15 | .10 |
| 143 | Gary Zimmerman | .05 | .02 |
| 144 | Ernie Jones | .07 | .04 |
| 145 | Cortez Kennedy | .10 | .06 |
| 146 | Jeff Cross | .05 | .02 |
| 147 | Floyd Turner | .05 | .02 |
| 148 | Mike Tomczak | .08 | .05 |
| 149 | Lorenzo White | .15 | .10 |
| 150 | Mark Carrier | .08 | .05 |
| 151 | John Stephens | .07 | .04 |
| 152 | Jerry Rice | .40 | .25 |
| 153 | Jim Kelly | .35 | .20 |
| 154 | Al Smith | .05 | .02 |
| 155 | Duane Bickett | .05 | .02 |
| 156 | Brett Perriman | .07 | .04 |
| 157 | Boomer Esiason | .12 | .07 |
| 158 | Neil Smith | .05 | .02 |
| 159 | Eddie Anderson | .05 | .02 |
| 160 | Browning Nagle | .80 | .50 |
| 161 | John Friesz | .10 | .06 |
| 162 | Robert Delpino | .07 | .04 |
| 163 | Darren Lewis | .15 | .10 |
| 164 | Roger Craig | .08 | .05 |
| 165 | Keith McCants | .07 | .04 |
| 166 | Stephone Paige | .07 | .04 |
| 167 | Steve Broussard | .10 | .06 |
| 168 | Gaston Green | .10 | .06 |
| 169 | Ethan Horton | .07 | .04 |
| 170 | Lewis Billups | .05 | .02 |
| 171 | Mike Merriweather | .05 | .02 |
| 172 | Randall Cunningham | .15 | .10 |
| 173 | Leonard Marshall | .05 | .02 |
| 174 | Jay Novacek | .08 | .05 |
| 175 | Irvin Fryar | .07 | .04 |
| 176 | Randal Hill | .12 | .07 |
| 177 | Keith Henderson | .07 | .04 |
| 178 | Brad Baxter | .12 | .07 |
| 179 | William Fuller | .05 | .02 |
| 180 | Leslie O'Neal | .07 | .04 |
| 181 | Steve Smith | .05 | .02 |
| 182 | Joe Montana | .40 | .25 |
| 183 | Eric Green | .10 | .06 |
| 184 | Rodney Peete | .12 | .07 |
| 185 | Lawrence Dawsey | .12 | .07 |
| 186 | Brian Mitchell | .07 | .04 |
| 187 | Rickey Jackson | .07 | .04 |
| 188 | Christian Okoye | .10 | .06 |
| 189 | David Wyman | .05 | .02 |
| 190 | Jessie Tuggle | .05 | .02 |
| 191 | Ronnie Harmon | .05 | .02 |
| 192 | Andre Reed | .12 | .07 |
| 193 | Chris Doleman | .08 | .05 |
| 194 | Leroy Hoard | .12 | .07 |
| 195 | Mark Ingram | .05 | .02 |
| 196 | Willie Gault | .07 | .04 |
| 197 | Eugene Lockhart | .05 | .02 |
| 198 | Jim Everett | .12 | .07 |
| 199 | Doug Smith | .05 | .02 |
| 200 | Clarence Verdin | .07 | .04 |
| 201 | Steve Bono | .35 | .20 |
| 202 | Mark Vlasic | .08 | .05 |
| 203 | Fred Barnett | .15 | .10 |
| 204 | Henry Thomas | .05 | .02 |
| 205 | Shaun Gayle | .05 | .02 |
| 206 | Rod Bernstine | .07 | .04 |
| 207 | Harold Green | .15 | .10 |
| 208 | Dan McGwire | .40 | .25 |
| 209 | Marv Cook | .07 | .04 |
| 210 | Emmitt Smith | 1.50 | .90 |
| 211 | Merrill Hoge | .07 | .04 |
| 212 | Darion Conner | .05 | .02 |
| 213 | Mike Sherrard | .07 | .04 |
| 214 | Jeff George | .25 | .15 |
| 215 | Craig Heyward | .07 | .04 |
| 216 | Henry Ellard | .07 | .04 |
| 217 | Lawrence Taylor | .12 | .07 |
| 218 | Jerry Ball | .05 | .02 |
| 219 | Tom Rathman | .07 | .04 |
| 220 | Warren Moon | .20 | .12 |
| 221 | Ricky Proehl | .08 | .05 |
| 222 | Sterling Sharpe | .20 | .12 |
| 223 | Ernest Byner | .07 | .04 |
| 224 | Jay Schroeder | .10 | .06 |
| 225 | Vance Johnson | .08 | .05 |
| 226 | Cornelius Bennett | .12 | .07 |
| 227 | Ken O'Brien | .10 | .06 |
| 228 | Ferrell Edmunds | .05 | .02 |
| 229 | Eric Allen | .05 | .02 |
| 230 | Derrick Thomas | .20 | .12 |
| 231 | Cris Carter | .20 | .12 |
| 232 | Jon Vaughn | .12 | .07 |
| 233 | Eric Metcalf | .12 | .07 |
| 234 | William Perry | .07 | .04 |
| 235 | Vinny Testaverde | .10 | .06 |
| 236 | Chip Banks | .05 | .02 |
| 237 | Brian Blades | .07 | .04 |
| 238 | Calvin Williams | .08 | .05 |
| 239 | Andre Rison | .15 | .10 |
| 240 | Neil O'Donnell | .50 | .30 |
| 241 | Michael Irvin | .25 | .15 |
| 242 | Gary Plummer | .05 | .02 |
| 243 | Nick Bell | .20 | .12 |
| 244 | Ray Crockett | .05 | .02 |
| 245 | Sam Mills | .07 | .04 |

| | | | |
|---|---|---|---|
| 246 | Haywood Jeffries | .20 | .12 |
| 247 | Steve Young | .30 | .18 |
| 248 | Martin Bayless | .05 | .02 |
| 249 | Dan Marino | .25 | .15 |
| 250 | Carl Banks | .05 | .02 |
| 251 | Keith McKeller | .05 | .02 |
| 252 | Aaron Wallace | .07 | .04 |
| 253 | Lamar Lathon | .05 | .02 |
| 254 | Derrick Fenner | .07 | .04 |
| 255 | Vai Sikahema | .05 | .02 |
| 256 | Keith Sims | .05 | .02 |
| 257 | Rohn Stark | .05 | .02 |
| 258 | Reggie Roby | .05 | .02 |
| 259 | Tony Zendejas | .05 | .02 |
| 260 | Harris Barton | .05 | .02 |
| 261 | Checklist (1-100) | .05 | .02 |
| 262 | Checklist (101-200) | .05 | .02 |
| 263 | Checklist (201-300) | .05 | .02 |
| 264 | Rookies Checklist | .05 | .02 |
| 265 | Greats Checklist | .05 | .02 |
| 266 | Joe Namath | .12 | .07 |
| 267 | Joe Namath | .12 | .07 |
| 268 | Joe Namath | .12 | .07 |
| 269 | Joe Namath | .12 | .07 |
| 270 | Joe Namath | .12 | .07 |
| 271 | Jim Brown | .12 | .07 |
| 272 | Jim Brown | .12 | .07 |
| 273 | Jim Brown | .12 | .07 |
| 274 | Jim Brown | .12 | .07 |
| 275 | Jim Brown | .12 | .07 |
| 276 | Vince Lomabardi (G) | .12 | .07 |
| 277 | Jim Thorpe (G) | .10 | .06 |
| 278 | Tom Fears (G) | .05 | .02 |
| 279 | J. Henry Johnson(G) | .07 | .04 |
| 280 | Gale Sayers (G) | .12 | .07 |
| 281 | Willie Brown (G) | .07 | .04 |
| 282 | Doak Walker (G) | .08 | .05 |
| 283 | Night Train Lane (G) | .07 | .04 |
| 284 | Otto Graham (G) | .12 | .07 |
| 285 | Hugh McElhenny (G) | .10 | .06 |
| 286 | Roger Staubach (G) | .15 | .10 |
| 287 | Steve Largent (G) | .10 | .06 |
| 288 | Otis Taylor (G) | .08 | .05 |
| 289 | Sam Huff (G) | .10 | .06 |
| 290 | Harold Carmichael (G) | .08 | .05 |
| 291 | Steve Van Buren (G) | .08 | .05 |
| 292 | Gino Marchetti (G) | .08 | .05 |
| 293 | Tony Dorsett (G) | .12 | .07 |
| 294 | Leo Nomellini (G) | .08 | .05 |
| 295 | Jack Lambert (G) | .10 | .06 |
| 296 | Joe Theismann (G) | .10 | .06 |
| 297 | Bobby Layne (G) | .12 | .07 |
| 298 | John Stallworth (G) | .08 | .05 |
| 299 | Paul Hornung (G) | .12 | .07 |
| 300 | Don Maynard (G) | .10 | .06 |

# BOWMAN

## 1948 Bowman

The black and white cards in this 108-cards set measure 2-1/16" by 2-1/2" and are among the most sought after in the hobby. One-third of the cards are considered extremely scarce. Those cards (with card numbers divisible by three) were in the third 36-card sheet printed by Bowman and were produced in smaller quantities than the first two sheets.

| | | NR/MT | EX |
|---|---|---|---|
| Complete Set (108) | | 6,600.00 | 3,275.00 |
| Commons | | 20.00 | 10.00 |
| Commons (3,6,9,12 etc) | | 80.00 | 38.00 |

| | | | |
|---|---|---|---|
| 1 | Joe Tereshinski | 180.00 | 80.00 |
| 2 | Larry Olsonoski | 20.00 | 10.00 |
| 3 | John Lujack (R) | 275.00 | 130.00 |
| 4 | Ray Poole | 20.00 | 10.00 |
| 5 | Bill DeCorrevont | 20.00 | 10.00 |
| 6 | Paul Briggs | 80.00 | 38.00 |
| 7 | S. Van Buren(R) | 140.00 | 60.00 |
| 8 | K. Washington(R) | 48.00 | 22.00 |
| 9 | Nolan Luhn | 80.00 | 38.00 |
| 10 | Chris Iversen | 20.00 | 10.00 |
| 11 | Jack Wiley | 20.00 | 10.00 |
| 12 | C. Conerly (R) | 260.00 | 120.00 |
| 13 | Hugh Taylor | 25.00 | 12.00 |
| 14 | Frank Seno | 20.00 | 10.00 |
| 15 | Gil Bouley | 80.00 | 38.00 |
| 16 | Tommy Thompson | 35.00 | 15.00 |
| 17 | Charlie Trippi (R) | 125.00 | 55.00 |
| 18 | Vince Banonis | 80.00 | 38.00 |

| | | | |
|---|---|---:|---:|
| 19 | Art Faircloth | 20.00 | 10.00 |
| 20 | Clyde Goodnight | 20.00 | 10.00 |
| 21 | Bill Chipley | 80.00 | 38.00 |
| 22 | Sammy Baugh (R) | 375.00 | 175.00 |
| 23 | Don Kindt | 20.00 | 10.00 |
| 24 | John Koniszewski | 80.00 | 38.00 |
| 25 | Pat McHugh | 20.00 | 10.00 |
| 26 | Bob Waterfield (R) | 180.00 | 80.00 |
| 27 | Tony Compagno | 80.00 | 38.00 |
| 28 | Paul Governali | 20.00 | 10.00 |
| 29 | Pat Harder | 35.00 | 15.00 |
| 30 | Vic Lindskog | 80.00 | 38.00 |
| 31 | Salvatore Rosato | 20.00 | 10.00 |
| 32 | John Mastrangelo | 20.00 | 10.00 |
| 33 | Fred Gehrke | 80.00 | 38.00 |
| 34 | Bosh Pritchard | 20.00 | 10.00 |
| 35 | Mike Micka | 20.00 | 10.00 |
| 36 | Bulldog Turner (R) | 180.00 | 80.00 |
| 37 | Len Younce | 20.00 | 10.00 |
| 38 | Pat West | 20.00 | 10.00 |
| 39 | Russ Thomas | 80.00 | 38.00 |
| 40 | James Peebles | 20.00 | 10.00 |
| 41 | Bob Skoglund | 20.00 | 10.00 |
| 42 | Walt Stickle | 80.00 | 38.00 |
| 43 | Whitey Wistert | 20.00 | 10.00 |
| 44 | Paul Christman (R) | 48.00 | 22.00 |
| 45 | Jay Rhodemyre | 80.00 | 38.00 |
| 46 | Skip Minisi | 20.00 | 10.00 |
| 47 | Bob Mann | 20.00 | 10.00 |
| 48 | Mal Kutner | 80.00 | 38.00 |
| 49 | Dick Poillon | 20.00 | 10.00 |
| 50 | Charles Cherundolo | 20.00 | 10.00 |
| 51 | Gerald Cowhig | 80.00 | 38.00 |
| 52 | Neil Armstrong | 25.00 | 12.00 |
| 53 | Frank Maznicki | 20.00 | 10.00 |
| 54 | John Sanchez | 80.00 | 38.00 |
| 55 | Frank Reagan | 20.00 | 10.00 |
| 56 | Jim Hardy | 20.00 | 10.00 |
| 57 | John Badaczewski | 80.00 | 38.00 |
| 58 | Robert Nussbaumer | 20.00 | 10.00 |
| 59 | Marvin Pregulman | 20.00 | 10.00 |
| 60 | Elbie Nickel (R) | 90.00 | 42.00 |
| 61 | Alex Wojciechowicz (R) | 90.00 | 42.00 |
| 62 | Walt Schlinkman | 20.00 | 10.00 |
| 63 | Pete Pihos (R) | 200.00 | 90.00 |
| 64 | Joseph Sulaitis | 20.00 | 10.00 |
| 65 | Mike Holovak (R) | 35.00 | 15.00 |
| 66 | Cecil Souders | 80.00 | 38.00 |
| 67 | Paul McKee | 20.00 | 10.00 |
| 68 | Bill Moore | 20.00 | 10.00 |
| 69 | Frank Minini | 80.00 | 38.00 |
| 70 | Jack Ferrante | 20.00 | 10.00 |
| 71 | Leslie Horvath | 35.00 | 15.00 |
| 72 | Ted Fritsch | 80.00 | 38.00 |
| 73 | Tex Coulter | 20.00 | 10.00 |
| 74 | Boley Dancewicz | 20.00 | 10.00 |
| 75 | Dante Mangani | 80.00 | 38.00 |
| 76 | James Hefti | 20.00 | 10.00 |
| 77 | Paul Sarringhaus | 20.00 | 10.00 |
| 78 | Joe Scott | 80.00 | 38.00 |
| 79 | Bucko Kilroy | 25.00 | 12.00 |
| 80 | Bill Dudley (R) | 125.00 | 55.00 |
| 81 | Marshall Goldberg | 80.00 | 38.00 |
| 82 | John Cannady | 20.00 | 10.00 |
| 83 | Perry Moss | 20.00 | 10.00 |
| 84 | Harold Crisler | 80.00 | 38.00 |
| 85 | Bill Gray | 20.00 | 10.00 |
| 86 | John Clement | 20.00 | 10.00 |
| 87 | Dan Sandifer | 80.00 | 38.00 |
| 88 | Ben Kish | 20.00 | 10.00 |
| 89 | Herbert Banta | 20.00 | 10.00 |
| 90 | Bill Garnaas | 80.00 | 38.00 |
| 91 | Jim White | 20.00 | 10.00 |
| 92 | Frank Barzilauskas | 20.00 | 10.00 |
| 93 | Vic Sears | 80.00 | 38.00 |
| 94 | John Adams | 20.00 | 10.00 |
| 95 | George McAfee (R) | 100.00 | 48.00 |
| 96 | Ralph Heywood | 80.00 | 38.00 |
| 97 | Joe Muha | 20.00 | 10.00 |
| 98 | Fred Enke | 20.00 | 10.00 |
| 99 | Harry Gilmer (R) | 125.00 | 55.00 |
| 100 | Bill Miklich | 20.00 | 10.00 |
| 101 | Joe Gottlieb | 20.00 | 10.00 |
| 102 | Bud Angsman | 80.00 | 38.00 |
| 103 | Tom Farmer | 20.00 | 10.00 |
| 104 | Bruce Smith | 35.00 | 15.00 |
| 105 | Bob Cifers | 80.00 | 38.00 |
| 106 | Ernie Steele | 20.00 | 10.00 |
| 107 | Sid Luckman (R) | 200.00 | 90.00 |
| 108 | Buford Ray | 425.00 | 180.00 |

# 1950 Bowman

This 144-card set marks Bowman's first use of color on football cards. The cards measure 2-1/16" by 2-1/2" with vertical close-up player images on the card fronts and horizontal card backs.

| | | NR/MT | EX |
|---|---|---|---|
| | **Complete Set (144)** | 4,250.00 | 2,000.00 |
| | **Commons** | 14.00 | 7.00 |
| | | | |
| 1 | Doak Walker | 125.00 | 55.00 |
| 2 | John Greene | 14.00 | 7.00 |
| 3 | Bob Nowasky | 14.00 | 7.00 |
| 4 | Jonathan Jenkins | 14.00 | 7.00 |
| 5 | Y.A. Tittle (R) | 275.00 | 125.00 |
| 6 | Lou Groza (R) | 125.00 | 55.00 |
| 7 | Alex Agase (R) | 20.00 | 10.00 |
| 8 | Mac Speedie (R) | 20.00 | 10.00 |
| 9 | Tony Canadeo (R) | 35.00 | 15.00 |
| 10 | Larry Craig | 14.00 | 7.00 |
| 11 | Ted Fritsch, Sr. | 14.00 | 7.00 |
| 12 | Joe Goldring | 14.00 | 7.00 |
| 13 | Martin Ruby | 14.00 | 7.00 |
| 14 | George Taliaferro | 20.00 | 10.00 |
| 15 | Tank Younger (R) | 25.00 | 12.00 |
| 16 | Glenn Davis (R) | 125.00 | 55.00 |
| 17 | Bob Waterfield | 60.00 | 28.00 |
| 18 | Val Jansante | 14.00 | 7.00 |
| 19 | Joe Geri | 14.00 | 7.00 |
| 20 | Jerry Nuzum | 14.00 | 7.00 |
| 21 | Elmer Angsman | 14.00 | 7.00 |
| 22 | Billy Dewell | 14.00 | 7.00 |
| 23 | Steve Van Buren | 50.00 | 22.50 |
| 24 | Cliff Patton | 14.00 | 7.00 |
| 25 | Bosh Pritchard | 14.00 | 7.00 |
| 26 | John Lujack | 60.00 | 28.00 |
| 27 | Sid Luckman | 60.00 | 28.00 |
| 28 | Bulldog Turner | 35.00 | 15.00 |
| 29 | Bill Dudley | 30.00 | 14.00 |
| 30 | Hugh Taylor | 14.00 | 7.00 |
| 31 | George Thomas | 14.00 | 7.00 |
| 32 | Ray Poole | 14.00 | 7.00 |
| 33 | Travis Tidwell | 14.00 | 7.00 |
| 34 | Gail Bruce | 14.00 | 7.00 |
| 35 | Joe Perry (R) | 125.00 | 55.00 |
| 36 | Frankie Albert (R) | 30.00 | 14.00 |
| 37 | Bobby Layne | 125.00 | 55.00 |
| 38 | Leon Hart | 25.00 | 12.00 |
| 39 | B. Hoernschemeyer | 14.00 | 7.00 |
| 40 | Dick Barwegan | 14.00 | 7.00 |
| 41 | Adrian Burk | 14.00 | 7.00 |
| 42 | Barry French | 14.00 | 7.00 |
| 43 | Marion Motley (R) | 80.00 | 38.00 |
| 44 | Jim Martin | 14.00 | 7.00 |
| 45 | Otto Graham (R) | 550.00 | 250.00 |
| 46 | Al Baldwin | 14.00 | 7.00 |
| 47 | Larry Coutre | 14.00 | 7.00 |
| 48 | John Rauch | 14.00 | 7.00 |
| 49 | Sam Tamburo | 14.00 | 7.00 |
| 50 | Mike Swistowicz | 14.00 | 7.00 |
| 51 | Tom Fears (R) | 75.00 | 35.00 |
| 52 | Elroy Hirsch (R) | 135.00 | 60.00 |
| 53 | Dick Huffman | 14.00 | 7.00 |
| 54 | Bob Gage | 14.00 | 7.00 |
| 55 | Bob Tinsley | 14.00 | 7.00 |
| 56 | Bill Blackburn | 14.00 | 7.00 |
| 57 | John Cochran | 14.00 | 7.00 |
| 58 | Bill Fischer | 14.00 | 7.00 |
| 59 | Whitey Wistert | 14.00 | 7.00 |
| 60 | Clyde Scott | 14.00 | 7.00 |
| 61 | Walter Barnes | 14.00 | 7.00 |
| 62 | Bob Perina | 14.00 | 7.00 |
| 63 | Bill Wightkin | 14.00 | 7.00 |
| 64 | Bob Goode | 14.00 | 7.00 |
| 65 | Al Demao | 14.00 | 7.00 |
| 66 | Harry Gilmer | 18.00 | 9.00 |
| 67 | Bill Austin | 14.00 | 7.00 |
| 68 | Joe Scott | 14.00 | 7.00 |
| 69 | Tex Coulter | 14.00 | 7.00 |
| 70 | Paul Salata | 14.00 | 7.00 |
| 71 | Emil Sitko | 14.00 | 7.00 |
| 72 | Bill Johnson | 14.00 | 7.00 |
| 73 | Don Doll | 14.00 | 7.00 |
| 74 | Dan Sandifer | 14.00 | 7.00 |
| 75 | John Panelli | 14.00 | 7.00 |
| 76 | Bill Leonard | 14.00 | 7.00 |
| 77 | Bob Kelly | 14.00 | 7.00 |
| 78 | Dante Lavelli (R) | 50.00 | 22.50 |
| 79 | Tony Adamie | 14.00 | 7.00 |
| 80 | Dick Wildung | 14.00 | 7.00 |
| 81 | Tobin Rote (R) | 25.00 | 12.00 |
| 82 | Paul Burris | 14.00 | 7.00 |
| 83 | Lowell Tew | 14.00 | 7.00 |
| 84 | Barney Poole | 14.00 | 7.00 |
| 85 | Fred Naumetz | 14.00 | 7.00 |
| 86 | Dick Hoerner | 14.00 | 7.00 |

| 87 | Bob Reinhard | 14.00 | 7.00 |
| 88 | Howard Hartley | 14.00 | 7.00 |
| 89 | Darrell Hogan | 14.00 | 7.00 |
| 90 | Jerry Shipkey | 14.00 | 7.00 |
| 91 | Frank Tripucka | 20.00 | 10.00 |
| 92 | Garrard Ramsey | 14.00 | 7.00 |
| 93 | Pat Harder | 18.00 | 9.00 |
| 94 | Vic Sears | 14.00 | 7.00 |
| 95 | Tommy Thompson | 14.00 | 7.00 |
| 96 | Bucko Kilroy | 18.00 | 9.00 |
| 97 | George Connor | 28.00 | 13.00 |
| 98 | Fred Morrison | 14.00 | 7.00 |
| 99 | Jim Keane | 14.00 | 7.00 |
| 100 | Sammy Baugh | 125.00 | 55.00 |
| 101 | Harry Ulinski | 14.00 | 7.00 |
| 102 | Frank Spaniel | 14.00 | 7.00 |
| 103 | Charley Conerly | 60.00 | 28.00 |
| 104 | Dick Hensley | 14.00 | 7.00 |
| 105 | Eddie Price | 14.00 | 7.00 |
| 106 | Ed Carr | 14.00 | 7.00 |
| 107 | Leo Nomellini | 38.00 | 18.00 |
| 108 | Verl Lillywhite | 14.00 | 7.00 |
| 109 | Wallace Triplett | 14.00 | 7.00 |
| 110 | Joe Watson | 14.00 | 7.00 |
| 111 | Cloyce Box | 14.00 | 7.00 |
| 112 | Billy Stone | 14.00 | 7.00 |
| 113 | Earl Murray | 14.00 | 7.00 |
| 114 | Chet Mutryn | 14.00 | 7.00 |
| 115 | Ken Carpenter | 14.00 | 7.00 |
| 116 | Lou Rymkus | 18.00 | 9.00 |
| 117 | Dub Jones (R) | 25.00 | 12.00 |
| 118 | C. Tonnemaker | 14.00 | 7.00 |
| 119 | Walt Schlinkman | 14.00 | 7.00 |
| 120 | Billy Grimes | 14.00 | 7.00 |
| 121 | G. Ratterman (R) | 20.00 | 10.00 |
| 122 | Bob Mann | 14.00 | 7.00 |
| 123 | Buddy Young (R) | 28.00 | 13.00 |
| 124 | Jack Zilly | 14.00 | 7.00 |
| 125 | Tom Kalmanir | 14.00 | 7.00 |
| 126 | Frank Sinkovitz | 14.00 | 7.00 |
| 127 | Elbie Nickel | 14.00 | 7.00 |
| 128 | Jim Finks (R) | 25.00 | 12.00 |
| 129 | Charlie Trippi | 28.00 | 13.00 |
| 130 | Tom Wham | 14.00 | 7.00 |
| 131 | Ventan Yablonski | 14.00 | 7.00 |
| 132 | Chuck Bednarik | 50.00 | 22.50 |
| 133 | Joe Muha | 14.00 | 7.00 |
| 134 | Pete Pihos | 30.00 | 14.00 |
| 135 | Washington Serini | 14.00 | 7.00 |
| 136 | George Gulyanics | 14.00 | 7.00 |
| 137 | Ken Kavanaugh | 20.00 | 10.00 |
| 138 | Howie Livingston | 14.00 | 7.00 |
| 139 | Joe Tereshinski | 14.00 | 7.00 |
| 140 | Jim White | 14.00 | 7.00 |
| 141 | Gene Roberts | 14.00 | 7.00 |
| 142 | William Swiacki | 14.00 | 7.00 |
| 143 | Norm Standlee | 14.00 | 7.00 |
| 144 | Knox Ramsey | 48.00 | 20.00 |

## 1951 Bowman

This 144-card set features hand drawn color portraits traced from black and white photographs on the card fronts and vertical card backs printed in blue and burgandy. Bowman enlarged the size of the cards to 2-1/16" by 3-1/8".

| | | NR/MT | EX |
| --- | --- | --- | --- |
| Complete Set (144) | | 3,250.00 | 1,500.00 |
| Commons | | 14.00 | 7.00 |

| 1 | Weldon Humble | 50.00 | 20.00 |
| --- | --- | --- | --- |
| 2 | Otto Graham | 125.00 | 55.00 |
| 3 | Mac Speedie | 14.00 | 7.00 |
| 4 | Norm Van Brocklin (R) | 210.00 | 95.00 |
| 5 | Woodley Lewis | 14.00 | 7.00 |
| 6 | Tom Fears | 28.00 | 13.00 |
| 7 | George Musacco | 14.00 | 7.00 |
| 8 | George Taliaferro | 14.00 | 7.00 |
| 9 | Barney Poole | 14.00 | 7.00 |
| 10 | Steve Van Buren | 35.00 | 15.00 |
| 11 | Whitey Wistert | 14.00 | 7.00 |
| 12 | Chuck Bednarik | 38.00 | 16.00 |
| 13 | Bulldog Turner | 30.00 | 14.00 |
| 14 | Bob Williams | 14.00 | 7.00 |
| 15 | John Lujack | 35.00 | 15.00 |
| 16 | Roy Steiner | 14.00 | 7.00 |
| 17 | Earl Girard | 14.00 | 7.00 |
| 18 | Bill Neal | 14.00 | 7.00 |
| 19 | Travis Tidwell | 14.00 | 7.00 |

| # | Name | | |
|---|------|------|------|
| 20 | Tom Landry (R) | 550.00 | 250.00 |
| 21 | Arnie Weinmeister (R) | 35.00 | 15.00 |
| 22 | Joe Geri | 14.00 | 7.00 |
| 23 | Bill Walsh (R) | 18.00 | 9.00 |
| 24 | Fran Rogel | 14.00 | 7.00 |
| 25 | Doak Walker | 38.00 | 16.00 |
| 26 | Leon Hart | 25.00 | 12.00 |
| 27 | Thurman McGraw | 14.00 | 7.00 |
| 28 | Buster Ramsey | 14.00 | 7.00 |
| 29 | Frank Tripucka | 20.00 | 10.00 |
| 30 | Don Paul | 14.00 | 7.00 |
| 31 | Alex Loyd | 14.00 | 7.00 |
| 32 | Y.A. Tittle | 100.00 | 48.00 |
| 33 | Verl Lillywhite | 14.00 | 7.00 |
| 34 | Sammy Baugh | 110.00 | 50.00 |
| 35 | Chuck Drazenovich | 14.00 | 7.00 |
| 36 | Bob Goode | 14.00 | 7.00 |
| 37 | Horace Gillom | 14.00 | 7.00 |
| 38 | Lou Rymkus | 14.00 | 7.00 |
| 39 | Ken Carpenter | 14.00 | 7.00 |
| 40 | Bob Waterfield | 40.00 | 18.00 |
| 41 | Vitamin Smith | 14.00 | 7.00 |
| 42 | Glenn Davis | 30.00 | 14.00 |
| 43 | Dan Edwards | 14.00 | 7.00 |
| 44 | John Rauch | 14.00 | 7.00 |
| 45 | Zollie Toth | 14.00 | 7.00 |
| 46 | Pete Pihos | 25.00 | 12.00 |
| 47 | Russ Craft | 14.00 | 7.00 |
| 48 | Walter Barnes | 14.00 | 7.00 |
| 49 | Fred Morrison | 14.00 | 7.00 |
| 50 | Ray Bray | 14.00 | 7.00 |
| 51 | Ed Sprinkle | 14.00 | 7.00 |
| 52 | Floyd Reid | 14.00 | 7.00 |
| 53 | Billy Grimes | 14.00 | 7.00 |
| 54 | Ted Fritsch | 14.00 | 7.00 |
| 55 | Al DeRogatis | 14.00 | 7.00 |
| 56 | Charley Conerly | 45.00 | 20.00 |
| 57 | Jon Baker | 14.00 | 7.00 |
| 58 | Tom McWilliams | 14.00 | 7.00 |
| 59 | Jerry Shipkey | 14.00 | 7.00 |
| 60 | Lynn Chandnois | 14.00 | 7.00 |
| 61 | Don Doll | 14.00 | 7.00 |
| 62 | Lou Creekmur | 18.00 | 9.00 |
| 63 | B. Hoernschemeyer | 14.00 | 7.00 |
| 64 | Tom Wham | 14.00 | 7.00 |
| 65 | Bill Fischer | 14.00 | 7.00 |
| 66 | Robert Nussbaumer | 14.00 | 7.00 |
| 67 | Gordon Soltau | 14.00 | 7.00 |
| 68 | Visco Grgich | 14.00 | 7.00 |
| 69 | John Strzykalski | 14.00 | 7.00 |
| 70 | Pete Stout | 14.00 | 7.00 |
| 71 | Paul Lipscomb | 14.00 | 7.00 |
| 72 | Harry Gilmer | 14.00 | 7.00 |
| 73 | Dante Lavelli | 28.00 | 13.00 |
| 74 | Dub Jones | 18.00 | 9.00 |
| 75 | Lou Groza | 65.00 | 30.00 |
| 76 | Elroy Hirsch | 38.00 | 16.00 |
| 77 | Tom Kalmanir | 14.00 | 7.00 |
| 78 | Jack Zilly | 14.00 | 7.00 |
| 79 | Bruce Alford | 14.00 | 7.00 |
| 80 | Art Weiner | 14.00 | 7.00 |
| 81 | Brad Ecklund | 14.00 | 7.00 |
| 82 | Bosh Pritchard | 14.00 | 7.00 |
| 83 | John Green | 14.00 | 7.00 |
| 84 | Ebert Van Buren | 14.00 | 7.00 |
| 85 | Julie Rykovich | 14.00 | 7.00 |
| 86 | Fred Davis | 14.00 | 7.00 |
| 87 | John Hoffman | 14.00 | 7.00 |
| 88 | Tobin Rote | 20.00 | 10.00 |
| 89 | Paul Burris | 14.00 | 7.00 |
| 90 | Tony Canadeo | 25.00 | 12.00 |
| 91 | Emlen Tunnell (R) | 75.00 | 35.00 |
| 92 | Otto Schnellbacher | 14.00 | 7.00 |
| 93 | Ray Poole | 14.00 | 7.00 |
| 94 | Darrell Hogan | 14.00 | 7.00 |
| 95 | Frank Sinkovitz | 14.00 | 7.00 |
| 96 | Ernie Stautner (R) | 75.00 | 30.00 |
| 97 | Elmer Angsman | 14.00 | 7.00 |
| 98 | Jack Jennings | 14.00 | 7.00 |
| 99 | Jerry Groom | 14.00 | 7.00 |
| 100 | John Prichlik | 14.00 | 7.00 |
| 101 | J. Robert Smith | 14.00 | 7.00 |
| 102 | Bobby Layne | 75.00 | 35.00 |
| 103 | Frankie Albert | 20.00 | 10.00 |
| 104 | Gail Bruce | 14.00 | 7.00 |
| 105 | Joe Perry | 35.00 | 15.00 |
| 106 | Leon Heath | 14.00 | 7.00 |
| 107 | Ed Quirk | 14.00 | 7.00 |
| 108 | Hugh Taylor | 14.00 | 7.00 |
| 109 | Marion Motley | 35.00 | 15.00 |
| 110 | Tony Adamle | 14.00 | 7.00 |
| 111 | Alex Agase | 14.00 | 7.00 |
| 112 | Tank Younger | 18.00 | 9.00 |
| 113 | Bob Boyd | 14.00 | 7.00 |
| 114 | Jerry Williams | 14.00 | 7.00 |
| 115 | Joe Golding | 14.00 | 7.00 |
| 116 | Sherman Howard | 14.00 | 7.00 |
| 117 | John Wozniak | 14.00 | 7.00 |
| 118 | Frank Reagan | 14.00 | 7.00 |
| 119 | Vic Sears | 14.00 | 7.00 |
| 120 | Clyde Scott | 14.00 | 7.00 |
| 121 | George Gulyanics | 14.00 | 7.00 |
| 122 | Bill Wightkin | 14.00 | 7.00 |
| 123 | Chuck Hunsinger | 14.00 | 7.00 |
| 124 | Jack Cloud | 14.00 | 7.00 |
| 125 | Abner Wimberly | 14.00 | 7.00 |
| 126 | Dick Wildung | 14.00 | 7.00 |
| 127 | Eddie Price | 14.00 | 7.00 |
| 128 | Joe Scott | 14.00 | 7.00 |
| 129 | Jerry Nuzum | 14.00 | 7.00 |
| 130 | Jim Finks | 16.00 | 8.00 |
| 131 | Bob Gage | 14.00 | 7.00 |

| 132 | William Swiacki | 14.00 | 7.00 |
|---|---|---|---|
| 133 | Joe Watson | 14.00 | 7.00 |
| 134 | Ollie Cline | 14.00 | 7.00 |
| 135 | Jack Lininger | 14.00 | 7.00 |
| 136 | Fran Polsfoot | 14.00 | 7.00 |
| 137 | Charlie Trippi | 28.00 | 13.00 |
| 138 | Ventan Yablonski | 14.00 | 7.00 |
| 139 | Emil Sitko | 14.00 | 7.00 |
| 140 | Leo Nomellini | 30.00 | 14.00 |
| 141 | Norm Standlee | 14.00 | 7.00 |
| 142 | Eddie Saenz | 14.00 | 7.00 |
| 143 | Al Demao | 14.00 | 7.00 |
| 144 | Bill Dudley | 50.00 | 20.00 |

# 1952 Bowman Large

The cards in this 144-card set measure 2-1/2" by 3-3/4". Card fronts feature close-up portraits drawn from black and white photos. Card backs are horizontal. Several cards in this edition were short printed and are considered scarce. Those cards are indicated in the checklist below as (SP).

| | | NR/MT | EX |
|---|---|---|---|
| **Complete Set (144)** | | 13,750.00 | 6,000.00 |
| **Commons (1-72)** | | 20.00 | 10.00 |
| **Commons (73-144)** | | 30.00 | 15.00 |

| 1 | Norm Van Brocklin | 350.00 | 125.00 |
|---|---|---|---|
| 2 | Otto Graham | 180.00 | 80.00 |
| 3 | Doak Walker | 48.00 | 22.00 |
| 4 | Steve Owen | 48.00 | 22.00 |
| 5 | Frankie Albert | 25.00 | 12.00 |
| 6 | Laurie Niemi | 20.00 | 10.00 |
| 7 | Chuck Hunsinger | 20.00 | 10.00 |

| 8 | Ed Modzelewski | 20.00 | 10.00 |
|---|---|---|---|
| 9 | Joe Spencer (SP) | 50.00 | 22.50 |
| 10 | Chuck Bednarik (SP) | 80.00 | 38.00 |
| 11 | Barney Poole | 20.00 | 10.00 |
| 12 | Charlie Trippi | 40.00 | 18.00 |
| 13 | Tom Fears | 48.00 | 22.00 |
| 14 | Paul Brown (R) | 125.00 | 55.00 |
| 15 | Leon Hart | 25.00 | 12.00 |
| 16 | Frank Gifford (R) | 700.00 | 325.00 |
| 17 | Y.A. Tittle | 140.00 | 60.00 |
| 18 | Charlie Justice (SP) | 90.00 | 42.00 |
| 19 | George Connor (SP) | 80.00 | 38.00 |
| 20 | Lynn Chandnois | 20.00 | 10.00 |
| 21 | Bill Howton (R) | 32.00 | 14.00 |
| 22 | Kenneth Snyder | 20.00 | 10.00 |
| 23 | Gino Marchetti (R) | 120.00 | 50.00 |
| 24 | John Karras | 20.00 | 10.00 |
| 25 | Tank Younger | 25.00 | 12.00 |
| 26 | Tommy Thompson | 25.00 | 12.00 |
| 27 | Bob Miller (R)(SP) | 225.00 | 100.00 |
| 28 | Kyle Rote (R)(SP) | 100.00 | 48.00 |
| 29 | H. McElhenny (R) | 160.00 | 70.00 |
| 30 | Sammy Baugh | 280.00 | 125.00 |
| 31 | Jim Dooley (R) | 25.00 | 12.00 |
| 32 | Ray Mathews | 20.00 | 10.00 |
| 33 | Fred Cone | 20.00 | 10.00 |
| 34 | Al Pollard | 20.00 | 10.00 |
| 35 | Brad Ecklund | 20.00 | 10.00 |
| 36 | John Lee Hancock (R) (SP) | 275.00 | 120.00 |
| 37 | Elroy Hirsch (SP) | 90.00 | 42.00 |
| 38 | Keever Jankovich | 20.00 | 10.00 |
| 39 | Emlen Tunnell | 60.00 | 28.00 |
| 40 | Steve Dowden | 20.00 | 10.00 |
| 41 | Claude Hipps | 20.00 | 10.00 |
| 42 | Norm Standlee | 20.00 | 10.00 |
| 43 | Dick Todd | 20.00 | 10.00 |
| 44 | Babe Parilli | 35.00 | 15.00 |
| 45 | S. Van Buren(SP) | 140.00 | 60.00 |
| 46 | Art Donovan (R) (SP) | 180.00 | 80.00 |
| 47 | Bill Fischer | 20.00 | 10.00 |
| 48 | George Halas (R) | 160.00 | 70.00 |
| 49 | Jerrell Price | 20.00 | 10.00 |
| 50 | John Sandusky (R) | 25.00 | 12.00 |
| 51 | Ray Beck | 20.00 | 10.00 |
| 52 | Jim Martin | 20.00 | 10.00 |
| 53 | Joe Bach | 20.00 | 10.00 |
| 54 | Glen Christian (SP) | 50.00 | 20.00 |
| 55 | Andy Davis (SP) | 50.00 | 20.00 |
| 56 | Tobin Rote | 25.00 | 12.00 |
| 57 | Wayne Millner (R) | 70.00 | 30.00 |
| 58 | Zollie Toth | 20.00 | 10.00 |
| 59 | Jack Jennings | 20.00 | 10.00 |
| 60 | Bill McColl | 20.00 | 10.00 |
| 61 | Les Richter (R) | 28.00 | 13.00 |
| 62 | Walt Michaels (R) | 35.00 | 15.00 |

| | | | |
|---|---|---|---|
| 63 | Charley Conerly (SP) | 400.00 | 180.00 |
| 64 | Howard Hartley (SP) | 50.00 | 20.00 |
| 65 | Jerome Smith | 20.00 | 10.00 |
| 66 | James Clark | 20.00 | 10.00 |
| 67 | Dick Logan | 20.00 | 10.00 |
| 68 | Wayne Robinson | 20.00 | 10.00 |
| 69 | James Hammond | 20.00 | 10.00 |
| 70 | Gene Schroeder | 20.00 | 10.00 |
| 71 | Tex Coulter | 20.00 | 10.00 |
| 72 | John Schweder (R) (SP) | 350.00 | 150.00 |
| 73 | Vitamin Smith (SP) | 90.00 | 40.00 |
| 74 | Joe Campanella | 30.00 | 15.00 |
| 75 | Joe Kuharich (R) | 35.00 | 17.50 |
| 76 | Herman Clark | 30.00 | 15.00 |
| 77 | Dan Edwards | 30.00 | 15.00 |
| 78 | Bobby Layne | 150.00 | 70.00 |
| 79 | Bob Hoernschemeyer | 30.00 | 15.00 |
| 80 | John Blount | 30.00 | 15.00 |
| 81 | John Kastan (SP) | 90.00 | 40.00 |
| 82 | Harry Minarik (SP) | 90.00 | 40.00 |
| 83 | Joe Perry | 80.00 | 38.00 |
| 84 | Ray Parker | 30.00 | 15.00 |
| 85 | Andy Robustelli (R) | 150.00 | 70.00 |
| 86 | Dub Jones | 35.00 | 15.00 |
| 87 | Mal Cook | 30.00 | 15.00 |
| 88 | Billy Stone | 30.00 | 15.00 |
| 89 | George Taliaferro | 30.00 | 15.00 |
| 90 | Thomas Johnson (SP) | 90.00 | 40.00 |
| 91 | Leon Heath (SP) | 80.00 | 35.00 |
| 92 | Pete Pihos | 60.00 | 28.00 |
| 93 | Fred Benners | 30.00 | 15.00 |
| 94 | George Tarasovic | 30.00 | 15.00 |
| 95 | Lawrence Shaw | 30.00 | 15.00 |
| 96 | Bill Wightkin | 30.00 | 15.00 |
| 97 | John Wozniak | 30.00 | 15.00 |
| 98 | Bobby Dillon | 30.00 | 15.00 |
| 99 | Joe Stydahar (R) (SP) | 500.00 | 225.00 |
| 100 | Dick Alban (SP) | 90.00 | 40.00 |
| 101 | Arnie Weinmeister | 60.00 | 28.00 |
| 102 | Bobby Joe Cross | 30.00 | 15.00 |
| 103 | Don Paul | 30.00 | 15.00 |
| 104 | Buddy Young | 35.00 | 17.50 |
| 105 | Lou Groza | 90.00 | 40.00 |
| 106 | Ray Pelfrey | 30.00 | 15.00 |
| 107 | Maurice Nipp | 30.00 | 15.00 |
| 108 | Hubert Johnston (R) (SP) | 375.00 | 175.00 |
| 109 | Volney Quinlan (SP) | 80.00 | 35.00 |
| 110 | Jack Simmons | 30.00 | 15.00 |
| 111 | George Ratterman | 30.00 | 15.00 |
| 112 | John Badaczewski | 30.00 | 15.00 |
| 131 | Bill Reichardt | 30.00 | 15.00 |
| 114 | Art Weiner | 30.00 | 15.00 |
| 115 | Keith Flowers | 30.00 | 15.00 |
| 116 | Russ Craft | 30.00 | 15.00 |
| 117 | Jim O'Donahue (SP) | 90.00 | 40.00 |
| 118 | Darrell Hogan (SP) | 80.00 | 35.00 |
| 119 | Frank Ziegler | 30.00 | 15.00 |
| 120 | Dan Towler | 35.00 | 17.50 |
| 121 | Fred Williams | 30.00 | 15.00 |
| 122 | Jimmy Phelan | 30.00 | 15.00 |
| 123 | Eddie Price | 30.00 | 15.00 |
| 124 | Chet Ostrowski | 30.00 | 15.00 |
| 125 | Leo Nomellini | 60.00 | 28.00 |
| 126 | Steve Romanik (R) (SP) | 280.00 | 125.00 |
| 127 | Ollie Matson (R) (SP) | 250.00 | 110.00 |
| 128 | Dante Lavelli | 60.00 | 28.00 |
| 129 | Jack Christiansen (R) | 125.00 | 55.00 |
| 130 | Dom Moselle | 30.00 | 15.00 |
| 131 | John Rapacz | 30.00 | 15.00 |
| 132 | Chuck Ortman | 30.00 | 15.00 |
| 133 | Bob Williams | 30.00 | 15.00 |
| 134 | Chuck Ulrich | 30.00 | 15.00 |
| 135 | Gene Ronzani (R) (SP) | 450.00 | 200.00 |
| 136 | Bert Rechichar (SP) | 80.00 | 35.00 |
| 137 | Bob Waterfield | 90.00 | 40.00 |
| 138 | Bobby Walston (R) | 35.00 | 17.50 |
| 139 | Jerry Shipkey | 30.00 | 15.00 |
| 140 | Yale Lary (R) | 125.00 | 55.00 |
| 141 | Gordon Soltau | 30.00 | 15.00 |
| 142 | Tom Landry | 550.00 | 250.00 |
| 143 | John Papit | 30.00 | 15.00 |
| 144 | Jim Lansford (R) | 2,500.00 | 500.00 |

# 1952 Bowman Small

This 144-card set is identical to the 1952 Bowman Large set except for the card size which was reduced to 2-1/16" by 3-1/8".

|  | NR/MT | EX |
|---|---|---|
| **Complete Set (144)** | 5,400.00 | 2,500.00 |
| **Commons (1-72)** | 16.00 | 8.00 |
| **Commons (73-144)** | 20.00 | 10.00 |

| | | NR/MT | EX |
|---|---|---|---|
| 1 | Norm Van Brocklin | 200.00 | 90.00 |
| 2 | Otto Graham | 140.00 | 60.00 |
| 3 | Doak Walker | 25.00 | 12.00 |
| 4 | Steve Owen (R) | 30.00 | 14.00 |
| 5 | Frankie Albert | 20.00 | 10.00 |
| 6 | Laurie Niemi | 16.00 | 8.00 |
| 7 | Chuck Hunsinger | 16.00 | 8.00 |
| 8 | Ed Modzelewski | 16.00 | 8.00 |
| 9 | Joe Spencer | 16.00 | 8.00 |
| 10 | Chuck Bednarik | 35.00 | 15.00 |
| 11 | Barney Poole | 16.00 | 8.00 |
| 12 | Charlie Trippi | 25.00 | 12.00 |
| 13 | Tom Fears | 25.00 | 15.00 |
| 14 | Paul Brown (R) | 80.00 | 38.00 |
| 15 | Leon Hart | 20.00 | 10.00 |
| 16 | Frank Gifford (R) | 550.00 | 250.00 |
| 17 | Y.A Tittle | 90.00 | 40.00 |
| 18 | Charlie Justice | 25.00 | 12.00 |
| 19 | George Connor | 25.00 | 12.00 |
| 20 | Lynn Chandnois | 16.00 | 8.00 |
| 21 | Bill Howton (R) | 25.00 | 12.00 |
| 22 | Kenneth Snyder | 16.00 | 8.00 |
| 23 | Gino Marchetti (R) | 80.00 | 38.00 |
| 24 | John Karras | 16.00 | 8.00 |
| 25 | Tank Younger | 20.00 | 10.00 |
| 26 | Tommy Thompson | 18.00 | 9.00 |
| 27 | Bob Miller | 16.00 | 8.00 |
| 28 | Kyle Rote (R) | 40.00 | 18.00 |
| 29 | Hugh McElhenny (R) | 100.00 | 45.00 |
| 30 | Sammy Baugh | 150.00 | 70.00 |
| 31 | Jim Dooley (R) | 20.00 | 10.00 |
| 32 | Ray Mathews | 16.00 | 8.00 |
| 33 | Fred Cone | 16.00 | 8.00 |
| 34 | Al Pollard | 16.00 | 8.00 |
| 35 | Brad Ecklund | 16.00 | 8.00 |
| 36 | John Lee Hancock | 16.00 | 8.00 |
| 37 | Elroy Hirsch | 35.00 | 15.00 |
| 38 | Keever Jankovich | 16.00 | 8.00 |
| 39 | Emlen Tunnell | 35.00 | 15.00 |
| 40 | Steve Dowden | 16.00 | 8.00 |
| 41 | Claude Hipps | 16.00 | 8.00 |
| 42 | Norm Standlee | 16.00 | 8.00 |
| 43 | Dick Todd | 16.00 | 8.00 |
| 44 | Babe Parilli | 25.00 | 12.00 |
| 45 | Steve Van Buren | 35.00 | 15.00 |
| 46 | Art Donovan (R) | 80.00 | 38.00 |
| 47 | Bill Fischer | 16.00 | 8.00 |
| 48 | George Halas (R) | 80.00 | 38.00 |
| 49 | Jerrell Price | 16.00 | 8.00 |
| 50 | John Sandusky (R) | 18.00 | 9.00 |
| 51 | Ray Beck | 16.00 | 8.00 |
| 52 | Jim Martin | 16.00 | 8.00 |
| 53 | Joe Bach | 16.00 | 8.00 |
| 54 | Glen Christian | 16.00 | 8.00 |
| 55 | Andy Davis | 16.00 | 8.00 |
| 56 | Tobin Rote | 20.00 | 10.00 |
| 57 | Wayne Millner (R) | 40.00 | 18.00 |
| 58 | Zollie Toth | 16.00 | 8.00 |
| 59 | Jack Jennings | 16.00 | 8.00 |
| 60 | Bill McColl | 16.00 | 8.00 |
| 61 | Les Richter (R) | 18.00 | 9.00 |
| 62 | Walt Michaels (R) | 20.00 | 10.00 |
| 63 | Charley Conerly | 60.00 | 28.00 |
| 64 | Howard Hartley | 16.00 | 8.00 |
| 65 | Jerom Smith | 16.00 | 8.00 |
| 66 | James Clark | 16.00 | 8.00 |
| 67 | Dick Logan | 16.00 | 8.00 |
| 68 | Wayne Robinson | 16.00 | 8.00 |
| 69 | James Hammond | 16.00 | 8.00 |
| 70 | Gene Schroeder | 16.00 | 8.00 |
| 71 | Tex Coulter | 16.00 | 8.00 |
| 72 | John Schweder | 16.00 | 8.00 |
| 73 | Vitamin Smith | 20.00 | 10.00 |
| 74 | Joe Campanella | 20.00 | 10.00 |
| 75 | Joe Kuharich (R) | 22.00 | 11.00 |
| 76 | Herman Clark | 20.00 | 10.00 |
| 77 | Dan Edwards | 20.00 | 10.00 |
| 78 | Bobby Layne | 100.00 | 48.00 |
| 79 | B. Hoernschemeyer | 20.00 | 10.00 |
| 80 | John Blount | 20.00 | 10.00 |
| 81 | John Kastan | 20.00 | 10.00 |
| 82 | Harry Minarik | 20.00 | 10.00 |
| 83 | Joe Perry | 45.00 | 20.00 |
| 84 | Ray Parker | 20.00 | 10.00 |

| 85 | Andy Robustelli (R) | 80.00 | 38.00 |
|---|---|---|---|
| 86 | Dub Jones | 22.00 | 11.00 |
| 87 | Mal Cook | 20.00 | 10.00 |
| 88 | Billy Stone | 20.00 | 10.00 |
| 89 | George Taliaferro | 20.00 | 10.00 |
| 90 | Thomas Johnson | 20.00 | 10.00 |
| 91 | Leon Heath | 20.00 | 10.00 |
| 92 | Pete Pihos | 35.00 | 15.00 |
| 93 | Fred Benners | 20.00 | 10.00 |
| 94 | George Tarasovic | 20.00 | 10.00 |
| 95 | Lawrence Shaw | 20.00 | 10.00 |
| 96 | Bill Wightkin | 20.00 | 10.00 |
| 97 | John Wozniak | 20.00 | 10.00 |
| 98 | Bobby Dillon | 20.00 | 10.00 |
| 99 | Joe Stydahar (R) | 45.00 | 20.00 |
| 100 | Dick Alban | 20.00 | 10.00 |
| 101 | Arnie Weinmeister | 30.00 | 14.00 |
| 102 | Bobby Joe Cross | 20.00 | 10.00 |
| 103 | Don Paul | 20.00 | 10.00 |
| 104 | Buddy Young | 22.00 | 11.00 |
| 105 | Lou Groza | 48.00 | 22.00 |
| 106 | Ray Pelfrey | 20.00 | 10.00 |
| 107 | Maurice Nipp | 20.00 | 10.00 |
| 108 | Hubert Johnston | 20.00 | 10.00 |
| 109 | Volney Quinlan | 20.00 | 10.00 |
| 110 | Jack Simmons | 20.00 | 10.00 |
| 111 | George Ratterman | 22.00 | 11.00 |
| 112 | John Badaczewski | 20.00 | 10.00 |
| 113 | Bill Reichardt | 20.00 | 10.00 |
| 114 | Art Weiner | 20.00 | 10.00 |
| 115 | Keith Flowers | 20.00 | 10.00 |
| 116 | Russ Craft | 20.00 | 10.00 |
| 117 | Jim O'Donahue | 20.00 | 10.00 |
| 118 | Darrell Hogan | 20.00 | 10.00 |
| 119 | Frank Ziegler | 20.00 | 10.00 |
| 120 | Dan Towler | 22.00 | 11.00 |
| 121 | Fred Williams | 20.00 | 10.00 |
| 122 | Jimmy Phelan | 20.00 | 10.00 |
| 123 | Eddie Price | 20.00 | 10.00 |
| 124 | Chet Ostrowski | 20.00 | 10.00 |
| 125 | Leo Nomellini | 35.00 | 15.00 |
| 126 | Steve Romanik | 20.00 | 10.00 |
| 127 | Ollie Matson (R) | 95.00 | 42.00 |
| 128 | Dante Lavelli | 30.00 | 14.00 |
| 129 | Jack Christiansen(R) | 75.00 | 35.00 |
| 130 | Dom Moselle | 20.00 | 10.00 |
| 131 | John Rapacz | 20.00 | 10.00 |
| 132 | Chuck Ortman | 20.00 | 10.00 |
| 133 | Bob Williams | 20.00 | 10.00 |
| 134 | Chuck Ulrich | 20.00 | 10.00 |
| 135 | Gene Ronzani | 20.00 | 10.00 |
| 136 | Bert Rechichar | 20.00 | 10.00 |
| 137 | Bob Waterfield | 45.00 | 20.00 |
| 138 | Bobby Walston (R) | 25.00 | 12.00 |
| 139 | Jerry Shipkey | 20.00 | 10.00 |
| 140 | Yale Lary (R) | 75.00 | 35.00 |
| 141 | Gordon Soltau | 20.00 | 10.00 |
| 142 | Tom Landry | 275.00 | 125.00 |
| 143 | John Papit | 20.00 | 10.00 |
| 144 | Jim Lansford | 125.00 | 35.00 |

# 1953 Bowman

Though Bowman reduced the number of cards in their 1953 set they retained the larger card size from the previous year with each card measuring 2-1/2" by 3-3/4". Nearly two dozen cards in the set were short-printed and are considered scarce. Those cards carry the initials (SP) in the checklist below.

|  |  | NR/MT | EX |
|---|---|---|---|
| Complete Set (96) | | 3,000.00 | 1,400.00 |
| Commons | | 15.00 | 7.00 |

| 1 | Eddie LeBaron (R) | 150.00 | 40.00 |
|---|---|---|---|
| 2 | John Dottley | 15.00 | 7.00 |
| 3 | Babe Parilli | 20.00 | 9.00 |
| 4 | Bucko Kilroy | 15.00 | 7.00 |
| 5 | Joe Tereshinski | 15.00 | 7.00 |
| 6 | Doak Walker | 30.00 | 14.00 |
| 7 | Fran Polsfoot | 15.00 | 7.00 |
| 8 | Sisto Averno | 15.00 | 7.00 |
| 9 | Marion Motley | 30.00 | 14.00 |
| 10 | Pat Brady | 15.00 | 7.00 |
| 11 | Norm Van Brocklin | 80.00 | 38.00 |
| 12 | Bill McColl | 15.00 | 7.00 |
| 13 | Jerry Groom | 15.00 | 7.00 |
| 14 | Al Pollard | 15.00 | 7.00 |
| 15 | Dante Lavelli | 25.00 | 12.00 |
| 16 | Eddie Price | 15.00 | 7.00 |

| 17 | Charlie Trippi | 25.00 | 12.00 |
|----|----------------|-------|-------|
| 18 | Elbie Nickel | 15.00 | 7.00 |
| 19 | George Taliaferro | 15.00 | 7.00 |
| 20 | Charley Conerly | 48.00 | 22.00 |
| 21 | Bobby Layne | 75.00 | 35.00 |
| 22 | Elroy Hirsch | 35.00 | 16.00 |
| 23 | Jim Finks | 18.00 | 8.00 |
| 24 | Chuck Bednarik | 35.00 | 16.00 |
| 25 | Kyle Rote | 25.00 | 12.00 |
| 26 | Otto Graham | 150.00 | 70.00 |
| 27 | Harry Gilmer | 15.00 | 7.00 |
| 28 | Tobin Rote | 20.00 | 9.00 |
| 29 | Billy Stone | 15.00 | 7.00 |
| 30 | Buddy Young | 20.00 | 9.00 |
| 31 | Leon Hart | 20.00 | 9.00 |
| 32 | Hugh McElhenny | 35.00 | 16.00 |
| 33 | Dale Samuels | 15.00 | 7.00 |
| 34 | Lou Creekmur | 15.00 | 7.00 |
| 35 | Tom Catlin | 15.00 | 7.00 |
| 36 | Tom Fears | 25.00 | 12.00 |
| 37 | George Connor | 25.00 | 12.00 |
| 38 | Bill Walsh | 15.00 | 7.00 |
| 39 | Leo Sanford (SP) | 20.00 | 9.00 |
| 40 | Horace Gillom | 15.00 | 7.00 |
| 41 | John Schweder (SP) | 20.00 | 9.00 |
| 42 | Tom O'Connell | 15.00 | 7.00 |
| 43 | Frank Gifford (SP) | 375.00 | 175.00 |
| 44 | Frank Continetti (SP) | 20.00 | 9.00 |
| 45 | John Olszewski (SP) | 20.00 | 9.00 |
| 46 | Dub Jones | 18.00 | 8.00 |
| 47 | Don Paul (SP) | 20.00 | 9.00 |
| 48 | Gerald Weatherly | 15.00 | 7.00 |
| 49 | Fred Bruney (SP) | 20.00 | 9.00 |
| 50 | Jack Scarbath | 15.00 | 7.00 |
| 51 | John Karras | 15.00 | 7.00 |
| 52 | Al Conway | 15.00 | 7.00 |
| 53 | Emlen Tunnell (SP) | 60.00 | 28.00 |
| 54 | Gern Nagler (SP) | 20.00 | 9.00 |
| 55 | Kenneth Snyder (SP) | 20.00 | 9.00 |
| 56 | Y.A. Tittle | 80.00 | 38.00 |
| 57 | John Rapacz (SP) | 20.00 | 9.00 |
| 58 | Harley Sewell (SP) | 20.00 | 9.00 |
| 59 | Don Bingham | 15.00 | 7.00 |
| 60 | Darrell Hogan | 15.00 | 7.00 |
| 61 | Tony Curcillo | 15.00 | 7.00 |
| 62 | Ray Renfro (R)(SP) | 28.00 | 13.00 |
| 63 | Leon Heath | 15.00 | 7.00 |
| 64 | Tex Coulter (SP) | 20.00 | 9.00 |
| 65 | Dewayne Douglas | 15.00 | 7.00 |
| 66 | Robert Smith (SP) | 20.00 | 9.00 |
| 67 | Bob McChesney (SP) | 20.00 | 9.00 |
| 68 | Dick Alban (SP) | 20.00 | 9.00 |
| 69 | Andy Kozar | 15.00 | 7.00 |
| 70 | Merwin Hodel (SP) | 20.00 | 9.00 |

| 71 | Thurman McGraw | 15.00 | 7.00 |
|----|----------------|-------|-------|
| 72 | Cliff Anderson | 15.00 | 7.00 |
| 73 | Pete Pihos | 25.00 | 12.00 |
| 74 | Julie Rykovich | 15.00 | 7.00 |
| 75 | John Kreamcheck | 20.00 | 9.00 |
| 76 | Lynn Chandnois | 15.00 | 7.00 |
| 77 | Cloyce Box (SP) | 22.00 | 10.00 |
| 78 | Ray Matthews | 15.00 | 7.00 |
| 79 | Bobby Walston | 15.00 | 7.00 |
| 80 | Jim Dooley | 15.00 | 7.00 |
| 81 | Pat Harder (SP) | 22.00 | 10.00 |
| 82 | Jerry Shipkey | 15.00 | 7.00 |
| 83 | Bobby Thomason | 15.00 | 7.00 |
| 84 | Hugh Taylor | 15.00 | 7.00 |
| 85 | George Ratterman | 18.00 | 8.00 |
| 86 | Don Stonesifer | 15.00 | 7.00 |
| 87 | John Williams (SP) | 20.00 | 9.00 |
| 88 | Leo Nomellini | 30.00 | 14.00 |
| 89 | Frank Ziegler | 15.00 | 7.00 |
| 90 | Don Paul | 15.00 | 7.00 |
| 91 | Tom Dublinski | 15.00 | 7.00 |
| 92 | Ken Carpenter | 15.00 | 7.00 |
| 93 | Ted Marchibroda (R) | 25.00 | 12.00 |
| 94 | Chuck Drazenovich | 15.00 | 7.00 |
| 95 | Lou Groza | 75.00 | 35.00 |
| 96 | William Cross (SP) | 70.00 | 25.00 |

# 1954 Bowman

The 128-cards in this set each measure 2-1/2" by 3-3/4" and feature close up portraits on the card fronts with the player's name and team in a small pennant-shaped design at the bottom. The horizontal card backs include a football trivia question with an upside-down answer and the player's personal data and statistics from the previous season.

| | | NR/MT | EX |
|---|---|---|---|
| | **Complete Set (128)** | 1,850.00 | 900.00 |
| | **Commons (1-64)** | 6.50 | 3.00 |
| | **Commons (65-96)** | 12.00 | 5.00 |
| | **Commons (97-128)** | 6.50 | 3.00 |
| 1 | Ray Matthews | 25.00 | 8.00 |
| 2 | John Huzvar | 6.50 | 3.00 |
| 3 | Jack Scarbath | 6.50 | 3.00 |
| 4 | Doug Atkins (R) | 40.00 | 18.00 |
| 5 | Bill Stits | 6.50 | 3.00 |
| 6 | Joe Perry | 24.00 | 10.00 |
| 7 | Kyle Rote | 12.50 | 5.50 |
| 8 | Norm Van Brocklin | 40.00 | 18.00 |
| 9 | Pete Pihos | 18.00 | 8.00 |
| 10 | Babe Parilli | 12.00 | 5.00 |
| 11 | Zeke Bratkowski (R) | 18.00 | 8.00 |
| 12 | Ollie Matson | 24.00 | 10.00 |
| 13 | Pat Brady | 6.50 | 3.00 |
| 14 | Fred Enke | 6.50 | 3.00 |
| 15 | Harry Ulinski | 6.50 | 3.00 |
| 16 | Bobby Garrett | 6.50 | 3.00 |
| 17 | Bill Bowman | 6.50 | 3.00 |
| 18 | Leo Rucka | 6.50 | 3.00 |
| 19 | John Cannady | 6.50 | 3.00 |
| 20 | Tom Fears | 16.00 | 7.00 |
| 21 | Norm Willey | 6.50 | 3.00 |
| 22 | Floyd Reid | 6.50 | 3.00 |
| 23 | George Blanda (R) | 325.00 | 150.00 |
| 24 | Don Doheney | 6.50 | 3.00 |
| 25 | John Schweder | 6.50 | 3.00 |
| 26 | Bert Rechichar | 6.50 | 3.00 |
| 27 | Harry Dowda | 6.50 | 3.00 |
| 28 | John Sandusky | 6.50 | 3.00 |
| 29 | Les Bingaman (R) | 10.00 | 4.50 |
| 30 | Joe Arenas | 6.50 | 3.00 |
| 31 | Ray Wietecha | 6.50 | 3.00 |
| 32 | Elroy Hirsch | 20.00 | 9.00 |
| 33 | Harold Giancanelli | 6.50 | 3.00 |
| 34 | Bill Howton | 10.00 | 4.50 |
| 35 | Fred Morrison | 6.50 | 3.00 |
| 36 | Bobby Cavazos | 6.50 | 3.00 |
| 37 | Darrell Hogan | 6.50 | 3.00 |
| 38 | Buddy Young | 6.50 | 3.00 |
| 39 | Charlie Justice | 12.00 | 5.00 |
| 40 | Otto Graham | 80.00 | 38.00 |
| 41 | Doak Walker | 18.00 | 8.00 |
| 42 | Y.A. Tittle | 48.00 | 22.00 |
| 43 | Buford Long | 6.50 | 3.00 |
| 44 | Volney Quinlan | 6.50 | 3.00 |
| 45 | Bobby Thomason | 6.50 | 3.00 |
| 46 | Fred Cone | 6.50 | 3.00 |
| 47 | Gerald Weatherly | 6.50 | 3.00 |
| 48 | Don Stonesifer | 6.50 | 3.00 |
| 49 | Lynn Chandnois | 6.50 | 3.00 |
| 50 | George Taliaferro | 6.50 | 3.00 |
| 51 | Dick Alban | 6.50 | 3.00 |
| 52 | Lou Groza | 30.00 | 14.00 |
| 53 | Bobby Layne | 45.00 | 20.00 |
| 54 | Hugh McElhenny | 25.00 | 12.00 |
| 55 | Frank Gifford | 140.00 | 60.00 |
| 56 | Leon McLaughlin | 6.50 | 3.00 |
| 57 | Chuck Bednarik | 20.00 | 9.00 |
| 58 | Art Hunter | 6.50 | 3.00 |
| 59 | Bill McColl | 6.50 | 3.00 |
| 60 | Charlie Trippi | 16.00 | 7.00 |
| 61 | Jim Finks | 8.00 | 3.50 |
| 62 | Bill Lange | 6.50 | 3.00 |
| 63 | Lauri Niemi | 6.50 | 3.00 |
| 64 | Ray Renfro | 6.50 | 3.00 |
| 65 | Dick Chapman | 12.00 | 5.00 |
| 66 | Bob Hantla | 12.00 | 5.00 |
| 67 | Ralph Starkey | 12.00 | 5.00 |
| 68 | Don Paul | 12.00 | 5.00 |
| 69 | Kenneth Snyder | 12.00 | 5.00 |
| 70 | Tobin Rote | 15.00 | 7.00 |
| 71 | Arthur DeCarlo | 12.00 | 5.00 |
| 72 | Tom Keane | 12.00 | 5.00 |
| 73 | Hugh Taylor | 12.00 | 5.00 |
| 74 | Warren Lahr | 12.00 | 5.00 |
| 75 | Jim Neal | 12.00 | 5.00 |
| 76 | Leo Nomellini | 35.00 | 16.00 |
| 77 | Dick Yelvington | 12.00 | 5.00 |
| 78 | Les Richter | 12.00 | 5.00 |
| 79 | Bucko Kilroy | 12.00 | 5.00 |
| 80 | John Martinkovic | 12.00 | 5.00 |
| 81 | Dale Dodrill | 12.00 | 5.00 |
| 82 | Ken Jackson | 12.00 | 5.00 |
| 83 | Paul Lipscomb | 12.00 | 5.00 |
| 84 | John Bauer | 12.00 | 5.00 |
| 85 | Lou Creekmur | 12.00 | 5.00 |
| 86 | Eddie Price | 12.00 | 5.00 |
| 87 | Kenneth Farragut | 12.00 | 5.00 |
| 88 | Dave Hanner | 12.00 | 5.00 |
| 89 | Don Boll | 12.00 | 5.00 |
| 90 | Chet Hanulak | 12.00 | 5.00 |
| 91 | Thurman McGraw | 12.00 | 5.00 |
| 92 | Don Heinrich (R) | 15.00 | 7.00 |
| 93 | Dan McKown | 12.00 | 5.00 |
| 94 | Bob Fleck | 12.00 | 5.00 |
| 95 | Jerry Hilgenberg | 12.00 | 5.00 |
| 96 | Bill Walsh | 12.00 | 5.00 |
| 97A | Tom Finnin (ER) (Name Incorrect) | 25.00 | 12.00 |
| 97B | Tom Finnan (Cor) | 6.50 | 3.00 |
| 98 | Paul Barry | 6.50 | 3.00 |
| 99 | Harry Jagade | 6.50 | 3.00 |
| 100 | Jack Christiansen | 18.00 | 8.00 |
| 101 | Gordon Soltau | 6.50 | 3.00 |

| 102 | Emlen Tunnell | 20.00 | 9.00 |
| 103 | Stan West | 6.50 | 3.00 |
| 104 | Jerry Williams | 6.50 | 3.00 |
| 105 | Veryl Switzer | 6.50 | 3.00 |
| 106 | Billy Stone | 6.50 | 3.00 |
| 107 | Jerry Watford | 6.50 | 3.00 |
| 108 | Elbie Nickel | 6.50 | 3.00 |
| 109 | Ed Sharkey | 6.50 | 3.00 |
| 110 | Steve Meilinger | 6.50 | 3.00 |
| 111 | Dante Lavelli | 16.00 | 7.00 |
| 112 | Leon Hart | 10.00 | 4.50 |
| 113 | Charley Conerly | 28.00 | 13.00 |
| 114 | Richard Lemmon | 6.50 | 3.00 |
| 115 | Al Carmichael | 6.50 | 3.00 |
| 116 | George Connor | 16.00 | 7.00 |
| 117 | John Olszewski | 6.50 | 3.00 |
| 118 | Ernie Stautner | 20.00 | 9.00 |
| 119 | Ray Smith | 6.50 | 3.00 |
| 120 | Neil Worden | 6.50 | 3.00 |
| 121 | Jim Dooley | 6.50 | 3.00 |
| 122 | Arnold Galiffa (R) | 8.00 | 3.50 |
| 123 | Kline Gilbert | 6.50 | 3.00 |
| 124 | Bob Hoernschemeyer | 6.50 | 3.00 |
| 125 | Whizzer White (R) | 12.00 | 5.00 |
| 126 | Art Spinney | 6.50 | 3.00 |
| 127 | Joe Koch | 6.50 | 3.00 |
| 128 | John Lattner | 85.00 | 25.00 |

# 1955 Bowman

The cards in this 160-card set measure 2-1/2" by 3-3/4". Card fronts feature close up color portraits while the vertical card backs contain the player's personal data and statistics from the previous season. This was Bowman's last football card set until 1991 when Topps issued a set under the Bowman name.

| | | NR/MT | EX |
| --- | --- | --- | --- |
| Complete Set (160) | | 1,650.00 | 770.00 |
| Commons (1-64) | | 4.00 | 2.00 |
| Commons (65-160) | | 5.00 | 2.50 |
| | | | |
| 1 | Doak Walker | 48.00 | 15.00 |
| 2 | Mike McCormack (R) | 35.00 | 16.00 |
| 3 | John Olszewski | 4.00 | 2.00 |
| 4 | Dorne Dibble | 4.00 | 2.00 |
| 5 | Lindon Crow | 4.00 | 2.00 |
| 6 | Hugh Taylor | 4.00 | 2.00 |
| 7 | Frank Gifford | 100.00 | 45.00 |
| 8 | Alan Ameche (R) | 32.00 | 15.00 |
| 9 | Doo Stonesifer | 4.00 | 2.00 |
| 10 | Pete Pihos | 10.00 | 4.50 |
| 11 | Bill Austin | 4.00 | 2.00 |
| 12 | Dick Alban | 4.00 | 2.00 |
| 13 | Bobby Walston | 4.00 | 2.00 |
| 14 | Len Ford (R) | 30.00 | 14.00 |
| 15 | Jug Girard | 4.00 | 2.00 |
| 16 | Charley Conerly | 28.00 | 13.00 |
| 17 | Volney Peters | 4.00 | 2.00 |
| 18 | Max Boydston | 4.00 | 2.00 |
| 19 | Leon Hart | 7.00 | 3.00 |
| 20 | Bert Rechichar | 4.00 | 2.00 |
| 21 | Lee Riley | 4.00 | 2.00 |
| 22 | Johnny Carson | 4.00 | 2.00 |
| 23 | Harry Thompson | 4.00 | 2.00 |
| 24 | Ray Wietecha | 4.00 | 2.00 |
| 25 | Ollie Matson | 18.00 | 8.00 |
| 26 | Eddie LeBaron | 10.00 | 4.50 |
| 27 | Jack Simmons | 4.00 | 2.00 |
| 28 | Jack Christiansen | 12.00 | 5.00 |
| 29 | Bucko Kilroy | 4.00 | 2.00 |
| 30 | Tom Keane | 4.00 | 2.00 |
| 31 | Dave Leggett | 4.00 | 2.00 |
| 32 | Norm Van Brocklin | 30.00 | 14.00 |
| 33 | Harlon Hill (R) | 7.50 | 3.50 |
| 34 | Robert Haner | 4.00 | 2.00 |
| 35 | Veryl Switzer | 4.00 | 2.00 |
| 36 | Dick Stanfel (R) | 5.00 | 2.50 |
| 37 | Lou Groza | 28.00 | 13.00 |
| 38 | Tank Younger | 7.00 | 3.00 |
| 39 | Dick Flanagan | 4.00 | 2.00 |
| 40 | Jim Dooley | 4.00 | 2.00 |
| 41 | Ray Collins | 4.00 | 2.00 |
| 42 | John Henry Johnson (R) | 38.00 | 17.00 |
| 43 | Tom Fears | 10.00 | 4.50 |
| 44 | Joe Perry | 18.00 | 8.00 |
| 45 | Gene Brito (R) | 5.00 | 2.50 |
| 46 | Bill Johnson | 4.00 | 2.00 |
| 47 | Dan Towler | 4.00 | 2.00 |
| 48 | Dick Moegle | 4.00 | 2.00 |
| 49 | Kline Gilbert | 4.00 | 2.00 |
| 50 | Les Gobel | 4.00 | 2.00 |

| | | | |
|---|---|---|---|
| 51 | Ray Krouse | 4.00 | 2.00 |
| 52 | Pat Summerall (R) | 50.00 | 22.50 |
| 53 | Ed Brown (R) | 8.00 | 3.75 |
| 54 | Lynn Chandnois | 4.00 | 2.00 |
| 55 | Joe Heap | 4.00 | 2.00 |
| 56 | John Hoffman | 4.00 | 2.00 |
| 57 | Howard Ferguson | 4.00 | 2.00 |
| 58 | Bobby Watkins | 4.00 | 2.00 |
| 59 | Charlie Ane | 4.00 | 2.00 |
| 60 | Ken MacAfee (R) | 6.00 | 2.75 |
| 61 | Ralph Guglielmi (R) | 6.00 | 2.75 |
| 62 | George Blanda | 100.00 | 45.00 |
| 63 | Kenneth Snyder | 4.00 | 2.00 |
| 64 | Chet Ostrowski | 4.00 | 2.00 |
| 65 | Buddy Young | 5.00 | 2.50 |
| 66 | Gordon Soltau | 5.00 | 2.50 |
| 67 | Eddie Bell | 5.00 | 2.50 |
| 68 | Ben Agajanian (R) | 7.00 | 3.00 |
| 69 | Tom Dahms | 5.00 | 2.50 |
| 70 | Jim Ringo (R) | 45.00 | 20.00 |
| 71 | Bobby Layne | 40.00 | 18.00 |
| 72 | Y.A. Tittle | 40.00 | 18.00 |
| 73 | Bob Gaona | 5.00 | 2.50 |
| 74 | Tobin Rote | 7.50 | 3.50 |
| 75 | Hugh McElhenny | 22.00 | 11.00 |
| 76 | John Kreamcheck | 5.00 | 2.50 |
| 77 | Al Dorow | 5.00 | 2.50 |
| 78 | Bill Wade (R) | 10.00 | 4.50 |
| 79 | Dale Dodrill | 5.00 | 2.50 |
| 80 | Chuck Drazenovich | 5.00 | 2.50 |
| 81 | Billy Wilson (R) | 7.50 | 3.50 |
| 82 | Les Richter | 5.00 | 2.50 |
| 83 | Pat Brady | 5.00 | 2.50 |
| 84 | Bob Hoernschemeyer | 5.00 | 2.50 |
| 85 | Joe Arenas | 5.00 | 2.50 |
| 86 | Len Szafaryn | 5.00 | 2.50 |
| 87 | Rick Casares (R) | 10.00 | 4.50 |
| 88 | Leon McLaughlin | 5.00 | 2.50 |
| 89 | Charley Toogood | 5.00 | 2.50 |
| 90 | Tom Bettis | 5.00 | 2.50 |
| 91 | John Sandusky | 5.00 | 2.50 |
| 92 | Bill Wightkin | 5.00 | 2.50 |
| 93 | Darrell Brewster | 5.00 | 2.50 |
| 94 | Marion Campbell | 7.50 | 3.50 |
| 95 | Floyd Reid | 5.00 | 2.50 |
| 96 | Harry Jagade | 5.00 | 2.50 |
| 97 | George Taliaferro | 5.00 | 2.50 |
| 98 | Carleton Massey | 5.00 | 2.50 |
| 99 | Fran Rogel | 5.00 | 2.50 |
| 100 | Alex Sandusky | 5.00 | 2.50 |
| 101 | Bob St. Clair (R) | 35.00 | 16.00 |
| 102 | Al Carmichael | 5.00 | 2.50 |
| 103 | Carl Taseff (R) | 6.00 | 2.75 |
| 104 | Leo Nomellini | 18.00 | 8.00 |
| 105 | Tom Scott | 5.00 | 2.50 |
| 106 | Ted Marchibroda | 7.50 | 3.50 |
| 107 | Art Spinney | 5.00 | 2.50 |
| 108 | Wayne Robinson | 5.00 | 2.50 |
| 109 | Jim Ricca | 5.00 | 2.50 |
| 110 | Lou Ferry | 5.00 | 2.50 |
| 111 | Roger Zatkoff | 5.00 | 2.50 |
| 112 | Lou Creekmur | 5.00 | 2.50 |
| 113 | Kenny Konz | 5.00 | 2.50 |
| 114 | Dou Eggers | 5.00 | 2.50 |
| 115 | Bobby Thomason | 5.00 | 2.50 |
| 116 | Bill McPeak | 5.00 | 2.50 |
| 117 | William Brown | 5.00 | 2.50 |
| 118 | Royce Womble | 5.00 | 2.50 |
| 119 | Frank Gatski (R) | 30.00 | 14.00 |
| 120 | Jim Finks | 7.00 | 3.00 |
| 121 | Andy Robustelli | 18.00 | 8.00 |
| 122 | Bobby Dillon | 5.00 | 2.50 |
| 123 | Leo Sanford | 5.00 | 2.50 |
| 124 | Elbert Nickel | 5.00 | 2.50 |
| 125 | Wayne Hansen | 5.00 | 2.50 |
| 126 | Buck Lansford | 5.00 | 2.50 |
| 127 | Gern Nagler | 5.00 | 2.50 |
| 128 | Jim Salsbury | 5.00 | 2.50 |
| 129 | Dale Atkeson | 5.00 | 2.50 |
| 130 | John Schweder | 5.00 | 2.50 |
| 131 | Dave Hanner | 5.00 | 2.50 |
| 132 | Eddie Price | 5.00 | 2.50 |
| 133 | Vic Janowicz (R) | 12.00 | 5.00 |
| 134 | Ernie Stautner | 18.00 | 8.00 |
| 135 | James Parmer | 5.00 | 2.50 |
| 136 | Emlen Tunnell | 18.00 | 8.00 |
| 137 | Kyle Rote | 10.00 | 4.50 |
| 138 | Norm Willey | 5.00 | 2.50 |
| 139 | Charlie Trippi | 12.00 | 5.00 |
| 140 | Bill Howton | 7.50 | 3.50 |
| 141 | Bobby Clatterbuck | 5.00 | 2.50 |
| 142 | Bob Boyd | 5.00 | 2.50 |
| 143 | Bob Toneff | 5.00 | 2.50 |
| 144 | Jerry Helluin | 5.00 | 2.50 |
| 145 | Adrian Burk | 5.00 | 2.50 |
| 146 | Walt Michaels | 7.50 | 3.50 |
| 147 | Zollie Toth | 5.00 | 2.50 |
| 148 | Frank Varrichione (R) | 7.00 | 3.00 |
| 149 | Dick Bielski | 5.00 | 2.50 |
| 150 | George Ratterman | 5.00 | 2.50 |
| 151 | Mike Jarmoluk | 5.00 | 2.50 |
| 152 | Tom Landry | 225.00 | 100.00 |
| 153 | Ray Renfro | 5.00 | 2.50 |
| 154 | Zeke Bratkowski | 7.50 | 3.50 |
| 155 | Jerry Norton | 5.00 | 2.50 |
| 156 | Maurice Bassett | 5.00 | 2.50 |
| 157 | Volney Quinlan | 5.00 | 2.50 |
| 158 | Chuck Bednarik | 20.00 | 9.00 |
| 159 | Don Colo | 5.00 | 2.50 |
| 160 | L.G. Dupre | 28.00 | 8.00 |

# 1991 Bowman

This 561-card set marks the return of the Bowman name under the Topps banner. Card fronts feature full-color action photos framed by a blue and orange border. The player's name is printed in white type within a purple stripe below the photo. Card backs are vertical and printed in green and black type. Three noted subsets contain gold foil stamping including Rookie Superstars (1-11), League Leaders (LL) and Road To The Super Bowl (547-557).

|  |  | MINT | NR/MT |
|---|---|---|---|
| Complete Set (561) |  | 12.50 | 8.00 |
| Commons |  | .05 | .03 |

| | | | |
|---|---|---|---|
| 1 | Jeff George (RS) | .25 | .15 |
| 2 | Richmond Webb (RS) | .07 | .04 |
| 3 | Emmitt Smith (RS) | .90 | .55 |
| 4 | Mark Carrier (RS) | .08 | .05 |
| 5 | Steve Christie (RS) | .05 | .03 |
| 6 | Keith Sims (RS) | .05 | .03 |
| 7 | Rob Moore (R) | .20 | .12 |
| 8 | Johnny Johnson (RS) | .12 | .07 |
| 9 | Eric Green (RS) | .10 | .06 |
| 10 | Ben Smith (RS) | .07 | .04 |
| 11 | Tory Epps (RS) | .05 | .03 |
| 12 | Andre Rison | .30 | .18 |
| 13 | Shawn Collins | .05 | .03 |
| 14 | Chris Hinton | .05 | .03 |
| 15 | Deion Sanders | .30 | .18 |
| 16 | Darion Conner | .05 | .03 |
| 17 | Michael Haynes | .25 | .15 |
| 18 | Chris Miller | .30 | .18 |
| 19 | Jessie Tuggle | .05 | .03 |
| 20 | Scott Fulhage | .05 | .03 |
| 21 | Bill Fralic | .05 | .03 |
| 22 | Floyd Dixon | .05 | .03 |
| 23 | Oliver Barnett | .05 | .03 |
| 24 | Mike Rozier | .05 | .03 |
| 25 | Tory Epps | .05 | .03 |
| 26 | Tim Green | .05 | .03 |
| 27 | Steve Broussard | .08 | .05 |
| 28 | Bruce Pickens (R) | .20 | .12 |
| 29 | Mike Pritchard (R) | .50 | .30 |
| 30 | Andre Reed | .12 | .07 |
| 31 | Darryl Talley | .07 | .04 |
| 32 | Nate Odomes | .05 | .03 |
| 33 | Jamie Mueller | .05 | .03 |
| 34 | Leon Seals | .05 | .03 |
| 35 | Keith McKeller | .07 | .04 |
| 36 | Al Edwards (R) | .07 | .04 |
| 37 | Butch Rolle | .05 | .03 |
| 38 | Jeff Wright (R) | .07 | .04 |
| 39 | Will Wolford | .05 | .03 |
| 40 | James Williams | .05 | .03 |
| 41 | Kent Hull | .05 | .03 |
| 42 | James Lofton | .20 | .12 |
| 43 | Frank Reich | .07 | .04 |
| 44 | Bruce Smith | .08 | .05 |
| 45 | Thurman Thomas | .40 | .25 |
| 46 | Leonard Smith | .05 | .03 |
| 47 | Shane Conlan | .08 | .05 |
| 48 | Steve Tasker | .05 | .03 |
| 49 | Ray Bentley | .05 | .03 |
| 50 | Cornelius Bennett | .10 | .06 |
| 51 | Stan Thomas (R) | .07 | .04 |
| 52 | Shaun Gayle | .05 | .03 |
| 53 | Wendell Davis | .12 | .07 |
| 54 | James Thornton | .05 | .03 |
| 55 | Mark Carrier (Chi) | .08 | .05 |
| 56 | Richard Dent | .07 | .04 |
| 57 | Ron Morris | .05 | .03 |
| 58 | Mike Singletary | .10 | .06 |
| 59 | Jay Hilgenberg | .05 | .03 |
| 60 | Donnell Woolford | .05 | .03 |
| 61 | Jim Covert | .05 | .03 |
| 62 | Jim Harbaugh | .12 | .07 |
| 63 | Neal Anderson | .15 | .10 |
| 64 | Brad Muster | .08 | .05 |
| 65 | Kevin Butler | .05 | .03 |
| 66 | Trace Armstrong | .05 | .03 |
| 67 | Ron Cox | .05 | .03 |
| 68 | Peter Tom Willis | .12 | .07 |
| 69 | Johnny Bailey | .07 | .04 |
| 70 | Mark Bortz | .05 | .03 |
| 71 | Chris Zorich (R) | .10 | .06 |
| 72 | Lamar Rogers (R) | .15 | .10 |
| 73 | David Grant | .05 | .03 |
| 74 | Lewis Billups | .05 | .03 |
| 75 | Harold Green | .20 | .12 |
| 76 | Ickey Woods | .07 | .04 |
| 77 | Eddie Brown | .08 | .05 |
| 78 | David Fulcher | .05 | .03 |
| 79 | Anthony Munoz | .08 | .05 |

| | | | |
|---|---|---|---|
| 80 | Carl Zander | .05 | .03 |
| 81 | Rodney Holman | .08 | .05 |
| 82 | James Brooks | .07 | .04 |
| 83 | Tim McGee | .08 | .05 |
| 84 | Boomer Esiason | .12 | .07 |
| 85 | Leon White | .05 | .03 |
| 86 | James Francis | .10 | .06 |
| 87 | Mitchell Price (R) | .08 | .05 |
| 88 | Ed King (R) | .08 | .05 |
| 89 | Eric Turner (R) | .25 | .15 |
| 90 | Rob Burnett (R) | .08 | .05 |
| 91 | Leroy Hoard | .08 | .05 |
| 92 | Kevin Mack | .07 | .04 |
| 93 | Thane Gash | .05 | .03 |
| 94 | Gregg Rakoczy | .05 | .03 |
| 95 | Clay Matthews | .05 | .03 |
| 96 | Eric Metcalf | .10 | .06 |
| 97 | Stephen Braggs | .05 | .03 |
| 98 | Frank Minnifield | .05 | .03 |
| 99 | Reggie Langhorne | .05 | .03 |
| 100 | Mike Johnson | .05 | .03 |
| 101 | Brian Brennan | .05 | .03 |
| 102 | Anthony Pleasant | .05 | .03 |
| 103 | Godfrey Myles (R) | .08 | .05 |
| 104 | Russell Maryland (R) | .40 | .25 |
| 105 | James Washington (R) | .08 | .05 |
| 106 | Nate Newton | .05 | .03 |
| 107 | Jimmie Jones | .05 | .03 |
| 108 | Jay Novacek | .08 | .05 |
| 109 | Alexander Wright | .08 | .05 |
| 110 | Jack Del Rio | .05 | .03 |
| 111 | Jim Jeffcoat | .07 | .04 |
| 112 | Mike Saxon | .05 | .03 |
| 113 | Troy Aikman | 1.00 | .70 |
| 114 | Issiac Holt | .05 | .03 |
| 115 | Ken Norton | .05 | .03 |
| 116 | Kelvin Martin | .07 | .04 |
| 117 | Emmitt Smith | 1.75 | 1.00 |
| 118 | Ken Willis | .05 | .03 |
| 119 | Daniel Stubbs | .05 | .03 |
| 120 | Michael Irvin | .50 | .30 |
| 121 | Danny Noonan | .05 | .03 |
| 122 | Alvin Harper (R) | .80 | .50 |
| 123 | Reggie Johnson (R) | .15 | .10 |
| 124 | Vance Johnson | .07 | .04 |
| 125 | Steve Atwater | .10 | .06 |
| 126 | Greg Kragen | .05 | .03 |
| 127 | John Elway | .25 | .15 |
| 128 | Simon Fletcher | .05 | .03 |
| 129 | Wymon Henderson | .05 | .03 |
| 130 | Ricky Nattiel | .05 | .03 |
| 131 | Shannon Sharpe | .08 | .05 |
| 132 | Ron Holmes | .05 | .03 |
| 133 | Karl Mecklenburg | .08 | .05 |
| 134 | Bobby Humphrey | .10 | .06 |
| 135 | Clarence Kay | .05 | .03 |
| 136 | Dennis Smith | .05 | .03 |
| 137 | Jim Juriga | .05 | .03 |
| 138 | Melvin Bratton | .05 | .03 |
| 139 | Mark Jackson | .05 | .03 |
| 140 | Michael Brooks | .05 | .03 |
| 141 | Alton Montgomery | .05 | .03 |
| 142 | Mike Croel (R) | .35 | .20 |
| 143 | Mel Gray | .05 | .03 |
| 144 | Michael Cofer | .05 | .03 |
| 145 | Jeff Campbell | .05 | .03 |
| 146 | Dan Owens | .05 | .03 |
| 147 | Robert Clark | .05 | .03 |
| 148 | Jim Arnold | .05 | .03 |
| 149 | William White | .05 | .03 |
| 150 | Rodney Peete | .08 | .05 |
| 151 | Jerry Ball | .05 | .03 |
| 152 | Bennie Blades | .07 | .04 |
| 153 | Barry Sanders | .80 | .50 |
| 154 | Andre Ware | .07 | .04 |
| 155 | Lomas Brown | .05 | .03 |
| 156 | Chris Spielman | .07 | .04 |
| 157 | Kelvin Pritchett (R) | .35 | .20 |
| 158 | Herman Moore (R) | .50 | .30 |
| 159 | Chris Jacke | .05 | .03 |
| 160 | Tony Mandarich | .05 | .03 |
| 161 | Perry Kemp | .05 | .03 |
| 162 | Johnny Holland | .05 | .03 |
| 163 | Mark Lee | .05 | .03 |
| 164 | Anthony Dilweg | .05 | .03 |
| 165 | Scott Stephen (R) | .07 | .04 |
| 166 | Ed West | .05 | .03 |
| 167 | Mark Murphy | .05 | .03 |
| 168 | Darrell Thompson | .10 | .06 |
| 169 | James Campen (R) | .07 | .04 |
| 170 | Jeff Query (R) | .08 | .05 |
| 171 | Brian Noble | .05 | .03 |
| 172 | Sterling Sharpe | .35 | .20 |
| 173 | Robert Brown | .05 | .03 |
| 174 | Tim Harris | .07 | .04 |
| 175 | LeRoy Butler | .05 | .03 |
| 176 | Don Majkowski | .12 | .07 |
| 177 | Vinnie Clark (R) | .10 | .06 |
| 178 | Esera Tuaolo (R) | .08 | .05 |
| 179 | Lorenzo White | .15 | .10 |
| 180 | Warren Moon | .30 | .18 |
| 181 | Sean Jones | .05 | .03 |
| 182 | Curtis Duncan | .05 | .03 |
| 183 | Al Smith | .05 | .03 |
| 184 | Richard Johnson (R) | .07 | .04 |
| 185 | Tony Jones | .05 | .03 |
| 186 | Bubba McDowell | .05 | .03 |
| 187 | Bruce Matthews | .05 | .03 |
| 188 | Ray Childress | .08 | .05 |
| 189 | Haywood Jeffires | .20 | .12 |
| 190 | Ernest Givins | .15 | .10 |
| 191 | Mike Munchak | .05 | .03 |
| 192 | Greg Montgomery | .05 | .03 |

| | | | |
|---|---|---|---|
| 193 | Cody Carlson (R) | .15 | .10 |
| 194 | Johnny Meads | .05 | .03 |
| 195 | Drew Hill | .08 | .05 |
| 196 | Mike Dumas (R) | .10 | .06 |
| 197 | Darryll Lewis (R) | .12 | .07 |
| 198 | Rohn Stark | .05 | .03 |
| 199 | Clarence Verdin | .07 | .04 |
| 200 | Mike Prior | .05 | .03 |
| 201 | Eugene Daniel | .05 | .03 |
| 202 | Dean Biasucci | .05 | .03 |
| 203 | Jeff Herrod | .05 | .03 |
| 204 | Keith Taylor | .05 | .03 |
| 205 | Jon Hand | .05 | .03 |
| 206 | Pat Beach | .05 | .03 |
| 207 | Duane Bickett | .05 | .03 |
| 208 | Jessie Hester | .05 | .03 |
| 209 | Chip banks | .07 | .04 |
| 210 | Ray Donaldson | .05 | .03 |
| 211 | Bill Brooks | .05 | .03 |
| 212 | Jeff George | .35 | .20 |
| 213 | Tony Siragusa (R) | .08 | .05 |
| 214 | Albert Bentley | .05 | .03 |
| 215 | Joe Valerio (R) | .08 | .05 |
| 216 | Chris Martin | .05 | .03 |
| 217 | Christian Okoye | .08 | .05 |
| 218 | Stephone Paige | .08 | .05 |
| 219 | Percy Snow | .08 | .05 |
| 220 | David Szott (R) | .07 | .04 |
| 221 | Derrick Thomas | .20 | .12 |
| 222 | Todd McNair | .05 | .03 |
| 223 | Albert Lewis | .07 | .04 |
| 224 | Neil Smith | .05 | .03 |
| 225 | Barry Word | .25 | .15 |
| 226 | Robb Thomas | .05 | .03 |
| 227 | John Alt | .05 | .03 |
| 228 | Jonathan Hayes | .05 | .03 |
| 229 | Kevin Ross | .05 | .03 |
| 230 | Nick Lowery | .07 | .04 |
| 231 | Tim Grunhard | .05 | .03 |
| 232 | Dan Saleaumua | .05 | .03 |
| 233 | Steve DeBerg | .08 | .05 |
| 234 | Harvey Williams (R) | .40 | .25 |
| 235 | Nick Bell (R) | .40 | .25 |
| 236 | Mervyn Fernandez | .07 | .04 |
| 237 | Howie Long | .07 | .04 |
| 238 | Marcus Allen | .10 | .06 |
| 239 | Eddie Anderson | .05 | .03 |
| 240 | Ethan Horton | .05 | .03 |
| 241 | Lionel Washington | .05 | .03 |
| 242 | Steve Wisniewski | .05 | .03 |
| 243 | Bo Jackson | .30 | .18 |
| 244 | Greg Townsend | .05 | .03 |
| 245 | Jeff Jaeger | .05 | .03 |
| 246 | Aaron Wallace | .07 | .04 |
| 247 | Garry Lewis | .05 | .03 |
| 248 | Steve Smith | .05 | .03 |
| 249 | Willie Gault | .07 | .04 |
| 250 | Scott Davis | .05 | .03 |
| 251 | Jay Schroeder | .08 | .05 |
| 252 | Don Mosebar | .05 | .03 |
| 253 | Todd Marinovich (R) | .80 | .50 |
| 254 | Irv Pankey | .05 | .03 |
| 255 | Flipper Anderson | .07 | .04 |
| 256 | Tom Newberry | .05 | .03 |
| 257 | Kevin Greene | .07 | .04 |
| 258 | Mike Wilcher | .05 | .03 |
| 259 | Bern Brostek | .05 | .03 |
| 260 | Buford McGee | .05 | .03 |
| 261 | Cleveland Gary | .12 | .07 |
| 262 | Jackie Slater | .07 | .04 |
| 263 | Henry Ellard | .07 | .04 |
| 264 | Alvin Wright | .05 | .03 |
| 265 | Darryl Henley (R) | .10 | .06 |
| 266 | Damone Johnson (R) | .07 | .04 |
| 267 | Frank Stams | .05 | .03 |
| 268 | Jerry Gray | .05 | .03 |
| 269 | Jim Everett | .12 | .07 |
| 270 | Pat Terrell | .05 | .03 |
| 271 | Todd Lyght (R) | .25 | .15 |
| 272 | Aaron Cox | .05 | .03 |
| 273 | Barry Sanders (LL) | .30 | .18 |
| 274 | Jerry Rice (LL) | .20 | .12 |
| 275 | Derrick Thomas (LL) | .10 | .06 |
| 276 | Mark Carrier (LL) | .07 | .04 |
| 277 | Warren Moon (LL) | .12 | .07 |
| 278 | Randall Cunningham (LL) | .10 | .06 |
| 279 | Nick Lowery (LL) | .07 | .04 |
| 280 | Clarence Verdin (LL) | .07 | .04 |
| 281 | Thurman Thomas (LL) | .20 | .12 |
| 282 | Mike Horan (LL) | .05 | .03 |
| 283 | Flipper Anderson (LL) | .07 | .04 |
| 284 | John Offerdahl | .08 | .05 |
| 285 | Dan Marino | .35 | .20 |
| 286 | Mark Clayton | .10 | .06 |
| 287 | Tony Paige | .05 | .03 |
| 288 | Keith Sims | .05 | .03 |
| 289 | Jeff Cross | .05 | .03 |
| 290 | Pete Stoyanovich | .05 | .03 |
| 291 | Ferrell Edmunds | .05 | .03 |
| 292 | Reggie Roby | .05 | .03 |
| 293 | Louis Oliver | .07 | .04 |
| 294 | Jarvis Williams | .05 | .03 |
| 295 | Sammie Smith | .08 | .05 |
| 296 | Richmond Webb | .07 | .04 |
| 297 | J.B. Brown | .05 | .03 |
| 298 | Jim Jensen | .05 | .03 |
| 299 | Mark Duper | .07 | .04 |
| 300 | David Griggs | .05 | .03 |
| 301 | Randal Hill (R) | .35 | .20 |
| 302 | Aaron Craver (R) | .10 | .06 |
| 303 | Keith Millard | .07 | .04 |
| 304 | Steve Jordan | .05 | .03 |

| | | | |
|---|---|---|---|
| 305 Anthony Carter | .08 | .05 | |
| 306 Mike Merriweather | .07 | .04 | |
| 307 Audray McMillian | .05 | .03 | |
| 308 Randall McDaniel | .05 | .03 | |
| 309 Gary Zimmerman | .05 | .03 | |
| 310 Carl Lee | .05 | .03 | |
| 311 Reggie Rutland | .05 | .03 | |
| 312 Hassan Jones | .07 | .04 | |
| 313 Kirk Lowdermilk | .05 | .03 | |
| 314 Herschel Walker | .12 | .07 | |
| 315 Chris Doleman | .07 | .04 | |
| 316 Joey Browner | .07 | .04 | |
| 317 Wade Wilson | .08 | .05 | |
| 318 Henry Thomas | .05 | .03 | |
| 319 Rich Gannon | .25 | .15 | |
| 320 Al Noga | .05 | .03 | |
| 321 Pat Harlow (R) | .08 | .05 | |
| 322 Bruce Armstrong | .05 | .03 | |
| 323 Maurice Hurst | .05 | .03 | |
| 324 Brent Williams | .05 | .03 | |
| 325 Chris Singleton (R) | .07 | .04 | |
| 326 Jason Staurovsky | .05 | .03 | |
| 327 Marvin Allen | .05 | .03 | |
| 328 Hart Lee Dykes | .08 | .05 | |
| 329 Johnny Rembert | .07 | .04 | |
| 330 Andre Tippett | .07 | .04 | |
| 331 Greg McMurtry | .08 | .05 | |
| 332 John Stephens | .08 | .05 | |
| 333 Ray Agnew | .05 | .03 | |
| 334 Tommy Hodson | .08 | .05 | |
| 335 Ronnie Lippett | .05 | .03 | |
| 336 Marv Cook | .07 | .04 | |
| 337 Tommy Barnhardt (R) | .07 | .04 | |
| 338 Dalton Hilliard | .07 | .04 | |
| 339 Sam Mills | .07 | .04 | |
| 340 Morten Andersen | .07 | .04 | |
| 341 Stan Brock | .05 | .03 | |
| 342 Brett Maxie | .05 | .03 | |
| 343 Steve Walsh | .08 | .05 | |
| 344 Vaughan Johnson | .05 | .03 | |
| 345 Rickey Jackson | .07 | .04 | |
| 346 Renaldo Turnbull (R) | .07 | .04 | |
| 347 Joel Hilgenberg | .05 | .03 | |
| 348 Toi Cook (R) | .07 | .04 | |
| 349 Robert Massey | .05 | .03 | |
| 350 Pat Swilling | .10 | .06 | |
| 351 Eric Martin | .07 | .04 | |
| 352 Rueben Mayes | .05 | .03 | |
| 353 Vince Buck | .05 | .03 | |
| 354 Brett Perriman | .05 | .03 | |
| 355 Wesley Carroll (R) | .25 | .15 | |
| 356 Jarrod Bunch (R) | .25 | .15 | |
| 357 Pepper Johnson | .05 | .03 | |
| 358 Dave Meggett | .12 | .07 | |
| 359 Mark Collins | .07 | .04 | |
| 360 Sean Landeta | .05 | .03 | |
| 361 Maurice Carthon | .05 | .03 | |

| | | | |
|---|---|---|---|
| 362 Mike Fox (R) | .07 | .04 | |
| 363 Jeff Hostetler | .15 | .10 | |
| 364 Phil Simms | .10 | .06 | |
| 365 Leonard Marshall | .07 | .04 | |
| 366 Gary Reasons | .05 | .03 | |
| 367 Rodney Hampton | .35 | .20 | |
| 368 Greg Jackson (R) | .08 | .05 | |
| 369 Jumbo Elliott | .05 | .03 | |
| 370 Bob Kratch (R) | .07 | .04 | |
| 371 Lawrence Taylor | .12 | .07 | |
| 372 Erik Howard | .05 | .03 | |
| 373 Carl Banks | .08 | .05 | |
| 374 Stephen Baker | .07 | .04 | |
| 375 Mark Ingram | .07 | .04 | |
| 376 Browning Nagle (R) | 1.00 | .70 | |
| 377 Jeff Lageman | .07 | .04 | |
| 378 Ken O'Brien | .08 | .05 | |
| 379 Al Toon | .08 | .05 | |
| 380 Joe Prokop | .05 | .03 | |
| 381 Tony Stargell | .07 | .04 | |
| 382 Blair Thomas | .25 | .15 | |
| 383 Erik McMillan | .07 | .04 | |
| 384 Dennis Byrd | .05 | .03 | |
| 385 Freeman McNeil | .07 | .04 | |
| 386 Brad Baxter | .12 | .07 | |
| 387 Mark Boyer | .05 | .03 | |
| 388 Terance Mathis | .12 | .07 | |
| 389 Jim Sweeney | .05 | .03 | |
| 390 Kyle Clifton | .05 | .03 | |
| 391 Pat Leahy | .05 | .03 | |
| 392 Rob Moore | .40 | .25 | |
| 393 James Hasty | .05 | .03 | |
| 394 Blaise Bryant (R) | .07 | .04 | |
| 395A Jesse Campbell | 1.25 | .80 | |
| (R) (Wrong Photo) | | | |
| 395B Jesse Campbell (R) | .10 | .06 | |
| 396 Keith Jackson | .15 | .10 | |
| 397 Jerome Brown | .07 | .04 | |
| 398 Keith Byars | .08 | .05 | |
| 399 Seth Joyner | .07 | .04 | |
| 400 Mike Bellamy | .07 | .04 | |
| 401 Fred Barnett | .25 | .15 | |
| 402 Reggie Singletary | .05 | .03 | |
| 403 Reggie White | .10 | .06 | |
| 404 Randall Cunningham | .15 | .10 | |
| 405 Byron Evans | .05 | .03 | |
| 406 Wes Hopkins | .05 | .03 | |
| 407 Ben Smith | .07 | .04 | |
| 408 Roger Ruzek | .05 | .03 | |
| 409 Eric Allen | .05 | .03 | |
| 410 Anthony Toney | .05 | .03 | |
| 411 Clyde Simmons | .08 | .05 | |
| 412 Andre Waters | .05 | .03 | |
| 413 Calvin Williams | .10 | .06 | |
| 414 Eric Swann (R) | .15 | .10 | |
| 415 Eric Hill | .05 | .03 | |
| 416 Tim McDonald | .05 | .03 | |

| | | | |
|---|---|---|---|
| 417 Luis Sharpe | .05 | .03 | |
| 418 Ernie Jones | .05 | .03 | |
| 419 Ken Harvey | .05 | .03 | |
| 420 Ricky Proehl | .08 | .05 | |
| 421 Johnny Johnson | .12 | .07 | |
| 422 Anthony Bell | .05 | .03 | |
| 423 Timm Rosenbach | .12 | .07 | |
| 424 Rich Camarillo | .05 | .03 | |
| 425 Walter Reeves | .05 | .03 | |
| 426 Freddie Joe Nunn | .05 | .03 | |
| 427 Anthony Thompson | .10 | .06 | |
| 428 Bill Lewis | .05 | .03 | |
| 429 Jim Wahler (R) | .07 | .04 | |
| 430 Cedric Mack | .05 | .03 | |
| 431 Michael Jones (R) | .08 | .05 | |
| 432 Ernie Mills (R) | .25 | .15 | |
| 433 Tim Worley | .07 | .04 | |
| 434 Greg Lloyd | .05 | .03 | |
| 435 Dermontti Dawson | .05 | .03 | |
| 436 Louis Lipps | .07 | .04 | |
| 437 Eric Green | .15 | .10 | |
| 438 Donald Evans | .05 | .03 | |
| 439 David Johnson (R) | .07 | .04 | |
| 440 Tunch Ilkin | .05 | .03 | |
| 441 Bubby Brister | .10 | .06 | |
| 442 Chris Calloway | .05 | .03 | |
| 443 David Little | .05 | .03 | |
| 444 Thomas Everett | .07 | .04 | |
| 445 Carnell Lake | .05 | .03 | |
| 446 Rod Woodson | .08 | .05 | |
| 447 Gary Anderson | .05 | .03 | |
| 448 Merril Hoge | .07 | .04 | |
| 449 Gerald Williams | .05 | .03 | |
| 450 Eric Moten (R) | .07 | .04 | |
| 451 Marion Butts | .10 | .06 | |
| 452 Leslie O'Neal | .07 | .04 | |
| 453 Ronnie Harmon | .07 | .04 | |
| 454 Gil Byrd | .07 | .04 | |
| 455 Junior Seau | .20 | .12 | |
| 456 Nate Lewis (R) | .12 | .07 | |
| 457 Leo Goeas | .05 | .03 | |
| 458 Burt Grossman | .07 | .04 | |
| 459 Courtney Hall | .05 | .03 | |
| 460 Anthony Miller | .08 | .05 | |
| 461 Gary Plummer | .05 | .03 | |
| 462 Billy Joe Tolliver | .08 | .05 | |
| 463 Lee Williams | .05 | .03 | |
| 464 Arthur Cox | .05 | .03 | |
| 465 John Kidd | .05 | .03 | |
| 466 Frank Cornish | .05 | .03 | |
| 467 John Carney | .05 | .03 | |
| 468 Eric Bieniemy (R) | .20 | .12 | |
| 469 Don Griffin | .05 | .03 | |
| 470 Jerry Rice | .35 | .20 | |
| 471 Keith DeLong | .05 | .03 | |
| 472 John Taylor | .15 | .10 | |
| 473 Brent Jones | .07 | .04 | |
| 474 Pierce Holt | .05 | .03 |
| 475 Kevin Fagan | .05 | .03 |
| 476 Bill Romanowski | .05 | .03 |
| 477 Dexter Carter | .08 | .05 |
| 478 Guy McIntyre | .05 | .03 |
| 479 Joe Montana | .50 | .30 |
| 480 Charles Haley | .08 | .05 |
| 481 Mike Cofer | .05 | .03 |
| 482 Jesse Sapolu | .05 | .03 |
| 483 Eric Davis | .05 | .03 |
| 484 Mike Sherrad | .07 | .04 |
| 485 Steve Young | .35 | .20 |
| 486 Darryl Pollard | .05 | .03 |
| 487 Tom Rathman | .07 | .04 |
| 488 Michael Carter | .07 | .04 |
| 489 Ricky Watters (R) | 1.75 | 1.00 |
| 490 John Johnson (R) | .08 | .05 |
| 491 Eugene Robinson | .05 | .03 |
| 492 Andy Heck | .05 | .03 |
| 493 John L. Williams | .07 | .04 |
| 494 Norm Johnson | .05 | .03 |
| 495 David Wyman | .05 | .03 |
| 496 Derrick Fenner | .08 | .05 |
| 497 Rick Donnelly | .05 | .03 |
| 498 Tony Woods | .05 | .03 |
| 499 Derek Loville (R) | .07 | .04 |
| 500 Dave Krieg | .12 | .07 |
| 501 Joe Nash | .05 | .03 |
| 502 Brian Blades | .08 | .05 |
| 503 Cortez Kennedy | .20 | .12 |
| 504 Jeff Bryant | .05 | .03 |
| 505 Tommy Kane | .08 | .05 |
| 506 Travis McNeal | .05 | .03 |
| 507 Terry Wooden | .05 | .03 |
| 508 Chris Warren | .07 | .04 |
| 509A Dan McGwire (ER) | 1.50 | .90 |
| (Wrong Photo) | | |
| 509B Dan McGwire (Cor) | .90 | .60 |
| 510 Mark Robinson | .05 | .03 |
| 511 Ron Hall | .05 | .03 |
| 512 Paul Gruber | .07 | .04 |
| 513 Harry Hamilton | .05 | .03 |
| 514 Keith McCants | .08 | .05 |
| 515 Reggie Cobb | .15 | .10 |
| 516 Steve Christie | .05 | .03 |
| 517 Broderick Thomas | .08 | .05 |
| 518 Mark Carrier (TB) | .08 | .05 |
| 519 Vinny Testaverde | .08 | .05 |
| 520 Ricky Reynolds | .05 | .03 |
| 521 Jesse Anderson | .05 | .03 |
| 522 Reuben Davis | .05 | .03 |
| 523 Wayne Haddix | .07 | .04 |
| 524 Gary Anderson | .07 | .04 |
| 525 Bruce Hill | .05 | .03 |
| 526 Kevin Murphy | .05 | .03 |
| 527 Lawrence Dawsey (R) | .40 | .25 |
| 528 Ricky Ervins (R) | .90 | .60 |

| 529 | Charles Mann | .05 | .03 |
|-----|--------------|-----|-----|
| 530 | Jim Lachey | .07 | .04 |
| 531 | Mark Rypien | .15 | .10 |
| 532 | Darrell Green | .10 | .06 |
| 533 | Stan Humphries | .25 | .15 |
| 534 | Jeff Bostic | .05 | .03 |
| 535 | Earnest Byner | .07 | .04 |
| 536 | Art Monk | .15 | .10 |
| 537 | Don Warren | .05 | .03 |
| 538 | Darryl Grant | .05 | .03 |
| 539 | Wilbur Marshall | .08 | .05 |
| 540 | Kurt Gouveia (R) | .08 | .05 |
| 541 | Marcus Koch | .08 | .05 |
| 542 | Andre Collins | .05 | .03 |
| 543 | Chip Lohmiller | .05 | .03 |
| 544 | Alvin Walton | .05 | .03 |
| 545 | Gary Clark | .12 | .07 |
| 546 | Ricky Sanders | .08 | .05 |
| 547 | Redskins vs Eagles | .10 | .06 |
| 548 | Bengals vs. Oilers | .07 | .04 |
| 549 | Dolphins vs. Chiefs | .08 | .05 |
| 550 | Bears vs. Saints | .07 | .04 |
| 551 | Bills vs. Dolphins | .15 | .10 |
| 552 | 49ers vs. Redskins | .07 | .04 |
| 553 | Giants vs. Bears | .07 | .04 |
| 554 | Raiders vs. Gengals | .15 | .10 |
| 555 | AFC Championship | .07 | .04 |
| 556 | NFC Championship | .07 | .04 |
| 557 | Super Bowl XXV | .07 | .04 |
| 558 | Checklist 1-140 | .05 | .03 |
| 559 | Checklist 141-280 | .05 | .03 |
| 560 | Checklist 281-420 | .05 | .03 |
| 561 | Checklist 421-561 | .05 | .03 |

# 1992 Bowman

This 573-card set features full color action photos on the front printed on a glossy white stock. The player's name appears in a color bar below the photo while the Bowman logo is printed in the top corner. The set contains gold foil cards of Team Leaders (TL), Longest Plays (LP) and Playoff Leaders (PL). One gold foil card was distributed in each foil pack. All cards measure 2-1/2" by 3-1/2".

|  |  | MINT | NR/MT |
|--|--|------|-------|
| Complete Set (573) | | 140.00 | 80.00 |
| Commons | | .20 | .12 |

| 1 | Reggie White | .25 | .15 |
|---|--------------|-----|-----|
| 2 | Johnny Meads | .20 | .12 |
| 3 | Chip Lohmiller | .20 | .12 |
| 4 | James Lofton | .25 | .15 |
| 5 | Ray Horton | .20 | .12 |
| 6 | Rich Moran | .20 | .12 |
| 7 | Howard Cross | .20 | .12 |
| 8 | Mike Horan | .20 | .12 |
| 9 | Erik Kramer | .35 | .20 |
| 10 | Steve Wisniewski | .20 | .12 |
| 11 | Michael Haynes | .30 | .18 |
| 12 | Donald Evans | .20 | .12 |
| 13 | Michael Irvin (PL) | 2.50 | 1.40 |
| 14 | Gary Zimmerman | .20 | .12 |
| 15 | John Friesz | .25 | .15 |
| 16 | Mark Carrier | .20 | .12 |
| 17 | Mark Duper | .20 | .12 |
| 18 | James Thornton | .20 | .12 |
| 19 | Jon Hand | .20 | .12 |
| 20 | Sterling Sharpe | 1.50 | .90 |
| 21 | Jacob Green | .20 | .12 |
| 22 | Wesley Carroll | .25 | .15 |
| 23 | Clay Matthews | .20 | .12 |
| 24 | Kevin Greene | .20 | .12 |
| 25 | Brad Baxter | .25 | .15 |
| 26 | Don Griffin | .20 | .12 |
| 27 | Robert Delpino | .25 | .15 |
| 28 | Lee Johnson | .20 | .12 |
| 29 | Jim Wahler | .20 | .12 |
| 30 | Leonard Russell | .75 | .45 |
| 31 | Eric Moore | .20 | .12 |
| 32 | Dino Hackett | .20 | .12 |
| 33 | Simon Fletcher | .20 | .12 |
| 34 | Al Edwards | .20 | .12 |
| 35 | Brad Edwards | .20 | .12 |
| 36 | James Joseph | .25 | .15 |
| 37 | Rodney Peete | .30 | .18 |
| 38 | Ricky Reynolds | .20 | .12 |
| 39 | Eddie Anderson | .20 | .12 |
| 40 | Ken Clarke | .20 | .12 |
| 41 | Tony Bennett | .20 | .12 |
| 42 | Larry Brown | .20 | .12 |
| 43 | Ray Childress | .25 | .15 |
| 44 | Mike Kenn | .20 | .12 |

| | | | |
|---|---|---|---|
| 45 | Vestee Jackson | .20 | .12 |
| 46 | Neil O'Donnell | 1.25 | .80 |
| 47 | Bill Brooks | .20 | .12 |
| 48 | Kevin Butler | .20 | .12 |
| 49 | Joe Phillips | .20 | .12 |
| 50 | Cortez Kennedy | .30 | .18 |
| 51 | Rickey Jackson | .25 | .15 |
| 52 | Vinnie Clark | .20 | .12 |
| 53 | Michael Jackson | .30 | .18 |
| 54 | Ernie Jones | .25 | .15 |
| 55 | Tom Newberry | .20 | .12 |
| 56 | Pat Harlow | .20 | .12 |
| 57 | Craig Taylor | .20 | .12 |
| 58 | Joe Prokop | .20 | .12 |
| 59 | Warren Moon (PL) | .90 | .60 |
| 60 | Jeff Lageman | .25 | .15 |
| 61 | Neil Smith | .20 | .12 |
| 62 | Jim Jeffcoat | .20 | .12 |
| 63 | Bill Fralic | .20 | .12 |
| 64 | Mark Schlereth (R) | .25 | .15 |
| 65 | Keith Byars | .25 | .15 |
| 66 | Jeff Hostetler | .30 | .18 |
| 67 | Joey Browner | .20 | .12 |
| 68 | Bobby Hebert (PL) | .35 | .20 |
| 69 | Keith Sims | .20 | .12 |
| 70 | Warren Moon | .50 | .30 |
| 71 | Pio Sagapolutele (R) | .25 | .15 |
| 72 | Cornelius Bennett | .25 | .15 |
| 73 | Greg Davis | .20 | .12 |
| 74 | Ronnie Harmon | .25 | .15 |
| 75 | Ron Hall | .20 | .12 |
| 76 | Howie Long | .25 | .15 |
| 77 | Greg Lewis | .30 | .18 |
| 78 | Carnell Lake | .20 | .12 |
| 79 | Ray Crockett | .20 | .12 |
| 80 | Tom Waddle | .25 | .15 |
| 81 | Vincent Brown | .20 | .12 |
| 82 | Bill Brooks | .20 | .12 |
| 83 | John L. Williams | .25 | .15 |
| 84 | Floyd Turner | .20 | .12 |
| 85 | Scott Radecic | .20 | .12 |
| 86 | Anthony Munoz | .25 | .15 |
| 87 | Ronnie Young | .20 | .12 |
| 88 | Dexter Carter | .25 | .15 |
| 89 | Tony Zendejas | .20 | .12 |
| 90 | Tim Jorden | .20 | .12 |
| 91 | Leroy Butler | .20 | .12 |
| 92 | Richard Brown (R) | .25 | .15 |
| 93 | Erric Pegram | .25 | .15 |
| 94 | Sean Landeta | .20 | .12 |
| 95 | Clyde Simmons | .25 | .15 |
| 96 | Martin Mayhew | .20 | .12 |
| 97 | Jarvis Williams | .20 | .12 |
| 98 | Barry Word | .30 | .18 |
| 99 | John Taylor (LP) | .50 | .30 |
| 100 | Emmitt Smith | 14.00 | 8.00 |
| 101 | Leon Seals | .20 | .12 |
| 102 | Marion Butts | .25 | .15 |
| 103 | Mike Merriweather | .20 | .12 |
| 104 | Ernest Givins | .30 | .18 |
| 105 | Wymon Henderson | .20 | .12 |
| 106 | Robert Wilson | .25 | .15 |
| 107 | Bobby Hebert | .25 | .15 |
| 108 | Terry McDaniel | .20 | .12 |
| 109 | Jerry Ball | .20 | .12 |
| 110 | John Taylor | .30 | .18 |
| 111 | Rob Moore | .25 | .15 |
| 112 | Thurman Thomas (TL) | 5.00 | 3.00 |
| 113 | Checklist | .20 | .12 |
| 114 | Brian Blades | .20 | .12 |
| 115 | Larry Kelm | .20 | .12 |
| 116 | James Francis | .25 | .15 |
| 117 | Rod Woodson | .25 | .15 |
| 118 | Trace Armstrong | .20 | .12 |
| 119 | Eugene Daniel | .20 | .12 |
| 120 | Andre Tippett | .25 | .15 |
| 121 | Chris Jacke | .20 | .12 |
| 122 | Jesse Tuggle | .20 | .12 |
| 123 | Chris Chandler | .25 | .15 |
| 124 | Tim Johnson | .20 | .12 |
| 125 | Mark Collins | .20 | .12 |
| 126 | Aeneas Williams | .25 | .15 |
| 127 | James Jones | .20 | .12 |
| 128 | George Jameson | .20 | .12 |
| 129 | Deron Cherry | .20 | .12 |
| 130 | Mark Clayton | .30 | .18 |
| 131 | Keith DeLong | .20 | .12 |
| 132 | Marcus Allen | .25 | .15 |
| 133 | Joe Walter (R) | .25 | .15 |
| 134 | Reggie Rutland | .20 | .12 |
| 135 | Kent Hull | .20 | .12 |
| 136 | Jeff Feagles | .20 | .12 |
| 137 | Ronnie Lott (TL) | .35 | .20 |
| 138 | Henry Rolling | .20 | .12 |
| 139 | Gary Anderson | .20 | .12 |
| 140 | Morten Andersen | .25 | .15 |
| 141 | Cris Dishman | .20 | .12 |
| 142 | David Treadwell | .20 | .12 |
| 143 | Kevin Gogan | .20 | .12 |
| 144 | James Hasty | .20 | .12 |
| 145 | Robert Delpino | .25 | .15 |
| 146 | Patrick Hunter | .20 | .12 |
| 147 | Gary Anderson | .20 | .12 |
| 148 | Chip Banks | .20 | .12 |
| 149 | Dan Fike | .20 | .12 |
| 150 | Chris Miller | .35 | .20 |
| 151 | Hugh Millen | .30 | .18 |
| 152 | Courtney Hall | .20 | .12 |
| 153 | Gary Clark | .30 | .18 |
| 154 | Michael Brooks | .20 | .12 |
| 155 | Jay Hilgenberg | .20 | .12 |
| 156 | Jim McDonald | .20 | .12 |
| 157 | Andre Tippett | .25 | .15 |
| 158 | Doug Riesenberg | .20 | .12 |

| | | | |
|---|---|---|---|
| 159 | Bill Maas | .20 | .12 |
| 160 | Fred Barnett | .40 | .25 |
| 161 | Pierce Holt | .20 | .12 |
| 162 | Brian Noble | .20 | .12 |
| 163 | Harold Green | .40 | .25 |
| 164 | Joel Hilgenberg | .20 | .12 |
| 165 | Mervyn Fernandez | .25 | .15 |
| 166 | John Offerdahl | .25 | .15 |
| 167 | Shane Conlan | .25 | .15 |
| 168 | Mark Higgs (TL) | .80 | .50 |
| 169 | Bubba McDowell | .20 | .12 |
| 170 | Barry Sanders | 7.00 | 4.00 |
| 171 | Larry Roberts | .20 | .12 |
| 172 | Herschel Walker | .30 | .18 |
| 173 | Steve McMichael | .20 | .12 |
| 174 | Kelly Stouffer | .25 | .15 |
| 175 | Louis Lipps | .20 | .12 |
| 176 | Jim Everett | .30 | .18 |
| 177 | Tony Folbert | .20 | .12 |
| 178 | Mike Baab | .20 | .12 |
| 179 | Eric Swann | .25 | .15 |
| 180 | Emmitt Smith (TL) | 28.00 | 18.00 |
| 181 | Tim Brown | .25 | .15 |
| 182 | Dennis Smith | .20 | .12 |
| 183 | Moe Gardner | .20 | .12 |
| 184 | Derrick Walker | .25 | .15 |
| 185 | Reyna Thompson | .20 | .12 |
| 186 | Esera Tuapolo | .20 | .12 |
| 187 | Jeff Wright | .20 | .12 |
| 188 | Mark Rypien | .30 | .18 |
| 189 | Quinn Early | .20 | .12 |
| 190 | Christian Okoye | .30 | .18 |
| 191 | Keith Jackson | .30 | .18 |
| 192 | Doug Smith | .20 | .12 |
| 193 | John Elway (PL) | 1.25 | .80 |
| 194 | Reggie Cobb | .30 | .18 |
| 195 | Reggie Roby | .20 | .12 |
| 196 | Clarence Verdin | .20 | .12 |
| 197 | Jim Breech | .20 | .12 |
| 198 | Jim Sweeney | .20 | .12 |
| 199 | Marv Cook | .25 | .15 |
| 200 | Ronnie Lott | .30 | .18 |
| 201 | Mel Gray | .20 | .12 |
| 202 | Maury Buford | .20 | .12 |
| 203 | Lorenzo Lynch | .20 | .12 |
| 204 | Jesse Sapolu | .20 | .12 |
| 205 | Steve Jordan | .20 | .12 |
| 206 | Don Majkowski | .25 | .15 |
| 207 | Flipper Anderson | .25 | .15 |
| 208 | Ed King | .20 | .12 |
| 209 | Tony Woods | .20 | .12 |
| 210 | Ron Heller | .20 | .12 |
| 211 | Greg Kragen | .20 | .12 |
| 212 | Scott Case | .20 | .12 |
| 213 | Tommy Barnhardt | .20 | .12 |
| 214 | Charles Mann | .20 | .12 |
| 215 | David Griggs | .20 | .12 |
| 216 | Kenneth Davis | .30 | .18 |
| 217 | Lamar Lathon | .25 | .15 |
| 218 | Nate Odomes | .20 | .12 |
| 219 | Vinny Testaverde | .25 | .15 |
| 220 | Rod Bernstine | .25 | .15 |
| 221 | Barry Sanders (TL) | 12.00 | 8.00 |
| 222 | Carlton Haselrig | .20 | .12 |
| 223 | Steve Beuerlein | .30 | .18 |
| 224 | John Alt | .20 | .12 |
| 225 | Pepper Johnson | .20 | .12 |
| 226 | Checklist | .20 | .12 |
| 227 | Irv Eatman | .20 | .12 |
| 228 | Greg Townsend | .20 | .12 |
| 229 | Mark Jackson | .25 | .15 |
| 230 | Robert Blackmon | .20 | .12 |
| 231 | Terry Allen | 2.00 | 1.25 |
| 232 | Bennie Blades | .20 | .12 |
| 233 | Sam Mills | .25 | .15 |
| 234 | Richmond Webb | .25 | .15 |
| 235 | Richard Dent | .25 | .15 |
| 236 | Alonzo Mitz (R) | .25 | .15 |
| 237 | Steve Young | .80 | .50 |
| 238 | Pat Swilling | .30 | .18 |
| 239 | James Campen | .20 | .12 |
| 240 | Earnest Byner | .25 | .15 |
| 241 | Pat Terrell | .20 | .12 |
| 242 | Carwell Gardner | .20 | .12 |
| 243 | Charles McRae | .20 | .12 |
| 244 | Vince Newsome | .20 | .12 |
| 245 | Eric Hill | .20 | .12 |
| 246 | Steve Young (TL) | 2.00 | 1.25 |
| 247 | Nate Lewis | .20 | .12 |
| 248 | William Fuller | .20 | .12 |
| 249 | Andre Waters | .20 | .12 |
| 250 | Dean Biasucci | .20 | .12 |
| 251 | Andre Rison | .35 | .20 |
| 252 | Brent Williams | .20 | .12 |
| 253 | Todd McNair | .20 | .12 |
| 254 | Jeff Davidson (R) | .25 | .15 |
| 255 | Art Monk | .35 | .20 |
| 256 | Kirk Lowdermilk | .20 | .12 |
| 257 | Bob Golic | .20 | .12 |
| 258 | Michael Irvin | 1.25 | .80 |
| 259 | Eric Green | .25 | .15 |
| 260 | David Fulcher | .20 | .12 |
| 261 | Damone Johnson | .20 | .12 |
| 262 | Marc Spindler | .20 | .12 |
| 263 | Alfred Williams | .20 | .12 |
| 264 | Donnie Elder | .20 | .12 |
| 265 | Keith McKeller | .25 | .15 |
| 266 | Steve Bono (R) | 1.00 | .70 |
| 267 | Jumbo Elliott | .20 | .12 |
| 268 | Randy Hilliard (R) | .25 | .15 |
| 269 | Rufus Porter | .20 | .12 |
| 270 | Neal Anderson | .25 | .15 |
| 271 | Dalton Hilliard | .25 | .15 |
| 272 | Michael Zordich (R) | .25 | .15 |

| | | | |
|---|---|---|---|
| 273 | Cornelius Bennett (PL) | .30 | .18 |
| 274 | Louie Aguiar (R) | .25 | .15 |
| 275 | Aaron Craver | .25 | .15 |
| 276 | Tony Bennett | .20 | .12 |
| 277 | Terry Wooden | .20 | .12 |
| 278 | Mike Munchak | .20 | .12 |
| 279 | Chris Hinton | .20 | .12 |
| 280 | John Elway | .60 | .35 |
| 281 | Randall McDaniel | .20 | .12 |
| 282 | Brad Baxter | .25 | .15 |
| 283 | Wes Hopkins | .20 | .12 |
| 284 | Scott Davis | .20 | .12 |
| 285 | Mark Turner | .20 | .12 |
| 286 | Broderick Thompson | .20 | .12 |
| 287 | Henry Ellard | .25 | .15 |
| 288 | Adrian Cooper | .20 | .12 |
| 289 | Don Warren | .20 | .12 |
| 290 | Rodney Hampton | .60 | .35 |
| 291 | Kevin Ross | .20 | .12 |
| 292 | Mark Carrier | .25 | .15 |
| 293 | Ian Beckles | .20 | .12 |
| 294 | Gene Atkins | .20 | .12 |
| 295 | Mark Rypien (PL) | 1.00 | .60 |
| 296 | Eric Metcalf | .25 | .15 |
| 297 | Howard Ballard | .20 | .12 |
| 298 | Nate Newton | .20 | .12 |
| 299 | Dan Owens | .20 | .12 |
| 300 | Tim McGee | .25 | .15 |
| 301 | Greg McMurtry | .25 | .15 |
| 302 | Walter Reeves | .20 | .12 |
| 303 | Jeff Herrod | .20 | .12 |
| 304 | Darren Comeaux | .20 | .12 |
| 305 | Pete Stoyanovich | .20 | .12 |
| 306 | Johnny Holland | .20 | .12 |
| 307 | Jay Novacek | .25 | .15 |
| 308 | Steve Broussard | .25 | .15 |
| 309 | Darrell Green | .30 | .18 |
| 310 | Sam Mills | .25 | .15 |
| 311 | Tim Barnett | .30 | .18 |
| 312 | Steve Atwater | .25 | .15 |
| 313 | Tom Waddle (PL) | .40 | .25 |
| 314 | Felix Wright | .20 | .12 |
| 315 | Sean Jones | .20 | .12 |
| 316 | Jim Harbaugh | .30 | .18 |
| 317 | Eric Allen | .20 | .12 |
| 318 | Don Mosebar | .20 | .12 |
| 319 | Rob Taylor | .20 | .12 |
| 320 | Terance Mathis | .20 | .12 |
| 321 | Leroy Hoard | .25 | .15 |
| 322 | Kenneth Davis | .30 | .18 |
| 323 | Guy McIntyre | .20 | .12 |
| 324 | Deron Cherry | .20 | .12 |
| 325 | Tunch Ilkin | .20 | .12 |
| 326 | Willie Green | .25 | .15 |
| 327 | Darryl Henley | .20 | .12 |
| 328 | Shawn Jefferson | .25 | .15 |
| 329 | Greg Jackson | .20 | .12 |
| 330 | John Roper | .20 | .12 |
| 331 | Bill Lewis | .20 | .12 |
| 332 | Rodney Holman | .20 | .12 |
| 333 | Bruce Armstrong | .20 | .12 |
| 334 | Robb Thomas | .20 | .12 |
| 335 | Alvin Harper | .75 | .45 |
| 336 | Brian Jordan | .25 | .15 |
| 337 | Morten Andersen | .25 | .15 |
| 338 | Dermontti Dawson | .20 | .12 |
| 339 | Checklist | .20 | .12 |
| 340 | Louis Oliver | .25 | .15 |
| 341 | Paul McJulien (R) | .25 | .15 |
| 342 | Karl Mecklenburg | .25 | .15 |
| 343 | Lawrence Dawsey | .30 | .18 |
| 344 | Kyle Clifton | .20 | .12 |
| 345 | Jeff Bostic | .20 | .12 |
| 346 | Cris Carter | .30 | .18 |
| 347 | Al Smith | .20 | .12 |
| 348 | Mark Kelso | .20 | .12 |
| 349 | Art Monk (TL) | 1.25 | .80 |
| 350 | Michael Carter | .20 | .12 |
| 351 | Ethan Horton | .25 | .15 |
| 352 | Andy Heck | .20 | .12 |
| 353 | Gill Fenerty | .20 | .12 |
| 354 | David Brandon (R) | .25 | .15 |
| 355 | Anthony Johnson | .20 | .12 |
| 356 | Mike Golic | .20 | .12 |
| 357 | Ferrell Edmonds | .20 | .12 |
| 358 | Dennis Gibson | .20 | .12 |
| 359 | Gill Byrd | .20 | .12 |
| 360 | Todd Lyght | .25 | .15 |
| 361 | Jayice Pearson (R) | .25 | .15 |
| 362 | John Rade | .20 | .12 |
| 363 | Keith Van Horne | .20 | .12 |
| 364 | John Kasay | .20 | .12 |
| 365 | Broderick Thomas | .20 | .12 |
| 366 | Ken Harvey | .20 | .12 |
| 367 | Rich Gannon | .30 | .18 |
| 368 | Darrell Thompson | .25 | .15 |
| 369 | Jon Vaughn | .30 | .18 |
| 370 | Jesse Solomon | .20 | .12 |
| 371 | Erik McMillan | .20 | .12 |
| 372 | Bruce Matthews | .20 | .12 |
| 373 | Wilber Marshall | .20 | .12 |
| 374 | Brian Blades | .20 | .12 |
| 375 | Vance Johnson | .25 | .15 |
| 376 | Eddie Brown | .25 | .15 |
| 377 | Don Beebe | .30 | .18 |
| 378 | Brent Jones | .25 | .15 |
| 379 | Matt Bahr | .20 | .12 |
| 380 | Dwight Stone | .20 | .12 |
| 381 | Tony Casillas | .25 | .15 |
| 382 | Jay Schroeder | .25 | .15 |
| 383 | Byron Evans | .20 | .12 |
| 384 | Dan Saleaumua | .20 | .12 |
| 385 | Wendell Davis | .25 | .15 |
| 386 | Ron Holmes | .20 | .12 |

| # | Name | | |
|---|------|---|---|
| 387 | George Thomas (R) | .25 | .15 |
| 388 | Ray Berry | .20 | .12 |
| 389 | Eric Martin | .25 | .15 |
| 390 | Kevin Mack | .25 | .15 |
| 391 | Natu Tautagaloa (R) | .25 | .15 |
| 392 | Bill Romanowski | .20 | .12 |
| 393 | Nick Bell (PL) | 1.00 | .60 |
| 394 | Grant Feasel | .20 | .12 |
| 395 | Eugene Lockhart | .20 | .12 |
| 396 | Lorenzo White | .30 | .18 |
| 397 | Mike Farr | .20 | .12 |
| 398 | Eric Bieniemy | .25 | .15 |
| 399 | Kevin Murphy | .20 | .12 |
| 400 | Luis Sharpe | .20 | .12 |
| 401 | Jessie Tuggle | .20 | .12 |
| 402 | Cleveland Gary | .25 | .15 |
| 403 | Tony Mandarich | .20 | .12 |
| 404 | Bryan Cox | .25 | .15 |
| 405 | Marvin Washington | .20 | .12 |
| 406 | Fred Stokes | .20 | .12 |
| 407 | Duane Bickett | .20 | .12 |
| 408 | Leonard Marshall | .25 | .15 |
| 409 | Barry Foster | 4.00 | 2.75 |
| 410 | Thurman Thomas | 3.50 | 2.00 |
| 411 | Willie Gault | .25 | .15 |
| 412 | Vinson Smith | .25 | .15 |
| 413 | Mark Bortz | .20 | .12 |
| 414 | Johnny Johnson | .30 | .18 |
| 415 | Rodney Hampton (TL) | 2.00 | 1.25 |
| 416 | Steve Wallace | .20 | .12 |
| 417 | Fuad Reveiz | .20 | .12 |
| 418 | Derrick Thomas | .35 | .20 |
| 419 | Jackie Harris (R) | .60 | .35 |
| 420 | Derek Russell | .25 | .15 |
| 421 | David Grant | .20 | .12 |
| 422 | Tommy Kane | .25 | .15 |
| 423 | Stan Brock | .20 | .12 |
| 424 | Haywood Jeffires | .35 | .20 |
| 425 | Broderick Thomas | .20 | .12 |
| 426 | John Kidd | .20 | .12 |
| 427 | Shawn McCarthy (LP) | .40 | .25 |
| 428 | Jim Arnold | .20 | .12 |
| 429 | Scott Fulhage | .20 | .12 |
| 430 | Jackie Slater | .25 | .15 |
| 431 | Scott Galbraith (R) | .30 | .18 |
| 432 | Roger Ruzek | .20 | .12 |
| 433 | Irving Fryar | .25 | .15 |
| 434 | Derrick Thomas (TL) | 1.25 | .80 |
| 435 | David Johnson | .20 | .12 |
| 436 | Jim Jensen | .20 | .12 |
| 437 | James Washington | .20 | .12 |
| 438 | Phil Hansen | .20 | .12 |
| 439 | Rohn Stark | .20 | .12 |
| 440 | Jarrod Bunch | .30 | .18 |
| 441 | Todd Marinovich | .70 | .40 |
| 442 | Brett Perriman | .25 | .15 |
| 443 | Eugene Robinson | .20 | .12 |
| 444 | Robert Massey | .20 | .12 |
| 445 | Nick Lowery | .25 | .15 |
| 446 | Rickey Dixon | .20 | .12 |
| 447 | Jim Lachey | .25 | .15 |
| 448 | Johnny Hector | .20 | .12 |
| 449 | Gary Plummer | .20 | .12 |
| 450 | Robert Brown | .20 | .12 |
| 451 | Gaston Green | .30 | .18 |
| 452 | Checklist | .20 | .12 |
| 453 | Darion Conner | .20 | .12 |
| 454 | Mike Cofer | .20 | .12 |
| 455 | Craig Heyward | .25 | .15 |
| 456 | Anthony Carter | .25 | .15 |
| 457 | Pat Coleman (R) | .25 | .15 |
| 458 | Jeff Bryant | .20 | .12 |
| 459 | Mark Gunn (R) | .25 | .15 |
| 460 | Stan Thomas | .20 | .12 |
| 461 | Simon Fletcher | .20 | .12 |
| 462 | Ray Agnew | .20 | .12 |
| 463 | Jessie Hester | .20 | .12 |
| 464 | Rob Burnett | .25 | .15 |
| 465 | Mike Croel | .30 | .18 |
| 466 | Mike Pitts | .20 | .12 |
| 467 | Darryl Talley | .25 | .15 |
| 468 | Rich Camarillo | .20 | .12 |
| 469 | Reggie White (TL) | 1.00 | .60 |
| 470 | Nick Bell | .50 | .30 |
| 471 | Tracy Hayworth (R) | .25 | .15 |
| 472 | Eric Thomas | .20 | .12 |
| 473 | Paul Gruber | .20 | .12 |
| 474 | David Richard | .20 | .12 |
| 475 | T.J. Turner | .20 | .12 |
| 476 | Mark Ingram | .20 | .12 |
| 477 | Tim Grunhard | .20 | .12 |
| 478 | Marion Butts | .30 | .18 |
| 479 | Tom Rathman | .25 | .15 |
| 480 | Brian Mitchell | .25 | .15 |
| 481 | Bryce Paup | .20 | .12 |
| 482 | Mike Pritchard | .40 | .25 |
| 483 | Ken Norton | .20 | .12 |
| 484 | Roman Phifer | .20 | .12 |
| 485 | Greg Lloyd | .20 | .12 |
| 486 | Brett Maxie | .20 | .12 |
| 487 | Richard Dent | .25 | .15 |
| 488 | Curtis Duncan | .25 | .15 |
| 489 | Chris Burkett | .20 | .12 |
| 490 | Travis McNeal | .20 | .12 |
| 491 | Carl Lee | .20 | .12 |
| 492 | Clarence Kay | .20 | .12 |
| 493 | Tom Thayer | .20 | .12 |
| 494 | Erik Kramer (PL) | 1.00 | .60 |
| 495 | Perry Kemp | .20 | .12 |
| 496 | Jeff Jaeger | .20 | .12 |
| 497 | Eric Sanders | .20 | .12 |
| 498 | Burt Grossman | .25 | .15 |
| 499 | John Smith | .20 | .12 |
| 500 | Keith McCants | .25 | .15 |

| | | | |
|---|---|---|---|
| 501 | John Stephens | .25 | .15 |
| 502 | John Rienstra | .20 | .12 |
| 503 | Jim Ritcher | .20 | .12 |
| 504 | Harris Barton | .20 | .12 |
| 505 | Andre Rison (TL) | 1.00 | .60 |
| 506 | Chris Martin | .20 | .12 |
| 507 | Freddie Joe Nunn | .20 | .12 |
| 508 | Mark Higgs | .40 | .25 |
| 509 | Norm Johnson | .20 | .12 |
| 510 | Stephen Baker | .20 | .12 |
| 511 | Ricky Sanders | .25 | .15 |
| 512 | Ray Donaldson | .20 | .12 |
| 513 | David Fulcher | .20 | .12 |
| 514 | Gerald Williams | .20 | .12 |
| 515 | Toi Cook | .20 | .12 |
| 516 | Chris Warren | .25 | .15 |
| 517 | Jeff Gossett | .20 | .12 |
| 518 | Ken Lanier | .20 | .12 |
| 519 | Haywood Jeffires (TL) | 1.00 | .60 |
| 520 | Kevin Glover | .20 | .12 |
| 521 | Mo Lewis | .25 | .15 |
| 522 | Bern Brostek | .20 | .12 |
| 523 | Bo Orlando (R) | .25 | .15 |
| 524 | Mike Saxon | .20 | .12 |
| 525 | Seth Joyner | .25 | .15 |
| 526 | John Carney | .20 | .12 |
| 527 | Jeff Cross | .20 | .12 |
| 528 | Gary Anderson | .20 | .12 |
| 529 | Chuck Cecil | .20 | .12 |
| 530 | Tim Green | .20 | .12 |
| 531 | Kevin Porter | .20 | .12 |
| 532 | Chris Spielman | .25 | .15 |
| 533 | Willie Drewrey | .20 | .12 |
| 534 | Chris Singleton | .25 | .15 |
| 535 | Matt Stover | .20 | .12 |
| 536 | Andre Collins | .25 | .15 |
| 537 | Erik Howard | .20 | .12 |
| 538 | Steve Tasker | .20 | .12 |
| 539 | Anthony Thompson | .25 | .15 |
| 540 | Charles Haley | .25 | .15 |
| 541 | Mike Merriweather | .20 | .12 |
| 542 | Henry Thomas | .20 | .12 |
| 543 | Scott Stephen | .20 | .12 |
| 544 | Bruce Kozerski | .20 | .12 |
| 545 | Tim McKyer | .20 | .12 |
| 546 | Chris Doleman | .20 | .12 |
| 547 | Riki Ellison | .20 | .12 |
| 548 | Mike Prior | .20 | .12 |
| 549 | Dwayne Harper | .20 | .12 |
| 550 | Bubby Brister | .25 | .15 |
| 551 | Dave Meggett | .30 | .18 |
| 552 | Greg Montgomery | .20 | .12 |
| 553 | Kevin Mack | .25 | .15 |
| 554 | Mark Strepnoski | .20 | .12 |
| 555 | Kenny Walker | .25 | .15 |
| 556 | Eric Moten | .20 | .12 |
| 557 | Michael Stewart | .20 | .12 |

| | | | |
|---|---|---|---|
| 558 | Calvin Williams | .25 | .15 |
| 559 | Johnny Hector | .20 | .12 |
| 560 | Tony Paige | .20 | .12 |
| 561 | Tim Newton | .20 | .12 |
| 562 | Brad Muster | .25 | .15 |
| 563 | Aeneas Williams | .25 | .15 |
| 564 | Herman Moore | .60 | .35 |
| 565 | Checklist | .20 | .12 |
| 566 | Jerome Henderson | .20 | .12 |
| 567 | Danny Copeland | .20 | .12 |
| 568 | Alexander Wright (LP) | .30 | .18 |
| 569 | Tim Harris | .20 | .12 |
| 570 | Jonathan Hayes | .20 | .12 |
| 571 | Tony Jones | .20 | .12 |
| 572 | Carlton Bailey (R) | .25 | .15 |
| 573 | Vaughan Johnson | .25 | .15 |

# CLASSIC

## 1991 Classic Draft Picks

Ricky Watters

This 50-card set is Classic's first football set and includes the top draft picks from the 1991 NFL draft. The cards, which measure 2-1/2" by 3-1/2", picture players wearing their college uniforms framed by white borders with gray swirls on the card fronts. The players name and position appears in a small blue box below the photograph.

|  | | MINT | NR/MT |
|---|---|---|---|
| **Complete Set (50)** | | 12.00 | 7.75 |
| **Commons** | | .10 | .06 |

| 1 | Rocket Ismail | 4.00 | 2.75 |
|---|---|---|---|
| 2 | Russell Maryland | .70 | .40 |
| 3 | Eric Turner | .45 | .28 |
| 4 | Bruce Pickens | .20 | .12 |
| 5 | Mike Croel | .80 | .50 |
| 6 | Todd Lyght | .40 | .25 |
| 7 | Eric Swann | .20 | .12 |
| 8 | Antone Davis | .12 | .07 |
| 9 | Stanley Richard | .25 | .15 |
| 10 | Pat Harlow | .12 | .07 |
| 11 | Alvin Harper | .90 | .60 |
| 12 | Mike Pritchard | .75 | .45 |
| 13 | Leonard Russell | 1.00 | .70 |
| 14 | Dan McGwire | .80 | .50 |
| 15 | Bobby Wilson | .20 | .12 |
| 16 | Alfred Williams | .20 | .12 |
| 17 | Vinnie Clark | .20 | .12 |
| 18 | Kelvin Pritchett | .25 | .15 |
| 19 | Harvey Williams | .70 | .40 |
| 20 | Stan Thomas | .10 | .06 |
| 21 | Randal Hill | .70 | .40 |
| 22 | Todd Marinovich | 1.25 | .80 |
| 23 | Henry Jones | .10 | .06 |
| 24 | Jarrod Bunch | .25 | .15 |
| 25 | Mike Dumas | .15 | .10 |
| 26 | Ed King | .10 | .06 |
| 27 | Reggie Johnson | .12 | .07 |
| 28 | Roman Phifer | .12 | .07 |
| 29 | Mike Jones | .10 | .06 |
| 30 | Brett Favre | 1.50 | .90 |
| 31 | Browning Nagle | 1.25 | .80 |
| 32 | Esera Tuaolo | .12 | .07 |
| 33 | George Thornton | .10 | .06 |
| 34 | Dixon Edwards | .12 | .07 |
| 35 | Darryl Lewis | .20 | .12 |
| 36 | Eric Bieniemy | .30 | .18 |
| 37 | Shane Curry | .10 | .06 |
| 38 | Jerome Henderson | .12 | .07 |
| 39 | Wesley Carroll | .30 | .18 |
| 40 | Nick Bell | .70 | .40 |
| 41 | John Flannery | .10 | .06 |
| 42 | Ricky Watters | 1.00 | .70 |
| 43 | Jeff Graham | .20 | .12 |
| 44 | Eric Moten | .10 | .06 |
| 45 | Jesse Campbell | .10 | .06 |
| 46 | Chris Zorich | .35 | .20 |
| 47 | Doug Thomas | .10 | .06 |
| 48 | Phil Hansen | .10 | .06 |
| 49 | Kanavis McGhee | .25 | .15 |
| 50 | Reggie Barrett | .25 | .15 |

# 1992 Classic Draft Picks

This 100-card set features the top draft picks from the 1992 NFL draft. The cards were issued in both blister packs and foil packs. Card fronts include action photos of players in their college uniforms framed by black borders. Cards measure 2-1/2" by 3-1/2". 10 Gold Stamped bonus insert cards were issued randomly in foil packs. Those inserts are featured at the end of this checklist but are not included in the complete set price below.

|  | | MINT | NR/MT |
|---|---|---|---|
| **Complete Set (100)** | | 15.00 | 10.00 |
| **Commons** | | .10 | .06 |

| 1 | Desmond Howard | 2.00 | 1.25 |
|---|---|---|---|
| 2 | David Klingler | 1.50 | .90 |
| 3 | Quentin Coryatt | .70 | .40 |
| 4 | Bill Johnson | .12 | .07 |
| 5 | Eugene Chung | .12 | .07 |
| 6 | Derek Brown | .60 | .35 |
| 7 | Carl Pickens | .50 | .30 |
| 8 | Chris Mims | .35 | .20 |
| 9 | Charles Davenport | .25 | .15 |
| 10 | Ray Roberts | .10 | .06 |
| 11 | Chuck Smith | .12 | .07 |
| 12 | Joe Bowden | .10 | .06 |
| 13 | Mirko Jurkovic | .12 | .07 |
| 14 | Tony Smith | .40 | .25 |
| 15 | Ken Swilling | .12 | .07 |
| 16 | Greg Skrepenak | .15 | .10 |
| 17 | Phillippi Sparks | .12 | .07 |
| 18 | Alonzo Spellman | .30 | .18 |
| 19 | Bernard Dafney | .10 | .06 |
| 20 | Edgar Bennett | .30 | .18 |
| 21 | Shane Dronett | .12 | .07 |

| # | Name | | |
|---|---|---|---|
| 22 | Jeremy Lincoln | .10 | .06 |
| 23 | Dion Lambert | .10 | .06 |
| 24 | Siran Stacy | .30 | .18 |
| 25 | Tony Sacca | .35 | .20 |
| 26 | Sean Lumpkin | .10 | .06 |
| 27 | Tommy Vardell | .70 | .40 |
| 28 | Keith Hamilton | .12 | .07 |
| 29 | Ashley Ambrose | .20 | .12 |
| 30 | Sean Gilbert | .35 | .20 |
| 31 | Casey Weldon | .30 | .18 |
| 32 | Marc Boutte | .12 | .07 |
| 33 | Santana Dotson | .35 | .20 |
| 34 | Ronnie West | .10 | .06 |
| 35 | Michael Bankston | .10 | .06 |
| 36 | Mike Pawlawski | .15 | .10 |
| 37 | Dale Carter | .25 | .15 |
| 38 | Carlos Snow | .25 | .15 |
| 39 | Corey Barlow | .10 | .06 |
| 40 | Mark D'Onofrio | .15 | .10 |
| 41 | Matt Blundin | .35 | .20 |
| 42 | George Rooks | .10 | .06 |
| 43 | Patrick Rowe | .25 | .15 |
| 44 | Dwight Hollier | .10 | .06 |
| 45 | Joel Steed | .12 | .07 |
| 46 | Erick Anderson | .15 | .10 |
| 47 | Rodney Culver | .25 | .15 |
| 48 | Chris Hakel | .12 | .07 |
| 49 | Luke Fisher | .10 | .06 |
| 50 | Kevin Smith | .25 | .15 |
| 51 | Robert Brooks | .12 | .07 |
| 52 | Bucky Richardson | .20 | .12 |
| 53 | Steve Israel | .15 | .10 |
| 54 | Marco Coleman | .50 | .30 |
| 55 | Johnny Mitchell | .40 | .25 |
| 56 | Scottie Graham | .20 | .12 |
| 57 | Keith Goganious | .12 | .07 |
| 58 | Tommy Maddox | 1.00 | .70 |
| 59 | Terrell Buckley | .75 | .45 |
| 60 | Dana Hall | .20 | .12 |
| 61 | Ty Detmer | .35 | .20 |
| 62 | Darryl Williams | .20 | .12 |
| 63 | Jason Hanson | .10 | .06 |
| 64 | Leon Searcy | .10 | .06 |
| 65 | Gene McGuire | .10 | .06 |
| 66 | Will Furrer | .30 | .18 |
| 67 | Darren Woodson | .10 | .06 |
| 68 | Tracy Scroggins | .15 | .10 |
| 69 | Corey Widmer | .10 | .06 |
| 70 | Robert Harris | .10 | .06 |
| 71 | Larry Tharpe | .10 | .06 |
| 72 | Lance Olberding | .10 | .06 |
| 73 | Stacecy Dillard | .10 | .06 |
| 74 | Anthony Hamlet | .10 | .06 |
| 75 | Tommy Jeter | .10 | .06 |
| 76 | Mike Evans | .10 | .06 |
| 77 | Shane Collins | .15 | .10 |
| 78 | Mark Thomas | .10 | .06 |
| 79 | Chester McGlockton | .20 | .12 |
| 80 | Robert Porcher | .12 | .07 |
| 81 | Marquez Pope | .12 | .07 |
| 82 | Rico Smith | .12 | .07 |
| 83 | Tyrone Williams | .10 | .06 |
| 84 | Rod Smith | .10 | .06 |
| 85 | Tyrone Legette | .12 | .07 |
| 86 | Wayne Hawkins | .10 | .06 |
| 87 | Derrick Moore | .12 | .07 |
| 88 | Tim Lester | .10 | .06 |
| 89 | Calvin Holmes | .10 | .06 |
| 90 | Reggie Dwight | .10 | .06 |
| 91 | Eddie Robinson | .12 | .07 |
| 92 | Robert Jones | .25 | .15 |
| 93 | Ricardo McDonald | .15 | .10 |
| 94 | Howard Dinkins | .10 | .06 |
| 95 | Todd Collins | .10 | .06 |
| 96 | Eddie Blake | .10 | .06 |
| 97 | Classic QB's | .50 | .30 |
| 98 | Back to Back Heisman | .40 | .25 |
| 99 | Checklist | .10 | .06 |
| 100 | Checklist | .10 | .06 |
| BC1 | Desmond Howard (Gold) | 8.00 | 5.00 |
| BC2 | David Klingler (Gold) | 10.00 | 7.00 |
| BC3 | Siran Stacy (Gold) | 3.00 | 2.00 |
| BC4 | Casey Weldon (Gold) | 5.00 | 3.00 |
| BC5 | Sean Gilbert (Gold) | 2.50 | 1.50 |
| BC6 | Matt Blundin (Gold) | 5.00 | 3.00 |
| BC7 | Tommy Maddox (Gold) | 8.00 | 5.00 |
| BC8 | Derek Brown (Gold) | 4.00 | 2.75 |
| BC9 | Tony Smith (Gold) | 4.00 | 2.75 |
| BC10 | Tony Sacca (Gold) | 4.00 | 2.75 |

# 1993 Classic Draft Picks

This 100-card set features the NFL's top draft picks pictured in their college uniforms. Card fronts consist of action shots framed by a blue border. The player's name and position appear in a gold color bar below the photo along with an NFL 1993 Draft logo. The Classic logo is printed in the top left corner. Card backs include personal data, stats and highlights. All cards measure 2-1/2" by 3-1/2".

|  |  | MINT | NR/MT |
|---|---|---|---|
| Complete Set (100) | | 16.00 | 10.00 |
| Commons | | .10 | .06 |

| | | | |
|---|---|---|---|
| 1 | Drew Bledsoe | 4.00 | 2.50 |
| 2 | Rick Mirer | 2.75 | 1.50 |
| 3 | Garrison Hearst | 3.50 | 2.00 |
| 4 | Marvin Jones | .75 | .45 |
| 5 | John Copeland | .25 | .15 |
| 6 | Eric Curry | .25 | .15 |
| 7 | Curtis Conway | .80 | .50 |
| 8 | Willie Roaf | .15 | .10 |
| 9 | Lincoln Kennedy | .15 | .10 |
| 10 | Jerome Bettis | .50 | .30 |
| 11 | Mike Compton | .12 | .07 |
| 12 | John Gerak | .12 | .07 |
| 13 | Will Shields | .12 | .07 |
| 14 | Ben Coleman | .12 | .07 |
| 15 | Ernest Dye | .12 | .07 |
| 16 | Lester Holmes | .12 | .07 |
| 17 | Brad Hopkins | .12 | .07 |
| 18 | Everett Lindsay | .12 | .07 |
| 19 | Todd Rucci | .10 | .06 |
| 20 | Lance Gunn | .12 | .07 |
| 21 | Elvis Grbac | .30 | .18 |
| 22 | Shane Matthews | .75 | .45 |
| 23 | Rudy Harris | .20 | .12 |
| 24 | Richie Anderson | .15 | .10 |
| 25 | Derek Brown | .15 | .10 |
| 26 | Roger Harper | .10 | .06 |
| 27 | Terry Kirby | .40 | .25 |
| 28 | Natrone Means | .50 | .30 |
| 29 | Glyn Milburn | .50 | .30 |
| 30 | Adrian Murrell | .15 | .10 |
| 31 | Lorenzo Neal | .20 | .12 |
| 32 | Roosevelt Potts | .30 | .18 |
| 33 | Kevin Williams | .25 | .15 |
| 34 | Russell Copeland | .20 | .12 |
| 35 | Fred Baxter | .10 | .06 |
| 36 | Troy Drayton | .15 | .10 |
| 37 | Chris Gedney | .15 | .10 |
| 38 | Irv Smith | .20 | .12 |
| 39 | Olanda Truitt | .15 | .10 |
| 40 | Victor Bailey | .20 | .12 |
| 41 | Horace Copeland | .20 | .12 |
| 42 | Ron Dickerson, Jr. | .15 | .10 |
| 43 | Willie Harris | .15 | .10 |
| 44 | Tyrone Hughes | .15 | .10 |
| 45 | Qadry Ismail | .40 | .25 |
| 46 | Reggie Brooks | .30 | .18 |
| 47 | Sean LaChapelle | .20 | .12 |
| 48 | O.J. McDuffie | .40 | .25 |
| 49 | Larry Ryans | .15 | .10 |
| 50 | Kenny Shedd | .15 | .10 |
| 51 | Brian Stablein | .12 | .07 |
| 52 | Lamar Thomas | .15 | .10 |
| 53 | Kevin Williams | .25 | .15 |
| 54 | Othello Henderson | .12 | .07 |
| 55 | Kevin Henry | .12 | .07 |
| 56 | Todd Kelly | .20 | .12 |
| 57 | Devon McDonald | .10 | .06 |
| 58 | Michael Strahan | .12 | .07 |
| 59 | Dan Williams | .15 | .10 |
| 60 | Gilbert Brown | .12 | .07 |
| 61 | Mark Caesar | .12 | .07 |
| 62 | Ronnie Dixon | .10 | .06 |
| 63 | John Parrella | .10 | .06 |
| 64 | Leonard Renfro | .12 | .07 |
| 65 | Coleman Rudolph | .15 | .10 |
| 66 | Ronnie Bradford | .10 | .06 |
| 67 | Tom Carter III | .25 | .15 |
| 68 | Deon Figures | .25 | .15 |
| 69 | Derrick Frazier | .12 | .07 |
| 70 | Darrien Gordon | .25 | .15 |
| 71 | Carlton Gray | .20 | .12 |
| 72 | Adrian Hardy | .10 | .06 |
| 73 | Mike Reid | .10 | .06 |
| 74 | Thomas Smith | .20 | .12 |
| 75 | Robert O'Neal | .20 | .12 |
| 76 | Chad Brown | .12 | .07 |
| 77 | Demetrius DuBose | .20 | .12 |
| 78 | Reggie Givens | .10 | .06 |

| | | | |
|---|---|---|---|
| 79 | Travis Hill | .12 | .07 |
| 80 | Rich McKenzie | .10 | .06 |
| 81 | Barry Minter | .10 | .06 |
| 82 | Darrin Smith | .10 | .06 |
| 83 | Steve Tovar | .10 | .06 |
| 84 | Patrick Bates | .25 | .15 |
| 85 | Dan Footman | .20 | .12 |
| 86 | Ryan McNeil | .20 | .12 |
| 87 | Danan Hughes | .20 | .12 |
| 88 | Mark Brunell | .30 | .18 |
| 89 | Ron Moore | .15 | .10 |
| 90 | Antonio London | .12 | .07 |
| 91 | Steve Everitt | .15 | .10 |
| 92 | Wayne Simmons | .12 | .07 |
| 93 | Robert Smith | .40 | .25 |
| 94 | Dana Stubblefield | .20 | .12 |
| 95 | George Teague | .20 | .12 |
| 96 | Carl Simpson | .12 | .07 |
| 97 | Billy Joe Hobert | .40 | .25 |
| 98 | Gino Torretta | .40 | .25 |
| 99 | Checklist #1 | .10 | .06 |
| 100 | Checklist #2 | .10 | .06 |

# COLLECTORS EDGE

## 1992 Collectors Edge

The cards in this 175-card set are the first from Denver-based Collectors Edge. The cards are printed on a damage-proof vinyl-type stock and only 100,000 cards of each player were printed. Each player card is sequentially numbered on the back. The cards, which measure 2-1/2" by 3-1/2", feature full color photos on the front framed by black borders. A team helmut appears in the bottom right corner. The vertical card backs contain a small portrait shot, player stats and a brief bio. 2,500 autographed cards of John Elway and Ken O'Brien were randomly inserted into foil packs. The value of those autographed inserts are included at the end of this checklist but are not included in the complete set price below.

| | | MINT | NR/MT |
|---|---|---|---|
| **Complete Set (175)** | | 100.00 | 70.00 |
| **Commons** | | .25 | .15 |
| | | | |
| 1 | Chris Miller | .70 | .40 |
| 2 | Steve Broussard | .30 | .18 |
| 3 | Mike Pritchard | 1.25 | .80 |
| 4 | Tim Green | .25 | .15 |

| | | | | | | | |
|---|---|---|---|---|---|---|---|
| 5 | Andre Rison | 1.00 | .70 | 62 | Richard Johnson | .25 | .15 |
| 6 | Deion Sanders | 1.50 | .90 | 63 | Eric Dickerson | 1.00 | .70 |
| 7 | Jim Kelly | 2.50 | 1.50 | 64 | Jessie Hester | .25 | .15 |
| 8 | James Lofton | .50 | .30 | 65 | Rohn Stark | .25 | .15 |
| 9 | Andre Reed | .60 | .35 | 66 | Clarence Verdin | .25 | .15 |
| 10 | Bruce Smith | .35 | .20 | 67 | Dean Biasucci | .25 | .15 |
| 11 | Thurman Thomas | 2.50 | 1.50 | 68 | Duane Bickett | .25 | .15 |
| 12 | Cornelius Bennett | .40 | .25 | 69 | Jeff George | .90 | .60 |
| 13 | Jim Harbaugh | .50 | .30 | 70 | Christian Okoye | .60 | .35 |
| 14 | William Perry | .25 | .15 | 71 | Derrick Thomas | .90 | .60 |
| 15 | Mike Singletary | .30 | .18 | 72 | Stephone Paige | .30 | .18 |
| 16 | Mark Carrier | .30 | .18 | 73 | Dan Saleaumua | .25 | .15 |
| 17 | Kevin Butler | .25 | .15 | 74 | Deron Cherry | .25 | .15 |
| 18 | Tom Waddle | .70 | .40 | 75 | Kevin Ross | .25 | .15 |
| 19 | Boomer Esiason | .40 | .25 | 76 | Barry Word | .70 | .40 |
| 20 | David Fulcher | .25 | .15 | 77 | Ronnie Lott | .75 | .45 |
| 21 | Anthony Munoz | .30 | .18 | 78 | Greg Townsend | .30 | .18 |
| 22 | Tim McGee | .30 | .18 | 79 | Willie Gault | .30 | .18 |
| 23 | Harold Green | .75 | .45 | 80 | Howie Long | .35 | .20 |
| 24 | Rickey Dixon | .25 | .15 | 81 | Winston Moss | .25 | .15 |
| 25 | Bernie Kosar | .60 | .35 | 82 | Steve Smith | .25 | .15 |
| 26 | Michael Dean Perry | .40 | .25 | 83 | Jay Schroeder | .35 | .20 |
| 27 | Mike Baab | .25 | .15 | 84 | Jim Everett | .60 | .35 |
| 28 | Brian Brennan | .25 | .15 | 85 | Flipper Anderson | .35 | .20 |
| 29 | Michael Jackson | .75 | .45 | 86 | Henry Ellard | .30 | .18 |
| 30 | Eric Metcalf | .75 | .45 | 87 | Tony Zendejas | .25 | .15 |
| 31 | Troy Aikman | 5.50 | 3.25 | 88 | Robert Delpino | .30 | .18 |
| 32 | Emmitt Smith | 7.50 | 4.50 | 89 | Pat Terrell | .25 | .15 |
| 33 | Michael Irvin | 2.00 | 1.25 | 90 | Dan Marino | 2.50 | 1.50 |
| 34 | Jay Novacek | .40 | .25 | 91 | Mark Clayton | .50 | .30 |
| 35 | Issiac Holt | .25 | .15 | 92 | Jim Jensen | .25 | .15 |
| 36 | Ken Norton | .25 | .15 | 93 | Reggie Roby | .25 | .15 |
| 37 | John Elway | .90 | .60 | 94 | Sammie Smith | .50 | .30 |
| 38 | Gaston Green | .40 | .25 | 95 | Tony Martin | .25 | .15 |
| 39 | Charles Dimry | .25 | .15 | 96 | Jeff Cross | .25 | .15 |
| 40 | Vance Johnson | .30 | .18 | 97 | Anthony Carter | .35 | .20 |
| 41 | Dennis Smith | .25 | .15 | 98 | Chris Doleman | .35 | .20 |
| 42 | David Treadwell | .25 | .15 | 99 | Wade Wilson | .35 | .20 |
| 43 | Michael Young | .25 | .15 | 100 | Cris Carter | .60 | .35 |
| 44 | Bennie Blades | .30 | .18 | 101 | Mike Merriweather | .25 | .15 |
| 45 | Mel Gray | .25 | .15 | 102 | Gary Zimmerman | .25 | .15 |
| 46 | Andre Ware | .30 | .18 | 103 | Chris Singleton | .25 | .15 |
| 47 | Rodney Peete | .30 | .18 | 104 | Bruce Armstrong | .25 | .15 |
| 48 | Toby Caston | .25 | .15 | 105 | Marv Cook | .30 | .18 |
| 49 | Herman Moore | 1.00 | .70 | 106 | Andre Tippett | .30 | .18 |
| 50 | Brian Noble | .25 | .15 | 107 | Tommy Hodson | .35 | .20 |
| 51 | Sterling Sharpe | 1.25 | .80 | 108 | Greg McMurtry | .35 | .20 |
| 52 | Mike Tomczak | .30 | .18 | 109 | Jon Vaughn | .50 | .30 |
| 53 | Vinnie Clark | .25 | .15 | 110 | Vaughan Johnson | .25 | .15 |
| 54 | Tony Mandarich | .25 | .15 | 111 | Craig Heyward | .30 | .18 |
| 55 | Ed West | .25 | .15 | 112 | Floyd Turner | .25 | .15 |
| 56 | Warren Moon | 1.25 | .80 | 113 | Pat Swilling | .60 | .35 |
| 57 | Ray Childress | .30 | .18 | 114 | Rickey Jackson | .30 | .18 |
| 58 | Haywood Jeffires | .80 | .50 | 115 | Steve Walsh | .35 | .20 |
| 59 | Al Smith | .25 | .15 | 116 | Phil Simms | .60 | .35 |
| 60 | Cris Dishman | .25 | .15 | 117 | Carl Banks | .30 | .18 |
| 61 | Ernest Givins | .70 | .40 | 118 | Mark Ingram | .25 | .15 |

| | | | |
|---|---|---|---|
| 119 | Bart Oates | .25 | .15 |
| 120 | Lawrence Taylor | .80 | .50 |
| 121 | Jeff Hostetler | .70 | .40 |
| 122 | Rob Moore | .80 | .50 |
| 123 | Ken O'Brien | .50 | .30 |
| 124 | Bill Pickel | .25 | .15 |
| 125 | Irv Eatman | .25 | .15 |
| 126 | Browning Nagle | 2.00 | 1.25 |
| 127 | Al Toon | .50 | .30 |
| 128 | Randall Cunningham | 1.00 | .70 |
| 129 | Eric Allen | .25 | .15 |
| 130 | Mike Golic | .25 | .15 |
| 131 | Fred Barnett | .80 | .50 |
| 132 | Keith Byars | .30 | .18 |
| 133 | Calvin Williams | .50 | .30 |
| 134 | Randal Hill | .90 | .60 |
| 135 | Ricky Proehl | .40 | .25 |
| 136 | Lance Smith | .25 | .15 |
| 137 | Ernie Jones | .30 | .18 |
| 138 | Timm Rosenbach | .75 | .45 |
| 139 | Anthony Thompson | .50 | .30 |
| 140 | Bubby Brister | .70 | .40 |
| 141 | Merril Hoge | .30 | .18 |
| 142 | Louis Lipps | .30 | .18 |
| 143 | Eric Green | .50 | .30 |
| 144 | Gary Anderson | .25 | .15 |
| 145 | Neil O'Donnell | 2.00 | 1.25 |
| 146 | Rod Bernstine | .30 | .18 |
| 147 | John Friesz | .60 | .35 |
| 148 | Anthony Miller | .75 | .45 |
| 149 | Junior Seau | .60 | .35 |
| 150 | Leslie O'Neal | .30 | .18 |
| 151 | Nate Lewis | .30 | .18 |
| 152 | Steve Young | 1.50 | .90 |
| 153 | Kevin Fagan | .25 | .15 |
| 154 | Charles Haley | .30 | .18 |
| 155 | Tom Rathman | .30 | .18 |
| 156 | Jerry Rice | 2.50 | 1.50 |
| 157 | John Taylor | .80 | .50 |
| 158 | Brian Blades | .30 | .18 |
| 159 | Patrick Hunter | .25 | .15 |
| 160 | Cortez Kennedy | .60 | .35 |
| 161 | Vann McElroy | .25 | .15 |
| 162 | Dan McGwire | 1.25 | .80 |
| 163 | John L. Williams | .30 | .18 |
| 164 | Gary Anderson | .30 | .18 |
| 165 | Broderick Thomas | .40 | .25 |
| 166 | Vinny Testaverde | .50 | .30 |
| 167 | Lawrence Dawsey | .75 | .45 |
| 168 | Paul Gruber | .25 | .15 |
| 169 | Keith McCants | .30 | .18 |
| 170 | Mark Rypien | 1.25 | .80 |
| 171 | Gary Clark | .70 | .40 |
| 172 | Earnest Byner | .40 | .25 |
| 173 | Brian Mitchell | .40 | .25 |
| 174 | Monte Coleman | .25 | .15 |
| 175 | Joe Jacoby | .25 | .15 |

| | | | |
|---|---|---|---|
| BC1 | John Elway | 175.00 | 100.00 |
| | (Autographed) | | |
| BC2 | Ken O'Brien | 75.00 | 45.00 |
| | (Autographed) | | |

# 1992 Collectors Edge Rookie Update

This 75-card Update set is a continuation of the regular series and contains mostly rookies. The card design is identical to the regular edition. The set contains random inserts of autographed Ronnie Lott cards. All cards measure 2-1/2" by 3-1/2".

| | | MINT | NR/MT |
|---|---|---|---|
| **Complete Set (75)** | | 55.00 | 32.50 |
| **Commons** | | .30 | .18 |

| | | | |
|---|---|---|---|
| 176 | Tommy Vardell (R) | 2.00 | 1.25 |
| 177 | Troy Vincent (R) | .90 | .60 |
| 178 | Robert Jones (R) | .90 | .60 |
| 179 | Marc Boutte (R) | .40 | .25 |
| 180 | Marco Coleman (R) | 1.50 | .90 |
| 181 | Chris Mims (R) | 1.50 | .90 |
| 182 | Tony Casillas | .35 | .20 |
| 183 | Shane Dronett (R) | .60 | .35 |
| 184 | Sean Gilbert (R) | .60 | .35 |
| 185 | Siran Stacy (R) | .60 | .35 |
| 186 | Tommy Maddox (R) | 4.00 | 2.75 |
| 187 | Steve Israel (R) | .40 | .25 |
| 188 | Brad Muster | .30 | .18 |
| 189 | Shane Collins (R) | .40 | .25 |
| 190 | Terrell Buckley (R) | 2.00 | 1.25 |
| 191 | Eugene Chung (R) | .40 | .25 |

| 192 | Leon Searcy (R) | .40 | .25 |
|---|---|---|---|
| 193 | Chuck Smith (R) | .40 | .25 |
| 194 | Patrick Rowe (R) | .75 | .45 |
| 195 | Bill Johnson (R) | .35 | .20 |
| 196 | Gerald Dixon (R) | .40 | .25 |
| 197 | Robert Porcher (R) | .40 | .25 |
| 198 | Tracy Scroggins (R) | .50 | .30 |
| 199 | Jason Hanson (R) | .35 | .20 |
| 200 | Corey Harris (R) | .40 | .25 |
| 201 | Eddie Robinson (R) | .40 | .25 |
| 202 | Steve Emtman (R) | 3.00 | 2.00 |
| 203 | Ashley Ambrose (R) | .50 | .30 |
| 204 | Greg Skrepenak (R) | .35 | .20 |
| 205 | Todd Collins (R) | .35 | .20 |
| 206 | Derek Brown (R) | .90 | .60 |
| 207 | Kurt Barber (R) | .35 | .20 |
| 208 | Tony Sacca (R) | 1.00 | .70 |
| 209 | Mark Wheeler (R) | .35 | .20 |
| 210 | Kevin Smith (R) | .90 | .60 |
| 211 | John Fina (R) | .35 | .20 |
| 212 | Johnny Mitchell (R) | 1.25 | .80 |
| 213 | Dale Carter (R) | 1.25 | .80 |
| 214 | Bobby Spitulski (R) | .35 | .20 |
| 215 | Phillippi Sparks (R) | .40 | .25 |
| 216 | Levon Kirkland (R) | .40 | .25 |
| 217 | Mike Sherrard (R) | .30 | .18 |
| 218 | Marquez Pope (R) | .35 | .20 |
| 219 | Courtney Hawkins (R) | .90 | .60 |
| 220 | Tyji Armstrong (R) | .40 | .25 |
| 221 | Keith Jackson | .35 | .20 |
| 222 | Clayton Holmes (R) | .40 | .25 |
| 223 | Quentin Coryatt (R) | 2.50 | 1.40 |
| 224 | Troy Auzenne (R) | .40 | .25 |
| 225 | David Klingler (R) | 6.00 | 3.75 |
| 226 | Darryl Williams (R) | .60 | .35 |
| 227 | Carl Pickens (R) | 1.75 | 1.00 |
| 228 | Jimmy Smith (R) | .60 | .35 |
| 229 | Chester McGlockton (R) | .40 | .25 |
| 230 | Robert Brooks (R) | .35 | .20 |
| 231 | Alonzo Spellman (R) | .80 | .50 |
| 232 | Darren Woodson (R) | .35 | .20 |
| 233 | Lewis Billups | .30 | .18 |
| 234 | Edgar Bennett (R) | 1.00 | .70 |
| 235 | Vaughn Dunbar (R) | 1.75 | 1.00 |
| 236 | Steve Bono (R) | 1.00 | .70 |
| 237 | Clarence Kay | .30 | .18 |
| 238 | Chris Hinton | .30 | .18 |
| 239 | Jimmie Jones | .30 | .18 |
| 240 | Vai Sikahema | .30 | .18 |
| 241 | Russell Maryland | .50 | .30 |
| 242 | Neal Anderson | .35 | .20 |
| 243 | Charles Mann | .30 | .18 |
| 244 | Hugh Millen | .40 | .25 |
| 245 | Roger Craig | .35 | .20 |
| 246 | Rich Gannon | .40 | .25 |
| 247 | Ricky Ervins | .60 | .35 |
| 248 | Leonard Marshall | .30 | .18 |
| 249 | Eric Dickerson | .90 | .60 |
| 250 | Joe Montana | 1.75 | 1.00 |
| RU1 | Terrell Buckley | 5.00 | 3.50 |
| RU2 | Tommy Maddox | 8.50 | 5.50 |
| BC1 | Ronnie Lott (Autographed) | 125.00 | 80.00 |

# 1993 Collectors Edge

This 250-card set is similar to last years edition except for the border color. Cards are printed on damage-resistant vinyl-type stock and feature full color action photos on the fronts framed by a blue border. The card backs are seqentially numbered and only 100,000 cards of each player are printed. The backs include a smaller photo, stats and brief highlights. All cards measure 2-1/2" by 3-1/2".

|  |  | MINT | NR/MT |
|---|---|---|---|
| **Complete Set (250)** | | 80.00 | 48.00 |
| **Commons** | | .30 | .18 |
| 1 | Atlanta Falcons | .30 | .18 |
| 2 | Chris Miller | .50 | .28 |
| 3 | Michael Haynes | 1.00 | .60 |
| 4 | Mike Pritchard | .80 | .50 |
| 5 | Andre Rison | .50 | .28 |
| 6 | Deion Sanders | .70 | .40 |
| 7 | Chuck Smith | .30 | .18 |
| 8 | Drew Hill | .30 | .18 |
| 9 | Bobby Hebert | .40 | .25 |
| 10 | Buffalo Bills | .30 | .18 |

| 11 | Jim Kelly | 1.50 | .90 |
|----|-----------|------|-----|
| 12 | Matt Darby | .30 | .18 |
| 13 | John Fina | .30 | .18 |
| 14 | James Patton | .30 | .18 |
| 15 | Andre Reed | .60 | .35 |
| 16 | Thurman Thomas | 2.50 | 1.50 |
| 17 | James Lofton | .50 | .28 |
| 18 | Bruce Smith | .35 | .20 |
| 19 | Chicago Bears | .30 | .18 |
| 20 | Jim Harbaugh | .50 | .28 |
| 21 | Neal Anderson | .40 | .25 |
| 22 | Troy Auzenne | .30 | .18 |
| 23 | Alonzo Spellman | .30 | .18 |
| 24 | Tom Waddle | .60 | .35 |
| 25 | Darren Lewis | .40 | .25 |
| 26 | Wendell Davis | .40 | .25 |
| 27 | Will Furrer | .35 | .20 |
| 28 | Cincinnati Bengals | .30 | .18 |
| 29 | David Klingler | 3.00 | 1.75 |
| 30 | Ricardo McDonald | .30 | .18 |
| 31 | Carl Pickens | .80 | .50 |
| 32 | Harold Green | 1.00 | .60 |
| 33 | Anthony Munoz | .35 | .20 |
| 34 | Darryl Williams | .30 | .18 |
| 35 | Jay Schroeder | .35 | .20 |
| 36 | Cleveland Browns | .30 | .18 |
| 37 | Bernie Kosar | .50 | .28 |
| 38 | Michael Jackson | .60 | .35 |
| 39 | Pio Sagapolu | .30 | .18 |
| 40 | Tommy Vardell | .80 | .50 |
| 41 | Michael Dean Perry | .35 | .20 |
| 42 | Bill Johnson | .30 | .18 |
| 43 | Vinny Testaverde | .35 | .20 |
| 44 | Dallas Cowboys | .75 | .45 |
| 45 | Troy Aikman | 4.00 | 2.50 |
| 46 | Alvin Harper | 1.25 | .70 |
| 47 | Michael Irvin | 2.00 | 1.25 |
| 48 | Russell Maryland | .35 | .20 |
| 49 | Emmitt Smith | 8.00 | 5.00 |
| 50 | Kenneth Gant | .30 | .18 |
| 51 | Jay Novacek | .60 | .35 |
| 52 | Robert Jones | .40 | .25 |
| 53 | Clayton Holmes | .30 | .18 |
| 54 | Denver Broncos | .30 | .18 |
| 55 | John Elway | 1.00 | .60 |
| 56 | Mike Croel | .35 | .20 |
| 57 | Shane Dronett | .30 | .18 |
| 58 | Kenny Walker | .35 | .20 |
| 59 | Tommy Maddox | 1.25 | .70 |
| 60 | Dennis Smith | .30 | .18 |
| 61 | Karl Mecklenberg | .35 | .20 |
| 62 | Steve Atwater | .35 | .20 |
| 63 | Vance Johnson | .35 | .20 |
| 64 | Detroit Lions | .30 | .18 |
| 65 | Rodney Peete | .40 | .25 |
| 66 | Barry Sanders | 4.00 | 2.50 |
| 67 | Andre Ware | .40 | .25 |
| 68 | Pat Swilling | .35 | .20 |
| 69 | Jason Hanson | .30 | .18 |
| 70 | Willie Green | .70 | .40 |
| 71 | Herman Moore | 1.00 | .60 |
| 72 | Erik Kramer | .40 | .25 |
| 73 | Robert Porcher | .35 | .20 |
| 74 | Green Bay Packers | .30 | .18 |
| 75 | Brett Favre | 3.00 | 1.75 |
| 76 | Terrell Buckley | .75 | .45 |
| 77 | Reggie White | .40 | .25 |
| 78 | Don Majkowski | .35 | .20 |
| 79 | Edgar Bennett | .30 | .18 |
| 80 | Ty Detmer | .40 | .25 |
| 81 | Sanjay Beach | .35 | .20 |
| 82 | Sterling Sharpe | 2.00 | 1.25 |
| 83 | Houston Oilers | .30 | .18 |
| 84 | Warren Moon | 1.00 | .60 |
| 85 | Gary Brown | .30 | .18 |
| 86 | Ernest Givens | .60 | .35 |
| 87 | Haywood Jeffires | .75 | .45 |
| 88 | Corey Harris | .30 | .18 |
| 89 | Eddie Robinson | .30 | .18 |
| 90 | Lorenzo White | .50 | .28 |
| 91 | Bo Orlando | .30 | .18 |
| 92 | Indianapolis Colts | .30 | .18 |
| 93 | Jeff George | 1.25 | .70 |
| 94 | Quentin Coryatt | .80 | .50 |
| 95 | Steve Emtman | 1.00 | .60 |
| 96 | Jesse Hester | .35 | .20 |
| 97 | Rohn Stark | .30 | .18 |
| 98 | Ashley Ambrose | .35 | .20 |
| 99 | John Baylor | .30 | .18 |
| 100 | Kansas City Chiefs | .30 | .18 |
| 101 | Joe Montana | 1.50 | .90 |
| 102 | Tim Barnett | .60 | .35 |
| 103 | Derrick Thomas | .75 | .45 |
| 104 | Barry Word | .40 | .25 |
| 105 | Dale Carter | .80 | .50 |
| 106 | Jayice Pearson | .30 | .18 |
| 107 | Tracy Simien | .30 | .18 |
| 108 | Harvey Williams | .50 | .28 |
| 109 | Dave Krieg | .35 | .20 |
| 110 | Christian Okoye | .40 | .25 |
| 111 | Miami Dolphins | .30 | .18 |
| 112 | Dan Marino | 1.75 | 1.00 |
| 113 | James Brown | .30 | .18 |
| 114 | Marco Coleman | .80 | .50 |
| 115 | Mark Clayton | .40 | .25 |
| 116 | Mark Higgs | .60 | .35 |
| 117 | Bryan Cox | .35 | .20 |
| 118 | Chuck Klingbell | .30 | .18 |
| 119 | Troy Vincent | .40 | .25 |
| 120 | Keith Jackson | .50 | .28 |
| 121 | Bruce Alexander | .30 | .18 |
| 122 | Minnesota Vikings | .30 | .18 |
| 123 | Rich Gannon | .40 | .25 |
| 124 | Terry Allen | 1.00 | .60 |

| | | | |
|---|---|---|---|
| 125 | Todd Scott | .30 | .18 |
| 126 | Cris Carter | .50 | .28 |
| 127 | Sean Salisbury | .35 | .20 |
| 128 | Mike Merriweather | .30 | .18 |
| 129 | Chris Doleman | .30 | .18 |
| 130 | Anthony Carter | .35 | .20 |
| 131 | New England Patriots | .30 | .18 |
| 132 | Tommy Hodson | .40 | .25 |
| 133 | Eugene Chung | .30 | .18 |
| 134 | Todd Collins | .30 | .18 |
| 135 | Leonard Russell | .80 | .50 |
| 136 | Jon Vaughn | .50 | .28 |
| 137 | Kevin Turner | .30 | .18 |
| 138 | New Orleans Saints | .30 | .18 |
| 139 | Steve Walsh | .40 | .25 |
| 140 | Wesley Carroll | .40 | .25 |
| 141 | Richard Cooper | .30 | .18 |
| 142 | Vaughn Dunbar | 1.00 | .60 |
| 143 | Fred McAfee | .40 | .25 |
| 144 | Torrence Small | .30 | .18 |
| 145 | Tyrone Legette | .30 | .18 |
| 146 | New York Giants | .30 | .18 |
| 147 | Phil Simms | .40 | .25 |
| 148 | Jarrod Bunch | .40 | .25 |
| 149 | Carl Banks | .30 | .18 |
| 150 | Lawrence Taylor | .50 | .28 |
| 151 | Rodney Hampton | 1.25 | .80 |
| 152 | Phillippi Sparks | .30 | .18 |
| 153 | Derek Brown | .40 | .25 |
| 154 | New York Jets | .30 | .18 |
| 155 | Boomer Esiason | .40 | .25 |
| 156 | Johnny Mitchell | .40 | .25 |
| 157 | Rob Moore | .40 | .25 |
| 158 | Ronnie Lott | .40 | .25 |
| 159 | Browning Nagle | .75 | .45 |
| 160 | Johnny Johnson | .50 | .28 |
| 161 | Dwayne White | .30 | .18 |
| 162 | Mike Brim | .30 | .18 |
| 163 | Philadelphia Eagles | .30 | .18 |
| 164 | Randall Cunningham | .80 | .50 |
| 165 | Fred Barnett | .75 | .45 |
| 166 | Siran Stacy | .40 | .25 |
| 167 | Keith Byars | .35 | .20 |
| 168 | Calvin Williams | .35 | .20 |
| 169 | Jeff Snyder | .30 | .18 |
| 170 | Tommy Jeter | .30 | .18 |
| 171 | Ben Smith | .30 | .18 |
| 172 | Phoenix Cardinals | .30 | .18 |
| 173 | Steve Beuerlein | .60 | .35 |
| 174 | Randal Hill | .60 | .35 |
| 175 | Timm Rosenbach | .35 | .20 |
| 176 | Ed Cunningham | .30 | .18 |
| 177 | Tony Sacca | .75 | .45 |
| 178 | Michael Zordich | .30 | .18 |
| 179 | Gary Clark | .40 | .25 |
| 180 | Pittsburgh Steelers | .30 | .18 |
| 181 | Neil O'Donnell | 1.50 | .90 |
| 182 | Barry Foster | 3.00 | 1.75 |
| 183 | Leon Searcy | .30 | .18 |
| 184 | Bubby Brister | .35 | .20 |
| 185 | Levon Kirkland | .30 | .18 |
| 186 | Joel Steed | .30 | .18 |
| 187 | Los Angeles Raiders | .30 | .18 |
| 188 | Jeff Hostetler | .40 | .25 |
| 189 | Nick Bell | .50 | .28 |
| 190 | Eric Dickerson | .50 | .28 |
| 191 | Nolan Harrison | .30 | .18 |
| 192 | Greg Skrepenak | .30 | .18 |
| 193 | Howie Long | .35 | .20 |
| 194 | Todd Marinovich | 1.00 | .60 |
| 195 | Chester McGlocklin | .30 | .18 |
| 196 | Los Angeles Rams | .30 | .18 |
| 197 | Jim Everett | .40 | .25 |
| 198 | Sean Gilbert | .50 | .28 |
| 199 | Steve Israel | .30 | .18 |
| 200 | Marc Boutte | .30 | .18 |
| 201 | Joe Milinichick | .30 | .18 |
| 202 | Henry Ellard | .35 | .20 |
| 203 | Robert Delpino | .40 | .25 |
| 204 | San Diego Chargers | .30 | .18 |
| 205 | Eric Bieniemy | .40 | .25 |
| 206 | Marion Butts | .40 | .25 |
| 207 | Nate Lewis | .40 | .25 |
| 208 | Junior Seau | .90 | .60 |
| 209 | Steve Hendricks | .30 | .18 |
| 210 | Chris Mims | .60 | .35 |
| 211 | Harry Swayne | .30 | .18 |
| 212 | Marquez Pope | .35 | .20 |
| 213 | Donald Frank | .30 | .18 |
| 214 | Ray Ethridge | .40 | .25 |
| 215 | Seattle Seahawks | .30 | .18 |
| 216 | Dan McGwire | .50 | .28 |
| 217 | Cortez Kennedy | .90 | .60 |
| 218 | Kelly Stouffer | .35 | .20 |
| 219 | Chris Warren | .50 | .28 |
| 220 | Brian Blades | .35 | .20 |
| 221 | Jeff Graham | .35 | .20 |
| 222 | San Francisco 49ers | .30 | .18 |
| 223 | Steve Young | 1.75 | 1.00 |
| 224 | Jerry Rice | 2.00 | 1.25 |
| 225 | Ricky Watters | 2.75 | 1.40 |
| 226 | Tom Rathman | .35 | .20 |
| 227 | Dana Hall | .30 | .18 |
| 228 | Amp Lee | .60 | .35 |
| 229 | Brian Bollinger | .30 | .18 |
| 230 | Steve Bono | .60 | .35 |
| 231 | John Taylor | .60 | .35 |
| 232 | Tampa Bay Bucs | .30 | .18 |
| 233 | Tyji Armstrong | .30 | .18 |
| 234 | Lawrence Dawsey | .50 | .28 |
| 235 | Mark Wheeler | .30 | .18 |
| 236 | Vince Workman | .30 | .18 |
| 237 | Reggie Cobb | .75 | .45 |
| 238 | Tony Mayberry | .30 | .18 |

| | | | |
|---|---|---|---|
| 239 | Marty Carter | .30 | .18 |
| 240 | Courtney Hawkins | .40 | .25 |
| 241 | Ray Seals | .30 | .18 |
| 242 | Washington Redskins | .30 | .18 |
| 243 | Mark Rypien | .75 | .45 |
| 244 | Ricky Ervins | .50 | .28 |
| 245 | Shane Collins | .30 | .18 |
| 246 | Art Monk | .40 | .25 |
| 247 | Mark Schlereth | .30 | .18 |
| 248 | Sidney Jackson | .30 | .18 |
| 249 | Chris Hakel | .30 | .18 |
| 250 | Paul Siever | .30 | .18 |

# COURTSIDE

## 1992 Courtside Draft Picks

This 140-card set features nearly all of the top picks from the 1992 NFL draft. Card fronts include action photos of players in their college uniforms framed by a white border. Card backs feature full color close up photos, brief bio's and each players college stats. Ten limited bonus cards were randomly inserted into the company's foil packs. Those bonus cards are listed at the end of this checklist but are not inlcuded in the complete set price. All cards measure 2-1/2" by 3-1/2".

| | | MINT | NR/MT |
|---|---|---|---|
| Complete Set (140) | | 12.00 | 8.00 |
| Commons | | .06 | .03 |
| | | | |
| 1 | Steve Emtman | 1.00 | .70 |
| 2 | Quentin Coryatt | .70 | .40 |
| 3 | Ken Swilling | .08 | .05 |
| 4 | Jay Leeuwenburg | .08 | .05 |
| 5 | Mazio Royster | .12 | .07 |
| 6 | Matt Veatch | .06 | .03 |
| 7 | Scott Lockwood | .12 | .07 |
| 8 | Todd Collins | .08 | .05 |
| 9 | Gene McGuire | .08 | .05 |
| 10 | Dale Carter | .35 | .20 |
| 11 | Michael Bankston | .10 | .06 |
| 12 | Jeremy Lincoln | .10 | .06 |
| 13 | Troy Auzenne | .12 | .07 |
| 14 | Rod Smith | .12 | .07 |
| 15 | Andy Kelly | .08 | .05 |
| 16 | Chris Holder | .08 | .05 |
| 17 | Rico Smith | .15 | .10 |
| 18 | Chris Pedersen | .06 | .03 |
| 19 | Brian Treggs | .06 | .03 |
| 20 | Eugene Chung | .12 | .07 |
| 21 | Joel Steed | .12 | .07 |
| 22 | Ricardo McDonald | .12 | .07 |
| 23 | Nate Turner | .10 | .06 |
| 24 | Sean Lumpkin | .08 | .05 |
| 25 | Ty Detmer | .60 | .35 |
| 26 | Matt Darby | .08 | .05 |
| 27 | Michael Warfield | .06 | .03 |
| 28 | Tracy Scroggins | .15 | .10 |
| 29 | Carl Pickens | .75 | .45 |
| 30 | Chris Mims | .20 | .12 |
| 31 | Mark D'Onofrio | .15 | .10 |
| 32 | Dwight Hollier | .06 | .03 |
| 33 | Siupeli Malamala | .10 | .06 |
| 34 | Mark Barsotti | .10 | .06 |
| 35 | Charles Davenport | .25 | .15 |
| 36 | Brian Bollinger | .08 | .05 |
| 37 | Willie McClendon | .08 | .05 |
| 38 | Calvin Holmes | .10 | .06 |
| 39 | Phillippi Sparks | .15 | .10 |
| 40 | Darryl Williams | .20 | .12 |
| 41 | Greg Skrepenak | .15 | .10 |
| 42 | Larry Webster | .08 | .05 |
| 43 | Dion Lambert | .06 | .03 |
| 44 | Sam Gash | .12 | .07 |
| 45 | Patrick Rowe | .20 | .12 |
| 46 | Scottie Graham | .25 | .15 |
| 47 | Darian Hagan | .15 | .10 |
| 48 | Arthur Marshall | .06 | .03 |
| 49 | Amp Lee | .60 | .35 |
| 50 | Tommy Vardell | .75 | .45 |
| 51 | Robert Porcher | .15 | .10 |

| # | Player | | |
|---|---|---|---|
| 52 | Reggie Dwight | .08 | .05 |
| 53 | Torrance Small | .12 | .07 |
| 54 | Ronnie West | .08 | .05 |
| 55 | Tony Brooks | .30 | .18 |
| 56 | Anthony McDowell | .08 | .05 |
| 57 | Chris Hakel | .15 | .10 |
| 58 | Ed Cunningham | .06 | .03 |
| 59 | Ashley Ambrose | .15 | .10 |
| 60 | Alonzo Spellman | .25 | .15 |
| 61 | Harold Heath | .06 | .03 |
| 62 | Ron Lopez | .06 | .03 |
| 63 | Bill Johnson | .12 | .07 |
| 64 | Kent Graham | .08 | .05 |
| 65 | Aaron Pierce | .10 | .06 |
| 66 | Bucky Richardson | .20 | .12 |
| 67 | Todd Kinchen | .15 | .10 |
| 68 | Ken Ealy | .06 | .03 |
| 69 | Carlos Snow | .15 | .10 |
| 70 | Dana Hall | .20 | .12 |
| 71 | Matt Rodgers | .15 | .10 |
| 72 | Howard Dinkins | .10 | .06 |
| 73 | Tim Lester | .06 | .03 |
| 74 | Mark Chmura | .08 | .05 |
| 75 | Johnny Mitchell | .25 | .15 |
| 76 | Mirko Jurkovic | .10 | .06 |
| 77 | Anthony Lynn | .06 | .03 |
| 78 | Roosevelt Collins | .06 | .03 |
| 79 | Tony Sands | .06 | .03 |
| 80 | Kevin Smith | .20 | .12 |
| 81 | Tony Brown | .08 | .05 |
| 82 | Bobby Fuller | .06 | .03 |
| 83 | Darryl Ashmore | .06 | .03 |
| 84 | Tyrone Legette | .12 | .07 |
| 85 | Mike Gaddis | .20 | .12 |
| 86 | Gerald Dixon | .10 | .06 |
| 87 | T.J. Rubley | .20 | .12 |
| 88 | Mark Thomas | .10 | .06 |
| 89 | Corey Widmer | .08 | .05 |
| 90 | Robert Jones | .20 | .12 |
| 91 | Eddie Robinson | .20 | .12 |
| 92 | Rob Tomlinson | .06 | .03 |
| 93 | Russ Campbell | .06 | .03 |
| 94 | Keith Goganious | .10 | .06 |
| 95 | Rod Moore | .06 | .03 |
| 96 | Jerry Ostroski | .06 | .03 |
| 97 | Tyji Armstrong | .06 | .03 |
| 98 | Ronald Humphrey | .06 | .03 |
| 99 | Corey Harris | .12 | .07 |
| 100 | Terrell Buckley | .80 | .50 |
| 101 | Cal Dixon | .06 | .03 |
| 102 | Tyrone Williams | .08 | .05 |
| 103 | Joe Bowden | .08 | .05 |
| 104 | Santana Dotson | .25 | .15 |
| 105 | Jeff Blake | .20 | .12 |
| 106 | Erick Anderson | .20 | .12 |
| 107 | Steve Israel | .15 | .10 |
| 108 | Chad Roghair | .06 | .03 |
| 109 | Todd Harrison | .08 | .05 |
| 110 | Chester McGlockton | .20 | .12 |
| 111 | Marquez Pope | .15 | .10 |
| 112 | George Rooks | .08 | .05 |
| 113 | Dion Johnson | .08 | .05 |
| 114 | Tim Simpson | .06 | .03 |
| 115 | Chris Walsh | .06 | .03 |
| 116 | Mark Bouttte | .15 | .10 |
| 117 | Jamie Gill | .06 | .03 |
| 118 | Willie Clay | .06 | .03 |
| 119 | Tim Paulk | .06 | .03 |
| 120 | Ray Roberts | .12 | .07 |
| 121 | Jeff Thomason | .06 | .03 |
| 122 | Leodis Flowers | .08 | .05 |
| 123 | Robert Brooks | .10 | .06 |
| 124 | Jeff Ellis | .06 | .03 |
| 125 | Jon Fina | .12 | .07 |
| 126 | Michael Smith | .06 | .03 |
| 127 | Mike Saunders | .06 | .03 |
| 128 | John Brown | .06 | .03 |
| 129 | Reggie Yarbrough | .06 | .03 |
| 130 | Leon Searcy | .12 | .07 |
| 131 | Marcus Woods | .06 | .03 |
| 132 | Shane Collins | .12 | .07 |
| 133 | Chuck Smith | .12 | .07 |
| 134 | Keith Hamilton | .12 | .07 |
| 135 | Rodney Blackshear | .06 | .03 |
| 136 | Corey Barlow | .06 | .03 |
| 137 | Robert Harris | .10 | .06 |
| 138 | Tony Smith | .60 | .35 |
| 139 | Checklist 1 | .06 | .03 |
| 140 | Checklist 2 | .06 | .03 |
| BC1 | Steve Emtman (Outland Trophy) | 3.00 | 2.00 |
| BC2 | Ty Detmer (Heisman) | 2.50 | 1.50 |
| BC3 | Steve Emtman (Lombardi Trophy) | 3.00 | 2.00 |
| BC4 | Terrell Buckley (Thorpe Award) | 2.50 | 1.50 |
| BC5 | Erick Anderson (Butkus Award) | 1.50 | .90 |
| BC6 | Carl Pickens (All-America) | 2.50 | 1.50 |
| BC7 | Dale Carter (All-America) | 1.50 | .90 |
| BC8 | Tommy Vardell (All-America) | 2.50 | 1.50 |
| BC9 | Amp Lee (All-America) | 2.50 | 1.50 |
| BC10 | Leon Searcy (All-America) | 1.00 | .70 |

# FLEER

## 1960 Fleer

Fleer's first football set is devoted exclusively to players from the American Football League. The cards, which measure 2-1/2" by 3-1/2", feature player photos on the fronts with the player's name and position in a diagonal box in the lower left corner and the player's team in the lower right corner. The card backs, printed in red and black, contain the player's personal data and brief biography's. Many of the cards in the set are either miscut or off-center making it impossible to put together a mint set.

|  | | NR/MT | EX |
|---|---|---|---|
| Complete Set (132) | | 675.00 | 325.00 |
| Commons | | 1.75 | 1.00 |

| | | NR/MT | EX |
|---|---|---|---|
| 1 | Harvey White (RT) | 15.00 | 6.00 |
| 2 | Tom Tharp (R) | 1.75 | 1.00 |
| 3 | Dan McGrew (R) | 1.75 | 1.00 |
| 4 | Bob White (R) | 1.75 | 1.00 |
| 5 | Dick Jamieson (R) | 1.75 | 1.00 |
| 6 | Sam Salerno (R) | 1.75 | 1.00 |
| 7 | Sid Gillman (R) | 12.00 | 6.00 |
| 8 | Ben Preston (R) | 1.75 | 1.00 |
| 9 | George Blanch (R) | 1.75 | 1.00 |
| 10 | Bob Stransky (R) | 1.75 | 1.00 |
| 11 | Fran Curci (R) | 2.00 | 1.25 |
| 12 | George Shirkey (R) | 1.75 | 1.00 |
| 13 | Paul Larson (R) | 1.75 | 1.00 |
| 14 | John Stolte (R) | 1.75 | 1.00 |
| 15 | Serafino Fazio (R) | 2.00 | 1.25 |
| 16 | Tom Dimitroff (R) | 1.75 | 1.00 |

| | | | |
|---|---|---|---|
| 17 | Elbert Dubenion (R) | 7.50 | 3.75 |
| 18 | Hogan Wharton (R) | 1.75 | 1.00 |
| 19 | Tom O'Connell (R) | 1.75 | 1.00 |
| 20 | Sammy Baugh | 45.00 | 24.00 |
| 21 | Tony Sardisco (R) | 1.75 | 1.00 |
| 22 | Alan Cann (R) | 1.75 | 1.00 |
| 23 | Mike Hudock (R) | 1.75 | 1.00 |
| 24 | Bill Atkins (R) | 1.75 | 1.00 |
| 25 | Charlie Jackson (R) | 1.75 | 1.00 |
| 26 | Frank Tripucka | 5.00 | 2.75 |
| 27 | Tony Teresa (R) | 1.75 | 1.00 |
| 28 | Joe Amstutz (R) | 1.75 | 1.00 |
| 29 | Bob Fee (R) | 1.75 | 1.00 |
| 30 | Jim Baldwin (R) | 1.75 | 1.00 |
| 31 | Jim Yates (R) | 1.75 | 1.00 |
| 32 | Don Flynn (R) | 1.75 | 1.00 |
| 33 | Ken Adamson (R) | 1.75 | 1.00 |
| 34 | Ron Drzewiecki (R) | 1.75 | 1.00 |
| 35 | J.W. Slack (R) | 1.75 | 1.00 |
| 36 | Bob Yates (R) | 1.75 | 1.00 |
| 37 | Gary Cobb (R) | 1.75 | 1.00 |
| 38 | Jackie Lee (R) | 2.00 | 1.25 |
| 39 | Jack Spikes (R) | 3.50 | 1.75 |
| 40 | Jim Padgett (R) | 1.75 | 1.00 |
| 41 | Jack Larsheid (R) | 1.75 | 1.00 |
| 42 | Bob Reifsnyder (R) | 1.75 | 1.00 |
| 43 | Fran Rogel | 1.75 | 1.00 |
| 44 | Ray Moss | 1.75 | 1.00 |
| 45 | Tony Banfield (R) | 1.75 | 1.00 |
| 46 | George Herring (R) | 1.75 | 1.00 |
| 47 | Willie Smith (R) | 1.75 | 1.00 |
| 48 | Buddy Allen (R) | 1.75 | 1.00 |
| 49 | Bill Brown | 1.75 | 1.00 |
| 50 | Ken Ford (R) | 1.75 | 1.00 |
| 51 | Billy Kinard | 1.75 | 1.00 |
| 52 | Buddy Mayfield | 1.75 | 1.00 |
| 53 | Bill Krisher (R) | 1.75 | 1.00 |
| 54 | Frank Bernardi (R) | 1.75 | 1.00 |
| 55 | Lou Saban (R) | 4.00 | 2.25 |
| 56 | Gene Cockrell (R) | 1.75 | 1.00 |
| 57 | Sam Sanders (R) | 1.75 | 1.00 |
| 58 | George Blanda | 38.00 | 18.50 |
| 59 | Sherrill Headrick (R) | 3.50 | 1.75 |
| 60 | Carl Larpenter (R) | 1.75 | 1.00 |
| 61 | Gene Prebola (R) | 1.75 | 1.00 |
| 62 | Dick Chorovich (R) | 1.75 | 1.00 |
| 63 | Bob McNamara (R) | 1.75 | 1.00 |
| 64 | Tom Saidock (R) | 1.75 | 1.00 |
| 65 | Willie Evans (R) | 1.75 | 1.00 |
| 66 | Billy Cannon (R) | 15.00 | 8.00 |
| 67 | Sam McCord (R) | 1.75 | 1.00 |
| 68 | Mike Simmons (R) | 1.75 | 1.00 |
| 69 | Jim Swink (R) | 2.50 | 1.25 |
| 70 | Don Hitt (R) | 1.75 | 1.00 |
| 71 | Gerhard Schwedes (R) | 1.75 | 1.00 |
| 72 | Thurlow Cooper (R) | 1.75 | 1.00 |

| | | | |
|---|---|---|---|
| 73 | Abner Haynes (R) | 12.00 | 6.50 |
| 74 | Billy Shoemaker (R) | 1.75 | 1.00 |
| 75 | Marv Lasater (R) | 1.75 | 1.00 |
| 76 | Paul Lowe (R) | 10.00 | 5.00 |
| 77 | Bruce Hartman (R) | 1.75 | 1.00 |
| 78 | Blanche Martin (R) | 1.75 | 1.00 |
| 79 | Gene Grabosky (R) | 1.75 | 1.00 |
| 80 | Lou Rymkus (R) | 2.00 | 1.25 |
| 81 | Chris Burford (R) | 3.50 | 1.75 |
| 82 | Don Allen (R) | 1.75 | 1.00 |
| 83 | Bob Nelson (R) | 1.75 | 1.00 |
| 84 | Jim Woodard (R) | 1.75 | 1.00 |
| 85 | Tom Rychlec (R) | 1.75 | 1.00 |
| 86 | Bob Cox (R) | 1.75 | 1.00 |
| 87 | Jerry Cornelison (R) | 1.75 | 1.00 |
| 88 | Jack Work (R) | 1.75 | 1.00 |
| 89 | Sam DeLuca (R) | 1.75 | 1.00 |
| 90 | Rommie Loudd (R) | 1.75 | 1.00 |
| 91 | Teddy Edmondson (R) | 1.75 | 1.00 |
| 92 | Buster Ramsey (R) | 1.75 | 1.00 |
| 93 | Doug Asad (R) | 1.75 | 1.00 |
| 94 | Jimmy Harris (R) | 1.75 | 1.00 |
| 95 | Larry Cundiff (R) | 1.75 | 1.00 |
| 96 | Richie Lucas (R) | 3.00 | 1.50 |
| 97 | Don Norwood (R) | 1.75 | 1.00 |
| 98 | Larry Grantham (R) | 3.50 | 1.75 |
| 99 | Bill Mathis (R) | 2.50 | 1.25 |
| 100 | Mel Branch (R) | 3.50 | 1.75 |
| 101 | Marvin Terrell (R) | 1.75 | 1.00 |
| 102 | Charlie Flowres (R) | 2.00 | 1.25 |
| 103 | John McMullan (R) | 1.75 | 1.00 |
| 104 | Charlie Kaaihue (R) | 1.75 | 1.00 |
| 105 | Joe Schaffer (R) | 1.75 | 1.00 |
| 106 | Al Day (R) | 1.75 | 1.00 |
| 107 | John Carson (R) | 1.75 | 1.00 |
| 108 | Alan Goldstein (R) | 1.75 | 1.00 |
| 109 | Doug Cline (R) | 1.75 | 1.00 |
| 110 | Al Carmichael (R) | 1.75 | 1.00 |
| 111 | Bob Dee (R) | 1.75 | 1.00 |
| 112 | John Bredice (R) | 1.75 | 1.00 |
| 113 | Don Floyd (R) | 1.75 | 1.00 |
| 114 | Ronnie Cain (R) | 1.75 | 1.00 |
| 115 | Stan Flowers (R) | 1.75 | 1.00 |
| 116 | Hank Stram (R) | 18.00 | 9.50 |
| 117 | Bob Dougherty (R) | 1.75 | 1.00 |
| 118 | Ron Mix (R) | 35.00 | 17.50 |
| 119 | Roger Ellis (R) | 1.75 | 1.00 |
| 120 | Elvin Caldwell (R) | 1.75 | 1.00 |
| 121 | Bill Kimber (R) | 1.75 | 1.00 |
| 122 | Jim Matheny (R) | 1.75 | 1.00 |
| 123 | Curley Johnson (R) | 2.50 | 1.25 |
| 124 | Jack Kemp (R) | 300.00 | 140.00 |
| 125 | Ed Denk (R) | 1.75 | 1.00 |
| 126 | Jerry McFarland (R) | 1.75 | 1.00 |
| 127 | Dan Lanphear (R) | 1.75 | 1.00 |
| 128 | Paul Maguire (R) | 8.50 | 4.25 |
| 129 | Ray Collins (R) | 1.75 | 1.00 |
| 130 | Ron Burton (R) | 2.00 | 1.25 |
| 131 | Eddie Erdelatz (R) | 1.75 | 1.00 |
| 132 | Ron Beagle (R) | 15.00 | 6.00 |

# 1961 Fleer

This 220-card set contains players from both the National Football League (1-132) and the American Football League (133-220). Cards measure 2-1/2" by 3-1/2". Card fronts feature action photos framed by a white border. Card backs, printed in green and black on a white card stock, contain the player's personal data and a brief biography.

| | | NR/MT | EX |
|---|---|---|---|
| **Complete Set (220)** | | 1,550.00 | 725.00 |
| **Commons (1-132)** | | 1.75 | 1.00 |
| **Commons (133-220)** | | 4.00 | 2.25 |

| | | | |
|---|---|---|---|
| 1 | Ed Brown | 9.00 | 3.75 |
| 2 | Rick Casares | 4.00 | 2.25 |
| 3 | Willie Galimore | 3.50 | 2.00 |
| 4 | Jim Dooley | 1.75 | 1.00 |
| 5 | Harlon Hill | 2.50 | 1.40 |
| 6 | Stan Jones | 4.00 | 2.25 |
| 7 | J.C. Caroline | 1.75 | 1.00 |
| 8 | Joe Fortunato | 2.00 | 1.25 |
| 9 | Doug Atkins | 5.00 | 2.75 |
| 10 | Milt Plum | 3.50 | 2.00 |
| 11 | Jim Brown | 140.00 | 75.00 |
| 12 | Bobby Mitchell | 7.00 | 3.75 |
| 13 | Ray Renfro | 2.00 | 1.25 |
| 14 | Gern Nagler | 1.75 | 1.00 |
| 15 | Jim Shofner | 2.50 | 1.40 |
| 16 | Vince Costello | 1.75 | 1.00 |

| | | | | | | | |
|---|---|---|---|---|---|---|---|
| 17 | Galen Fiss | 1.75 | 1.00 | 74 | Sam Huff | 8.00 | 4.50 |
| 18 | Walt Michaels | 2.50 | 1.40 | 75 | Andy Robustelli | 5.00 | 2.75 |
| 19 | Bob Gain | 1.75 | 1.00 | 76 | Dick Modzelewski | 2.00 | 1.25 |
| 20 | Mal Hammack | 1.75 | 1.00 | 77 | Roosevelt Grier | 4.50 | 2.50 |
| 21 | Frank Mestnick | 1.75 | 1.00 | 78 | Earl Morrall | 5.00 | 2.75 |
| 22 | Bobby Joe Conrad | 2.50 | 1.40 | 79 | Jim Ninowski (R) | 2.00 | 1.25 |
| 23 | John David Crow | 3.50 | 2.00 | 80 | Nick Pietrosante (R) | 4.50 | 2.50 |
| 24 | Sonny Randle (R) | 3.50 | 2.00 | 81 | Howard Cassady | 3.00 | 1.75 |
| 25 | Don Gillis | 1.75 | 1.00 | 82 | Jim Gibbons (R) | 1.75 | 1.00 |
| 26 | Jerry Norton | 1.75 | 1.00 | 83 | Gail Cogdill (R) | 2.50 | 1.40 |
| 27 | Bill Stacy | 1.75 | 1.00 | 84 | Dick Lane | 6.00 | 3.25 |
| 28 | Leo Sugar | 1.75 | 1.00 | 85 | Yale Lary | 5.00 | 2.75 |
| 29 | Frank Fuller | 1.75 | 1.00 | 86 | Joe Schmidt | 6.50 | 3.50 |
| 30 | John Unitas | 70.00 | 38.00 | 87 | Darris McCord | 1.75 | 1.00 |
| 31 | Alan Ameche | 5.00 | 2.75 | 88 | Bart Starr | 40.00 | 24.00 |
| 32 | Lenny Moore | 7.00 | 3.75 | 89 | Jim Taylor | 32.00 | 18.00 |
| 33 | Raymond Berry | 7.00 | 3.75 | 90 | Paul Hornung | 38.00 | 22.00 |
| 34 | Jim Mutcheller | 1.75 | 1.00 | 91 | Tom Moore (R) | 4.00 | 2.25 |
| 35 | Jim Parker | 4.50 | 2.50 | 92 | Boyd Dowler (R) | 5.00 | 2.75 |
| 36 | Bill Pellington | 1.75 | 1.00 | 93 | Max McGee | 3.50 | 2.00 |
| 37 | Gino Marchetti | 6.50 | 3.50 | 94 | Forrest Gregg | 6.50 | 3.50 |
| 38 | Gene Lipscomb | 3.50 | 2.00 | 95 | Jerry Kramer | 6.00 | 3.25 |
| 39 | Art Donovan | 5.00 | 2.75 | 96 | Jim Ringo | 6.00 | 3.25 |
| 40 | Eddie LeBaron | 4.50 | 2.50 | 97 | Bill Forester | 2.00 | 1.25 |
| 41 | Don Meredith (R) | 175.00 | 90.00 | 98 | Frank Ryan | 3.50 | 2.00 |
| 42 | Don McIlhenny | 1.75 | 1.00 | 99 | Ollie Matson | 7.50 | 4.00 |
| 43 | L.G. Dupre | 2.00 | 1.25 | 100 | Jon Arnett | 2.50 | 1.40 |
| 44 | Fred Dugan | 1.75 | 1.00 | 101 | Dick Bass (R) | 3.00 | 1.75 |
| 45 | Bill Howton | 2.50 | 1.40 | 102 | Jim Phillips | 1.75 | 1.00 |
| 46 | Duane Putnam | 1.75 | 1.00 | 103 | Del Shofner | 2.50 | 1.40 |
| 47 | Gene Cronin | 1.75 | 1.00 | 104 | Art Hunter | 1.75 | 1.00 |
| 48 | Jerry Tubbs | 2.00 | 1.25 | 105 | Lindon Crow | 1.75 | 1.00 |
| 49 | Clarence Peaks | 1.75 | 1.00 | 106 | Les Richter | 2.00 | 1.25 |
| 50 | Ted Dean (R) | 2.00 | 1.25 | 107 | Lou Michaels | 2.50 | 1.40 |
| 51 | Tommy McDonald | 3.50 | 2.00 | 108 | Ralph Guglielmi | 2.00 | 1.25 |
| 52 | Bill Barnes | 1.75 | 1.00 | 109 | Don Bosseler | 1.75 | 1.00 |
| 53 | Pete Retzlaff | 2.00 | 1.25 | 110 | John Olszewski | 1.75 | 1.00 |
| 54 | Bobby Walston | 1.75 | 1.00 | 111 | Bill Anderson | 1.75 | 1.00 |
| 55 | Chuck Bednarik | 6.50 | 3.50 | 112 | Joe Walton | 2.00 | 1.25 |
| 56 | Maxie Baughan (R) | 5.00 | 2.75 | 113 | Jim Schrader | 1.75 | 1.00 |
| 57 | Bob Pellegrini | 1.75 | 1.00 | 114 | Gary Glick | 1.75 | 1.00 |
| 58 | Jesse Richardson | 1.75 | 1.00 | 115 | Ralph Felton | 1.75 | 1.00 |
| 59 | John Brodie (R) | 75.00 | 40.00 | 116 | Bob Toneff | 1.75 | 1.00 |
| 60 | J.D. Smith | 2.00 | 1.25 | 117 | Bobby Layne | 24.00 | 14.00 |
| 61 | Ray Norton (R) | 2.00 | 1.25 | 118 | John Henry Johnson | 6.50 | 3.50 |
| 62 | Monty Stickles (R) | 2.00 | 1.25 | 119 | Tom Tracy | 2.00 | 1.25 |
| 63 | Bob St. Clair | 5.00 | 2.75 | 120 | Jimmy Orr (R) | 4.50 | 2.50 |
| 64 | Dave Baker | 1.75 | 1.00 | 121 | John Nisby | 1.75 | 1.00 |
| 65 | Abe Woodson | 1.75 | 1.00 | 122 | Dean Derby | 1.75 | 1.00 |
| 66 | Matt Hazeltine | 1.75 | 1.00 | 123 | John Reger | 1.75 | 1.00 |
| 67 | Leo Nomellini | 5.00 | 2.75 | 124 | George Tarasovic | 1.75 | 1.00 |
| 68 | Charley Conerly | 14.00 | 8.00 | 125 | Ernie Stautner | 5.00 | 2.75 |
| 69 | Kyle Rote | 3.50 | 2.00 | 126 | George Shaw | 2.00 | 1.25 |
| 70 | Jack Stroud | 1.75 | 1.00 | 127 | Hugh McElhenny | 6.50 | 3.50 |
| 71 | Roosevelt Brown | 5.00 | 2.75 | 128 | Dick Haley | 1.75 | 1.00 |
| 72 | Jim Patton | 1.75 | 1.00 | 129 | Dave Middleton | 1.75 | 1.00 |
| 73 | Erich Barnes | 2.50 | 1.40 | 130 | Perry Richards | 1.75 | 1.00 |

| # | Name | | |
|---|---|---|---|
| 131 | Gene Johnson | 1.75 | 1.00 |
| 132 | Don Joyce | 1.75 | 1.00 |
| 133 | John Green | 4.00 | 2.25 |
| 134 | Wray Carlton (R) | 5.00 | 2.75 |
| 135 | Richie Lucas | 4.00 | 2.25 |
| 136 | Elbert Dubenion | 4.00 | 2.25 |
| 137 | Tom Rychlec | 4.00 | 2.25 |
| 138 | Mack Yoho | 4.00 | 2.25 |
| 139 | Phil Blazer | 4.00 | 2.25 |
| 140 | Dan McGrew | 4.00 | 2.25 |
| 141 | Bill Atkins | 4.00 | 2.25 |
| 142 | Archie Matsos (R) | 4.00 | 2.25 |
| 143 | Gene Grabosky | 4.00 | 2.25 |
| 144 | Frank Tripucka | 4.50 | 2.50 |
| 145 | Al Carmichael | 4.00 | 2.25 |
| 146 | Bob McNamara | 4.00 | 2.25 |
| 147 | Lionel Taylor (R) | 10.00 | 6.00 |
| 148 | Eldon Danenhauer (R) | 4.00 | 2.25 |
| 149 | Willie Smith | 4.00 | 2.25 |
| 150 | Carl Larpenter | 4.00 | 2.25 |
| 151 | Ken Adamson | 4.00 | 2.25 |
| 152 | Goose Gonsoulin | 4.50 | 2.50 |
| 153 | Joe Young | 4.00 | 2.25 |
| 154 | Gordy Molz | 4.00 | 2.25 |
| 155 | Jack Kemp | 160.00 | 85.00 |
| 156 | Charlie Flowers | 4.00 | 2.25 |
| 157 | Paul Lowe | 5.00 | 2.50 |
| 158 | Don Norton | 4.00 | 2.25 |
| 159 | Howard Clark | 4.00 | 2.25 |
| 160 | Paul Maguire | 4.50 | 2.50 |
| 161 | Ernie Wright (R) | 4.50 | 2.50 |
| 162 | Ron Mix | 15.00 | 8.00 |
| 163 | Fred Cole | 4.00 | 2.25 |
| 164 | Jim Sears | 4.00 | 2.25 |
| 165 | Volney Peters | 4.00 | 2.25 |
| 166 | George Blanda | 35.00 | 20.00 |
| 167 | Jacky Lee | 4.00 | 2.25 |
| 168 | Bob White | 4.00 | 2.25 |
| 169 | Doug Cline | 4.00 | 2.25 |
| 170 | Dave Smith | 4.00 | 2.25 |
| 171 | Billy Cannon | 7.50 | 4.00 |
| 172 | Bill Groman (R) | 4.50 | 2.50 |
| 173 | Al Jamison | 4.00 | 2.25 |
| 174 | Jim Norton | 4.00 | 2.25 |
| 175 | Dennis Morris | 4.00 | 2.25 |
| 176 | Don Floyd | 4.00 | 2.25 |
| 177 | Butch Songin | 4.00 | 2.25 |
| 178 | Billy Lott (R) | 4.50 | 2.50 |
| 179 | Ron Burton | 4.00 | 2.25 |
| 180 | Jim Colclough (R) | 4.00 | 2.25 |
| 181 | Charley Leo | 4.00 | 2.25 |
| 182 | Walt Cudzik | 4.00 | 2.25 |
| 183 | Fred Bruney | 4.00 | 2.25 |
| 184 | Ross O'Hanley | 4.00 | 2.25 |
| 185 | Tony Sardisco | 4.00 | 2.25 |
| 186 | Harry Jacobs | 4.00 | 2.25 |
| 187 | Bob Dee | 4.00 | 2.25 |
| 188 | Tom Flores (R) | 16.00 | 9.00 |
| 189 | Jack Larsheid | 4.00 | 2.25 |
| 190 | Dick Christy | 4.00 | 2.25 |
| 191 | Alan Miller | 4.00 | 2.25 |
| 192 | Jim Smith | 4.00 | 2.25 |
| 193 | Gerald Burch | 4.00 | 2.25 |
| 194 | Gene Prebola | 4.00 | 2.25 |
| 195 | Alan Goldstein | 4.00 | 2.25 |
| 196 | Don Manoukian | 4.00 | 2.25 |
| 197 | Jim Otto (R) | 50.00 | 28.00 |
| 198 | Wayne Crow | 4.00 | 2.25 |
| 199 | Cotton Davidson (R) | 5.00 | 2.75 |
| 200 | Randy Duncan | 4.50 | 2.50 |
| 201 | Jack Spikes | 4.50 | 2.50 |
| 202 | Johnny Robinson (R) | 8.50 | 4.50 |
| 203 | Abner Haynes | 8.00 | 4.25 |
| 204 | Chris Burford | 4.50 | 2.50 |
| 205 | Bill Krisher | 4.00 | 2.25 |
| 206 | Marvin Terrell | 4.00 | 2.25 |
| 207 | Jimmy Harris | 4.00 | 2.25 |
| 208 | Mel Branch | 4.00 | 2.25 |
| 209 | Paul Miller | 4.00 | 2.25 |
| 210 | Al Dorow | 4.00 | 2.25 |
| 211 | Dick Jamieson | 4.00 | 2.25 |
| 212 | Pete Hart | 4.00 | 2.25 |
| 213 | Bill Shockley | 4.00 | 2.25 |
| 214 | Dewey Bohling | 4.00 | 2.25 |
| 215 | Don Maynard (R) | 75.00 | 40.00 |
| 216 | Bob Mischak | 4.00 | 2.25 |
| 217 | Mike Hudock | 4.00 | 2.25 |
| 218 | Bob Reifsnyder | 4.00 | 2.25 |
| 219 | Tom Saidock | 4.00 | 2.25 |
| 220 | Sid Youngelman | 24.00 | 8.00 |

# 1962 Fleer

The cards in this 88-card set feature players from the American Football League. Card fronts contain action photos surrounded by a white border. The player's name, team and position are located in a box below the photograph. The vertical card backs include the player's personal data and biographical information. Cards measure 2-1/2" by 3-1/2".

|  |  | NR/MT | EX |
|---|---|---|---|
|  | Complete Set (88) | 675.00 | 350.00 |
|  | Commons | 4.50 | 2.50 |
|  |  |  |  |
| 1 | Billy Lott | 15.00 | 6.00 |
| 2 | Ron Burton | 4.50 | 2.50 |
| 3 | Gino Cappelletti (R) | 15.00 | 8.00 |
| 4 | Babe Parilli | 5.00 | 2.75 |
| 5 | Jim Colclough | 4.50 | 2.50 |
| 6 | Tony Sardisco | 4.50 | 2.50 |
| 7 | Walt Cudzik | 4.50 | 2.50 |
| 8 | Bob Dee | 4.50 | 2.50 |
| 9 | Tommy Addison | 4.50 | 2.50 |
| 10 | Harry Jacobs | 4.50 | 2.50 |
| 11 | Ross O'Hanley | 4.50 | 2.50 |
| 12 | Art Baker | 4.50 | 2.50 |
| 13 | John Green | 4.50 | 2.50 |
| 14 | Elbert Dubenion | 4.50 | 2.50 |
| 15 | Tom Rychlec | 4.50 | 2.50 |
| 16 | Billy Shaw (R) | 5.00 | 2.75 |
| 17 | Ken Rice | 4.50 | 2.50 |
| 18 | Bill Atkins | 4.50 | 2.50 |
| 19 | Richie Lucas | 4.50 | 2.50 |
| 20 | Archie Matsos | 4.50 | 2.50 |
| 21 | Laverne Torczon | 4.50 | 2.50 |
| 22 | Warren Rabb | 4.50 | 2.50 |
| 23 | Jack Spikes | 4.50 | 2.50 |
| 24 | Cotton Davidson | 5.00 | 2.75 |
| 25 | Abner Haynes | 6.50 | 3.50 |
| 26 | Jimmy Saxton | 4.50 | 2.50 |
| 27 | Chris Burford | 5.00 | 2.75 |
| 28 | Bill Miller | 4.50 | 2.50 |
| 29 | Sherrill Headrick | 4.50 | 2.50 |
| 30 | E.J. Holub (R) | 7.50 | 4.00 |
| 31 | Jerry Mays (R) | 6.50 | 3.50 |
| 32 | Mel Branch | 5.00 | 2.75 |
| 33 | Paul Rochester | 4.50 | 2.50 |
| 34 | Frank Tripucka | 5.00 | 2.75 |
| 35 | Gene Mingo | 4.50 | 2.50 |
| 36 | Lionel Taylor | 8.00 | 4.50 |
| 37 | Ken Adamson | 4.50 | 2.50 |
| 38 | Eldon Danenhauer | 4.50 | 2.50 |
| 39 | Goose Gonsoulin | 4.50 | 2.50 |
| 40 | Gordy Holz | 4.50 | 2.50 |
| 41 | Bud McFadin | 4.50 | 2.50 |
| 42 | Jim Stinnette | 4.50 | 2.50 |
| 43 | Bob Hudson | 4.50 | 2.50 |
| 44 | George Herring | 4.50 | 2.50 |
| 45 | Charley Tolar (R) | 5.00 | 2.75 |
| 46 | George Blanda | 48.00 | 26.00 |
| 47 | Billy Cannon | 7.00 | 3.75 |
| 48 | Charlie Hennigan (R) | 10.00 | 6.00 |
| 49 | Bill Groman | 4.50 | 2.50 |
| 50 | Al Jamison | 4.50 | 2.50 |
| 51 | Tony Banfield | 4.50 | 2.50 |
| 52 | Jim Norton | 4.50 | 2.50 |
| 53 | Dennis Morris | 4.50 | 2.50 |
| 54 | Don Floyd | 4.50 | 2.50 |
| 55 | Ed Hussmann | 4.50 | 2.50 |
| 56 | Robert Brooks | 4.50 | 2.50 |
| 57 | Al Dorow | 4.50 | 2.50 |
| 58 | Dick Christy | 4.50 | 2.50 |
| 59 | Don Maynard | 30.00 | 16.00 |
| 60 | Art Powell | 7.50 | 4.00 |
| 61 | Mike Hudock | 4.50 | 2.50 |
| 62 | Bill Mathis | 4.50 | 2.50 |
| 63 | Butch Songin | 4.50 | 2.50 |
| 64 | Larry Grantham | 5.00 | 2.75 |
| 65 | Nick Mumley | 4.50 | 2.50 |
| 66 | Tom Saidock | 4.50 | 2.50 |
| 67 | Alan Miller | 4.50 | 2.50 |
| 68 | Tom Flores | 8.00 | 4.50 |
| 69 | Bob Coolbaugh | 4.50 | 2.50 |
| 70 | George Fleming | 4.50 | 2.50 |
| 71 | Wayne Hawkins | 4.50 | 2.50 |
| 72 | Jim Otto | 15.00 | 8.00 |
| 73 | Wayne Crow | 4.50 | 2.50 |
| 74 | Fred Williamson (R) | 12.00 | 7.00 |
| 75 | Tom Louderback | 4.50 | 2.50 |
| 76 | Volney Peters | 4.50 | 2.50 |
| 77 | Charley Powell | 4.50 | 2.50 |
| 78 | Don Norton | 4.50 | 2.50 |
| 79 | Jack Kemp | 125.00 | 65.00 |
| 80 | Paul Lowe | 6.00 | 3.50 |

| 81 | Dave Kocourek | 4.50 | 2.50 |
|----|---------------|------|------|
| 82 | Ron Mix | 10.00 | 6.00 |
| 83 | Ernie Wright | 4.50 | 2.50 |
| 84 | Dick Harris | 4.50 | 2.50 |
| 85 | Bill Hudson | 4.50 | 2.50 |
| 86 | Ernie Ladd (R) | 20.00 | 12.00 |
| 87 | Earl Faison (R) | 5.00 | 2.75 |
| 88 | Ron Nery (R) | 12.50 | 5.00 |

# 1963 Fleer

CARLTON (Cookie) GILCHRIST
FULLBACK
BUFFALO BILLS

This 88-card set includes only players from the American Football League and is similar in design to Fleer's 1962 set. Cards measure 2-1/2" by 3-1/2" and feature action photos on the front. The vertical cards backs, printed in red and black type on a white cardboard stock, include the player's personal data and brief biography's. Two cards (#6 and #64) were short printed (SP) and are considered extremely scarce.

| | | NR/MT | EX |
|---|---|-------|-----|
| | Complete Set (88) | 1,875.00 | 975.00 |
| | Commons | 5.00 | 2.75 |
| | | | |
| 1 | Larry Garron (R) | 16.00 | 6.00 |
| 2 | Babe Parilli | 8.00 | 4.25 |
| 3 | Ron Burton | 6.00 | 3.25 |
| 4 | Jim Colclough | 5.00 | 2.75 |
| 5 | Gino Cappelletti | 8.50 | 4.50 |
| 6 | Charles Long (SP) | 225.00 | 125.00 |
| 7 | Bill Neighbors (R) | 8.50 | 4.50 |

| 8 | Dick Felt | 5.00 | 2.75 |
|----|-----------|------|------|
| 9 | Tommy Addison | 5.00 | 2.75 |
| 10 | Nick Buoniconti (R) | 52.00 | 30.00 |
| 11 | Larry Eisenhauer (R) | 8.50 | 4.50 |
| 12 | Bill Mathis | 7.00 | 3.75 |
| 13 | Lee Grosscup (R) | 9.00 | 4.75 |
| 14 | Dick Christy | 5.00 | 2.75 |
| 15 | Don Maynard | 40.00 | 22.50 |
| 16 | Alex Kroll (R) | 7.50 | 4.00 |
| 17 | Bob Mischak | 5.00 | 2.75 |
| 18 | Dainard Paulson | 5.00 | 2.75 |
| 19 | Lee Riley | 5.00 | 2.75 |
| 20 | Larry Grantham | 7.00 | 3.75 |
| 21 | Hubert Bobo | 5.00 | 2.75 |
| 22 | Nick Mumley | 5.00 | 2.75 |
| 23 | Cookie Gilchrist (R) | 15.00 | 8.00 |
| 24 | Jack Kemp | 140.00 | 75.00 |
| 25 | Wray Carlton | 6.00 | 3.25 |
| 26 | Elbert Dubenion | 6.50 | 3.50 |
| 27 | Ernie Warlick | 5.00 | 2.75 |
| 28 | Billy Shaw | 5.00 | 2.75 |
| 29 | Ken Rice | 5.00 | 2.75 |
| 30 | Booker Edgerson | 5.00 | 2.75 |
| 31 | Ray Abbruzzese | 5.00 | 2.75 |
| 32 | Mike Stratton (R) | 7.50 | 4.00 |
| 33 | Tom Sestak (R) | 6.50 | 3.50 |
| 34 | Charley Tolar | 6.50 | 3.50 |
| 35 | Dave Smith | 5.00 | 2.75 |
| 36 | George Blanda | 60.00 | 32.00 |
| 37 | Billy Cannon | 9.00 | 4.75 |
| 38 | Charlie Hennigan | 7.50 | 4.00 |
| 39 | Bob Talamini (R) | 7.50 | 4.00 |
| 40 | Jim Norton | 5.00 | 2.75 |
| 41 | Tony Banfield | 5.00 | 2.75 |
| 42 | Dou Cline | 5.00 | 2.75 |
| 43 | Don Floyd | 5.00 | 2.75 |
| 44 | Ed Husmann | 5.00 | 2.75 |
| 45 | Curtis McClinton (R) | 8.50 | 4.50 |
| 46 | Jack Spikes | 6.00 | 3.25 |
| 47 | Len Dawson (R) | 175.00 | 95.00 |
| 48 | Abner Haynes | 10.00 | 6.00 |
| 49 | Chris Burford | 6.50 | 3.50 |
| 50 | Fred Arbanas (R) | 8.50 | 4.50 |
| 51 | Johnny Robinson | 7.00 | 3.75 |
| 52 | E.J. Holub | 7.50 | 4.00 |
| 53 | Sherrill Headrick | 7.00 | 3.75 |
| 54 | Mel Branch | 7.50 | 4.00 |
| 55 | Jerry Mays | 7.00 | 3.75 |
| 56 | Cotton Davidson | 6.50 | 3.50 |
| 57 | Clem Daniels (R) | 12.50 | 7.00 |
| 58 | Bo Robertson | 5.00 | 2.75 |
| 59 | Art Powell | 8.00 | 4.25 |
| 60 | Bob Coolbaugh | 5.00 | 2.75 |
| 61 | Wayne Hawkins | 5.00 | 2.75 |
| 62 | Jim Otto | 25.00 | 14.00 |
| 63 | Fred Williamson | 8.50 | 4.50 |
| 64 | Bob Dougherty (SP) | 240.00 | 125.00 |

| | | MINT | NR/MT |
|---|---|---|---|
| 65 | Dalva Allen | 5.00 | 2.75 |
| 66 | Chuck McMutry | 5.00 | 2.75 |
| 67 | Gerry McDougall | 5.00 | 2.75 |
| 68 | Tobin Rote | 8.00 | 4.25 |
| 69 | Paul Lowe | 8.50 | 4.50 |
| 70 | Keith Lincoln (R) | 15.00 | 8.00 |
| 71 | Dave Kocourek | 6.00 | 3.25 |
| 72 | Lance Alworth (R) | 175.00 | 95.00 |
| 73 | Ron Mix | 15.00 | 8.00 |
| 74 | Charles McNeil (R) | 8.00 | 4.25 |
| 75 | Emil Karas | 5.00 | 2.75 |
| 76 | Ernie Ladd | 12.00 | 6.50 |
| 77 | Earl Faison | 6.50 | 3.50 |
| 78 | Jim Stinnette | 5.00 | 2.75 |
| 79 | Frank Tripucka | 8.00 | 4.25 |
| 80 | Don Stone | 5.00 | 2.75 |
| 81 | Bob Scarpito | 5.00 | 2.75 |
| 82 | Lionel Taylor | 8.50 | 4.50 |
| 83 | Jerry Tarr | 5.00 | 2.75 |
| 84 | Eldon Dananhauer | 5.00 | 2.75 |
| 85 | Goose Gonsoulin | 5.00 | 2.75 |
| 86 | Jim Fraser | 5.00 | 2.75 |
| 87 | Chuck Gavin | 5.00 | 2.75 |
| 88 | Bud McFadin | 12.00 | 5.50 |
| ___ | Checklist | 400.00 | 85.00 |

## 1990 Fleer

Fleer's first regular edition football card set since 1963 contains 400 standard-size cards measuring 2-1/2" by 3-1/2". Card fronts feature full-color action shots inside a white border. A small frame line reflecting the player's team colors separates the border from the photograph. The vertical card backs include a small head shot inside an oval frame along with the player's personal data and stats.

| | | MINT | NR/MT |
|---|---|---|---|
| | Complete Set (400) | 12.00 | 8.00 |
| | Commons | .05 | .03 |
| | | | |
| 1 | Harris Barton | .05 | .03 |
| 2 | Chet Brooks | .05 | .03 |
| 3 | Michael Carter | .05 | .03 |
| 4 | Mike Cofer | .05 | .03 |
| 5 | Roger Craig | .12 | .07 |
| 6 | Kevin Fagan (R) | .08 | .05 |
| 7 | Charles Haley | .08 | .05 |
| 8 | Pierce Holt (R) | .07 | .04 |
| 9 | Ronnie Loft | .12 | .07 |
| 10a | Joe Montana (Er) | 1.00 | .70 |
| | (Wrong stats on back) | | |
| 10b | Joe Montana (Cor) | .75 | .45 |
| 11 | Bubba Paris | .05 | .03 |
| 12 | Tom Rathman | .10 | .06 |
| 13 | Jerry Rice | .80 | .50 |
| 14 | John Taylor | .20 | .12 |
| 15 | Kenna Turner | .05 | .03 |
| 16 | Mike Walter | .05 | .03 |
| 17 | Steve Young | .40 | .25 |
| 18 | Steve Atwater | .08 | .05 |
| 19 | Tyrone Braxton | .05 | .03 |
| 20 | Michael Brooks (R) | .08 | .05 |
| 21 | John Elway | .20 | .12 |
| 22 | Simon Fletcher | .05 | .03 |
| 23 | Bobby Humphrey | .15 | .10 |
| 24 | Mark Jackson | .05 | .03 |
| 25 | Vance Johnson | .05 | .03 |
| 26 | Greg Kragen | .05 | .03 |
| 27 | Ken Lanier (R) | .07 | .04 |
| 28 | Karl Mecklenburg | .08 | .05 |
| 29 | Orson Mobley (R) | .08 | .05 |
| 30 | Steve Sewell | .05 | .03 |
| 31 | Dennis Smith | .05 | .03 |
| 32 | David Treadwell | .05 | .03 |
| 33 | Flipper Anderson | .10 | .06 |
| 34 | Greg Bell | .07 | .04 |
| 35 | Henry Ellard | .08 | .05 |
| 36 | Jim Everett | .15 | .10 |
| 37 | Jerry Gray | .05 | .03 |
| 38 | Kevin Green | .07 | .04 |
| 39 | Pete Holohan | .05 | .03 |
| 40 | LeRoy Irvin | .05 | .03 |
| 41 | Mike Lansford | .05 | .03 |
| 42 | Buford McGee (R) | .15 | .10 |
| 43 | Tom Newberry | .05 | .03 |
| 44 | Vince Newsome (R) | .08 | .05 |
| 45 | Jackie Slater | .07 | .04 |
| 46 | Mike Wilcher | .05 | .03 |

| # | Player | | |
|---|---|---|---|
| 47 | Matt Bahr | .05 | .03 |
| 48 | Brian Brennan | .05 | .03 |
| 49 | Thane Gash (R) | .10 | .06 |
| 50 | Mike Johnson | .05 | .03 |
| 51 | Bernie Kosar | .05 | .03 |
| 52 | Reggie Langhorne | .05 | .03 |
| 53 | Tim Manoa (R) | .07 | .04 |
| 54 | Clay Matthews | .05 | .03 |
| 55 | Eric Metcalf | .15 | .10 |
| 56 | Frank Minnifield | .05 | .03 |
| 57 | Gregg Rakoczy (R) | .07 | .04 |
| 58 | Webster Slaughter | .08 | .05 |
| 59 | Bryan Wagner | .05 | .03 |
| 60 | Felix Wright | .05 | .03 |
| 61 | Raul Allegre | .05 | .03 |
| 62 | Ottis Anderson | .08 | .05 |
| 63 | Carl Banks | .07 | .04 |
| 64 | Mark Bavaro | .07 | .04 |
| 65 | Maurice Carthon | .07 | .04 |
| 66 | Mark Collins | .07 | .04 |
| 67 | Jeff Hostetler (R) | .50 | .30 |
| 68 | Erik Howard | .05 | .03 |
| 69 | Pepper Johnson | .07 | .04 |
| 70 | Sean Landeta | .05 | .03 |
| 71 | Lionel Manuel | .07 | .04 |
| 72 | Leonard Marshall | .07 | .04 |
| 73 | Dave Meggett | .12 | .07 |
| 74 | Bart Oates | .05 | .03 |
| 75 | Doug Riesenberg (R) | .05 | .03 |
| 76 | Phil Simms | .15 | .10 |
| 77 | Lawrence Taylor | .20 | .12 |
| 78 | Eric Allen | .05 | .03 |
| 79 | Jerome Brown | .07 | .04 |
| 80 | Keith Byars | .08 | .05 |
| 81 | Cris Carter | .20 | .12 |
| 82a | Randall Cunningham | .25 | .15 |
| 82b | Byron Evans (R)(Er) | .15 | .10 |
| | (Wrong card number) | | |
| 83a | Byron Evans (Cor) | .08 | .05 |
| 83b | Ron Heller (R)(Er) | .15 | .10 |
| | (Wrong card number) | | |
| 84 | Ron Heller (Cor) | .08 | .05 |
| 85 | Terry Hoage (R) | .08 | .05 |
| 86 | Keith Jackson | .20 | .12 |
| 87 | Seth Joyner | .05 | .03 |
| 88 | Mike Quick | .07 | .04 |
| 89 | Mike Schad (R) | .07 | .04 |
| 90 | Clyde Simmons | .08 | .05 |
| 91 | John Teltschik | .05 | .03 |
| 92 | Anthony Toney | .05 | .03 |
| 93 | Reggie White | .12 | .07 |
| 94 | Ray Berry | .05 | .03 |
| 95 | Joey Browner | .05 | .03 |
| 96 | Anthony Carter | .08 | .05 |
| 97 | Chris Doleman | .08 | .05 |
| 98 | Rick Fenney | .05 | .03 |
| 99 | Rich Gannon (R) | .75 | .45 |
| 100 | Hassan Jones | .08 | .05 |
| 101 | Steve Jordan | .05 | .03 |
| 102 | Rich Karlis | .05 | .03 |
| 103 | Andre Ware (R) | .20 | .12 |
| 104 | Kirk Lowdermilk | .05 | .03 |
| 105 | Keith Millard | .07 | .04 |
| 106 | Scott Studwell | .05 | .03 |
| 107 | Herschel Walker | .15 | .10 |
| 108 | Wade Wilson | .10 | .06 |
| 109 | Gary Zimmerman | .05 | .03 |
| 110 | Don Beebe | .08 | .05 |
| 111 | Cornelius Bennett | .10 | .06 |
| 112 | Shane Conlan | .08 | .05 |
| 113 | Jim Kelly | .50 | .30 |
| 114 | Scott Norwood | .05 | .03 |
| 115 | Mark Kelso | .05 | .03 |
| 116 | Larry Kinnebrew | .05 | .03 |
| 117 | Pete Metzelaars | .05 | .03 |
| 118 | Scott Radecic | .05 | .03 |
| 119 | Andre Reed | .20 | .12 |
| 120 | Jim Ritcher (R) | .08 | .05 |
| 121 | Bruce Smith | .12 | .07 |
| 122 | Leonard Smith | .05 | .03 |
| 123 | Art Still | .05 | .03 |
| 124 | Thurman Thomas | .75 | .45 |
| 125 | Steve Brown | .05 | .03 |
| 126 | Ray Childress | .07 | .04 |
| 127 | Ernest Givins | .20 | .12 |
| 128 | John Grimsley | .05 | .03 |
| 129 | Alonzo Highsmith | .05 | .03 |
| 130 | Drew Hill | .08 | .05 |
| 131 | Bruce Matthews | .05 | .03 |
| 132 | Johnny Meads | .05 | .03 |
| 133 | Warren Moon | .25 | .15 |
| 134 | Mike Munchak | .05 | .03 |
| 135 | Mike Rozier | .05 | .03 |
| 136 | Dean Steinkuhler | .05 | .03 |
| 137 | Lorenzo White (R) | .25 | .15 |
| 138 | Tony Zendejas | .05 | .03 |
| 139 | Gary Anderson | .05 | .03 |
| 140 | Bubby Brister | .15 | .10 |
| 141 | Thomas Everett (R) | .08 | .05 |
| 142 | Derek Hill (R) | .07 | .04 |
| 143 | Merril Hoge | .07 | .04 |
| 144 | Tim Johnson | .05 | .03 |
| 145 | Louis Lipps | .08 | .05 |
| 146 | David Little | .05 | .03 |
| 147 | Greg Lloyd | .07 | .04 |
| 148 | Mike Mularkey (R) | .07 | .04 |
| 149 | John Rienstra (R) | .07 | .04 |
| 150 | Gerald Williams (R) | .07 | .04 |
| 151 | Keith Willis | .05 | .03 |
| 152 | Rod Woodson | .10 | .06 |
| 153 | Tim Worley | .07 | .04 |
| 154 | Gary Clark | .20 | .12 |
| 155 | Darryl Grant | .07 | .04 |
| 156 | Darrell Green | .15 | .10 |

| | | | |
|---|---|---|---|
| 157 Joe Jacoby | .07 | .04 |
| 158 Jim Lachey | .08 | .05 |
| 159 Chip Lohmiller | .05 | .03 |
| 160 Charles Mann | .05 | .03 |
| 161 Wilber Marshall | .07 | .04 |
| 162 Mark May | .05 | .03 |
| 163 Ralf Mojsiejenko | .05 | .03 |
| 164 Art Monk | .25 | .15 |
| 165 Gerald Riggs | .07 | .04 |
| 166 Mark Rypien | .40 | .25 |
| 167 Ricky Sanders | .10 | .06 |
| 168 Don Warren | .07 | .04 |
| 169 Robert Brown (R) | .05 | .03 |
| 170 Blair Bush | .05 | .03 |
| 171 Brent Fullwood | .05 | .03 |
| 172 Tim Harris | .07 | .04 |
| 173 Chris Jacke | .05 | .03 |
| 174 Perry Kemp | .05 | .03 |
| 175 Don Majkowski | .10 | .06 |
| 176 Tony Mandarich | .07 | .04 |
| 177 Mark Murphy | .05 | .03 |
| 178 Brian Noble | .05 | .03 |
| 179 Ken Ruettgers | .05 | .03 |
| 180 Sterling Sharpe | .50 | .30 |
| 181 Ed West (R) | .07 | .04 |
| 182 Keith Woodside | .05 | .03 |
| 183 Morten Anderson | .07 | .04 |
| 184 Stan Brock | .05 | .03 |
| 185 Jim Dombrowski (R) | .07 | .04 |
| 186 John Fourcade (R) | .07 | .04 |
| 187 Bobby Hebert | .15 | .10 |
| 188 Craig Heyward | .07 | .04 |
| 189 Dalton Hilliard | .08 | .05 |
| 190 Rickey Jackson | .08 | .05 |
| 191 Buford Jordan (R) | .07 | .04 |
| 192 Eric Martin | .07 | .04 |
| 193 Robert Massey | .05 | .03 |
| 194 Sam Mills | .08 | .05 |
| 195 Pat Swilling | .12 | .07 |
| 196 Jim Wilks | .05 | .03 |
| 197 John Alt (R) | .05 | .03 |
| 198 Walker Lee Ashley | .05 | .03 |
| 199 Steve DeBerg | .10 | .06 |
| 200 Leonard Griffin (R) | .08 | .05 |
| 201 Albert Lewis | .07 | .04 |
| 202 Nick Lowery | .07 | .04 |
| 203 Bill Maas | .05 | .03 |
| 204 Pete Mandley | .05 | .03 |
| 205 Chris Martin (R) | .07 | .04 |
| 206 Christian Okoye | .15 | .10 |
| 207 Stephone Paige | .07 | .04 |
| 208 Kevin Porter (R) | .07 | .04 |
| 209 Derrick Thomas | .35 | .20 |
| 210 Lewis Billups | .05 | .03 |
| 211 James Brooks | .07 | .04 |
| 212 Jason Buck | .05 | .03 |
| 213 Rickey Dixon (R) | .12 | .07 |
| 214 Boomer Esiason | .15 | .10 |
| 215 David Fulcher | .05 | .03 |
| 216 Rodney Holman | .07 | .04 |
| 217 Lee Johnson | .05 | .03 |
| 218 Tim Krumrie | .05 | .03 |
| 219 Tim McGee | .08 | .05 |
| 220 Anthony Munoz | .08 | .05 |
| 221 Bruce Reimers (R) | .07 | .04 |
| 222 Leon White | .05 | .03 |
| 223 Ickey Woods | .07 | .04 |
| 224 Harvey Armstrong (R) | .07 | .04 |
| 225 Michael Ball (R) | .07 | .04 |
| 226 Chip Banks | .07 | .04 |
| 227 Pat Beach | .05 | .03 |
| 228 Duane Bickett | .05 | .03 |
| 229 Bill Brooks | .05 | .03 |
| 230 Jon Hand | .05 | .03 |
| 231 Andre Rison | .25 | .15 |
| 232 Rohn Stark | .05 | .03 |
| 233 Donnell Thompson | .05 | .03 |
| 234 Jack Trudeau | .08 | .05 |
| 235 Clarence Verdin | .08 | .05 |
| 236 Mark Clayton | .12 | .07 |
| 237 Jeff Cross | .05 | .03 |
| 238 Jeff Dellenbach (R) | .07 | .04 |
| 239 Mark Duper | .10 | .06 |
| 240 Ferrell Edmunds | .07 | .04 |
| 241 Hugh Green | .05 | .03 |
| 242 E.J. Junior | .05 | .03 |
| 243 Marc Logan | .05 | .03 |
| 244 Dan Marino | .40 | .25 |
| 245 John Offerdahl | .08 | .05 |
| 246 Reggie Roby | .05 | .03 |
| 247 Sammie Smith | .08 | .05 |
| 248 Pete Stoyanovich | .05 | .03 |
| 249 Marcus Allen | .10 | .06 |
| 250 Eddie Anderson (R) | .07 | .04 |
| 251 Steve Beuerlein | .12 | .07 |
| 252 Mike Dyal (R) | .07 | .04 |
| 253 Mervyn Fernandez | .10 | .06 |
| 254 Bob Golic | .05 | .03 |
| 255 Mike Harden | .05 | .03 |
| 256 Bo Jackson | .25 | .15 |
| 257 Howie Long | .07 | .04 |
| 258 Don Mosbar | .05 | .03 |
| 259 Jay Schroeder | .10 | .06 |
| 260 Steve Smith | .07 | .04 |
| 261 Greg Townsend | .08 | .05 |
| 262 Lionel Washington | .05 | .03 |
| 263 Brian Blades | .08 | .05 |
| 264 Jeff Bryant | .05 | .03 |
| 265 Grant Feasell (R) | .07 | .04 |
| 266 Jacob Green | .05 | .03 |
| 267 James Jefferson | .05 | .03 |
| 268 Norm Johnson | .05 | .03 |
| 269 Dave Krieg | .12 | .07 |
| 270 Travis McNeal (R) | .07 | .04 |

| 271 | Joe Nash | .05 | .03 |
| 272 | Rufus Porter | .05 | .03 |
| 273 | Kelly Stouffer | .12 | .07 |
| 274 | John L. Williams | .08 | .05 |
| 275 | Jim Arnold | .05 | .03 |
| 276 | Jerry Ball | .05 | .03 |
| 277 | Bennie Blades | .07 | .04 |
| 278 | Lomas Brown | .05 | .03 |
| 279 | Michael Cofer | .05 | .03 |
| 280 | Bob Gagliano | .07 | .04 |
| 281 | Richard Johnson | .07 | .04 |
| 282 | Eddie Murray | .05 | .03 |
| 283 | Rodney Peete | .20 | .12 |
| 284 | Barry Sanders | 1.00 | .70 |
| 285 | Eric Sanders (R) | .07 | .04 |
| 286 | Chris Spielman | .08 | .05 |
| 287 | Eric Williams (R) | .07 | .04 |
| 288 | Neal Anderson | .20 | .12 |
| 289A | Kevin Butler (Er) | .05 | .03 |
| | (Punter front & back) | .35 | .20 |
| 289B | Kevin Butler (Er) | .50 | .30 |
| | (Punter on front) | | |
| 289C | Kevin Butler | .50 | .30 |
| | (Punter on back) | | |
| 289D | Kevin Butler (Cor) | .05 | .03 |
| 290 | Jim Covert | .05 | .03 |
| 291 | Richard Dent | .07 | .04 |
| 292 | Dennis Gentry | .05 | .03 |
| 293 | Jim Harbaugh (R) | .30 | .18 |
| 294 | Jay Hilgenberg | .05 | .03 |
| 295 | Vestee Jackson | .05 | .03 |
| 296 | Steve McMichael | .07 | .04 |
| 297 | Ron Morris | .05 | .03 |
| 298 | Brad Muster | .10 | .06 |
| 299 | Mike Singletary | .12 | .07 |
| 300 | James Thornton | .05 | .03 |
| 301 | Mike Tomczak | .08 | .05 |
| 302 | Keith Van Horne | .05 | .03 |
| 303 | Chris Bahr | .05 | .03 |
| 304 | Martin Bayless (R) | .05 | .03 |
| 305 | Marion Butts | .15 | .10 |
| 306 | Gill Byrd | .05 | .03 |
| 307 | Arthur Cox | .05 | .03 |
| 308 | Burt Grossman | .05 | .03 |
| 309 | Jamie Holland | .05 | .03 |
| 310 | Jim McMahon | .12 | .07 |
| 311 | Anthony Miller | .25 | .15 |
| 312 | Leslie O'Neal | .05 | .03 |
| 313 | Billy Ray Smith | .05 | .03 |
| 314 | Tim Spencer | .05 | .03 |
| 315 | Broderick Thompson (R) | .12 | .07 |
| 316 | Lee Williams | .05 | .03 |
| 317 | Bruce Armstrong | .05 | .03 |
| 318 | Tim Goad (R) | .07 | .04 |
| 319 | Steve Grogan | .07 | .04 |
| 320 | Roland James | .05 | .03 |
| 321 | Cedric Jones | .05 | .03 |
| 322 | Fred Marion | .05 | .03 |
| 323 | Stanley Morgan | .07 | .04 |
| 324 | Robert Perryman | .05 | .03 |
| 325 | Johnny Rembert | .05 | .03 |
| 326 | Ed Reynolds | .05 | .03 |
| 327 | Kenneth Sims | .05 | .03 |
| 328 | John Stephens | .10 | .06 |
| 329 | Danny Villa (R) | .07 | .04 |
| 330 | Robert Awalt | .05 | .03 |
| 331 | Anthony Bell | .05 | .03 |
| 332 | Rich Camarillo | .05 | .03 |
| 333 | Earl Ferrell | .05 | .03 |
| 334 | Roy Green | .07 | .04 |
| 335 | Gary Hogeboom | .05 | .03 |
| 336 | Cedric Mack | .05 | .03 |
| 337 | Freddie Joe Nunn | .05 | .03 |
| 338 | Luis Sharpe | .05 | .03 |
| 339 | Vai Sikahema | .05 | .03 |
| 340 | J.T. Smith | .05 | .03 |
| 341 | Tom Tupa (R) | .12 | .07 |
| 342 | Percy Snow (R) | .12 | .07 |
| 343 | Mark Carrier (WR) | .12 | .07 |
| 344 | Randy Grimes | .05 | .03 |
| 345 | Paul Gruber | .07 | .04 |
| 346 | Ron Hall | .05 | .03 |
| 347 | Jeff George (R) | .80 | .50 |
| 348 | Bruce Hill | .05 | .03 |
| 349 | William Howard (R) | .07 | .04 |
| 350 | Donald Igwebuike | .05 | .03 |
| 351 | Chris Mohr (R) | .07 | .04 |
| 352 | Winston Moss (R) | .07 | .04 |
| 353 | Ricky Reynolds | .05 | .03 |
| 354 | Mark Robinson | .05 | .03 |
| 355 | Lars Tate | .07 | .04 |
| 356 | Vinny Testaverde | .12 | .07 |
| 357 | Broderick Thomas | .15 | .10 |
| 358 | Troy Benson | .05 | .03 |
| 359 | Jeff Criswell (R) | .07 | .04 |
| 360 | Tony Eason | .08 | .05 |
| 361 | James Hasty | .05 | .03 |
| 362 | Johnny Hector | .08 | .05 |
| 363 | Bobby Humphery | .05 | .03 |
| 364 | Pat Leahy | .05 | .03 |
| 365 | Erik McMillan | .07 | .04 |
| 366 | Freeman McNeil | .08 | .05 |
| 367 | Ken O'Brien | .10 | .06 |
| 368 | Ron Stallworth | .05 | .03 |
| 369 | Al Toon | .08 | .05 |
| 370 | Blair Thomas (R) | .35 | .20 |
| 371 | Aundray Bruce | .07 | .04 |
| 372 | Tony Casillas | .08 | .05 |
| 373 | Shawn Collins | .07 | .04 |
| 374 | Evan Cooper | .05 | .03 |
| 375 | Bill Fralic | .05 | .03 |
| 376 | Scott Funhage | .05 | .03 |
| 377 | Mike Gann | .05 | .03 |

| | | | |
|---|---|---|---|
| 378 | Ron Heller | .05 | .03 |
| 379 | Keith Jones | .05 | .03 |
| 380 | Mike Kenn | .07 | .04 |
| 381 | Chris Miller | .40 | .25 |
| 382 | Deion Sanders | .40 | .25 |
| 383 | John Settle | .05 | .03 |
| 384 | Troy Aikman | 1.50 | .90 |
| 385 | Bill Bates | .05 | .03 |
| 386 | Willie Broughton | .05 | .03 |
| 387 | Steve Folsom | .05 | .03 |
| 388 | Ray Horton | .05 | .03 |
| 389 | Michael Irvin | .60 | .35 |
| 390 | Jim Jeffcoat | .05 | .03 |
| 391 | Eugene Lockhart | .05 | .03 |
| 392 | Kelvin Martin (R) | .15 | .10 |
| 393 | Nate Newton | .05 | .03 |
| 394 | Mike Saxon | .05 | .03 |
| 395 | Derrick Shepard (R) | .07 | .04 |
| 396 | Steve Walsh | .12 | .07 |
| 397 | Montana/Rice (Super Bowl MVP's) | .25 | .15 |
| 398 | Checklist Card | .05 | .03 |
| 399 | Checklist Card | .05 | .03 |
| 400 | Checklist Card | .05 | .03 |

| | | MINT | NR/MT |
|---|---|---|---|
| **Complete Set (25)** | | 14.00 | 9.50 |
| **Commons** | | .25 | .15 |
| 1 | Joe Montana | 3.50 | 2.50 |
| 2 | Jerry Rice | 2.50 | 1.50 |
| 3 | Keith Jackson | .80 | .50 |
| 4 | Barry Sanders | 4.00 | 3.00 |
| 5 | Christian Okoye | .50 | .30 |
| 6 | Tom Newberry | .25 | .15 |
| 7 | Jim Covert | .25 | .15 |
| 8 | Anthony Munoz | .40 | .25 |
| 9 | Mike Munchak | .25 | .15 |
| 10 | Jay Hilgenberg | .25 | .15 |
| 11 | Chris Doleman | .40 | .25 |
| 12 | Keith Millard | .30 | .18 |
| 13 | Derrick Thomas | 1.25 | .80 |
| 14 | Lawrence Taylor | 1.50 | .90 |
| 15 | Karl Mecklenburg | .30 | .18 |
| 16 | Reggie White | .50 | .30 |
| 17 | Tim Harris | .30 | .18 |
| 18 | David Fulcher | .25 | .15 |
| 19 | Ronnie Lott | 1.25 | .80 |
| 20 | Eric Allen | .25 | .15 |
| 21 | Steve Atwater | .30 | .18 |
| 22 | Rich Camarillo | .25 | .15 |
| 23 | Morten Andersen | .30 | .18 |
| 24 | Andre Reed | 1.00 | .70 |
| 25 | Rod Woodson | .50 | .30 |

# 1990 Fleer All-Pro

These limited insert cards were randomly placed in 1990 Fleer Poly Packs. Card fronts are silver and contain two photographs including a large head shot and a smaller action figure. Card backs are vertical and feature career highlights written in paragraph form. Cards measure 2-1/2" by 3-1/2".

# 1990 Fleer Update

This 120-card set marks Fleer's first post-season football card set. The cards, which measure 2-1/2" by 3-1/2", are designed exactly like Fleer's regular 1992 edition. The numbers on the card backs are preceeded by the letter "U" for Update set.

|  |  | MINT | NR/MT |
|---|---|---|---|
| | **Complete Set (120)** | 36.00 | 24.00 |
| | **Commons** | .05 | .03 |
| 1 | Albert Bentley | .07 | .04 |
| 2 | Dean Biasucci | .05 | .03 |
| 3 | Ray Donaldson | .05 | .03 |
| 4 | Jeff George | 2.00 | 1.25 |
| 5 | Ray Agnew (R) | .12 | .07 |
| 6 | Greg McMurtry (R) | .50 | .30 |
| 7 | Chris Singleton (R) | .15 | .10 |
| 8 | James Francis (R) | .25 | .15 |
| 9 | Harold Green (R) | 1.50 | .90 |
| 10 | John Elliott (R) | .07 | .04 |
| 11 | Rodney Hampton (R) | 2.75 | 1.75 |
| 12 | Gary Reasons | .05 | .03 |
| 13 | Lewis Tillman | .07 | .04 |
| 14 | Everson Walls | .07 | .04 |
| 15 | David Alexander (R) | .07 | .04 |
| 16 | Jim McMahon | .12 | .07 |
| 17 | Ben Smith (R) | .15 | .10 |
| 18 | Andre Waters | .05 | .03 |
| 19 | Calvin Williams (R) | .60 | .35 |
| 20 | Earnest Byner | .10 | .06 |
| 21 | Andre Collin (R) | .20 | .12 |
| 22 | Russ Grimm | .07 | .04 |
| 23 | Stan Humphries (R) | 3.50 | 2.50 |
| 24 | Martin Mayhew (R) | .15 | .10 |
| 25 | Barry Foster (R) | 7.50 | 4.50 |
| 26 | Eric Green (R) | .80 | .50 |
| 27 | Tunch Ilkin | .05 | .03 |
| 28 | Hardy Nickerson | .05 | .03 |
| 29 | Jerrol Williams | .05 | .03 |
| 30 | Mike Baab | .05 | .03 |
| 31 | Leroy Hoard (R) | .50 | .30 |
| 32 | Eddie Johnson (R) | .07 | .04 |
| 33 | William Fuller | .07 | .04 |
| 34 | Haywood Jeffires (R) | 5.00 | 3.00 |
| 35 | Don Maggs (R) | .07 | .04 |
| 36 | Allen Pinkett | .07 | .04 |
| 37 | Robert Awalt | .05 | .03 |
| 38 | Dennis McKinnon | .05 | .03 |
| 39 | Ken Norton (R) | .40 | .25 |
| 40 | Emmitt Smith (R) | 25.00 | 18.00 |
| 41 | Alexander Wright (R) | .50 | .30 |
| 42 | Eric Hill | .07 | .04 |
| 43 | Johnny Johnson (R) | 1.25 | .80 |
| 44 | Timm Rosenbach | .12 | .07 |
| 45 | Anthony Thompson (R) | .50 | .30 |
| 46 | Dexter Carter (R) | .50 | .30 |
| 47 | Eric Davis (R) | .10 | .06 |
| 48 | Keith DeLong | .05 | .03 |
| 49 | Brent Jones (R) | .50 | .30 |
| 50 | Darryl Pollard (R) | .10 | .06 |
| 51 | Steve Wallace (R) | .08 | .05 |
| 52 | Bern Brostek (R) | .08 | .05 |
| 53 | Aaron Cox | .07 | .04 |
| 54 | Cleveland Garry | .50 | .30 |
| 55 | Fred Strickland (R) | .10 | .06 |
| 56 | Pat Terrell (R) | .12 | .07 |
| 57 | Steve Broussard (R) | .25 | .15 |
| 58 | Scott Case | .05 | .03 |
| 59 | Brian Jordan (R) | .80 | .50 |
| 60 | Andre Rison | .75 | .45 |
| 61 | Kevin Haverdink (R) | .08 | .05 |
| 62 | Rueben Mayes | .05 | .03 |
| 63 | Steve Walsh | .12 | .07 |
| 64 | Greg Bell | .07 | .04 |
| 65 | Tim Brown | .15 | .10 |
| 66 | Willie Gault | .08 | .05 |
| 67 | Vance Mueller (R) | .12 | .07 |
| 68 | Bill Pickel | .05 | .03 |
| 69 | Aaron Wallace (R) | .50 | .30 |
| 70 | Glenn Parker (R) | .08 | .05 |
| 71 | Frank Reich | .10 | .06 |
| 72 | Leon Seals (R) | .12 | .07 |
| 73 | Darryl talley | .12 | .07 |
| 74 | Brad Baxter (R) | .75 | .45 |
| 75 | Jeff Criswell | .05 | .03 |
| 76 | Jeff Lageman | .10 | .06 |
| 77 | Rob Moore (R) | 2.00 | 1.25 |
| 78 | Blair Thomas | 1.25 | .80 |
| 79 | Louis Oliver | .12 | .07 |
| 80 | Tony Paige | .07 | .04 |
| 81 | Richmond Webb (R) | .35 | .20 |
| 82 | Robert Blackmon (R) | .12 | .07 |
| 83 | Derrick Fenner (R) | .50 | .30 |
| 84 | Andy Heck | .05 | .03 |
| 85 | Cortez Kennedy (R) | 1.50 | .90 |
| 86 | Terry Wooden (R) | .12 | .07 |
| 87 | Jeff Donaldson | .05 | .03 |
| 88 | Tim Grunhard (R) | .10 | .06 |
| 89 | Emile Harry (R) | .10 | .06 |
| 90 | Dan Saleaumua | .08 | .05 |
| 91 | Percy Snow | .12 | .07 |
| 92 | Andre Ware | .30 | .18 |
| 93 | Darrell Fullington (R) | .07 | .04 |
| 94 | Mike Merriweather | .05 | .03 |
| 95 | Henry Thomas | .05 | .03 |
| 96 | Robert Brown | .05 | .03 |
| 97 | LeRoy Butler (R) | .15 | .10 |
| 98 | Anthony Dilweg | .10 | .06 |
| 99 | Darrell Thompson (R) | .40 | .25 |
| 100 | Keith Woodside | .07 | .04 |
| 101 | Gary Plummer | .07 | .04 |
| 102 | Junior Seau (R) | .80 | .50 |
| 103 | Billy Joe Tolliver | .15 | .10 |
| 104 | Mark Vlasic | .10 | .06 |
| 105 | Gary Anderson | .07 | .04 |
| 106 | Ian Beckles (R) | .07 | .04 |
| 107 | Reggie Cobb (R) | 1.50 | .90 |
| 108 | Keith McCants (R) | .40 | .25 |

| 109 | Mark Bortz (R) | .10 | .06 |
| 110 | Maury Buford | .05 | .03 |
| 111 | Mark Carrier (R)(Chi) | .50 | .30 |
| 112 | Dan Hampton | .12 | .07 |
| 113 | William Perry | .10 | .06 |
| 114 | Ron Rivera | .05 | .03 |
| 115 | Lemuel Stinson | .08 | .05 |
| 116 | Melvin Bratton (R) | .10 | .06 |
| 117 | Gary Kubiak (R) | .10 | .06 |
| 118 | Alton Montgomery (R) | .10 | .06 |
| 119 | Ricky Nattiel | .08 | .05 |
| 120 | Checklist | .05 | .03 |

# 1991 Fleer

This 432-card set features full color action photos on the card fronts surrounded by a green border. Card backs contain a full color photo on the top half and the player's stats on the bottom half. Cards measure 2-1/2" by 3-1/2". Key subsets included League Leaders (LL) (408-419), Hitters (H) (396-407) and Rookies (R) (420-428). The set also includes 10 Pro-Vision Insert Cards created by artist Terry Smith which were randomly distributed in Fleer football packs. Those inserts are listed at the end of this checklist but are not included in the complete set price below.

| | | MINT | NR/MT |
| --- | --- | --- | --- |
| Complete Set (432) | | 10.00 | 6.50 |
| Commons | | .05 | .02 |
| 1 | Shane Conlan | .07 | .04 |

| 2 | John Davis (R) | .08 | .05 |
| 3 | Kent Hull | .05 | .02 |
| 4 | James Lofton | .15 | .10 |
| 5 | Keith McKeller | .05 | .02 |
| 6 | Scott Norwood | .05 | .02 |
| 7 | Nate Odomes | .05 | .02 |
| 8 | Andre Reed | .12 | .07 |
| 9 | Jim Ritcher | .05 | .02 |
| 10 | Leon Seals | .05 | .02 |
| 11 | Bruce Smith | .12 | .07 |
| 12 | Leonard Smith | .05 | .02 |
| 13 | Steve Tasker | .05 | .02 |
| 14 | Thurman Thomas | .40 | .25 |
| 15 | Lewis Billups | .05 | .02 |
| 16 | James Brooks | .07 | .04 |
| 17 | Eddie Brown | .07 | .04 |
| 18 | Carl Carter (R) | .05 | .02 |
| 19 | Boomer Esiason | .12 | .07 |
| 20 | James Francis | .08 | .05 |
| 21 | David Fulcher | .05 | .02 |
| 22 | Harold Green | .20 | .12 |
| 23 | Rodney Holman | .07 | .04 |
| 24 | Bruce Kozerski | .05 | .02 |
| 25 | Tim McGee | .07 | .04 |
| 26 | Anthony Munoz | .08 | .05 |
| 27 | Bruce Reimers | .05 | .02 |
| 28 | Ickey Woods | .05 | .02 |
| 29 | Carl Zander | .05 | .02 |
| 30 | Mike Baab | .05 | .02 |
| 31 | Brian Brennan | .05 | .02 |
| 32 | Rob Burnett (R) | .07 | .04 |
| 33 | Paul Farren | .05 | .02 |
| 34 | Thane Gash | .05 | .02 |
| 35 | David Grayson | .05 | .02 |
| 36 | Mike Johnson | .05 | .02 |
| 37 | Reggie Langhorne | .05 | .02 |
| 38 | Kevin Mack | .07 | .04 |
| 39 | Eric Metcalf | .12 | .07 |
| 40 | Frank Minnifield | .05 | .02 |
| 41 | Gregg Rakoczy | .05 | .02 |
| 42 | Felix Wright | .05 | .02 |
| 43 | Steve Atwater | .08 | .05 |
| 44 | Michael Brooks | .05 | .02 |
| 45 | John Elway | .15 | .10 |
| 46 | Simon Fletcher | .05 | .02 |
| 47 | Bobby Humphrey | .12 | .07 |
| 48 | Mark Jackson | .07 | .04 |
| 49 | Keith Kartz (R) | .07 | .04 |
| 50 | Clarence Kay | .05 | .02 |
| 51 | Greg Kragen | .05 | .02 |
| 52 | Karl Mecklenburg | .07 | .04 |
| 53 | Warren Powers | .05 | .02 |
| 54 | Dennis Smith | .05 | .02 |
| 55 | Jim Szymanski (R) | .07 | .04 |
| 56 | David Treadwell | .05 | .02 |
| 57 | Michael Young | .05 | .02 |
| 58 | Ray Childress | .07 | .04 |

| # | Player | | |
|---|--------|---|---|
| 59 | Curtis Duncan | .07 | .04 |
| 60 | William Fuller | .07 | .04 |
| 61 | Ernest Givins | .12 | .07 |
| 62 | Drew Hill | .08 | .05 |
| 63 | Haywood Jeffires | .15 | .10 |
| 64 | Richard Johnson | .05 | .02 |
| 65 | Sean Jones | .05 | .02 |
| 66 | Don Maggs | .05 | .02 |
| 67 | Bruce Matthews | .05 | .02 |
| 68 | Johnny Meads | .05 | .02 |
| 69 | Greg Montgomery | .05 | .02 |
| 70 | Warren Moon | .20 | .12 |
| 71 | Mike Munchak | .05 | .02 |
| 72 | Allen Pinkett | .07 | .04 |
| 73 | Lorenzo White | .20 | .12 |
| 74 | Pat Beach | .05 | .02 |
| 75 | Albert Bentley | .05 | .02 |
| 76 | Dean Biasucci | .05 | .02 |
| 77 | Duane Bickett | .05 | .02 |
| 78 | Bill Brooks | .05 | .02 |
| 79 | Sam Clancy | .05 | .02 |
| 80 | Ray Donaldson | .05 | .02 |
| 81 | Jeff George | .25 | .15 |
| 82 | Alan Grant (R) | .05 | .02 |
| 83 | Jessie Hester | .05 | .02 |
| 84 | Jeff Herrod | .05 | .02 |
| 85 | Rohn Stark | .05 | .02 |
| 86 | Jack Trudeau | .07 | .04 |
| 87 | Clarence Verdin | .08 | .05 |
| 88 | John Alt | .05 | .02 |
| 89 | Steve DeBerg | .10 | .06 |
| 90 | Tim Grunhard | .05 | .02 |
| 91 | Dino Hackett | .05 | .02 |
| 92 | Jonathan Hayes | .05 | .02 |
| 93 | Albert Lewis | .05 | .02 |
| 94 | Nick Lowery | .07 | .04 |
| 95 | Bill Maas | .05 | .02 |
| 96 | Christian Okoye | .10 | .06 |
| 97 | Stephone Paige | .08 | .05 |
| 98 | Kevin Porter | .05 | .02 |
| 99 | David Szott (R) | .07 | .04 |
| 100 | Derrick Thomas | .20 | .12 |
| 101 | Barry Word | .20 | .12 |
| 102 | Marcus Allen | .10 | .06 |
| 103 | Tom Benson | .05 | .02 |
| 104 | Tim Brown | .10 | .06 |
| 105 | Riki Eillison | .05 | .02 |
| 106 | Mervyn Fernandez | .08 | .05 |
| 107 | Willie Gault | .07 | .04 |
| 108 | Bob Golic | .05 | .02 |
| 109 | Ethan Horton | .07 | .04 |
| 110 | Bo Jackson | .25 | .15 |
| 111 | Howie Long | .07 | .04 |
| 112 | Don Mosebar | .05 | .02 |
| 113 | Jerry Robinson | .05 | .02 |
| 114 | Jay Schroeder | .10 | .06 |
| 115 | Steve Smith | .07 | .04 |
| 116 | Greg Townsend | .07 | .04 |
| 117 | Steve Wisniewski | .05 | .02 |
| 118 | Mark Clayton | .10 | .06 |
| 119 | Mark Duper | .07 | .04 |
| 120 | Ferrell Edmunds | .05 | .02 |
| 121 | Hugh Green | .05 | .02 |
| 122 | David Griggs | .05 | .02 |
| 123 | Jim Jensen | .05 | .02 |
| 124 | Dan Marino | .35 | .20 |
| 125 | Tim McKyer | .05 | .02 |
| 126 | John Offerdahl | .07 | .04 |
| 127 | Louis Oliver | .07 | .04 |
| 128 | Tony Paige | .05 | .02 |
| 129 | Reggie Roby | .05 | .02 |
| 130 | Keith Sims | .05 | .02 |
| 131 | Sammie Smith | .08 | .05 |
| 132 | Pete Stoyanovich | .05 | .02 |
| 133 | Richmond Webb | .07 | .04 |
| 134 | Bruce Armstrong | .05 | .02 |
| 135 | Vincent Brown | .05 | .02 |
| 136 | Hart Lee Dykes | .07 | .04 |
| 137 | Irvin Fryar | .07 | .04 |
| 138 | Tim Goad | .05 | .02 |
| 139 | Tommy Hodson | .10 | .06 |
| 140 | Maurice Hurst | .05 | .02 |
| 141 | Ronnie Lippett | .05 | .02 |
| 142 | Greg McMurtry | .08 | .05 |
| 143 | Ed Reynolds | .05 | .02 |
| 144 | John Stephens | .07 | .04 |
| 145 | Andre Tippett | .07 | .04 |
| 146 | Danny Villa | .05 | .02 |
| 147 | Brad Baxter | .20 | .12 |
| 148 | Kyle Clifton | .05 | .02 |
| 149 | Jeff Criswell | .05 | .02 |
| 150 | James Hasty | .05 | .02 |
| 151 | Jeff Lageman | .07 | .04 |
| 152 | Pat Leahy | .05 | .02 |
| 153 | Rob Moore | .25 | .15 |
| 154 | Al Toon | .07 | .04 |
| 155 | Gary Anderson | .05 | .02 |
| 156 | Bubby Brister | .15 | .10 |
| 157 | Chris Calloway | .07 | .04 |
| 158 | Donald Evans | .05 | .02 |
| 159 | Eric Green | .15 | .10 |
| 160 | Bryan Hinkle | .05 | .02 |
| 161 | Merril Hoge | .07 | .04 |
| 162 | Tunch Ilkin | .05 | .02 |
| 163 | Louis Lipps | .07 | .04 |
| 164 | David Little | .05 | .02 |
| 165 | Mike Mularkey | .05 | .02 |
| 166 | Gerald Williams | .05 | .02 |
| 167 | Warren Williams | .05 | .02 |
| 168 | Rod Woodson | .10 | .06 |
| 169 | Tim Worley | .08 | .05 |
| 170 | Martin Bayless | .05 | .02 |
| 171 | Marion Butts | .12 | .07 |
| 172 | Gill Byrd | .05 | .02 |

| 173 | Frank Cornish | .05 | .02 |
| 174 | Arthur Cox | .05 | .02 |
| 175 | Burt Grossman | .07 | .04 |
| 176 | Anthony Miller | .12 | .07 |
| 177 | Leslie O'Neal | .07 | .04 |
| 178 | Gary Plummer | .05 | .02 |
| 179 | Junio Seau | .12 | .07 |
| 180 | Billy Joe Tolliver | .07 | .04 |
| 181 | Derrick Walker (R) | .10 | .06 |
| 182 | Lee Williams | .05 | .02 |
| 183 | Robert Blackmon | .05 | .02 |
| 184 | Brian Blades | .07 | .04 |
| 185 | Grant Feasel | .05 | .02 |
| 186 | Derrick Fenner | .12 | .07 |
| 187 | Andy Heck | .05 | .02 |
| 188 | Norm Johnson | .05 | .02 |
| 189 | Tommy Kane | .08 | .05 |
| 190 | Cortez Kennedy | .12 | .07 |
| 191 | Dave Krieg | .12 | .07 |
| 192 | Travis McNeal | .05 | .02 |
| 193 | Eugene Robinson | .05 | .02 |
| 194 | Chris Warren | .07 | .04 |
| 195 | John L. Williams | .08 | .05 |
| 196 | Steve Broussard | .08 | .05 |
| 197 | Scott Case | .05 | .02 |
| 198 | Shawn Collins | .05 | .02 |
| 199 | Darion Conner | .05 | .02 |
| 200 | Tory Epps | .05 | .02 |
| 201 | Bill Fralic | .05 | .02 |
| 202 | Michael Haynes | .35 | .20 |
| 203 | Chris Hinton | .05 | .02 |
| 204 | Keith Jones | .05 | .02 |
| 205 | Brian Jordan | .12 | .07 |
| 206 | Mike Kenn | .05 | .02 |
| 207 | Chris Miller | .25 | .15 |
| 208 | Andre Rison | .20 | .12 |
| 209 | Mike Rozier | .07 | .04 |
| 210 | Deion Sanders | .20 | .12 |
| 211 | Gary Wilkins (R) | .07 | .04 |
| 212 | Neal Anderson | .12 | .07 |
| 213 | Trace Armstrong | .05 | .02 |
| 214 | Mark Bortz | .05 | .02 |
| 215 | Kevin Butler | .05 | .02 |
| 216 | Mark Carrier (Chi) | .08 | .05 |
| 217 | Wendell Davis | .12 | .07 |
| 218 | Richard Dent | .07 | .04 |
| 219 | Dennis Gentry | .05 | .02 |
| 220 | Jim Harbaugh | .15 | .10 |
| 221 | Jay Hilgenberg | .05 | .02 |
| 222 | Steve McMichael | .07 | .04 |
| 223 | Ron Morris | .05 | .02 |
| 224 | Brad Muster | .10 | .06 |
| 225 | Mike Singletary | .08 | .05 |
| 226 | James Thornton | .05 | .02 |
| 227 | Tommie Agee | .05 | .02 |
| 228 | Troy Aikman | .90 | .60 |
| 229 | Jack Del Rio | .05 | .02 |
| 230 | Issiac Holt | .05 | .02 |
| 231 | Ray Horton | .05 | .02 |
| 232 | Jim Jeffcoat | .05 | .02 |
| 233 | Eugene Lockhart | .05 | .02 |
| 234 | Kelvin Martin | .08 | .05 |
| 235 | Nate Newton | .05 | .02 |
| 236 | Mike Saxon | .05 | .02 |
| 237 | Emmitt Smith | 1.50 | .90 |
| 238 | Danny Stubbs | .05 | .02 |
| 239 | Jim Arnold | .05 | .02 |
| 240 | Jerry Ball | .05 | .02 |
| 241 | Bennie Blades | .07 | .04 |
| 242 | Lomas Brown | .05 | .02 |
| 243 | Robert Clark | .05 | .02 |
| 244 | Mike Cofer | .05 | .02 |
| 245 | Mel Gray | .05 | .02 |
| 246 | Rodney Peete | .10 | .06 |
| 247 | Barry Sanders | .80 | .50 |
| 248 | Andre Ware | .10 | .06 |
| 249 | Matt Brock (R) | .07 | .04 |
| 250 | Robert Brown | .05 | .02 |
| 251 | Anthony Dilweg | .07 | .04 |
| 252 | Johnny Holland | .05 | .02 |
| 253 | Tim Harris | .07 | .04 |
| 254 | Chris Jacke | .05 | .02 |
| 255 | Perry Kemp | .05 | .02 |
| 256 | Don Majkowski | .12 | .07 |
| 257 | Tony Mandarich | .05 | .02 |
| 258 | Mark Murphy | .05 | .02 |
| 259 | Brian Noble | .05 | .02 |
| 260 | Jeff Query | .07 | .04 |
| 261 | Sterling Sharpe | .25 | .15 |
| 262 | Ed West | .05 | .02 |
| 263 | Keith Woodside | .05 | .02 |
| 264 | Flipper Anderson | .08 | .05 |
| 265 | Aaron Cox | .05 | .02 |
| 266 | Henry Ellard | .07 | .04 |
| 267 | Jim Everett | .15 | .10 |
| 268 | Cleveland Gary | .10 | .06 |
| 269 | Kevin Greene | .07 | .04 |
| 270 | Pete Holohan | .05 | .02 |
| 271 | Mike Lansford | .05 | .02 |
| 272 | Duval Love (R) | .07 | .04 |
| 273 | Buford McGee | .05 | .02 |
| 274 | Tom Newberry | .05 | .02 |
| 275 | Jackie Slater | .07 | .04 |
| 276 | Frank Stams | .05 | .02 |
| 277 | Alfred Anderson | .05 | .02 |
| 278 | Joey Browner | .07 | .04 |
| 279 | Anthony Carter | .08 | .05 |
| 280 | Chris Doleman | .07 | .04 |
| 281 | Rick Fenney | .05 | .02 |
| 282 | Rich Gannon | .20 | .12 |
| 283 | Hassan Jones | .07 | .04 |
| 284 | Steve Jordan | .05 | .02 |
| 285 | Carl Lee | .05 | .02 |
| 286 | Randall McDaniel | .05 | .02 |

| No. | Player | | |
|---|---|---|---|
| 287 | Keith Millard | .07 | .04 |
| 288 | Herschel Walker | .15 | .10 |
| 289 | Wade Wilson | .08 | .05 |
| 290 | Gary Zimmerman | .05 | .02 |
| 291 | Morten Andersen | .07 | .04 |
| 292 | Jim Dombrowski | .05 | .02 |
| 293 | Gill Fenerty | .05 | .02 |
| 294 | Craig Heyward | .07 | .04 |
| 295 | Dalton Hilliard | .08 | .05 |
| 296 | Rickey Jackson | .07 | .04 |
| 297 | Vaughan Johnson | .07 | .04 |
| 298 | Eric Martin | .08 | .05 |
| 299 | Robert Massey | .05 | .02 |
| 300 | Rueben Mayes | .05 | .02 |
| 301 | Sam Mills | .07 | .04 |
| 302 | Brett Perriman | .05 | .02 |
| 303 | Pat Swilling | .10 | .06 |
| 304 | Steve Walsh | .10 | .06 |
| 305 | Ottis Anderson | .12 | .07 |
| 306 | Matt Bahr | .05 | .02 |
| 307 | Mark Bavaro | .05 | .02 |
| 308 | Maurice Carthon | .05 | .02 |
| 309 | Mark Collins | .05 | .02 |
| 310 | John Elliott | .05 | .02 |
| 311 | Rodney Hampton | .50 | .30 |
| 312 | Jeff Hostetler | .20 | .12 |
| 313 | Erik Howard | .05 | .02 |
| 314 | Pepper Johnson | .05 | .02 |
| 315 | Sean Landeta | .05 | .02 |
| 316 | Dave Meggett | .10 | .06 |
| 317 | Bart Oates | .05 | .02 |
| 318 | Phil Simms | .10 | .06 |
| 319 | Lawrence Taylor | .15 | .10 |
| 320 | Reyna Thompson | .05 | .02 |
| 321 | Everson Walls | .05 | .02 |
| 322 | Eric Allen | .05 | .02 |
| 323 | Fred Barnett | .20 | .12 |
| 324 | Jerome Brown | .07 | .04 |
| 325 | Keith Byars | .07 | .04 |
| 326 | Randall Cunningham | .20 | .12 |
| 327 | Byron Evans | .05 | .02 |
| 328 | Ron Heller | .05 | .02 |
| 329 | Keith Jackson | .10 | .06 |
| 330 | Seth Joyner | .07 | .04 |
| 331 | Heath Sherman | .08 | .05 |
| 332 | Clyde Simmons | .07 | .04 |
| 333 | Ben Smith | .05 | .02 |
| 334 | Anthony Toney | .05 | .02 |
| 335 | Andre Waters | .05 | .02 |
| 336 | Reggie White | .10 | .06 |
| 337 | Calvin Williams | .10 | .06 |
| 338 | Anthony Bell | .05 | .02 |
| 339 | Rich Camarillo | .05 | .02 |
| 340 | Roy Green | .07 | .04 |
| 341 | Tim Jorden (R) | .07 | .04 |
| 342 | Cedric Mack | .05 | .02 |
| 343 | Dexter Manley | .05 | .02 |
| 344 | Freddie Joe Nunn | .05 | .02 |
| 345 | Ricky Proehl | .15 | .10 |
| 346 | Tootie Robbins | .05 | .02 |
| 347 | Timm Rosenbach | .10 | .06 |
| 348 | Luis Sharpe | .05 | .02 |
| 349 | Vai Sikahema | .05 | .02 |
| 350 | Anthony Thompson | .08 | .05 |
| 351 | Lonnie Young | .05 | .02 |
| 352 | Dexter Carter | .08 | .05 |
| 353 | Mike Cofer | .05 | .02 |
| 354 | Kevin Fagan | .05 | .02 |
| 355 | Don Griffin | .05 | .02 |
| 356 | Charles Haley | .08 | .05 |
| 357 | Pierce Holt | .05 | .02 |
| 358 | Brent Jones | .08 | .05 |
| 359 | Guy McIntyre | .05 | .02 |
| 360 | Joe Montana | .50 | .30 |
| 361 | Darryl Pollard | .05 | .02 |
| 362 | Tom Rathman | .08 | .05 |
| 363 | Jerry Rice | .40 | .25 |
| 364 | Bill Romanowski | .05 | .02 |
| 365 | John Taylor | .15 | .10 |
| 366 | Steve Wallace | .05 | .02 |
| 367 | Steve Young | .25 | .15 |
| 368 | Gary Anderson | .05 | .02 |
| 369 | Ian Beckles | .05 | .02 |
| 370 | Mark Carrier (TB) | .10 | .06 |
| 371 | Reggie Cobb | .15 | .10 |
| 372 | Reuben Davis | .05 | .02 |
| 373 | Randy Grimes | .05 | .02 |
| 374 | Wayne Haddix | .05 | .02 |
| 375 | Ron Hall | .05 | .02 |
| 376 | Harry Hamilton | .05 | .02 |
| 377 | Bruce Hill | .05 | .02 |
| 378 | Keith McCants | .08 | .05 |
| 379 | Bruce Perkins (R) | .07 | .04 |
| 380 | Vinny Testaverde | .12 | .07 |
| 381 | Broderick Thomas | .08 | .05 |
| 382 | Jeff Bostic | .05 | .02 |
| 383 | Earnest Byner | .08 | .05 |
| 384 | Gary Clark | .15 | .10 |
| 385 | Darryl Grant | .05 | .02 |
| 386 | Darrell Green | .10 | .06 |
| 387 | Stan Humphries | .35 | .20 |
| 388 | Jim Lachey | .07 | .04 |
| 389 | Charles Mann | .05 | .02 |
| 390 | Wilber Marshall | .07 | .04 |
| 391 | Art Monk | .15 | .10 |
| 392 | Gerald Riggs | .08 | .05 |
| 393 | Mark Rypien | .20 | .12 |
| 394 | Ricky Sanders | .07 | .04 |
| 395 | Don Warren | .05 | .02 |
| 396 | Bruce Smith (H) | .07 | .04 |
| 397 | Reggie White (H) | .08 | .05 |
| 398 | Lawrence Taylor (H) | .10 | .06 |
| 399 | David Fulcher (H) | .05 | .02 |
| 400 | Derrick Thomas (H) | .10 | .06 |

| | | | |
|---|---|---|---|
| 401 | Mark Carrier (H) | .07 | .04 |
| 402 | Mike Singletary (H) | .08 | .05 |
| 403 | Charles Haley (H) | .07 | .04 |
| 404 | Jeff Cross (H) | .05 | .02 |
| 405 | Leslie O'Neal (H) | .05 | .02 |
| 406 | Tim Harris (H) | .05 | .02 |
| 407 | Steve Atwater (H) | .07 | .04 |
| 408 | Joe Montana (LL) | .25 | .15 |
| 409 | Randall Cunningham (LL) | .10 | .06 |
| 410 | Warren Moon (LL) | .10 | .06 |
| 411 | Andre Rison (LL) | .10 | .06 |
| 412 | Haywood Jeffires (LL) | .10 | .06 |
| 413 | Stephone Paige (LL) | .05 | .02 |
| 414 | Phil Simms (LL) | .07 | .04 |
| 415 | Barry Sanders (LL) | .20 | .12 |
| 416 | Bo Jackson (LL) | .15 | .10 |
| 417 | Thurman Thomas (LL) | .20 | .12 |
| 418 | Emmitt Smith (LL) | .75 | .45 |
| 419 | John L. Williams (LL) | .05 | .02 |
| 420 | Nick Bell (R) | .50 | .30 |
| 421 | Eric Bieniemy (R) | .20 | .12 |
| 422 | Mike Dumas (R) | .10 | .06 |
| 423 | Russell Maryland (R) | .30 | .18 |
| 424 | Derek Russell (R) | .20 | .12 |
| 425 | Chris Smith (R) | .08 | .05 |
| 426 | Mike Stonebreaker (R) | .08 | .05 |
| 427 | Patrick Tyrance (R) | .07 | .04 |
| 428 | Kenny Walker (R) | .20 | .12 |
| 429 | Checklist 1 | .05 | .02 |
| 430 | Checklist 2 | .05 | .02 |
| 431 | Checklist 3 | .05 | .02 |
| 432 | Checklist 4 | .05 | .02 |
| PV1 | Joe Montana | 1.25 | .80 |
| PV2 | Barry Sanders | 1.50 | .90 |
| PV3 | Lawrence Taylor | .50 | .30 |
| PV4 | Mike Singletary | .30 | .18 |
| PV5 | Dan Marino | 1.00 | .70 |
| PV6 | Bo Jackson | .75 | .45 |
| PV7 | Randall Cunningham | .50 | .30 |
| PV8 | Bruce Smith | .30 | .18 |
| PV9 | Derrick Thomas | 1.00 | .70 |
| PV10 | Howie Long | .30 | .18 |

# 1991 Fleer All-Pro

These limited insert cards were distributed randomly in 1991 Fleer football packs. Card fronts contain two photographs, a large portrait shot and a smaller action figure. The vertical card backs feature the player's career highlights in a story format. Cards measure 2-1/2" by 3-1/2".

| | | MINT | NR/MT |
|---|---|---|---|
| **Complete Set (26)** | | 8.50 | 5.50 |
| **Commons** | | .10 | .06 |
| 1 | Andre Reed | .75 | .45 |
| 2 | Bobby Humphrey | .25 | .15 |
| 3 | Kent Hull | .10 | .06 |
| 4 | Mark Bortz | .10 | .06 |
| 5 | Bruce Smith | .25 | .15 |
| 6 | Greg Townsend | .15 | .10 |
| 7 | Ray Childress | .15 | .10 |
| 8 | Andre Rison | .80 | .50 |
| 9 | Barry Sanders | 1.50 | .90 |
| 10 | Bo Jackson | .80 | .50 |
| 11 | Neal Anderson | .50 | .30 |
| 12 | Keith Jackson | .25 | .15 |
| 13 | Derrick Thomas | .90 | .60 |
| 14 | John Offerdahl | .20 | .12 |
| 15 | Lawrence Taylor | .50 | .30 |
| 16 | Darrell Green | .25 | .15 |
| 17 | Mark Carrier | .25 | .15 |
| 18 | David Fulcher | .10 | .06 |
| 19 | Joe Montana | 1.25 | .80 |
| 20 | Jerry Rice | 1.25 | .80 |
| 21 | Charles Haley | .15 | .10 |
| 22 | Mike Singletary | .25 | .15 |
| 23 | Nick Lowery | .10 | .06 |
| 24 | Jim Lachey | .10 | .06 |
| 25 | Anthony Munoz | .20 | .12 |
| 26 | Thurman Thomas | 1.25 | .80 |

# 1991 Fleer Ultra

This 300-card set marks Fleer's first upscale premium football card product. The card fronts feature full color action photos with silver borders at the top and bottom. The player's name, team and position is printed across the bottom of the card. The card backs contain three photos including a large head shot of the player and two smaller action shots.. The player's personal data and statistics are printed just below the photos. Cards measure 2-1/2" by 3-1/2". This edition also includes two limited edition 10-card insert sets, Ultra All-Stars (AS) and Ultra Performances (P). These cards were randomly distributed in Fleer Ultra packs and are listed at the end of this checklist but are not included in the complete set price below.

|  |  | MINT | NR/MT |
|---|---|---|---|
| Complete Set (300) | | 12.50 | 8.50 |
| Commons | | .05 | .03 |
| | | | |
| 1 | Don Beebe | .08 | .05 |
| 2 | Shane Conlan | .08 | .05 |
| 3 | Pete Metzelaars | .05 | .03 |
| 4 | Jamie Mueller | .05 | .03 |
| 5 | Scott Norwood | .05 | .03 |
| 6 | Andre Reed | .12 | .07 |
| 7 | Leon Seals | .05 | .03 |
| 8 | Bruce Smith | .10 | .06 |
| 9 | Leonard Smith | .05 | .03 |
| 10 | Thurman Thomas | .75 | .45 |
| 11 | Lewis Billups | .05 | .03 |
| 12 | Jim Breech | .05 | .03 |
| 13 | James Brooks | .07 | .04 |
| 14 | Eddie Brown | .08 | .05 |
| 15 | Boomer Esiason | .12 | .07 |
| 16 | David Fulcher | .05 | .03 |
| 17 | Rodney Holman | .07 | .04 |
| 18 | Bruce Kozerski | .05 | .03 |
| 19 | Tim Krumrie | .05 | .03 |
| 20 | Tim McGee | .08 | .05 |
| 21 | Anthony Munoz | .10 | .06 |
| 22 | Leon White | .05 | .03 |
| 23 | Ickey Woods | .05 | .03 |
| 24 | Carl Zander | .05 | .03 |
| 25 | Brian Brennan | .05 | .03 |
| 26 | Thane Gash | .05 | .03 |
| 27 | Leroy Hoard | .15 | .10 |
| 28 | Mike Johnson | .05 | .03 |
| 29 | Reggie Langhorne | .05 | .03 |
| 30 | Kevin Mack | .07 | .04 |
| 31 | Clay Matthews | .05 | .03 |
| 32 | Eric Metcalf | .12 | .07 |
| 33 | Steve Atwater | .10 | .06 |
| 34 | Melvin Bratton | .05 | .03 |
| 35 | John Elway | .20 | .12 |
| 36 | Bobby Humphrey | .12 | .07 |
| 37 | Mark Jackson | .07 | .04 |
| 38 | Vance Johnson | .07 | .04 |
| 39 | Ricky Nattiel | .07 | .04 |
| 40 | Steve Sewell | .05 | .03 |
| 41 | Dennis Smith | .05 | .03 |
| 42 | David Treadwell | .05 | .03 |
| 43 | Mike Young | .05 | .03 |
| 44 | Ray Childress | .07 | .04 |
| 45 | Cris Dishman (R) | .15 | .10 |
| 46 | William Fuller | .07 | .04 |
| 47 | Ernest Givins | .15 | .10 |
| 48 | John Grimsley | .05 | .03 |
| 49 | Drew Hill | .08 | .05 |
| 50 | Haywood Jeffires | .20 | .12 |
| 51 | Sean Jones | .05 | .03 |
| 52 | Johnny Meads | .05 | .03 |
| 53 | Warren Moon | .30 | .18 |
| 54 | Al Smith | .05 | .03 |
| 55 | Lorenzo White | .20 | .12 |
| 56 | Albert Bentley | .05 | .03 |
| 57 | Duane Bickett | .05 | .03 |
| 58 | Bill Brooks | .05 | .03 |
| 59 | Jeff George | .50 | .30 |
| 60 | Mike Prior | .05 | .03 |
| 61 | Rohn Stark | .05 | .03 |
| 62 | Jack Trudeau | .08 | .05 |
| 63 | Clarence Verdin | .08 | .05 |
| 64 | Steve DeBerg | .10 | .06 |
| 65 | Emile Harry | .05 | .03 |
| 66 | Albert Lewis | .05 | .03 |
| 67 | Nick Lowery | .07 | .04 |
| 68 | Todd McNair | .05 | .03 |
| 69 | Christian Okoye | .12 | .07 |
| 70 | Stephone Paige | .08 | .05 |
| 71 | Kevin Porter | .05 | .03 |
| 72 | Derrick Thomas | .20 | .12 |
| 73 | Robb Thomas | .05 | .03 |

| | | | |
|---|---|---|---|
| 74 | Barry Word | .20 | .12 |
| 75 | Marcus Allen | .12 | .07 |
| 76 | Eddie Anderson | .05 | .03 |
| 77 | Tim Brown | .12 | .07 |
| 78 | Mervyn Fernandez | .08 | .05 |
| 79 | Willie Gault | .07 | .04 |
| 80 | Ethan Horton | .05 | .03 |
| 81 | Howie Long | .07 | .04 |
| 82 | Vance Mueller | .05 | .03 |
| 83 | Jay Schroeder | .10 | .06 |
| 84 | Steve Smith | .05 | .03 |
| 85 | Greg Townsend | .07 | .04 |
| 86 | Mark Clayton | .10 | .06 |
| 87 | Jim Jensen | .05 | .03 |
| 88 | Dan Marino | .60 | .35 |
| 89 | Tim McKyer | .05 | .03 |
| 90 | John Offerdahl | .08 | .05 |
| 91 | Louis Olier | .07 | .04 |
| 92 | Reggie Roby | .05 | .03 |
| 93 | Sammie Smith | .10 | .06 |
| 94 | Hart Lee Dykes | .05 | .03 |
| 95 | Irving Fryar | .07 | .04 |
| 96 | Tommy Hodson | .10 | .06 |
| 97 | Maurice Hurst | .05 | .03 |
| 98 | John Stephens | .08 | .05 |
| 99 | Andre Tippett | .08 | .05 |
| 100 | Mark Boyer | .05 | .03 |
| 101 | Kyle Clifton | .05 | .03 |
| 102 | James Hasty | .05 | .03 |
| 103 | Erik McMillan | .05 | .03 |
| 104 | Rob Moore | .40 | .25 |
| 105 | Joe Mott | .05 | .03 |
| 106 | Ken O'Brien | .10 | .06 |
| 107 | Ron Stallworth | .05 | .03 |
| 108 | Al Toon | .10 | .06 |
| 109 | Gary Anderson | .05 | .03 |
| 110 | Bubby Brister | .15 | .10 |
| 111 | Thomas Everett | .05 | .03 |
| 112 | Merril Hoge | .08 | .05 |
| 113 | Louis Lipps | .08 | .05 |
| 114 | Greg Lloyd | .05 | .03 |
| 115 | Hardy Nickerson | .05 | .03 |
| 116 | Dwight Stone | .05 | .03 |
| 117 | Rod Woodson | .12 | .07 |
| 118 | Tim Worley | .08 | .05 |
| 119 | Rod Bernstine | .10 | .06 |
| 120 | Marion Butts | .12 | .07 |
| 121 | Gill Byrd | .07 | .04 |
| 122 | Arthur Cox | .05 | .03 |
| 123 | Burt Grossman | .07 | .04 |
| 124 | Ronnie Harmon | .07 | .04 |
| 125 | Anthony Miller | .12 | .07 |
| 126 | Leslie O'Neal | .08 | .05 |
| 127 | Gary Plummer | .05 | .03 |
| 128 | Sam Seale | .05 | .03 |
| 129 | Junior Seau | .20 | .12 |
| 130 | Broderick Thompson | .05 | .03 |
| 131 | Billy Joe Tolliver | .08 | .05 |
| 132 | Brian Blades | .08 | .05 |
| 133 | Jeff Bryant | .05 | .03 |
| 134 | Derrick Fenner | .15 | .10 |
| 135 | Jacob Green | .05 | .03 |
| 136 | Andy Heck | .05 | .03 |
| 137 | Patrick Hunter (R) | .10 | .06 |
| 138 | Norm Johnson | .05 | .03 |
| 139 | Tommy Kane | .08 | .05 |
| 140 | Dave Krieg | .12 | .07 |
| 141 | John L. Williams | .08 | .05 |
| 142 | Terry Wooden | .05 | .03 |
| 143 | Steve Broussard | .12 | .07 |
| 144 | Keith Jones | .05 | .03 |
| 145 | Brian Jordan | .15 | .10 |
| 146 | Chris Miller | .30 | .18 |
| 147 | John Rade | .05 | .03 |
| 148 | Andre Rison | .25 | .15 |
| 149 | Mike Rozier | .08 | .05 |
| 150 | Deion Sanders | .25 | .15 |
| 151 | Neal Anderson | .15 | .10 |
| 152 | Trace Armstrong | .07 | .04 |
| 153 | Kevin Butler | .05 | .03 |
| 154 | Mark Carrier (Chi) | .10 | .06 |
| 155 | Richard Dent | .08 | .05 |
| 156 | Dennis Gentry | .05 | .03 |
| 157 | Jim Harbaugh | .20 | .12 |
| 158 | Brad Muster | .10 | .06 |
| 159 | William Perry | .08 | .05 |
| 160 | Mike Singletary | .12 | .07 |
| 161 | Lemuel Stinson | .05 | .03 |
| 162 | Troy Aikman | .90 | .60 |
| 163 | Michael Irvin | .40 | .25 |
| 164 | Mike Saxon | .05 | .03 |
| 165 | Emmitt Smith | 1.75 | 1.00 |
| 166 | Jerry Ball | .05 | .03 |
| 167 | Michael Cofer | .05 | .03 |
| 168 | Rodney Peete | .12 | .07 |
| 169 | Barry Sanders | 1.00 | .70 |
| 170 | Robert Brown | .05 | .03 |
| 171 | Anthony Dilweg | .08 | .05 |
| 172 | Tim Harris | .07 | .04 |
| 173 | Johnny Holland | .05 | .03 |
| 174 | Perry Kemp | .05 | .03 |
| 175 | Don Majkowski | .12 | .07 |
| 176 | Brian Noble | .05 | .03 |
| 177 | Jeff Query | .05 | .03 |
| 178 | Sterling Sharpe | .30 | .18 |
| 179 | Charles Wilson | .05 | .03 |
| 180 | Keith Woodside | .05 | .03 |
| 181 | Flipper Anderson | .12 | .07 |
| 182 | Bern Brostek | .05 | .03 |
| 183 | Pat Carter (R) | .10 | .06 |
| 184 | Aaron Cox | .05 | .03 |
| 185 | Henry Ellard | .08 | .05 |
| 186 | Jim Everett | .20 | .12 |
| 187 | Cleveland Gary | .12 | .07 |

| | | | |
|---|---|---|---|
| 188 | Jerry Gray | .05 | .03 |
| 189 | Kevin Greene | .07 | .04 |
| 190 | Mike Wilcher | .05 | .03 |
| 191 | Alfred Anderson | .05 | .03 |
| 192 | Joe Browner | .07 | .04 |
| 193 | Anthony Carter | .10 | .06 |
| 194 | Chris Doleman | .08 | .05 |
| 195 | Rick Fenney | .05 | .03 |
| 196 | Darrell Fullington | .05 | .03 |
| 197 | Rich Gannon | .20 | .12 |
| 198 | Hassan Jones | .08 | .05 |
| 199 | Steve Jordan | .05 | .03 |
| 200 | Mike Merriweather | .05 | .03 |
| 201 | Al Noga | .05 | .03 |
| 202 | Herschel Walker | .15 | .10 |
| 203 | Wade Wilson | .10 | .06 |
| 204 | Morten Andersen | .07 | .04 |
| 205 | Gene Atkins | .05 | .03 |
| 206 | Toi Cook (R) | .08 | .05 |
| 207 | Craig Heyward | .08 | .05 |
| 208 | Dalton Hilliard | .10 | .06 |
| 209 | Vaughan Johnson | .08 | .05 |
| 210 | Eric Martin | .10 | .06 |
| 211 | Brett Perriman | .05 | .03 |
| 212 | Pat Swilling | .15 | .10 |
| 213 | Steve Walsh | .10 | .06 |
| 214 | Ottis Anderson | .10 | .06 |
| 215 | Carl Banks | .08 | .05 |
| 216 | Maurice Carthon | .05 | .03 |
| 217 | Mark Collins | .05 | .03 |
| 218 | Rodney Hampton | .70 | .40 |
| 219 | Erik Howard | .05 | .03 |
| 220 | Mark Ingram | .07 | .04 |
| 221 | Pepper Johnson | .05 | .03 |
| 222 | Dave Meggett | .12 | .07 |
| 223 | Phil Simms | .12 | .07 |
| 224 | Lawrence Taylor | .15 | .10 |
| 225 | Lewis Tillman | .05 | .03 |
| 226 | Everson Walls | .05 | .03 |
| 227 | Fred Barnett | .20 | .12 |
| 228 | Jerome Brown | .08 | .05 |
| 229 | Keith Byars | .10 | .06 |
| 230 | Randall Cunningham | .25 | .15 |
| 231 | Byron Evans | .05 | .03 |
| 232 | Wes Hopkins | .05 | .03 |
| 233 | Keith Jackson | .12 | .07 |
| 234 | Heath Sherman | .08 | .05 |
| 235 | Anthony Toney | .05 | .03 |
| 236 | Reggie White | .12 | .07 |
| 237 | Rich Camarillo | .05 | .03 |
| 238 | Ken Harvey | .05 | .03 |
| 239 | Eric Hill | .05 | .03 |
| 240 | Johnny Johnson | .20 | .12 |
| 241 | Ernie Jones | .08 | .05 |
| 242 | Tim McDonald | .05 | .03 |
| 243 | Timm Rosenbach | .15 | .10 |
| 244 | Jay Taylor (R) | .07 | .04 |
| 245 | Dexter Carter | .10 | .06 |
| 246 | Mike Cofer | .05 | .03 |
| 247 | Kevin Fagan | .05 | .03 |
| 248 | Don Griffin | .05 | .03 |
| 249 | Charles Haley | .08 | .05 |
| 250 | Brent Jones | .12 | .07 |
| 251 | Joe Montana | .80 | .50 |
| 252 | Darryl Pollard | .05 | .03 |
| 253 | Tom Rathman | .10 | .06 |
| 254 | Jerry Rice | .50 | .30 |
| 255 | John Taylor | .20 | .12 |
| 256 | Steve Young | .40 | .25 |
| 257 | Gary Anderson | .05 | .03 |
| 258 | Mark Carrier (TB) | .12 | .07 |
| 259 | Chris Chandler | .10 | .06 |
| 260 | Reggie Cobb | .25 | .15 |
| 261 | Reuben Davis | .05 | .03 |
| 262 | Willie Drewrey | .05 | .03 |
| 263 | Ron Hall | .05 | .03 |
| 264 | Eugene Marve | .05 | .03 |
| 265 | Winston Moss | .05 | .03 |
| 266 | Vinny Testaverde | .12 | .07 |
| 267 | Broderick Thomas | .15 | .10 |
| 268 | Jeff Bostic | .05 | .03 |
| 269 | Earnest Byner | .08 | .05 |
| 270 | Gary Clark | .15 | .10 |
| 271 | Darrell Green | .12 | .07 |
| 272 | Jim Lachey | .08 | .05 |
| 273 | Wilber Marshall | .08 | .05 |
| 274 | Art Monk | .25 | .15 |
| 275 | Gerald Riggs | .08 | .05 |
| 276 | Mark Rypien | .30 | .18 |
| 277 | Ricky Sanders | .08 | .05 |
| 278 | Alvin Walton | .05 | .03 |
| 279 | Nick Bell (R) | .70 | .40 |
| 280 | Eric Bieniemy (R) | .20 | .12 |
| 281 | Jarrod Bunch (R) | .25 | .15 |
| 282 | Mike Croel (R) | .35 | .20 |
| 283 | Brett Favre (R) | 2.00 | 1.25 |
| 284 | Moe Gardner (R) | .15 | .10 |
| 285 | Pat Harlow (R) | .12 | .07 |
| 286 | Randal Hill (R) | .60 | .35 |
| 287 | Todd Marinovich (R) | 1.00 | .70 |
| 288 | Russell Maryland (R) | .40 | .25 |
| 289 | Dan McGwire (R) | .80 | .50 |
| 290 | Ernie Mills (R) | .35 | .20 |
| 291 | Herman Moore (R) | .70 | .40 |
| 292 | Godfrey Myles (R) | .10 | .06 |
| 293 | Browning Nagle (R) | 1.25 | .80 |
| 294 | Mike Pritchard (R) | .75 | .45 |
| 295 | Esera Tuaolo (R) | .12 | .07 |
| 296 | Mark Vander Poel (R) | .10 | .06 |
| 297 | Ricky Watters (R) | 1.75 | 1.00 |
| 298 | Chris Zorich (R) | .15 | .10 |
| 299 | Checklist | .15 | .10 |

| | | | |
|---|---|---|---|
| 300 | Checklist | .15 | .10 |
| AS1 | Barry Sanders | 3.00 | 2.00 |
| AS2 | Keith Jackson | .60 | .35 |
| AS3 | Bruce Smith | .75 | .45 |
| AS4 | Randall Cunningham | 1.25 | .80 |
| AS5 | Dan Marino | 2.50 | 1.50 |
| AS6 | Charles Haley | .60 | .35 |
| AS7 | John L. Williams | .60 | .35 |
| AS8 | Darrell Green | .75 | .45 |
| AS9 | Stephone Paige | .60 | .35 |
| AS10 | Kevin Greene | .60 | .35 |
| P1 | Emmitt Smith | 6.00 | 4.50 |
| P2 | Andre Rison | 1.75 | 1.00 |
| P3 | Derrick Thomas | 1.50 | .90 |
| P4 | Joe Montana | 2.50 | 1.50 |
| P5 | Warren Moon | 2.00 | 1.25 |
| P6 | Mike Singletary | .75 | .45 |
| P7 | Thurman Thomas | 3.50 | 2.50 |
| P8 | Rod Woodson | .75 | .45 |
| P9 | Jerry Rice | 3.50 | 2.50 |
| P10 | Reggie White | .75 | .45 |

# 1991 Fleer Ultra Update

RICKY ERVINS REDSKINS RUNNING BACK

This 100-card update set consists of mostly rookies and traded players. The card fronts are nearly identical to the regular Fleer Ultra set. Card backs contain just one player photo as opposed to three on the card backs of the regular Ultra set. Card numbers on the backs are preceeded by the letter "U" to signify an update set. All cards measure 2-1/2" by 3-1/2".

| | | MINT | NR/MT |
|---|---|---|---|
| | **Complete Set (100)** | 16.00 | 10.00 |
| | **Commons** | .05 | .03 |

| | | | |
|---|---|---|---|
| 1 | Brett Favre | 1.25 | .80 |
| 2 | Moe Gardner | .12 | .07 |
| 3 | Tim McKyer | .05 | .03 |
| 4 | Bruce Pickens (R) | .30 | .18 |
| 5 | Mike Pritchard | .60 | .35 |
| 6 | Cornelius Bennett | .12 | .07 |
| 7 | Phil Hansen (R) | .15 | .10 |
| 8 | Henry Jones (R) | .15 | .10 |
| 9 | Mark Kelso | .05 | .03 |
| 10 | James Lofton | .25 | .15 |
| 11 | Anthony Morgan (R) | .60 | .35 |
| 12 | Stan Thomas (R) | .10 | .06 |
| 13 | Chris Zorich | .10 | .06 |
| 14 | Reggie Rembert | .08 | .05 |
| 15 | Alfred Williams (R) | .35 | .20 |
| 16 | Michael Jackson (R) | .75 | .45 |
| 17 | Ed King (R) | .10 | .06 |
| 18 | Joe Morris | .08 | .05 |
| 19 | Vince Newsome | .05 | .03 |
| 20 | Tony Casillas | .12 | .07 |
| 21 | Russell Maryland | .25 | .15 |
| 22 | Jay Novacek | .10 | .06 |
| 23 | Mike Croel | .50 | .30 |
| 24 | Gaston Green | .25 | .15 |
| 25 | Kenny Walker (R) | .30 | .18 |
| 26 | Melvin Jenkins (R) | .20 | .12 |
| 27 | Herman Moore | .60 | .35 |
| 28 | Kelvin Pritchett (R) | .15 | .10 |
| 29 | Chris Spielman | .10 | .06 |
| 30 | Vinnie Clark (R) | .10 | .06 |
| 31 | Allen Rice | .05 | .03 |
| 32 | Vai Sikahema | .05 | .03 |
| 33 | Esera Tuaolo | .07 | .04 |
| 34 | Mike Dumas (R) | .12 | .07 |
| 35 | John Flannery (R) | .10 | .06 |
| 36 | Allen Pinkett | .07 | .04 |
| 37 | Tim Barnett (R) | .60 | .35 |
| 38 | Dan Saleaumua | .05 | .03 |
| 39 | Harvey Williams (R) | .80 | .50 |
| 40 | Nick Bell | .90 | .60 |
| 41 | Roger Craig | .12 | .07 |
| 42 | Ronnie Lott | .15 | .10 |
| 43 | Todd Marinovich | 1.00 | .70 |
| 44 | Robert Delpino | .10 | .06 |
| 45 | Todd Lyght (R) | .30 | .18 |
| 46 | Robert Young (R) | .15 | .10 |
| 47 | Aaron Craver (R) | .15 | .10 |
| 48 | Mark Higgs (R) | 1.00 | .70 |
| 49 | Vestee Jackson | .05 | .03 |
| 50 | Carl Lee | .05 | .03 |
| 51 | Felix Wright | .05 | .03 |
| 52 | Darrell Fullington | .05 | .03 |

| 53 | Pat Harlow | .07 | .04 |
| 54 | Eugene Lockhart | .05 | .03 |
| 55 | Hugh Millen (R) | .60 | .35 |
| 56 | Leonard Russell (R) | 1.25 | .80 |
| 57 | Jon Vaughn (R) | .35 | .20 |
| 58 | Quinn Early | .07 | .04 |
| 59 | Bobby Hebert | .20 | .12 |
| 60 | Rickey Jackson | .08 | .05 |
| 61 | Sam Mills | .08 | .05 |
| 62 | Jarrod Bunch | .25 | .15 |
| 63 | John Elliott | .05 | .03 |
| 64 | Jeff Hostetler | .25 | .15 |
| 65 | Ed McCaffrey (R) | .50 | .30 |
| 66 | Kanavis McGhee (R) | .25 | .15 |
| 67 | Mo Lewis (R) | .20 | .12 |
| 68 | Browning Nagle | 1.25 | .80 |
| 69 | Blair Thomas | .35 | .20 |
| 70 | Antone Davis (R) | .10 | .06 |
| 71 | Brad Goebel (R) | .12 | .07 |
| 72 | Jim McMahon | .10 | .06 |
| 73 | Clyde Simmons | .08 | .05 |
| 74 | Randal Hill | .60 | .35 |
| 75 | Eric Swann (R) | .20 | .12 |
| 76 | Tom Tupa | .08 | .05 |
| 77 | Jeff Graham (R) | .70 | .40 |
| 78 | Eric Green | .20 | .12 |
| 79 | Neil O'Donnell (R) | 1.75 | 1.00 |
| 80 | Huey Richardson (R) | .12 | .07 |
| 81 | Eric Bieniemy | .15 | .10 |
| 82 | John Friesz | .20 | .12 |
| 83 | Eric Moten (R) | .08 | .05 |
| 84 | Stanley Richard (R) | .20 | .12 |
| 85 | Todd Bowles | .05 | .03 |
| 86 | Merton Hanks (R) | .08 | .05 |
| 87 | Tim Harris | .08 | .05 |
| 88 | Pierce Holt | .05 | .03 |
| 89 | Ted Washington (R) | .15 | .10 |
| 90 | John Kasay (R) | .08 | .05 |
| 91 | Dan McGwire | .75 | .45 |
| 92 | Lawrence Dawsey (R) | .60 | .35 |
| 93 | Charles McRae (R) | .10 | .06 |
| 94 | Jesse Solomon | .05 | .03 |
| 95 | Robert Wilson (R) | .15 | .10 |
| 96 | Ricky Ervins (R) | 1.50 | .90 |
| 97 | Charles Mann | .05 | .03 |
| 98 | Bobby Wilson (R) | .12 | .07 |
| 99 | Jerry Rice (Pro Vision) | .40 | .25 |
| 100 | Checklist | .10 | .06 |

# 1992 Fleer

343

BARRY FOSTER

This 480-card set consists of full color action photos on the card fronts framed by a white border. A color bar below the photo contains the player's name and position with the team logo printed in the lower right corner. Card backs feature a large portrait shot along with the player's personal data and statistics. Key subsets include Rookies (R) (432-451), League Leaders (LL) (452-470) and Pro Vision art cards (PV) (471-476). All cards measure 2-1/2" by 3-1/2".

| | | MINT | NR/MT |
|---|---|---|---|
| Complete Set (480) | | 14.00 | 8.50 |
| Commons | | .05 | .02 |

| 1 | Steve Broussard | .08 | .05 |
|---|---|---|---|
| 2 | Rick Bryan | .05 | .02 |
| 3 | Scott Case | .05 | .02 |
| 4 | Tory Epps | .05 | .02 |
| 5 | Bill Fralic | .05 | .02 |
| 6 | Moe Gardner | .05 | .02 |
| 7 | Michael Haynes | .25 | .15 |
| 8 | Chris Hinton | .05 | .02 |
| 9 | Brian Jordan | .12 | .07 |
| 10 | Mike Kenn | .05 | .02 |
| 11 | Tim McKyer | .05 | .02 |
| 12 | Chris Miller | .25 | .15 |
| 13 | Erric Pegram | .08 | .05 |
| 14 | Mike Pritchard | .25 | .15 |
| 15 | Andre Rison | .25 | .15 |
| 16 | Jessie Tuggle | .05 | .02 |
| 17 | Carlton Bailey (R) | .08 | .05 |
| 18 | Howard Ballard | .05 | .02 |
| 19 | Don Beebe | .05 | .02 |
| 20 | Cornelius Bennett | .08 | .05 |
| 21 | Shane Conlan | .07 | .04 |
| 22 | Kent Hull | .05 | .02 |

| | | | |
|---|---|---|---|
| 23 Mark Kelso | .05 | .02 |
| 24 James Lofton | .20 | .12 |
| 26 Scott Norwood | .05 | .02 |
| 27 Nate Odomes | .05 | .02 |
| 28 Frank Reich | .07 | .04 |
| 29 Jim Ritcher | .05 | .02 |
| 30 Leon Seals | .05 | .02 |
| 31 Darryl Talley | .05 | .02 |
| 32 Steve Tasker | .05 | .02 |
| 33 Thurman Thomas | .35 | .20 |
| 34 Will Wolford | .05 | .02 |
| 35 Neal Anderson | .10 | .06 |
| 36 Trace Armstrong | .05 | .02 |
| 37 Mark Carrier | .08 | .05 |
| 38 Richard Dent | .07 | .04 |
| 39 Shaun Gayle | .05 | .02 |
| 40 Jim Harbaugh | .10 | .06 |
| 41 Jay Hilgenberg | .05 | .02 |
| 42 Darren Lewis | .15 | .10 |
| 43 Steve McMichael | .05 | .02 |
| 44 Brad Muster | .07 | .04 |
| 45 William Perry | .07 | .04 |
| 46 John Roper | .05 | .02 |
| 47 Lemuel Stinson | .05 | .02 |
| 48 Stan Thomas | .05 | .02 |
| 49 Keith Van Horne | .05 | .02 |
| 50 Tom Waddle | .15 | .10 |
| 51 Donnell Woolford | .05 | .02 |
| 52 Chris Zorich | .10 | .06 |
| 53 Eddie Brown | .07 | .04 |
| 54 James Francis | .07 | .04 |
| 55 David Fulcher | .05 | .02 |
| 56 David Grant | .05 | .02 |
| 57 Harold Green | .20 | .12 |
| 58 Rodney Holman | .05 | .02 |
| 59 Lee Johnson | .05 | .02 |
| 60 Tim Krumrie | .05 | .02 |
| 61 Anthony Munoz | .08 | .05 |
| 62 Joe Walter (R) | .07 | .04 |
| 63 Mike Baab | .05 | .02 |
| 64 Stephen Braggs | .05 | .02 |
| 65 Richard Brown (R) | .07 | .04 |
| 66 Dan Fike | .05 | .02 |
| 67 Scott Galbraith (R) | .08 | .05 |
| 68 Randy Hillard (R) | .07 | .04 |
| 69 Michael Jackson | .20 | .12 |
| 70 Tony Jones | .05 | .02 |
| 71 Ed King | .05 | .02 |
| 72 Kevin Mack | .05 | .02 |
| 73 Clay Matthews | .05 | .02 |
| 74 Eric Metcalf | .12 | .07 |
| 75 Vince Newsome | .05 | .02 |
| 76 John Rienstra | .05 | .02 |
| 77 Steve Beuerlein | .10 | .06 |
| 78 Larry Brown | .05 | .02 |
| 79 Tony Casillas | .05 | .02 |
| 80 Alvin Harper | .25 | .15 |

| | | |
|---|---|---|
| 81 Issiac Holt | .05 | .02 |
| 82 Ray Horton | .05 | .02 |
| 83 Michael Irvin | .30 | .18 |
| 84 Daryl Johnston | .05 | .02 |
| 85 Kelvin Martin | .05 | .02 |
| 86 Nate Newton | .05 | .02 |
| 87 Ken Norton | .05 | .02 |
| 88 Jay Novacek | .08 | .05 |
| 89 Emmitt Smith | 1.50 | .90 |
| 90 Vinson Smith (R) | .08 | .05 |
| 91 Mark Stepnoski | .05 | .02 |
| 92 Steve Atwater | .08 | .05 |
| 93 Mike Croel | .15 | .10 |
| 94 John Elway | .20 | .12 |
| 95 Simon Fletcher | .05 | .02 |
| 96 Gaston Green | .10 | .06 |
| 97 Mark Jackson | .07 | .04 |
| 98 Keith Kartz | .05 | .02 |
| 99 Greg Kragen | .05 | .02 |
| 100 Greg Lewis | .12 | .07 |
| 101 Karl Mecklenburg | .08 | .05 |
| 102 Derek Russell | .10 | .06 |
| 103 Steve Sewell | .05 | .02 |
| 104 Dennis Smith | .05 | .02 |
| 105 David Treadwell | .05 | .02 |
| 106 Kenny Walker | .10 | .06 |
| 107 Doug Widell | .05 | .02 |
| 108 Michael Young | .05 | .02 |
| 109 Jerry Ball | .05 | .02 |
| 110 Bennie Blades | .07 | .04 |
| 111 Lomas Brown | .05 | .02 |
| 112 Scott Conover (R) | .07 | .04 |
| 113 Ray Crockett | .05 | .02 |
| 114 Mike Farr | .05 | .02 |
| 115 Mel Gray | .05 | .02 |
| 116 Willie Green | .30 | .18 |
| 117 Tracy Hayworth (R) | .08 | .05 |
| 118 Erik Kramer | .35 | .20 |
| 119 Herman Moore | .20 | .12 |
| 120 Dan Owens | .05 | .02 |
| 121 Rodney Peete | .12 | .07 |
| 122 Brett Perriman | .05 | .02 |
| 123 Barry Sanders | .80 | .50 |
| 124 Chris Spielman | .07 | .04 |
| 125 Marc Spindler | .05 | .02 |
| 126 Tony Bennett | .05 | .02 |
| 127 Matt Brock | .05 | .02 |
| 128 LeRoy Butler | .05 | .02 |
| 129 Johnny Holland | .05 | .02 |
| 130 Perry Kemp | .05 | .02 |
| 131 Don Majkowski | .12 | .07 |
| 132 Mark Murphy | .05 | .02 |
| 133 Brian Noble | .05 | .02 |
| 134 Bryce Paup | .05 | .02 |
| 135 Sterling Sharpe | .25 | .15 |
| 136 Scott Stephen | .05 | .02 |
| 137 Darrell Thompson | .08 | .05 |

| | | | | | | | |
|---|---|---|---|---|---|---|---|
| 138 | Mike Tomczak | .08 | .05 | 195 | Willie Gault | .07 | .04 |
| 139 | Esera Tuaolo | .05 | .02 | 196 | Jeff Gossett | .05 | .02 |
| 140 | Keith Woodside | .05 | .02 | 197 | Ethan Horton | .07 | .04 |
| 141 | Ray Childress | .08 | .05 | 198 | Jeff Jaeger | .05 | .02 |
| 142 | Cris Dishman | .07 | .04 | 199 | Howie Long | .07 | .04 |
| 143 | Curtis Duncan | .05 | .02 | 200 | Ronnie Lott | .15 | .10 |
| 144 | John Flannery | .05 | .02 | 201 | Todd Marinovich | .40 | .25 |
| 145 | William Fuller | .05 | .02 | 202 | Don Mosbar | .05 | .02 |
| 146 | Ernest Givins | .12 | .07 | 203 | Jay Schroeder | .10 | .06 |
| 147 | Haywood Jeffires | .20 | .12 | 204 | Greg Townsend | .07 | .04 |
| 148 | Sean Jones | .05 | .02 | 205 | Lionel Washington | .05 | .02 |
| 149 | Lamar Lathon | .05 | .02 | 206 | Steve Wisniewski | .05 | .02 |
| 150 | Bruce Matthews | .05 | .02 | 207 | Flipper Anderson | .08 | .05 |
| 151 | Bubba McDowell | .05 | .02 | 208 | Bern Brostek | .05 | .02 |
| 152 | Johnny Meads | .05 | .02 | 209 | Robert Delpino | .08 | .05 |
| 153 | Warren Moon | .25 | .15 | 210 | Henry Ellard | .07 | .04 |
| 154 | Mike Munchak | .05 | .02 | 211 | Jim Everett | .15 | .10 |
| 155 | Al Smith | .05 | .02 | 212 | Cleveland Gary | .08 | .05 |
| 156 | Doug Smith | .05 | .02 | 213 | Kevin Greene | .07 | .04 |
| 157 | Lorenze White | .15 | .10 | 214 | Darryl Henley | .05 | .02 |
| 158 | Michael Ball | .05 | .02 | 215 | Damone Johnson | .05 | .02 |
| 159 | Chip Banks | .05 | .02 | 216 | Larry Kelm | .05 | .02 |
| 160 | Duane Bickett | .05 | .02 | 217 | Todd Lyght | .12 | .07 |
| 161 | Bill Brooks | .05 | .02 | 218 | Jackie Slater | .05 | .02 |
| 162 | Ken Clark | .05 | .02 | 219 | Michael Stewart | .05 | .02 |
| 163 | Jon Hand | .05 | .02 | 220 | Pat Terrell | .05 | .02 |
| 164 | Jeff Herrod | .05 | .02 | 221 | Robert Young | .05 | .02 |
| 165 | Jessie Hester | .05 | .02 | 222 | Mark Clayton | .12 | .07 |
| 166 | Scott Radecic | .05 | .02 | 223 | Bryan Cox | .05 | .02 |
| 167 | Rohn Stark | .05 | .02 | 224 | Aaron Craver | .07 | .04 |
| 168 | Clarence Verdin | .07 | .04 | 225 | Jeff Cross | .05 | .02 |
| 169 | John Alt | .05 | .02 | 226 | Mark Duper | .08 | .05 |
| 170 | Tim Barnett | .15 | .10 | 227 | Harry Galbreath | .05 | .02 |
| 171 | Tim Grunhard | .05 | .02 | 228 | David Griggs | .05 | .02 |
| 172 | Dino Hackett | .05 | .02 | 229 | Mark Higgs | .20 | .12 |
| 173 | Jonathan Hayes | .05 | .02 | 230 | Vestee Jackson | .05 | .02 |
| 174 | Bill Maas | .05 | .02 | 231 | John Offerdahl | .08 | .05 |
| 175 | Chris Martin | .05 | .02 | 232 | Louis Oliver | .07 | .04 |
| 176 | Christian Okoye | .10 | .06 | 233 | Tony Paige | .05 | .02 |
| 177 | Stephone Paige | .07 | .04 | 234 | Reggie Roby | .05 | .02 |
| 178 | Jayice Pearson (R) | .08 | .05 | 235 | Sammie Smith | .08 | .05 |
| 179 | Kevin Porter | .05 | .02 | 236 | Pete Stoyanovich | .05 | .02 |
| 180 | Kevin Ross | .05 | .02 | 237 | Richmond Webb | .05 | .02 |
| 181 | Dan Saleaumua | .05 | .02 | 238 | Terry Allen | .30 | .18 |
| 182 | Tracy Simien (R) | .08 | .05 | 239 | Ray Berry | .05 | .02 |
| 183 | Neil Smith | .05 | .02 | 240 | Joey Browner | .07 | .04 |
| 184 | Derrick Thomas | .20 | .12 | 241 | Anthony Carter | .08 | .05 |
| 185 | Robb Thoms | .05 | .02 | 242 | Cris Carter | .15 | .10 |
| 186 | Mark Vlasic | .07 | .04 | 243 | Chris Doleman | .08 | .05 |
| 187 | Barry Word | .15 | .10 | 244 | Rich Gannon | .25 | .15 |
| 188 | Marcus Allen | .12 | .07 | 245 | Tim Irwin | .05 | .02 |
| 189 | Eddie Anderson | .05 | .02 | 246 | Steve Jordan | .05 | .02 |
| 190 | Nick Bell | .25 | .15 | 247 | Carl Lee | .05 | .02 |
| 191 | Tim Brown | .08 | .05 | 248 | Randall McDaniel | .05 | .02 |
| 192 | Scott Davis | .05 | .02 | 249 | Mike Merriweather | .05 | .02 |
| 193 | Riki Ellison | .05 | .02 | 250 | Harry Newsome | .05 | .02 |
| 194 | Mervyn Fernandez | .07 | .04 | 251 | John Randle | .05 | .02 |

| | | | |
|---|---|---|---|
| 252 Henry Thomas | .05 | .02 |
| 253 Herschel Walker | .10 | .06 |
| 254 Ray Agnew | .05 | .02 |
| 255 Bruce Armstrong | .05 | .02 |
| 256 Vincent Brown | .05 | .02 |
| 257 Marv Cook | .05 | .02 |
| 258 Irving Fryar | .07 | .04 |
| 259 Pat Harlow | .05 | .02 |
| 260 Tommy Hodson | .08 | .05 |
| 261 Maurice Hurst | .05 | .02 |
| 262 Ronnie Lippett | .05 | .02 |
| 263 Eugene Lockhart | .05 | .02 |
| 264 Greg McMurtry | .08 | .05 |
| 265 Hugh Millen | .20 | .12 |
| 266 Leonard Russell | .30 | .18 |
| 267 Andre Tippett | .07 | .04 |
| 268 Brent Williams | .05 | .02 |
| 269 Morten Andersen | .07 | .04 |
| 270 Gene Atkin | .05 | .02 |
| 271 Wesley Carroll | .12 | .07 |
| 272 Jim Dombrowski | .05 | .02 |
| 273 Quinn Early | .05 | .02 |
| 274 Gill Fenerty | .05 | .02 |
| 275 Bobby Hebert | .12 | .07 |
| 276 Joel Hilgenberg | .05 | .02 |
| 277 Rickey Jackson | .07 | .04 |
| 278 Vaughan Johnson | .07 | .04 |
| 279 Eric Martin | .08 | .05 |
| 280 Brett Maxie | .05 | .02 |
| 281 Fred McAfee (R) | .15 | .10 |
| 282 Sam Mills | .07 | .04 |
| 283 Pat Swilling | .12 | .07 |
| 284 Floyd Turner | .05 | .02 |
| 285 Steve Walsh | .08 | .05 |
| 286 Frank Warren | .05 | .02 |
| 287 Stephen Baker | .05 | .02 |
| 288 Maurice Carthon | .05 | .02 |
| 289 Mark Collins | .05 | .02 |
| 290 John Elliott | .05 | .02 |
| 291 Myron Guyton | .05 | .02 |
| 292 Rodney Hampton | .25 | .15 |
| 293 Jeff Hostetler | .15 | .10 |
| 294 Mark Ingram | .05 | .02 |
| 295 Pepper Johnson | .05 | .02 |
| 296 Sean Landeta | .05 | .02 |
| 297 Leonrd Marshall | .05 | .02 |
| 298 Dave Meggett | .10 | .06 |
| 299 Bart Oates | .05 | .02 |
| 300 Phil Simms | .12 | .07 |
| 301 Reyna Thompson | .05 | .02 |
| 302 Lewis Tillman | .05 | .02 |
| 303 Brad Baxter | .12 | .07 |
| 304 Kyle Clifton | .05 | .02 |
| 305 James Hasty | .05 | .02 |
| 306 Joe Kelly | .05 | .02 |
| 307 Jeff Lageman | .07 | .04 |
| 308 Mo Lewis | .05 | .02 |
| 309 Erik McMillan | .05 | .02 |
| 310 Rob Moore | .20 | .12 |
| 311 Tony Stargell | .05 | .02 |
| 312 Jim Sweeney | .05 | .02 |
| 313 Marvin Washington | .05 | .02 |
| 314 Lonnie Young | .05 | .02 |
| 315 Eric Allen | .05 | .02 |
| 316 Fred Barnett | .15 | .10 |
| 317 Jerome Brown | .07 | .04 |
| 318 Keith Byars | .07 | .04 |
| 319 Wes Hopkins | .05 | .02 |
| 320 Keith Jackson | .12 | .07 |
| 321 James Joseph | .08 | .05 |
| 322 Seth Joyner | .07 | .04 |
| 323 Jeff Kemp | .05 | .02 |
| 324 Roger Ruzek | .05 | .02 |
| 325 Clyde Simmons | .07 | .04 |
| 326 William Thomas | .05 | .02 |
| 327 Reggie White | .12 | .07 |
| 328 Calvin Williams | .05 | .02 |
| 329 Rich Camarillo | .05 | .02 |
| 330 Ken Harvey | .05 | .02 |
| 331 Eric Hill | .05 | .02 |
| 332 Johnny Johnson | .15 | .10 |
| 333 Ernie Jones | .05 | .02 |
| 334 Tim Jorden | .05 | .02 |
| 335 Tim McDonald | .05 | .02 |
| 336 Freddie Joe Nunn | .05 | .02 |
| 337 Luis Sharpe | .05 | .02 |
| 338 Eric Swann | .07 | .04 |
| 339 Aeneas Williams | .05 | .02 |
| 340 Gary Anderson | .05 | .02 |
| 341 Bubby Brister | .10 | .06 |
| 342 Adrian Cooper | .05 | .02 |
| 343 Barry Foster | .50 | .30 |
| 344 Eric Green | .12 | .07 |
| 345 Bryan Hinkle | .05 | .02 |
| 346 Tunch Ilkin | .05 | .02 |
| 347 Carnell Lake | .05 | .02 |
| 348 Louis Lipps | .07 | .04 |
| 349 David Little | .05 | .02 |
| 350 Greg Lloyd | .05 | .02 |
| 351 Neil O'Donnell | .75 | .45 |
| 352 Dwight Stone | .05 | .02 |
| 353 Rod Woodson | .08 | .05 |
| 354 Rod Bernstine | .07 | .04 |
| 355 Eric Bieniemy | .10 | .06 |
| 356 Marion Butts | .12 | .07 |
| 357 Gill Byrd | .05 | .02 |
| 358 John Friesz | .10 | .06 |
| 359 Burt Grossman | .05 | .02 |
| 360 Courtney Hall | .05 | .02 |
| 361 Ronnie Harmon | .05 | .02 |
| 362 Shawn Jefferson | .05 | .02 |
| 363 Nate Lewis | .05 | .02 |
| 364 Craig McEwen (R) | .08 | .05 |
| 365 Eric Moten | .05 | .02 |

| # | Player | | |
|---|---|---|---|
| 366 | Joe Phillips | .05 | .02 |
| 367 | Gary Plummer | .05 | .02 |
| 368 | Henry Rolling | .05 | .02 |
| 369 | Broderick Thompson | .05 | .02 |
| 370 | Harris Barton | .05 | .02 |
| 371 | Steve Bono (R) | .30 | .18 |
| 372 | Todd Bowles | .05 | .02 |
| 373 | Dexter Carter | .08 | .05 |
| 374 | Michael Carter | .05 | .02 |
| 375 | Mike Cofer | .05 | .02 |
| 376 | Keith DeLong | .05 | .02 |
| 377 | Charles Haley | .07 | .04 |
| 378 | Merton Hanks | .05 | .02 |
| 379 | Tim Harris | .07 | .04 |
| 380 | Brent Jones | .07 | .04 |
| 381 | Guy McIntyre | .05 | .02 |
| 382 | Tom Rathman | .07 | .04 |
| 383 | Bill Romanowski | .05 | .02 |
| 384 | Jesse Sapolu | .05 | .02 |
| 385 | John Taylor | .12 | .07 |
| 386 | Steve Young | .30 | .18 |
| 387 | Robert Blackmon | .05 | .02 |
| 388 | Brian Blades | .07 | .04 |
| 389 | Jacob Green | .05 | .02 |
| 390 | Dwayne Harper | .05 | .02 |
| 391 | Andy Heck | .05 | .02 |
| 392 | Tommy Kane | .05 | .02 |
| 393 | John Kasay | .05 | .02 |
| 394 | Cortez Kennedy | .08 | .05 |
| 395 | Bryan Millard | .05 | .02 |
| 396 | Rufus Porter | .05 | .02 |
| 397 | Eugene Robinson | .05 | .02 |
| 398 | John L. Williams | .07 | .04 |
| 399 | Terry Wooden | .05 | .02 |
| 400 | Gary Anderson | .05 | .02 |
| 401 | Ian Beckles | .05 | .02 |
| 402 | Mark Carrier (TB) | .08 | .05 |
| 403 | Reggie Cobb | .12 | .07 |
| 404 | Lawrence Dawsey | .15 | .10 |
| 405 | Ron Hall | .05 | .02 |
| 406 | Keith McCants | .07 | .04 |
| 407 | Charles McRae | .05 | .02 |
| 408 | Tim Newton | .05 | .02 |
| 409 | Jesse Solomon | .05 | .02 |
| 410 | Vinny Testaverde | .10 | .06 |
| 411 | Broderick Thomas | .08 | .05 |
| 412 | Robert Wilson | .05 | .02 |
| 413 | Jeff Bostic | .05 | .02 |
| 414 | Earnest Byner | .08 | .05 |
| 415 | Gary Clark | .12 | .07 |
| 416 | Andre Collins | .07 | .04 |
| 417 | Brad Edwards | .05 | .02 |
| 418 | Kurt Gouveia | .05 | .02 |
| 419 | Darrell Green | .12 | .07 |
| 420 | Joe Jacoby | .05 | .02 |
| 421 | Jim Lachey | .07 | .04 |
| 422 | Chip Lohmiller | .05 | .02 |
| 423 | Charles Mann | .05 | .02 |
| 424 | Wilber Marshall | .07 | .04 |
| 425 | Ron Middleton (R) | .08 | .05 |
| 426 | Brian Mitchell | .07 | .04 |
| 427 | Art Monk | .20 | .12 |
| 428 | Mark Rypien | .20 | .12 |
| 429 | Ricky Sanders | .07 | .04 |
| 430 | Mark Schlereth (R) | .08 | .05 |
| 431 | Fred Stokes | .05 | .02 |
| 432 | Edgar Bennett (R) | .25 | .15 |
| 433 | Brian Bollinger (R) | .07 | .04 |
| 434 | Joe Bowden (R) | .07 | .04 |
| 435 | Terrell Buckley (R) | .60 | .35 |
| 436 | Willie Clay (R) | .08 | .05 |
| 437 | Steve Gordon (R) | .07 | .04 |
| 438 | Keith Hamilton (R) | .10 | .06 |
| 439 | Carlos Huerta (R) | .07 | .04 |
| 440 | Matt LaBounty (R) | .07 | .04 |
| 441 | Amp Lee (R) | .70 | .40 |
| 442 | Ricardo McDonald (R) | .08 | .05 |
| 443 | Chris Mims (R) | .35 | .20 |
| 444 | Michael Mooney (R) | .08 | .05 |
| 445 | Patrick Rowe (R) | .20 | .12 |
| 446 | Leon Searcy (R) | .10 | .06 |
| 447 | Siran Stacy (R) | .20 | .12 |
| 448 | Kevin Turner (R) | .15 | .10 |
| 449 | Tommy Vardell (R) | .75 | .45 |
| 450 | Bob Whitfield (R) | .10 | .06 |
| 451 | Darryl Williams (R) | .12 | .07 |
| 452 | Thurman Thomas (LL) | .20 | .12 |
| 453 | Emmitt Smith (LL) | .75 | .45 |
| 454 | Haywood Jeffires (LL) | .10 | .06 |
| 455 | Michael Irvin (LL) | .15 | .10 |
| 456 | Mark Clayton (LL) | .08 | .05 |
| 457 | Barry Sanders (LL) | .25 | .15 |
| 458 | Pete Stoyanovich (LL) | .05 | .02 |
| 459 | Chip Lohmiller (LL) | .05 | .02 |
| 460 | William Fuller (LL) | .07 | .04 |
| 561 | Pat Swilling (LL) | .08 | .05 |
| 462 | Ronnie Lott (LL) | .08 | .05 |
| 463 | Ray Crockett (LL) | .05 | .03 |
| 464 | Tim McKyer (LL) | .05 | .02 |
| 465 | Aeneas Williams (LL) | .05 | .02 |
| 466 | Rod Woodson (LL) | .08 | .05 |
| 467 | Mel Gray (LL) | .05 | .02 |
| 468 | Nate Lewis (LL) | .05 | .02 |
| 469 | Steve Young (LL) | .12 | .07 |
| 470 | Reggie Roby (LL) | .05 | .02 |
| 471 | John Elway (PV) | .12 | .07 |
| 472 | Ronnie Lott (PV) | .10 | .06 |
| 473 | Art Monk (PV) | .10 | .06 |
| 474 | Warren Moon (PV) | .12 | .07 |
| 475 | Emmitt Smith (PV) | .80 | .50 |
| 476 | Thurman Thomas (PV) | .25 | .15 |
| 477 | Checklist | .05 | .02 |

| 478 | Checklist | .05 | .02 |
| 479 | Checklist | .05 | .02 |
| 480 | Checklist | .05 | .02 |

# 1992 Fleer All-Pro

These insert cards were distributed randomly in 1992 Fleer wax packs. Card fronts consist of action photos set inside an NFL logo surrounded by a dark blue border. The player's name and position are printed in gold foil stamping in the lower left corner. A Fleer All-Pro headline is printed in bold type across the top. Card backs feature a small head shot and individual player highlights. The cards measure 2-1/2" by 3-1/2".

|  |  | MINT | NR/MT |
|---|---|---|---|
| Complete Set (24) |  | 9.00 | 6.00 |
| Commons |  | .35 | .20 |
| | | | |
| 1 | Marv Cook | .35 | .20 |
| 2 | Mike Kenn | .35 | .20 |
| 3 | Steve Wisniewski | .35 | .20 |
| 4 | Jim Ritcher | .35 | .20 |
| 5 | Jim Lachey | .40 | .25 |
| 6 | Michael Irvin | 1.75 | 1.00 |
| 7 | Andre Rison | 1.00 | .70 |
| 8 | Thurman Thomas | 2.50 | 1.40 |
| 9 | Barry Sanders | 3.00 | 2.00 |
| 10 | Bruce Matthews | .35 | .20 |
| 11 | Mark Rypien | 1.00 | .70 |
| 12 | Jeff Jaeger | .35 | .20 |
| 13 | Reggie White | .75 | .45 |
| 14 | Clyde Simmons | .35 | .20 |
| 15 | Pat Swilling | .60 | .35 |
| 16 | Sam Mills | .35 | .20 |
| 17 | Ray Childress | .35 | .20 |
| 18 | Jerry Ball | .35 | .20 |
| 19 | Derrick Thomas | 1.00 | .70 |
| 20 | Darrell Green | .50 | .35 |
| 21 | Ronnie Lott | .75 | .45 |
| 22 | Steve Atwater | .40 | .25 |
| 23 | Mark Carrier (Chi) | .40 | .25 |
| 24 | Jeff Gossett | .35 | .20 |

# 1992 Fleer Rookie Sensations

This insert set was randomly distributed in 1992 Fleer cello packs. Card fronts feature action photos that are tilted slightly to the left and framed by a green border with white yardline markers. The player's name is printe din gold below the photograph. A Rookie Sensations headline is trimmed in gold above the photo. Card backs contain the player's career highlights. All cards measure 2-1/2" by 3-1/2".

|  |  | MINT | NR/MT |
|---|---|---|---|
| Complete Set (20) |  | 60.00 | 38.00 |
| Commons |  | 3.00 | 2.00 |
| | | | |
| 1 | Moe Gardner | 3.00 | 2.00 |
| 2 | Mike Pritchard | 7.50 | 5.50 |
| 3 | Stan Thomas | 3.00 | 2.00 |
| 4 | Larry Brown | 3.00 | 2.00 |
| 5 | Todd Lyght | 3.50 | 2.50 |
| 6 | James Joseph | 3.50 | 2.50 |
| 7 | Aeneas Williams | 3.00 | 2.00 |
| 8 | Michael Jackson | 5.00 | 3.50 |
| 9 | Ed King | 3.00 | 2.00 |
| 10 | Mike Croel | 6.00 | 4.00 |
| 11 | Kenny Walker | 3.50 | 2.50 |
| 12 | Tim Barnett | 5.00 | 3.50 |
| 13 | Nick Bell | 6.50 | 4.50 |
| 14 | Todd Marinovich | 8.50 | 5.75 |
| 15 | Leonard Russell | 7.00 | 5.00 |
| 16 | Pat Harlow | 3.00 | 2.00 |
| 17 | Mo Lewis | 3.00 | 2.00 |
| 18 | John Kasay | 3.00 | 2.00 |
| 19 | Lawrence Dawsey | 5.00 | 3.50 |
| 20 | Charles McRae | 3.00 | 2.00 |

# 1992 Fleer
# Team Leaders

The insert cards in this set were randomly distributed in 1992 Fleer rack packs. Card fronts feature full color action shots framed by a black border. The player's name, team and position are printed in gold foil stamping across the bottom of the card. A Team Leader logo appears in the lower right corner. Card backs contain a small head shot the player's career highlights. All cards measure 2-1/2" by 3-1/2".

|  |  | MINT | NR/MT |
|---|---|---|---|
| Complete Set (24) |  | 38.50 | 28.50 |
| Commons |  | 1.00 | .70 |
|  |  |  |  |
| 1 | Chris Miller | 2.50 | 1.50 |
| 2 | Neal Anderson | 2.00 | 1.25 |
| 3 | Emmitt Smith | 10.00 | 7.50 |
| 4 | Chris Spielman | 1.00 | .70 |
| 5 | Brian Noble | 1.00 | .70 |
| 6 | Jim Everett | 1.75 | 1.00 |
| 7 | Joey Browner | 1.00 | .70 |
| 8 | Sam Mills | 1.00 | .70 |
| 9 | Rodney Hampton | 4.50 | 3.00 |
| 10 | Reggie White | 1.50 | .90 |
| 11 | Tim McDonald | 1.00 | .70 |
| 12 | Charles Haley | 1.25 | .80 |
| 13 | Mark Rypien | 2.50 | 1.50 |
| 14 | Cornelius Bennett | 1.50 | .90 |
| 15 | Clay Matthews | 1.00 | .70 |
| 16 | John Elway | 3.00 | 2.00 |
| 17 | Warren Moon | 2.50 | 1.50 |
| 18 | Derrick Thomas | 2.50 | 1.50 |
| 19 | Greg Townsend | 1.00 | .70 |
| 20 | Bruce Armstrong | 1.00 | .70 |
| 21 | Brad Baxter | 1.50 | .90 |
| 22 | Rod Woodson | 1.25 | .80 |
| 23 | Marion Butts | 1.25 | .80 |
| 24 | Rufus Porter | 1.00 | .70 |

# 1992 Fleer Ultra

For the second straight year Fleer issued a high-end football set under the Ultra label. The set consists of 450-cards which feature full-bleed full color action photos on the card fronts. The player's name appears in a color bar below his photo. His team and position are printed in a smaller color bar below his name. Card backs feature full color action shots, persoanl data and stats. Two 10-card limited insert sets featuring quarterback Chris Miller and Defensive End Reggie White were randomly distributed in Ultra foil packs. Those cards are listed at the end of this checklist but are not included in the complete set price below. All cards measure 2-1/2" by 3-1/2".

|  |  | MINT | NR/MT |
|---|---|---|---|
| Complete Set (450) |  | 28.50 | 16.50 |
| Commons |  | .10 | .06 |
|  |  |  |  |
| 1 | Steve Broussard | .12 | .07 |
| 2 | Rick Bryan | .10 | .06 |
| 3 | Scott Case | .10 | .06 |
| 4 | Darrion Conner | .10 | .06 |
| 5 | Bill Fralic | .10 | .06 |
| 6 | Moe Gardner | .10 | .06 |
| 7 | Tim Green | .10 | .06 |
| 8 | Michael Haynes | .35 | .20 |
| 9 | Chris Hinton | .10 | .06 |
| 10 | Mike Kenn | .10 | .06 |
| 11 | Tim McKyer | .10 | .06 |
| 12 | Chris Miller | .40 | .25 |
| 13 | Erric Pegram | .12 | .07 |
| 14 | Mike Pritchard | .35 | .20 |
| 15 | Andre Rison | .35 | .20 |
| 16 | Jessie Tuggle | .10 | .06 |
| 17 | Carlton Bailey (R) | .15 | .10 |

| | | | |
|---|---|---|---|
| 18 Howard Ballard | .10 | .06 |
| 19 Cornelius Bennett | .20 | .12 |
| 20 Shane Conlan | .12 | .07 |
| 21 Kenneth Davis | .15 | .10 |
| 22 Kent Hull | .10 | .06 |
| 23 Mark Kelso | .10 | .06 |
| 24 James Lofton | .25 | .15 |
| 25 Keith McKeller | .12 | .07 |
| 26 Nate Odomes | .10 | .06 |
| 27 Jim Ritcher | .10 | .06 |
| 28 Leon Seals | .10 | .06 |
| 29 Darryl Talley | .12 | .07 |
| 30 Steve Tasker | .10 | .06 |
| 31 Thurman Thomas | 1.50 | .90 |
| 32 Will Wolford | .10 | .06 |
| 33 Jeff Wright | .10 | .06 |
| 34 Neal Anderson | .15 | .10 |
| 35 Trace Armstrong | .10 | .06 |
| 36 Mark Carrier (Chi) | .12 | .07 |
| 37 Wendell Davis | .20 | .12 |
| 38 Richard Dent | .12 | .07 |
| 39 Shaun Gayle | .10 | .06 |
| 40 Jim Harbaugh | .25 | .15 |
| 41 Jay Hilgenberg | .10 | .06 |
| 42 Darren Lewis | .20 | .12 |
| 43 Steve McMichael | .12 | .07 |
| 44 Anthony Morgan | .15 | .10 |
| 45 Brad Muster | .12 | .07 |
| 46 William Perry | .12 | .07 |
| 47 John Roper | .10 | .06 |
| 48 Lemuel Stinson | .10 | .06 |
| 49 Tom Waddle | .25 | .15 |
| 50 Donnell Woolford | .10 | .06 |
| 51 Leo Barker (R) | .12 | .07 |
| 52 Eddie Brown | .12 | .07 |
| 53 James Francis | .12 | .07 |
| 54 David Fulcher | .10 | .06 |
| 55 David Grant | .10 | .06 |
| 56 Harold Green | .40 | .25 |
| 57 Rodney Holman | .10 | .06 |
| 58 Lee Johnson | .10 | .06 |
| 59 Tim Krumrie | .10 | .06 |
| 60 Tim McGee | .12 | .07 |
| 61 Alonzo Mitz (R) | .12 | .07 |
| 62 Anthony Munoz | .15 | .10 |
| 63 Alfred Williams | .12 | .07 |
| 64 Stephen Braggs | .10 | .06 |
| 65 Richard Brown (R) | .15 | .10 |
| 66 Randy Hilliard (R) | .12 | .07 |
| 67 Leroy Hoard | .15 | .10 |
| 68 Michael Jackson | .30 | .18 |
| 69 Mike Johnson | .10 | .06 |
| 70 James Jones | .10 | .06 |
| 71 Tony Jones | .10 | .06 |
| 72 Ed King | .10 | .06 |
| 73 Kevin Mack | .12 | .07 |
| 74 Clay Matthews | .10 | .06 |

| | | | |
|---|---|---|---|
| 75 Eric Metcalf | .15 | .10 |
| 76 Vince Newsome | .10 | .06 |
| 77 Steve Beuerlein | .20 | .12 |
| 78 Larry Brown | .10 | .06 |
| 79 Tony Casillas | .12 | .07 |
| 80 Alvin Harper | .60 | .35 |
| 81 Issiac Holt | .10 | .06 |
| 82 Ray Horton | .10 | .06 |
| 83 Michael Irvin | .75 | .45 |
| 84 Daryl Johnston | .10 | .06 |
| 85 Kelvin Martin | .12 | .07 |
| 86 Ken Norton | .10 | .06 |
| 87 Jay Novacek | .15 | .10 |
| 88 Emmitt Smith | 4.50 | 2.75 |
| 89 Vinson Smith (R) | .15 | .10 |
| 90 Mark Stepnoski | .10 | .06 |
| 91 Tony Tolbert | .10 | .06 |
| 92 Alexander Wright | .15 | .10 |
| 93 Steve Atwater | .15 | .10 |
| 94 Tyrone Braxton | .10 | .06 |
| 95 Michael Brooks | .10 | .06 |
| 96 Mike Croel | .25 | .15 |
| 97 John Elway | .35 | .20 |
| 98 Simon Fletcher | .10 | .06 |
| 99 Gaston Green | .25 | .15 |
| 100 Mark Jackson | .12 | .07 |
| 101 Keith Kartz | .10 | .06 |
| 102 Greg Kragen | .10 | .06 |
| 103 Greg Lewis | .12 | .07 |
| 104 Karl Mecklenburg | .12 | .07 |
| 105 Derek Russell | .15 | .10 |
| 106 Steve Sewell | .10 | .06 |
| 107 Dennis Smith | .10 | .06 |
| 108 David Treadwell | .10 | .06 |
| 109 Kenny Walker | .15 | .10 |
| 110 Michael Young | .10 | .06 |
| 111 Jerry Ball | .10 | .06 |
| 112 Bennie Blades | .12 | .07 |
| 113 Lomas Brown | .10 | .06 |
| 114 Scott Conover (R) | .12 | .07 |
| 115 Ray Crockett | .10 | .06 |
| 116 Mel Gray | .10 | .06 |
| 117 Willie Green | .30 | .18 |
| 118 Erik Kramer | .25 | .15 |
| 119 Dan Owens | .10 | .06 |
| 120 Rodney Peete | .20 | .12 |
| 121 Brett Perriman | .12 | .07 |
| 122 Barry Sanders | 3.00 | 2.00 |
| 123 Chris Spielman | .12 | .07 |
| 124 Mark Spindler | .10 | .06 |
| 125 Willie White | .10 | .06 |
| 126 Tony Bennett | .15 | .10 |
| 127 Matt Brock | .10 | .06 |
| 128 Leroy Butler | .10 | .06 |
| 129 Chuck Cecil | .10 | .06 |
| 130 Johnny Holland | .10 | .06 |
| 131 Perry Kemp | .10 | .06 |

| | | | |
|---|---|---|---|
| 132 | Don Majkowski | .20 | .12 |
| 133 | Tony Mandarich | .10 | .06 |
| 134 | Brian Noble | .10 | .06 |
| 135 | Bryce Paup | .10 | .06 |
| 136 | Sterling Sharpe | .60 | .35 |
| 137 | Darrell Thompson | .15 | .10 |
| 138 | Mike Tomczak | .12 | .07 |
| 139 | Vince Workman | .12 | .07 |
| 140 | Ray Childress | .12 | .07 |
| 141 | Cris Dishman | .12 | .07 |
| 142 | Curtis Duncan | .12 | .07 |
| 143 | William Fuller | .10 | .06 |
| 144 | Ernest Givens | .25 | .15 |
| 145 | Haywood Jeffires | .40 | .25 |
| 146 | Sean Jones | .10 | .06 |
| 147 | Lamar Lathon | .12 | .07 |
| 148 | Bruce Matthews | .10 | .06 |
| 149 | Bubba McDowell | .10 | .06 |
| 150 | Johnny Meads | .10 | .06 |
| 151 | Warren Moon | .35 | .20 |
| 152 | Mike Munchak | .10 | .06 |
| 153 | Bo Orlando (R) | .15 | .10 |
| 154 | Al Smith | .10 | .06 |
| 155 | Doug Smith | .10 | .06 |
| 156 | Lorenzo White | .25 | .15 |
| 157 | Chip Banks | .10 | .06 |
| 158 | Duane Bickett | .10 | .06 |
| 159 | Bill Brooks | .10 | .06 |
| 160 | Jon Hand | .10 | .06 |
| 161 | Jeff Herrod | .10 | .06 |
| 162 | Jessie Hester | .10 | .06 |
| 163 | Scott Radecic | .10 | .06 |
| 164 | Rohn Stark | .10 | .06 |
| 165 | Clarence Verdin | .12 | .07 |
| 166 | Eugene Daniel | .10 | .06 |
| 167 | John Alt | .10 | .06 |
| 168 | Tim Barnett | .25 | .15 |
| 169 | Tim Grunhard | .10 | .06 |
| 170 | Dino Hackett | .10 | .06 |
| 171 | Jonathan Hayes | .10 | .06 |
| 172 | Bill Maas | .10 | .06 |
| 173 | Chris Martin | .10 | .06 |
| 174 | Christian Okoye | .25 | .15 |
| 175 | Stephone Paige | .12 | .07 |
| 176 | Jayice Pearson (R) | .15 | .10 |
| 177 | Kevin Porter | .10 | .06 |
| 178 | Kevin Ross | .10 | .06 |
| 179 | Dan Saleaumua | .10 | .06 |
| 180 | Tracy Simien (R) | .15 | .10 |
| 181 | Neil Smith | .10 | .06 |
| 182 | Derrick Thomas | .35 | .20 |
| 183 | Robb Thomas | .10 | .06 |
| 184 | Barry Word | .30 | .18 |
| 185 | Marcus Allen | .20 | .12 |
| 186 | Eddie Anderson | .10 | .06 |
| 187 | Nick Bell | .40 | .25 |
| 188 | Tim Brown | .20 | .12 |
| 189 | Mervyn Fernandez | .15 | .10 |
| 190 | Willie Gault | .10 | .06 |
| 191 | Jeff Gossett | .10 | .06 |
| 192 | Ethan Horton | .12 | .07 |
| 193 | Jeff Jaeger | .10 | .06 |
| 194 | Howie Long | .12 | .07 |
| 195 | Ronnie Lott | .25 | .15 |
| 196 | Todd Marinovich | 1.00 | .70 |
| 197 | Don Mosebar | .10 | .06 |
| 198 | Jay Schroeder | .20 | .12 |
| 199 | Anthony Smith | .10 | .06 |
| 200 | Greg Townsend | .12 | .07 |
| 201 | Lionel Washington | .10 | .06 |
| 202 | Steve Wisniewski | .10 | .06 |
| 203 | Willie Anderson | .15 | .10 |
| 204 | Robert Delpino | .15 | .10 |
| 205 | Henry Ellard | .12 | .07 |
| 206 | Jim Everett | .20 | .12 |
| 207 | Kevin Greene | .10 | .06 |
| 208 | Darryl Henley | .10 | .06 |
| 209 | Damone Johnson | .10 | .06 |
| 210 | Larry Kelm | .10 | .06 |
| 211 | Todd Lyght | .20 | .12 |
| 212 | Jackie Slater | .12 | .07 |
| 213 | Michael Stewart | .10 | .06 |
| 214 | Pat Terrell | .10 | .06 |
| 215 | Robert Young | .10 | .06 |
| 216 | Mark Clayton | .25 | .15 |
| 217 | Bryan Cox | .10 | .06 |
| 218 | Jeff Cross | .10 | .06 |
| 219 | Mark Duper | .15 | .10 |
| 220 | Harry Galbreath | .10 | .06 |
| 221 | David Griggs | .10 | .06 |
| 222 | Mark Higgs | .30 | .18 |
| 224 | John Offerdahl | .12 | .07 |
| 225 | Louis Oliver | .12 | .07 |
| 226 | Tony Paige | .10 | .06 |
| 227 | Reggie Roby | .10 | .06 |
| 228 | Pete Stoyanovich | .10 | .06 |
| 229 | Richmond Webb | .12 | .07 |
| 230 | Terry Allen | 1.00 | .70 |
| 231 | Ray Berry | .10 | .06 |
| 232 | Anthony Carter | .15 | .10 |
| 233 | Cris Carter | .30 | .18 |
| 234 | Chris Doleman | .12 | .07 |
| 235 | Rich Gannon | .25 | .15 |
| 236 | Steve Jordan | .10 | .06 |
| 237 | Carl Lee | .10 | .06 |
| 238 | Randall McDaniel | .10 | .06 |
| 239 | Mike Merriweather | .10 | .06 |
| 240 | Harry Newsome | .10 | .06 |
| 241 | John Randle | .10 | .06 |
| 242 | Harry Newsome | .10 | .06 |
| 243 | Bruce Armstrong | .10 | .06 |
| 244 | Vincent Brown | .10 | .06 |
| 245 | Marv Cook | .12 | .07 |
| 246 | Irving Fryar | .12 | .07 |

| | | | |
|---|---|---|---|
| 247 Pat Harlow | .10 | .06 |
| 248 Maurice Hurst | .10 | .06 |
| 249 Eugene Lockhart | .10 | .06 |
| 250 Greg McMurtry | .15 | .10 |
| 251 Hugh Millen | .30 | .18 |
| 252 Leonard Russell | .75 | .45 |
| 253 Chris Singleton | .12 | .07 |
| 254 Andre Tippett | .12 | .07 |
| 255 Jon Vaughn | .30 | .18 |
| 256 Morten Andersen | .12 | .07 |
| 257 Gene Atkins | .10 | .06 |
| 258 Wesley Carroll | .30 | .18 |
| 259 Jim Dombrowski | .10 | .06 |
| 260 Quinn Early | .12 | .07 |
| 261 Bobby Hebert | .20 | .12 |
| 262 Joel Hilgenberg | .10 | .06 |
| 263 Rickey Jackson | .12 | .07 |
| 264 Vaughan Johnson | .12 | .07 |
| 265 Eric Martin | .12 | .07 |
| 266 Brett Maxie | .10 | .06 |
| 267 Fred McAfee (R) | .25 | .15 |
| 268 Sam Mills | .12 | .07 |
| 269 Pat Swilling | .20 | .12 |
| 270 Floyd Turner | .10 | .06 |
| 271 Steve Walsh | .15 | .10 |
| 272 Stephen Baker | .10 | .06 |
| 273 Jarrod Bunch | .25 | .15 |
| 274 Mark Collins | .12 | .07 |
| 275 John Elliott | .10 | .06 |
| 276 Myron Guyton | .10 | .06 |
| 277 Rodney Hampton | .60 | .35 |
| 278 Jeff Hostetler | .20 | .12 |
| 279 Mark Ingram | .12 | .07 |
| 280 Pepper Johnson | .12 | .07 |
| 281 Sean Landeta | .10 | .06 |
| 282 Leonard Marshall | .12 | .07 |
| 283 Kanavis McGhee | .15 | .10 |
| 284 Dave Meggett | .20 | .12 |
| 285 Bart Oates | .10 | .06 |
| 286 Phil Simms | .20 | .12 |
| 287 Reyna Thompson | .10 | .06 |
| 288 Lewis Tillman | .10 | .06 |
| 289 Brad Baxter | .15 | .10 |
| 290 Mike Brim (R) | .12 | .07 |
| 291 Chris Burkett | .10 | .06 |
| 292 Kyle Clifton | .10 | .06 |
| 293 James Hasty | .10 | .06 |
| 294 Joe Kelly | .10 | .06 |
| 295 Jeff Lageman | .12 | .07 |
| 296 Mo Lewis | .12 | .07 |
| 297 Erik McMillan | .10 | .06 |
| 298 Scott Mersereau | .10 | .06 |
| 299 Rob Moore | .30 | .18 |
| 300 Tony Stargell | .10 | .06 |
| 301 Jim Sweeney | .10 | .06 |
| 302 Marvin Washington | .10 | .06 |
| 303 Lonnie Young | .10 | .06 |
| 304 Eric Allen | .10 | .06 |
| 305 Fred Barnett | .35 | .20 |
| 306 Keith Byars | .12 | .07 |
| 307 Byron Evans | .10 | .06 |
| 308 Wes Hopkins | .10 | .06 |
| 309 Keith Jackson | .20 | .12 |
| 310 James Joseph | .15 | .10 |
| 311 Seth Joyner | .12 | .07 |
| 312 Roger Ruzek | .10 | .06 |
| 313 Clyde Simmons | .12 | .07 |
| 314 William Thomas | .10 | .06 |
| 315 Reggie White | .20 | .12 |
| 316 Calvin Williams | .15 | .10 |
| 317 Rich Camarillo | .10 | .06 |
| 318 Jeff Faulkner | .10 | .06 |
| 319 Ken Harvey | .10 | .06 |
| 320 Eric Hill | .10 | .06 |
| 321 Johnny Johnson | .25 | .15 |
| 322 Ernie Jones | .15 | .10 |
| 323 Tim McDonald | .10 | .06 |
| 324 Freddie Joe Nunn | .10 | .06 |
| 325 Luis Sharpe | .10 | .06 |
| 326 Eric Swann | .12 | .07 |
| 327 Aeneas Williams | .10 | .06 |
| 328 Mike Zordich (R) | .12 | .07 |
| 329 Gary Anderson | .10 | .06 |
| 330 Bubby Brister | .15 | .10 |
| 331 Barry Foster | 1.50 | .90 |
| 332 Eric Green | .20 | .12 |
| 333 Bryan Hinkle | .10 | .06 |
| 334 Tunch Ilkin | .10 | .06 |
| 335 Carnell Lake | .10 | .06 |
| 336 Louis Lipps | .10 | .06 |
| 337 David Little | .10 | .06 |
| 338 Greg Lloyd | .10 | .06 |
| 339 Neil O'Donnell | .80 | .50 |
| 340 Rod Woodson | .20 | .12 |
| 341 Rod Bernstine | .12 | .07 |
| 342 Marion Butts | .20 | .12 |
| 343 Gill Byrd | .10 | .06 |
| 344 John Friesz | .15 | .10 |
| 345 Burt Grossman | .12 | .07 |
| 346 Courtney Hall | .10 | .06 |
| 347 Ronnie Harmon | .12 | .07 |
| 348 Shawn Jefferson | .15 | .10 |
| 349 Nate Lewis | .15 | .10 |
| 350 Craig McEwen | .15 | .10 |
| 351 Eric Moten | .10 | .06 |
| 352 Gary Plummer | .10 | .06 |
| 353 Henry Rolling | .10 | .06 |
| 354 Broderick Thompson | .10 | .06 |
| 355 Derrick Walker | .15 | .10 |
| 356 Harris Barton | .10 | .06 |
| 357 Steve Bono (R) | .80 | .50 |
| 358 Todd Bowles | .10 | .06 |
| 359 Dexter Carter | .15 | .10 |
| 360 Michael Carter | .10 | .06 |

| | | | |
|---|---|---|---|
| 361 | Keith DeLong | .10 | .06 |
| 362 | Charles Haley | .12 | .07 |
| 363 | Merton Hanks | .10 | .06 |
| 364 | Tim Harris | .10 | .06 |
| 365 | Brent Jones | .15 | .10 |
| 366 | Guy McIntyre | .10 | .06 |
| 367 | Tom Rathman | .15 | .10 |
| 368 | Bill Romanowski | .10 | .06 |
| 369 | Jesse Sapolu | .10 | .06 |
| 370 | John Taylor | .25 | .15 |
| 371 | Steve Young | .50 | .30 |
| 372 | Robert Blackmon | .10 | .06 |
| 373 | Brain Blades | .12 | .07 |
| 374 | Jacob Green | .10 | .06 |
| 375 | Dwayne Harper | .10 | .06 |
| 376 | Andy Heck | .10 | .06 |
| 377 | Tommy Kane | .12 | .07 |
| 378 | John Kasay | .10 | .06 |
| 379 | Cortez Kennedy | .15 | .10 |
| 380 | Bryan Millard | .10 | .06 |
| 381 | Rufus Porter | .10 | .06 |
| 382 | Eugene Robinson | .10 | .06 |
| 383 | John L. Williams | .12 | .07 |
| 384 | Terry Wooden | .10 | .06 |
| 385 | Gary Anderson | .10 | .06 |
| 386 | Ian Beckles | .10 | .06 |
| 387 | Mark Carrier (TB) | .12 | .07 |
| 388 | Reggie Cobb | .25 | .15 |
| 389 | Tony Covington | .10 | .06 |
| 390 | Lawrence Dawsey | .25 | .15 |
| 391 | Ron Hall | .10 | .06 |
| 392 | Keith McCants | .12 | .07 |
| 393 | Charles McRae | .10 | .06 |
| 394 | Tim Newton | .10 | .06 |
| 395 | Jesse Solomon | .10 | .06 |
| 396 | Vinny Testaverde | .20 | .12 |
| 397 | Broderick Thomas | .15 | .10 |
| 398 | Robert Wilson | .12 | .07 |
| 399 | Earnest Byner | .12 | .07 |
| 400 | Gary Clark | .30 | .18 |
| 401 | Andre Collins | .12 | .07 |
| 402 | Brad Edwards | .10 | .06 |
| 403 | Kurt Gouveia | .10 | .06 |
| 404 | Darrell Green | .20 | .12 |
| 405 | Joe Jacoby | .10 | .06 |
| 407 | Chip Lohmiller | .10 | .06 |
| 408 | Charles Mann | .10 | .06 |
| 409 | Wilber Marshall | .12 | .07 |
| 410 | Brian Mitchell | .15 | .10 |
| 411 | Art Monk | .40 | .25 |
| 412 | Mark Rypien | .25 | .15 |
| 413 | Ricky Sanders | .15 | .10 |
| 414 | Mark Schlereth (R) | .15 | .10 |
| 415 | Fred Stokes | .10 | .06 |
| 416 | Bobby Wilson | .10 | .06 |
| 417 | Corey Barlow (R) | .15 | .10 |
| 418 | Edgar Bennett (R) | .60 | .35 |

| | | | |
|---|---|---|---|
| 419 | Eddie Blake (R) | .20 | .12 |
| 420 | Terrell Buckley (R) | .75 | .45 |
| 421 | Willie Clay (R) | .20 | .12 |
| 422 | Rodney Culver (R) | .25 | .15 |
| 423 | Ed Cunningham (R) | .15 | .10 |
| 424 | Mark D'Onofrio (R) | .15 | .10 |
| 425 | Matt Darby (R) | .15 | .10 |
| 426 | Charles Davenport (R) | .30 | .18 |
| 427 | Will Furrer (R) | .70 | .40 |
| 428 | Keith Goganious (R) | .15 | .10 |
| 429 | Mario Bailey (R) | .12 | .07 |
| 430 | Chris Hakel (R) | .15 | .10 |
| 431 | Keith Hamilton (R) | .20 | .12 |
| 432 | Aaron Pierce (R) | .15 | .10 |
| 433 | Amp Lee (R) | 1.25 | .80 |
| 434 | Scott Lockwood (R) | .15 | .10 |
| 435 | Ricardo McDonald (R) | .20 | .12 |
| 436 | Dexter McNabb (R) | .25 | .15 |
| 437 | Chris Mims (R) | .30 | .18 |
| 438 | Mike Mooney (R) | .15 | .10 |
| 439 | Ray Roberts (R) | .15 | .10 |
| 440 | Patrick Rowe (R) | .25 | .15 |
| 441 | Leon Searcy (R) | .15 | .10 |
| 442 | Siran Stacy (R) | .50 | .30 |
| 443 | Kevin Turner (R) | .25 | .15 |
| 444 | Tommy Vardell (R) | 1.50 | .90 |
| 445 | Bob Whitfield (R) | .20 | .12 |
| 446 | Darryl Williams (R) | .35 | .20 |
| 447 | Checklist | .10 | .06 |
| 448 | Checklist | .10 | .06 |
| 449 | Checklist | .10 | .06 |
| 450 | Checklist | .10 | .06 |
| BC | Chris Miller Inserts ea. | 3.00 | 2.00 |
| BC | Chris Miller(Signed) | 100.00 | 60.00 |
| BC | Reggie White Inserts ea. | 3.00 | 2.00 |
| BC | Reggie White(Signed) | 100.00 | 60.00 |

# 1992 Fleer Ultra Award Winners

These random inserts were distributed in Fleer Ultra foil packs. The card fronts feature full color action shots with the Ultra logo in the top corner and an Award Winner plaque in the lower corner. Card backs feature a close-up head shot with the player's name printed in a banner below the photo, a brief description of the award and a bio. All cards measure 2-1.2" by 3-1/2".

|   |   | MINT | NR/MT |
|---|---|------|-------|
| Complete Set (10) | | 48.00 | 32.00 |
| Commons | | 2.00 | 1.25 |
| | | | |
| 1 | Mark Rypien | 3.00 | 2.00 |
| 2 | Cornelius Bennett | 2.00 | 1.25 |
| 3 | Anthony Munoz | 2.00 | 1.25 |
| 4 | Lawrence Dawsey | 3.00 | 2.00 |
| 5 | Thurman Thomas | 8.50 | 5.50 |
| 6 | Michael Irvin | 8.00 | 5.00 |
| 7 | Mike Croel | 2.50 | 1.50 |
| 8 | Barry Sanders | 10.00 | 7.00 |
| 9 | Pat Swilling | 2.50 | 1.50 |
| 10 | Leonard Russell | 3.50 | 2.25 |

# 1993 Fleer

This 500-card set features huge full-color player photos on the front framed by a gray border. The player's last name is superimposed in clear block letters across the bottom of the card. His team and position are printed in smaller white type in the lower right corner. The horizontal card backs contain a large posed photo, personal data, stats and a paragraph devoted to 1992 highlights. Key subsets include League Leaders (LL), Award Winners (AW) and Pro Visions (PV). All cards measure 2-1/2" by 3-1/2".

|   |   | MINT | NR/MT |
|---|---|------|-------|
| Complete Set (500) | | 16.00 | 10.00 |
| Commons | | .05 | .02 |
| | | | |
| 1 | Dan Saleaumoa | .05 | .02 |
| 2 | Bryan Cox | .15 | .10 |
| 3 | Dermontti Dawson | .05 | .02 |
| 4 | Michael Jackson | .15 | .10 |
| 5 | Calvin Williams | .10 | .06 |
| 6 | Terry McDaniel | .05 | .02 |
| 7 | Jack Del Rio | .05 | .02 |
| 8 | Steve Atwater | .08 | .05 |
| 9 | Ernie Jones | .12 | .07 |
| 10 | Brad Muster | .08 | .05 |
| 11 | Harold Green | .20 | .12 |
| 12 | Eric Bieniemy | .12 | .07 |
| 13 | Eric Dorsey | .05 | .02 |
| 14 | Fred Barnett | .15 | .10 |
| 15 | Cleveland Gary | .12 | .07 |
| 16 | Darion Conner | .05 | .02 |
| 17 | Jerry Ball | .05 | .02 |
| 18 | Tony Casillas | .07 | .04 |
| 19 | Brian Blades | .07 | .04 |
| 20 | Tony Bennett | .08 | .05 |
| 21 | Reggie Cobb | .15 | .10 |

| | | | |
|---|---|---|---|
| 22 Kurt Gouveia | .05 | .02 |
| 23 Greg McMurtry | .08 | .05 |
| 24 Kyle Clifton | .05 | .02 |
| 25 Trace Armstrong | .05 | .02 |
| 26 Terry Allen | .35 | .20 |
| 27 Steve Bono | .25 | .15 |
| 28 Barry Word | .15 | .10 |
| 29 Mark Duper | .08 | .05 |
| 30 Nate Newton | .05 | .02 |
| 31 Will Wolford | .05 | .02 |
| 32 Curtis Duncan | .08 | .05 |
| 33 Nick Bell | .20 | .12 |
| 34 Don Beebe | .15 | .10 |
| 35 Mike Croel | .10 | .06 |
| 36 Rich Camarillo | .05 | .02 |
| 37 Wade Wilson | .15 | .10 |
| 38 John Taylor | .12 | .07 |
| 39 Marion Butts | .10 | .06 |
| 40 Rodney Hampton | .25 | .15 |
| 41 Seth Joyner | .07 | .04 |
| 42 Wilber Marshall | .08 | .05 |
| 43 Bobby Hebert | .15 | .10 |
| 44 Bennie Blades | .07 | .04 |
| 45 Thomas Everett | .05 | .02 |
| 46 Ricky Sanders | .08 | .05 |
| 47 Matt Brock | .05 | .02 |
| 48 Lawrence Dawsey | .15 | .10 |
| 49 Brad Edwards | .05 | .02 |
| 50 Vincent Brown | .05 | .02 |
| 51 Jeff Lageman | .07 | .04 |
| 52 Mark Carrier (Chi) | .08 | .05 |
| 53 Cris Carter | .12 | .07 |
| 54 Brent Jones | .08 | .05 |
| 55 Barry Foster | .50 | .30 |
| 56 Derrick Thomas | .20 | .12 |
| 57 Scott Zolak | .15 | .10 |
| 58 Mark Strepnoski | .05 | .02 |
| 59 Eric Metcalf | .15 | .10 |
| 60 Al Smith | .07 | .04 |
| 61 Ronnie Harmon | .15 | .10 |
| 62 Cornelius Bennett | .10 | .06 |
| 63 Karl Mecklenburg | .07 | .04 |
| 64 Chris Chandler | .15 | .10 |
| 65 Toi Cook | .05 | .02 |
| 66 Tim Krumrie | .05 | .02 |
| 67 Gill Byrd | .05 | .02 |
| 68 Mark Jackson | .08 | .05 |
| 69 Tim Harris | .05 | .02 |
| 70 Shane Conlan | .07 | .04 |
| 71 Moe Gardner | .05 | .02 |
| 72 Lomas Brown | .05 | .02 |
| 73 Charles Haley | .08 | .05 |
| 74 Mark Rypien | .20 | .12 |
| 75 LeRoy Butler | .05 | .02 |
| 76 Steve DeBerg | .10 | .06 |
| 77 Darrell Green | .10 | .06 |
| 78 Marv Cook | .08 | .05 |

| | | | |
|---|---|---|---|
| 79 Chris Burkett | .05 | .02 |
| 80 Richard Dent | .07 | .04 |
| 81 Roger Craig | .08 | .05 |
| 82 Amp Lee | .30 | .18 |
| 83 Eric Green | .10 | .06 |
| 84 Willie Davis | .05 | .02 |
| 85 Mark Higgs | .15 | .10 |
| 86 Carlton Haselrig | .05 | .02 |
| 87 Tommy Vardell | .30 | .18 |
| 88 Haywood Jeffires | .15 | .10 |
| 89 Tim Brown | .15 | .10 |
| 90 Randall McDaniel | .05 | .02 |
| 91 John Elway | .20 | .12 |
| 92 Ken Harvey | .05 | .02 |
| 93 Joel Hilgenberg | .05 | .02 |
| 94 Steve Wallace | .05 | .02 |
| 95 Stan Humphries | .25 | .15 |
| 96 Greg Jackson | .05 | .02 |
| 97 Clyde Simmons | .07 | .04 |
| 98 Jim Everett | .12 | .07 |
| 99 Michael Haynes | .20 | .12 |
| 100 Mel Gray | .05 | .02 |
| 101 Alvin Harper | .25 | .15 |
| 102 Art Monk | .15 | .10 |
| 103 Brett Favre | .60 | .35 |
| 104 Keith McCants | .05 | .02 |
| 105 Charles Mann | .05 | .02 |
| 106 Leonard Russell | .20 | .12 |
| 107 Mo Lewis | .05 | .02 |
| 108 Shaun Gayle | .05 | .02 |
| 109 Chris Doleman | .07 | .04 |
| 110 Tim McDonald | .07 | .04 |
| 111 Louis Oliver | .07 | .04 |
| 112 Greg Lloyd | .05 | .02 |
| 113 Chip Banks | .05 | .02 |
| 114 Sean Jones | .05 | .02 |
| 115 Ethan Hortan | .07 | .04 |
| 116 Kenneth Davis | .10 | .06 |
| 117 Simon Fletcher | .05 | .02 |
| 118 Johnny Johnson | .15 | .10 |
| 119 Vaughn Johnson | .07 | .04 |
| 120 Derrick Fenner | .12 | .07 |
| 121 Nate Lewis | .05 | .02 |
| 122 Pepper Johnson | .05 | .02 |
| 123 Heath Sherman | .08 | .05 |
| 124 Darryl Henley | .05 | .02 |
| 125 Pierce Holt | .05 | .02 |
| 126 Herman Moore | .20 | .12 |
| 127 Michael Irvin | .30 | .18 |
| 128 Tommy Kane | .08 | .05 |
| 129 Jackie Harris | .05 | .02 |
| 130 Hardy Nickerson | .05 | .02 |
| 131 Chip Lohmiller | .05 | .02 |
| 132 Andre Tippett | .07 | .04 |
| 133 Leonard Marshall | .07 | .04 |
| 134 Craig Heyward | .10 | .06 |
| 135 Anthony Carter | .10 | .06 |

| # | Name | | |
|---|---|---|---|
| 136 | Tom Rathman | .08 | .05 |
| 137 | Lorenzo White | .15 | .10 |
| 138 | Nick Lowery | .07 | .04 |
| 139 | John Offerdahl | .07 | .04 |
| 140 | Neil O'Donnell | .40 | .25 |
| 141 | Clarence Verdin | .08 | .05 |
| 142 | Ernest Givens | .12 | .07 |
| 143 | Todd Marinovich | .25 | .15 |
| 144 | Jeff Wright | .05 | .02 |
| 145 | Michael Brooks | .05 | .02 |
| 146 | Freddie Joe Nunn | .05 | .02 |
| 147 | William Perry | .07 | .04 |
| 148 | Daniel Stubbs | .05 | .02 |
| 149 | Morten Andersen | .08 | .05 |
| 150 | Dave Meggett | .12 | .07 |
| 151 | Andre Waters | .05 | .02 |
| 152 | Todd Lyght | .07 | .04 |
| 153 | Chris Miller | .15 | .10 |
| 154 | Rodney Peete | .12 | .07 |
| 155 | Jim Jeffcoat | .05 | .02 |
| 156 | Cortez Kennedy | .20 | .12 |
| 157 | Johnny Holland | .05 | .02 |
| 158 | Ricky Reynolds | .05 | .02 |
| 159 | Kevin Greene | .07 | .04 |
| 160 | Jeff Herrod | .05 | .02 |
| 161 | Bruce Matthews | .05 | .02 |
| 162 | Anthony Smith | .05 | .02 |
| 163 | Henry Jones | .05 | .02 |
| 164 | Rob Burnett | .08 | .05 |
| 165 | Eric Swann | .07 | .04 |
| 166 | Tom Waddle | .12 | .07 |
| 167 | Alfred Williams | .05 | .02 |
| 168 | Darren Carrington | .05 | .02 |
| 169 | Mike Sherrard | .08 | .05 |
| 170 | Frank Reich | .12 | .07 |
| 171 | Anthony Newman | .05 | .02 |
| 172 | Mike Pritchard | .20 | .12 |
| 173 | Andre Ware | .12 | .07 |
| 174 | Daryl Johnston | .08 | .05 |
| 175 | Rufus Porter | .05 | .02 |
| 176 | Reggie White | .15 | .10 |
| 177 | Charles Mincy | .05 | .02 |
| 178 | Pete Stoyanovich | .05 | .02 |
| 179 | Rod Woodson | .08 | .05 |
| 180 | Anthony Johnson | .08 | .05 |
| 181 | Cody Carlson | .12 | .07 |
| 182 | Gaston Green | .10 | .06 |
| 183 | Audray McMillian | .05 | .02 |
| 184 | Mike Johnson | .05 | .02 |
| 185 | Aeneas Williams | .08 | .05 |
| 186 | Jarrod Bunch | .15 | .10 |
| 187 | Dennis Smith | .05 | .02 |
| 188 | Quinn Early | .07 | .04 |
| 189 | James Hasty | .07 | .04 |
| 190 | Darryl Talley | .07 | .04 |
| 191 | Jon Vaughn | .10 | .06 |
| 192 | Andre Rison | .20 | .12 |
| 193 | Kelvin Pritchett | .12 | .07 |
| 194 | Ken Norton | .07 | .04 |
| 195 | Chris Warren | .12 | .07 |
| 196 | Sterling Sharpe | .25 | .15 |
| 197 | Christian Okoye | .10 | .06 |
| 198 | Richmond Webb | .05 | .02 |
| 199 | James Francis | .05 | .02 |
| 200 | Reggie Langhorne | .08 | .05 |
| 201 | J.J. Birden | .05 | .02 |
| 202 | Aaron Wallace | .05 | .02 |
| 203 | Henry Thomas | .05 | .02 |
| 204 | Clay Matthews | .05 | .02 |
| 205 | Robert Massey | .05 | .02 |
| 206 | Donnell Woolford | .05 | .02 |
| 207 | Ricky Watters | .50 | .30 |
| 208 | Wayne Martin | .07 | .04 |
| 209 | Rob Moore | .12 | .07 |
| 210 | Steve Tasker | .05 | .02 |
| 211 | Jackie Slater | .07 | .04 |
| 212 | Steve Young | .40 | .25 |
| 213 | Barry Sanders | .75 | .45 |
| 214 | Jay Novacek | .12 | .07 |
| 215 | Eugene Robinson | .05 | .02 |
| 216 | Duane Bickett | .05 | .02 |
| 217 | Broderick Thomas | .05 | .02 |
| 218 | David Fulcher | .05 | .02 |
| 219 | Rohn Stark | .05 | .02 |
| 220 | Warren Moon | .20 | .12 |
| 221 | Steve Wisniewski | .05 | .02 |
| 222 | Nate Odomes | .05 | .02 |
| 223 | Shannon Sharpe | .07 | .04 |
| 224 | Byron Evans | .05 | .02 |
| 225 | Mark Collins | .08 | .05 |
| 226 | Rod Bernstine | .15 | .10 |
| 227 | Sam Mills | .07 | .04 |
| 228 | Marvin Washington | .05 | .02 |
| 229 | Thurman Thomas | .30 | .18 |
| 230 | Brent Williams | .05 | .02 |
| 231 | Jessie Tuggle | .05 | .02 |
| 232 | Chris Spielman | .05 | .02 |
| 233 | Emmitt Smith | 1.50 | .90 |
| 234 | John L. Williams | .08 | .05 |
| 235 | Jeff Cross | .05 | .02 |
| 236 | Chris Doleman (AW) | .07 | .04 |
| 237 | John Elway (AW) | .15 | .10 |
| 238 | Barry Foster (AW) | .35 | .20 |
| 239 | Cortez Kennedy (AW) | .15 | .10 |
| 240 | Steve Young (AW) | .35 | .20 |
| 241 | Barry Foster (LL) | .35 | .20 |
| 242 | Warren Moon (LL) | .15 | .10 |
| 243 | Sterling Sharpe (LL) | .20 | .12 |
| 244 | Emmitt Smith (LL) | .75 | .45 |
| 245 | Thurman Thomas (LL) | .20 | .12 |
| 246 | Michael Irvin (PV) | .15 | .10 |
| 247 | Steve Young (PV) | .20 | .12 |
| 248 | Barry Foster (PV) | .25 | .15 |
| 249 | Checklist | .05 | .02 |

| | | | | | | | |
|---|---|---|---|---|---|---|---|
| 250 | Checklist | .05 | .02 | 307 | Blair Thomas | .12 | .07 |
| 251 | Checklist | .05 | .02 | 308 | Tim McGee | .10 | .06 |
| 252 | Checklist | .05 | .02 | 309 | Donald Evans | .05 | .02 |
| 253 | Troy Aikman (AW) | .60 | .35 | 310 | Randal Hill | .15 | .10 |
| 254 | Jason Hanson (AW) | .05 | .02 | 311 | Kenny Walker | .07 | .04 |
| 255 | Carl Pickens (AW) | .12 | .07 | 312 | Dalton Hilliard | .08 | .05 |
| 256 | Santana Dotson (AW) | .07 | .04 | 313 | Howard Ballard | .05 | .02 |
| 257 | Dale Carter (AW) | .08 | .05 | 314 | Phil Simms | .12 | .07 |
| 258 | Clyde Simmons (LL) | .05 | .02 | 315 | Jerry Rice | .30 | .18 |
| 259 | Audray McMillian (LL) | .05 | .02 | 316 | Courtney Hall | .05 | .02 |
| 260 | Henry Jones (LL) | .05 | .02 | 317 | Darren Lewis | .08 | .05 |
| 261 | Deion Sanders (LL) | .10 | .06 | 318 | Greg Montgomery | .05 | .02 |
| 262 | Haywood Jeffires (LL) | .10 | .06 | 319 | Paul Gruber | .05 | .02 |
| 263 | Deion Sanders (PV) | .10 | .06 | 320 | George Koonce | .05 | .02 |
| 264 | Andre Reed (PV) | .08 | .05 | 321 | Eugene Chung | .05 | .02 |
| 265 | Vince Workman | .07 | .04 | 322 | Mike Brim | .05 | .02 |
| 266 | Robert Brown | .05 | .02 | 323 | Patrick Hunter | .05 | .02 |
| 267 | Ray Agnew | .05 | .02 | 324 | Todd Scott | .05 | .02 |
| 268 | Ronnie Lott | .12 | .07 | 325 | Steve Emtman | .30 | .18 |
| 269 | Wesley Carroll | .12 | .07 | 326 | Andy Harmon | .05 | .02 |
| 270 | John Randle | .05 | .02 | 327 | Larry Brown | .05 | .02 |
| 271 | Rodney Culver | .08 | .05 | 328 | Chuck Cecil | .05 | .02 |
| 272 | David Alexander | .05 | .02 | 329 | Tim McKyer | .05 | .02 |
| 273 | Troy Aikman | .75 | .45 | 330 | Jeff Bryant | .05 | .02 |
| 274 | Bernie Kosar | .12 | .07 | 331 | Tim Barnett | .12 | .07 |
| 275 | Scott Case | .05 | .02 | 332 | Irving Fryar | .08 | .05 |
| 276 | Dan McGwire | .20 | .12 | 333 | Tyji Armstrong | .05 | .02 |
| 277 | John Alt | .05 | .02 | 334 | Brad Baxter | .08 | .05 |
| 278 | Dan Marino | .30 | .18 | 335 | Shane Collins | .05 | .02 |
| 279 | Santana Dotson | .10 | .06 | 336 | Jeff Graham | .12 | .07 |
| 280 | Johnny Mitchell | .15 | .10 | 337 | Ricky Proehl | .12 | .07 |
| 281 | Desmond Howard | .40 | .25 | 338 | Tommy Maddox | .40 | .25 |
| 282 | Adrian Cooper | .05 | .02 | 339 | Jim Dombrowski | .05 | .02 |
| 283 | Gary Clark | .15 | .10 | 340 | Bill Brooks | .05 | .02 |
| 284 | Arthur Marshall | .05 | .02 | 341 | Dave Brown | .05 | .02 |
| 285 | Eric Martin | .05 | .02 | 342 | Eric Davis | .05 | .02 |
| 286 | Jesse Solomon | .05 | .02 | 343 | Leslie O'Neal | .08 | .05 |
| 287 | Carl Banks | .07 | .04 | 344 | Jim Morrissey | .05 | .02 |
| 288 | Harris Barton | .05 | .02 | 345 | Mike Munchak | .07 | .04 |
| 289 | Jim Harbaugh | .12 | .07 | 346 | Ron Hall | .05 | .02 |
| 290 | Bubba McDowell | .05 | .02 | 347 | Brian Noble | .05 | .02 |
| 291 | Anthony McDowell | .05 | .02 | 348 | Chris Singleton | .05 | .02 |
| 292 | Terrell Buckley | .20 | .12 | 349 | Boomer Esiason | .12 | .07 |
| 293 | Bruce Armstrong | .05 | .02 | 350 | Ray Roberts | .05 | .02 |
| 294 | Kurt Barber | .05 | .02 | 351 | Gary Zimmerman | .05 | .02 |
| 295 | Reginald Jones | .05 | .02 | 352 | Quentin Coryatt | .30 | .18 |
| 296 | Steve Jordan | .05 | .02 | 353 | Willie Green | .12 | .07 |
| 297 | Kerry Cash | .05 | .02 | 354 | Randall Cunningham | .15 | .10 |
| 298 | Ray Crockett | .05 | .02 | 355 | Kevin Smith | .05 | .02 |
| 299 | Keith Byars | .08 | .05 | 356 | Michael Dean Perry | .07 | .04 |
| 300 | Russell Maryland | .08 | .05 | 357 | Tim Green | .05 | .02 |
| 301 | Johnny Bailey | .08 | .05 | 358 | Dwayne Harper | .05 | .02 |
| 302 | Vinnie Clark | .05 | .02 | 359 | Dale Carter | .20 | .12 |
| 303 | Terry Wooden | .05 | .02 | 360 | Keith Jackson | .15 | .10 |
| 304 | Harvey Williams | .20 | .12 | 361 | Martin Mayhew | .05 | .02 |
| 305 | Marco Coleman | .10 | .06 | 362 | Brian Washington | .05 | .02 |
| 306 | Mark Wheeler | .05 | .02 | 363 | Earnest Byner | .08 | .05 |

| | | | |
|---|---|---|---|
| 364 David Johnson | .05 | .02 |
| 365 Timm Rosenbach | .08 | .05 |
| 366 Doug Widell | .05 | .02 |
| 367 Vaughn Dunbar | .35 | .20 |
| 368 Phil Hansen | .05 | .02 |
| 369 John Elliott | .05 | .02 |
| 370 Dana Hall | .05 | .02 |
| 371 Junior Seau | .15 | .10 |
| 372 Steve McMichael | .07 | .04 |
| 373 Eddie Robinson | .05 | .02 |
| 374 Milton Mack | .05 | .02 |
| 375 Mike Prior | .05 | .02 |
| 376 Jerome Henderson | .05 | .02 |
| 377 Scott Mersereau | .05 | .02 |
| 378 Neal Anderson | .10 | .06 |
| 379 Harry Newsome | .05 | .02 |
| 380 John Baylor | .05 | .02 |
| 381 Bill Fralic | .05 | .02 |
| 382 Mark Bavaro | .07 | .04 |
| 383 Robert Jones | .08 | .05 |
| 384 Tyrone Stowe | .05 | .02 |
| 385 Deion Sanders | .20 | .12 |
| 386 Robert Blackmon | .05 | .02 |
| 387 Neil Smith | .07 | .04 |
| 388 Mark Ingram | .07 | .04 |
| 389 Mark Carrier (Cleve) | .10 | .06 |
| 390 Browning Nagle | .40 | .25 |
| 391 Ricky Ervins | .30 | .18 |
| 392 Carnell Lake | .05 | .02 |
| 393 Luis Sharpe | .05 | .02 |
| 394 Greg Kragen | .05 | .02 |
| 395 Tommy Barnhardt | .05 | .02 |
| 396 Mark Kelso | .05 | .02 |
| 397 Kent Graham | .05 | .02 |
| 398 Bill Romanowski | .05 | .02 |
| 399 Anthony Lewis | .05 | .02 |
| 400 John Roper | .05 | .02 |
| 401 Lamar Rogers | .05 | .02 |
| 402 Herschel Walker | .12 | .07 |
| 403 Webster Slaughter | .15 | .10 |
| 404 David Brandon | .05 | .02 |
| 405 Chris Hinton | .05 | .02 |
| 406 Andy Heck | .05 | .02 |
| 407 Jim McMahon | .10 | .06 |
| 408 Troy Vincent | .10 | .06 |
| 409 Jason Hanson | .05 | .02 |
| 410 Rod Jones | .05 | .02 |
| 411 Al Noga | .05 | .02 |
| 412 Ernie Mills | .12 | .07 |
| 413 Willie Gault | .08 | .05 |
| 414 Henry Ellard | .08 | .05 |
| 415 Rickey Jackson | .07 | .04 |
| 416 Bruce Smith | .12 | .07 |
| 417 Derek Brown | .20 | .12 |
| 418 Kevin Fagan | .05 | .02 |
| 419 Gary Plummer | .05 | .02 |
| 420 Wendell Davis | .12 | .07 |
| 421 Craig Thompson | .05 | .02 |
| 422 Mark McMillian | .05 | .02 |
| 423 Ray Childress | .08 | .05 |
| 424 Eric Turner | .10 | .06 |
| 425 Howie Long | .07 | .04 |
| 426 Shane Dronett | .07 | .04 |
| 427 Sean Salisbury | .12 | .07 |
| 428 Dwight Hollier | .05 | .02 |
| 429 Brett Perriman | .08 | .05 |
| 430 Donald Hollas | .15 | .10 |
| 431 Jim Lachey | .10 | .06 |
| 432 Darren Perry | .08 | .05 |
| 433 Lionel Washington | .05 | .02 |
| 434 Sean Gilbert | .15 | .10 |
| 435 Gene Atkins | .05 | .02 |
| 436 Jim Kelly | .25 | .15 |
| 437 Ed McCaffrey | .08 | .05 |
| 438 Don Griffin | .05 | .02 |
| 439 Jerrol Williams | .07 | .04 |
| 440 Bryce Paup | .05 | .02 |
| 441 Darryl Williams | .08 | .05 |
| 442 Vai Sikahema | .05 | .02 |
| 443 Cris Dishman | .05 | .02 |
| 444 Kevin Mack | .08 | .05 |
| 445 Winston Moss | .05 | .02 |
| 446 Tyrone Braxton | .07 | .04 |
| 447 Mike Merriweather | .05 | .02 |
| 448 Tony Paige | .05 | .02 |
| 449 Robert Porcher | .08 | .05 |
| 450 Ricardo McDonald | .08 | .05 |
| 451 Danny Copeland | .08 | .05 |
| 452 Tony Tolbert | .05 | .02 |
| 453 Eric Dickerson | .20 | .12 |
| 454 Willie Andersom | .10 | .06 |
| 455 Dave Krieg | .10 | .06 |
| 456 Brad Lamb | .05 | .02 |
| 457 Bart Oates | .05 | .02 |
| 458 Guy McIntyre | .05 | .02 |
| 459 Stanley Richard | .08 | .05 |
| 460 Edgar Bennett | .08 | .05 |
| 461 Pat Carter | .05 | .02 |
| 462 Eric Allen | .05 | .02 |
| 463 William Fuller | .05 | .02 |
| 464 James Jones | .05 | .02 |
| 465 Chester McGlockton | .07 | .04 |
| 466 Charles Dimry | .05 | .02 |
| 467 Tim Grunhard | .05 | .02 |
| 468 Jarvis Williams | .08 | .05 |
| 469 Tracy Scroggins | .05 | .02 |
| 470 David Klingler | 1.00 | .60 |
| 471 Andre Collins | .07 | .04 |
| 472 Erik Williams | .05 | .02 |
| 473 Eddie Anderson | .05 | .02 |
| 474 Marc Boutte | .08 | .05 |
| 475 Joe Montana | .60 | .35 |
| 476 Andre Reed | .15 | .10 |
| 477 Lawrence Taylor | .15 | .10 |

| | | | |
|---|---|---|---|
| 478 | Jeff George | .25 | .15 |
| 479 | Chris Mims | .12 | .07 |
| 480 | Ken Ruettgers | .05 | .02 |
| 481 | Roman Phifer | .05 | .02 |
| 482 | William Thomas | .05 | .02 |
| 483 | Lamar Lathon | .07 | .04 |
| 484 | Vinny Testaverde | .08 | .05 |
| 485 | Mike Kenn | .05 | .02 |
| 486 | Greg Lewis | .05 | .02 |
| 487 | Chris Martin | .05 | .02 |
| 488 | Maurice Hurst | .05 | .02 |
| 489 | Pat Swilling | .12 | .07 |
| 490 | Carl Pickens | .30 | .18 |
| 491 | Tony Smith | .15 | .10 |
| 492 | James Washington | .05 | .02 |
| 493 | Jeff Hostetler | .12 | .07 |
| 494 | Jeff Chadwick | .05 | .02 |
| 495 | Kevin Ross | .05 | .02 |
| 496 | Jim Ritcher | .05 | .02 |
| 497 | Jessie Hester | .07 | .04 |
| 498 | Burt Grossman | .07 | .04 |
| 499 | Keith Van Horne | .05 | .02 |
| 500 | Gerald Robinson | .05 | .02 |

| | | | |
|---|---|---|---|
| 18 | Clyde Simmons | .25 | .15 |
| 19 | Emmitt Smith | 4.50 | 2.75 |
| 20 | Derrick Thomas | .75 | .45 |
| 21 | Steve Wallace | .25 | .15 |
| 22 | Richmond Webb | .25 | .15 |
| 23 | Steve Wisniewski | .25 | .15 |
| 25 | Rod Woodson | .30 | .18 |
| 25 | Steve Young | 1.00 | .60 |

## 1993 Fleer Prospects

These random inserts feature the NFL's top draft picks. Card fronts include gold foil stamping and an isolated action photo set against a gold background. The pictures are framed by a gold and blue border. The player's name is printed in gold across the bottom of the card. All cards measure 2-1/2" by 3-1/2".

| | | MINT | NR/MT |
|---|---|---|---|
| **Complete Set (30)** | | 60.00 | 38.00 |
| **Commons** | | 1.75 | 1.00 |

## 1993 Fleer All-Pro

The card fronts in this set are horizontal and feature two images and gold foil stamping. There's a four color portrait in the foreground with a black and white action shot in tha background. The cards were randomly distributed in Fleer wax packs and measure 3-1/2" by 2-1/2".

| | | MINT | NR/MT |
|---|---|---|---|
| **Complete Set (25)** | | 12.00 | 8.00 |
| **Commons** | | .25 | .15 |
| 1 | Steve Atwater | .30 | .18 |
| 2 | Rich Camarillo | .25 | .15 |
| 3 | Ray Childress | .35 | .20 |
| 4 | Chris Doleman | .25 | .15 |
| 5 | Barry Foster | 1.50 | .90 |
| 6 | Henry Jones | .25 | .15 |
| 7 | Cortez Kennedy | .75 | .45 |
| 8 | Nick Lowery | .25 | .15 |
| 9 | Wilber Marshall | .30 | .18 |
| 10 | Bruce Matthews | .25 | .15 |
| 11 | Randall McDaniel | .25 | .15 |
| 12 | Audray McMillian | .25 | .15 |
| 13 | Sam Mills | .25 | .15 |
| 14 | Jay Novacek | .35 | .20 |
| 15 | Jerry Rice | 1.25 | .80 |
| 16 | Junior Seau | .60 | .35 |
| 17 | Sterling Sharpe | 1.50 | .90 |

| | | | |
|---|---|---|---|
| 1 | Drew Bledsoe | 8.50 | 5.50 |
| 2 | Garrison Hearst | 7.00 | 4.00 |
| 3 | John Copeland | 2.50 | 1.50 |
| 4 | Eric Curry | 2.50 | 1.50 |
| 5 | Curtis Conway | 4.00 | 2.75 |
| 6 | Lincoln Kennedy | 2.00 | 1.25 |
| 7 | Jerome Bettis | 3.50 | 2.00 |
| 8 | Patrick Bates | 2.00 | 1.25 |
| 9 | Brad Hopkins | 1.75 | 1.00 |
| 10 | Tom Carter | 2.00 | 1.25 |
| 11 | Irv Smith | 2.00 | 1.25 |
| 12 | Robert Smith | 3.00 | 1.75 |
| 13 | Deon Figures | 2.00 | 1.25 |
| 14 | Leonard Renfro | 1.75 | 1.00 |
| 15 | O.J. McDuffie | 3.00 | 1.75 |
| 16 | Dana Stubblefield | 2.50 | 1.50 |
| 17 | Todd Kelly | 2.50 | 1.50 |
| 18 | George Teague | 1.75 | 1.00 |
| 19 | Demetrius DuBose | 2.00 | 1.25 |
| 20 | Coleman Rudolph | 2.00 | 1.25 |
| 21 | Carlton Gray | 2.00 | 1.25 |
| 22 | Troy Drayton | 1.75 | 1.00 |
| 23 | Natrone Means | 2.50 | 1.50 |
| 24 | Qadry Ismail | 3.00 | 1.75 |
| 25 | Gino Torretta | 2.00 | 1.25 |
| 26 | Carl Simpson | 1.75 | 1.00 |
| 27 | Glyn Milburn | 3.00 | 1.75 |
| 28 | Chad Brown | 1.75 | 1.00 |
| 29 | Reggie Brooks | 2.00 | 1.25 |
| 30 | Billy Joe Hobert | 2.00 | 1.25 |

# GAMEDAY

## 1992 NFL GameDay

RANDALL CUNNINGHAM
®GAMEDAY

This 500-card set was produced by NFL Properties and was patterned after the 1965 Topps set. Cards measure 2-1/2" by 4-11/16". The fronts feature full color action photos while the player's team, name and a GameDay logo are centered below the photograph. The card backs are horizontal and include a small photo, the player's personal data, statistics and highlights. This series contains a Quad-Cards subset that features four players per card. Total GameDay production was limited to 17,500 cases.

|  |  | MINT | NR/MT |
|---|---|---|---|
| Complete Set (500) | | 75.00 | 48.00 |
| Commons | | .08 | .05 |
| 1 | Jim Kelly | .75 | .45 |
| 2 | Mark Ingram | .08 | .05 |
| 3 | Travis McNeal | .08 | .05 |
| 4 | Ricky Ervins | 1.00 | .70 |
| 5 | Joe Montana | .60 | .35 |
| 6 | Broderick Thompson | .08 | .05 |
| 7 | Darion Conner | .08 | .05 |
| 8 | Jim Harbaugh | .15 | .10 |
| 9 | Harvey Williams | .40 | .25 |
| 10 | Chip Banks | .08 | .05 |
| 11 | Henry Thomas | .08 | .05 |
| 12 | Derek Brown (R) | .30 | .18 |
| 13 | James Joseph | .15 | .10 |
| 14 | Kevin Fagan | .08 | .05 |
| 15 | Chuck Klingbeil (R) | .10 | .06 |
| 16 | Harlon Barnett | .08 | .05 |
| 17 | Jim Price | .08 | .05 |
| 18 | Terrell Buckley (R) | 1.00 | .70 |
| 19 | Paul McJulian (R) | .10 | .06 |
| 20 | James Hasty | .08 | .05 |
| 21 | James Francis | .10 | .06 |
| 22 | Andre Tippett | .08 | .05 |
| 23 | John Elway | .25 | .15 |
| 24 | Eric Dickerson | .35 | .20 |
| 25 | James Jefferson | .08 | .05 |
| 26 | Danny Noonan | .08 | .05 |
| 27 | Warren Moon | .25 | .15 |
| 28 | Gene Atkins | .08 | .05 |
| 29 | Jessie Hester | .08 | .05 |
| 30 | Mike Mooney | .15 | .10 |
| | Kevin Smith | | |
| | Ron Humphrey | | |
| | Tracy Boyd | .08 | .05 |
| 31 | Toby Caston (R) | .10 | .06 |
| 32 | Howard Dinkins (R) | .12 | .07 |
| 33 | James Patton (R) | .12 | .07 |
| 34 | Walter Reeves | .08 | .05 |
| 35 | Johnny Mitchell (R) | .30 | .18 |
| 36 | Michael Brim (R) | .12 | .07 |
| 37 | Irving Fryar | .10 | .06 |
| 38 | Lewis Billups | .08 | .05 |
| 39 | Alonzo Spellman (R) | .25 | .15 |
| 40 | John Friesz | .12 | .07 |
| 41 | Patrick Hunter | .08 | .05 |
| 42 | Reuben Davis | .08 | .05 |
| 43 | Tom Mylinski | .10 | .06 |
| | Shawn Harper | | |
| | Mark Thomas | | |
| | Mike Frier | | |
| 44 | Siran Stacy (R) | .30 | .18 |
| 45 | Stephone Paige | .10 | .06 |
| 46 | Eddie Robinson (R) | .15 | .10 |
| 47 | Tracy Scroggins (R) | .12 | .07 |
| 48 | David Klingler (R) | 2.50 | 1.50 |
| 49 | Deion Sanders | .30 | .18 |
| 50 | Tom Waddle | .15 | .10 |
| 51 | Gary Anderson | .08 | .05 |
| 52 | Kevin Butler | .08 | .05 |
| 53 | Bruce Smith | .15 | .10 |
| 54 | Steve Sewell | .08 | .05 |
| 55 | Hugh Green | .08 | .05 |
| 56 | Lawrence Taylor | .25 | .15 |
| 57 | Mike Merriweather | .08 | .05 |
| 58 | Roman Phifer | .08 | .05 |
| 59 | Shaun Gayle | .08 | .05 |
| 60 | Marc Boutte (R) | .12 | .07 |
| 61 | Tony Mayberry (R) | .10 | .06 |
| 62 | Antone Davis | .08 | .05 |
| 63 | Rod Bernstine | .12 | .07 |
| 64 | Shane Collins (R) | .12 | .07 |

| | | | |
|---|---|---|---|
| 65 | Martin Bayless | .08 | .05 |
| 66 | Corey Harris (R) | .15 | .10 |
| 67 | Jason Hanson (R) | .10 | .06 |
| 68 | John Fina (R) | .12 | .07 |
| 69 | Cornelius Bennett | .15 | .10 |
| 70 | Mark Bortz | .08 | .05 |
| 71 | Gary Anderson | .08 | .05 |
| 72 | Paul Siever (R) | .10 | .06 |
| 73 | Willie Anderson | .12 | .07 |
| 74 | Shane Dronett (R) | .15 | .10 |
| 75 | Brian Noble | .08 | .05 |
| 76 | Tim Green | .08 | .05 |
| 77 | Percy Snow | .10 | .06 |
| 78 | Greg McMurtry | .15 | .10 |
| 79 | Dana Hall (R) | .25 | .15 |
| 80 | Tyji Armstrong (R) | .15 | .10 |
| 81 | Gary Clark | .20 | .12 |
| 82 | Steve Emtman (R) | 1.25 | .80 |
| 83 | Eric Moore | .08 | .05 |
| 84 | Brent Jones | .12 | .07 |
| 85 | Ray Seale (R) | .10 | .06 |
| 86 | James Jones | .08 | .05 |
| 87 | Jeff Hostetler | .20 | .12 |
| 88 | Keith Jackson | .20 | .12 |
| 89 | Gary Plummer | .08 | .05 |
| 90 | Robert Blackmon | .08 | .05 |
| 91 | Larry Tharpe | .15 | .10 |
| | Mike Brandon | | |
| | Anthony Hamlet | | |
| | Mike Pawlawski | | |
| 92 | Greg Skrepenak (R) | .12 | .07 |
| 93 | Kevin Call | .08 | .05 |
| 94 | Clarence Kay | .08 | .05 |
| 95 | William Fuller | .10 | .06 |
| 96 | Troy Auzenne (R) | .12 | .07 |
| 97 | Carl Pickens (R) | 1.00 | .70 |
| 98 | Lorenzo White | .20 | .12 |
| 99 | Doug Smith | .08 | .05 |
| 100 | Dale Carter (R) | .35 | .20 |
| 101 | Fred McAfee | .25 | .15 |
| 102 | Jack Del Rio | .08 | .05 |
| 103 | Vaughn Dunbar (R) | 1.00 | .70 |
| 104 | Corey Miller | .08 | .05 |
| 105 | Harris Barton | .08 | .05 |
| 106 | Ray Ethridge (R) | .15 | .10 |
| 107 | John Gesek | .08 | .05 |
| 108 | Mike Singletary | .15 | .10 |
| 109 | Mark Rypien | .25 | .15 |
| 110 | Robb Thomas | .08 | .05 |
| 111 | Joe Kelly | .08 | .05 |
| 112 | Ben Smith | .08 | .05 |
| 113 | Neil O'Donnell | .75 | .45 |
| 114 | John L. Williams | .10 | .06 |
| 115 | Mike Sherrard | .12 | .07 |
| 116 | Chad Hennings (R) | .15 | .10 |
| 117 | Henry Ellard | .10 | .06 |
| 118 | Dan Stryzinski | .08 | .05 |
| 119 | Charles Dimry | .08 | .05 |
| 120 | Chuck Smith (R) | .12 | .07 |
| 121 | Brian Mitchell | .10 | .06 |
| 122 | Eric Allen | .08 | .05 |
| 123 | Nate Lewis | .12 | .07 |
| 124 | Kevin Ross | .08 | .05 |
| 125 | Jimmy Smith (R) | .20 | .12 |
| 126 | Kevin Smith (R) | .20 | .12 |
| 127 | Larry Webster (R) | .10 | .06 |
| 128 | Marv Cook | .10 | .06 |
| 129 | Calvin Williams | .15 | .10 |
| 130 | Harry Swayne (R) | .10 | .06 |
| 131 | Jimmie Jones | .08 | .05 |
| 132 | Ethan Horton | .08 | .05 |
| 133 | Chris Mims (R) | .30 | .18 |
| 134 | Derrick Thomas | .25 | .15 |
| 135 | Gerald Dixon (R) | .10 | .06 |
| 136 | Gary Zimmerman | .08 | .05 |
| 137 | Robert Jones (R) | .30 | .18 |
| 138 | Steve Broussard | .12 | .07 |
| 139 | David Wyman | .08 | .05 |
| 140 | Ian Beckler | .08 | .05 |
| 141 | Steve Bono | .50 | .30 |
| 142 | Cris Carter | .20 | .12 |
| 143 | Anthony Carter | .12 | .07 |
| 144 | Greg Townsend | .08 | .05 |
| 145 | Al Smith | .08 | .05 |
| 146 | Troy Vincent (R) | .40 | .25 |
| 147 | Jessie Tuggle | .08 | .05 |
| 148 | David Fulcher | .08 | .05 |
| 149 | Johnny Rembert | .10 | .06 |
| 150 | Ernie Jones | .12 | .07 |
| 151 | Mark Royals | .08 | .05 |
| 152 | Jeff Bryant | .08 | .05 |
| 153 | Vai Sikahema | .08 | .05 |
| 154 | Tony Woods | .08 | .05 |
| 155 | Joe Bowden | .12 | .07 |
| | Doug Rigby | | |
| | Marcus Dowdell | | |
| | Vincent Brownlee | | |
| 156 | Mark Carrier | .10 | .06 |
| 157 | Joe Nash | .08 | .05 |
| 158 | Keith Van Horne | .08 | .05 |
| 159 | Kelvin Martin | .15 | .10 |
| 160 | Peter Tom Willis | .20 | .12 |
| 161 | Richard Johnson | .08 | .05 |
| 162 | Louis Oliver | .10 | .06 |
| 163 | Nick Lowery | .08 | .05 |
| 164 | Ricky Froehl | .15 | .10 |
| 165 | Terance Mathis | .12 | .07 |
| 166 | Keith Sims | .08 | .05 |
| 167 | E.J. Junior | .08 | .05 |
| 168 | Scott Mersereau | .08 | .05 |
| 169 | Tom Rathman | .12 | .07 |
| 170 | Robert Harris (R) | .12 | .07 |
| 171 | Ashley Ambrose (R) | .30 | .18 |
| 172 | David Treadwell | .08 | .05 |

| | | | |
|---|---|---|---|
| 173 | Mark Green | .08 | .05 |
| 174 | Clayton Holmes (R) | .12 | .07 |
| 175 | Tony Sacca (R) | .50 | .30 |
| 176 | Wes Hopkins | .08 | .05 |
| 177 | Mark Wheeler (R) | .12 | .07 |
| 178 | Robert Clark | .08 | .05 |
| 179 | Jeff Query | .12 | .07 |
| 180 | Rob Burnett | .12 | .07 |
| 181 | Al Edwards | .08 | .05 |
| 182 | Clarence Verdin | .10 | .06 |
| 183 | Tom Newberry | .08 | .05 |
| 184 | Mike Jones | .08 | .05 |
| 185 | Roy Foster | .08 | .05 |
| 186 | Leslie O'Neal | .10 | .06 |
| 187 | Izel Jenkins | .08 | .05 |
| 188 | Willie Clay | .35 | .20 |
| | Ty Detmer | | |
| | Mike Evans | | |
| | Ed McDaniel | | |
| 189 | Mike Tomczak | .10 | .06 |
| 190 | Leonard Wheeler (R) | .10 | .06 |
| 191 | Gaston Green | .20 | .12 |
| 192 | Maury Buford | .08 | .05 |
| 193 | Jeremy Lincoln (R) | .12 | .07 |
| 194 | Todd Collins (R) | .12 | .07 |
| 195 | Billy Ray Smith | .08 | .05 |
| 196 | Renaldo Turnbull | .10 | .06 |
| 197 | Michael Carter | .08 | .05 |
| 198 | Rod Milstead | .12 | .07 |
| | Dion Lambert | | |
| | Hesham Ismail | | |
| | Reggie White | | |
| 199 | Shawn Collins | .10 | .06 |
| 200 | Issaic Holt | .08 | .05 |
| 201 | Irv Eatman | .08 | .05 |
| 202 | Anthony Thompson | .12 | .07 |
| 203 | Chester McGlockton (R) | .20 | .12 |
| 204 | Greg Briggs | .12 | .07 |
| | Chris Crooms | | |
| | Ephesiana Bartley | | |
| | Curtis Whitley | | |
| 205 | James Brown (R) | .12 | .07 |
| 206 | Marvin Washington | .08 | .05 |
| 207 | Richard Cooper (R) | .12 | .07 |
| 208 | Jim Jensen | .08 | .05 |
| 209 | Sam Seale | .08 | .05 |
| 210 | Andre Reed | .15 | .10 |
| 211 | Thane Gash | .08 | .05 |
| 212 | Randal Hill | .25 | .15 |
| 213 | Brad Baxter | .15 | .10 |
| 214 | Van Waiters | .08 | .05 |
| 215 | Ray Crockett | .08 | .05 |
| 216 | Tony Mandarich | .08 | .05 |
| 217 | Warren Williams | .08 | .05 |
| 218 | Erik Kramer | .25 | .15 |
| 219 | Bubby Brister | .12 | .07 |
| 220 | Steve Young | .40 | .25 |
| 221 | Jeff George | .30 | .18 |
| 222 | James Washington | .08 | .05 |
| 223 | Bruce Alexander (R) | .12 | .07 |
| 224 | Broderick Thomas | .12 | .07 |
| 225 | Bern Brostek | .08 | .05 |
| 226 | Brian Blades | .10 | .06 |
| 227 | Troy Aikman | .80 | .50 |
| 228 | Aaron Wallace | .10 | .06 |
| 229 | Tom Jeter (R) | .12 | .07 |
| 230 | Russell Maryland | .30 | .18 |
| 231 | Charles Haley | .10 | .06 |
| 232 | James Lofton | .20 | .12 |
| 233 | William White | .08 | .05 |
| 234 | Tim McGee | .10 | .06 |
| 235 | Haywood Jeffires | .25 | .15 |
| 236 | Charles Mann | .08 | .05 |
| 237 | Robert Lyles | .08 | .05 |
| 238 | Rohn Stark | .08 | .05 |
| 239 | Jim Morrissey | .08 | .05 |
| 240 | Mel Gray | .08 | .05 |
| 241 | Barry Word | .25 | .15 |
| 242 | Dave Widdell (R) | .10 | .06 |
| 243 | Sean Gilbert (R) | .15 | .10 |
| 244 | Tommy Maddox (R) | 1.50 | .90 |
| 245 | Bernie Kosar | .15 | .10 |
| 246 | John Roper | .08 | .05 |
| 247 | Mark Higgs | .30 | .18 |
| 248 | Rob Moore | .25 | .15 |
| 249 | Dan Fike | .08 | .05 |
| 250 | Dan Saleaumia | .08 | .05 |
| 251 | Tim Krumrie | .08 | .05 |
| 252 | Tony Casillas | .10 | .06 |
| 253 | Jayice Pearson (R) | .12 | .07 |
| 254 | Dan Marino | .60 | .35 |
| 255 | Tony Martin | .08 | .05 |
| 256 | Mike Fox | .08 | .05 |
| 257 | Courtney Hawkins (R) | .30 | .18 |
| 258 | Leonard Marshall | .10 | .06 |
| 259 | Willie Gault | .10 | .06 |
| 260 | Al Toon | .12 | .07 |
| 261 | Browning Nagle (R) | 1.00 | .70 |
| 262 | Ronnie Lott | .15 | .10 |
| 263 | Sean Jones | .08 | .05 |
| 264 | Ernest Givins | .15 | .10 |
| 265 | Ray Donaldson | .08 | .05 |
| 266 | Vaughn Johnson | .10 | .06 |
| 267 | Tom Hodson | .12 | .07 |
| 268 | Chris Doleman | .10 | .06 |
| 269 | Pat Swilling | .15 | .10 |
| 270 | Merril Hoge | .10 | .06 |
| 271 | Bill Maas | .08 | .05 |
| 272 | Sterling Sharpe | .25 | .15 |
| 273 | Mitchell Price | .08 | .05 |
| 274 | Richard Brown (R) | .12 | .07 |
| 275 | Randall Cunningham | .25 | .15 |
| 276 | Harry Sydney | .08 | .05 |

| | | | |
|---|---|---|---|
| 277 | Courtney Hall | .08 | .05 |
| 278 | Michael Walter | .08 | .05 |
| 279 | Ricardo McDonald | .20 | .12 |
| | David Wilson | | |
| | Sean Lumpkin | | |
| | Tony Brooks | | |
| 280 | Bill Brooks | .08 | .05 |
| 281 | Jay Schroeder | .12 | .07 |
| 282 | John Stephens | .15 | .10 |
| 283 | William Perry | .10 | .06 |
| 284 | Floyd Turner | .08 | .05 |
| 285 | Carnell Lake | .08 | .05 |
| 286 | Joel Steed (R) | .12 | .07 |
| 287 | Vinnie Clark | .12 | .07 |
| 288 | Ken Norton | .08 | .05 |
| 289 | Eric Thomas | .08 | .05 |
| 290 | Derreck Fenner | .15 | .10 |
| 291 | Tony Smith (R) | .80 | .50 |
| 292 | Eric Metcalf | .12 | .07 |
| 293 | Roger Craig | .12 | .07 |
| 294 | Leon Searcy (R) | .12 | .07 |
| 295 | Tyrone Legette (R) | .12 | .07 |
| 296 | Rob Taylor | .08 | .05 |
| 297 | Eric Williams | .08 | .05 |
| 298 | David Little | .08 | .05 |
| 299 | Wayne Martin | .08 | .05 |
| 300 | Eric Martin | .12 | .07 |
| 301 | Jim Everett | .15 | .10 |
| 302 | Michael Dean Perry | .15 | .10 |
| 303 | Dwayne White (R) | .12 | .07 |
| 304 | Greg Lloyd | .08 | .05 |
| 305 | Ricky Reynolds | .08 | .05 |
| 306 | Anthony Smith | .08 | .05 |
| 307 | Robert DelPino | .10 | .06 |
| 308 | Ken Clark | .08 | .05 |
| 309 | Chris Jacke | .08 | .05 |
| 310 | Reggie Dwight | .12 | .07 |
| | Craig Thompson | | |
| | Anthony McCoy | | |
| | Klaus Wilmsmeyer | | |
| 311 | Doug Widdell | .08 | .05 |
| 312 | Sammie Smith | .12 | .07 |
| 313 | Ken O'Brien | .15 | .10 |
| 314 | Timm Rosenbach | .15 | .10 |
| 315 | Jesse Sapolu | .08 | .05 |
| 316 | Ronnie Harmon | .08 | .05 |
| 317 | Bill Pickel | .08 | .05 |
| 318 | Lonnie Young | .08 | .05 |
| 319 | Chris Burkett | .08 | .05 |
| 320 | Ervin Randle | .08 | .05 |
| 321 | Ed West | .08 | .05 |
| 322 | Tom Thayer | .08 | .05 |
| 323 | Keith McKeller | .08 | .05 |
| 324 | Webster Slaughter | .08 | .05 |
| 325 | Duane Pickett | .08 | .05 |
| 326 | Howie Long | .10 | .06 |
| 327 | Sam Mills | .10 | .06 |

| | | | |
|---|---|---|---|
| 328 | Mike Golic | .08 | .05 |
| 329 | Bruce Armstrong | .08 | .05 |
| 330 | Pat Terrell | .10 | .06 |
| 331 | Mike Pritchard | .25 | .15 |
| 332 | Audray McMillian | .08 | .05 |
| 333 | Marquez Pope (R) | .12 | .07 |
| 334 | Pierce Holt | .08 | .05 |
| 335 | Erik Howard | .08 | .05 |
| 336 | Jerry Rice | .60 | .35 |
| 337 | Vinnie Testaverde | .15 | .10 |
| 338 | Bart Oates | .08 | .05 |
| 339 | Nolan Harrison (R) | .12 | .07 |
| 340 | Chris Goode | .08 | .05 |
| 341 | Ken Ruttgers | .08 | .05 |
| 342 | Brad Muster | .12 | .07 |
| 343 | Paul Farren | .08 | .05 |
| 344 | Corey Miller (R) | .12 | .07 |
| 345 | Brian Washington | .08 | .05 |
| 346 | Jim Sweeney | .08 | .05 |
| 347 | Keith McCants | .12 | .07 |
| 348 | Louis Lipps | .10 | .06 |
| 349 | Keith Byars | .10 | .06 |
| 350 | Steve Walsh | .12 | .07 |
| 351 | Tim Newton | .08 | .05 |
| 352 | Christian Okoye | .20 | .12 |
| 353 | Cris Dishman | .10 | .06 |
| 354 | Keith Hartz | .08 | .05 |
| 355 | Harold Green | .30 | .18 |
| 356 | Richard Shelton (R) | .12 | .07 |
| 357 | Jacob Green | .08 | .05 |
| 358 | Al Noga | .08 | .05 |
| 359 | Dean Biassucci | .08 | .05 |
| 360 | Jeff Harrod | .08 | .05 |
| 361 | Bennie Blades | .10 | .06 |
| 362 | Mark Vlasic | .10 | .06 |
| 363 | Chris Miller | .30 | .18 |
| 364 | Bubba McDowell | .08 | .05 |
| 365 | Tyronne Stowe (R) | .12 | .07 |
| 366 | Jon Vaughn | .25 | .15 |
| 367 | Winston Moss | .08 | .05 |
| 368 | Levon Kirkland (R) | .15 | .10 |
| 369 | Ted Washington | .08 | .05 |
| 370 | Cortez Kennedy | .12 | .07 |
| 371 | Jeff Feagles | .08 | .05 |
| 372 | Aundray Bruce | .08 | .05 |
| 373 | Michael Irvin | .30 | .18 |
| 374 | Lemuel Stinson | .08 | .05 |
| 375 | Billy Joe Tolliver | .12 | .07 |
| 376 | Anthony Munoz | .12 | .07 |
| 377 | Nate Newton | .08 | .05 |
| 378 | Steve Smith | .08 | .05 |
| 379 | Eugene Chung (R) | .12 | .07 |
| 380 | Bryan Hinkle | .08 | .05 |
| 381 | Dan McGwire | .60 | .35 |
| 382 | Jeff Cross | .08 | .05 |
| 383 | Ferrell Edmunds | .08 | .05 |
| 384 | Craig Heyward | .10 | .06 |

| | | | |
|---|---|---|---|
| 385 | Shannon Sharpe | .08 | .05 |
| 386 | Anthony Miller | .15 | .10 |
| 387 | Eugene Lockhart | .08 | .05 |
| 388 | Darryl Henley | .08 | .05 |
| 389 | Leroy Butler | .08 | .05 |
| 390 | Scott Fulhage | .08 | .05 |
| 391 | Andre Ware | .25 | .15 |
| 392 | Lionel Washington | .08 | .05 |
| 393 | Rick Fenney | .08 | .05 |
| 394 | John Taylor | .20 | .12 |
| 395 | Chris Singleton | .12 | .07 |
| 396 | Monte Coleman | .08 | .05 |
| 397 | Brett Perriman | .10 | .06 |
| 398 | Hugh Millen | .30 | .18 |
| 399 | Dennis Gentry | .08 | .05 |
| 400 | Eddie Anderson | .08 | .05 |
| 401 | Lance Olberding | .12 | .07 |
| | Eddie Miller | | |
| | Dwayne Sabb | | |
| | Corey Widmer | | |
| 402 | Brent Williams | .08 | .05 |
| 403 | Tony Zendejas | .08 | .05 |
| 404 | Donnell Woolford | .08 | .05 |
| 405 | Boomer Esiason | .15 | .10 |
| 406 | Gill Fenarty | .08 | .05 |
| 407 | Kurt Barber (R) | .12 | .07 |
| 408 | Williams Thomas | .08 | .05 |
| 409 | Keith Henderson | .10 | .06 |
| 410 | Paul Gruber | .08 | .05 |
| 411 | Alfred Oglesby | .08 | .05 |
| 412 | Wendell Davis | .15 | .10 |
| 413 | Robert Brooks (R) | .20 | .12 |
| 414 | Ken Willis | .08 | .05 |
| 415 | Aaron Cox | .08 | .05 |
| 416 | Thruman Thomas | .75 | .45 |
| 417 | Alton Montgomery | .08 | .05 |
| 418 | Mike Prior | .08 | .05 |
| 419 | Albert Bentley | .08 | .05 |
| 420 | John Randle | .08 | .05 |
| 421 | Dermontti Dawson | .08 | .05 |
| 422 | Phillippi Sparks (R) | .15 | .10 |
| 423 | Michael Jackson | .25 | .15 |
| 424 | Carl Banks | .08 | .05 |
| 425 | Darren Comeaux | .08 | .05 |
| 426 | Dwight Stone | .08 | .05 |
| 427 | Bryan Millard | .08 | .05 |
| 428 | Neal Anderson | .15 | .10 |
| 429 | Michael Haynes | .30 | .18 |
| 430 | Michael Young | .08 | .05 |
| 431 | Dennis Byrd | .08 | .05 |
| 432 | Fred Barnett | .25 | .15 |
| 433 | Junior Seau | .15 | .10 |
| 434 | Mark Clayton | .15 | .10 |
| 435 | Marco Coleman (R) | .50 | .35 |
| 436 | Lee Williams | .08 | .05 |
| 437 | Stan Thomas | .08 | .05 |
| 438 | Lawrence Dawsey | .20 | .12 |
| 439 | Tommy Vardell (R) | .80 | .50 |
| 440 | Steve Israel (R) | .20 | .12 |
| 441 | Ray Childress | .10 | .06 |
| 442 | Darren Woodson (R) | .12 | .07 |
| 443 | Lamar Lathon | .10 | .06 |
| 444 | Reggie Roby | .08 | .05 |
| 445 | Eric Green | .20 | .12 |
| 446 | Mark Carrier | .10 | .06 |
| 447 | Kevin Walker | .08 | .05 |
| 448 | Vince Workman | .12 | .07 |
| 449 | Leonard Griffin | .08 | .05 |
| 450 | Robert Porcher | .20 | .12 |
| 451 | Hart Lee Dykes | .10 | .06 |
| 452 | Thomas McLemore (R) | .12 | .07 |
| 453 | Jamie Dukes (R) | .12 | .07 |
| 454 | Bill Romanowski | .08 | .05 |
| 455 | Deron Cherry | .08 | .05 |
| 456 | Burt Grossman | .08 | .05 |
| 457 | Lance Smith | .08 | .05 |
| 458 | Jay Novacek | .10 | .06 |
| 459 | Erric Pegram | .15 | .10 |
| 460 | Reggie Rutland | .08 | .05 |
| 461 | Rickey Jackson | .10 | .06 |
| 462 | Dennis Brown | .08 | .05 |
| 463 | Neil Smith | .08 | .05 |
| 464 | Rich Gannon | .25 | .15 |
| 465 | Herman Moore | .30 | .18 |
| 466 | Rodney Peete | .12 | .07 |
| 467 | Alvin Harper | .35 | .20 |
| 468 | Andre Rison | .30 | .18 |
| 469 | Rufus Porter | .08 | .05 |
| 470 | Robert Wilson | .08 | .05 |
| 471 | Phil Simms | .12 | .07 |
| 472 | Art Monk | .35 | .20 |
| 473 | Mike Tice | .08 | .05 |
| 474 | Quentin Coryatt (R) | .75 | .45 |
| 475 | Chris Hinton | .08 | .05 |
| 476 | Vance Johnson | .12 | .07 |
| 477 | Kyle Clinton | .08 | .05 |
| 478 | Garth Jax | .08 | .05 |
| 479 | Ray Agnew | .08 | .05 |
| 480 | Patrick Rowe (R) | .30 | .18 |
| 481 | Joe Jacoby | .08 | .05 |
| 482 | Bruce Pickens | .20 | .12 |
| 483 | Keith DeLong | .08 | .05 |
| 484 | Eric Swann | .12 | .07 |
| 485 | Steve McMichael | .10 | .06 |
| 486 | Leroy Hoard | .15 | .10 |
| 487 | Rickey Dixon | .08 | .05 |
| 488 | Robert Perryman | .08 | .05 |
| 489 | Darryl Williams (R) | .30 | .18 |
| 490 | Emmitt Smith | 2.00 | 1.25 |
| 491 | Dino Hackett | .08 | .05 |
| 492 | Earnest Byner | .10 | .06 |
| 493 | Bucky Richardson | .30 | .18 |
| | Bernard Dafney | | |

| | | | |
|---|---|---|---|
| | Anthony Davis | | |
| | Tony Brown | | |
| 494 | Bill Johnson (R) | .12 | .07 |
| 495 | Darryl Ashmore | .12 | .07 |
| | Joe Campbell | | |
| | Kelvin Harris | | |
| | Tim Lester | | |
| 496 | Nick Bell | .40 | .25 |
| 497 | Jerry Ball | .08 | .05 |
| 498 | Edgar Bennett | .50 | .30 |
| | Mark Chmura | | |
| | Chris Holder | | |
| | Mario Royster | | |
| 499 | Steve Christie | .08 | .05 |
| 500 | Kenneth Davis | .12 | .07 |

# LEAF

## 1948 Leaf

GEORGE CONNOR

The cards in this 98-card set measure 2-3/8" by 2-7/8". Card fronts feature posed black and white shots printed on a color background. The vertical card backs contain the player's personal data and a brief biography. Cards #50 through #98 are extremely scarce.

| | NR/MT | EX |
|---|---|---|
| Complete Set (98) | 6,200.00 | 3,200.00 |
| Commons (1-49) | 18.00 | 9.00 |
| Commons (50-98) | 75.00 | 38.00 |

| 1 | Sid Luckman (R) | 250.00 | 120.00 |
|---|---|---|---|
| 2 | Steve Suhey (R) | 18.00 | 9.00 |
| 3 | Bulldog Turner (R) | 100.00 | 48.00 |
| 4 | Doak Walker (R) | 100.00 | 48.00 |
| 5 | Levi Jackson (R) | 18.00 | 9.00 |
| 6 | Bobby Layne (R) | 240.00 | 110.00 |
| 7 | Bill Fischer (R) | 18.00 | 9.00 |
| 8 | Vince Banonis (R) | 18.00 | 9.00 |
| 9 | Tommy Thompson (R) | 28.00 | 12.50 |
| 10 | Perry Moss (R) | 18.00 | 9.00 |
| 11 | Terry Brennan (R) | 20.00 | 9.50 |
| 12 | William Swiacki (R) | 18.00 | 9.00 |
| 13 | Johnny Lujack (R) | 100.00 | 48.00 |
| 14 | Mal Kutner (R) | 18.00 | 9.00 |
| 15 | Charlie Justice (R) | 50.00 | 24.00 |
| 16 | Pete Pihos (R) | 75.00 | 36.00 |
| 17 | Kenny Washington (R) | 28.00 | 12.50 |
| 18 | Harry Gilmer (R) | 25.00 | 11.00 |
| 19 | George McAfee (R) | 75.00 | 36.00 |
| 20 | George Taliaferro (R) | 20.00 | 9.50 |
| 21 | Paul Christman (R) | 35.00 | 16.50 |
| 22 | Steve Van Buren (R) | 110.00 | 50.00 |
| 23 | Ken Kavanaugh (R) | 25.00 | 11.00 |
| 24 | Jim Martin (R) | 20.00 | 9.50 |
| 25 | Bud Angsman (R) | 18.00 | 9.00 |
| 26 | Bob Waterfield (R) | 140.00 | 65.00 |
| 27 | Fred Davis (R) | 18.00 | 9.00 |
| 28 | Whitey Wistert (R) | 18.00 | 9.00 |
| 29 | Charlie Trippi (R) | 75.00 | 36.00 |
| 30 | Paul Governali (R) | 18.00 | 9.00 |
| 31 | Tom McWilliams (R) | 18.00 | 9.00 |
| 32 | Larry Zimmerman (R) | 18.00 | 9.00 |
| 33 | Pat Harder (R) | 20.00 | 9.50 |
| 34 | Sammy Baugh (R) | 325.00 | 150.00 |
| 35 | Ted Fritsch (R) | 18.00 | 9.00 |
| 36 | Bill Dudley (R) | 75.00 | 36.00 |
| 37 | George Connor (R) | 60.00 | 28.00 |
| 38 | Frank Dancewicz (R) | 18.00 | 9.00 |
| 39 | Billy Dewell (R) | 18.00 | 9.00 |
| 40 | John Nolan (R) | 18.00 | 9.00 |
| 41 | Harry Szulborski (R) | 18.00 | 9.00 |
| 42 | Tex Coulter (R) | 18.00 | 9.00 |
| 43 | Rbt. Nussbaumer (R) | 18.00 | 9.00 |
| 44 | Bob Mann (R) | 18.00 | 9.00 |
| 45 | Jim White (R) | 18.00 | 9.00 |
| 46 | Jack Jacobs (R) | 18.00 | 9.00 |
| 47 | John Clement (R) | 18.00 | 9.00 |
| 48 | Frank Reagan (R) | 18.00 | 9.00 |
| 49 | Frank Tripucka (R) | 48.00 | 22.00 |
| 50 | John Rauch (R) | 75.00 | 38.00 |
| 51 | Mike Dimitro (R) | 75.00 | 38.00 |

| 52 | Leo Nomelini (R) | 225.00 | 105.00 |
|----|------------------|--------|--------|
| 53 | Charley Conerly (R) | 250.00 | 120.00 |
| 54 | Chuck Bednarik (R) | 250.00 | 120.00 |
| 55 | Chick Jagade (R) | 75.00 | 38.00 |
| 56 | Bob Folsom (R) | 75.00 | 38.00 |
| 57 | Eugene Rossides (R) | 75.00 | 38.00 |
| 58 | Art Weiner (R) | 75.00 | 38.00 |
| 59 | Alex Sarkistian (R) | 75.00 | 38.00 |
| 60 | Dick Harris (R) | 75.00 | 38.00 |
| 61 | Len Younce (R) | 75.00 | 38.00 |
| 62 | Gene Derricotte (R) | 75.00 | 38.00 |
| 63 | Roy Steiner (R) | 75.00 | 38.00 |
| 64 | Frank Seno (R) | 75.00 | 38.00 |
| 65 | Bob Hendren (R) | 75.00 | 38.00 |
| 66 | Jack Cloud (R) | 75.00 | 38.00 |
| 67 | Harrell Collins (R) | 75.00 | 38.00 |
| 68 | Clyde LeForce (R) | 75.00 | 38.00 |
| 69 | Larry Joe (R) | 75.00 | 38.00 |
| 70 | Phil O'Reilly (R) | 75.00 | 38.00 |
| 71 | Paul Campbell (R) | 75.00 | 38.00 |
| 72 | Ray Evans (R) | 75.00 | 38.00 |
| 73 | Jackie Jensen (R) | 250.00 | 120.00 |
| 74 | Russ Steger (R) | 75.00 | 38.00 |
| 75 | Tony Minisi (R) | 75.00 | 38.00 |
| 76 | Clay Tonnemaker (R) | 75.00 | 38.00 |
| 77 | George Savitsky (R) | 75.00 | 38.00 |
| 78 | Clarence Self (R) | 75.00 | 38.00 |
| 79 | Rod Franz (R) | 75.00 | 38.00 |
| 80 | Jim Youle (R) | 75.00 | 38.00 |
| 81 | Billy Bye (R) | 75.00 | 38.00 |
| 82 | Fred Enke (R) | 75.00 | 38.00 |
| 83 | Fred Folger (R) | 75.00 | 38.00 |
| 84 | Jug Girard (R) | 75.00 | 38.00 |
| 85 | Joe Scott (R) | 75.00 | 38.00 |
| 86 | Bob Demoss (R) | 75.00 | 38.00 |
| 87 | Dave Templeton (R) | 75.00 | 38.00 |
| 88 | Herb Siegert (R) | 75.00 | 38.00 |
| 89 | Bucky O'Conner (R) | 75.00 | 38.00 |
| 90 | Joe Whisler (R) | 75.00 | 38.00 |
| 91 | Leon Hart (R) | 125.00 | 60.00 |
| 92 | Earl Banks (R) | 75.00 | 38.00 |
| 93 | F. Aschenbrenner (R) | 75.00 | 38.00 |
| 94 | John Goldsberry (R) | 75.00 | 38.00 |
| 95 | Porter Payne (R) | 75.00 | 38.00 |
| 96 | Pete Perini (R) | 75.00 | 38.00 |
| 97 | Jay Rhodemyre (R) | 75.00 | 38.00 |
| 98 | Al DiMarco (R) | 125.00 | 50.00 |

# 1949 Leaf

This 49 card set is similar to Leaf's 1948 edition. Cards measure 2-3/8" by 2-7/8". Card fronts contain black and white shots superimposed on a color background.

The vertical card backs feature the player's personal data, a brief bio and a special mail-in offer for a team pennant. Although the set contains only 49 cards, for unknown reasons the card backs are numbered from 1-150.

| | | NR/MT | EX |
|---|---|-------|-----|
| **Complete Set (49)** | | 1,650.00 | 800.00 |
| **Commons** | | 14.00 | 7.00 |
| | | | |
| 1 | Bob Hendren | 60.00 | 20.00 |
| 2 | Joe Scott | 14.00 | 7.00 |
| 3 | Frank Reagan | 14.00 | 7.00 |
| 4 | John Rauch | 14.00 | 7.00 |
| 7 | Bill Fischer | 14.00 | 7.00 |
| 9 | Bud Angsman | 14.00 | 7.00 |
| 10 | Billy Dewell | 14.00 | 7.00 |
| 13 | Tommy Thompson | 24.00 | 11.00 |
| 15 | Sid Luckman | 100.00 | 48.00 |
| 16 | Charlie Trippi | 32.00 | 15.00 |
| 17 | Bob Mann | 14.00 | 7.00 |
| 19 | Paul Christman | 25.00 | 12.00 |
| 22 | Bill Dudley | 32.00 | 15.00 |
| 23 | Clyde LeForce | 14.00 | 7.00 |
| 26 | Sammy Baugh | 165.00 | 80.00 |
| 28 | Pete Pihos | 35.00 | 16.50 |
| 31 | Tex Coulter | 14.00 | 7.00 |
| 32 | Mal Kutner | 14.00 | 7.00 |
| 35 | Whitey Wistert | 14.00 | 7.00 |
| 37 | Ted Fritsch | 14.00 | 7.00 |
| 38 | Vince Banonis | 14.00 | 7.00 |
| 39 | Jim White | 14.00 | 7.00 |
| 40 | George Connor | 32.00 | 15.00 |

| 41 | George McAfee | 32.00 | 15.00 |
| 43 | Frank Tripucka | 25.00 | 12.00 |
| 47 | Fred Enke | 14.00 | 7.00 |
| 49 | Charley Conerly | 70.00 | 32.50 |
| 51 | Ken Kavanaugh | 25.00 | 12.00 |
| 52 | Bob Demoss | 14.00 | 7.00 |
| 56 | John Lujack | 60.00 | 28.00 |
| 57 | Jim Youle | 14.00 | 7.00 |
| 62 | Harry Gilmer | 16.00 | 8.00 |
| 65 | Robert Nussbaumer | 14.00 | 7.00 |
| 67 | Bobby Layne | 120.00 | 55.00 |
| 70 | Herb Siegert | 14.00 | 7.00 |
| 74 | Tony Minisi | 14.00 | 7.00 |
| 79 | Steve Van Buren | 60.00 | 28.00 |
| 81 | Perry Moss | 14.00 | 7.00 |
| 89 | Bob Waterfield | 70.00 | 32.50 |
| 90 | Jack Jacobs | 14.00 | 7.00 |
| 95 | Kenny Washington | 24.00 | 11.00 |
| 101 | Pat Harder | 20.00 | 9.00 |
| 110 | William Swiacki | 14.00 | 7.00 |
| 118 | Fred Davis | 14.00 | 7.00 |
| 126 | Jay Rhodemyre | 14.00 | 7.00 |
| 127 | Frank Seno | 14.00 | 7.00 |
| 134 | Chuck Bednarik | 75.00 | 36.00 |
| 144 | George Savitsky | 14.00 | 7.00 |
| 150 | Bulldog Turner | 80.00 | 38.00 |

# 1991 Pacific Plus I

This 550-card set was the premier football issue from Pacific Trading Cards. The card fronts feature full color photos with the player's name printed vertically down the left border. The player's team and position appear in a diagonal box below the photo. A small Pacific pennant is located below the player's name. The card backs are diagonal and include a small head shot of the player along with his personal data, stats and a brief biography. Five checklist cards were randomly inserted into the company's foil packs. Those cards are listed at the end of this checklist but are not included in the complete set price below. All cards measure 2-1/2" by 3-1/2".

| | | MINT | NR/MT |
|---|---|---|---|
| **Complete Set (550)** | | 12.00 | 7.00 |
| **Commons** | | .05 | .02 |
| | | | |
| 1 | Deion Sanders | .20 | .12 |
| 2 | Steve Broussard | .08 | .05 |
| 3 | Aundray Bruce | .05 | .02 |
| 4 | Rick Bryan (R) | .05 | .02 |
| 5 | John Rade | .05 | .02 |
| 6 | Scott Case | .05 | .02 |
| 7 | Tony Casillas | .07 | .04 |
| 8 | Shawn Collins | .05 | .02 |
| 9 | Darion Conner | .08 | .05 |
| 10 | Tory Epps | .05 | .02 |
| 11 | Bill Fralic | .05 | .02 |
| 12 | Mike Gann | .05 | .02 |
| 13 | Tim Green | .05 | .02 |
| 14 | Chris Hinton | .05 | .02 |
| 15 | Houston Hoover | .05 | .02 |
| 16 | Chris Miller | .25 | .15 |
| 17 | Andre Rison | .20 | .12 |
| 18 | Mike Rozier | .05 | .02 |
| 19 | Jessie Tuggle | .05 | .02 |
| 20 | Don Beebe | .08 | .05 |
| 21 | Ray Bentley | .05 | .02 |
| 22 | Shane Conlan | .07 | .04 |
| 23 | Kent Hull | .05 | .02 |
| 24 | Mark Kelso | .05 | .02 |
| 25 | James Lofton | .20 | .12 |
| 26 | Scott Norwood | .05 | .02 |
| 27 | Andre Reed | .15 | .10 |
| 28 | Leonard Smith | .05 | .02 |
| 29 | Bruce Smith | .08 | .05 |
| 30 | Leon Seals | .05 | .02 |
| 31 | Darryl Talley | .07 | .04 |
| 32 | Steve Tasker | .05 | .02 |
| 33 | Thurman Thomas | .60 | .35 |
| 34 | James Williams | .05 | .02 |
| 35 | Will Wolford | .05 | .02 |
| 36 | Frank Reich | .07 | .04 |
| 37 | Jeff Wright (R) | .07 | .04 |
| 38 | Neal Anderson | .15 | .10 |
| 39 | Trace Armstrong | .05 | .02 |
| 40 | Johnny Bailey | .05 | .02 |
| 41 | Mark Bortz | .05 | .02 |
| 42 | Cap Boso (R) | .07 | .04 |

| | | | |
|---|---|---|---|
| 43 Kevin Butler | .05 | .02 |
| 44 Mark Carrier (Chi) | .08 | .05 |
| 45 Jim Covert | .05 | .02 |
| 46 Wendell Davis | .10 | .06 |
| 47 Richard Dent | .07 | .04 |
| 48 Shaun Gayle | .05 | .02 |
| 49 Jim Harbaugh | .15 | .10 |
| 50 Jay Hilgenberg | .05 | .02 |
| 51 Brad Muster | .08 | .05 |
| 52 William Perry | .07 | .04 |
| 53 Mike Singletary | .10 | .06 |
| 54 Pete Tom Willis | .15 | .10 |
| 55 Donnell Woolford | .05 | .02 |
| 56 Steve McMichael | .05 | .02 |
| 57 Eric Ball | .05 | .02 |
| 58 Lewis Billups | .05 | .02 |
| 59 Jim Breech | .05 | .02 |
| 60 James Brooks | .07 | .04 |
| 61 Eddie Brown | .10 | .06 |
| 62 Rickey Dixon | .05 | .02 |
| 63 Boomer Esiason | .12 | .07 |
| 64 James Francis | .08 | .05 |
| 65 David Fulcher | .05 | .02 |
| 66 David Grant | .05 | .02 |
| 67 Harold Green | .20 | .12 |
| 68 Rodney Holman | .05 | .02 |
| 69 Stanford Jennings | .05 | .02 |
| 70 Tim Krumrie | .05 | .02 |
| 71 Tim McGee | .07 | .04 |
| 72 Anthony Munoz | .08 | .05 |
| 73 Mitchell Price (R) | .07 | .04 |
| 74 Eric Thomas | .05 | .02 |
| 75 Ickey Woods | .05 | .02 |
| 76 Mike Baab | .05 | .02 |
| 77 Thane Gash | .05 | .02 |
| 78 David Grayson | .05 | .02 |
| 79 Mike Johnson | .05 | .02 |
| 80 Reggie Langhorne | .05 | .02 |
| 81 Kevin Mack | .07 | .04 |
| 82 Clay Matthews | .05 | .02 |
| 83 Eric Metcalf | .15 | .10 |
| 84 Frank Minnifield | .05 | .02 |
| 85 Mike Oliphant | .05 | .02 |
| 86 Mike Pagel | .05 | .02 |
| 87 John Talley (R) | .07 | .04 |
| 88 Lawyer Tillman | .05 | .02 |
| 89 Gregg Rakoczy | .05 | .02 |
| 90 Bryan Wagner | .05 | .02 |
| 91 Rob Burnett (R) | .07 | .04 |
| 92 Tommie Agee | .05 | .02 |
| 93 Troy Aikman | .80 | .50 |
| 94 Bill Bates | .05 | .02 |
| 95 Jack Del Rio | .05 | .02 |
| 96 Issiac Holt | .05 | .02 |
| 97 Michael Irvin | .30 | .18 |
| 98 Jim Jeffcoat | .05 | .02 |
| 99 Jimmy Jones | .05 | .02 |

| | | | |
|---|---|---|---|
| 100 Kelvin Martin | .08 | .05 |
| 101 Nate Newton | .05 | .02 |
| 102 Danny Noonan | .05 | .02 |
| 103 Ken Norton | .05 | .02 |
| 104 Jay Novacek | .07 | .04 |
| 105 Mike Saxon | .05 | .02 |
| 106 Derrick Sheppard | .05 | .02 |
| 107 Emmitt Smith | 1.75 | 1.00 |
| 108 Daniel Stubbs | .05 | .02 |
| 109 Tony Tolbert | .05 | .02 |
| 110 Alexander Wright | .08 | .05 |
| 111 Steve Atwater | .08 | .05 |
| 112 Melvin Bratton | .05 | .02 |
| 113 Tyrone Braxton | .05 | .02 |
| 114 Alphonso Carreker | .05 | .02 |
| 115 John Elway | .20 | .12 |
| 116 Simon Fletcher | .05 | .02 |
| 117 Bobby Humphrey | .10 | .06 |
| 118 Mark Jackson | .07 | .04 |
| 119 Vance Johnson | .08 | .05 |
| 120 Greg Kragen | .05 | .02 |
| 121 Karl Mecklenburg | .08 | .05 |
| 122A Orsen Mobley (Er) | .35 | .20 |
| (First name wrong) | | |
| 122B Orson Mobley (Cor) | .05 | .02 |
| 123 Alton Montgomery | .05 | .02 |
| 124 Ricky Nattiel | .07 | .04 |
| 125 Steve Sewell | .05 | .02 |
| 126 Shannon Sharpe | .07 | .04 |
| 127 Dennis Smith | .05 | .02 |
| 128A Andie Townsend | .35 | .20 |
| (First name wrong) | | |
| 128B Andre Townsend | .05 | .02 |
| 129 Mike Horan | .05 | .02 |
| 130 Jerry Ball | .05 | .02 |
| 131 Bennie Blades | .07 | .04 |
| 132 Lomas Brown | .05 | .02 |
| 133 Jeff Campbell | .05 | .02 |
| 134 Robert Clark | .05 | .02 |
| 135 Michael Cofer | .05 | .02 |
| 136 Dennis Gibson | .05 | .02 |
| 137 Mel Gray | .05 | .02 |
| 138 LeRoy Irvin | .07 | .04 |
| 139 George Jamison (R) | .07 | .04 |
| 140 Richard Johnson | .05 | .02 |
| 141 Eddie Murray | .05 | .02 |
| 142 Dan Owens | .05 | .02 |
| 143 Rodney Peete | .12 | .07 |
| 144 Barry Sanders | .70 | .40 |
| 145 Chris Spielman | .07 | .04 |
| 146 Mark Spindler | .05 | .02 |
| 147 Andre Ware | .15 | .10 |
| 148 William White | .05 | .02 |
| 149 Tony Bennett | .07 | .04 |
| 150 Robert Brown | .05 | .02 |
| 151 LeRoy Butler | .05 | .02 |
| 152 Anthony Dilweg | .07 | .04 |

| | | | |
|---|---|---|---|
| 153 | Michael Haddix | .05 | .02 |
| 154 | Ron Hallstrom | .05 | .02 |
| 155 | Tim Harris | .07 | .04 |
| 156 | Johnny Holland | .05 | .02 |
| 157 | Chris Jacke | .05 | .02 |
| 158 | Perry Kemp | .05 | .02 |
| 159 | Mark Lee | .05 | .02 |
| 160 | Don Majkowski | .12 | .07 |
| 161 | Tony Mandarich | .05 | .02 |
| 162 | Mark Murphy | .05 | .02 |
| 163 | Brian Noble | .05 | .02 |
| 164 | Shawn Patterson (R) | .08 | .05 |
| 165 | Jeff Query | .08 | .05 |
| 166 | Sterling Sharpe | .20 | .12 |
| 167 | Darrell Thompson | .12 | .07 |
| 168 | Ed West | .05 | .02 |
| 169 | Ray Childress | .07 | .04 |
| 170A | Chris Dishman (Er) (First name wrong) | .25 | .15 |
| 170B | Cris Dishman (Cor) | .10 | .06 |
| 171 | Curtis Duncan | .07 | .04 |
| 172 | William Fuller | .05 | .02 |
| 173 | Ernest Givins | .10 | .06 |
| 174 | Drew Hill | .08 | .05 |
| 175A | Haywood Jeffries (Er) (Last name wrong) | .40 | .25 |
| 175B | Haywood Jeffires (Cor) | .20 | .12 |
| 176 | Sean Jones | .05 | .02 |
| 177 | Lamar Lathon | .07 | .04 |
| 178 | Bruce Matthews | .05 | .02 |
| 179 | Bubba McDowell | .05 | .02 |
| 180 | Johnny Meads | .05 | .02 |
| 181 | Warren Moon | .25 | .15 |
| 182 | Mike Munchak | .05 | .02 |
| 183 | Allen Pinkett | .05 | .02 |
| 184 | Dean Steinkuhler | .05 | .02 |
| 185 | Lorenzo White | .15 | .10 |
| 186 | John Grimsley | .05 | .02 |
| 187 | Pat Beach | .05 | .02 |
| 188 | Albert Bentley | .05 | .02 |
| 189 | Dean Biasucci | .05 | .02 |
| 190 | Duane Bickett | .05 | .02 |
| 191 | Bill Brooks | .05 | .02 |
| 192 | Eugene Daniel | .05 | .02 |
| 193 | Jeff George | .25 | .15 |
| 194 | Jon Hand | .05 | .02 |
| 195 | Jeff Herrod | .05 | .02 |
| 196A | Jesse Hester (Er) (First name wrong) | .35 | .20 |
| 196B | Jessie Hester (Cor) | .08 | .05 |
| 197 | Mike Prior | .05 | .02 |
| 198 | Stacey Simmons | .05 | .02 |
| 199 | Rohn Stark | .05 | .02 |
| 200 | Pat Tomberlin (R) | .07 | .04 |
| 201 | Clarence Verdin | .07 | .04 |
| 202 | Keith Taylor | .05 | .02 |
| 203 | Jack Trudeau | .10 | .06 |
| 204 | Chip Banks | .05 | .02 |
| 205 | John Alt | .05 | .02 |
| 206 | Deron Cherry | .05 | .02 |
| 207 | Steve DeBerg | .10 | .06 |
| 208 | Tim Grunhard | .05 | .02 |
| 209 | Albert Lewis | .05 | .02 |
| 210 | Nick Lowery | .07 | .04 |
| 211 | Bill Maas | .05 | .02 |
| 212 | Chris Martin | .05 | .02 |
| 213 | Todd McNair | .05 | .02 |
| 214 | Christian Okoye | .12 | .07 |
| 215 | Stephone Paige | .08 | .05 |
| 216 | Steve Pelluer | .08 | .05 |
| 217 | Kevin Porter | .05 | .02 |
| 218 | Kevin Ross | .05 | .02 |
| 219 | Dan Saleaumua | .05 | .02 |
| 220 | Neil Smith | .05 | .02 |
| 221 | David Szott (R) | .07 | .04 |
| 222 | Derrick Thomas | .20 | .12 |
| 223 | Barry Word | .20 | .12 |
| 224 | Percy Snow | .08 | .05 |
| 225 | Marcus Allen | .12 | .07 |
| 226 | Eddie Anderson | .05 | .02 |
| 227 | Steve Beuerlein | .12 | .07 |
| 228A | Tim Brown (Er (No position on back) | .35 | .20 |
| 228B | Tim Brown (Cor) | .12 | .07 |
| 229 | Scott Davis | .05 | .02 |
| 230 | Mike Dyal | .05 | .02 |
| 231 | Mervyn Fernandez | .08 | .05 |
| 232 | Willie Gault | .07 | .04 |
| 233 | Ethan Horton | .07 | .04 |
| 234 | Bo Jackson | .25 | .15 |
| 235 | Howie Long | .07 | .04 |
| 236 | Terry McDaniel | .05 | .02 |
| 237 | Max Montoya | .05 | .02 |
| 238 | Don Mosbar | .05 | .02 |
| 239 | Jay Schroeder | .10 | .06 |
| 240 | Steve Smith | .05 | .02 |
| 241 | Greg Townsend | .07 | .04 |
| 242 | Aaron Wallace | .07 | .04 |
| 243 | Lionel Washington | .05 | .02 |
| 244A | Steve Winsiewski (Er) (Last name wrong) | .35 | .20 |
| 244B | Steve Wisniewski (Cor) | .08 | .05 |
| 245 | Flipper Anderson | .08 | .05 |
| 246 | Latin Berry (R) | .05 | .02 |
| 247 | Robert Delpino | .07 | .04 |
| 248 | Marcus Dupree | .07 | .04 |
| 249 | Henry Ellard | .07 | .04 |
| 250 | Jim Everett | .15 | .10 |
| 251 | Cleveland Gary | .08 | .05 |
| 252 | Jerry Gray | .05 | .02 |
| 253 | Kevin Greene | .07 | .04 |
| 254 | Pete Holohan | .05 | .02 |

| # | Player | | |
|---|---|---|---|
| 255 | Buford McGee | .05 | .02 |
| 256 | Tom Newberry | .05 | .02 |
| 257 | Irv Pankey | .05 | .02 |
| 258 | Jackie Slater | .07 | .04 |
| 259 | Doug Smith | .05 | .02 |
| 260 | Frank Stams | .05 | .02 |
| 261 | Michael Stewart | .05 | .02 |
| 262 | Fred Strickland | .05 | .02 |
| 263 | J.B. Brown | .05 | .02 |
| 264 | Mark Clayton | .12 | .07 |
| 265 | Jeff Cross | .05 | .02 |
| 266 | Mark Dennis (R) | .07 | .04 |
| 267 | Mark Duper | .08 | .04 |
| 268 | Ferrell Edmunds | .05 | .02 |
| 269 | Dan Marino | .40 | .25 |
| 270 | John Offerdahl | .08 | .05 |
| 271 | Louis Oliver | .07 | .04 |
| 272 | Tony Paige | .05 | .02 |
| 273 | Reggie Roby | .05 | .02 |
| 274 | Sammie Smith | .08 | .05 |
| 275 | Keith Sims | .05 | .02 |
| 276 | Brian Sochia | .05 | .02 |
| 277 | Pete Stoyanovich | .05 | .02 |
| 278 | Richmond Webb | .07 | .04 |
| 279 | Jarvis Williaams | .05 | .02 |
| 280 | Tim McKyer | .05 | .02 |
| 281 | Jim Jensen | .05 | .02 |
| 282 | Scott Secules | .05 | .02 |
| 283 | Ray Berry | .05 | .02 |
| 284 | Joey Browner | .07 | .04 |
| 285 | Anthony Carter | .10 | .06 |
| 286A | Chris Carter (Er) | 1.00 | .70 |
| | First name wrong) | | |
| 286B | Cris Carter (Cor) | .35 | .20 |
| 287 | Chris Doleman | .08 | .05 |
| 288 | Mark Dusbabek (R) | .07 | .04 |
| 289 | Hassan Jones | .07 | .04 |
| 290 | Steve Jordan | .05 | .02 |
| 291 | Carl Lee | .05 | .02 |
| 292 | Kirk Lowdermilk | .05 | .02 |
| 293 | Randall McDaniel | .05 | .02 |
| 294 | Mike Merriweather | .05 | .02 |
| 295A | Keith Millard (Er) | .35 | .20 |
| | (No position on back) | | |
| 295B | Keith Millard | .08 | .05 |
| 296 | Al Noga | .05 | .02 |
| 297 | Scott Studwell | .05 | .02 |
| 298 | Henry Thomas | .05 | .02 |
| 299 | Herschel Walker | .15 | .10 |
| 300 | Gary Zimmerman | .05 | .02 |
| 301 | Rick Gannon | .20 | .12 |
| 302 | Wade Wilson | .10 | .06 |
| 303 | Vincent Brown | .05 | .02 |
| 304 | Marv Cook | .05 | .02 |
| 305 | Hart Lee Dykes | .07 | .04 |
| 306 | Irving Fryar | .07 | .04 |
| 307 | Tommy Hodson | .10 | .06 |
| 308 | Maurice Hurst | .05 | .02 |
| 309 | Ronnie Lippett | .05 | .02 |
| 310 | Fred Mario | .05 | .02 |
| 311 | Greg McMurtry | .12 | .07 |
| 312 | Johnny Rembert | .05 | .02 |
| 313 | Chris Singleton | .07 | .04 |
| 314 | Ed Reynolds | .05 | .02 |
| 315 | Andre Tippett | .07 | .04 |
| 316 | Garin Veris | .05 | .02 |
| 317 | Brent Williams | .05 | .02 |
| 318A | John Stevens (Er) | .35 | .20 |
| | (First name wrong) | | |
| 318B | John Stephens (Cor) | .12 | .07 |
| 319 | Sammy Martin | .05 | .02 |
| 320 | Bruce Armstrong | .05 | .02 |
| 321A | Morten Anderson | .35 | .20 |
| | (Er) (Last name wrong) | | |
| 321B | Morten Andersen (Cor) | .08 | .05 |
| 322 | Gene Atkins | .05 | .02 |
| 323 | Vince Buck | .05 | .02 |
| 324 | John Fourcade | .07 | .04 |
| 325 | Kevin Haverdink | .05 | .02 |
| 326 | Bobby Hebert | .15 | .10 |
| 327 | Craig Heyward | .07 | .04 |
| 328 | Dalton Hilliard | .08 | .05 |
| 329 | Rickey Jackson | .07 | .04 |
| 330 | Vaughan Johnson | .07 | .04 |
| 331 | Eric Martin | .08 | .05 |
| 332 | Wayne Martin | .05 | .02 |
| 333 | Reuben Mayes | .05 | .02 |
| 334 | Sam Mills | .07 | .04 |
| 335 | Brett Perriman | .07 | .04 |
| 336 | Pat Swilling | .10 | .06 |
| 337 | Renaldo Turnbull | .07 | .04 |
| 338 | Lonzell Hill | .05 | .02 |
| 339 | Steve Walsh | .08 | .05 |
| 340 | Carl Banks | .05 | .02 |
| 341 | Mark Bavaro | .07 | .04 |
| 342 | Maurice Carthon | .05 | .02 |
| 343 | Pat Harlow (R) | .08 | .05 |
| 344 | Eric Dorsey | .05 | .02 |
| 345 | John Elliott | .05 | .02 |
| 346 | Rodney Hampton | .50 | .30 |
| 347 | Jeff Hostetler | .15 | .10 |
| 348 | Erik Howard | .05 | .02 |
| 349 | Pepper Johnson | .05 | .02 |
| 350 | Sean Landeta | .05 | .02 |
| 351 | Leonard Marshall | .05 | .02 |
| 352 | David Meggett | .12 | .07 |
| 353A | Bart Oats (Er) | .35 | .20 |
| | (Last name wrong) | | |
| 353B | Bart Oates (Cor) | .07 | .04 |
| 354 | Gary Reasons | .05 | .02 |
| 355 | Phil Simms | .10 | .06 |
| 356 | Lawrence Taylor | .15 | .10 |
| 357 | Reyna Thompson | .05 | .02 |

| # | Player | | |
|---|--------|---|---|
| 358 | Brian Williams | .05 | .02 |
| 359 | Matt Bahr | .05 | .02 |
| 360 | Mark Ingram | .05 | .02 |
| 361 | Brad Baxter | .15 | .10 |
| 362 | Mark Boyer | .05 | .02 |
| 363 | Dennis Byrd | .05 | .02 |
| 364 | Dave Cadigan | .05 | .02 |
| 365 | Kyle Clifton | .05 | .02 |
| 366 | James Hasty | .05 | .02 |
| 367 | Joe Kelly | .05 | .02 |
| 368 | Jeff Lageman | .07 | .04 |
| 369 | Pat Leahy | .05 | .02 |
| 370 | Terance Mathis | .07 | .04 |
| 371 | Erik McMillan | .05 | .02 |
| 372 | Rob Moore | .25 | .15 |
| 373 | Ken O'Brien | .10 | .06 |
| 374 | Tony Stargell | .05 | .02 |
| 375 | Jim Sweeney | .05 | .02 |
| 376 | Al Toon | .08 | .05 |
| 377 | Johnny Hector | .05 | .02 |
| 378 | Jeff Criswell | .05 | .02 |
| 379 | Mike Haight (R) | .07 | .04 |
| 380 | Troy Benson | .05 | .02 |
| 381 | Eric Allen | .05 | .02 |
| 382 | Fred Barnett | .20 | .12 |
| 383 | Jerome Brown | .07 | .04 |
| 384 | Keith Byars | .07 | .04 |
| 385 | Randall Cunningham | .20 | .12 |
| 386 | Byron Evans | .05 | .02 |
| 387 | Wes Hopkins | .05 | .02 |
| 388 | Keith Jackson | .15 | .10 |
| 389 | Seth Joyner | .07 | .04 |
| 390 | Bobby Wilson (R) | .08 | .05 |
| 391 | Heath Sherman | .07 | .04 |
| 392 | Clyde Simmons | .07 | .04 |
| 393 | Ben Smith | .05 | .02 |
| 394 | Andre Waters | .05 | .02 |
| 395 | Reggie White | .12 | .07 |
| 396 | Calvin Williams | .10 | .06 |
| 397 | Al Harris | .05 | .02 |
| 398 | Anthony Toney | .05 | .02 |
| 399 | Mike Quick | .07 | .04 |
| 400 | Anthony Bell | .05 | .02 |
| 401 | Rich Camarillo | .05 | .02 |
| 402 | Roy Green | .07 | .04 |
| 403 | Ken Harvey | .05 | .02 |
| 404 | Eric Hill | .05 | .02 |
| 405 | Garth Jax (R) | .07 | .04 |
| 406 | Ernie Jones | .05 | .02 |
| 407 | Cedric Mack | .05 | .02 |
| 408 | Dexter Manley | .05 | .02 |
| 409 | Tim McDonald | .05 | .02 |
| 410 | Freddie Joe Nunn | .05 | .02 |
| 411 | Ricky Proehl | .08 | .05 |
| 412 | Moe Gardner (R) | .10 | .06 |
| 413 | Timm Rosenbach | .12 | .07 |
| 414 | Luis Sharpe | .05 | .02 |
| 415 | Vai Sikahema | .05 | .02 |
| 416 | Anthony Thompson | .08 | .05 |
| 417 | Ron Wolfley | .05 | .02 |
| 418 | Lonnie Young | .05 | .02 |
| 419 | Gary Anderson | .05 | .02 |
| 420 | Bubby Brister | .10 | .06 |
| 421 | Thomas Everett | .05 | .02 |
| 422 | Eric Green | .12 | .07 |
| 423 | Delton Hall | .05 | .02 |
| 424 | Bryan Hinkle | .05 | .02 |
| 425 | Merril Hoge | .07 | .04 |
| 426 | Carnell Lake | .05 | .02 |
| 427 | Louis Lipps | .07 | .04 |
| 428 | David Little | .05 | .02 |
| 429 | Greg Lloyd | .05 | .02 |
| 430 | Mike Mularkey | .05 | .02 |
| 431 | Keith Willis | .05 | .02 |
| 432 | Dwayne Woodruff | .05 | .02 |
| 433 | Rod Woodson | .10 | .06 |
| 434 | Tim Worley | .07 | .04 |
| 435 | Warren Williams | .05 | .02 |
| 436 | Terry Long | .05 | .02 |
| 437 | Martin Bayless | .05 | .02 |
| 438 | Jarrod Bunch (R) | .25 | .15 |
| 439 | Marion Butts | .10 | .06 |
| 440 | Gill Byrd | .05 | .02 |
| 441 | Arthur Cox | .05 | .02 |
| 442 | John Friesz | .10 | .06 |
| 443 | Leo Goeas | .05 | .02 |
| 444 | Burt Grossman | .07 | .04 |
| 445 | Courtney Hall | .05 | .02 |
| 446 | Ronnie Harmon | .05 | .02 |
| 447 | Nate Lewis (R) | .12 | .07 |
| 448 | Anthony Miller | .12 | .07 |
| 449 | Leslie O'Neal | .07 | .04 |
| 450 | Gary Plummer | .05 | .02 |
| 451 | Junior Seau | .12 | .07 |
| 452 | Billy Ray Smith | .05 | .02 |
| 453 | Billy Joe Tolliver | .08 | .05 |
| 454 | Broderick Thompson | .05 | .02 |
| 455 | Lee Williams | .05 | .02 |
| 456 | Michael Carter | .05 | .02 |
| 457 | Mike Cofer | .05 | .02 |
| 458 | Kevin Fagan | .05 | .02 |
| 459 | Charles Haley | .07 | .04 |
| 460 | Piece Holt | .05 | .02 |
| 461 | Johnny Jackson (R) | .08 | .05 |
| 462 | Brent Jones | .07 | .04 |
| 463 | Guy McIntyre | .05 | .02 |
| 464 | Joe Montana | .60 | .35 |
| 465A | Bubba Parris (Er) (Last name wrong) | .35 | .20 |
| 465B | Bubba Paris (Cor) | .08 | .05 |
| 466 | Tom Rathman | .08 | .05 |
| 467 | Jerry Rice | .40 | .25 |
| 468 | Mike Sherrard | .08 | .05 |
| 469 | John Taylor | .15 | .10 |

| No. | Player | | |
|---|---|---|---|
| 470 | Steve Young | .25 | .15 |
| 471 | Dennis Brown | .05 | .02 |
| 472 | Dexter Carter | .08 | .05 |
| 473 | Bill Romanowski | .05 | .02 |
| 474 | Dave Waymer | .05 | .02 |
| 475 | Robert Blackmon | .05 | .02 |
| 476 | Derrick Fenner | .08 | .05 |
| 477 | Nesby Glasgow | .05 | .02 |
| 478 | Jacob Green | .05 | .02 |
| 479 | Andy Heck | .05 | .02 |
| 480 | Norm Johnson | .05 | .02 |
| 481 | Tommy Kane | .07 | .04 |
| 482 | Cortez Kennedy | .08 | .05 |
| 483 | Dave Krieg | .12 | .07 |
| 484 | Bryan Millard | .05 | .02 |
| 485 | Joe Nash | .05 | .02 |
| 486 | Rufus Porter | .05 | .02 |
| 487 | Eugene Robinson | .05 | .02 |
| 488 | Mike Tice (R) | .07 | .04 |
| 489 | Chris Warren | .05 | .02 |
| 490 | John L. Williams | .07 | .04 |
| 491 | Terry Wooden | .05 | .02 |
| 492 | Tony Woods | .05 | .02 |
| 493 | Brian Blades | .07 | .04 |
| 494 | Paul Skansi | .05 | .02 |
| 495 | Gary Anderson | .05 | .02 |
| 496 | Mark Carrier | .08 | .05 |
| 497 | Chris Chandler | .10 | .06 |
| 498 | Steve Christie | .05 | .02 |
| 499 | Reggie Cobb | .15 | .10 |
| 500 | Reuben Davis | .05 | .02 |
| 501 | Willie Drewrey | .05 | .02 |
| 502 | Randy Grimes | .05 | .02 |
| 503 | Paul Gruber | .05 | .02 |
| 504 | Wayne Haddix | .05 | .02 |
| 505 | Ron Hall | .05 | .02 |
| 506 | Harry Hamilton | .05 | .02 |
| 507 | Bruce Hill | .05 | .02 |
| 508 | Eugene Marve | .05 | .02 |
| 509 | Keith McCants | .08 | .05 |
| 510 | Winston Moss | .05 | .02 |
| 511 | Kevin Murphy | .05 | .02 |
| 512 | Mark Robinson | .05 | .02 |
| 513 | Vinny Testaverde | .12 | .07 |
| 514 | Broderick Thomas | .08 | .05 |
| 515 | Jeff Bostic | .05 | .02 |
| 516 | Todd Bowles | .05 | .02 |
| 517 | Earnest Byner | .08 | .05 |
| 518 | Gary Clark | .15 | .10 |
| 519 | Craig Erickson (R) | .15 | .10 |
| 520 | Darryl Grant | .05 | .02 |
| 521 | Darrell Green | .10 | .06 |
| 522 | Russ Grimm | .05 | .02 |
| 523 | Stan Humphries | .30 | .18 |
| 524 | Joe Jacoby | .05 | .02 |
| 525 | Jim Lachey | .07 | .04 |
| 526 | Chip Lohmiller | .05 | .02 |
| 527 | Charles Mann | .05 | .02 |
| 528 | Wilber Marshall | .07 | .04 |
| 529 | Art Monk | .20 | .12 |
| 530 | Tracy Rocker | .05 | .02 |
| 531 | Mark Rypien | .20 | .12 |
| 532 | Ricky Sanders | .08 | .05 |
| 533 | Alvin Walton | .05 | .02 |
| 534 | Todd Marinovich (R) | .80 | .50 |
| 535 | Mike Dumas (R) | .08 | .05 |
| 536 | Russell Maryland (R) | .25 | .15 |
| 537 | Eric Turner (R) | .20 | .12 |
| 538 | Ernie Mills (R) | .20 | .12 |
| 539 | Ed King (R) | .08 | .05 |
| 540 | Michael Stonbreaker (R) | .08 | .05 |
| 541 | Chris Zorich (R) | .10 | .06 |
| 542 | Mike Croel (R) | .30 | .18 |
| 543 | Eric Moten (R) | .08 | .05 |
| 544 | Dan McGwire (R) | .60 | .35 |
| 545 | Keith Cash (R) | .08 | .05 |
| 546 | Kenny Walker (R) | .25 | .15 |
| 547 | Leroy Hoard | .15 | .10 |
| 548 | Luis Chrisobol (R) | .07 | .04 |
| 549 | Stacy Danley (R) | .08 | .05 |
| 550 | Todd Lyght (R) | .25 | .15 |
| CL1 | Checklist | 1.75 | 1.00 |
| CL2 | Checklist | 1.75 | 1.00 |
| CL3 | Checklist | 1.75 | 1.00 |
| CL4 | Checklist | 1.75 | 1.00 |
| CL5 | Checklist | 1.75 | 1.00 |

# 1991 Pacific Plus II

This 110-card update set is identical in design to Pacific's regular edition. The set contains mostly rookie cards and is considered limited compared with Pacific's first edition. The card number sequence on the backs pick up where the first series left off, staring with #551. All cards measure 2-1/2" by 3-1/2".

|  | MINT | NR/MT |
|---|---|---|
| Complete Set (110) | 12.50 | 7.50 |
| Commons | .05 | .02 |
| | | |
| 551 Brett Favre (R) | 2.00 | 1.25 |
| 552 Mike Pritchard (R) | .50 | .30 |
| 553 Moe Gardner | .10 | .06 |
| 554 Tim McKyer | .05 | .02 |
| 555 Erric Pegram (R) | .20 | .12 |
| 556 Norm Johnson | .05 | .02 |
| 557 Bruce Pickens (R) | .20 | .12 |
| 558 Henry Jones (R) | .25 | .15 |
| 559 Phil Hansen (R) | .15 | .10 |
| 560 Cornelius Bennett | .10 | .06 |
| 561 Stan Thomas (R) | .08 | .05 |
| 562 Chris Zorich | .08 | .05 |
| 563 Anthony Morgan (R) | .35 | .20 |
| 564 Darren Lewis (R) | .35 | .20 |
| 565 Mike Stonebreaker | .08 | .05 |
| 566 Alfred Williams (R) | .25 | .15 |
| 567 Lamar Rogers (R) | .20 | .12 |
| 568 Erik Wilhelm (R) | .15 | .10 |
| 569 Ed King | .07 | .04 |
| 570 Michael Jackson (R) | .60 | .35 |
| 571 James Jones (R) | .08 | .05 |
| 572 Russell Maryland | .12 | .07 |
| 573 Dixon Edwards (R) | .10 | .06 |
| 574 Darrick Brownlow (R) | .08 | .05 |
| 575 Larry Brown (R) | .12 | .07 |
| 576 Mike Croel | .30 | .18 |
| 577 Keith Traylor (R) | .08 | .05 |
| 578 Kenny Walker | .15 | .10 |
| 579 Reggie Johnnson (R) | .15 | .10 |
| 580 Herman Moore (R) | .75 | .45 |
| 581 Kelvin Pritchett (R) | .20 | .12 |
| 582 Kevin Scott (R) | .12 | .07 |
| 583 Vinnie Clark (R) | .12 | .07 |
| 584 Esera Tuaolo (R) | .08 | .05 |
| 585 Don Davey (R) | .08 | .05 |
| 586 Blair Kiel (R) | .10 | .06 |
| 587 Mike Dumas | .07 | .04 |
| 588 Darryll Lewis (R) | .10 | .06 |
| 589 John Flannery (R) | .08 | .05 |
| 590 Kevin Donnally (R) | .08 | .05 |
| 591 Shane Curry (R) | .08 | .05 |
| 592 Mark Vander Poel (R) | .08 | .05 |
| 593 Dave McCloughan (R) | .08 | .05 |
| 594 Mel Agee (R) | .12 | .07 |
| 595 Kerry Cash (R) | .08 | .05 |
| 596 Harvey Williams (R) | .60 | .35 |
| 597 Joe Valerio (R) | .08 | .05 |
| 598 Tim Barnett (R) | .40 | .25 |
| 599 Todd Marinovich (R) | .90 | .60 |
| 600 Nick Bell (R) | .75 | .45 |
| 601 Roger Craig | .10 | .06 |
| 602 Ronnie Lott | .15 | .10 |
| 603 Mike Jones (R) | .10 | .06 |
| 604 Todd Lyght (R) | .20 | .12 |
| 605 Roman Phifer (R) | .08 | .05 |
| 606 David Lang (R) | .12 | .07 |
| 607 Aaron Craver (R) | .15 | .10 |
| 608 Mark Higgs (R) | .50 | .30 |
| 609 Chris Green (R) | .08 | .05 |
| 610 Randy Baldwin (R) | .10 | .06 |
| 611 Pat Harlow | .08 | .05 |
| 612 Leonard Russell (R) | .90 | .60 |
| 613 Jerome Henderson (R) | .15 | .10 |
| 614 Scott Zolak (R) | .40 | .25 |
| 615 Jon Vaughn (R) | .30 | .18 |
| 616 Harry Colon (R) | .10 | .06 |
| 617 Wesley Carroll (R) | .35 | .20 |
| 618 Quinn Early | .05 | .02 |
| 619 Reggie Jones (R) | .10 | .06 |
| 620 Jarrod Bunch (R) | .20 | .12 |
| 621 Kanavis McGhee (R) | .20 | .12 |
| 622 Ed McCaffrey (R) | .50 | .30 |
| 623 Browning Nagle (R) | 1.25 | .90 |
| 624 Mo Lewis (R) | .15 | .10 |
| 625 Blair Thomas | .15 | .10 |
| 626 Antone Davis (R) | .08 | .05 |
| 627 Jim McMahon | .10 | .06 |
| 628 Scott Kowalkowski (R) | .10 | .06 |
| 629 Brad Goebel (R) | .12 | .07 |
| 630 William Thomas (R) | .08 | .05 |
| 631 Eric Swann (R) | .20 | .12 |
| 632 Mike Jones (R) | .10 | .06 |

| | | | | | MINT | NR/MT |
|---|---|---|---|---|---|---|
| 633 | Aeneas Williams (R) | .15 | .10 | | | |
| 634 | Dexter Davis (R) | .08 | .05 | **Complete Set (25)** | 200.00 | 125.00 |
| 635 | Tom Tupa | .08 | .05 | **Commons** | 5.00 | 3.50 |
| 636 | Johnny Johnson | .25 | .15 | | | |
| 637 | Randal Hill (R) | .70 | .40 | | | |
| 638 | Jeff Graham (R) | .40 | .25 | 1 Russell Maryland | 10.00 | 7.00 |
| 639 | Ernie Mills (R) | .10 | .06 | 2 Andre Reed | 8.50 | 5.50 |
| 640 | Adrian Cooper (R) | .12 | .07 | 3 Jerry Rice | 20.00 | 14.00 |
| 641 | Stanley Richard (R) | .25 | .15 | 4 Keith Jackson | 6.00 | 3.75 |
| 642 | Eric Bieniemy (R) | .35 | .20 | 5 Jim Lachey | 5.00 | 3.00 |
| 643 | Eric Moten | .05 | .02 | 6 Anthony Munoz | 7.50 | 4.50 |
| 644 | Shawn Jefferson (R) | .25 | .15 | 7 Randall McDaniel | 5.00 | 3.00 |
| 645 | Ted Washington (R) | .15 | .10 | 8 Bruce Matthews | 5.00 | 3.00 |
| 646 | John Johnson (R) | .08 | .05 | 9 Kent Hull | 5.00 | 3.00 |
| 647 | Dan McGwire | .50 | .30 | 10 Joe Montana | 20.00 | 14.00 |
| 648 | Doug Thomas (R) | .10 | .06 | 11 Barry Sanders | 25.00 | 18.00 |
| 649 | David Daniels (R) | .08 | .05 | 12 Thurman Thomas | 20.00 | 14.00 |
| 650 | John Kasay (R) | .08 | .05 | 13 Morten Anderson | 5.00 | 3.00 |
| 651 | Jeff Kemp | .08 | .05 | 14 Jerry Ball | 5.00 | 3.00 |
| 652 | Charles McRae (R) | .10 | .06 | 15 Jerome Brown | 5.00 | 3.00 |
| 653 | Lawrence Dawsey (R) | .60 | .35 | 16 Reggie White | 7.50 | 4.50 |
| 654 | Robert Wilson (R) | .20 | .12 | 17 Bruce Smith | 6.00 | 3.75 |
| 655 | Dexter Manley | .05 | .02 | 18 Derrick Thomas | 12.00 | 8.50 |
| 656 | Chuck Weatherspoon (R) | .10 | .06 | 19 Lawrence Taylor | 12.00 | 8.50 |
| 657 | Tim Ryan (R) | .07 | .04 | 20 Charles Haley | 6.00 | 3.75 |
| 658 | Bobby Wilson | .08 | .05 | 21 Albert Lewis | 5.00 | 3.00 |
| 659 | Ricky Ervins (R) | .90 | .60 | 22 Rod Woodson | 6.00 | 3.75 |
| 660 | Matt Millen | .07 | .04 | 23 David Fulcher | 5.00 | 3.00 |
| | | | | 24 Joey Browner | 5.00 | 3.00 |
| | | | | 25 Sean Landeta | 5.00 | 3.00 |

# 1991 Pacific Picks The Pros Gold Inserts

The cards in this 25-card limited insert set were distributed randomly in Pacific's foil and wax packs. The card fronts feature full color action shots with gold foil borders. The player's name and position appear below the photo. The headline "Pacific Picks The Pros" is printed vertically to the left of the photo. Card backs are diagonal and consist of career highlights on a red and blue background. Only 10,000 gold insert cards were produced. The cards measure 2-1/2" by 3-1/2".

# 1991 Pacific Picks The Pros Silver Inserts

The cards in this limited insert set were distributed randomly in Pacific's cello packs and are identical in design to the gold inserts except for silver foil borders. Only 10,000 cards were produced. The cards measure 2-1/2" by 3-1/2".

| | MINT | NR/MT |
|---|---|---|
| **Complete Set (25)** | 200.00 | 125.00 |
| **Commons** | 5.00 | 3.00 |

| | | | |
|---|---|---|---|
| 1 | Russell Maryland | 10.00 | 7.00 |
| 2 | Andre Reed | 8.50 | 5.50 |
| 3 | Jerry Rice | 20.00 | 14.00 |
| 4 | Keith Jackson | 6.00 | 3.75 |
| 5 | Jim Lachey | 5.00 | 3.00 |
| 6 | Anthony Munoz | 7.50 | 4.50 |
| 7 | Randall McDaniel | 5.00 | 3.00 |
| 8 | Bruce Matthews | 5.00 | 3.00 |
| 9 | Kent Hull | 5.00 | 3.00 |
| 10 | Joe Montana | 20.00 | 14.00 |
| 11 | Barry Sanders | 25.00 | 18.00 |
| 12 | Thurman Thomas | 20.00 | 14.00 |
| 13 | Morten Anderson | 5.00 | 3.00 |
| 14 | Jerry Ball | 5.00 | 3.00 |
| 15 | Jerome Brown | 5.00 | 3.00 |
| 16 | Reggie White | 7.50 | 4.50 |
| 17 | Bruce Smith | 6.00 | 3.75 |
| 18 | Derrick Thomas | 12.00 | 8.50 |
| 19 | Lawrence Taylor | 12.00 | 8.50 |
| 20 | Charles Haley | 6.00 | 3.75 |
| 21 | Albert Lewis | 5.00 | 3.00 |
| 22 | Rod Woodson | 6.00 | 3.75 |
| 23 | David Fulcher | 5.00 | 3.00 |
| 24 | Joey Browner | 5.00 | 3.00 |
| 25 | Sean Landeta | 5.00 | 3.00 |

# 1992 Pacific Plus I

This set is the first of two series of 1992 NFL football cards issued by Pacific Trading Cards. The fronts are similar to 1991's edition with full color action shots and the player's name printed vertically down the left side of the card. A team helmet appear below the player's name. Card backs are horizontal and feature a close up head shot and career highlights. The set included limited bonus cards honoring the career of Steve Largent.

Checklist cards were randomly inserted in the company's foil packs. Both the checklist cards and the Largent inserts are listed at the end of this checklist but are not included in the complete set price below. All cards measure 2-1/2" by 3-12".

| | | MINT | NR/MT |
|---|---|---|---|
| Complete Set (330) | | 10.00 | 6.50 |
| Commons | | .05 | .02 |

| | | | |
|---|---|---|---|
| 1 | Steve Broussard | .08 | .05 |
| 2 | Darion Conner | .05 | .02 |
| 3 | Tory Epps | .05 | .02 |
| 4 | Michael Haynes | .15 | .10 |
| 5 | Chris Hinton | .05 | .02 |
| 6 | Mike Kenn | .05 | .02 |
| 7 | Tim McKyer | .05 | .02 |
| 8 | Chris Miller | .15 | .10 |
| 9 | Erric Pegram | .10 | .06 |
| 10 | Mike Pritchard | .25 | .10 |
| 11 | Moe Gardner | .07 | .04 |
| 12 | Tim Green | .05 | .02 |
| 13 | Norm Johnson | .05 | .02 |
| 14 | Don Beebe | .07 | .04 |
| 15 | Cornelius Bennett | .12 | .07 |
| 16 | Al Edwards | .05 | .02 |
| 17 | Mark Kelso | .05 | .02 |
| 18 | James Lofton | .15 | .10 |
| 19 | Frank Reich | .05 | .02 |
| 20 | Leon Seals | .05 | .02 |
| 21 | Darryl Talley | .07 | .04 |
| 22 | Thurman Thomas | .35 | .20 |
| 23 | Kent Hull | .05 | .02 |
| 24 | Jeff Wright | .05 | .02 |
| 25 | Nate Odomes | .05 | .02 |
| 26 | Carwel Gardner | .05 | .02 |
| 27 | Neal Anderson | .12 | .07 |
| 28 | Mark Carrier | .08 | .05 |
| 29 | Johnny Bailey | .05 | .02 |
| 30 | Jim Harbaugh | .12 | .07 |
| 31 | Jay Hilgenberg | .05 | .02 |
| 32 | William Perry | .07 | .04 |
| 33 | Wendell Davis | .12 | .07 |
| 34 | Donnell Woolford | .05 | .02 |
| 35 | Keith Van Horne | .05 | .02 |
| 36 | Shaun Gayle | .05 | .02 |
| 37 | Tom Waddle | .12 | .07 |
| 38 | Chris Zorich | .08 | .05 |
| 39 | Tom Thayer | .05 | .02 |
| 40 | Rickey Dixon | .05 | .02 |
| 41 | James Francis | .08 | .05 |
| 42 | David Fulcher | .05 | .02 |
| 43 | Reggie Reimbert | .07 | .04 |
| 44 | Anthony Munoz | .08 | .05 |

| No. | Player | | |
|---|---|---|---|
| 45 | Harold Green | .15 | .10 |
| 46 | Mitchell Price | .05 | .02 |
| 47 | Rodney Holman | .05 | .02 |
| 48 | Bruce Kozerski | .05 | .02 |
| 49 | Bruce Reimers | .05 | .02 |
| 50 | Erik Wilhelm | .08 | .05 |
| 51 | Harlon Barnett | .05 | .02 |
| 52 | Mike Johnson | .05 | .02 |
| 53 | Brian Brennan | .05 | .02 |
| 54 | Ed King | .05 | .02 |
| 55 | Reggie Langhorne | .05 | .02 |
| 56 | James Jones | .05 | .02 |
| 57 | Mike Baab | .05 | .02 |
| 58 | Dan Fike | .05 | .02 |
| 59 | Frank Minnifield | .05 | .02 |
| 60 | Clay Matthews | .05 | .02 |
| 61 | Kevin Mack | .07 | .04 |
| 62 | Tony Casillas | .07 | .04 |
| 63 | Jay Novacek | .08 | .05 |
| 64 | Larry Brown | .05 | .02 |
| 65 | Michael Irvin | .25 | .15 |
| 66 | Jack Del Rio | .05 | .02 |
| 67 | Ken Willis | .05 | .02 |
| 68 | Emmitt Smith | 1.50 | .90 |
| 69 | Alan Veingrad | .05 | .02 |
| 70 | John Gesek | .05 | .02 |
| 71 | Steve Beuerlein | .15 | .10 |
| 72 | Vinson Smith (R) | .08 | .05 |
| 73 | Steve Atwater | .08 | .05 |
| 74 | Mike Croel | .12 | .07 |
| 75 | John Elway | .20 | .12 |
| 76 | Gaston Green | .12 | .07 |
| 77 | Mike Horan | .05 | .02 |
| 78 | Vance Johnson | .08 | .05 |
| 79 | Karl Mecklenburg | .07 | .04 |
| 80 | Shannon Sharpe | .08 | .05 |
| 81 | David Treadwell | .05 | .02 |
| 82 | Kenny Walker | .12 | .07 |
| 83 | Greg Lewis | .10 | .06 |
| 84 | Shawn Moore | .12 | .07 |
| 85 | Alton Montgomery | .05 | .02 |
| 86 | Michael Young | .05 | .02 |
| 87 | Jerry Ball | .05 | .02 |
| 88 | Bennie Blades | .07 | .04 |
| 89 | Mel Gray | .05 | .02 |
| 90 | Herman Moore | .20 | .12 |
| 91 | Erik Kramer | .20 | .12 |
| 92 | Willie Green | .30 | .18 |
| 93 | George Jamison | .05 | .02 |
| 94 | Chris Spielman | .07 | .04 |
| 95 | Kelvin Pritchett | .05 | .02 |
| 96 | William White | .05 | .02 |
| 97 | Mike Utley | .08 | .05 |
| 98 | Tony Bennett | .05 | .02 |
| 99 | LeRoy Butler | .05 | .02 |
| 100 | Vinnie Clark | .05 | .02 |
| 101 | Ron Hallstrom | .05 | .02 |
| 102 | Chris Jacke | .05 | .02 |
| 103 | Tony Mandarich | .05 | .02 |
| 104 | Sterling Sharpe | .25 | .15 |
| 105 | Don Majkowski | .12 | .07 |
| 106 | Johnny Holland | .05 | .02 |
| 107 | Esera Tuaolo | .05 | .02 |
| 108 | Darrell Thompson | .08 | .05 |
| 109 | Bubba McDowell | .05 | .02 |
| 110 | Curtis Duncan | .05 | .02 |
| 111 | Lamar Lathon | .07 | .04 |
| 112 | Drew Hill | .07 | .04 |
| 113 | Bruce Matthews | .05 | .02 |
| 114 | Bo Orlando (R) | .10 | .06 |
| 115 | Don Maggs | .05 | .02 |
| 116 | Lorenzo White | .15 | .10 |
| 117 | Ernest Givins | .12 | .07 |
| 118 | Tony Jones | .05 | .02 |
| 119 | Dean Steinkuhler | .05 | .02 |
| 120 | Dean Biasucci | .05 | .02 |
| 121 | Duane Bickett | .05 | .02 |
| 122 | Bill Brooks | .05 | .02 |
| 123 | Ken Clark | .05 | .02 |
| 124 | Jessie Hester | .05 | .02 |
| 125 | Anthony Johnson | .05 | .02 |
| 126 | Chip Banks | .05 | .02 |
| 127 | Mike Prior | .05 | .02 |
| 128 | Rohn Stark | .05 | .02 |
| 130 | Clarence Verdin | .07 | .04 |
| 131 | Tim Manoa | .05 | .02 |
| 132 | Brian Baldinger (R) | .08 | .05 |
| 133 | Tim Barnett | .15 | .10 |
| 134 | J.J. Birden | .05 | .02 |
| 135 | Deron Cherry | .05 | .02 |
| 136 | Steve DeBerg | .10 | .06 |
| 137 | Nick Lowery | .07 | .04 |
| 138 | Todd McNair | .05 | .02 |
| 139 | Christian Okoye | .12 | .07 |
| 140 | Mark Vlasic | .07 | .04 |
| 141 | Dan Saleaumua | .05 | .02 |
| 142 | Neil Smith | .05 | .02 |
| 143 | Robb Thomas | .05 | .02 |
| 144 | Eddie Anderson | .05 | .02 |
| 145 | Nick Bell | .25 | .15 |
| 146 | Tim Brown | .10 | .06 |
| 147 | Roger Craig | .08 | .05 |
| 148 | Jeff Gossett | .05 | .02 |
| 149 | Ethan Horton | .05 | .02 |
| 150 | Jamie Holland | .05 | .02 |
| 151 | Jeff Jaeger | .05 | .02 |
| 152 | Todd Marinovich | .50 | .30 |
| 153 | Marcus Allen | .10 | .06 |
| 154 | Steve Smith | .05 | .02 |
| 155 | Flipper Anderson | .08 | .05 |
| 156 | Robert Delpino | .08 | .05 |
| 157 | Cleveland Gary | .08 | .05 |
| 158 | Kevin Greene | .07 | .04 |
| 159 | Dale Hatcher | .05 | .02 |

| | | | |
|---|---|---|---|
| 160 Duval Love | .05 | .02 |
| 161 Ron Brown | .05 | .02 |
| 162 Jackie Slater | .07 | .04 |
| 163 Doug Smith | .05 | .02 |
| 164 Aaron Cox | .05 | .02 |
| 165 Larry Kelm | .05 | .02 |
| 166 Mark Clayton | .10 | .06 |
| 167 Louis Oliver | .07 | .04 |
| 168 Mark Higgs | .20 | .12 |
| 169 Aaron Craver | .07 | .04 |
| 170 Sammie Smith | .08 | .05 |
| 171 Tony Paige | .05 | .02 |
| 172 Jeff Cross | .05 | .02 |
| 173 David Griggs | .05 | .02 |
| 174 Richmond Webb | .07 | .04 |
| 175 Vestee Jackson | .05 | .02 |
| 176 Jim Jensen | .05 | .02 |
| 177 Anthony Carter | .08 | .05 |
| 178 Cris Carter | .15 | .10 |
| 179 Chris Doleman | .07 | .04 |
| 180 Rich Gannon | .20 | .12 |
| 181 Al Noga | .05 | .02 |
| 182 Randall McDaniel | .05 | .02 |
| 183 Todd Scott | .05 | .02 |
| 184 Henry Thomas | .05 | .02 |
| 185 Felix Wright | .05 | .02 |
| 186 Gary Zimmerman | .05 | .02 |
| 187 Herschel Walker | .10 | .06 |
| 188 Vincent Brown | .05 | .02 |
| 189 Harry Colon | .05 | .02 |
| 190 Irving Fryar | .07 | .04 |
| 191 Marv Cook | .05 | .02 |
| 192 Leonard Russell | .35 | .20 |
| 193 Hugh Millen | .15 | .10 |
| 194 Pat Harlow | .05 | .02 |
| 195 Jon Vaughn | .12 | .07 |
| 196 Ben Coates (R) | .08 | .05 |
| 197 Johnny Rembert | .05 | .02 |
| 198 Greg McMurtry | .10 | .06 |
| 199 Morten Andersen | .05 | .02 |
| 200 Tommy Barnhardt | .05 | .02 |
| 201 Bobby Hebert | .12 | .07 |
| 202 Dalton Hilliard | .07 | .04 |
| 203 Sam Mills | .07 | .04 |
| 204 Pat Swilling | .12 | .07 |
| 205 Rickey Jackson | .07 | .04 |
| 206 Stan Brock | .05 | .02 |
| 207 Reggie Jones | .05 | .02 |
| 208 Gill Fenerty | .05 | .02 |
| 209 Eric Martin | .07 | .04 |
| 210 Matt Bahr | .05 | .02 |
| 211 Rodney Hampton | .25 | .15 |
| 212 Jeff Hostetler | .15 | .10 |
| 213 Pepper Johnson | .05 | .02 |
| 214 Leonard Marshall | .05 | .02 |
| 215 Doug Riesenberg | .05 | .02 |
| 216 Stephen Baker | .05 | .02 |
| 217 Mike Fox | .05 | .02 |
| 218 Bart Oates | .05 | .02 |
| 219 Everson Walls | .05 | .02 |
| 220 Gary Reasons | .05 | .02 |
| 221 Jeff Lageman | .07 | .04 |
| 222 Joe Kelly | .05 | .02 |
| 223 Mo Lewis | .05 | .02 |
| 224 Tony Stargell | .05 | .02 |
| 225 Jim Sweeney | .05 | .02 |
| 226 Freeman McNeil | .08 | .05 |
| 227 Brian Washington | .05 | .02 |
| 228 Johnny Hector | .07 | .04 |
| 229 Terance Mathis | .07 | .04 |
| 230 Rob Moore | .20 | .12 |
| 231 Brad Baxter | .08 | .05 |
| 232 Eric Allen | .05 | .02 |
| 233 Fred Barnett | .12 | .07 |
| 234 Jerome Brown | .07 | .04 |
| 235 Keith Byars | .07 | .04 |
| 236 William Thomas | .05 | .02 |
| 237 Jessie Small | .05 | .02 |
| 238 Robert Drummond | .05 | .02 |
| 239 Reggie White | .12 | .07 |
| 240 James Joseph | .08 | .05 |
| 241 Brad Goebel | .07 | .04 |
| 242 Clyde Simmons | .07 | .04 |
| 243 Rich Camarillo | .05 | .02 |
| 244 Ken Harvey | .05 | .02 |
| 245 Garth Jax | .05 | .02 |
| 246 Johnny Johnson | .15 | .10 |
| 247 Mike Jones | .05 | .02 |
| 248 Ernie Jones | .05 | .02 |
| 249 Tom Tupa | .07 | .04 |
| 250 Ron Wolfley | .05 | .02 |
| 251 Luis Sharpe | .05 | .02 |
| 252 Eric Swann | .08 | .05 |
| 253 Anthony Thompson | .08 | .05 |
| 254 Gary Anderson | .05 | .02 |
| 255 Dermontti Dawson | .05 | .02 |
| 256 Jeff Graham | .15 | .10 |
| 257 Eric Green | .10 | .06 |
| 258 Louis Lipps | .07 | .04 |
| 259 Neil O'Donnell | .70 | .40 |
| 260 Rod Woodson | .08 | .05 |
| 261 Dwight Stone | .05 | .02 |
| 262 Aaron Jones | .05 | .02 |
| 263 Keith Willis | .05 | .02 |
| 264 Ernie Mills | .08 | .05 |
| 265 Martin Bayless | .05 | .02 |
| 266 Rod Bernstine | .07 | .04 |
| 267 John Carney | .05 | .02 |
| 268 John Friesz | .10 | .06 |
| 269 Nate Lewis | .07 | .04 |
| 270 Shawn Jefferson | .10 | .06 |
| 271 Burt Grossman | .07 | .04 |
| 272 Eric Moten | .05 | .02 |
| 273 Gary Plummer | .05 | .02 |

| | | | |
|---|---|---|---|
| 274 | Henry Rolling | .05 | .02 |
| 275 | Steve Hendrickson (R) | .10 | .06 |
| 276 | Michael Carter | .05 | .02 |
| 277 | Steve Bono | .25 | .15 |
| 278 | Dexter Carter | .08 | .05 |
| 279 | Mike Cofer | .05 | .02 |
| 280 | Charles Haley | .07 | .04 |
| 282 | Tom Rathman | .08 | .05 |
| 283 | John Taylor | .15 | .10 |
| 284 | Dave Waymer | .05 | .02 |
| 285 | Steve Wallace | .05 | .02 |
| 286 | Jamie Williams | .05 | .02 |
| 287 | Brian Blades | .07 | .04 |
| 288 | Jeff Bryant | .05 | .02 |
| 289 | Grant Feasel | .05 | .02 |
| 290 | Jacob Green | .05 | .02 |
| 291 | Andy Heck | .05 | .02 |
| 292 | Kelly Stouffer | .10 | .06 |
| 293 | John Kasay | .05 | .02 |
| 294 | Cortez Kennedy | .08 | .05 |
| 295 | Bryan Millard | .05 | .02 |
| 296 | Eugene Robinson | .05 | .02 |
| 297 | Tony Woods | .05 | .02 |
| 298 | Jesse Anderson | .05 | .02 |
| 299 | Gary Anderson | .05 | .02 |
| 300 | Mark Carrier (TB) | .07 | .04 |
| 301 | Reggie Cobb | .12 | .07 |
| 302 | Robert Wilson | .07 | .04 |
| 303 | Jesse Solomon | .05 | .02 |
| 304 | Broderick Thomas | .08 | .05 |
| 305 | Lawrence Dawsey | .15 | .10 |
| 306 | Charles McRae | .05 | .02 |
| 307 | Paul Gruber | .05 | .02 |
| 308 | Vinny Testaverde | .10 | .06 |
| 309 | Brian Mitchell | .05 | .02 |
| 310 | Darrell Green | .08 | .05 |
| 311 | Art Monk | .20 | .12 |
| 312 | Russ Grimm | .05 | .02 |
| 313 | Mark Rypien | .20 | .12 |
| 314 | Bobby Wilson | .05 | .02 |
| 315 | Wilber Marshall | .07 | .04 |
| 316 | Gerald Riggs | .07 | .04 |
| 317 | Chip Lohmiller | .05 | .02 |
| 318 | Joe Jacoby | .05 | .02 |
| 319 | Martin Mayhew | .05 | .02 |
| 320 | Amp Lee (R) | .70 | .40 |
| 321 | Terrell Buckley (R) | .50 | .30 |
| 322 | Tommy Vardell (R) | .70 | .40 |
| 323 | Ricardo McDonald (R) | .10 | .06 |
| 324 | Joe Bowden (R) | .08 | .05 |
| 325 | Darryl Williams (R) | .15 | .10 |
| 326 | Carlos Huerta (R) | .07 | .04 |
| 327 | Patrick Rowe (R) | .20 | .12 |
| 328 | Siran Stacy (R) | .20 | .12 |
| 329 | Dexter McNabb (R) | .20 | .12 |
| 330 | Willie Clay (R) | .10 | .06 |
| CL1 | Checklist (1-110) | 1.25 | .80 |
| CL2 | Checklist (111-220) | 1.25 | .80 |
| CL3 | Checklist (221-330) | 1.25 | .80 |
| CL4 | Checklist (Hghlights) | 1.25 | .80 |
| BC1-9 | Steve Largent | 1.00 ea | .70 ea |
| | Inserts | | |

# 1992 Pacific Plus II

This 330-card set is the second series of 1992 Pacific Plus Football cards. The card design is the same as Series I. The second series includes a limited 9-card Bob Griese Legends insert set. Those insert cards are are listed at the end of this checklist but are not included in the complete set price below. All cards measure 2-1/2" by 3-1/2".

| | | MINT | NR/MT |
|---|---|---|---|
| **Complete Set (330)** | | 10.00 | 6.50 |
| **Commons** | | .05 | .02 |
| 331 | Oliver Barnett | .08 | .05 |
| 332 | Audray Bruce | .05 | .02 |
| 333 | Ken Tippins (R) | .08 | .05 |
| 334 | Jesse Tuggle | .05 | .02 |
| 335 | Brian Jordan | .12 | .07 |
| 336 | Andre Rison | .20 | .12 |
| 337 | Houston Hoover | .05 | .02 |
| 338 | Bill Fralic | .05 | .02 |
| 339 | Pat Chaffey (R) | .10 | .06 |
| 340 | Keith Jones | .05 | .02 |
| 341 | Jamie Dukes (R) | .08 | .05 |
| 342 | Chris Mohr | .05 | .02 |
| 343 | John Davis | .05 | .02 |
| 344 | Ray Bentley | .05 | .02 |
| 345 | Scott Norwood | .05 | .02 |
| 346 | Shane Conlan | .08 | .05 |
| 347 | Steve Tasker | .05 | .02 |

| | | | | | | | |
|---|---|---|---|---|---|---|---|
| 348 | Will Wolford | .05 | .02 | 405 | Keith Traylor | .05 | .02 |
| 349 | Gary Baldinger (R) | .07 | .04 | 406 | Doug Widell | .05 | .02 |
| 350 | Kirby Jackson | .05 | .02 | 407 | Dennis Smith | .05 | .02 |
| 351 | Jamie Mueller | .05 | .02 | 408 | Marc Spindler | .05 | .02 |
| 352 | Pete Metzelaars | .05 | .02 | 409 | Lomas Brown | .05 | .02 |
| 353 | Richard Dent | .07 | .04 | 410 | Robert Clark | .05 | .02 |
| 354 | Ron Rivera | .05 | .02 | 411 | Sheldon White | .05 | .02 |
| 355 | Jim Morrissey | .05 | .02 | 412 | Mike Farr | .05 | .02 |
| 356 | John Roper | .05 | .02 | 413 | Ray Crockett | .05 | .02 |
| 357 | Steve McMichael | .07 | .04 | 414 | Jeff Campbell | .05 | .02 |
| 358 | Ron Morris | .05 | .02 | 415 | Dan Owens | .05 | .02 |
| 359 | Darren Lewis | .15 | .10 | 416 | Jim Arnold | .05 | .02 |
| 360 | Anthony Morgan | .15 | .10 | 417 | Barry Sanders | .60 | .35 |
| 361 | Stan Thomas | .05 | .02 | 417 | Eddie Murray | .05 | .02 |
| 362 | James Thornton | .05 | .02 | 419 | Vince Workman | .10 | .06 |
| 363 | Brad Muster | .08 | .05 | 420 | Ed West | .05 | .02 |
| 364 | Tim Krumrie | .05 | .02 | 421 | Charles Wilson | .05 | .02 |
| 365 | Lee Johnson | .05 | .02 | 422 | Perry Kemp | .05 | .02 |
| 366 | Eric Ball | .05 | .02 | 423 | Chuck Cecil | .05 | .02 |
| 367 | Alonzo Mitz (R) | .06 | .05 | 424 | James Campen | .05 | .02 |
| 368 | David Grant | .05 | .02 | 425 | Robert Brown | .05 | .02 |
| 369 | Lynn James | .05 | .02 | 426 | Brian Noble | .05 | .02 |
| 370 | Lewis Billups | .05 | .02 | 427 | Rich Moran | .05 | .02 |
| 371 | Jim Breech | .05 | .02 | 428 | Vai Sikahema | .05 | .02 |
| 372 | Alfred Williams | .08 | .05 | 429 | Allen Rice | .05 | .02 |
| 373 | Wayne Haddix | .05 | .02 | 430 | Haywood Jeffires | .20 | .12 |
| 374 | Tim McGee | .07 | .04 | 431 | Warren Moon | .20 | .12 |
| 375 | Michael Jackson | .20 | .12 | 432 | Greg Montgomery | .05 | .02 |
| 376 | Leroy Hoard | .08 | .05 | 433 | Sean Jones | .05 | .02 |
| 377 | Tony Jones | .05 | .02 | 434 | Richard Johnson | .05 | .02 |
| 378 | Vince Newsome | .05 | .02 | 435 | Al Smith | .05 | .02 |
| 379 | Todd Philcox (R) | .35 | .18 | 436 | Johnny Meads | .05 | .02 |
| 380 | Eric Metcalf | .10 | .06 | 437 | William Fuller | .05 | .02 |
| 381 | John Rienstra | .05 | .02 | 438 | Mike Munchak | .05 | .02 |
| 382 | Matt Stover | .05 | .02 | 439 | Ray Childress | .07 | .04 |
| 383 | Brian Hansen | .05 | .02 | 440 | Cody Carlson | .25 | .15 |
| 384 | Joe Morris | .05 | .02 | 441 | Scott Radecic | .05 | .02 |
| 385 | Anthony Pleasant | .05 | .02 | 442 | Quintus McDonald (R) | .08 | .05 |
| 386 | Mark Stepnoski | .05 | .02 | 443 | Eugene Daniel | .05 | .02 |
| 387 | Erik Williams | .05 | .02 | 444 | Mark Herrmann (R) | .08 | .05 |
| 388 | Jimmie Jones | .05 | .02 | 445 | John Baylor (R) | .08 | .05 |
| 389 | Kevin Gogan | .05 | .02 | 446 | Dave McCloughan | .05 | .02 |
| 390 | Manny Hendrix (R) | .08 | .05 | 447 | Mark VanderPoel | .05 | .02 |
| 391 | Issiac Holt | .05 | .02 | 448 | Randy Dixon | .05 | .02 |
| 392 | Ken Norton | .05 | .02 | 449 | Keith Taylor | .05 | .02 |
| 393 | Tommie Agee | .05 | .02 | 450 | Alan Grant | .05 | .02 |
| 394 | Alvin Harper | .25 | .15 | 451 | Tony Siragusa | .05 | .02 |
| 395 | Alexander Wright | .08 | .05 | 452 | Rich Baldinger | .05 | .02 |
| 396 | Mike Saxon | .05 | .02 | 453 | Derrick Thomas | .15 | .10 |
| 397 | Michael Brooks | .05 | .02 | 454 | Bill Jones (R) | .08 | .05 |
| 398 | Bobby Humphrey | .10 | .06 | 455 | Troy Stradford | .05 | .02 |
| 399 | Ken Lanier | .05 | .02 | 456 | Barry Word | .15 | .10 |
| 400 | Steve Sewell | .05 | .02 | 457 | Tim Grunhard | .05 | .02 |
| 401 | Robert Perryman | .05 | .02 | 458 | Chris Martin | .05 | .02 |
| 402 | Wymon Henderson | .05 | .02 | 459 | Jayice Pearson (R) | .08 | .05 |
| 403 | Keith Kartz | .05 | .02 | 460 | Dino Hackett | .05 | .02 |
| 404 | Clarence Kay | .05 | .02 | 461 | David Lutz | .05 | .02 |

| | | | |
|---|---|---|---|
| 462 Albert Lewis | .05 | .02 |
| 463 Fred Jones (R) | .10 | .06 |
| 464 Winston Moss | .05 | .02 |
| 465 Sam Graddy | .15 | .10 |
| 466 Steve Wisniewski | .05 | .02 |
| 467 Jay Schroeder | .10 | .06 |
| 468 Ronnie Lott | .10 | .06 |
| 469 Willie Gault | .07 | .04 |
| 470 Greg Townsend | .07 | .04 |
| 471 Max Montoya | .05 | .02 |
| 472 Howie Long | .07 | .04 |
| 473 Lionel Washington | .05 | .02 |
| 474 Riki Ellison | .05 | .02 |
| 475 Tom Newberry | .05 | .02 |
| 476 Damone Johnson | .05 | .02 |
| 477 Pat Terrell | .05 | .02 |
| 478 Marcus Dupree | .08 | .05 |
| 479 Todd Lyght | .12 | .07 |
| 480 Buford McGee | .05 | .02 |
| 481 Bern Brostek | .05 | .02 |
| 482 Jim Price | .05 | .02 |
| 483 Robert Young | .05 | .02 |
| 484 Tony Zendejas | .05 | .02 |
| 485 Robert Bailey (R) | .08 | .05 |
| 486 Alvin Wright | .05 | .02 |
| 487 Pat Carter | .05 | .02 |
| 488 Pete Stoyanovich | .05 | .02 |
| 489 Reggie Roby | .05 | .02 |
| 490 Harry Galbreath | .05 | .02 |
| 491 Michael McGruder | .05 | .02 |
| 492 J.B. Brown | .05 | .02 |
| 493 E.J. Junior | .05 | .02 |
| 494 Ferrell Edmunds | .05 | .02 |
| 495 Scott Secules | .08 | .05 |
| 496 Greg Baty (R) | .08 | .05 |
| 497 Mike Iaquaniello | .05 | .02 |
| 498 Keith Sims | .05 | .02 |
| 499 John Randle | .05 | .02 |
| 500 Joey Browner | .07 | .04 |
| 501 Steve Jordan | .05 | .02 |
| 502 Darrin Nelson | .07 | .04 |
| 503 Audray McMillian | .07 | .04 |
| 504 Harry Newsome | .05 | .02 |
| 505 Hassan Jones | .08 | .05 |
| 506 Ray Berry | .05 | .02 |
| 507 Mike Merriweather | .05 | .02 |
| 508 Leo Lewis | .05 | .02 |
| 509 Tim Irwin | .05 | .02 |
| 510 Kirk Lowdermilk | .05 | .02 |
| 511 Alfred Anderson | .05 | .02 |
| 512 Michael Timpson (R) | .12 | .07 |
| 513 Jerome Henderson | .07 | .04 |
| 514 Andre Tippett | .08 | .05 |
| 515 Chris Singleton | .08 | .05 |
| 516 John Stephens | .10 | .06 |
| 517 Ronnie Lippett | .05 | .02 |
| 518 Bruce Armstrong | .05 | .02 |

| | | | |
|---|---|---|---|
| 519 Marion Hobby (R) | .08 | .05 |
| 520 Tim Goad | .05 | .02 |
| 521 Mickey Washington (R) | .08 | .05 |
| 522 Fred Smerlas | .05 | .02 |
| 523 Wayne Martin | .05 | .02 |
| 524 Frank Warren | .05 | .02 |
| 525 Floyd Turner | .05 | .02 |
| 526 Wesley Carroll | .15 | .10 |
| 527 Gene Atkins | .05 | .02 |
| 528 Vaughan Johnson | .07 | .04 |
| 529 Hoby Brenner | .05 | .02 |
| 530 Renaldo Turnbull | .07 | .04 |
| 531 Joel Hilgenberg | .05 | .02 |
| 532 Craig Heyward | .07 | .04 |
| 533 Vince Buck | .05 | .02 |
| 534 Jim Dombrowski | .05 | .02 |
| 535 Fred McAfee (R) | .20 | .12 |
| 536 Phil Simms | .10 | .06 |
| 537 Lewis Tillman | .05 | .02 |
| 538 John Elliott | .05 | .02 |
| 539 David Meggett | .12 | .07 |
| 540 Mark Collins | .07 | .04 |
| 541 Ottis Anderson | .08 | .05 |
| 542 Bobby Abrams (R) | .08 | .05 |
| 543 Sean Landeta | .05 | .02 |
| 544 Brian Williams | .05 | .02 |
| 545 Erik Howard | .05 | .02 |
| 546 Mark Ingram | .07 | .04 |
| 547 Kanavis McGhee | .08 | .05 |
| 548 Kyle Clifton | .05 | .02 |
| 549 Marvin Washington | .05 | .02 |
| 550 Jeff Criswell | .05 | .02 |
| 551 Dave Cadigan | .05 | .02 |
| 552 Chris Burkett | .07 | .04 |
| 553 Erik McMillan | .05 | .02 |
| 554 James Hasty | .05 | .02 |
| 555 Louie Aguiar (R) | .08 | .05 |
| 556 Troy Johnson (R) | .10 | .06 |
| 557 Troy Taylor (R) | .25 | .15 |
| 558 Pat Kelly (R) | .08 | .05 |
| 559 Heath Sherman | .08 | .05 |
| 560 Roger Ruzek | .05 | .02 |
| 561 Andre Waters | .05 | .02 |
| 562 Izel Jenkins | .05 | .02 |
| 563 Keith Jackson | .15 | .10 |
| 564 Byron Evans | .05 | .02 |
| 565 Wes Hopkins | .05 | .02 |
| 566 Rich Miano | .05 | .02 |
| 567 Seth Joyner | .07 | .04 |
| 568 Thomas Sanders | .05 | .02 |
| 569 David Alexander | .05 | .02 |
| 570 Jeff Kemp | .08 | .05 |
| 571 Jock Jones (R) | .08 | .05 |
| 572 Craig Patterson (R) | .08 | .05 |
| 573 Robert Massey | .05 | .02 |
| 574 Bill Lewis | .05 | .02 |

| # | Player | | |
|---|--------|---|---|
| 575 | Freddie Joe Nunn | .05 | .02 |
| 576 | Aeneas Williams | .07 | .04 |
| 577 | John Jackson | .05 | .02 |
| 578 | Tim McDonald | .05 | .02 |
| 579 | Michael Zordich (R) | .08 | .05 |
| 580 | Eric Hills | .05 | .02 |
| 581 | Lorenzo Lynch | .05 | .02 |
| 582 | Vernice Smith (R) | .08 | .05 |
| 583 | Greg Lloyd | .05 | .02 |
| 584 | Carnell Lake | .05 | .02 |
| 585 | Hardy Nickerson | .05 | .02 |
| 586 | Delton Hall | .05 | .02 |
| 587 | Gerald Williams | .05 | .02 |
| 588 | Bryan Hinkle | .05 | .02 |
| 589 | Barry Foster | .45 | .28 |
| 590 | Bubby Brister | .10 | .06 |
| 591 | Rick Strom (R) | .15 | .10 |
| 592 | David Little | .05 | .02 |
| 593 | Leroy Thompson | .05 | .02 |
| 594 | Eric Bieniemy | .12 | .07 |
| 595 | Courtney Hall | .05 | .02 |
| 596 | Gerorge Thornton | .05 | .02 |
| 597 | Donnie Elder | .05 | .02 |
| 598 | Billy Ray Smith | .05 | .02 |
| 599 | Gill Byrd | .05 | .02 |
| 600 | Marion Butts | .10 | .06 |
| 601 | Ronnie Harmon | .05 | .02 |
| 602 | Anthony Shelton | .05 | .02 |
| 603 | Mark May | .05 | .02 |
| 604 | Craig McEwen (R) | .10 | .06 |
| 605 | Steve Young | .20 | .12 |
| 606 | Keith Henderson | .08 | .05 |
| 607 | Pierce Holt | .05 | .02 |
| 608 | Roy Foster | .05 | .02 |
| 609 | Don Griffin | .05 | .02 |
| 610 | Harry Sydney | .05 | .02 |
| 611 | Todd Bowles | .05 | .02 |
| 612 | Ted Washington | .08 | .05 |
| 613 | Johnnie Jackson | .05 | .02 |
| 614 | Jesse Sapolu | .05 | .02 |
| 615 | Brent Jones | .08 | .05 |
| 616 | Travis McNeal | .05 | .02 |
| 617 | Darrick Brilz (R) | .08 | .05 |
| 618 | Terry Wooden | .05 | .02 |
| 619 | Tommy Kane | .08 | .05 |
| 620 | Nesby Glasgow | .05 | .02 |
| 621 | Dwayne Harper | .05 | .02 |
| 622 | Rick Tuten | .05 | .02 |
| 623 | Chris Warren | .05 | .02 |
| 624 | John L. Williams | .07 | .04 |
| 625 | Rufus Porter | .05 | .02 |
| 626 | David Daniels | .05 | .02 |
| 627 | Keith McCants | .07 | .04 |
| 628 | Reuben Davis | .05 | .02 |
| 629 | Mark Royals | .05 | .02 |
| 630 | Marty Carter (R) | .08 | .05 |
| 631 | Ian Beckles | .05 | .02 |

| # | Player | | |
|---|--------|---|---|
| 632 | Ron Hall | .05 | .02 |
| 633 | Eugene Marve | .05 | .02 |
| 634 | Willie Drewrey | .05 | .02 |
| 635 | Tom McHale (R) | .08 | .05 |
| 636 | Kevin Murphy | .05 | .02 |
| 637 | Robert Hardy (R) | .10 | .06 |
| 638 | Ricky Sanders | .08 | .05 |
| 639 | Gary Clark | .15 | .10 |
| 640 | Andre Collins | .08 | .05 |
| 641 | Brad Edwards | .05 | .02 |
| 642 | Monte Coleman | .05 | .02 |
| 643 | Clarence Vaughn (R) | .08 | .05 |
| 644 | Fred Stokes | .05 | .02 |
| 645 | Charles Mann | .05 | .02 |
| 646 | Earnest Byner | .07 | .04 |
| 647 | Jim Lachey | .07 | .04 |
| 648 | Jeff Bostic | .05 | .02 |
| 649 | Chris Mims (R) | .25 | .15 |
| 650 | George Williams (R) | .08 | .05 |
| 651 | Ed Cunningham (R) | .07 | .04 |
| 652 | Tony Smith (R) | .60 | .35 |
| 653 | Will Furrer (R) | .35 | .20 |
| 654 | Matt Elliott (R) | .08 | .05 |
| 655 | Mike Mooney (R) | .08 | .05 |
| 656 | Eddie Blake (R) | .10 | .06 |
| 657 | Leon Searcy (R) | .10 | .06 |
| 658 | Kevin Turner (R) | .15 | .10 |
| 659 | Keith Hamilton (R) | .10 | .06 |
| 660 | Alan Haller (R) | .10 | .06 |
| BC10-18 | Bob Griese Inserts | 1.00ea | .70ea |

# 1992 Pacific
# Picks The Pros
# Gold Inserts

This 25-card limited insert set features full color action photos on the front framed in gold foil borders. The headline "Pacific Picks The Pros" is printed vertically down the left side of the caerd front. The player's name and position appear below the photograph. The card backs are diagonal and printed in a rainbow color scheme. These inserts were randomly distributed in Pacific's foil packs. All cards measure 2-1/2" by 3-12".

|  | | MINT | NR/MT |
|---|---|---|---|
| | Complete Set (25) | 125.00 | 80.00 |
| | Commons | 4.50 | 2.75 |
| 1 | Mark Rypien | 10.00 | 6.50 |
| 2 | Marv Cook | 4.50 | 2.75 |
| 3 | Jim Lachey | 5.00 | 3.00 |
| 4 | Darrell Green | 6.00 | 3.75 |
| 5 | Derrick Thomas | 10.00 | 6.50 |
| 6 | Thurman Thomas | 25.00 | 18.00 |
| 7 | Kent Hull | 4.50 | 2.75 |
| 8 | Tim McDonald | 4.50 | 2.75 |
| 9 | Mike Croel | 8.00 | 5.00 |
| 10 | Anthony Munoz | 6.50 | 4.00 |
| 11 | Jerome Brown | 4.50 | 2.75 |
| 12 | Reggie White | 8.50 | 5.50 |
| 13 | Gill Byrd | 4.50 | 2.75 |
| 14 | Jessie Tuggle | 4.50 | 2.75 |
| 15 | Randall McDaniel | 4.50 | 2.75 |
| 16 | Sam Mills | 4.50 | 2.75 |
| 17 | Pat Swilling | 6.00 | 3.75 |
| 18 | Eugene Robinson | 4.50 | 2.75 |
| 19 | Michael Irvin | 15.00 | 10.00 |
| 20 | Emmitt Smith | 32.00 | 24.00 |
| 21 | Jeff Gossett | 4.50 | 2.75 |
| 22 | Jeff Jaeger | 4.50 | 2.75 |
| 23 | William Fuller | 4.50 | 2.75 |
| 24 | Mike Munchak | 4.50 | 2.75 |
| 25 | Andre Rison | 12.00 | 8.00 |

| 2 | Marv Cook | 4.50 | 2.75 |
|---|---|---|---|
| 3 | Jim Lachey | 5.00 | 3.00 |
| 4 | Darrell Green | 6.00 | 3.75 |
| 5 | Derrick Thomas | 10.00 | 6.50 |
| 6 | Thurman Thomas | 25.00 | 18.00 |
| 7 | Kent Hull | 4.50 | 2.75 |
| 8 | Tim McDonald | 4.50 | 2.75 |
| 9 | Mike Croel | 8.00 | 5.00 |
| 10 | Anthony Munoz | 6.50 | 4.00 |
| 11 | Jerome Brown | 4.50 | 2.75 |
| 12 | Reggie White | 8.50 | 5.50 |
| 13 | Gill Byrd | 4.50 | 2.75 |
| 14 | Jessie Tuggle | 4.50 | 2.75 |
| 15 | Randall McDaniel | 4.50 | 2.75 |
| 16 | Sam Mills | 4.50 | 2.75 |
| 17 | Pat Swilling | 6.00 | 3.75 |
| 18 | Eugene Robinson | 4.50 | 2.75 |
| 19 | Michael Irvin | 15.00 | 10.00 |
| 20 | Emmitt Smith | 32.00 | 24.00 |
| 21 | Jeff Gossett | 4.50 | 2.75 |
| 22 | Jeff Jaeger | 4.50 | 2.75 |
| 23 | William Fuller | 4.50 | 2.75 |
| 24 | Mike Munchak | 4.50 | 2.75 |
| 25 | Andre Rison | 12.00 | 8.00 |

# 1992 Pacific Picks The Pros Silver Inserts

This 25-card limited insert set is identical to the gold inserts except the card fronts feature silver borders. The silver inserts were randomly distributed in Pacific's jumbo packs. All cards measure 2-1/2" by 3-1/2".

|  | | MINT | NR/MT |
|---|---|---|---|
| | Complete Set (25) | 125.00 | 80.00 |
| | Commons | 4.50 | 2.75 |
| 1 | Mark Rypien | 10.00 | 6.50 |

# 1992 Pacific Stat Leaders

The cards in this limited insert set were randomly distributed in Pacific's foil packs and feature the statistical leaders from each NFL team plus the NFC and AFC rushing leaders. Card fronts consist of full color action photos framed by a white border. A multi-colored box below the picture includes the player's name and feat. The vertical card backs contain small photos of three other team leaders and their accomplishments. All cards measure 2-1/2" by 3-1/2".

| | | MINT | NR/MT |
|---|---|---|---|
| | Complete Set (30) | 20.00 | 12.50 |
| | Commons | .40 | .25 |
| | | | |
| 1 | Chris Miller | .75 | .45 |
| 2 | Thurman Thomas | 2.50 | 1.50 |
| 3 | Jim Harbaugh | .60 | .35 |
| 4 | Jim Breech | .40 | .25 |
| 5 | Kevin Mack | .40 | .25 |
| 6 | Emmitt Smith | 4.50 | 2.75 |
| 7 | Gaston Green | .75 | .45 |
| 8 | Barry Sanders | 3.50 | 2.00 |
| 9 | Tony Bennett | .40 | .25 |
| 10 | Warren Moon | .80 | .50 |
| 11 | Bill Brooks | .40 | .25 |
| 12 | Christian Okoye | .60 | .35 |
| 13 | Jay Schroeder | .50 | .30 |
| 14 | Robert Delpino | .40 | .25 |
| 15 | Mark Higgs | .60 | .35 |
| 16 | John Randle | .40 | .25 |
| 17 | Leonard Russell | 1.00 | .70 |
| 18 | Pat Swilling | .60 | .35 |
| 19 | Rodney Hampton | 1.00 | .70 |
| 20 | Terance Mathis | .40 | .25 |
| 21 | Fred Barnett | .75 | .45 |
| 22 | Aeneas Williams | .40 | .25 |
| 23 | Neil O'Donnell | .80 | .50 |
| 24 | Marion Butts | .75 | .45 |
| 25 | Steve Young | 1.00 | .70 |
| 26 | John L. Williams | .40 | .25 |
| 27 | Reggie Cobb | .60 | .35 |
| 28 | Mark Rypien | .75 | .45 |
| 29 | Thurman Thomas (AFC) | 1.50 | .90 |
| 30 | Emmitt Smith (NFC) | 2.50 | 1.50 |

# 1992 Pacific Prisms

The 10 cards in this limited edition are printed on a unique foil stock that give the cards a prism effect. The standard size cards were randomly inserted into Pacific's foil packs.

| | | MINT | NR/MT |
|---|---|---|---|
| | Complete Set (10) | 75.00 | 48.00 |
| | Commons | 5.00 | 3.00 |
| | | | |
| 1 | Thurman Thomas | 10.00 | 6.50 |
| 2 | Gaston Green | 5.00 | 3.00 |
| 3 | Christian Okoye | 6.00 | 3.50 |
| 4 | Leonard Russell | 7.50 | 4.50 |
| 5 | Mark Higgs | 6.50 | 3.75 |
| 6 | Emmitt Smith | 18.00 | 12.50 |
| 7 | Barry Sanders | 12.00 | 8.00 |
| 8 | Rodney Hampton | 8.50 | 5.50 |
| 9 | Earnest Byner | 5.00 | 3.00 |
| 10 | Herschel Walker | 6.50 | 3.75 |

# PHILADELPHIA GUM

## 1964 Philadelphia

JOHN UNITAS
BALTIMORE COLTS    QUARTERBACK

This 198 card set was the first issue from the philadephia Gum Company and included players from the National Football League. The cards feature posed player shots on the front with the player's name, team and position located below the picture. The vertical card backs contain the player's stats, and a cartoon at the bottom with a question about the player along with the answer that is printed upside down. The set also includes team cards and a coaches card that features a team play. All cards measure 2-1/2" by 3-1/2".

| | | NR/MT | EX |
|---|---|---|---|
| | Complete Set (198) | 950.00 | 500.00 |
| | Commons | 1.25 | .65 |
| 1 | Raymond Berry | 22.00 | 10.00 |
| 2 | Tom Gilburg | 1.25 | .65 |
| 3 | John Mackey (R) | 25.00 | 12.00 |
| 4 | Gino Marchetti | 5.00 | 2.25 |
| 5 | Jim Martin | 1.25 | .65 |
| 6 | Tom Matte (R) | 5.00 | 2.25 |
| 7 | Jimmy Orr | 2.00 | .90 |
| 8 | Jim Parker | 4.00 | 1.75 |
| 9 | Bill Pellington | 1.25 | .65 |
| 10 | Alex Sandusky | 1.25 | .65 |
| 11 | Dick Szymanski | 1.25 | .65 |
| 12 | John Unitas | 55.00 | 25.00 |
| 13 | Baltimore Colts | 3.00 | 1.25 |
| 14 | Colts Play (Shula) | 18.00 | 8.00 |
| 15 | Doug Atkins | 5.00 | 2.25 |
| 16 | Ron Bull | 1.50 | .70 |
| 17 | Mike Ditka | 28.00 | 13.50 |
| 18 | Joe Fortunato | 1.25 | .65 |
| 19 | Willie Galimore | 1.75 | .80 |
| 20 | Joe Marconi | 1.25 | .65 |
| 21 | Bennie McRae (R) | 1.75 | .80 |
| 22 | Johnny Morris | 1.75 | .80 |
| 23 | Richie Petitbon | 2.00 | .90 |
| 24 | Mike Pyle | 1.25 | .65 |
| 25 | Roosevelt Taylor (R) | 4.00 | 1.75 |
| 26 | Bill Wade | 2.00 | .90 |
| 27 | Chicago Bears | 3.00 | 1.25 |
| 28 | Bears Play (Halas) | 12.00 | 5.00 |
| 29 | Johnny Brewer | 1.25 | .65 |
| 30 | Jim Brown | 80.00 | 38.00 |
| 31 | Gary Collins (R) | 5.00 | 2.25 |
| 32 | Vince Costello | 1.25 | .65 |
| 33 | Galen Fiss | 1.25 | .65 |
| 34 | Bill Glass | 1.25 | .65 |
| 35 | Ernie Green (R) | 3.50 | 1.50 |
| 36 | Rich Kreitling | 1.25 | .65 |
| 37 | John Morrow | 1.25 | .65 |
| 38 | Frank Ryan | 2.50 | 1.10 |
| 39 | Charlie Scales (R) | 1.75 | .80 |
| 40 | Dick Schafrath (R) | 2.50 | 1.10 |
| 41 | Cleveland Browns | 3.00 | 1.25 |
| 42 | Browns Play (Collier) | 1.75 | .80 |
| 43 | Don Bishop | 1.25 | .65 |
| 44 | Frank Clarke (R) | 3.00 | 1.25 |
| 45 | Mike Connelly | 1.25 | .65 |
| 46 | Lee Folkins | 1.25 | .65 |
| 47 | Cornell Green (R) | 4.50 | 2.00 |
| 48 | Bob Lilly | 22.00 | 10.00 |
| 49 | Amos Marsh | 1.25 | .65 |
| 50 | Tommy McDonald | 2.50 | 1.10 |
| 51 | Don Meredith | 36.00 | 17.00 |
| 52 | Pettis Norman (R) | 2.00 | .90 |
| 53 | Don Perkins | 2.50 | 1.10 |
| 54 | Guy Reese | 1.25 | .65 |
| 55 | Dallas Cowboys | 3.00 | 1.25 |
| 56 | Cowboys Play (Landry) | 15.00 | 7.00 |
| 57 | Terry Barr | 1.25 | .65 |
| 58 | Roger Brown | 1.50 | .70 |
| 59 | Gail Cogdill | 1.25 | .65 |
| 60 | John Gordy | 1.25 | .65 |
| 61 | Dick Lane | 5.00 | 2.25 |
| 62 | Yale Lary | 3.50 | 1.50 |
| 63 | Dan Lewis | 1.25 | .65 |
| 64 | Darris McCord | 1.25 | .65 |
| 65 | Earl Morrall | 3.00 | 1.25 |
| 66 | Joe Schmidt | 3.50 | 1.50 |
| 67 | Pat Studstill (R) | 4.00 | 1.75 |

| | | | |
|---|---|---:|---:|
| 68 | Wayne Walker (R) | 4.00 | 1.75 |
| 69 | Detroit Lions | 3.00 | 1.25 |
| 70 | Lions Play (Wilson) | 1.75 | .80 |
| 71 | Herb Adderley (R) | 35.00 | 16.00 |
| 72 | Willie Davis (R) | 35.00 | 16.00 |
| 73 | Forrest Gregg | 4.50 | 2.00 |
| 74 | Paul Hornung | 25.00 | 12.00 |
| 75 | Henry Jordan | 1.50 | .70 |
| 76 | Jerry Kramer | 4.50 | 2.00 |
| 77 | Tom Moore | 1.25 | .65 |
| 78 | Jim Ringo | 4.00 | 1.75 |
| 79 | Bart Starr | 30.00 | 14.00 |
| 80 | Jim Taylor | 12.00 | 5.00 |
| 81 | Jesse Whittenton (R) | 2.00 | .90 |
| 82 | Willie Wood | 6.00 | 2.75 |
| 83 | Green Bay Packers | 3.00 | 1.25 |
| 84 | Packers Play (Lombardi) | 30.00 | 14.00 |
| 85 | Jon Arnett | 2.00 | .90 |
| 86 | Pervis Atkins (R) | 1.50 | .70 |
| 87 | Dick Bass | 1.75 | .80 |
| 88 | Carroll Dale | 1.75 | .80 |
| 89 | Roman Gabriel | 5.00 | 2.25 |
| 90 | Ed Meador | 1.25 | .65 |
| 91 | Merlin Olsen (R) | 75.00 | 36.00 |
| 92 | Jack Pardee (R) | 10.00 | 4.50 |
| 93 | Jim Phillips | 1.25 | .65 |
| 94 | Carver Shannon | 1.25 | .65 |
| 95 | Frank Villanueva | 1.25 | .65 |
| 97 | Los Angeles Rams | 3.00 | 1.25 |
| 98 | Rams Play (Svare) | 1.75 | .80 |
| 99 | Grady Alderman (R) | 2.50 | 1.10 |
| 100 | Larry Bowie | 1.25 | .65 |
| 101 | Bill Brown (R) | 4.50 | 2.00 |
| 102 | Paul Flatley (R) | 1.75 | .80 |
| 103 | Rip Hawkins | 1.25 | .65 |
| 104 | Jim Marshall | 4.00 | 1.75 |
| 105 | Tommy Mason | 1.50 | .70 |
| 106 | Jim Prestel | 1.25 | .65 |
| 107 | Jerry Reichow | 1.25 | .65 |
| 108 | Ed Sharockman | 1.25 | .65 |
| 109 | Fran Tarkenton | 45.00 | 20.00 |
| 110 | Mick Tingelhoff (R) | 5.00 | 2.25 |
| 111 | Minnesota Vikings | 3.00 | 1.25 |
| 112 | Vikings Play (Van Brocklin) | 4.00 | 1.75 |
| 113 | Erich Barnes | 1.50 | .70 |
| 114 | Roosevelt Brown | 3.50 | 1.50 |
| 115 | Don Chandler | 1.75 | .80 |
| 116 | Darrell Dess | 1.25 | .65 |
| 117 | Frank Gifford | 50.00 | 24.00 |
| 118 | Dick James | 1.25 | .65 |
| 119 | Jim Katcavage | 1.25 | .65 |
| 120 | John Lovetere | 1.25 | .65 |
| 121 | Dick Lynch (R) | 3.00 | 1.25 |
| 122 | Jim Patton | 1.50 | .70 |
| 123 | Del Shofner | 1.75 | .80 |
| 124 | Y.A. Tittle | 20.00 | 9.00 |
| 125 | New York Giants | 3.00 | 1.25 |
| 126 | Giants Play (Sherman) | 2.00 | .90 |
| 127 | Sam Baker | 1.25 | .65 |
| 128 | Maxie Baughan | 1.50 | .70 |
| 129 | Timmy Brown | 1.50 | .70 |
| 130 | Mike Clark | 1.25 | .65 |
| 131 | Irv Cross (R) | 7.50 | 3.50 |
| 132 | Ted Dean | 1.25 | .65 |
| 133 | Ron Goodwin | 1.25 | .65 |
| 134 | King Hill | 1.75 | .80 |
| 135 | Clarence Peaks | 1.25 | .65 |
| 136 | Pete Retzlaff | 1.25 | .65 |
| 137 | Jim Schrader | 1.25 | .65 |
| 138 | Norm Snead | 3.50 | 1.50 |
| 139 | Philadelphia Eagles | 3.00 | 1.25 |
| 140 | Eagles Play (Skorich) | 1.75 | .80 |
| 141 | Gary Ballman (R) | 2.00 | .90 |
| 142 | Charley Bradshaw | 1.25 | .65 |
| 143 | Ed Brown | 1.75 | .80 |
| 144 | John Henry Johnson | 4.50 | 2.00 |
| 145 | Joe Krupa | 1.25 | .65 |
| 146 | Bill Mack | 1.25 | .65 |
| 147 | Lou Michaels | 1.75 | .80 |
| 148 | Buzz Nutter | 1.25 | .65 |
| 149 | Myron Pottios | 1.25 | .65 |
| 150 | John Reger | 1.25 | .65 |
| 151 | Mike Sandusky | 1.25 | .65 |
| 152 | Clendon Thomas | 1.25 | .65 |
| 153 | Pittsburgh Steelers | 3.00 | 1.25 |
| 154 | Steelers Play (Parker) | 1.75 | .80 |
| 155 | Kermit Alexander (R) | 4.50 | 2.00 |
| 156 | Bernie Casey | 1.75 | .80 |
| 157 | Dan Colchico | 1.25 | .65 |
| 158 | Clyde Conner | 1.25 | .65 |
| 159 | Tommy Davis | 1.25 | .65 |
| 160 | Matt Hazeltine | 1.25 | .65 |
| 161 | Jim Johnson (R) | 3.50 | 1.50 |
| 162 | Don Lisbon (R) | 1.50 | .70 |
| 163 | Lamar McHan | 1.25 | .65 |
| 164 | Bob St. Clair | 4.50 | 2.00 |
| 165 | J.D. Smith | 1.50 | .70 |
| 166 | Abe Woodson | 1.75 | .80 |
| 167 | San Francisco 49ers | 3.00 | 1.25 |
| 168 | 49ers Play (Hickey) | 1.75 | .80 |
| 169 | Garland Boyette | 1.25 | .65 |
| 170 | Bobby Joe Conrad | 2.00 | .90 |
| 171 | Bob DeMarco (R) | 2.50 | 1.10 |
| 172 | Ken Gray (R) | 2.50 | 1.10 |
| 173 | Jimmy Hill | 1.25 | .65 |
| 174 | Charlie Johnson | 3.50 | 1.50 |
| 175 | Ernie McMillan | 1.50 | .70 |
| 176 | Dale Meinert | 1.25 | .65 |
| 177 | Luke Owens | 1.25 | .65 |
| 178 | Sonny Randle | 2.00 | .90 |
| 179 | Joe Robb | 1.25 | .65 |

| | | | |
|---|---|---|---|
| 180 | Bill Stacy | 1.25 | .65 |
| 181 | St. Louis Cardinals | 3.00 | 1.25 |
| 182 | Cardinals Play (Lemm) | 1.75 | .80 |
| 183 | Bill Barnes | 1.25 | .65 |
| 184 | Don Bosseler | 1.25 | .65 |
| 185 | Sam Huff | 6.00 | 2.75 |
| 186 | Sonny Jurgensen | 25.00 | 12.00 |
| 187 | Bob Khayat | 1.25 | .65 |
| 188 | Riley Mattson | 1.25 | .65 |
| 189 | Bobby Mitchell | 5.00 | 2.25 |
| 190 | John Nisby | 1.25 | .65 |
| 191 | Vince Promuto | 1.25 | .65 |
| 192 | Joe Rutgens | 1.25 | .65 |
| 193 | Lonnie Sanders | 1.25 | .65 |
| 194 | Jim Steffen | 1.25 | .65 |
| 195 | Washington Redskins | 3.00 | 1.25 |
| 196 | Redskins Play (McPeak) | 1.75 | .80 |
| 197 | Checklist (Er) (Wrong year listed) | 25.00 | 8.00 |
| 198 | Checklist 2 (Er) (Wrong year listed) | 40.00 | 12.50 |

# 1965 Philadelphia

BART STARR

This 198-card set features players from the National Football League. Card fronts show posed photographs framed by a white border. The player's name, team and position are located in a small box below the photo. The vertical card backs include the player's statistics and a question with a rub-off answer. This set includes team cards and a coaches subset that features a diagram of a play. All cards measure 2-1/2" by 3-1/2".

| | | NR/MT | EX |
|---|---|---|---|
| **Complete Set (198)** | | 800.00 | 450.00 |
| **Commons** | | 1.00 | .55 |
| | | | |
| 1 | Baltimore Colts | 8.50 | 3.50 |
| 2 | Raymond Berry | 5.00 | 2.25 |
| 3 | Bob Boyd | 1.00 | .55 |
| 4 | Wendell Harris | 1.00 | .55 |
| 5 | Jerry Logan | 1.00 | .55 |
| 6 | Tony Lorick | 1.00 | .55 |
| 7 | Lou Michaels | 1.00 | .55 |
| 8 | Lenny Moore | 6.00 | 2.75 |
| 9 | Jimmy Orr | 2.00 | .90 |
| 10 | Jim Parker | 4.00 | 1.75 |
| 11 | Dick Szymanski | 1.00 | .55 |
| 12 | John Unitas | 38.00 | 18.00 |
| 13 | Bob Vogel (R) | 1.75 | .80 |
| 14 | Colts Play (Shula) | 6.00 | 2.75 |
| 15 | Chicago Bears | 3.00 | 1.25 |
| 16 | Jon Arnett | 2.00 | .90 |
| 17 | Doug Atkins | 4.00 | 1.75 |
| 18 | Rudy Bukich (R) | 2.00 | .90 |
| 19 | Mike Ditka | 15.00 | 7.00 |
| 20 | Dick Evey | 1.00 | .55 |
| 21 | Joe Fortunato | 1.00 | .55 |
| 22 | Bobby Joe Green (R) | 3.00 | 1.25 |
| 23 | Johnny Morris | 1.75 | .80 |
| 24 | Mike Pyle | 1.00 | .55 |
| 25 | Roosevelt Taylor | 2.00 | .90 |
| 26 | Bill Wade | 2.00 | .90 |
| 27 | Bob Wetoska | 1.00 | .55 |
| 28 | Bears Play (Halas) | 6.00 | 2.75 |
| 29 | Cleveland Browns | 3.00 | 1.25 |
| 30 | Walter Beach | 1.00 | .55 |
| 31 | Jim Brown | 70.00 | 32.00 |
| 32 | Gary Collins | 2.00 | .90 |
| 33 | Bill Glass | 1.25 | .60 |
| 34 | Ernie Green | 1.25 | .60 |
| 35 | Jim Houston (R) | 2.50 | 1.10 |
| 36 | Dick Modzelewski | 1.25 | .60 |
| 37 | Bernie Parrish | 1.00 | .55 |
| 38 | Walter Roberts | 1.00 | .55 |
| 39 | Frank Ryan | 2.50 | 1.10 |
| 40 | Dick Schafrath | 1.00 | .55 |
| 41 | Paul Warfield (R) | 80.00 | 38.00 |
| 42 | Browns Play (Collier) | 1.50 | .70 |
| 43 | Dallas Cowboys | 3.00 | 1.25 |
| 44 | Frank Clarke | 1.00 | .55 |
| 45 | Mike Connelly | 1.00 | .55 |
| 46 | Buddy Dial | 2.00 | .90 |
| 47 | Bob Lilly | 10.00 | 4.50 |
| 48 | Tony Liscio (R) | 1.50 | .70 |
| 49 | Tommy McDonald | 2.00 | .90 |
| 50 | Don Meredith | 25.00 | 12.00 |
| 51 | Pettis Norman | 1.25 | .60 |
| 52 | Don Perkins | 2.50 | 1.10 |

| # | Player | | |
|---|---|---|---|
| 53 | Mel Renfro (R) | 12.00 | 5.00 |
| 54 | Jim Ridlon | 1.00 | .55 |
| 55 | Jerry Tubbs | 1.50 | .70 |
| 56 | Cowboys Play (Landry) | 8.00 | 3.75 |
| 57 | Detroit Lions | 3.00 | 1.25 |
| 58 | Terry Barr | 1.00 | .55 |
| 59 | Roger Brown | 1.25 | .60 |
| 60 | Gail Cogdill | 1.00 | .55 |
| 61 | Jim Gibbons | 1.00 | .55 |
| 62 | John Gordy | 1.00 | .55 |
| 63 | Yale Lary | 4.00 | 1.75 |
| 64 | Dick LeBeau (R) | 4.00 | 1.75 |
| 65 | Earl Morrall | 3.00 | 1.25 |
| 66 | Nick Pietrosante | 1.75 | .80 |
| 67 | Pat Studstill | 1.50 | .70 |
| 68 | Wayne Walker | 1.25 | .60 |
| 69 | Tom Watkins | 1.00 | .55 |
| 70 | Lion Play (Wilson) | 1.50 | .70 |
| 71 | Green Bay Packers | 3.00 | 1.25 |
| 72 | Herb Adderley | 7.50 | 3.50 |
| 73 | Willie Davis | 7.50 | 3.50 |
| 74 | Boyd Dowler | 2.50 | 1.10 |
| 75 | Forrest Gregg | 4.00 | 1.75 |
| 76 | Paul Hornung | 24.00 | 10.50 |
| 77 | Henry Jordan | 1.25 | .60 |
| 78 | Tom Moore | 1.25 | .60 |
| 79 | Ray Nitschke | 10.00 | 4.50 |
| 80 | Elija Pitts (R) | 3.00 | 1.25 |
| 81 | Bart Starr | 28.00 | 12.50 |
| 82 | Jim Taylor | 8.50 | 4.00 |
| 83 | Willie Wood | 7.50 | 3.50 |
| 84 | Packers Play (Lombardi) | 10.00 | 4.50 |
| 85 | Los Angeles Rams | 3.00 | 1.25 |
| 86 | Dick Bass | 1.50 | .70 |
| 87 | Roman Gabriel | 4.00 | 1.75 |
| 88 | Roosevelt Grier | 4.00 | 1.75 |
| 89 | Deacon Jones | 6.50 | 3.00 |
| 90 | Lamar Lundy (R) | 3.00 | 1.25 |
| 91 | Marlin McKeever (R) | 1.50 | .70 |
| 92 | Ed Meador | 1.25 | .60 |
| 93 | Bill Munson (R) | 4.00 | 1.75 |
| 94 | Merlin Olsen | 18.00 | 8.00 |
| 95 | Bobby Smith | 1.00 | .55 |
| 96 | Frank Varrichione | 1.00 | .55 |
| 97 | Ben Wilson | 1.00 | .55 |
| 98 | Rams Play (Svare) | 1.50 | .70 |
| 99 | Minnesota Vikings | 3.00 | 1.25 |
| 100 | Grady Alderman | 1.25 | .60 |
| 101 | Hal Bedsole (R) | 1.75 | .80 |
| 102 | Bill Brown | 1.75 | .80 |
| 103 | Bill Butler | 1.00 | .55 |
| 104 | Fred Cox (R) | 2.50 | 1.10 |
| 105 | Carl Eller (R) | 15.00 | 7.00 |
| 106 | Paul Flatley | 1.00 | .55 |
| 107 | Jim Marshall | 3.50 | 1.50 |
| 108 | Tommy Mason | 1.50 | .70 |
| 109 | George Rose | 1.00 | .55 |
| 110 | Fran Tarkenton | 38.00 | 18.00 |
| 111 | Mick Tingelhoff | 2.00 | .90 |
| 112 | Vikings Play (Van Brocklin) | 3.50 | 1.50 |
| 113 | New York Giants | 3.00 | 1.25 |
| 114 | Erich Barnes | 1.25 | .60 |
| 115 | Roosevelt Brown | 4.00 | 1.75 |
| 116 | Clarence Childs | 1.00 | .55 |
| 117 | Jerry Hillebrand | 1.00 | .55 |
| 118 | Greg Larson (R) | 2.00 | .90 |
| 119 | Dick Lynch | 1.25 | .60 |
| 120 | Joe Morrison (R) | 3.50 | 1.25 |
| 121 | Lou Slaby | 1.00 | .55 |
| 122 | Aaron Thomas (R) | 2.00 | .90 |
| 123 | Steve Thurlow | 1.00 | .55 |
| 124 | Ernie Wheelwright | 1.00 | .55 |
| 125 | Gary Wood (R) | 1.75 | .80 |
| 126 | Giants Play (Sherman) | 1.50 | .70 |
| 127 | Philadelphia Eagles | 3.00 | 1.25 |
| 128 | Sam Baker | 1.25 | .60 |
| 129 | Maxie Baughan | 2.00 | .90 |
| 130 | Timmy Brown | 1.75 | .80 |
| 131 | Jack Concannon (R) | 3.00 | 1.25 |
| 132 | Irv Cross | 3.50 | 1.50 |
| 133 | Earl Gros | 1.00 | .55 |
| 134 | Dave Lloyd | 1.00 | .55 |
| 135 | Floyd Peters (R) | 3.50 | 1.50 |
| 136 | Nate Ramsey | 1.00 | .55 |
| 137 | Pete Retzlaff | 1.50 | .70 |
| 138 | Jim Ringo | 4.00 | 1.75 |
| 139 | Norm Snead | 3.00 | 1.25 |
| 140 | Eagles Play (Kuharich) | 1.50 | .70 |
| 141 | Pittsburgh Steelers | 3.00 | 1.25 |
| 142 | John Baker | 1.00 | .55 |
| 143 | Gary Ballman | 1.25 | .60 |
| 144 | Charley Bradshaw | 1.00 | .55 |
| 145 | Ed Brown | 1.25 | .60 |
| 146 | Dick Haley | 1.00 | .55 |
| 147 | John Henry Johnson | 4.50 | 2.00 |
| 148 | Brady Keys | 1.00 | .55 |
| 149 | Ray Lemek | 1.00 | .55 |
| 150 | Ben McGee | 1.00 | .55 |
| 151 | Clarence Peaks | 1.00 | .55 |
| 152 | Myron Pottios | 1.00 | .55 |
| 153 | Clendon Thomas | 1.00 | .55 |
| 154 | Steelers Play (Parker) | 1.50 | .70 |
| 155 | St. Louis Cardinals | 3.00 | 1.25 |
| 156 | Jim Bakken (R) | 4.50 | 2.00 |
| 157 | Joe Childress | 1.00 | .55 |
| 158 | Bobby Joe Conrad | 1.50 | .70 |
| 159 | Bob DeMarco | 1.00 | .55 |
| 160 | Pat Fischer (R) | 4.00 | 1.75 |

# 1966 Philadelphia

| | | | |
|---|---|---|---|
| 161 | Irv Goode | 1.00 | .55 |
| 162 | Ken Gray (R) | 1.25 | .60 |
| 163 | Charlie Johnson | 3.00 | 1.25 |
| 164 | Bill Koman | 1.00 | .55 |
| 165 | Dale Meinert | 1.00 | .55 |
| 166 | Jerry Stoval (R) | 3.00 | 1.25 |
| 167 | Abe Woodson | 1.25 | .60 |
| 168 | Cardinals Play (Lemm) | 1.50 | .70 |
| 169 | San Francisco 49ers | 3.00 | 1.25 |
| 170 | Kermit Alexander | 2.50 | 1.10 |
| 171 | John Brodie | 8.50 | 4.00 |
| 172 | Bernie Casey | 1.50 | .70 |
| 173 | John David Crow | 2.50 | 1.10 |
| 174 | Tommy Davis | 1.00 | .55 |
| 175 | Matt Hazeltine | 1.00 | .55 |
| 176 | Jim Johnson | 1.50 | .70 |
| 177 | Charlie Krueger (R) | 3.00 | 1.25 |
| 178 | Roland Lakes | 1.00 | .55 |
| 179 | George Mira (R) | 3.50 | 1.50 |
| 180 | Dave Parks (R) | 4.00 | 1.75 |
| 181 | John Thomas | 1.00 | .55 |
| 182 | 49ers Play (Christiansen) | 1.75 | .80 |
| 183 | Washington Redskins | 3.00 | 1.25 |
| 184 | Pervis Atkins | 1.00 | .55 |
| 185 | Preston Carpenter | 1.00 | .55 |
| 186 | Angelo Coia | 1.00 | .55 |
| 187 | Sam Huff | 6.00 | 2.75 |
| 188 | Sonny Jurgensen | 18.50 | 8.50 |
| 189 | Paul Krause (R) | 8.50 | 4.00 |
| 190 | Jim Martin | 1.00 | .55 |
| 19i1 | Bobby Mitchell | 5.00 | 2.25 |
| 192 | John Nisby | 1.00 | .55 |
| 193 | John Paluck | 1.00 | .55 |
| 194 | Vince Promuto | 1.00 | .55 |
| 195 | Charley Taylor (R) | 50.00 | 22.50 |
| 196 | Redskins Play (McPeak) | 1.50 | .70 |
| 197 | Checklist 1 | 22.00 | 8.50 |
| 198 | Checklist 2 | 40.00 | 15.00 |

This 198-card set features only NFL players and consists of posed photographs on the fronts framed by a white border. The player's name, team and position appear in a box across the top of the card. An NFL logo is printed in the upper left corner. The card backs are horizontal and include the player's personal data, highlights and a quiz question. The answer appears on another card. The set contains team cards and a subset featuring team plays. All cards measure 2-1/2" by 3-1/2".

| | | NR/MT | EX |
|---|---|---|---|
| **Complete Set (198)** | | 875.00 | 475.00 |
| **Commons** | | 1.00 | .55 |

| | | | |
|---|---|---|---|
| 1 | Atlanta Falcons | 7.50 | 3.50 |
| 2 | Larry Benz | 1.00 | .55 |
| 3 | Dennis Claridge | 1.00 | .55 |
| 4 | Perry Lee Dunn | 1.00 | .55 |
| 5 | Dan Grimm | 1.00 | .55 |
| 6 | Alex Hawkins | 1.25 | .60 |
| 7 | Ralph Heck | 1.00 | .55 |
| 8 | Frank Lasky | 1.00 | .55 |
| 9 | Guy Reese | 1.00 | .55 |
| 10 | Bob Richards | 1.00 | .55 |
| 11 | Ron Smith (R) | 1.50 | .70 |
| 12 | Ernie Wheelwright | 1.00 | .55 |
| 13 | Falcons Roster | 1.75 | .80 |
| 14 | Baltimor Colts | 2.50 | 1.10 |
| 15 | Raymond Berry | 5.00 | 2.25 |
| 16 | Bob Boyd | 1.00 | .55 |
| 17 | Jerry Logan | 1.00 | .55 |
| 18 | John Mackey | 6.00 | 2.75 |
| 19 | Tom Matte | 1.75 | .80 |
| 20 | Lou Michaels | 1.50 | .70 |
| 21 | Lenny Moore | 6.00 | 2.75 |

| 22 | Jimmy Orr | 1.75 | .80 |
|---|---|---|---|
| 23 | Jim Parker | 3.50 | 1.50 |
| 24 | John Unitas | 35.00 | 16.50 |
| 25 | Bob Vogel | 1.00 | .55 |
| 26 | Colts Play (Moore) | 2.50 | 1.10 |
| 27 | Chicago Bears | 2.50 | 1.10 |
| 28 | Doug Atkins | 4.00 | 1.75 |
| 29 | Rudy Bukich | 1.25 | .60 |
| 30 | Ron Bull | 1.75 | .80 |
| 31 | Dick Butkus (R) | 190.00 | 95.00 |
| 32 | Mike Ditka | 15.00 | 7.00 |
| 33 | Joe Fortunato | 1.00 | .55 |
| 34 | Bobby Joe Green | 1.25 | .60 |
| 35 | Roger LeClerc | 1.00 | .55 |
| 36 | Johnny Morris | 1.50 | .70 |
| 37 | Mike Pyle | 1.00 | .55 |
| 38 | Gale Sayers (R) | 240.00 | 110.00 |
| 39 | Bears Play (Sayers) | 10.00 | 4.50 |
| 40 | Cleveland Browns | 2.50 | 1.10 |
| 41 | Jim Brown | 70.00 | 32.50 |
| 42 | Gary Collins | 1.75 | .80 |
| 43 | Ross Fichtner | 1.00 | .55 |
| 44 | Ernie Green | 1.00 | .55 |
| 45 | Gene Hickerson (R) | 2.00 | .90 |
| 46 | Jim Houston | 1.25 | .60 |
| 47 | John Morrow | 1.00 | .55 |
| 48 | Walter Roberts | 1.00 | .55 |
| 49 | Frank Ryan | 2.00 | .90 |
| 50 | Dick Schafrath | 1.00 | .55 |
| 51 | Paul Wiggin (R) | 2.00 | .90 |
| 52 | Browns Play (Green) | 1.50 | .70 |
| 53 | Dallas Cowboys | 2.50 | 1.10 |
| 54 | George Andrie (R) | 1.50 | .70 |
| 55 | Frank Clarke | 1.00 | .55 |
| 56 | Mike Connelly | 1.00 | .55 |
| 57 | Cornell Green | 1.75 | .80 |
| 58 | Bob Hayes (R) | 8.50 | 4.00 |
| 59 | Chuck Howley (R) | 4.50 | 2.00 |
| 60 | Bob Lilly | 8.00 | 3.75 |
| 61 | Don Meredith | 22.00 | 10.00 |
| 62 | Don Perkins | 1.75 | .80 |
| 63 | Mel Renfro | 3.50 | 1.50 |
| 64 | Danny Villanueva | 1.00 | .55 |
| 65 | Cowboys Play | 1.50 | .70 |
| 66 | Detroit Lions | 2.50 | 1.10 |
| 67 | Roger Brown | 1.50 | .70 |
| 68 | John Gordy | 1.00 | .55 |
| 69 | Alex Karras | 8.50 | 4.00 |
| 70 | Dick LeBeau | 1.50 | .70 |
| 71 | Amos Marsh | 1.00 | .55 |
| 72 | Milt Plum | 2.00 | .90 |
| 73 | Bobby Smith | 1.00 | .55 |
| 74 | Wayne Rasmussen | 1.00 | .55 |
| 75 | Pat Studstill | 1.25 | .60 |
| 76 | Wayne Walker | 1.25 | .60 |
| 77 | Tom Watkins | 1.00 | .55 |
| 78 | Lions Play | 1.50 | .70 |
| 79 | Green Bay Packers | 2.50 | 1.10 |
| 80 | Herb Adderley | 5.00 | 2.25 |
| 81 | Lee Roy Caffey (R) | 1.75 | .80 |
| 82 | Don Chandler | 1.75 | .80 |
| 83 | Willie Davis | 4.50 | 2.00 |
| 84 | Boyd Dowler | 1.50 | .70 |
| 85 | Forrest Gregg | 3.50 | 1.50 |
| 86 | Tom Moore | 1.00 | .55 |
| 87 | Ray Nitschke | 7.50 | 3.50 |
| 88 | Bart Starr | 25.00 | 12.00 |
| 89 | Jim Taylor | 7.50 | 3.50 |
| 90 | Willie Wood | 5.00 | 2.25 |
| 91 | Packers Play | 1.50 | .70 |
| 92 | Los Angeles Rams | 2.50 | 1.10 |
| 93 | Willie Brown (R) | 1.50 | .70 |
| 94 | D. Bass/R. Gabriel | 3.50 | 1.50 |
| 95 | Bruce Gossett (R) | 1.75 | .80 |
| 96 | Deacon Jones | 5.00 | 2.25 |
| 97 | Tommy McDonald | 1.75 | .80 |
| 98 | Marlin McKeever | 1.00 | .55 |
| 99 | Aaron Martin | 1.00 | .55 |
| 100 | Ed Meador | 1.00 | .55 |
| 101 | Bill Munson | 1.75 | .80 |
| 102 | Merlin Olsen | 10.00 | 4.50 |
| 103 | Jim Stiger | 1.00 | .55 |
| 104 | Rams PPlay | 1.50 | .70 |
| 105 | Minnesota Vikings | 2.50 | 1.10 |
| 106 | Grady Alderman | 1.25 | .60 |
| 107 | Bill Brown | 1.75 | .80 |
| 108 | Fred Cox | 1.50 | .70 |
| 109 | Paul Flatley | 1.00 | .55 |
| 110 | Rip Hawkins | 1.00 | .55 |
| 111 | Tommy Mason | 1.50 | .70 |
| 112 | Ed Sharockman | 1.00 | .55 |
| 113 | Gordon Smith | 1.00 | .55 |
| 114 | Fran Tarkenton | 32.00 | 15.00 |
| 115 | Mick Tingelhoff | 1.75 | .80 |
| 116 | Bobby Walden (R) | 1.75 | .80 |
| 117 | Vikings Play | 1.50 | .70 |
| 118 | New York Giants | 2.50 | 1.10 |
| 119 | Roosevelt Brown | 4.00 | 1.75 |
| 120 | Henry Carr (R) | 2.00 | .90 |
| 121 | Clarence Childs | 1.00 | .55 |
| 122 | Tucker Frederickson | 2.50 | 1.10 |
| 123 | Jerry Hillebrand | 1.00 | .55 |
| 124 | Greg Larson | 1.00 | .55 |
| 125 | Spider Lockhart (R) | 2.50 | 1.10 |
| 126 | Dick Lynch | 1.00 | .55 |
| 127 | E. Morrall/B. Scholtz | 2.50 | 1.10 |
| 128 | Joe Morrison | 2.00 | .90 |
| 129 | Steve Thurlow | 1.00 | .55 |
| 130 | Giants Play | 1.50 | .70 |
| 131 | Philadelphia Eagles | 2.50 | 1.10 |
| 132 | Sam Baker | 1.25 | .60 |
| 133 | Maxie Baughan | 1.75 | .80 |
| 134 | Bob Brown (R) | 4.00 | 1.75 |
| 135 | Timmy Brown | 1.50 | .70 |

| | | | |
|---|---|---|---|
| 136 | Irv Cross | 2.50 | 1.10 |
| 137 | Earl Gros | 1.00 | .55 |
| 138 | Ray Poage | 1.00 | .55 |
| 139 | Nate Ramsey | 1.00 | .55 |
| 140 | Pete Retzlaff | 1.25 | .60 |
| 141 | Jim Ringo | 4.00 | 1.75 |
| 142 | Norm Snead | 2.50 | 1.10 |
| 143 | Eagles Play | 1.50 | .70 |
| 144 | Pittsburgh Steelers | 2.50 | 1.10 |
| 145 | Gary Ballman | 1.25 | .60 |
| 146 | Charley Bradshaw | 1.00 | .55 |
| 147 | Jim Butler | 1.00 | .55 |
| 148 | Mike Clark | 1.00 | .55 |
| 149 | Dick Hoak (R) | 2.00 | .90 |
| 150 | Roy Jefferson (R) | 2.50 | 1.10 |
| 151 | Frank Lambert | 1.00 | .55 |
| 152 | Mike Lind | 1.00 | .55 |
| 153 | Bill Nelsen (R) | 3.00 | 1.25 |
| 154 | Clarence Peaks | 1.00 | .55 |
| 155 | Clendon Thomas | 1.00 | .55 |
| 156 | Steelers Play | 1.50 | .70 |
| 157 | St. Louis Cardinals | 2.50 | 1.10 |
| 158 | Jim Bakken | 1.50 | .70 |
| 159 | Bobby Joe Conrad | 1.50 | .70 |
| 160 | Willis Crenshaw (R) | 1.75 | .80 |
| 161 | Bob DeMarco | 1.00 | .55 |
| 162 | Pat Fischer | 1.75 | .80 |
| 163 | Charlie Johnson | 2.50 | 1.10 |
| 164 | Dale Meinert | 1.00 | .55 |
| 165 | Sonny Randle | 1.50 | .70 |
| 166 | Sam Silas (R) | 1.50 | .70 |
| 167 | Bill Triplett | 1.00 | .55 |
| 168 | Larry Wilson | 4.50 | 2.00 |
| 169 | Cardinals Play | 1.50 | .70 |
| 170 | San Francisco 49ers | 2.50 | 1.10 |
| 171 | Kermit Alexander | 1.75 | .80 |
| 172 | Bruce Bosley | 1.00 | .55 |
| 173 | John Brodie | 8.50 | 4.00 |
| 174 | Bernie Casey | 1.50 | .70 |
| 175 | John David Crow | 2.00 | .90 |
| 176 | Tommy Davis | 1.00 | .55 |
| 177 | Jim Johnson | 1.25 | .60 |
| 178 | Gary Lewis | 1.00 | .55 |
| 179 | Dave Parks | 1.50 | .70 |
| 180 | Walter Rock | 1.00 | .55 |
| 181 | Ken Willard (R) | 4.00 | 1.75 |
| 182 | 49ers Play | 1.50 | .70 |
| 183 | Washington Redskins | 2.50 | 1.10 |
| 184 | Rickie Harris | 1.00 | .55 |
| 185 | Sonny Jurgensen | 12.00 | 5.00 |
| 186 | Paul Krause | 3.00 | 1.25 |
| 187 | Bobby Mitchell | 5.00 | 2.25 |
| 188 | Vince Promuto | 1.00 | .55 |
| 189 | Pat Richter (R) | 2.00 | .90 |
| 190 | Joe Rutgens | 1.00 | .55 |
| 191 | John Sample | 1.50 | .70 |
| 192 | Lonnie Sanders | 1.00 | .55 |
| 193 | Jim Steffen | 1.00 | .55 |
| 194 | Charley Taylor | 12.00 | 5.00 |
| 195 | Redskins Play | 1.50 | .70 |
| 196 | Referee Signals | 3.50 | 1.25 |
| 197 | Checklist 1 | 20.00 | 7.50 |
| 198 | Checklist 2 | 35.00 | 12.50 |

# 1967 Philadelphia

This 198-crd set is devoted exclusively to NFL players and marks Philadelphia Gum's final edition. Card fronts feature posed photos framed by a yellow border. The player's name, team and position appear in a box across the bottom of the card. The horizontal card backs consist of career hghlights and some include a question about the player. Subsets include team cards, logo cards and play cards. All cards measure 2-1/2" by 3-1/2".

| | NR/MT | EX |
|---|---|---|
| Complete Set (198) | 615.00 | 330.00 |
| Commons | 1.00 | .55 |

| | | | |
|---|---|---|---|
| 1 | Atlanta Falcons | 5.00 | 2.25 |
| 2 | Junior Coffey (R) | 1.50 | .70 |
| 3 | Alex Hawkins | 1.50 | .70 |
| 4 | Randy Johnson (R) | 2.00 | .90 |
| 5 | Lou Kirouac | 1.00 | .55 |
| 6 | Billy Martin | 1.00 | .55 |
| 7 | Tommy Nobis (R) | 10.00 | 4.50 |
| 8 | Jerry Richardson (R) | 1.50 | .70 |
| 9 | Marion Rushing | 1.00 | .55 |
| 10 | Ron Smith | 1.00 | .55 |
| 11 | Ernie Wheelwright | 1.00 | .55 |

| | | | |
|---|---|---:|---:|
| 12 | Falcons Logo | 1.50 | .70 |
| 13 | Baltimore Colts | 2.50 | 1.10 |
| 14 | Raymond Berry | 4.00 | 1.75 |
| 15 | Bob Boyd | 1.00 | .55 |
| 16 | Ordell Braase | 1.00 | .55 |
| 17 | Alvin Haymond | 1.00 | .55 |
| 18 | Tony Lorick | 1.00 | .55 |
| 19 | Lenny Lyles | 1.00 | .55 |
| 20 | John Mackey | 5.00 | 2.25 |
| 21 | Tom Matte | 1.75 | .80 |
| 22 | Lou Michaels | 1.50 | .70 |
| 23 | John Unitas | 30.00 | 14.00 |
| 24 | Colts Logo | 1.50 | .70 |
| 25 | Chicago Bears | 2.50 | 1.10 |
| 26 | Rudy Bukich | 1.50 | .70 |
| 27 | Ron Bull | 1.50 | .70 |
| 28 | Dick Butkus | 50.00 | 24.00 |
| 29 | Mike Ditka | 8.00 | 3.75 |
| 30 | Dick Gordon (R) | 2.00 | .90 |
| 31 | Roger LeClerc | 1.00 | .55 |
| 32 | Bennie McRae | 1.00 | .55 |
| 33 | Richie Petitbon | 1.50 | .70 |
| 34 | Mike Pyle | 1.00 | .55 |
| 35 | Gale Sayers | 85.00 | 40.00 |
| 36 | Bears Logo | 1.50 | .70 |
| 37 | Cleveland Browns | 2.50 | 1.10 |
| 38 | Johnny Brewer | 1.00 | .55 |
| 39 | Gary Collins | 1.25 | .60 |
| 40 | Ross Fichtner | 1.00 | .55 |
| 41 | Ernie Green | 1.00 | .55 |
| 42 | Gene Hickerson | 1.00 | .55 |
| 43 | Leroy Kelly (R) | 15.00 | 7.00 |
| 44 | Frank Ryan | 2.00 | .90 |
| 45 | Dick Schafrath | 1.00 | .55 |
| 46 | Paul Warfield | 16.00 | 7.50 |
| 47 | John Wooten | 1.00 | .55 |
| 48 | Browns Logo | 1.50 | .70 |
| 49 | Dallas Cowboys | 2.50 | 1.10 |
| 50 | George Andrie | 1.00 | .55 |
| 51 | Cornell Green | 1.50 | .70 |
| 52 | Bob Hayes | 4.00 | 1.75 |
| 53 | Chuck Howley | 2.00 | .90 |
| 54 | Lee Roy Jordan (R) | 18.00 | 8.50 |
| 55 | Bob Lilly | 6.00 | 2.75 |
| 56 | Dave Manders (R) | 1.25 | .60 |
| 57 | Don Meredith | 20.00 | 9.00 |
| 58 | Dan Reeves (R) | 15.00 | 7.00 |
| 59 | Mel Renfro | 2.50 | 1.10 |
| 60 | Cowboys Logo | 1.50 | .70 |
| 61 | Detroit Lions | 2.50 | 1.10 |
| 62 | Roger Brown | 1.50 | .70 |
| 63 | Gail Cogdill | 1.00 | .55 |
| 64 | John Gordy | 1.00 | .55 |
| 65 | Ron Kramer (R) | 1.25 | .60 |
| 66 | Dick LeBeau | 1.50 | .70 |
| 67 | Mike Lucci (R) | 3.50 | 1.50 |
| 68 | Amos Marsh | 1.00 | .55 |
| 69 | Tom Nowatzke | 1.00 | .55 |
| 70 | Pat Studstill | 1.25 | .60 |
| 71 | Karl Sweetan | 1.25 | .60 |
| 72 | Lions Logo | 1.50 | .70 |
| 73 | Green Bay Packers | 2.50 | 1.10 |
| 74 | Herb Adderley | 3.50 | 1.50 |
| 75 | Lee Roy Caffey | 1.00 | .55 |
| 76 | Willie Davis | 3.00 | 1.25 |
| 77 | Forrest Gregg | 3.00 | 1.25 |
| 78 | Henry Jordan | 1.25 | .60 |
| 79 | Ray Nitschke | 5.00 | 2.25 |
| 80 | Dave Robinson (R) | 3.50 | 1.50 |
| 81 | Bob Skoronski | 1.00 | .55 |
| 82 | Bart Starr | 28.00 | 13.50 |
| 83 | Willie Wood | 3.00 | 1.25 |
| 84 | Packers Logo | 1.50 | .70 |
| 85 | Los Angeles Rams | 2.50 | 1.10 |
| 86 | Dick Bass | 1.50 | .70 |
| 87 | Maxie Baughan | 1.25 | .60 |
| 88 | Roman Gabriel | 3.50 | 1.50 |
| 89 | Bruce Gossett | 1.00 | .55 |
| 90 | Deacon Jones | 5.00 | 2.25 |
| 91 | Tommy McDonald | 2.00 | .90 |
| 92 | Marlin McKeever | 1.00 | .55 |
| 93 | Tom Moore | 1.00 | .55 |
| 94 | Merlin Olsen | 6.00 | 2.75 |
| 95 | Clancy Williams | 1.00 | .55 |
| 96 | Rams Logo | 1.50 | .70 |
| 97 | Minnesota Vikings | 2.50 | 1.10 |
| 98 | Grady Alderman | 1.00 | .55 |
| 99 | Bill Brown | 1.50 | .70 |
| 100 | Fred Cox | 1.25 | .60 |
| 101 | Paul Flatley | 1.00 | .55 |
| 102 | Dale Hackbart (R) | 1.25 | .60 |
| 103 | Jim Marshall | 3.00 | 1.25 |
| 104 | Tommy Mason | 1.25 | .60 |
| 105 | Milt Sunde (R) | 1.25 | .60 |
| 106 | Fran Tarkenton | 28.00 | 13.00 |
| 107 | Mick Tingelhoff | 1.75 | .80 |
| 108 | Vikings Logo | 1.50 | .70 |
| 109 | New York Giants | 2.50 | 1.10 |
| 110 | Henry Carr | 1.25 | .60 |
| 111 | Clarence Childs | 1.00 | .55 |
| 112 | Allen Jacobs | 1.00 | .55 |
| 113 | Homer Jones (R) | 2.00 | .90 |
| 114 | Tom Kennedy (R) | 1.25 | .60 |
| 115 | Spider Lockhart | 1.25 | .60 |
| 116 | Joe Morrison | 1.75 | .80 |
| 117 | Francis Peay | 1.00 | .55 |
| 118 | Jeff Smith | 1.00 | .55 |
| 119 | Aaron Thomas | 1.00 | .55 |
| 120 | Giants Logo | 1.50 | .70 |
| 121 | Saints Logo | 2.00 | .90 |
| 122 | Charley Bradshaw | 1.00 | .55 |
| 123 | Paul Hornung | 18.00 | 8.50 |
| 124 | Elbert Kimbrough | 1.00 | .55 |
| 125 | Earl Leggett | 1.00 | .55 |

| 126 | Obert Logan | 1.00 | .55 |
|---|---|---|---|
| 127 | Riley Mattson | 1.00 | .55 |
| 128 | John Morrow | 1.00 | .55 |
| 129 | Bob Scholtz | 1.00 | .55 |
| 130 | Dave Whitsell (R) | 1.25 | .60 |
| 131 | Gary Wood (R) | 1.25 | .60 |
| 132 | New Orleans Saints | 2.50 | 1.10 |
| 133 | Philadelphia Eagles | 2.50 | 1.10 |
| 134 | Sam Baker | 1.25 | .60 |
| 135 | Bob Brown | 1.50 | .70 |
| 136 | Timmy Brown | 1.50 | .70 |
| 137 | Earl Gros | 1.00 | .55 |
| 138 | Dave Lloyd | 1.00 | .55 |
| 139 | Floyd Peters | 1.00 | .55 |
| 140 | Pete Retzlaff | 1.25 | .60 |
| 141 | Joe Scarpati | 1.00 | .55 |
| 142 | Norm Snead | 2.50 | 1.10 |
| 143 | Jim Skaggs | 1.00 | .55 |
| 144 | Eagles Logo | 1.50 | .70 |
| 145 | Pittsburgh Steelers | 2.50 | 1.10 |
| 146 | Bill Asbury | 1.00 | .55 |
| 147 | John Baker | 1.00 | .55 |
| 148 | Gary Ballman | 1.00 | .55 |
| 149 | Mike Clark | 1.00 | .55 |
| 150 | Riley Gunnels | 1.00 | .55 |
| 151 | John Hilton | 1.00 | .55 |
| 152 | Roy Jefferson | 1.50 | .70 |
| 153 | Brady Keys | 1.00 | .55 |
| 154 | Ben McGee | 1.00 | .55 |
| 155 | Bill Nelsen | 1.75 | .80 |
| 156 | Steelers Logo | 1.50 | .70 |
| 157 | St. Louis Cardinals | 2.50 | 1.10 |
| 158 | Jim Bakken | 1.25 | .60 |
| 159 | Bobby Joe Conrad | 1.25 | .60 |
| 160 | Ken Gray | 1.00 | .55 |
| 161 | Charlie Johnson | 2.00 | .90 |
| 162 | Joe Robb | 1.00 | .55 |
| 163 | Johnny Roland (R) | 4.00 | 1.75 |
| 164 | Roy Shivers | 1.25 | .60 |
| 165 | Jackie Smith (R) | 5.00 | 2.25 |
| 166 | Jerry Stovall | 1.50 | .70 |
| 167 | Larry Wilson | 3.50 | 1.50 |
| 168 | Cardinals Logo | 1.50 | .70 |
| 169 | San Francisco 49ers | 2.50 | 1.10 |
| 170 | Kermit Alexander | 1.50 | .70 |
| 171 | Bruce Bosley | 1.00 | .55 |
| 172 | John Brodie | 6.50 | 3.00 |
| 173 | Bernie Casey | 1.25 | .60 |
| 174 | Tommy Davis | 1.00 | .55 |
| 175 | Howard Mudd | 1.00 | .55 |
| 176 | Dave Parks | 1.25 | .60 |
| 177 | John Thomas | 1.00 | .55 |
| 178 | Dave Wilcox (R) | 3.00 | 1.25 |
| 179 | Ken Willard | 1.75 | .80 |
| 180 | 49ers Logo | 1.50 | .70 |
| 181 | Washington Redskins | 2.50 | 1.10 |
| 182 | Charlie Gogolak (R) | 1.75 | .80 |

| 183 | Chris Hanburger (R) | 5.00 | 2.25 |
|---|---|---|---|
| 184 | Len Hauss (R) | 2.00 | .90 |
| 185 | Sonny Jurgensen | 10.00 | 4.50 |
| 186 | Bobby Mitchell | 5.00 | 2.25 |
| 187 | Brig Owens | 1.00 | .55 |
| 188 | Jim Shorter | 1.00 | .55 |
| 189 | Jerry Smith (R) | 4.00 | 1.75 |
| 190 | Charley Taylor | 7.50 | 3.50 |
| 191 | A.D. Whitfield | 1.00 | .55 |
| 192 | Redskins Logo | 1.50 | .70 |
| 193 | Browns Play (Kelly) | 2.50 | 1.10 |
| 194 | Giants Play (Morrison) | 2.00 | .90 |
| 195 | Falcons Play (Wheelright) | 1.25 | .60 |
| 196 | Referee Signals | 1.75 | .80 |
| 197 | Checklist 1 | 18.00 | 6.00 |
| 198 | Checklist 2 | 35.00 | 12.50 |

# PRO LINE

## 1991 Pro Line Portraits

This 300-card set features posed full color photographs of some of the NFL's top stars in non-game action shots. The borderless fronts contain a Pro Line logo at the bottom of the photograph. Card backs include a close up head shot and a quote from the player. A 7-card Spirit subset, featuring the wives of some of the top players, was included in the set. Those cards (SC1-SC7) are listed at

the end of this checklist but are not
included in the complete set price below.
Two special limited bonus cards were
randomly inserted into Pro Line wax
packs. Those cards feature the Ahmad
Rashad family and professional golfer
Payne Stewart. Both are listed as bonus
cards (BC) at the end of this checklist. All
cards measure 2-1/2" by 3-1/2".

|  |  | MINT | NR/MT |
|---|---|---|---|
| **Complete Set (307)** |  | 10.00 | 6.50 |
| **Commons** |  | .04 | .02 |
| | | | |
| 1 | Jim Kelly | .60 | .35 |
| 2 | Carl Banks | .07 | .04 |
| 3 | Neal Anderson | .12 | .07 |
| 4 | James Brooks | .04 | .02 |
| 5 | Reggie Langhorne | .04 | .02 |
| 6 | Robert Awalt | .04 | .02 |
| 7 | Greg Kragen | .04 | .02 |
| 8 | Steve Young | .30 | .18 |
| 9 | Nick Bell (R) | .75 | .45 |
| 10 | Ray Childress | .07 | .04 |
| 11 | Albert Bentley | .04 | .02 |
| 12 | Albert Lewis | .04 | .02 |
| 13 | Howie Long | .08 | .05 |
| 14 | Flipper Anderson | .07 | .04 |
| 15 | Mark Clayton | .12 | .07 |
| 16 | Jarrod Bunch (R) | .40 | .25 |
| 17 | Bruce Armstrong | .04 | .02 |
| 18 | Vinnie Clark (R) | .12 | .07 |
| 19 | Rob Moore | .60 | .35 |
| 20 | Eric Allen | .04 | .02 |
| 21 | Timm Rosenbach | .10 | .06 |
| 22 | Gary Anderson | .04 | .02 |
| 23 | Martin Bayless | .04 | .02 |
| 24 | Kevin Fagan | .04 | .02 |
| 25 | Brian Blades | .06 | .03 |
| 26 | Gary Anderson | .04 | .02 |
| 27 | Earnest Byner | .07 | .04 |
| 28 | O.J. Simpson | .20 | .12 |
| 29 | Dan Henning | .04 | .02 |
| 30 | Sean Landeta | .04 | .02 |
| 31 | James Lofton | .20 | .12 |
| 32 | Mike Singletary | .10 | .06 |
| 33 | David Fulcher | .04 | .02 |
| 34 | Mark Murphy | .04 | .02 |
| 35 | Issiac Holt | .04 | .02 |
| 36 | Dennis Smith | .04 | .02 |
| 37 | Lomas Brown | .04 | .02 |
| 38 | Ernest Givins | .12 | .07 |
| 39 | Duane Bickett | .04 | .02 |
| 40 | Barry Word | .35 | .20 |
| 41 | Tony Mandarich | .04 | .02 |
| 42 | Cleveland Gary | .08 | .05 |
| 43 | Ferrell Edmunds | .04 | .02 |
| 44 | Randal Hill (R) | .60 | .35 |
| 45 | Irving Fryar | .08 | .05 |
| 46 | Henry Jones (R) | .30 | .18 |
| 47 | Blair Thomas | .25 | .15 |
| 48 | Andre Waters | .04 | .02 |
| 49 | J.T. Smith | .04 | .02 |
| 50 | Thomas Everett | .04 | .02 |
| 51 | Marion Butts | .12 | .07 |
| 52 | Tom Rathman | .08 | .05 |
| 53 | Vann McElroy | .04 | .02 |
| 54 | Mark Carrier (TB) | .06 | .03 |
| 55 | Jim Lachey | .07 | .04 |
| 56 | Joe Theismann | .15 | .10 |
| 57 | Jerry Glanville | .04 | .02 |
| 58 | Doug Riesenberg | .04 | .02 |
| 59 | Cornelius Bennett | .10 | .06 |
| 60 | Mark Carrier (Chi) | .08 | .05 |
| 61 | Rodney Holman | .04 | .02 |
| 62 | Leroy Hoard | .12 | .07 |
| 63 | Michael Irvin | .35 | .20 |
| 64 | Bobby Humphrey | .12 | .07 |
| 65 | Mel Gray | .04 | .02 |
| 66 | Brian Noble | .04 | .02 |
| 67 | Al Smith | .04 | .02 |
| 68 | Eric Dickerson | .25 | .15 |
| 69 | Steve DeBerg | .10 | .06 |
| 70 | Jay Schroeder | .12 | .07 |
| 71 | Irv Pankey | .04 | .02 |
| 72 | Reggie Roby | .04 | .02 |
| 73 | Wade Wilson | .08 | .05 |
| 74 | Johnny Rembert | .04 | .02 |
| 75 | Russell Maryland (R) | .50 | .30 |
| 76 | Al Toon | .08 | .05 |
| 77 | Randall Cunningham | .20 | .12 |
| 78 | Lonnie Young | .04 | .02 |
| 79 | Carnell Lake | .04 | .02 |
| 80 | Burt Grossman | .04 | .02 |
| 81 | Jim Mora | .04 | .02 |
| 82 | Dave Krieg | .10 | .06 |
| 83 | Bruce Hill | .04 | .02 |
| 84 | Ricky Sanders | .08 | .05 |
| 85 | Roger Staubach | .25 | .15 |
| 86 | Richard Williamson | .04 | .02 |
| 87 | Everson Walls | .04 | .02 |
| 88 | Shane Conlan | .07 | .04 |
| 89 | Mike Ditka | .07 | .04 |
| 90 | Mark Bortz | .04 | .02 |
| 91 | Tim McGee | .08 | .05 |
| 92 | Michael Dean Perry | .15 | .10 |
| 93 | Danny Noonan | .04 | .02 |
| 94 | Mark Jackson | .04 | .02 |
| 95 | Chris Miller | .25 | .15 |
| 96 | Ed McCaffrey (R) | .30 | .18 |
| 97 | Lorenzo White | .15 | .10 |
| 98 | Ray Donaldson | .04 | .02 |

| | | | |
|---|---|---|---|
| 99 | Nick Lowery | .07 | .04 |
| 100 | Steve Smith | .04 | .02 |
| 101 | Jackie Slater | .06 | .03 |
| 102 | Louis Oliver | .07 | .04 |
| 103 | Kanavis McGhee (R) | .20 | .12 |
| 104 | Ray Agnew | .04 | .02 |
| 105 | Sam Mills | .07 | .04 |
| 106 | Bill Pickel | .04 | .02 |
| 107 | Keith Byars | .08 | .05 |
| 108 | Ricky Proehl | .12 | .07 |
| 109 | Merril Hoge | .07 | .04 |
| 110 | Rod Bernstine | .07 | .04 |
| 111 | Andy Heck | .04 | .02 |
| 112 | Broderick Thomas | .08 | .05 |
| 113 | Andre Collins | .06 | .03 |
| 114 | Paul Warfield | .15 | .10 |
| 115 | Bill Belichick | .04 | .02 |
| 116 | Ottis Anderson | .08 | .05 |
| 117 | Andre Reed | .15 | .10 |
| 118 | Andre Rison | .25 | .15 |
| 119 | Dexter Carter | .08 | .05 |
| 120 | Anthony Munoz | .08 | .05 |
| 121 | Bernie Kosar | .15 | .10 |
| 122 | Alonzo Highsmith | .04 | .02 |
| 123 | David Treadwell | .04 | .02 |
| 124 | Rodney Peete | .12 | .07 |
| 125 | Haywood Jeffires | .25 | .15 |
| 126 | Clarence Verdin | .07 | .04 |
| 127 | Christian Okoye | .12 | .07 |
| 128 | Greg Townsend | .04 | .02 |
| 129 | Tom Newberry | .04 | .02 |
| 130 | Keith Sims | .04 | .02 |
| 131 | Myron Guyton | .04 | .02 |
| 132 | Andre Tippett | .07 | .04 |
| 133 | Steve Walsh | .10 | .06 |
| 134 | Erik McMillan | .04 | .02 |
| 135 | Jim McMahon | .10 | .06 |
| 136 | Derek Hill | .04 | .02 |
| 137 | David Johnson | .07 | .04 |
| 138 | Leslie O'Neal | .07 | .04 |
| 139 | Pierce Holt | .04 | .02 |
| 140 | Cortez Kennedy | .20 | .12 |
| 141 | Danny Peebles | .04 | .02 |
| 142 | Alvin Walton | .04 | .02 |
| 143 | Drew Pearson | .08 | .05 |
| 144 | Dick MacPherson | .04 | .02 |
| 145 | Erik Howard | .04 | .02 |
| 146 | Steve Tasker | .04 | .02 |
| 147 | Bill Fralic | .04 | .02 |
| 148 | Don Warren | .04 | .02 |
| 149 | Eric Thomas | .04 | .02 |
| 150 | Jack Pardee | .04 | .02 |
| 151 | Gary Zimmerman | .04 | .02 |
| 152 | Leonard Marshall | .06 | .03 |
| 153 | Chris Spielman | .04 | .02 |
| 154 | Sam Wyche | .04 | .02 |
| 155 | Rohn Stark | .04 | .02 |
| 156 | Stephone Paige | .07 | .04 |
| 157 | Lionel Washington | .04 | .02 |
| 158 | Henry Ellard | .07 | .04 |
| 159 | Dan Marino | .50 | .30 |
| 160 | Lindy Infante | .04 | .02 |
| 161 | Dan McGwire (R) | .60 | .35 |
| 162 | Ken O'Brien | .10 | .06 |
| 163 | Tim McDonald | .04 | .02 |
| 164 | Louis Lipps | .07 | .04 |
| 165 | Billy Joe Tolliver | .08 | .05 |
| 166 | Harris Barton | .04 | .02 |
| 167 | Tony Woods | .04 | .02 |
| 168 | Matt Millen | .04 | .02 |
| 169 | Gale Sayers | .20 | .12 |
| 170 | Ron Meyer | .04 | .02 |
| 171 | William Roberts | .04 | .02 |
| 172 | Thurman Thomas | .60 | .35 |
| 173 | Steve McMichael | .07 | .04 |
| 174 | Ickey Woods | .04 | .02 |
| 175 | Eugene Lockhart | .04 | .02 |
| 176 | George Seifert | .04 | .02 |
| 177 | Keith Jones | .04 | .02 |
| 178 | Jack Trudeau | .08 | .05 |
| 179 | Kevin Porter | .04 | .02 |
| 180 | Ronnie Lott | .12 | .07 |
| 181 | M. Schottenheimer | .04 | .02 |
| 182 | Morten Andersen | .07 | .04 |
| 183 | Anthony Thompson | .08 | .05 |
| 184 | Tim Worley | .08 | .05 |
| 185 | Billy Ray Smith | .04 | .02 |
| 186 | David Whitmore (R) | .08 | .05 |
| 187 | Jacob Green | .04 | .02 |
| 188 | Browning Nagle (R) | 1.25 | .80 |
| 189 | Franco Harris | .15 | .10 |
| 190 | Art Shell | .04 | .02 |
| 191 | Bart Oates | .04 | .02 |
| 192 | William Perry | .07 | .04 |
| 193 | Chuck Noll | .08 | .05 |
| 194 | Troy Aikman | 1.00 | .70 |
| 195 | Jeff George | .35 | .20 |
| 196 | Derrick Thomas | .20 | .12 |
| 197 | Roger Craig | .08 | .05 |
| 198 | John Fourcade | .07 | .04 |
| 199 | Rod Woodson | .08 | .05 |
| 200 | Anthony Miller | .15 | .10 |
| 201 | Jerry Rice | .40 | .25 |
| 202 | Eugene Robinson | .04 | .02 |
| 203 | Charles Mann | .04 | .02 |
| 204 | Mel Blount | .08 | .05 |
| 205 | Don Shula | .12 | .07 |
| 206 | Jumbo Elliott | .04 | .02 |
| 207 | Jay Hilgenberg | .04 | .02 |
| 208 | Deron Cherry | .04 | .02 |
| 209 | Dan Reeves | .04 | .02 |
| 210 | Roman Phifer (R) | .10 | .06 |
| 211 | David Little | .04 | .02 |
| 212 | Lee Williams | .04 | .02 |

| No. | Player | | |
|---|---|---|---|
| 213 | John Taylor | .15 | .10 |
| 214 | Monte Coleman | .04 | .02 |
| 215 | Walter Payton | .25 | .15 |
| 216 | John Robinson | .04 | .02 |
| 217 | Pepper Johnson | .04 | .02 |
| 218 | Tom Thayer | .04 | .02 |
| 219 | Dan Saleaumua | .04 | .02 |
| 220 | Ernest Spears (R) | .07 | .04 |
| 221 | Bubby Brister | .10 | .06 |
| 222 | Junior Seau | .20 | .12 |
| 223 | Brent Jones | .07 | .04 |
| 224 | Rufus Porter | .04 | .02 |
| 225 | Jack Kemp | .25 | .15 |
| 226 | Wayne Fontes | .04 | .02 |
| 227 | Phil Simms | .10 | .06 |
| 228 | Shaun Gayle | .04 | .02 |
| 229 | Bill Maas | .04 | .02 |
| 230 | Renaldo Turnbull | .06 | .03 |
| 231 | Bryan Hinkle | .04 | .02 |
| 232 | Gary Plummer | .04 | .02 |
| 233 | Jerry Burns | .04 | .02 |
| 234 | Lawrence Taylor | .15 | .10 |
| 235 | Joe Gibbs | .04 | .02 |
| 236 | Neil Smith | .04 | .02 |
| 237 | Rich Kotite | .04 | .02 |
| 238 | Jim Covert | .04 | .02 |
| 239 | Tim Grunhard | .04 | .02 |
| 240 | Joe Bugel | .04 | .02 |
| 241 | Dave Wyman | .04 | .02 |
| 242 | Maury Buford | .04 | .02 |
| 243 | Kevin Ross | .04 | .02 |
| 244 | Jimmy Johnson | .04 | .02 |
| 245 | Jim Morrissey (R) | .08 | .05 |
| 246 | Jeff Hostetler | .20 | .12 |
| 247 | Andre Ware | .15 | .10 |
| 248 | Steve Largent | .15 | .10 |
| 249 | Chuck Knox | .04 | .02 |
| 250 | Boomer Esiason | .12 | .07 |
| 251 | Kevin Butler | .04 | .02 |
| 252 | Bruce Smith | .10 | .06 |
| 253 | Webster Slaughter | .04 | .02 |
| 254 | Mike Sherrard | .08 | .05 |
| 255 | Steve Broussard | .10 | .06 |
| 256 | Warren Moon | .20 | .12 |
| 257 | John Elway | .20 | .12 |
| 258 | Bob Golic | .04 | .02 |
| 259 | Jim Everett | .15 | .10 |
| 260 | Bruce Coslet | .04 | .02 |
| 261 | James Francis | .08 | .05 |
| 262 | Eric Dorsey | .04 | .02 |
| 263 | Marcus Dupree | .07 | .04 |
| 264 | Hart Lee Dykes | .07 | .04 |
| 265 | Vinny Testaverde | .10 | .06 |
| 266 | Chip Lohmiller | .04 | .02 |
| 267 | John Riggins | .12 | .07 |
| 268 | Mike Schad | .04 | .02 |
| 269 | Kevin Greene | .04 | .02 |
| 270 | Dean Biasucci | .04 | .02 |
| 271 | Mike Pritchard (R) | .40 | .25 |
| 272 | Ted Washington (R) | .10 | .06 |
| 273 | Alfred Williams (R) | .20 | .12 |
| 274 | Chris Zorich (R) | .12 | .07 |
| 275 | Reggie Barrett (R) | .15 | .10 |
| 276 | Chris Hinton | .04 | .02 |
| 277 | Tracy Johnson (R) | .08 | .05 |
| 278 | Jim Harbaugh | .15 | .10 |
| 279 | John Roper | .04 | .02 |
| 280 | Mike Dumas (R) | .10 | .06 |
| 281 | Herman Moore (R) | .70 | .40 |
| 282 | Eric Turner (R) | .25 | .15 |
| 283 | Steve Atwater | .08 | .05 |
| 284 | Michael Cofer | .04 | .02 |
| 285 | Darion Conner | .04 | .02 |
| 286 | Darryl Talley | .07 | .04 |
| 287 | Donnell Woolford | .04 | .02 |
| 288 | Keith McCants | .07 | .04 |
| 289 | Ray Handley | .04 | .02 |
| 290 | Ahmad Rashad | .08 | .05 |
| 291 | Eric Swann (R) | .15 | .10 |
| 292 | Dalton Hilliard | .08 | .05 |
| 293 | Rickey Jackson | .07 | .04 |
| 294 | Vaughan Johnson | .07 | .04 |
| 295 | Eric Martin | .08 | .05 |
| 296 | Pat Swilling | .10 | .06 |
| 297 | Anthony Carter | .08 | .05 |
| 298 | Guy McIntyre | .04 | .02 |
| 299 | Bennie Blades | .07 | .04 |
| 300 | Paul Farren | .04 | .02 |
| SC1 | Jennifer Montana | .50 | .30 |
| SC2 | Babette Kosar | .12 | .07 |
| SC3 | Janet Elway | .12 | .07 |
| SC4 | Michelle Oates | .12 | .07 |
| SC5 | Toni Lipps | .12 | .07 |
| SC6 | Stacy O'Brien | .12 | .07 |
| SC7 | Phylicia Rashad | .25 | .15 |
| BC1 | Rashad Family | 20.00 | 14.00 |
| BC2 | Payne Stewart | 20.00 | 14.00 |

# 1992 Pro Line Portraits

The 1992 version of Pro Line Portraits is a continuation of the 1991 set. Starting with card number 301, this 167-card set features posed photographs of players in non-game action situations on the card fronts. The backs include a small head shot. The set also includes 16 new NFL Spirit cards (SC) featuring player's wives, 6 additional Bonus Cards (BC) and a 5 card Team NFL subset featuring athletes and celebrities who promote NFL licensed merchandise. All cards measure 2-1/2" by 3-1/2".

|  | MINT | NR/MT |
|---|---|---|
| Complete Set (167) | 10.00 | 6.50 |
| Commons | .05 | .02 |

| | | MINT | NR/MT |
|---|---|---|---|
| 301 | Steve Emtman (R) | 1.00 | .70 |
| 302 | Al Edwards | .05 | .02 |
| 303 | Wendell Davis | .10 | .06 |
| 304 | Lewis Billups | .05 | .02 |
| 305 | Brian Brennan | .05 | .02 |
| 306 | John Giesek | .05 | .02 |
| 307 | Terrell Buckley (R) | .60 | .35 |
| 308 | Johnny Mitchell (R) | .25 | .15 |
| 309 | LeRoy Butler | .05 | .02 |
| 310 | William Fuller | .05 | .02 |
| 311 | Bill Brooks | .05 | .02 |
| 312 | Dino Hackett | .05 | .02 |
| 313 | Willie Gault | .07 | .04 |
| 314 | Aaron Cox | .05 | .02 |
| 315 | Jeff Cross | .05 | .02 |
| 316 | Emmitt Smith | 1.50 | .90 |
| 317 | Marv Cook | .10 | .06 |
| 318 | Gill Fenerty | .05 | .02 |
| 319 | Jeff Carlson (R) | .15 | .10 |
| 320 | Brad Baxter | .10 | .06 |
| 321 | Fred Barnett | .15 | .10 |
| 322 | Kurt Barber (R) | .10 | .06 |
| 323 | Eric Green | .12 | .07 |
| 324 | Greg Clark (R) | .08 | .05 |
| 325 | Keith DeLong | .05 | .02 |
| 326 | Patrick Hunter | .05 | .02 |
| 327 | Troy Vincent (R) | .20 | .12 |
| 328 | Gary Clark | .15 | .10 |
| 329 | Joe Montana | .40 | .25 |
| 330 | Michael Haynes | .20 | .12 |
| 331 | Edgar Bennett (R) | .25 | .15 |
| 332 | Darren Lewis | .15 | .10 |
| 333 | Derrick Fenner | .10 | .06 |
| 334 | Rob Burnett | .07 | .04 |
| 335 | Alvin Harper | .30 | .18 |
| 336 | Vance Johnson | .08 | .05 |
| 337 | William White | .05 | .02 |
| 338 | Sterling Sharpe | .25 | .15 |
| 339 | Sean Jones | .05 | .02 |
| 340 | Jeff Herrod | .05 | .02 |
| 341 | Chris Martin | .05 | .02 |
| 342 | Ethan Horton | .07 | .04 |
| 343 | Robert Delpino | .07 | .04 |
| 344 | Mark Higgs | .25 | .15 |
| 345 | Chris Doleman | .08 | .05 |
| 346 | Tommy Hodson | .10 | .06 |
| 347 | Craig Heyward | .08 | .05 |
| 348 | Cary Conklin | .10 | .06 |
| 349 | James Hasty | .05 | .02 |
| 350 | Antone Davis | .05 | .02 |
| 351 | Ernie Jones | .08 | .05 |
| 352 | Greg Lloyd | .05 | .02 |
| 353 | John Friesz | .10 | .06 |
| 354 | Charles Haley | .07 | .04 |
| 355 | Tracy Scroggins | .05 | .02 |
| 356 | Paul Gruber | .05 | .02 |
| 357 | Ricky Ervins | .35 | .20 |
| 358 | Brad Muster | .08 | .05 |
| 359 | Deion Sanders | .25 | .15 |
| 360 | Mitch Frerotte (R) | .12 | .07 |
| 361 | Stan Thomas | .05 | .02 |
| 362 | Harold Green | .25 | .15 |
| 363 | Eric Metcalf | .10 | .06 |
| 364 | Ken Norton | .05 | .02 |
| 365 | Dave & Doug Widell | .05 | .02 |
| 366 | Mike Tomczak | .08 | .05 |
| 367 | Bubba McDowell | .05 | .02 |
| 368 | Jessie Hester | .05 | .02 |
| 369 | Ervin Randle | .05 | .02 |
| 370 | Anthony Smith | .05 | .02 |
| 371 | Pat Terrell | .05 | .02 |
| 372 | Jim Jensen | .05 | .02 |
| 373 | Mike Merriweather | .05 | .02 |
| 374 | Chris Singleton | .07 | .04 |
| 375 | Floyd Turner | .05 | .02 |
| 376 | Jim Sweeney | .05 | .02 |

| | | | |
|---|---|---:|---:|
| 377 | Keith Jackson | .15 | .10 |
| 378 | Walter Reeves | .05 | .02 |
| 379 | Neil O'Donnell | .50 | .30 |
| 380 | Nate Lewis | .10 | .06 |
| 381 | Keith Henderson | .08 | .05 |
| 382 | Kelly Stouffer | .10 | .06 |
| 383 | Ricky Reynolds | .05 | .02 |
| 384 | Joe Jacoby | .05 | .02 |
| 385 | Fred Biletnikoff | .10 | .06 |
| 386 | Jessie Tuggle | .05 | .02 |
| 387 | Tom Waddle | .12 | .07 |
| 388 | Dave Shula (R) | .07 | .04 |
| 389 | Van Waiters | .05 | .02 |
| 390 | Jay Novacek | .08 | .05 |
| 391 | Michael Young | .05 | .02 |
| 392 | Mike Holmgren (R) | .07 | .04 |
| 393 | Doug Smith | .05 | .02 |
| 394 | Mike Prior | .05 | .02 |
| 395 | Harvey Williams | .25 | .15 |
| 396 | Aaron Wallace | .07 | .04 |
| 397 | Tony Zendejas | .05 | .02 |
| 398 | Sammie Smith | .08 | .05 |
| 399 | Henry Thomas | .05 | .02 |
| 400 | Jon Vaughn | .15 | .10 |
| 401 | Brian Washington | .05 | .02 |
| 402 | Leon Searcy (R) | .10 | .06 |
| 403 | Lance Smith | .05 | .02 |
| 404 | Warren Williams | .05 | .02 |
| 405 | Bobby Ross (R) | .08 | .05 |
| 406 | Harry Sydney | .05 | .02 |
| 407 | John L. Williams | .08 | .05 |
| 408 | Ken Willis | .05 | .02 |
| 409 | Brian Mitchell | .10 | .06 |
| 410 | Dick Butkus | .15 | .10 |
| 411 | Chuck Knox | .05 | .02 |
| 412 | Robert Porcher (R) | .15 | .10 |
| 413 | Calvin Williams | .10 | .06 |
| 414 | Bill Cowher (R) | .08 | .05 |
| 415 | Eric Moore | .05 | .02 |
| 416 | Derek Brown (R) | .20 | .12 |
| 417 | Dennis Green (R) | .08 | .05 |
| 418 | Tom Flores | .07 | .04 |
| 419 | Dale Carter (R) | .35 | .20 |
| 420 | Tony Dorsett | .15 | .10 |
| 421 | Marco Coleman (R) | .30 | .18 |
| 422 | Sam Wyche | .05 | .02 |
| 423 | Ray Crockett | .05 | .02 |
| 424 | Dan Fouts | .12 | .07 |
| 425 | Hugh Millen | .20 | .12 |
| 426 | Quentin Coryatt (R) | .60 | .35 |
| 427 | Brian Jordan | .08 | .05 |
| 428 | Frank Gifford | .15 | .10 |
| 429 | Toby Gaston | .05 | .02 |
| 430 | Ted Marchibroda | .05 | .02 |
| 431 | Cris Carter | .15 | .10 |
| 432 | Tim Krumrie | .05 | .02 |
| 433 | Otto Graham | .12 | .07 |
| 434 | Vaughn Dunbar (R) | .60 | .35 |
| 435 | John Fina (R) | .08 | .05 |
| 436 | Sonny Jurgensen | .12 | .07 |
| 437 | Robert Jones (R) | .20 | .12 |
| 438 | Steve DeOssie | .05 | .02 |
| 439 | Eddie LeBaron | .10 | .06 |
| 440 | Chester McGlockton (R) | .15 | .10 |
| 441 | Ken Stabler | .12 | .07 |
| 442 | Joe DeLamielleure | .05 | .02 |
| 443 | Charley Taylor | .10 | .06 |
| 444 | Greg Skrepenak (R) | .10 | .06 |
| 445 | Y.A. Tittle | .12 | .07 |
| 446 | Chuck Smith (R) | .10 | .06 |
| 447 | Kellen Winslow | .10 | .06 |
| 448 | Kevin Smith (R) | .20 | .12 |
| 449 | Phillippi Sparks (R) | .12 | .07 |
| 450 | Alonzo Spellman (R) | .15 | .10 |
| 451 | Mark Rypien | .20 | .12 |
| 452 | Darryl Williams (R) | .20 | .12 |
| 453 | Tommy Vardell (R) | .75 | .45 |
| 454 | Tommy Maddox (R) | 1.00 | .70 |
| 455 | Steve Israel (R) | .12 | .07 |
| 456 | Marquez Pope (R) | .10 | .06 |
| 457 | Eugene Chung (R) | .10 | .06 |
| 458 | Lynn Swann | .10 | .06 |
| 459 | Sean Gilbert (R) | .25 | .15 |
| 460 | Chris Mims (R) | .30 | .18 |
| 461 | Al Davis | .07 | .04 |
| 462 | Richard Todd | .08 | .05 |
| 463 | Mike Fox | .05 | .02 |
| 464 | David Klingler (R) | 1.75 | 1.00 |
| 465 | Darren Woodson (R) | .10 | .06 |
| 466 | Jason Hanson (R) | .08 | .05 |
| 467 | Lem Barney | .10 | .06 |
| SC8 | Ortancis Carter | .12 | .07 |
| SC9 | Faith Cherry | .12 | .07 |
| SC10 | Kaye Cowher | .12 | .07 |
| SC11 | Datnnese Gault | .12 | .07 |
| SC12 | Kathie Lee Gifford | .25 | .15 |
| SC13 | Carole Hinton | .12 | .07 |
| SC14 | Diane Long | .12 | .07 |
| SC15 | Karen Lott | .15 | .10 |
| SC16 | Felicia Moon | .12 | .07 |
| SC17 | Cindy Noble | .12 | .07 |
| SC18 | Linda Seifert | .12 | .07 |
| SC19 | Mitzi Testaverde | .12 | .07 |
| SC20 | Robin Swilling | .12 | .07 |
| SC21 | Lesley Visser | .15 | .10 |
| SC22 | Toni Doleman | .12 | .07 |
| SC23 | Diana Ditka | .12 | .07 |
| BC3 | Chris Berman | 2.00 | 1.25 |
| BC4 | Joe Gibbs | 4.00 | 2.75 |
| BC5 | Gifford Family | 6.00 | 3.75 |
| BC6 | Dale Jarrett | 2.00 | 1.25 |

| | | MINT | NR/MT |
|---|---|---|---|
| BC7 | Paul Tagliabue | 2.00 | 1.25 |
| BC8 | Don & Dave Shula | 4.00 | 2.75 |
| TN1 | Muhammad Ali | 8.50 | 5.50 |
| TN2 | Milton Berle | 1.25 | .80 |
| TN3 | Don Mattingly | 2.50 | 1.50 |
| TN4 | Martin Mull | 1.00 | .70 |
| TN5 | Isiah Thomas | 2.50 | 1.50 |

# 1992 Pro Line Quarterback Gold

The cards in this limited edition subset were randomly distributed in Pro Line's 1992 foil packs. The cards feature full color action photos on the fronts with gold foil stamping. All cards measure 2-1/2" by 3-1/2".

| | | MINT | NR/MT |
|---|---|---|---|
| **Complete Set (18)** | | 30.00 | 18.00 |
| **Commons** | | 1.00 | .70 |
| | | | |
| 1 | Troy Aikman | 8.50 | 5.50 |
| 2 | Bubby Brister | 1.00 | .70 |
| 3 | Randall Cunningham | 3.00 | 2.00 |
| 4 | John Elway | 5.00 | 3.00 |
| 5 | Boomer Esiason | 1.50 | .90 |
| 6 | Jim Everett | 1.50 | .90 |
| 7 | Jeff George | 3.50 | 2.50 |
| 8 | Jim Harbaugh | 1.50 | .90 |
| 9 | Jeff Hostetler | 1.50 | .90 |
| 10 | Jim Kelly | 6.00 | 3.75 |
| 11 | Bernie Kosar | 1.50 | .90 |
| 12 | Dan Marino | 7.50 | 4.50 |
| 13 | Chris Miller | 3.00 | 2.00 |
| 14 | Joe Montana | 7.00 | 4.00 |

| | | | |
|---|---|---|---|
| 15 | Warren Moon | 4.00 | 2.75 |
| 16 | Mark Rypien | 2.50 | 1.50 |
| 17 | Phil Simms | 1.50 | .90 |
| 18 | Steve Young | 5.00 | 3.00 |

# 1992 Pro Line Rookie Gold

This 28-card limited insert set features the top rookies from the 1992 NFL draft. The cards were inserted randomly in Pro Line's jumbo packs. The cards consists of full color action shots on the front with gold foil stamping. All cards measure 2-1/2" by 3-1/2".

| | | MINT | NR/MT |
|---|---|---|---|
| **Complete Set (28)** | | 32.50 | 20.00 |
| **Commons** | | .50 | .30 |
| | | | |
| 1 | Tony Smith | 2.50 | 1.50 |
| 2 | John Fina | .50 | .30 |
| 3 | Alonzo Spellman | 1.00 | .70 |
| 4 | David Klingler | 4.00 | 2.75 |
| 5 | Tommy Vardell | 2.50 | 1.50 |
| 6 | Kevin Smith | 1.00 | .70 |
| 7 | Tommy Maddox | 2.50 | 1.50 |
| 8 | Robert Porcher | .80 | .50 |
| 9 | Terrell Buckley | 1.75 | 1.00 |
| 10 | Eddie Robinson | .75 | .45 |
| 11 | Steve Emtman | 3.00 | 2.00 |
| 12 | Quentin Coryatt | 2.00 | 1.25 |
| 13 | Dale Carter | 1.50 | .90 |
| 14 | Chester McGlockton | .75 | .45 |
| 15 | Sean Gilbert | 1.00 | .70 |
| 16 | Troy Vincent | 1.00 | .70 |

| | | MINT | NR/MT |
|---|---|---|---|
| 17 | Robert Harris | .50 | .30 |
| 18 | Eugene Chung | .50 | .30 |
| 19 | Vaughn Dunbar | 1.50 | .90 |
| 20 | Derek Brown | 1.25 | .80 |
| 21 | Johnny Mitchell | 1.25 | .80 |
| 22 | Siran Stacy | 1.50 | .90 |
| 23 | Tony Sacca | 1.25 | .80 |
| 24 | Leon Searcy | .80 | .50 |
| 25 | Chris Mims | 1.50 | .90 |
| 26 | Dana Hall | .80 | .50 |
| 27 | Courtney Hawkins | 1.00 | .70 |
| 28 | Shane Collins | .50 | .30 |

# 1992 Pro Line Profiles Series

This 495-card set features profiles of 55 top NFL stars, former stars and coaches. Each individual in the set is profiled on nine consecutively numbered cards. Since all nine cards of each individual carry the same value, only the first card of each person is included in the checklist below. An Art Monk series was available through a special mail-in offer. All cards measure 2-1/2" by 3-1/2".

| | | MINT | NR/MT |
|---|---|---|---|
| Complete Set (495) | | 12.50 | 8.00 |
| Commons | | .05 | .02 |
| | | | |
| 1 | Ronnie Lott | .10 | .06 |
| 10 | Rodney Peete | .12 | .07 |
| 19 | Carl Banks | .07 | .04 |
| 28 | Thurman Thomas | .50 | .30 |
| 37 | Roger Staubach | .20 | .12 |

| | | MINT | NR/MT |
|---|---|---|---|
| 46 | Jerry Rice | .40 | .25 |
| 55 | Vinny Testaverde | .10 | .06 |
| 64 | Anthony Carter | .07 | .04 |
| 73 | Sterling Sharpe | .25 | .15 |
| 82 | Anthony Munoz | .10 | .06 |
| 91 | Bubby Brister | .10 | .06 |
| 100 | Bernie Kosar | .12 | .07 |
| 109 | Art Shell | .07 | .04 |
| 118 | Don Shula | .08 | .05 |
| 127 | Joe Gibbs | .07 | .04 |
| 136 | Junior Seau | .12 | .07 |
| 145 | Al Toon | .07 | .04 |
| 154 | Jack Kemp | .20 | .12 |
| 163 | Jim Harbaugh | .12 | .07 |
| 172 | Dan McGwire | .25 | .15 |
| 181 | Troy Aikman | .75 | .45 |
| 190 | Keith Byars | .07 | .04 |
| 199 | Timm Rosenbach | .10 | .06 |
| 208 | Gary Clark | .15 | .10 |
| 217 | Chris Doleman | .07 | .04 |
| 226 | John Elway | .20 | .12 |
| 235 | Boomer Esiason | .12 | .07 |
| 244 | Jim Everett | .12 | .07 |
| 253 | Eric Green | .12 | .07 |
| 262 | Jerry Glanville | .05 | .02 |
| 271 | Jeff Hostetler | .15 | .10 |
| 280 | Haywood Jeffires | .20 | .12 |
| 289 | Michael Irvin | .25 | .15 |
| 298 | Steve Largent | .15 | .10 |
| 307 | Ken O'Brien | .10 | .06 |
| 316 | Christian Okoye | .12 | .07 |
| 325 | Michael Dean Perry | .10 | .06 |
| 334 | Chris Miller | .20 | .12 |
| 343 | Phil Simms | .10 | .06 |
| 352 | Bruce Smith | .10 | .06 |
| 361 | Derrick Thomas | .15 | .10 |
| 370 | Pat Swilling | .12 | .07 |
| 379 | Eric Dickerson | .25 | .15 |
| 388 | Howie Long | .07 | .04 |
| 397 | Mike Singletary | .10 | .06 |
| 406 | John Taylor | .12 | .07 |
| 415 | Andre Tippett | .05 | .02 |
| 424 | Jim Kelly | .50 | .30 |
| 433 | Mark Rypien | .20 | .12 |
| 442 | Warren Moon | .20 | .12 |
| 451 | Deion Sanders | .25 | .15 |
| 460 | Lawrence Taylor | .15 | .10 |
| 469 | Randall Cunningham | .15 | .10 |
| 478 | Earnest Byner | .07 | .04 |
| 487 | Mike Ditka | .12 | .07 |
| 496 | Art Monk (SP) | 1.75 | 1.00 |

# 1993 Pro Line Live

For the first time Pro Line has teamed up with Classic Games to produce a live action football card set. This 285-card series features full-color action photographs on the card fronts with the player's name printed vertically along a color stripe on the side of the card. The backs include a smaller photo, personal data, and statistics. The set includes limited autographed inserts and four new Spirit Cards featuring player's wives. All cards measure 2-1/2" by 3-1/2".

|  |  | MINT | NR/MT |
|---|---|---|---|
| Complete Set (285) | | 32.00 | 20.50 |
| Commons | | .05 | .02 |

| | | MINT | NR/MT |
|---|---|---|---|
| 1 | Michael Haynes | .25 | .15 |
| 2 | Chris Hinton | .05 | .02 |
| 3 | Pierce Holt | .05 | .02 |
| 4 | Chris Miller | .15 | .10 |
| 5 | Mike Pritchard | .25 | .15 |
| 6 | Andre Rison | .20 | .12 |
| 7 | Deion Sanders | .20 | .12 |
| 8 | Jessie Tuggle | .05 | .02 |
| 9 | Lincoln Kennedy (R) | .40 | .25 |
| 10 | Roger Harper (R) | .15 | .10 |
| 11 | Cornelius Bennett | .10 | .06 |
| 12 | Henry Jones | .05 | .02 |
| 13 | Jim Kelly | .35 | .20 |
| 14 | James Lofton | .12 | .07 |
| 15 | Nate Odomes | .05 | .02 |
| 16 | Andre Reed | .15 | .10 |
| 17 | Frank Reich | .15 | .10 |
| 18 | Bruce Smith | .10 | .06 |
| 19 | Steve Tasker | .05 | .02 |
| 20 | Thurman Thomas | .30 | .18 |
| 21 | Thomas Smith (R) | .20 | .12 |
| 22 | John Parrella (R) | .08 | .05 |
| 23 | Neal Anderson | .10 | .06 |
| 24 | Mark Carrier (Chi) | .08 | .05 |
| 25 | Jim Harbaugh | .15 | .10 |
| 26 | Darren Lewis | .15 | .10 |
| 27 | Steve McMichael | .07 | .04 |
| 28 | Alonzo Spellman | .05 | .02 |
| 29 | Tom Waddle | .15 | .10 |
| 30 | Curtis Conway (R) | .75 | .40 |
| 31 | Carl Simpson (R) | .15 | .10 |
| 32 | David Fulcher | .05 | .02 |
| 33 | Harold Green | .25 | .15 |
| 34 | David Klingler | 1.50 | .90 |
| 35 | Tim Krumrie | .05 | .02 |
| 36 | Carl Pickens | .40 | .25 |
| 37 | Alfred Williams | .05 | .02 |
| 38 | Darryl Williams | .05 | .02 |
| 39 | John Copeland (R) | .40 | .25 |
| 40 | Tony McGee (R) | .25 | .15 |
| 41 | Bernie Kosar | .15 | .10 |
| 42 | Kevin Mack | .08 | .05 |
| 43 | Clay Matthews | .05 | .02 |
| 44 | Eric Metcalf | .20 | .12 |
| 45 | Michael Dean Perry | .08 | .05 |
| 46 | Vinny Testaverde | .10 | .06 |
| 47 | Eric Turner | .12 | .07 |
| 48 | Tommy Vardell | .35 | .20 |
| 49 | Steve Everett (R) | .12 | .07 |
| 50 | Dan Footman (R) | .15 | .10 |
| 51 | Troy Aikman | 3.00 | 1.75 |
| 52 | Daryl Johnston | .12 | .07 |
| 53 | Tony Casillas | .07 | .04 |
| 54 | Charles Haley | .07 | .04 |
| 55 | Alvin Harper | .40 | .25 |
| 56 | Michael Irvin | .75 | .45 |
| 57 | Robert Jones | .10 | .06 |
| 58 | Russell Maryland | .10 | .06 |
| 59 | Nate Newton | .05 | .02 |
| 60 | Ken Norton | .07 | .04 |
| 61 | Jay Novacek | .15 | .10 |
| 62 | Emmitt Smith | 4.00 | 2.75 |
| 63 | Kevin Smith | .08 | .05 |
| 64 | Kevin Williams (R) | .50 | .28 |
| 65 | Darrin Smith (R) | .25 | .15 |
| 66 | Steve Atwater | .08 | .05 |
| 67 | Rod Bernstine | .15 | .10 |
| 68 | Mike Croel | .15 | .10 |
| 69 | John Elway | .25 | .15 |
| 70 | Tommy Maddox | .60 | .35 |
| 71 | Karl Mecklenberg | .07 | .04 |
| 72 | Shannon Sharpe | .08 | .05 |
| 73 | Dennis Smith | .05 | .02 |
| 74 | Dan Williams (R) | .20 | .12 |
| 75 | Glyn Milburn (R) | .50 | .28 |
| 76 | Pat Swilling | .10 | .06 |
| 77 | Bennie Blades | .07 | .04 |
| 78 | Herman Moore | .60 | .35 |

| No. | Player | | |
|---|---|---|---|
| 79 | Rodney Peete | .15 | .10 |
| 80 | Brett Perriman | .08 | .05 |
| 81 | Barry Sanders | 2.50 | 1.60 |
| 82 | Chris Spielman | .05 | .02 |
| 83 | Andre Ware | .15 | .10 |
| 84 | Ryan McNeill (R) | .30 | .18 |
| 85 | Antonio London (R) | .15 | .10 |
| 86 | Tony Bennett | .08 | .05 |
| 87 | Terrell Buckley | .35 | .20 |
| 88 | Brett Favre | 1.25 | .70 |
| 89 | Brian Noble | .05 | .02 |
| 90 | Ken O'Brien | .10 | .06 |
| 91 | Sterling Sharpe | .50 | .28 |
| 92 | Reggie White | .15 | .10 |
| 93 | John Stephans | .08 | .05 |
| 94 | Wayne Simmons (R) | .25 | .15 |
| 95 | George Teague (R) | .25 | .15 |
| 96 | Ray Childress | .08 | .05 |
| 97 | Curtis Duncan | .08 | .05 |
| 98 | Ernest Givens | .20 | .12 |
| 99 | Haywood Jeffires | .30 | .18 |
| 100 | Bubba McDowell | .05 | .02 |
| 101 | Warren Moon | .25 | .15 |
| 102 | Al Smith | .07 | .04 |
| 103 | Lorenzo White | .25 | .15 |
| 104 | Brad Hopkins (R) | .25 | .15 |
| 105 | Michael Barrow (R) | .20 | .12 |
| 106 | Duane Bickett | .05 | .02 |
| 107 | Quentin Coryatt | .40 | .25 |
| 108 | Steve Emtman | .60 | .35 |
| 109 | Jeff George | .20 | .12 |
| 110 | Anthony Johnson | .05 | .02 |
| 111 | Reggie Langhorne | .08 | .05 |
| 112 | Jack Trudeau | .10 | .06 |
| 113 | Clarence Verdin | .08 | .05 |
| 114 | Sean Dawkins (R) | .75 | .45 |
| 115 | Roosevelt Potts (R) | .40 | .25 |
| 116 | Dale Carter | .30 | .18 |
| 117 | Dave Krieg | .10 | .06 |
| 118 | Nick Lowery | .07 | .04 |
| 119 | Christian Okoye | .12 | .07 |
| 120 | Neil Smith | .05 | .02 |
| 121 | Derrick Thomas | .20 | .12 |
| 122 | Harvey Williams | .20 | .12 |
| 123 | Barry Word | .15 | .10 |
| 124 | Joe Montana | .75 | .45 |
| 125 | Darren Mickeil (R) | .15 | .10 |
| 126 | Marcus Allen | .15 | .10 |
| 127 | Nick Bell | .20 | .12 |
| 128 | Tim Brown | .20 | .12 |
| 129 | Eric Dickerson | .20 | .12 |
| 130 | Jeff Hostetler | .12 | .07 |
| 131 | Howie Long | .08 | .05 |
| 132 | Todd Marinovich | .30 | .18 |
| 133 | Greg Townsend | .05 | .02 |
| 134 | Patrick Bates (R) | .30 | .18 |
| 135 | Billy Joe Hobart (R) | .60 | .35 |
| 136 | Willie Anderson | .10 | .06 |
| 137 | Shane Conlan | .07 | .04 |
| 138 | Henry Ellard | .10 | .06 |
| 139 | Jim Everett | .15 | .10 |
| 140 | Cleveland Gary | .12 | .07 |
| 141 | Sean Gilbert | .15 | .10 |
| 142 | Todd Lyght | .08 | .05 |
| 143 | Jerome Bettis (R) | 1.25 | .70 |
| 144 | Troy Drayton (R) | .30 | .18 |
| 145 | Mark Clayton | .15 | .10 |
| 146 | Marco Coleman | .25 | .15 |
| 147 | Bryan Cox | .10 | .06 |
| 148 | Mark Duper | .12 | .07 |
| 149 | Irving Fryar | .08 | .05 |
| 150 | Mark Higgs | .25 | .15 |
| 151 | Keith Jackson | .20 | .12 |
| 152 | Dan Marino | .60 | .35 |
| 153 | Troy Vincent | .10 | .06 |
| 154 | Richmond Webb | .07 | .04 |
| 155 | O.J. McDuffie (R) | .60 | .35 |
| 156 | Terry Kirby (R) | .40 | .25 |
| 157 | Terry Allen | .35 | .20 |
| 158 | Anthony Carter | .10 | .06 |
| 159 | Cris Carter | .15 | .10 |
| 160 | Chris Doleman | .07 | .04 |
| 161 | Randall McDaniel | .05 | .02 |
| 162 | Jim McMahon | .10 | .06 |
| 163 | Henry Thomas | .05 | .02 |
| 164 | Gary Zimmerman | .05 | .02 |
| 165 | Robert Smith (R) | .60 | .35 |
| 166 | Qadry Ismail (R) | .60 | .35 |
| 167 | Vincent Brown | .05 | .02 |
| 168 | Marv Cook | .08 | .05 |
| 169 | Greg McMurtry | .08 | .05 |
| 170 | Jon Vaughn | .10 | .06 |
| 171 | Leonard Russell | .30 | .18 |
| 172 | Andre Tippett | .07 | .04 |
| 173 | Scott Zolak | .12 | .07 |
| 174 | Drew Bledsoe (R) | 4.50 | 3.00 |
| 175 | Chris Slade (R) | .25 | .15 |
| 176 | Morten Andersen | .07 | .04 |
| 177 | Vaughn Dunbar | .35 | .20 |
| 178 | Rickey Jackson | .07 | .04 |
| 179 | Vaughn Johnson | .07 | .04 |
| 180 | Eric Martin | .10 | .06 |
| 181 | Sam Mills | .07 | .04 |
| 182 | Brad Muster | .10 | .06 |
| 183 | Willie Roaf (R) | .25 | .15 |
| 184 | Irv Smith (R) | .40 | .25 |
| 185 | Reggie Freeman | .05 | .02 |
| 186 | Carl Banks | .07 | .04 |
| 187 | Dave Brown | .75 | .45 |
| 188 | Rodney Hampton | .35 | .20 |
| 189 | Pepper Johnson | .05 | .02 |
| 190 | Ed McCaffrey | .10 | .06 |
| 191 | Dave Meggett | .12 | .07 |
| 192 | Bart Oates | .05 | .02 |

| 193 | Phil Simms | .12 | .07 |
|---|---|---|---|
| 194 | Lawrence Taylor | .12 | .07 |
| 195 | Michael Strahan (R) | .25 | .15 |
| 196 | Brad Baxter | .08 | .05 |
| 197 | Johnny Johnson | .15 | .10 |
| 198 | Boomer Esiason | .15 | .10 |
| 199 | Ronnie Lott | .15 | .10 |
| 200 | Johnny Mitchell | .30 | .18 |
| 201 | Rob Moore | .20 | .12 |
| 202 | Browning Nagle | .30 | .18 |
| 203 | Blair Thomas | .15 | .10 |
| 204 | Marvin Jones (R) | .75 | .45 |
| 205 | Coleman Rudolph (R) | .25 | .15 |
| 206 | Eric Allen | .05 | .02 |
| 207 | Fred Barnett | .20 | .12 |
| 208 | Tim Harris | .05 | .02 |
| 209 | Randall Cunningham | .20 | .12 |
| 210 | Seth Joyner | .07 | .04 |
| 211 | Clyde Simmons | .07 | .04 |
| 212 | Herschel Walker | .20 | .12 |
| 213 | Calvin Williams | .10 | .06 |
| 214 | Lester Holmes (R) | .30 | .18 |
| 215 | Leonard Renfro (R) | .20 | .12 |
| 216 | Chris Chandler | .10 | .06 |
| 217 | Gary Clark | .20 | .12 |
| 218 | Ken Harvey | .05 | .02 |
| 219 | Randal Hill | .20 | .12 |
| 220 | Steve Beuerlein | .25 | .15 |
| 221 | Ricky Proehl | .15 | .10 |
| 222 | Timm Rosenbach | .10 | .06 |
| 223 | Garrison Hearst (R) | 3.50 | 2.00 |
| 224 | Ernest Dye (R) | .30 | .18 |
| 225 | Bubby Brister | .10 | .06 |
| 226 | Dermontti Dawson | .05 | .02 |
| 227 | Barry Foster | .80 | .50 |
| 228 | Kevin Greene | .07 | .04 |
| 229 | Merrill Hoge | .08 | .05 |
| 230 | Greg Lloyd | .05 | .02 |
| 231 | Neil O'Donnell | .80 | .50 |
| 232 | Rod Woodson | .08 | .05 |
| 233 | Deon Figures (R) | .30 | .18 |
| 234 | Chad Brown (R) | .20 | .12 |
| 235 | Marion Butts | .15 | .10 |
| 236 | Gill Byrd | .05 | .02 |
| 237 | Ronnie Harmon | .15 | .10 |
| 238 | Stan Humphries | 1.00 | .60 |
| 239 | Anthony Miller | .20 | .12 |
| 240 | Leslie O'Neal | .08 | .05 |
| 241 | Stanley Richard | .08 | .05 |
| 242 | Junior Seau | .20 | .12 |
| 243 | Darrien Gordon (R) | .30 | .18 |
| 244 | Natrone Means (R) | .40 | .25 |
| 245 | Dana Hall | .08 | .05 |
| 246 | Brent Jones | .08 | .05 |
| 247 | Tim McDonald | .05 | .02 |
| 248 | Steve Bono | .25 | .15 |
| 249 | Jerry Rice | .80 | .50 |
| 250 | John Taylor | .20 | .12 |
| 251 | Ricky Watters | .80 | .50 |
| 252 | Steve Young | .50 | .28 |
| 253 | Dana Stubblefield (R) | .35 | .20 |
| 254 | Todd Kelly (R) | .35 | .20 |
| 255 | Brian Blades | .07 | .04 |
| 256 | Ferrell Edmunds | .05 | .02 |
| 257 | Stan Gelbaugh | .10 | .06 |
| 258 | Cortez Kennedy | .20 | .12 |
| 259 | Dan McGwire | .35 | .20 |
| 260 | Chris Warren | .15 | .10 |
| 261 | John L. Williams | .08 | .05 |
| 262 | David Wyman | .05 | .02 |
| 263 | Rick Mirer (R) | 3.00 | 1.75 |
| 264 | Carlton Gray (R) | .30 | .18 |
| 265 | Marty Carter | .05 | .02 |
| 266 | Reggie Cobb | .15 | .10 |
| 267 | Lawrence Dawsey | .15 | .10 |
| 268 | Santana Dotson | .20 | .12 |
| 269 | Craig Erickson | .30 | .18 |
| 270 | Paul Gruber | .05 | .02 |
| 271 | Keith McCants | .05 | .02 |
| 272 | Broderick Thomas | .05 | .02 |
| 273 | Eric Curry (R) | .40 | .25 |
| 274 | Demetrius DuBose (R) | .40 | .25 |
| 275 | Earnest Byner | .08 | .05 |
| 276 | Ricky Ervins | .30 | .18 |
| 277 | Desmond Howard | .40 | .25 |
| 278 | Jim Lachey | .08 | .05 |
| 279 | Charles Mann | .05 | .02 |
| 280 | Wilber Marshall | .07 | .04 |
| 281 | Art Monk | .20 | .12 |
| 282 | Mark Rypien | .25 | .15 |
| 283 | Ricky Sanders | .10 | .06 |
| 284 | Tom Carter (R) | .30 | .18 |
| 285 | Reggie Brooks (R) | .35 | .20 |
| SC25 | Annette Rypien | .15 | .10 |
| SC26 | Ann Stark | .15 | .10 |
| SC27 | Cindy Walker | .15 | .10 |
| SC28 | Cindy Reed | .15 | .10 |

# 1993 Pro Line Portraits

This set is a continuation of 1992's Pro Line Portraits set but is considered part of the overall 1993 Pro Line set. Picking up with card number 468, the set features posed photographs of players in non-game action situations on the card fronts. The flip side contains a small head shot and some biographical information about the player. All cards measure 2-1/2" by 3-1/2".

|  | MINT | NR/MT |
|---|---|---|
| **Complete Set (40)** | 5.50 | 3.25 |
| **Commons** | .05 | .02 |
| | | |
| 468 Willie Roaf | .25 | .15 |
| 469 Terry Allen | .35 | .20 |
| 470 Jerry Ball | .05 | .02 |
| 471 Patrick Bates | .30 | .18 |
| 472 Ray Bentley | .05 | .02 |
| 473 Jerome Bettis | .75 | .45 |
| 474 Steve Beuerlein | .25 | .15 |
| 475 Drew Bledsoe | 2.00 | 1.25 |
| 476 Dave Brown | .60 | .35 |
| 477 Gill Byrd | .05 | .02 |
| 478 Tony Casillas | .07 | .04 |
| 479 Chuck Cecil | .05 | .02 |
| 480 Reggie Cobb | .15 | .10 |
| 481 Pat Harlow | .05 | .02 |
| 482 John Copeland | .30 | .18 |
| 483 Bryan Cox | .10 | .06 |
| 484 Eric Curry | .40 | .25 |
| 485 Jeff Lageman | .08 | .05 |
| 486 Brett Favre | 1.00 | .60 |
| 487 Barry Foster | .75 | .45 |
| 488 Gaston Green | .20 | .12 |
| 489 Rodney Hampton | .30 | .18 |
| 490 Tim Harris | .05 | .02 |
| 491 Garrison Hearst | 1.50 | .90 |
| 492 Tony Smith | .10 | .06 |
| 493 Marvin Jones | .50 | .28 |
| 494 Lincoln Kennedy | .25 | .15 |
| 495 Wilber Marshall | .07 | .04 |
| 496 Terry McDaniel | .05 | .02 |
| 497 Rick Mirer | 1.25 | .70 |
| 498 Art Monk | .15 | .10 |
| 499 Mike Munchak | .05 | .02 |
| 500 Frank Reich | .20 | .12 |
| 501 Barry Sanders | .80 | .50 |
| 502 Shannon Sharpe | .08 | .05 |
| 503 Gino Torretta | .30 | .18 |
| 504 Ricky Watters | .75 | .45 |
| 505 Richmond Webb | .05 | .02 |
| 506 Reggie White | .08 | .05 |

# 1993 Pro Line Profiles

This 115-card set is a continuation of last year's Pro Line Profiles series. Each player in the set is profiled on nine consecutively numbered cards. Since all nine cards of each player have the same value only the first card of each individual is included in the checklist below. All cards measure 2-1/2" by 3-1/2".

|  | MINT | NR/MT |
|---|---|---|
| **Complete Set (117)** | 20.00 | 12.50 |
| **Commons** | .07 | .04 |
| | | |
| 496 Ray Childress | .07 | .04 |
| 505 Jeff George | .12 | .07 |
| 514 Franco Harris | .12 | .07 |
| 523 Keith Jackson | .10 | .06 |
| 532 Jimmy Johnson | .08 | .05 |
| 541 James Lofton | .08 | .05 |
| 550 Dan Marino | .40 | .25 |
| 559 Joe Montana | .50 | .28 |
| 568 Jay Novacek | .10 | .06 |
| 577 Gale Sayers | .12 | .07 |
| 586 Emmitt Smith | 1.25 | .70 |
| 595 Herschel Walker | .10 | .06 |
| 604 Steve Young | .30 | .18 |

# PRO SET

## 1989 Pro Set

This set marked Pro Set's debut as a major card manufacturer. The 560-card set was released in two series, 440-cards in Series I and 100-cards in Series II. A 21-card Final Update set was released at the end of the season. Card fronts feature full color action photos while the side borders contain small horizontal white lines. The player's name, position and team are printed at the top between either and AFC or NFC logo and an NFL logo. Card backs consist of a small head shot, stats and career highlights. The set contains a number of errors but only those variations that increase the card's value are listed. All cards measure 2-1/2" by 3-1/2".

|  |  | MINT | NR/MT |
|---|---|---|---|
| **Complete Set (561)** |  | 35.00 | 22.00 |
| **Commons** |  | .05 | .02 |
| 1 | Stacey Bailey | .05 | .02 |
| 2 | Aundray Bruce (R) | .08 | .05 |
| 3 | Rick Bryan | .05 | .02 |
| 4 | Bobby Butler | .05 | .02 |
| 5 | Scott Case (R) | .08 | .05 |
| 6 | Tony Casillas | .08 | .05 |
| 7 | Floyd Dixon | .05 | .02 |
| 8 | Rick Donnelly | .05 | .02 |
| 9 | Bill Fralic | .05 | .02 |
| 10 | Mike Gann | .05 | .02 |
| 11 | Mike Kenn | .05 | .02 |
| 12 | Chris Miller (R) | 1.50 | .90 |
| 13 | John Rade | .05 | .02 |
| 14 | Gerald Riggs | .07 | .04 |
| 15 | John Settle (R) | .15 | .10 |
| 16 | Marion Campbell | .05 | .02 |
| 17 | Cornelius Bennett | .25 | .15 |
| 18 | Derrick Burroughs | .05 | .02 |
| 29 | Shane Conlan | .12 | .07 |
| 20 | Ronnie Harmon | .07 | .04 |
| 21 | Kent Hull (R) | .12 | .07 |
| 22 | Jim Kelly | .75 | .45 |
| 23 | Mark Kelson | .05 | .02 |
| 24 | Pete Metzelaars | .05 | .02 |
| 25 | Scott Norwood | .05 | .02 |
| 26 | Andre Reed | .25 | .15 |
| 27 | Fred Smerlas | .05 | .02 |
| 28 | Bruce Smith | .12 | .07 |
| 29 | Leonard Smith | .05 | .02 |
| 30 | Art Still | .05 | .02 |
| 31 | Darryl Talley | .08 | .05 |
| 32 | Thurman Thomas (R) | 4.00 | 2.50 |
| 33 | Will Wollford (R) | .08 | .05 |
| 34 | Marv Levy | .05 | .02 |
| 35 | Neal Anderson | .20 | .12 |
| 36 | Kevin Butler | .05 | .02 |
| 37 | Jim Covert | .05 | .02 |
| 38 | Richard Dent | .08 | .05 |
| 39 | Dave Duerson | .05 | .02 |
| 40 | Dennis Gentry | .08 | .05 |
| 41 | Dan Hampton | .08 | .05 |
| 42 | Jay Hilgenberg | .05 | .02 |
| 43 | Dennis McKinnon | .05 | .02 |
| 44 | Jim McMahon | .15 | .10 |
| 45 | Steve McMichael | .07 | .04 |
| 46 | Brad Muster (R) | .25 | .15 |
| 47a | William Perry (SP) | 7.00 | 4.50 |
| 47b | Ron Morris (R) | .10 | .06 |
| 48 | Ron Rivera | .05 | .02 |
| 49 | Vestee Jackson (R) | .10 | .06 |
| 50 | Mike Singletary | .12 | .07 |
| 51 | Mike Tomczak | .10 | .06 |
| 52 | Keith Van Horne (R) | .08 | .05 |
| 53 | Mike Ditka | .08 | .05 |
| 54 | Lewis Blllups | .05 | .02 |
| 55 | James Brooks | .07 | .04 |
| 56 | Eddie Brown | .10 | .06 |
| 57 | Jason Buck (R) | .10 | .06 |
| 58 | Boomer Esiason | .20 | .12 |
| 59 | David Fulcher | .05 | .02 |
| 60a | Rodney Holman (Er) (BENGALS in caps) | .15 | .10 |
| 60b | Rodney Holman (Cor) | 2.00 | 1.25 |
| 61 | Reggie Williams | .07 | .04 |
| 62 | Joe Kelly | .05 | .02 |
| 63 | Tim Krumrie | .05 | .02 |
| 64 | Tim McGee | .08 | .05 |
| 65 | Max Montoya | .05 | .02 |
| 66 | Anthony Munoz | .08 | .05 |
| 67 | Jim Skow | .05 | .02 |
| 68 | Eric Thomas (R) | .10 | .06 |
| 69 | Leon White | .05 | .02 |

| | | | | | | | |
|---|---|---|---|---|---|---|---|
| 70 | Ickey Woods (R) | .12 | .07 | 124 | Ed Murray | .05 | .02 |
| 71 | Carl Zander | .05 | .02 | 125 | Chris Spielman (R) | .20 | .12 |
| 72 | Sam Wyche | .05 | .02 | 126 | Dennis Gibson | .05 | .02 |
| 73 | Brian Brennan | .05 | .02 | 127 | Wayne Fontes | .05 | .02 |
| 74 | Earnest Byner | .10 | .06 | 128 | John Anderson | .05 | .02 |
| 75 | Hanford Dixon | .05 | .02 | 129 | Brent Fullwood (R) | .08 | .05 |
| 76 | Mike Pagel | .05 | .02 | 130 | Mark Cannon | .05 | .02 |
| 77 | Bernie Kosar | .15 | .10 | 131 | Tim Harris | .05 | .02 |
| 78 | Reggie Langhorne (R) | .15 | .10 | 132 | Mark Lee | .05 | .02 |
| 79 | Kevin Mack | .07 | .04 | 133 | Don Majkowski (R) | .50 | .30 |
| 80 | Clay Matthews | .05 | .02 | 134 | Mark Murphy | .05 | .02 |
| 81 | Gerald McNeil | .05 | .02 | 135 | Brian Noble | .05 | .02 |
| 82 | Frank Minnifield | .05 | .02 | 136 | Ken Ruettgers (R) | .08 | .05 |
| 83 | Cody Risien | .05 | .02 | 137 | Johnny Holland | .05 | .02 |
| 84 | Webster Slaughter | .12 | .07 | 138 | Randy Wright | .05 | .02 |
| 85 | Felix Wright | .05 | .02 | 139 | Lindy Infante | .05 | .02 |
| 86 | Bud Carson | .05 | .02 | 140 | Steve Brown | .05 | .02 |
| 87 | Bill Bates | .05 | .02 | 141 | Ray Childress | .08 | .05 |
| 88 | Kevin Brooks | .05 | .02 | 142 | Jeff Donaldson | .05 | .02 |
| 89 | Michael Irvin (R) | 2.50 | 1.50 | 143 | Ernest Givins | .20 | .12 |
| 90 | Jim Jeffcoat | .05 | .02 | 144 | John Grimsley | .05 | .02 |
| 91 | Ed Too Tall Jones | .08 | .05 | 145 | Alonzo Highsmith | .05 | .02 |
| 92 | Eugene Lockhart (R) | .10 | .06 | 146 | Drew Hill | .08 | .05 |
| 93 | Nate Newton (R) | .08 | .05 | 147 | Robert Lyles (R) | .07 | .04 |
| 94 | Danny Noonan (R) | .08 | .05 | 148 | Bruce Matthews (R) | .12 | .07 |
| 95 | Steve Pelluer | .08 | .05 | 149 | Warren Moon | .25 | .15 |
| 96 | Herschel Walker | .30 | .18 | 150 | Mike Munchak | .07 | .04 |
| 97 | Everson Walls | .05 | .02 | 151 | Allen Pinkett (R) | .15 | .10 |
| 98 | Jimmy Johnson | .05 | .02 | 152 | Mike Rozier | .07 | .04 |
| 99 | Keith Bishop | .05 | .02 | 153 | Tony Zendajas | .05 | .02 |
| 100a | John Elway (Er) (Drafted 1st Round) | 5.00 | 3.50 | 154 | Jerry Glanville | .05 | .02 |
| | | | | 155 | Albert Bentley | .05 | .02 |
| 100b | John Elway (Cor) (Acquired Trade) | .30 | .18 | 156 | Dean Biasucci | .05 | .02 |
| | | | | 157 | Duane Bickett | .05 | .02 |
| 101 | Simon Fletcher (R) | .15 | .10 | 158 | Bill Brooks | .05 | .02 |
| 102 | Mike Harden | .05 | .02 | 159 | Chris Chandler (R) | .25 | .15 |
| 103 | Mike Horan | .05 | .02 | 160 | Pat Beach | .05 | .02 |
| 104 | Mark Jackson | .08 | .05 | 161 | Ray Donaldson | .05 | .02 |
| 105 | Vance Johnson | .10 | .06 | 162 | Jon Hand | .05 | .02 |
| 106 | Rulon Jones | .05 | .02 | 163 | Chris Hinton | .05 | .02 |
| 107 | Clarence Kay | .05 | .02 | 164 | Rohn Stark | .05 | .02 |
| 108 | Karl Mecklenburg | .08 | .05 | 165 | Fredd Young | .05 | .02 |
| 109 | Ricky Nattiel | .08 | .05 | 166 | Ron Meyer | .05 | .02 |
| 110 | Steve Sewell (R) | .12 | .07 | 167 | Lloyd Burruss | .05 | .02 |
| 111 | Dennis Smith | .05 | .02 | 168 | Carlos Carson | .05 | .02 |
| 112 | Gerald Wilhite | .05 | .02 | 169 | Deron Cherry | .05 | .02 |
| 113 | Sammy Winder | .05 | .02 | 170 | Irv Eatman | .05 | .02 |
| 114 | Dan Reeves | .05 | .02 | 171 | Dino Hackett | .05 | .02 |
| 115 | Jim Arnold | .05 | .02 | 172 | Steve DeBerg | .10 | .06 |
| 116 | Jerry Ball (R) | .15 | .10 | 173 | Albert Lewis | .05 | .02 |
| 117 | Bennie Blades (R) | .15 | .10 | 174 | Nick Lowery | .07 | .04 |
| 118 | Lomas Brown | .05 | .02 | 175 | Bill Maas | .05 | .02 |
| 119 | Mike Cofer | .05 | .02 | 176 | Christian Okoye | .25 | .15 |
| 120 | Garry James | .05 | .02 | 177 | Stephone Paige | .08 | .05 |
| 121 | James Jones | .05 | .02 | 178 | Mark Adickes | .05 | .02 |
| 122 | Chuck Long | .08 | .05 | 179 | Kevin Ross (R) | .15 | .10 |
| 123 | Pete Mandley | .05 | .02 | 180 | Neil Smith (R) | .15 | .10 |

| 181 | Marty Schottenheimer | .05 | .02 |
|---|---|---|---|
| 182 | Marcus Allen | .15 | .10 |
| 183 | Tim Brown (R) | .80 | .50 |
| 184 | Willie Gault | .08 | .05 |
| 185 | Bo Jackson | .80 | .50 |
| 186 | Howie Long | .08 | .05 |
| 187 | Vann McElroy | .05 | .02 |
| 188 | Matt Millen | .05 | .02 |
| 189 | Don Mosebar (R) | .08 | .05 |
| 190 | Bill Pickel | .05 | .02 |
| 191 | Jerry Robinson | .05 | .02 |
| 192 | Jay Schroeder | .15 | .10 |
| 193a | Stacey Toran | .05 | .02 |
| 193b | Stacey Toran (Var) | .60 | .35 |
| | (1961-1989) | | |
| 194 | Mike Shananhan | .05 | .02 |
| 195 | Greg Bell | .07 | .04 |
| 196 | Ron Brown | .05 | .02 |
| 197 | Aaron Cox (R) | .12 | .07 |
| 198 | Henry Ellard | .08 | .05 |
| 199 | Jim Everett | .20 | .12 |
| 200 | Jerry Gray | .05 | .02 |
| 201 | Kevin Greene | .08 | .05 |
| 202 | Pete Hollohan | .05 | .02 |
| 203 | LeRoy Irvin | .07 | .04 |
| 204 | Mike Lansford | .05 | .02 |
| 205 | Tom Newberry (R) | .08 | .05 |
| 206 | Mel Owens | .05 | .02 |
| 207 | Jackie Slater | .08 | .05 |
| 208 | Doug Smith | .05 | .02 |
| 209 | Mike Wilcher | .05 | .02 |
| 210 | John Robinson | .05 | .02 |
| 211 | John Bosa | .05 | .02 |
| 212 | Mark Brown | .05 | .02 |
| 213 | Mark Clayton | .15 | .10 |
| 214a | Ferrell Edmonds (Er) | .75 | .45 |
| | (Last name wrong) | | |
| 214b | Ferrell Edmonds | .15 | .10 |
| | (Cor) | | |
| 215 | Roy Foster | .05 | .02 |
| 216 | Lorenzo Hampton | .05 | .02 |
| 217 | Jim Jensen (R) | .08 | .05 |
| 218 | William Judson | .05 | .02 |
| 219 | Eric Kumerow (R) | .08 | .05 |
| 220 | Dan Marino | .70 | .40 |
| 221 | John Offerdahl | .08 | .05 |
| 222 | Fuad Reveiz | .05 | .02 |
| 223 | Reggie Roby | .05 | .02 |
| 224 | Brian Sochia | .05 | .02 |
| 224 | Don Shula | .10 | .06 |
| 226 | Alfred Anderson | .05 | .02 |
| 227 | Joey Browner | .08 | .05 |
| 228 | Anthony Carter | .08 | .05 |
| 229 | Chris Doleman | .08 | .05 |
| 230 | Hassan Jones (R) | .15 | .10 |
| 231 | Steve Jordan | .07 | .04 |
| 232 | Tommy Kramer | .08 | .05 |
| 233 | Carl Lee (R) | .08 | .05 |
| 234 | Kirk Lowdermilk (R) | .07 | .04 |
| 235 | Randall McDaniel (R) | .12 | .07 |
| 236 | Doug Martin | .05 | .02 |
| 237 | Keith Millard | .08 | .05 |
| 238 | Darrin Nelson | .08 | .05 |
| 239 | Jesse Solomon | .05 | .02 |
| 240 | Scott Studwell | .05 | .02 |
| 241 | Wade Wilson | .10 | .06 |
| 242 | Gary Zimmerman | .05 | .02 |
| 243 | Jerry Burns | .05 | .02 |
| 244 | Bruce Armstrong (R) | .10 | .06 |
| 245 | Raymond Clayborn | .05 | .02 |
| 246 | Reggie Dupard (R) | .07 | .04 |
| 247 | Tony Eason | .08 | .05 |
| 248 | Sean Farrell | .05 | .02 |
| 249 | Doug Flutie | .15 | .10 |
| 250 | Brent Williams (R) | .07 | .04 |
| 251 | Roland James | .05 | .02 |
| 252 | Ronnie Lippett | .05 | .02 |
| 253 | Fred Marion | .05 | .02 |
| 254 | Larry McGrew | .05 | .02 |
| 255 | Stanley Morgan | .08 | .05 |
| 256 | Johnny Rembert (R) | .08 | .05 |
| 257 | John Stephens (R) | .35 | .20 |
| 258 | Andre Tippett | .08 | .05 |
| 259 | Garin Veris | .05 | .02 |
| 260a | Raymond Berry | .15 | .10 |
| | (No HOF stripe) | | |
| 260b | Raymond Berry | .30 | .18 |
| | (HOF stripe) | | |
| 261 | Morten Andersen | .07 | .04 |
| 262 | Hoby Brenner | .05 | .02 |
| 263 | Stan Brock | .05 | .02 |
| 264 | Brad Edelman | .05 | .02 |
| 265 | James Geathers | .05 | .02 |
| 266a | Bobby Hebert (Er) | .80 | .50 |
| | (Touchdown passers) | | |
| 266b | Bobby Hebert (Cor) | .15 | .10 |
| | (Touchdown passes) | | |
| 267 | Craig Heyward (R) | .20 | .12 |
| 268 | Lonzell Hill (R) | .07 | .04 |
| 269 | Dalton Hilliard | .10 | .06 |
| 270 | Rickey Jackson | .07 | .04 |
| 271 | Steve Korte | .05 | .02 |
| 272 | Eric Martin | .08 | .05 |
| 273 | Rueben Mayes | .07 | .04 |
| 274 | Sam Mills | .08 | .05 |
| 275 | Brett Perriman (R) | .30 | .18 |
| 276 | Pat Swilling | .20 | .12 |
| 277 | John Tice | .05 | .02 |
| 278 | Jim Mora | .05 | .02 |
| 279 | Eric Moore (R) | .07 | .04 |
| 280 | Carl Banks | .07 | .04 |
| 281 | Mark Bavaro | .07 | .04 |
| 282 | Maurice Carthon | .05 | .02 |

| | | | |
|---|---|---|---|
| 283 | Mark Collins (R) | .15 | .10 |
| 284 | Erik Howard | .05 | .02 |
| 285 | Terry Kinard | .05 | .02 |
| 286 | Sean Landeta | .05 | .02 |
| 287 | Lionel Manuel | .05 | .02 |
| 288 | Leonard Marshall | .07 | .04 |
| 289 | Joe Morris | .08 | .05 |
| 290 | Bart Oates | .05 | .02 |
| 291 | Phil Simms | .15 | .10 |
| 292 | Lawrence Taylor | .25 | .15 |
| 293 | Bill Parcells | .05 | .02 |
| 294 | Dave Cadigan | .05 | .02 |
| 295 | Kyle Clifton (R) | .10 | .06 |
| 296 | Alex Gordon | .05 | .02 |
| 297 | James Hasty (R) | .10 | .06 |
| 298 | Johnny Hector | .07 | .04 |
| 299 | Bobby Humphery | .05 | .02 |
| 300 | Pat Leahy | .05 | .02 |
| 301 | Marty Lyons | .05 | .02 |
| 302 | Reggie McElroy (R) | .07 | .04 |
| 303 | Erik McMillan | .05 | .02 |
| 304 | Freeman McNeil | .08 | .05 |
| 305 | Ken O'Brien | .15 | .10 |
| 306 | Pat Ryan | .05 | .02 |
| 307 | Mickey Shuler | .05 | .02 |
| 308 | Al Toon | .12 | .07 |
| 309 | Jo Jo Townsell | .05 | .02 |
| 310 | Roger Vick | .05 | .02 |
| 311 | Joe Walton | .05 | .02 |
| 312 | Jerome Brown | .08 | .05 |
| 313 | Keith Byars | .08 | .05 |
| 314 | Cris Carter (R) | .50 | .30 |
| 315 | Randall Cunningham | .50 | .30 |
| 316 | Terry Hoage | .05 | .02 |
| 317 | Wes Hopkins | .05 | .02 |
| 318 | Keith Jackson (R) | .75 | .45 |
| 319 | Mike Quick | .05 | .02 |
| 320 | Mike Reichenbach | .05 | .02 |
| 321 | Dave Rimington | .05 | .02 |
| 322 | John Teltschik | .05 | .02 |
| 323 | Anthony Toney | .07 | .04 |
| 324 | Andre Waters | .05 | .02 |
| 325 | Reggie White | .15 | .10 |
| 326 | Luis Zendejas | .05 | .02 |
| 237 | Buddy Ryan | .05 | .02 |
| 238 | Robert Awalt | .05 | .02 |
| 239 | Tim McDonald (R) | .12 | .07 |
| 330 | Roy Green | .08 | .05 |
| 331 | Neil Lomax | .08 | .05 |
| 332 | Cedric Mack | .05 | .02 |
| 333 | Stump Mitchell | .07 | .04 |
| 334 | Niko Noga (R) | .07 | .04 |
| 335 | Jay Novacek (R) | .80 | .50 |
| 336 | •Freddie Joe Nunn | .05 | .02 |
| 337 | Luis Sharpe | .05 | .02 |
| 338 | Vai Sikahema | .05 | .02 |
| 339 | J.T. Smith | .05 | .02 |

| | | | |
|---|---|---|---|
| 340 | Ron Wolfley | .05 | .02 |
| 341 | Gene Stallings | .05 | .02 |
| 342 | Gary Anderson | .05 | .02 |
| 343 | Bubby Brister (R) | .30 | .18 |
| 344 | Dermontti Dawson (R) | .08 | .05 |
| 345 | Thomas Everett (R) | .12 | .07 |
| 346 | Delton Hall (R) | .07 | .04 |
| 347 | Bryan Hinkle (R) | .05 | .02 |
| 348 | Merril Hoge (R) | .15 | .10 |
| 349 | Tunch Ilkin (R) | .08 | .05 |
| 350 | Aaron Jones (R) | .07 | .04 |
| 351 | Louis Lipps | .07 | .04 |
| 352 | David Little | .05 | .02 |
| 353 | Hardy Nickerson (R) | .08 | .05 |
| 354 | Rod Woodson (R) | .30 | .18 |
| 355 | Chuck Noll | .10 | .06 |
| 356 | Gary Anderson | .05 | .02 |
| 357 | Rod Bernstine (R) | .25 | .15 |
| 358 | Bill Byrne | .05 | .02 |
| 359 | Vencie Glenn | .05 | .02 |
| 360 | Dennis McKnight | .07 | .04 |
| 361 | Lionel James | .07 | .04 |
| 362 | Mark Malone | .07 | .04 |
| 363a | Anthony Miller (R) (Er) (TD's 14.8) | 1.50 | .90 |
| 363b | Anthony Miller (R) (Cor) (TD's 3) | 1.00 | .70 |
| 364 | Ralf Mojsiejenko | .05 | .02 |
| 365 | Leslie O'Neal | .10 | .06 |
| 366 | Jamie Holland (R) | .07 | .04 |
| 367 | Lee Williams | .07 | .04 |
| 368 | Dan Henning | .05 | .02 |
| 369 | Harris Barton (R) | .08 | .05 |
| 370 | Michael Carter | .05 | .02 |
| 371 | Mike Cofer (R) | .05 | .02 |
| 372 | Roger Craig | .08 | .05 |
| 373 | Riki Ellison (R) | .07 | .04 |
| 374 | Jim Fahnhorst | .05 | .02 |
| 375 | John Frank | .05 | .02 |
| 376 | Jeff Fuller | .05 | .02 |
| 377 | Don Griffin | .05 | .02 |
| 378 | Charles Haley | .08 | .05 |
| 379 | Ronnie Lott | .15 | .10 |
| 380 | Tim McKyer | .07 | .04 |
| 381 | Joe Montana | 1.00 | .70 |
| 382 | Tom Rathman | .08 | .05 |
| 383 | Jerry Rice | 1.00 | .70 |
| 384 | John Taylor (R) | .75 | .45 |
| 385 | Keena Turner | .05 | .02 |
| 386 | Michael Walter | .05 | .02 |
| 387 | Bubba Paris | .05 | .02 |
| 388 | Steve Young | .50 | .30 |
| 389 | George Seifert | .05 | .02 |
| 390 | Brian Blades (R) | .30 | .18 |
| 391a | Brian Bosworth (Er) (Seattle) | .50 | .30 |
| 391b | Brian Bosworth (Cor) | .08 | .05 |

| | | | |
|---|---|---|---|
| (Seahawks) | | | |
| 392 Jeff Bryant | .05 | .02 |
| 393 Jacob Green | .05 | .02 |
| 394 Norm Johnson | .05 | .02 |
| 395 Dave Krieg | .10 | .06 |
| 396 Steve Largent | .35 | .20 |
| 397 Bryan Millard (R) | .07 | .04 |
| 398 Paul Moyer | .05 | .02 |
| 399 Joe Nash | .05 | .02 |
| 400 Rufus Porter (R) | .10 | .06 |
| 401 Eugene Robinson (R) | .10 | .06 |
| 402 Bruce Scholtz | .05 | .02 |
| 403 Kelly Stouffer (R) | .30 | .18 |
| 404a Curt Warner (Er) | 3.00 | 2.00 |
|     (1,455 yards) | | |
| 404b Curt Warner (Cor) | .12 | .07 |
|     (6,074 yards) | | |
| 405 John L. Williams | .08 | .05 |
| 406 Tony Woods (R) | .07 | .04 |
| 407 David Wyman | .05 | .02 |
| 408 Chuck Knox | .05 | .02 |
| 409 Mark Carrier (TB)(R) | .20 | .12 |
| 410 Randy Grimes | .05 | .02 |
| 411 Paul Gruber (R) | .12 | .07 |
| 412 Harry Hamilton | .05 | .02 |
| 413 Ron Holmes | .05 | .02 |
| 414 Donald Igwebuike | .05 | .02 |
| 415 Dan Turk (R) | .07 | .04 |
| 416 Ricky Reynolds | .05 | .02 |
| 417 Bruce Hill | .05 | .02 |
| 418 Lars Tate (R) | .08 | .05 |
| 419 Vinny Testaverde | .15 | .10 |
| 420 James Wilder | .08 | .05 |
| 421 Ray Perkins | .05 | .02 |
| 422 Jeff Bostic | .05 | .02 |
| 423 Kelvin Bryant | .07 | .04 |
| 424 Gary Clark | .20 | .12 |
| 425 Monte Coleman | .05 | .02 |
| 426 Darrell Green | .15 | .10 |
| 427 Joe Jacoby | .05 | .02 |
| 428 Jim Lachey | .07 | .04 |
| 429 Charles Mann | .05 | .02 |
| 430 Dexter Manley | .05 | .02 |
| 431 Darryl Grant (R) | .08 | .05 |
| 432 Mark May (R) | .08 | .05 |
| 433 Art Monk | .30 | .18 |
| 434 Mark Rypien (R) | 1.50 | .90 |
| 435 Ricky Sanders | .08 | .05 |
| 436 Alvin Walton (R) | .08 | .05 |
| 437 Don Warren | .05 | .02 |
| 438 Jamie Morris | .07 | .04 |
| 439 Doug Williams | .10 | .06 |
| 440 Joe Gibbs | .08 | .05 |
| 441 Marcus Cotton (R) | .07 | .04 |
| 442 Joel Williams | .05 | .02 |
| 443 Joe Devlin | .05 | .02 |
| 444 Robb Riddick | .05 | .02 |

| | | | |
|---|---|---|---|
| 445 William Perry | .08 | .05 |
| 446 Thomas Sanders (R) | .08 | .05 |
| 447 Brian Blados | .05 | .02 |
| 448 Cris Collinsworth | .08 | .05 |
| 449 Stanford Jennings | .05 | .02 |
| 450 Barry Krauss | .05 | .02 |
| 451 Ozzie Newsome | .12 | .07 |
| 452 Mike Oliphant (R) | .07 | .04 |
| 453 Tony Dorsett | .25 | .15 |
| 454 Bruce McNorton | .05 | .02 |
| 455 Eric Dickerson | .50 | .30 |
| 456 Keith Bostic | .05 | .02 |
| 457 Sam Clancy (R) | .08 | .05 |
| 458 Jack Del Rio (R) | .10 | .06 |
| 459 Mike Webster | .07 | .04 |
| 460 Bob Golic | .05 | .02 |
| 461 Otis Wilson | .05 | .02 |
| 462 Mike Haynes | .07 | .04 |
| 463 Greg Townsend | .07 | .04 |
| 464 Mark Duper | .08 | .05 |
| 465 E.J. Junior | .05 | .02 |
| 466 Troy Stradford | .05 | .02 |
| 467 Mike Merriweather | .05 | .02 |
| 468 Irving Fryar | .07 | .04 |
| 469 Vaughan Johnson | .35 | .20 |
| 470 Pepper Johnson | .05 | .02 |
| 471 Gary Reasons (R) | .10 | .06 |
| 472 Perry Williams (R) | .07 | .04 |
| 473 Wesley Walker | .08 | .05 |
| 474 Anthony Bell (R) | .07 | .04 |
| 475 Earl Ferrell | .05 | .02 |
| 476 Craig Wolfley | .05 | .02 |
| 477 Billy Ray Smith | .05 | .02 |
| 478a Jim McMahon (Er) | .10 | .06 |
|     (No trade) | | |
| 478b Jim McMahon | .25 | .15 |
|     (Traded) | | |
| 479 Eric Wright | .05 | .02 |
| 480a Earnest Byner (Er) | .10 | .06 |
|     (No trade) | | |
| 480b Earnest Byner (Cor) | .25 | .15 |
|     (Traded) | | |
| 481 Russ Grimm | .05 | .02 |
| 482 Wilber Marshall | .07 | .04 |
| 483a Gerald Riggs (Er) | .10 | .06 |
|     (No trade) | | |
| 483b Gerald Riggs (Cor) | .25 | .15 |
|     (Traded) | | |
| 484 Brian Davis (R) | .07 | .04 |
| 485 Shawn Collins (R) | .12 | .07 |
| 486 Deion Sanders (R) | 2.00 | 1.25 |
| 487 Trace Armstrong (R) | .12 | .07 |
| 488 Donnell Woolford (R) | .10 | .06 |
| 489 Eric Metcalf (R) | .50 | .30 |
| 490 Troy Aikman (R) | 6.00 | 4.00 |
| 491 Steve Walsh (R) | .35 | .20 |
| 492 Steve Atwater (R) | .40 | .25 |

| | | | |
|---|---|---|---|
| 493 | Bobby Humphrey (R) | .60 | .35 |
| 494 | Barry Sanders (R) | 6.50 | 4.25 |
| 495 | Tony Mandarich (R) | .10 | .06 |
| 496 | David Williams (R) | .10 | .06 |
| 497 | Andre Rison (R) | 2.50 | 1.50 |
| 498 | Derrick Thomas (R) | 2.00 | 1.25 |
| 499 | Cleveland Gary (R) | .30 | .18 |
| 500 | Bill Hawkins (R) | .08 | .05 |
| 501 | Louis Oliver (R) | .20 | .12 |
| 502 | Sammie Smith (R) | .35 | .20 |
| 503 | Hart Lee Dykes (R) | .15 | .10 |
| 504 | Wayne Martin (R) | .10 | .06 |
| 505 | Brian Williams (R) | .10 | .06 |
| 506 | Jeff Lageman (R) | .15 | .10 |
| 507 | Eric Hill (R) | .10 | .06 |
| 508 | Joe Wolf (R) | .08 | .05 |
| 509 | Timm Rosenbach (R) | .50 | .30 |
| 510 | Tom Ricketts (R) | .07 | .04 |
| 511 | Tim Worley (R) | .12 | .07 |
| 512 | Burt Grossman (R) | .15 | .10 |
| 513 | Keith DeLong (R) | .15 | .10 |
| 514 | Andy Heck (R) | .08 | .05 |
| 515 | Broderick Thomas (R) | .40 | .25 |
| 516 | Don Beebe (R) | .25 | .15 |
| 517 | James Thornton (R) | .12 | .07 |
| 518 | Eric Kattus (R) | .07 | .04 |
| 519 | Bruce Kozerski (R) | .07 | .04 |
| 520 | Brian Washington (R) | .08 | .05 |
| 521 | Rodney Peete (R) | .60 | .35 |
| 522 | Erik Affholter (R) | .08 | .05 |
| 523 | Anthong Dilweg (R) | .15 | .10 |
| 524 | O'Brien Alston (R) | .08 | .05 |
| 525 | Mike Elkins (R) | .08 | .05 |
| 526 | Jonathan Hayes (R) | .08 | .05 |
| 527 | Terry McDaniel (R) | .15 | .10 |
| 528 | Frank Stams (R) | .10 | .06 |
| 529 | Darryl Ingram (R) | .08 | .05 |
| 530 | Henry Thomas (R) | .15 | .10 |
| 531 | Eric Coleman (R) | .08 | .05 |
| 532 | Sheldon White (R) | .08 | .05 |
| 533 | Eric Allen (R) | .15 | .10 |
| 534 | Robert Drummond (R) | .08 | .05 |
| 535a | Gizmo Williams (Er) (No scouting photo) | .35 | .20 |
| 535b | Gizmo Williams (Cor) (With scouting photo) | .12 | .07 |
| 536 | Billy Joe Tolliver (R) | .15 | .10 |
| 537 | Danny Stubbs (R) | .08 | .05 |
| 538 | Wesley Walls (R) | .08 | .05 |
| 539a | James Jefferson (Er) (No Prospect stripe) | .50 | .30 |
| 539a | James Jefferson (Cor) (W/prospect Stripe) | .15 | .10 |
| 540 | Tracy Rocker (R) | .10 | .06 |
| CC1 | Pete Rozelle SP | .05 | .02 |
| 541 | Art Shell | .12 | .07 |
| 542 | Lemuel Stinson (R) | .12 | .07 |

| | | | |
|---|---|---|---|
| 543 | Tyrone Braxton (R) | .10 | .06 |
| 544 | David Treadwell (R) | .07 | .04 |
| 545 | Flipper Anderson (R) | .60 | .35 |
| 546 | Dave Meggett (R) | .60 | .35 |
| 547 | Lewis Tillman (R) | .12 | .07 |
| 548 | Carnell Lake (R) | .12 | .07 |
| 549 | Marion Butts (R) | .80 | .50 |
| 550 | Sterling Sharpe (R) | 3.50 | 2.50 |
| 551 | Ezra Johnson | .05 | .02 |
| 552 | Clarence Verdin (R) | .10 | .06 |
| 553 | Mervyn Fernandez (R) | .25 | .15 |
| 554 | Ottis Anderson | .10 | .06 |
| 555 | Gary Hogeboom | .07 | .04 |
| 556 | Paul Palmer | .05 | .02 |
| 557 | Jesse Solomon | .05 | .02 |
| 558 | Chip Banks | .05 | .02 |
| 559 | Steve Pelluer | .05 | .02 |
| 560 | Darrin Nelson | .05 | .02 |
| 561 | Herschel Walker | .25 | .15 |
| SP1 | Pete Rozelle | 2.50 | 1.50 |

# 1990 Pro Set

ERIC METCALF

This 800-card set was issued in two series plus a Final Update. Card fronts feature full color action photos framed by top and bottom borders that reflect the player's team colors. The player's name, position and team are centered below the photograph. The horizontal card backs contain a small head shot, stats and highlights. Two cards were pulled from the set shortly after it was issued (#75 Cody Risien and #338 Eric Dickerson). Those cards are included in the checklist but the values are not included in the complete set price. The set also contains numerous errors. Those cards are listed only when there is a difference in value between the original error card and the variation. Key subsets include League Leaders (LL), Hall of Famers (HOF), Pro Bowlers (PB), Newsreels, American Bowls and Photo Contest. Random inserts include a Bonus Vince Lombardi Trophy Hologram card and five additional limited inserts. Those cards are listed at the end of this checklist but are not included in the complete set price. All cards measure 2-1/2" by 3-1/2".

|  |  | MINT | NR/MT |
|---|---|---|---|
| **Complete Set (800)** | | 22.50 | 14.50 |
| **Commons** | | .05 | .02 |
| 1 | Barry Sanders (Rookie of the year) | .60 | .35 |
| 2 | Joe Montana (Player of the year) | .30 | .18 |
| 3 | Lindy Infante (Coach of the year) | .05 | .02 |
| 4 | Warren Moon (Man of the Year) | .10 | .06 |
| 5 | Keith Millard (Defensive Player of the year) | .07 | .04 |
| 6 | Derrick Thomas (Defensive Rookie of the year) | .12 | .07 |
| 7 | Ottis Anderson (Comback Player of the year) | .07 | .04 |
| 8 | Joe Montana (LL) | .25 | .15 |
| 9 | Christian Okoye (LL) | .10 | .06 |
| 10 | Thurman Thomas (LL) | .25 | .15 |
| 11 | Mike Cofer (LL) | .05 | .02 |
| 12 | Dalton Hilliard (LL) | .07 | .04 |
| 13 | Sterling Sharpe (LL) | .25 | .15 |
| 14 | Rich Camarillo (LL) | .05 | .02 |
| 15a | Walter Stanley (LL) (Er) Wrong jersey number on back) | 1.50 | .90 |
| 15b | Walter Stanley (Cor) | .07 | .04 |
| 16 | Rod Woodson (LL) | .07 | .04 |
| 17 | Felix Wright (LL) | .05 | .02 |
| 18 | Chris Doleman (LL) | .07 | .04 |
| 19 | Andre Ware (Heisman) | .25 | .15 |
| 20 | Mohammed Elewonibi (Outland Trophy) | .07 | .04 |
| 21 | Percy Snow (Lombardi Award) | .10 | .06 |
| 22 | Anthony Thompson (Maxwell Award) | .20 | .12 |
| 23 | Buck Buchanan (HOF) | .07 | .04 |
| 24 | Bob Griese (HOF) | .08 | .05 |
| 25 | Franco Harris (HOF) | .08 | .05 |
| 26 | Ted Hendricks (HOF) | .07 | .04 |
| 27 | Jack Lambert (HOF) | .07 | .04 |
| 28 | Tom Landry (HOF) | .10 | .06 |
| 29 | Bob St. Clair (HOF) | .07 | .04 |
| 30 | Aundray Bruce | .05 | .02 |
| 31 | Tony Casillas | .07 | .04 |
| 32 | Shawn Collins | .05 | .02 |
| 33 | Marcus Cotton | .05 | .02 |
| 34 | Bill Fralic | .05 | .02 |
| 35 | Chris Miller | .25 | .15 |
| 36 | Deion Sanders | .30 | .18 |
| 37 | John Settle | .07 | .04 |
| 38 | Jerry Glanville | .05 | .02 |
| 39 | Cornilius Bennett | .10 | .06 |
| 40 | Jim Kelly | .35 | .20 |
| 41 | Mark Kelso | .05 | .02 |
| 42 | Scott Norwood | .05 | .02 |
| 43 | Nate Odomes (R) | .10 | .06 |
| 44 | Scott Radecic | .05 | .02 |
| 45 | Jim Ritcher (R) | .08 | .05 |
| 46 | Leonard Smith | .05 | .02 |
| 47 | Darryl Talley | .08 | .05 |
| 48 | Marv Levy | .05 | .02 |
| 49 | Neal Anderson | .12 | .07 |
| 50 | Kevin Butler | .05 | .02 |
| 51 | Jim Covert | .05 | .02 |
| 52 | Richard Dent | .07 | .04 |
| 53 | Jay Hilgenberg | .05 | .02 |
| 54 | Steve McMichael | .07 | .04 |
| 55 | Ron Morris | .05 | .02 |
| 56 | John Roper (R) | .08 | .05 |
| 57 | Mike Singletary | .12 | .07 |
| 58 | Keith Van Horne | .05 | .02 |
| 59 | Mike Ditka | .08 | .05 |
| 60 | Lewis Billups | .05 | .02 |
| 61 | Eddie Brown | .08 | .05 |
| 62 | Jason Buck | .05 | .02 |
| 63a | Rickey Dixon (R) (Er) (No bio on back) | .75 | .45 |
| 63b | Rickey Dixon (R) (Cor) | .15 | .10 |
| 64 | Tim McGee | .07 | .04 |
| 65 | Eric Thomas | .05 | .02 |
| 66 | Ickey Woods | .05 | .02 |

| | | | |
|---|---|---|---|
| 67 | Carl Zander | .05 | .02 |
| 68a | Sam Wyche (Er) | .50 | .30 |
| | (No bio on back) | | |
| 68b | Sam Wyche (Cor) | .05 | .02 |
| 69 | Paul Farren (R) | .07 | .04 |
| 70 | Thane Gash (R) | .08 | .05 |
| 71 | David Grayson | .05 | .02 |
| 72 | Bernie Kosar | .15 | .10 |
| 73 | Reggie Langhorne | .05 | .02 |
| 74 | Eric Metcalf | .12 | .07 |
| 75a | Cody Risien (Er) | 8.00 | 4.50 |
| | (Pulled from set) | | |
| 75b | Ozzie Newsome (Cor) | .10 | .06 |
| 76 | Felix Wright | .05 | .02 |
| 77 | Bud Carson | .05 | .02 |
| 78 | Troy Aikman | .75 | .45 |
| 79 | Michael Irvin | .30 | .18 |
| 80 | Jim Jeffcoat | .05 | .02 |
| 81 | Crawford Ker | .05 | .02 |
| 82 | Eugene Lockhard | .05 | .02 |
| 83 | Kelvin Martin (R) | .20 | .12 |
| 84 | Ken Norton (R) | .12 | .07 |
| 85 | Jimmy Johnson | .05 | .02 |
| 86 | Steve Atwater | .10 | .06 |
| 87 | Tyrone Braxton | .05 | .02 |
| 88 | John Elway | .20 | .12 |
| 89 | Simon Fletcher | .05 | .02 |
| 90 | Ron Holmes | .05 | .02 |
| 91 | Bobby Humphrey | .12 | .07 |
| 92 | Vance Johnson | .08 | .05 |
| 93 | Ricky Nattiel | .08 | .05 |
| 94 | Dan Reeves | .05 | .02 |
| 95 | Jim Arnold | .05 | .02 |
| 96 | Jerry Ball | .05 | .02 |
| 97 | Bennie Blades | .07 | .04 |
| 98 | Lomas Brown | .05 | .02 |
| 99 | Michael Cofer | .05 | .02 |
| 100 | Richard Johnson | .05 | .02 |
| 101 | Eddie Murray | .05 | .02 |
| 102 | Barry Sanders | .75 | .45 |
| 103 | Chris Spielman | .07 | .04 |
| 104 | William White (R) | .08 | .05 |
| 105 | Eric Williams (R) | .08 | .05 |
| 106 | Wayne Fontes | .05 | .02 |
| 107 | Brent Fullwood | .05 | .02 |
| 108 | Ron Hallstrom (R) | .08 | .05 |
| 109 | Tim Harris | .05 | .02 |
| 110a | Johnny Holland (Er) | 1.50 | .90 |
| | (No name on back) | | |
| 110b | Johnny Holland (Cor) | .07 | .04 |
| 111a | Perry Kemp (Er) | .50 | .30 |
| | (Wrong photo on back) | | |
| 111b | Perry Kemp (Cor) | .07 | .04 |
| 112 | Don Majkowski | .12 | .07 |
| 113 | Mark Murphy | .05 | .02 |
| 114a | Sterling Sharpe (Er) | .25 | .15 |
| | (Wrong birthplace) | | |

| | | | |
|---|---|---|---|
| 114b | Sterling Sharpe (Cor) | 1.50 | .90 |
| | (Born in Chicago) | | |
| 115 | Ed West (R) | .07 | .04 |
| 116 | Lindy Infante | .05 | .02 |
| 117 | Steve Brown | .05 | .02 |
| 118 | Ray Childress | .07 | .04 |
| 119 | Ernest Givins | .15 | .10 |
| 120 | John Grimsley | .05 | .02 |
| 121 | Alonzo Highsmith | .05 | .02 |
| 122 | Drew Hill | .08 | .05 |
| 123 | Bubba McDowell | .05 | .02 |
| 124 | Dean Steinkuhler | .05 | .02 |
| 125 | Lorenzo White | .20 | .12 |
| 126 | Tony Zendejas | .05 | .02 |
| 127 | Jack Pardee | .05 | .02 |
| 128 | Albert Bentley | .05 | .02 |
| 129 | Dean Biasucci | .05 | .02 |
| 130 | Duane Bickett | .05 | .02 |
| 131 | Bill Brooks | .05 | .02 |
| 132 | Jon Hand | .05 | .02 |
| 133 | Mike Prior | .05 | .02 |
| 134a | Andre Rison (Er) | .20 | .12 |
| | (No Trade stripe) | | |
| 134b | Andre Rison (Cor) | .50 | .30 |
| | (W/traded stripe) | | |
| 135 | Rohn Stark | .05 | .02 |
| 136 | Donnell Thompson | .05 | .02 |
| 137 | Clarence Verdin | .07 | .04 |
| 138 | Fredd Young | .05 | .02 |
| 139 | Ron Meyer | .05 | .02 |
| 140 | John Alt (R) | .08 | .05 |
| 141 | Steve DeBerg | .10 | .06 |
| 142 | Irv Eatman | .05 | .02 |
| 143 | Dino Hackett | .05 | .02 |
| 144 | Nick Lowery | .07 | .04 |
| 145 | Bill Maas | .05 | .02 |
| 146 | Stephone Paige | .08 | .05 |
| 147 | Neil Smith | .05 | .02 |
| 148 | Marty Schottenheimer | .05 | .02 |
| 149 | Steve Beuerlein | .15 | .10 |
| 150 | Tim Brown | .10 | .06 |
| 151 | Mike Dyal | .05 | .02 |
| 152 | Mervyn Fernandez | .10 | .06 |
| 153 | Willie Gault | .07 | .04 |
| 154 | Bob Golic | .05 | .02 |
| 155 | Bo Jackson | .35 | .20 |
| 156 | Don Mosebar | .05 | .02 |
| 157 | Steve Smith | .05 | .02 |
| 158 | Greg Townsend | .07 | .04 |
| 159 | Bruce Wilkerson (R) | .07 | .04 |
| 160 | Steve Wisniewski | .05 | .02 |
| 161a | Art Shell (Er) | .07 | .04 |
| | (Wrong birth date) | | |
| 161b | Art Shell (Cor) | .80 | .50 |
| | (Born 11/26/46) | | |
| 162 | Flipper Anderson | .08 | .05 |
| 163 | Greg Bell | .07 | .04 |

| 164 | Henry Ellard | .07 | .04 |
| 165 | Jim Everett | .15 | .10 |
| 166 | Jerry Gray | .05 | .02 |
| 167 | Kevin Greene | .05 | .02 |
| 168 | Pete Holohan | .05 | .02 |
| 169 | Larry Kelm (R) | .07 | .04 |
| 170 | Tom Newberry | .05 | .02 |
| 171 | Vince Newsome (R) | .08 | .05 |
| 172 | Irv Pankey | .05 | .02 |
| 173 | Jackie Slater | .07 | .04 |
| 174 | Fred Strickland (R) | .08 | .05 |
| 175 | Mike Wilcher | .05 | .02 |
| 176 | John Robinson | .05 | .02 |
| 177 | Mark Clayton | .12 | .07 |
| 178 | Roy Foster | .05 | .02 |
| 179 | Harry Galbreath (R) | .05 | .02 |
| 180 | Jim Jensen | .05 | .02 |
| 181 | Dan Marino | .40 | .25 |
| 182 | Louis Oliver | .07 | .04 |
| 183 | Sammie Smith | .08 | .05 |
| 184 | Brian Sochia | .05 | .02 |
| 185 | Don Shula | .08 | .05 |
| 186 | Joey Browner | .07 | .04 |
| 187 | Anthony Carter | .08 | .05 |
| 188 | Chris Doleman | .08 | .05 |
| 189 | Steve Jordan | .05 | .02 |
| 190 | Carl Lee | .05 | .02 |
| 191 | Randall McDaniel | .05 | .02 |
| 192 | Mike Merriweather | .05 | .02 |
| 193 | Keith Millard | .07 | .04 |
| 194 | Al Noga | .05 | .02 |
| 195 | Scott Studwell | .05 | .02 |
| 196 | Henry Thomas | .05 | .02 |
| 197 | Herschel Walker | .15 | .10 |
| 198 | Wade Wilson | .08 | .05 |
| 199 | Gary Zimmerman | .05 | .02 |
| 200 | Jerry Burns | .05 | .02 |
| 201 | Vincent Brown (R) | .07 | .04 |
| 202 | Hart Lee Dykes | .07 | .04 |
| 203 | Sean Farrell | .05 | .02 |
| 204 | Fred Marion | .05 | .02 |
| 205 | Stanley Morgan | .08 | .05 |
| 206 | Eric Sievers (R) | .08 | .05 |
| 207 | John Stephens | .10 | .06 |
| 208 | Andre Tippett | .08 | .05 |
| 209 | Rod Rust | .05 | .02 |
| 210a | Morten Andersen (Er) | .40 | .25 |
| | (Name and number on back printed in white) | | |
| 210b | Morten Andersen (Cor) Name and number on back printed in black) | .07 | .04 |
| 211 | Brad Edelman | .05 | .02 |
| 212 | John Fourcade | .07 | .04 |
| 213 | Dalton Hilliard | .08 | .05 |
| 214 | Rickey Jackson | .07 | .04 |
| 215 | Vaughan Johnson | .07 | .04 |
| 216a | Eric Martin (Er) | .40 | .25 |
| | (Name and number on back printed in white) | | |
| 216b | Eric Martin (Cor) | .08 | .05 |
| | (Name and number on back printed in black) | | |
| 217 | Sam Mills | .07 | .04 |
| 218 | Pat Swilling | .12 | .07 |
| 219 | Frank Warren (R) | .07 | .04 |
| 220 | Jim Wilks | .05 | .02 |
| 221a | Jim Mora (Er) | .40 | .25 |
| | (Name and number on back printed in white) | | |
| 221b | Jim Mora (Cor) | .05 | .02 |
| | (Name and number on back printed in black) | | |
| 222 | Raul Allegre | .05 | .02 |
| 223 | Carl Banks | .07 | .04 |
| 224 | John Elliott | .05 | .02 |
| 225 | Erik Howard | .05 | .02 |
| 226 | Pepper Johnson | .05 | .02 |
| 227 | Leonard Marshall | .07 | .04 |
| 228 | David Meggett | .15 | .10 |
| 229 | Bart Oates | .05 | .02 |
| 230 | Phil Simms | .10 | .06 |
| 231 | Lawrence Taylor | .15 | .10 |
| 232 | Bill Parcells | .05 | .02 |
| 233 | Troy Benson | .05 | .02 |
| 234 | Kyle Clifton | .05 | .02 |
| 235 | Johnny Hector | .07 | .04 |
| 236 | Jeff Lageman | .07 | .04 |
| 237 | Pat Leahy | .05 | .02 |
| 238 | Freeman McNeil | .07 | .04 |
| 239 | Ken O'Brien | .10 | .06 |
| 240 | Al Toon | .08 | .05 |
| 241 | Jo Jo Townsell | .05 | .02 |
| 242 | Bruce Coslet | .05 | .02 |
| 243 | Eric Allen | .05 | .02 |
| 244 | Jerome Brown | .07 | .04 |
| 245 | Keith Byars | .07 | .04 |
| 246 | Cris Carter | .20 | .12 |
| 247 | Randall Cunningham | .20 | .12 |
| 248 | Keith Jackson | .15 | .10 |
| 249 | Mike Quick | .05 | .02 |
| 250 | Clyde Simmons | .07 | .04 |
| 251 | Andre Waters | .05 | .02 |
| 252 | Reggie White | .12 | .07 |
| 253 | Buddy Ryan | .05 | .02 |
| 254 | Rich Camarillo | .05 | .02 |
| 255 | Earl Ferrell | .05 | .02 |
| 256 | Roy Green | .07 | .04 |
| 257 | Ken Harvey (R) | .10 | .06 |
| 258 | Ernie Jones (R) | .20 | .12 |
| 259 | Tim McDonald | .05 | .02 |
| 260 | Timm Rosenbach | .15 | .10 |
| 261 | Luis Sharpe | .05 | .02 |
| 262 | Vai Sikahema | .05 | .02 |

| # | Player | | |
|---|---|---|---|
| 263 | J.T. Smith | .05 | .02 |
| 264 | Ron Wolfey | .05 | .02 |
| 265 | Joe Bugel | .05 | .02 |
| 266 | Gary Anderson | .05 | .02 |
| 267 | Bubby Brister | .10 | .06 |
| 268 | Merril Hoge | .07 | .04 |
| 269 | Carnell Lake | .05 | .02 |
| 270 | Louis Lipps | .07 | .04 |
| 271 | David Little | .05 | .02 |
| 272 | Greg Lloyd | .05 | .02 |
| 273 | Keith Willis | .05 | .02 |
| 274 | Tim Worley | .08 | .05 |
| 275 | Chuck Noll | .08 | .05 |
| 276 | Marion Butts | .12 | .07 |
| 277 | Gill Byrd | .05 | .02 |
| 278 | Vencie Glenn | .05 | .02 |
| 279 | Burt Grossman | .07 | .04 |
| 280 | Gary Plummer | .05 | .02 |
| 281 | Billy Ray Smith | .05 | .02 |
| 282 | Billy Joe Tolliver | .08 | .05 |
| 283 | Dan Hennings | .05 | .02 |
| 284 | Harris Barton | .05 | .02 |
| 285 | Michael Carter | .05 | .02 |
| 286 | Mike Cofer | .05 | .02 |
| 287 | Roger Craig | .08 | .05 |
| 288 | Don Griffin | .05 | .02 |
| 289a | Charles Haley (Er) | .08 | .05 |
| | (4 fumble recoveries) | | |
| 289b | Charles Haley (Cor) | .50 | .30 |
| | (5 fumble recoveries) | | |
| 290 | Pierce Holt (R) | .08 | .05 |
| 291 | Ronnie Lott | .10 | .06 |
| 292 | Guy McIntyre | .05 | .02 |
| 293 | Joe Montana | .60 | .35 |
| 294 | Tom Rathman | .08 | .05 |
| 295 | Jerry Rice | .60 | .35 |
| 296 | Jesse Sapolu | .05 | .02 |
| 297 | John Taylor | .15 | .10 |
| 298 | Michael Walter | .05 | .02 |
| 299 | George Seifert | .05 | .02 |
| 300 | Jeff Bryant | .05 | .02 |
| 301 | Jacob Green | .05 | .02 |
| 302 | Norm Johnson | .05 | .02 |
| 303 | Bryan Millard | .05 | .02 |
| 304 | Joe Nash | .05 | .02 |
| 305 | Eugene Robinson | .07 | .04 |
| 306 | John L. Williams | .07 | .04 |
| 307 | Dave Wyman | .05 | .02 |
| 308 | Chuck Knox | .05 | .02 |
| 309 | Mark Carrier (TB) | .07 | .04 |
| 310 | Paul Gruber | .05 | .02 |
| 311 | Harry Hamilton | .05 | .02 |
| 312 | Bruce Hill | .05 | .02 |
| 313 | Donald Igwebuike | .05 | .02 |
| 314 | Kevin Murphy | .05 | .02 |
| 315 | Ervin Randle | .05 | .02 |
| 316 | Mark Robinson | .05 | .02 |
| 317 | Lars Tate | .07 | .04 |
| 318 | Vinny Testaverde | .12 | .07 |
| 319a | Ray Perkins (Er) | 1.50 | .90 |
| | (no name on back) | | |
| 319b | Ray Perkins (Cor) | .05 | .02 |
| 320 | Earnest Byner | .08 | .05 |
| 321 | Gary Clark | .15 | .10 |
| 322 | Darryl Grant | .05 | .02 |
| 323 | Darrell Green | .10 | .06 |
| 324 | Jim Lachey | .07 | .04 |
| 325 | Charles Mann | .05 | .02 |
| 326 | Wilber Marshall | .07 | .04 |
| 327 | Ralf Mojsiejenko | .05 | .02 |
| 328 | Art Monk | .25 | .15 |
| 329 | Gerald Riggs | .07 | .04 |
| 330 | Mark Rypien | .25 | .15 |
| 331 | Ricky Sanders | .08 | .05 |
| 332 | Alvin Walton | .05 | .02 |
| 333 | Joe Gibbs | .05 | .02 |
| 334 | Aloha Stadium | .05 | .02 |
| 335 | Brian Blades (PB) | .07 | .04 |
| 336 | James Brooks (PB) | .07 | .04 |
| 337 | Shane Conlan (PB) | .07 | .04 |
| 338 | Eric Dickerson(PB)SP | 15.00 | 9.00 |
| | (Card pulled from set) | | |
| 339 | Ray Donaldson (PB) | .05 | .02 |
| 340 | Ferrell Edmunds (PB) | .05 | .02 |
| 341 | Boomer Esiason (PB) | .08 | .05 |
| 342 | David Fulcher (PB) | .05 | .02 |
| 343 | Chris Hinton (PB) | .05 | .02 |
| 344 | Rodney Holman (PB) | .05 | .02 |
| 345 | Kent Hull (PB) | .05 | .02 |
| 346 | Tunch Ilkin (PB) | .05 | .02 |
| 347 | Mike Johnson (PB) | .05 | .02 |
| 348 | Greg Kragen (PB) | .05 | .02 |
| 349 | Dave Krieg (PB) | .08 | .05 |
| 350 | Albert Lewis (PB) | .05 | .02 |
| 351 | Howie Long (PB) | .07 | .04 |
| 352 | Bruce Matthews (PB) | .05 | .02 |
| 353 | Clay Matthews (PB) | .05 | .02 |
| 354 | Erik McMillan (PB) | .05 | .02 |
| 355 | Karl Mecklenburg (PB) | .07 | .04 |
| 356 | Anthony Miller (PB) | .08 | .05 |
| 357 | Frank Minnifield (PB) | .05 | .02 |
| 358 | Max Montoya (PB) | .05 | .02 |
| 359 | Warren Moon (PB) | .12 | .07 |
| 360 | Mike Munchak (PB) | .05 | .02 |
| 361 | Anthony Munoz (PB) | .07 | .04 |
| 362 | John Offerdahl (PB) | .05 | .02 |
| 363 | Christian Okoye (PB) | .08 | .05 |
| 364 | Leslie O'Neal (PB) | .05 | .02 |
| 365 | Rufus Porter (PB) | .05 | .02 |
| 366 | Andre Reed (PB) | .08 | .05 |
| 367 | Johnny Rembert (PB) | .05 | .02 |
| 368 | Reggie Roby (PB) | .05 | .02 |
| 369 | Kevin Ross (PB) | .05 | .02 |
| 370 | Webster Slaughter | .05 | .02 |

(PB)

| | | | |
|---|---|---|---|
| 371 | Bruce Smith (PB) | .08 | .05 |
| 372 | Dennis Smith (PB) | .05 | .02 |
| 373 | Derrick Thomas (PB) | .10 | .06 |
| 374 | Thurman Thomas (PB) | .25 | .15 |
| 375 | David Treadwell (PB) | .05 | .02 |
| 376 | Lee Williams (PB) | .05 | .02 |
| 377 | Rod Woodson (PB) | .07 | .04 |
| 378 | Bud Carson (PB) | .05 | .02 |
| 379 | Eric Allen (PB) | .05 | .02 |
| 380 | Neal Anderson (PB) | .08 | .05 |
| 381 | Jerry Ball (PB) | .05 | .02 |
| 382 | Joey Browner (PB) | .07 | .04 |
| 383 | Rich Camarillo (PB) | .05 | .02 |
| 384 | Mark Carrier (PB)(TB) | .07 | .04 |
| 385 | Roger Craig (PB) | .08 | .05 |
| 386 | Randall Cunningham (PB) | .10 | .06 |
| 387 | Chris Doleman (PB) | .07 | .04 |
| 388 | Henry Ellard (PB) | .07 | .04 |
| 389 | Bill Fralic (PB) | .05 | .02 |
| 390 | Brent Fullwood (PB) | .05 | .02 |
| 391 | Jerry Gray (PB) | .05 | .02 |
| 392 | Kevin Greene (PB) | .05 | .02 |
| 393 | Tim Harris (PB) | .05 | .02 |
| 394 | Jay Hilgenberg (PB) | .05 | .02 |
| 395 | Dalton Hilliard (PB) | .05 | .02 |
| 396 | Keith Jackson (PB) | .07 | .04 |
| 397 | Vaughan Johnson (PB) | .07 | .04 |
| 398 | Steve Jordan (PB) | .05 | .02 |
| 399 | Carl Lee (PB) | .05 | .02 |
| 400 | Ronnie Lott (PB) | .08 | .05 |
| 401 | Don Majkowski (PB) | .08 | .05 |
| 402 | Charles Mann (PB) | .05 | .02 |
| 403 | Randall McDaniel (PB) | .05 | .02 |
| 404 | Tim McDonald (PB) | .05 | .02 |
| 405 | Guy McIntyre (PB) | .05 | .02 |
| 406 | David Meggett (PB) | .08 | .05 |
| 407 | Keith Millard (PB) | .07 | .04 |
| 408 | Joe Montana (PB) | .25 | .15 |
| 409 | Eddie Murray (PB) | .05 | .02 |
| 410 | Tom Newberry (PB) | .05 | .02 |
| 411 | Jerry Rice (PB) | .30 | .18 |
| 412 | Mark Rypien (PB) | .20 | .12 |
| 413 | Barry Sanders (PB) | .50 | .30 |
| 414 | Luis Sharpe (PB) | .05 | .02 |
| 415 | Sterling Sharpe (PB) | .10 | .06 |
| 416 | Mike Singletary (PB) | .08 | .05 |
| 417 | Jackie Slater (PB) | .05 | .02 |
| 418 | Doug Smith (PB) | .05 | .02 |
| 419 | Chris Spielman (PB) | .05 | .02 |
| 420 | Pat Swilling (PB) | .08 | .05 |
| 421 | John Taylor (PB) | .08 | .05 |
| 422 | Lawrence Taylor (PB) | .10 | .06 |
| 423 | Reggie White (PB) | .08 | .05 |
| 424 | Ron Wolfley (PB) | .05 | .02 |
| 425 | Gary Zimmerman (PB) | .05 | .02 |
| 426 | John Robinson (PB) | .05 | .02 |
| 427 | Scott Case | .05 | .02 |
| 428 | Mike Kenn | .05 | .02 |
| 429 | Mike Gann | .05 | .02 |
| 430 | Tim Green (R) | .08 | .05 |
| 431 | Michael Haynes (R) | .80 | .50 |
| 432 | Jessie Tuggle (R) | .12 | .07 |
| 433 | John Rade | .05 | .02 |
| 434 | Andre Rison | .20 | .12 |
| 435 | Don Beebe | .08 | .05 |
| 436 | Ray Bentley | .05 | .02 |
| 437 | Shane Conlan | .07 | .04 |
| 438 | Kent Hull | .05 | .02 |
| 439 | Pete Metzelaars | .05 | .02 |
| 440 | Andre Reed | .15 | .10 |
| 441 | Frank Reich | .07 | .04 |
| 442 | Leon Seals (R) | .10 | .06 |
| 443 | Bruce Smith | .12 | .07 |
| 444 | Thurman Thomas | .75 | .45 |
| 445 | Will Wolford | .05 | .02 |
| 446 | Trace Armstrong | .05 | .02 |
| 447 | Mark Bortz (R) | .07 | .04 |
| 448 | Tom Thayer (R) | .07 | .04 |
| 449a | Dan Hampton (Er) (Listed as DE on back) | .35 | .20 |
| 449b | Dan Hampton (Cor) | .08 | .05 |
| 450 | Shaun Gayle (R) | .08 | .05 |
| 451 | Dennis Gentry | .05 | .02 |
| 452 | Jim Harbaugh | .20 | .12 |
| 453 | Vestee Jackson | .05 | .02 |
| 454 | Brad Muster | .08 | .05 |
| 455 | William Perry | .07 | .04 |
| 456 | Ron Rivera | .05 | .02 |
| 457 | James Thornton | .05 | .02 |
| 458 | Mike Tomczak | .07 | .04 |
| 459 | Donnell Woolford | .05 | .02 |
| 460 | Eric Ball | .05 | .02 |
| 461 | James Brooks | .07 | .04 |
| 462 | David Fulcher | .05 | .02 |
| 463 | Boomer Esiason | .15 | .10 |
| 464 | Rodney Holman | .05 | .02 |
| 465 | Bruce Kozerski | .05 | .02 |
| 466 | Tim Krumrie | .05 | .02 |
| 467 | Anthony Munoz | .08 | .05 |
| 468 | Brian Blados | .05 | .02 |
| 469 | Mike Baab | .05 | .02 |
| 470 | Brian Brennan | .05 | .02 |
| 471 | Raymond Clayborn | .05 | .02 |
| 472 | Mike Johnson | .05 | .02 |
| 473 | Kevin Mack | .07 | .04 |
| 474 | Clay Matthews | .05 | .02 |
| 475 | Frank Minnifield | .05 | .02 |
| 476 | Gregg Rakoczy (R) | .07 | .04 |
| 477 | Webster Slaughter | .07 | .04 |
| 478 | James Dixon (R) | .08 | .05 |
| 479 | Robert Awalt | .05 | .02 |

| # | Name | | |
|---|---|---|---|
| 480 | Dennis McKinnon | .05 | .02 |
| 481 | Danny Noonan | .05 | .02 |
| 482 | Jesse Solomon | .05 | .02 |
| 483 | Danny Stubbs | .05 | .02 |
| 484 | Steve Walsh | .10 | .06 |
| 485 | Michael Brooks (R) | .08 | .05 |
| 486 | Mark Jackson | .08 | .05 |
| 487 | Greg Kragen | .05 | .02 |
| 488 | Ken Lanier (R) | .08 | .05 |
| 489 | Karl Mecklenburg | .07 | .04 |
| 490 | Steve Sewell | .05 | .02 |
| 491 | Dennis Smith | .05 | .02 |
| 492 | David Treadwell | .05 | .02 |
| 493 | Michael Young (R) | .12 | .07 |
| 494 | Robert Clark (R) | .12 | .07 |
| 495 | Dennis Gibson | .05 | .02 |
| 496 | Kevin Glover (R) | .07 | .04 |
| 497 | Mel Gray | .05 | .02 |
| 498 | Rodney Peete | .12 | .07 |
| 499 | Dave Brown | .05 | .02 |
| 500 | Jerry Holmes | .05 | .02 |
| 501 | Chris Jacke | .05 | .02 |
| 502 | Alan Veingrad | .05 | .02 |
| 503 | Mark Lee | .05 | .02 |
| 504 | Tony Mandarich | .05 | .02 |
| 505 | Brian Noble | .05 | .02 |
| 506 | Jeff Query | .10 | .06 |
| 507 | Ken Ruettgers | .05 | .02 |
| 508 | Patrick Allen (R) | .08 | .05 |
| 509 | Curtis Duncan | .07 | .04 |
| 510 | William Fuller | .05 | .02 |
| 511 | Haywood Jeffires (R) | 1.00 | .70 |
| 512 | Sean Jones | .05 | .02 |
| 513 | Terry Kinard | .05 | .02 |
| 514 | Bruce Matthews | .05 | .02 |
| 515 | Gerald McNeil | .05 | .02 |
| 516 | Greg Montgomery (R) | .05 | .02 |
| 517 | Warren Moon | .20 | .12 |
| 518 | Mike Munchak | .05 | .02 |
| 519 | Allen Pinkett | .05 | .02 |
| 520 | Pat Beach | .05 | .02 |
| 521 | Eugene Daniel | .05 | .02 |
| 522 | Kevin Call | .05 | .02 |
| 523 | Ray Donaldson | .05 | .02 |
| 524 | Jeff Herrod (R) | .08 | .05 |
| 525 | Keith Taylor | .05 | .02 |
| 526 | Jack Trudeau | .08 | .05 |
| 527 | Deron Cherry | .05 | .02 |
| 528 | Jeff Donaldson | .05 | .02 |
| 529 | Albert Lewis | .05 | .02 |
| 530 | Pete Mandley | .05 | .02 |
| 531 | Chris Martin (R) | .08 | .05 |
| 532 | Christian Okoye | .15 | .10 |
| 533 | Steve Pelluer | .08 | .05 |
| 534 | Kevin Ross | .05 | .02 |
| 535 | Dan Saleaumua | .05 | .02 |
| 536 | Derrick Thomas | .35 | .20 |
| 537 | Mike Webster | .07 | .04 |
| 538 | Marcus Allen | .10 | .06 |
| 539 | Greg Bell | .07 | .04 |
| 540 | Thomas Benson | .05 | .02 |
| 541 | Ron Brown | .05 | .02 |
| 542 | Scott Davis | .05 | .02 |
| 543 | Riki Ellison | .05 | .02 |
| 544 | Jamie Holland | .05 | .02 |
| 545 | Howie Long | .07 | .04 |
| 546 | Terry McDaniel | .05 | .02 |
| 547 | Max Montoya | .05 | .02 |
| 548 | Jay Schroeder | .10 | .06 |
| 549 | Lionel Washington | .05 | .02 |
| 550 | Robert Delpino | .10 | .06 |
| 551 | Bobby Humphrey | .05 | .02 |
| 552 | Mike Lansford | .05 | .02 |
| 553 | Michael Stewart (R) | .07 | .04 |
| 554 | Doug Smith | .05 | .02 |
| 555 | Curt Warner | .07 | .04 |
| 556 | Alvin Wright (R) | .07 | .04 |
| 557 | Jeff Cross | .05 | .02 |
| 558 | Jeff Dellenbach (R) | .07 | .04 |
| 559 | Mark Duper | .08 | .05 |
| 560 | Ferrell Edmunds | .05 | .02 |
| 561 | Tim McKyer | .05 | .02 |
| 562 | John Offerdahl | .07 | .04 |
| 563 | Reggie Roby | .05 | .02 |
| 564 | Pete Stoyanovich | .05 | .02 |
| 565 | Alfred Anderson | .05 | .02 |
| 566 | Ray Berry | .05 | .02 |
| 567 | Rick Fenney | .05 | .02 |
| 568 | Rich Gannon (R) | .60 | .35 |
| 569 | Tim Irwin | .05 | .02 |
| 570 | Hassan Jones | .08 | .05 |
| 571 | Cris Carter | .20 | .12 |
| 572 | Kirk Lowdermilk | .05 | .02 |
| 573 | Reggie Rutland (R) | .07 | .04 |
| 574 | Ken Stills | .05 | .02 |
| 575 | Bruce Armstrong | .05 | .02 |
| 576 | Irving Fryar | .07 | .04 |
| 577 | Roland James | .05 | .02 |
| 578 | Robert Perryman | .07 | .04 |
| 579 | Cedric Jones | .05 | .02 |
| 580 | Steve Grogan | .07 | .04 |
| 581 | Johnny Rembert | .05 | .02 |
| 582 | Ed Reynolds | .05 | .02 |
| 583 | Brent Williams | .05 | .02 |
| 584 | Marc Wilson | .07 | .04 |
| 585 | Hoby Brenner | .05 | .02 |
| 586 | Stan Brock | .05 | .02 |
| 587 | Jim Dombrowski (R) | .08 | .05 |
| 588 | Joel Hilgenberg (R) | .07 | .04 |
| 589 | Robert Massey | .05 | .02 |
| 590 | Floyd Turner | .05 | .02 |
| 591 | Ottis Anderson | .08 | .05 |
| 592 | Mark Bavaro | .07 | .04 |
| 593 | Maurice Carthon | .05 | .02 |

| | | | | | | | | |
|---|---|---|---|---|---|---|---|
| 594 | Eric Dorsey (R) | .10 | .06 | 650 | Kelly Stouffer | .12 | .07 |
| 595 | Myron Guyton | .05 | .02 | 651 | Tony Woods | .05 | .02 |
| 596 | Jeff Hostetler (R) | .50 | .30 | 652 | Gary Anderson | .05 | .02 |
| 597 | Sean Landeta | .05 | .02 | 653 | Reuben Davis (R) | .08 | .05 |
| 598 | Lionel Manual | .05 | .02 | 654 | Randy Grimes | .05 | .02 |
| 599 | Odessa Turner (R) | .15 | .10 | 655 | Ron Hall | .05 | .02 |
| 600 | Perry Williams | .05 | .02 | 656 | Eugene Marve | .05 | .02 |
| 601 | James Hasty | .05 | .02 | 657 | Curt Jarvis | .05 | .02 |
| 602 | Erik McMillan | .05 | .02 | 658 | Ricky Reynolds | .05 | .02 |
| 603 | Alex Gordon | .05 | .02 | 659 | Broderick Thomas | .08 | .05 |
| 604 | Ron Stallworth | .05 | .02 | 660 | Jeff Bostic | .05 | .02 |
| 605 | Byron Evans (R) | .07 | .04 | 661 | Todd Bowles (R) | .07 | .04 |
| 606 | Ron Heller (R) | .07 | .04 | 662 | Ravin Caldwell (R) | .08 | .05 |
| 607 | Wes Hopkins | .05 | .02 | 663 | Russ Grimm | .05 | .02 |
| 608 | Mickey Shuler | .05 | .02 | 664 | Joe Jacoby | .07 | .04 |
| 609 | Seth Joyner | .07 | .04 | 665 | Mark May | .05 | .02 |
| 610 | Jim McMahon | .10 | .06 | 666 | Walter Stanley | .05 | .02 |
| 611 | Mike Pitts | .05 | .02 | 667 | Don Warren | .05 | .02 |
| 612 | Izel Jenkins (R) | .07 | .04 | 668 | Stan Humphries (R) | 1.00 | .70 |
| 613 | Anthony Bell | .05 | .02 | 669 | Jeff George (R) | 1.25 | .80 |
| 614 | David Galloway | .05 | .02 | 670 | Blair Thomas (R) | .40 | .25 |
| 615 | Eric Hill | .05 | .02 | 671 | Cortez Kennedy (R) | .75 | .45 |
| 616 | Cedric Mack | .05 | .02 | 672 | Keith McCants (R) | .20 | .12 |
| 617 | Freddie Joe Nunn | .05 | .02 | 673 | Junior Seau (R) | .30 | .18 |
| 618 | Tootie Robbins | .05 | .02 | 674 | Mark Carrier (R)(Chi) | .25 | .15 |
| 619 | Tom Tupa (R) | .12 | .07 | 675 | Andre Ware | .20 | .12 |
| 620 | Joe Wolf | .05 | .02 | 676 | Chris Singleton (R) | .15 | .10 |
| 621 | Dermontti Dawson | .05 | .02 | 677 | Richmond Webb (R) | .12 | .07 |
| 622 | Thomas Everett | .05 | .02 | 678 | Ray Agnew (R) | .10 | .06 |
| 623 | Tunch Ilkin | .05 | .02 | 679 | Anthony Smith (R) | .15 | .10 |
| 624 | Hardy Nickerson | .05 | .02 | 680 | James Francis (R) | .20 | .12 |
| 625 | Gerald Williams (R) | .08 | .05 | 681 | Percy Snow (R) | .20 | .12 |
| 626 | Rod Woodson | .10 | .06 | 682 | Renaldo Turnbull (R) | .12 | .07 |
| 627a | Rod Bernstine (TE) | .35 | .20 | 683 | Lamar Lathon (R) | .15 | .10 |
| 627b | Rod Bernstine (RB) | .15 | .10 | 684 | James Williams (R) | .08 | .05 |
| 628 | Courtney Hall | .05 | .02 | 685 | Emmitt Smith (R) | 3.00 | 2.00 |
| 629 | Ronnie Harmon | .05 | .02 | 686 | Tony Bennett (R) | .25 | .15 |
| 630 | Anthony Miller | .15 | .10 | 687 | Darrell Thompson (R) | .25 | .15 |
| 631 | Joe Phillips | .07 | .04 | 688 | Steve Broussard (R) | .20 | .12 |
| 632 | Leslie O'Neal | .15 | .10 | 689 | Eric Green (R) | .25 | .15 |
| 633 | David Richards | .05 | .02 | 690 | Ben Smith (R) | .08 | .05 |
| 634 | Mark Vlasic | .08 | .05 | 691 | Bern Brostek (R) | .08 | .05 |
| 635 | Lee Williams | .05 | .02 | 692 | Rodney Hampton (R) | 1.25 | .80 |
| 636 | Chet Brooks | .05 | .02 | 693 | Dexter Carter (R) | .20 | .12 |
| 637 | Keena Turner | .05 | .02 | 694 | Rob Moore (R) | .60 | .35 |
| 638 | Kevin Fagan (R) | .08 | .05 | 695 | Alexander Wright (R) | .15 | .10 |
| 639 | Brent Jones (R) | .15 | .10 | 696 | Darion Conner (R) | .10 | .06 |
| 640 | Matt Millen | .05 | .02 | 697 | Reggie Rembert (R) | .15 | .10 |
| 641 | Bubba Paris | .05 | .02 | 698 | Terry Wooden (R) | .10 | .06 |
| 642 | Bill Romanowski (R) | .08 | .05 | 699 | Reggie Cobb (R) | .60 | .35 |
| 643 | Fred Smerlas | .05 | .02 | 700 | Anthony Thompson | .15 | .10 |
| 644 | Dave Waymer | .05 | .02 | 701 | Fred Washington | .08 | .05 |
| 645 | Steve Young | .35 | .20 | | (Memorial version) | | |
| 646 | Brian Blades | .07 | .04 | 702 | Ron Cox (R) | .07 | .04 |
| 647 | Andy Heck | .05 | .02 | 703 | Robert Blackmon (R) | .08 | .05 |
| 648 | Dave Krieg | .10 | .06 | 704 | Dan Owens (R) | .10 | .06 |
| 649 | Rufus Porter | .05 | .02 | 705 | Anthony Johnson (R) | .12 | .07 |

| | | | |
|---|---|---|---|
| 706 Aaron Wallace (R) | .15 | .10 |
| 707 Harold Green (R) | .50 | .30 |
| 708 Keith Sims (R) | .08 | .05 |
| 709 Tim Grunhard (R) | .08 | .05 |
| 710 Jeff Alm (R) | .08 | .05 |
| 711 Carwell Gardner (R) | .10 | .06 |
| 712 Kenny Davidson (R) | .08 | .05 |
| 713 Vince Buck (R) | .12 | .07 |
| 714 Leroy Hoard (R) | .25 | .15 |
| 715 Andre Collins (R) | .15 | .10 |
| 716 Dennis Brown (R) | .08 | .05 |
| 717 LeRoy Butler (R) | .08 | .05 |
| 718 Pat Terrell (R) | .12 | .07 |
| 719 Mike Bellamy (R) | .12 | .07 |
| 720 Mike Fox (R) | .10 | .06 |
| 721 Alton Montgomery (R) | .10 | .06 |
| 722 Eric Davis (R) | .10 | .06 |
| 723 Oliver Barnett (R) | .12 | .07 |
| 724 Houston Hoover (R) | .08 | .05 |
| 725 Howard Ballard (R) | .08 | .05 |
| 726 Keith McKeller (R) | .15 | .10 |
| 727 Wendell Davis (R) | .25 | .15 |
| 728 Peter Tom Willis (R) | .25 | .15 |
| 729 Bernard Clark (R) | .07 | .04 |
| 730 Doug Widell (R) | .08 | .05 |
| 731 Eric Andolsek (R) | .07 | .04 |
| 732 Jeff Campbell (R) | .12 | .07 |
| 733 Marc Spindler (R) | .10 | .06 |
| 734 Keith Woodside (R) | .07 | .04 |
| 735 Willis Peguese (R) | .08 | .05 |
| 736 Frank Stams | .05 | .02 |
| 737 Jeff Uhlenhake | .05 | .02 |
| 738 Todd Kalis (R) | .07 | .04 |
| 739 Tommy Hodson (R) | .25 | .15 |
| 740 Greg McMurtry (R) | .20 | .12 |
| 741 Mike Buck (R) | .12 | .07 |
| 742 Kevin Haverdink (R) | .08 | .05 |
| 743 Johnny Bailey (R) | .15 | .10 |
| 744 Eric Moore (R) | .08 | .05 |
| 745 Tony Stargell (R) | .07 | .04 |
| 746 Fred Barnett (R) | .50 | .30 |
| 747 Walter Reeves | .05 | .02 |
| 748 Derek Hill (R) | .08 | .05 |
| 749 Quinn Early (R) | .08 | .05 |
| 750 Ronald Lewis (R) | .07 | .04 |
| 751 Ken Clark (R) | .07 | .04 |
| 752 Garry Lewis (R) | .07 | .04 |
| 753 James Lofton | .20 | .12 |
| 754 Steve Tasker | .07 | .04 |
| 755 Jim Shofner | .05 | .02 |
| 756 Jimmie Jones (R) | .07 | .04 |
| 757 Jay Novacek | .40 | .25 |
| 758 Jessie Hester (R) | .20 | .12 |
| 759 Barry Word (R) | .60 | .35 |
| 760 Eddie Anderson (R) | .08 | .05 |
| 761 Cleveland Gary (R) | .20 | .12 |
| 762 Marcus Dupree (R) | .15 | .10 |

| | | | |
|---|---|---|---|
| 763 David Griggs (R) | .10 | .06 |
| 764 Rueben Mayes | .07 | .04 |
| 765 Stephen Baker (R) | .10 | .06 |
| 766 Reyna Thompson (R) | .10 | .06 |
| 767 Everson Walls | .07 | .04 |
| 768 Brad Baxter (R) | .25 | .15 |
| 769 Steve Walsh | .08 | .05 |
| 770 Heath Sherman (R) | .25 | .15 |
| 771 Johnny Johnson (R) | .75 | .45 |
| 772 Dexter Manley | .07 | .04 |
| 773 Ricky Proehl (R) | .30 | .18 |
| 774 Frank Cornish (R) | .07 | .04 |
| 775 Tommy Kane (R) | .20 | .12 |
| 776 Derrick Fenner (R) | .35 | .20 |
| 777 Steve Christie (R) | .10 | .06 |
| 778 Wayne Haddix (R) | .12 | .07 |
| 779 Richard Williamson | .05 | .02 |
| 780 Brian Mitchell (R) | .30 | .18 |
| 781 American Bowl (London) | .05 | .02 |
| 782 American Bowl (Berlin) | .05 | .02 |
| 783 American Bowl (Tokyo) | .05 | .02 |
| 784 American Bowl(Mon) | .05 | .02 |
| 785 Berlin Wall | .05 | .02 |
| 786 Al Davis (Newsreel) | .10 | .06 |
| 787 Falcons (Newsreel) | .05 | .02 |
| 788 NFL/WLAF (Newsreel) | .05 | .02 |
| 789 Cheerleaders | .07 | .04 |
| 790 Photo Contest (Mularky) | .05 | .02 |
| 791 Photo Contest (Reasons) | .05 | .02 |
| 792 Photo Contest (Hurst) | .05 | .02 |
| 793 Photo Contest (Lott) | .08 | .05 |
| 794 Photo Contest (Sanders) | .25 | .15 |
| 795 Photo Contest (Seifert) | .05 | .02 |
| 796 Photo Contest (D. Smith) | .05 | .02 |
| 797 Photo Contest (Widell) | .05 | .02 |
| 798 Photo Contest (C. Carter) | .07 | .04 |
| 799 Ronnie Lott (Message) | .08 | .05 |
| 800 Emmitt Smith (Rookie Of The Year-Offense) | 2.00 | 1.25 |
| 800 Mark Carrier (Rookie Of The Year-Defense) | .15 | .10 |
| BC1 Lombardi Trophy (Hologram) | 200.00 | 110.00 |
| SP1 Payne Stewart | 1.50 | .90 |
| SP2 Super Pro | 1.50 | .90 |
| SP3 Santa Claus | 3.50 | 2.00 |
| SP4 Joe Robbie Memorial | 1.50 | .90 |
| SP5 Super Bowl Logo | 1.50 | .90 |

C2  Paul Tagliabue   1.50   .90

# 1991 Pro Set

This 850-card set was issued in two series. A Final Update set, released after the end of the '91 season, rounds out the set. Card fronts feature full bleed four color action photos with a Pro Set logo in the top right corner and the player's name, team and position printed at the bottom of the card front. The horizontal card backs contain a small photograph, stats and highlights. Key subsets include League Leaders (LL), Milestones (M), Hall of Famers (HOF), Heisman Winners (H), Super Bowl (SB), Replays (Rep), NFL Officials (OF), Pro Bowlers (PB), Newsreels (News), Legends (LG), Photo Contest, Message Cards and Draft Picks. There are two versions of card #1, honoring the Offensive and Defensive Rookies of the Year. There is no card #2 in the set. In addition, 13 different cards were produced in limited quantities and inserted randomly in Pro Set packs. Those cards, including autographed Lawrence Taylor cards, are listed at the end of this checklist but are not included in the complete set price. All cards measure 2-1/2" by 3-1/2".

|  | MINT | NR/MT |
|---|---|---|
| Complete Set (850) | 26.50 | 16.00 |
| Series I (1-405) | 9.50 | 6.00 |
| Series II (406-812) | 12.00 | 7.00 |

| | | | |
|---|---|---|---|
| | Final Update (813-850) | 5.00 | 3.00 |
| | Commons | .05 | .02 |
| 1 | Emmitt Smith (Rookie Of The Year-Offense) | 1.00 | .70 |
| 1a | Mark Carrier (Rookie Of The Year-Defense | .08 | .05 |
| 2 | No Card | .00 | .00 |
| 3 | Joe Montana (Player Of The Year) | .25 | .15 |
| 4 | Art Shell (Coach Of The Year) | .07 | .04 |
| 5 | Mike Singletary (Man Of The Year) | .08 | .05 |
| 6 | Bruce Smith (Player Of The Year-Defense) | .08 | .05 |
| 7 | Barry Word Comeback Of The Year) | .10 | .06 |
| 8 | Jim Kelly (LL) | .20 | .12 |
| 9 | Warren Moon (LL) | .12 | .07 |
| 10 | Barry Sanders (LL) | .30 | .18 |
| 11 | Jerry Rice (LL) | .25 | .15 |
| 12 | Jay Novacek (LL) | .07 | .04 |
| 13 | Thurman Thomas (LL) | .25 | .15 |
| 14 | Nick Lowery (LL) | .05 | .02 |
| 15 | Mike Horan (LL) | .05 | .02 |
| 16 | Clarence Verdin (LL) | .05 | .02 |
| 17 | Kevin Clark (LL) | .05 | .02 |
| 18 | Mark Carrier (LL) | .08 | .05 |
| 19a | Derrick Thomas(LL) (Er)(Bills helmet on front) | 12.00 | 7.50 |
| 19b | Derrick Thomas (LL) (Cor)(Chiefs helmut) | .12 | .07 |
| 20 | Ottis Anderson (M) | .08 | .05 |
| 21 | Roger Craig (M) | .08 | .05 |
| 22 | Art Monk (M) | .10 | .06 |
| 23 | Chuck Noll (M) | .07 | .04 |
| 24 | Randall Cunningham (M) | .08 | .05 |
| 25 | Dan Marino (M) | .15 | .10 |
| 26 | 49ers Road Record | .05 | .02 |
| 27 | Earl Campbell HOF | .10 | .06 |
| 28 | John Hannah HOF | .07 | .04 |
| 29 | Stan Jones HOF | .07 | .04 |
| 30 | Tex Schramm HOF | .05 | .02 |
| 31 | Jan Stenerud HOF | .07 | .04 |
| 32 | Russell Maryland (Outland Trophy) | .25 | .15 |
| 33 | Chris Zorich (Lombardi Trophy) | .10 | .06 |
| 34 | Darryl Lewis (Thorpe Trophy) | .12 | .07 |
| 35 | Alfred Williams (Butkus Trophy) | .12 | .07 |
| 36 | Rocket Ismail | 2.50 | 1.50 |

(Walter Camp Award)

| # | Player | | |
|---|---|---|---|
| 37 | Ty Detmer (Heisman) | 1.00 | .70 |
| 38 | Andre Ware (Heisman) | .10 | .06 |
| 39 | Barry Sanders (Heisman) | .25 | .15 |
| 40 | Tim Brown (Heisman) | .08 | .05 |
| 41 | Vinny Testaverde (Heisman) | .07 | .04 |
| 42 | Bob Jackson (Heisman) | .25 | .15 |
| 43 | Mike Rozier (Heisman) | .07 | .04 |
| 44 | Herschel Walker (Heisman) | .08 | .05 |
| 45 | Marcus Allen (Heisman) | .08 | .05 |
| 46 | James Lofton (SB) | .10 | .06 |
| 47 | Bruce Smith (SB) | .10 | .06 |
| 48 | Myron Guyton (SB) | .05 | .02 |
| 49 | Stephen Baker (SB) | .05 | .02 |
| 50 | Mark Ingram (SB) | .05 | .02 |
| 51 | Ottis Anderson (SB) | .07 | .04 |
| 52 | Thurman Thomas (SB) | .25 | .15 |
| 53 | Matt Bahr (SB) | .05 | .02 |
| 54 | Scott Norwood (SB) | .05 | .02 |
| 55 | Stephen Baker | .07 | .04 |
| 56 | Carl Banks | .07 | .04 |
| 57 | Mark Collins | .05 | .02 |
| 58 | Steve DeOssie | .05 | .02 |
| 59 | Eric Dorsey | .05 | .02 |
| 60 | John Elliott | .05 | .02 |
| 61 | Myron Guyton | .05 | .02 |
| 62 | Rodney Hampton | .35 | .20 |
| 63 | Jeff Hostetler | .15 | .10 |
| 64 | Erik Howard | .05 | .02 |
| 65 | Mark Ingram | .05 | .02 |
| 66 | Greg Jackson (R) | .07 | .04 |
| 67 | Leonard Marshall | .07 | .04 |
| 68 | David Meggett | .12 | .07 |
| 69 | Eric Moore | .05 | .02 |
| 70 | Bart Oates | .05 | .02 |
| 71 | Gary Reasons | .05 | .02 |
| 72 | Bill Parcells | .05 | .02 |
| 73 | Howard Ballard | .05 | .02 |
| 74a | Cornelius Bennett (NFLPA logo) | .30 | .18 |
| 74b | Cornelius Bennett (Without logo) | .10 | .06 |
| 75 | Shane Conlan | .07 | .04 |
| 76 | Kent Hull | .05 | .02 |
| 77 | Kirby Jackson (R) | .08 | .05 |
| 78a | Jim Kelly (NFLPA logo) | .75 | .45 |
| 78b | Jim Kelly (Without logo) | .25 | .15 |
| 79 | Mark Kelso | .05 | .02 |
| 80 | Nate Odomes | .05 | .02 |
| 81 | Andre Reed | .12 | .07 |
| 82 | Jim Ritcher | .05 | .02 |
| 83 | Bruce Smith | .10 | .06 |
| 84 | Darryl Talley | .07 | .04 |
| 85 | Steve Tasker | .05 | .02 |
| 86 | Thurman Thomas | .50 | .30 |
| 87 | James Williams | .05 | .02 |
| 88 | Will Wolford | .05 | .02 |
| 89 | Jeff Wright (R) | .08 | .05 |
| 90 | Marv Levy | .05 | .02 |
| 91 | Steve Brousaard | .08 | .05 |
| 92a | Darion Conner (Er) (Drafted '99) | 7.50 | 4.00 |
| 92b | Darion Conner (Cor) | .07 | .04 |
| 93 | Bill Fralic | .05 | .02 |
| 94 | Tim Green | .05 | .02 |
| 95 | Michael Haynes | .15 | .10 |
| 96 | Chris Hinton | .05 | .02 |
| 97 | Chris Miller | .25 | .15 |
| 98 | Deion Sanders | .25 | .15 |
| 99 | Jerry Glanville | .05 | .02 |
| 100 | Kevin Butler | .05 | .02 |
| 101 | Mark Carrier (Chi) | .08 | .05 |
| 102 | Jim Covert | .05 | .02 |
| 103 | Richard Dent | .07 | .04 |
| 104 | Jim Harbaugh | .15 | .10 |
| 105 | Brad Muster | .08 | .05 |
| 106 | Lemuel Stinson | .05 | .02 |
| 107 | Keith Van Horne | .05 | .02 |
| 108 | Mike Ditka | .07 | .04 |
| 109 | Lewis Billups | .05 | .02 |
| 110 | James Brooks | .07 | .04 |
| 111 | Boomer Esiason | .12 | .07 |
| 112 | James Francis | .08 | .05 |
| 113 | David Fulcher | .05 | .02 |
| 114 | Rodney Holman | .05 | .02 |
| 115 | Tim McGee | .07 | .04 |
| 116 | Anthony Munoz | .08 | .05 |
| 117 | Sam Wyche | .05 | .02 |
| 118 | Paul Farren | .05 | .02 |
| 119 | Thane Gash | .05 | .02 |
| 120 | Mike Johnson | .05 | .02 |
| 121a | Bernie Kosar (NFLPA logo) | .15 | .10 |
| 121b | Bernie Kosar (No Logo) | .10 | .06 |
| 122 | Clay Matthews | .05 | .02 |
| 123 | Eric Metcalf | .08 | .05 |
| 124 | Frank Minnifield | .05 | .02 |
| 125 | Webster Slaughter | .07 | .04 |
| 126 | Bill Belichick | .05 | .02 |
| 127 | Tommie Agee | .05 | .02 |
| 128 | Troy Aikman | .80 | .50 |
| 129 | Jack Del Rio | .05 | .02 |
| 130 | John Gesek (R) | .07 | .04 |
| 131 | Issiac Holt | .05 | .02 |

| | | | |
|---|---|---|---|
| 132 Michael Irvin | .35 | .20 |
| 133 Ken Norton | .05 | .02 |
| 134 Daniel Stubbs | .05 | .02 |
| 135 Jimmy Johnson | .05 | .02 |
| 136 Steve Atwater | .08 | .05 |
| 137 Michael Brooks | .05 | .02 |
| 138 John Elway | .20 | .12 |
| 139 Wyman Henderson | .05 | .02 |
| 140 Bobby Humphrey | .12 | .07 |
| 141 Mark Jackson | .07 | .04 |
| 142 Karl Mecklenburg | .07 | .04 |
| 143 Doug Widell | .05 | .02 |
| 144 Dan Reeves | .05 | .02 |
| 145 Eric Andolsek | .05 | .02 |
| 146 Jerry Ball | .05 | .02 |
| 147 Bennie Blades | .07 | .04 |
| 148 Lomas Brown | .05 | .02 |
| 149 Robert Clark | .05 | .02 |
| 150 Michael Cofer | .05 | .02 |
| 151 Dan Owens | .05 | .02 |
| 152 Rodney Peete | .10 | .06 |
| 153 Wayne Fontes | .05 | .02 |
| 154 Tim Harris | .05 | .02 |
| 155 Johnny Holland | .05 | .02 |
| 156 Dan Majkowski | .12 | .07 |
| 157 Tony Mandarich | .05 | .02 |
| 158 Mark Murphy | .05 | .02 |
| 159 Brian Noble | .05 | .02 |
| 160 Jeff Query | .08 | .05 |
| 161 Sterling Sharpe | .20 | .12 |
| 162 Lindy Infante | .05 | .02 |
| 163 Ray Childress | .07 | .04 |
| 164 Ernest Givins | .12 | .07 |
| 165 Richard Johnson | .05 | .02 |
| 166 Bruce Matthews | .05 | .02 |
| 167 Warren Moon | .20 | .12 |
| 168 Mike Munchak | .07 | .04 |
| 169 Al Smith | .05 | .02 |
| 170 Lorenzo White | .15 | .10 |
| 171 Jack Pardee | .05 | .02 |
| 172 Albert Bentley | .05 | .02 |
| 173 Duane Bickett | .05 | .02 |
| 174 Bill Brooks | .05 | .02 |
| 175a Eric Dickerson | 1.00 | .70 |
| (NFLPA logo) | .05 | .02 |
| 175b Eric Dickerson | .35 | .20 |
| (No Logo) | | |
| 176 Ray Donaldson | .05 | .02 |
| 177 Jeff George | .25 | .15 |
| 178 Jeff Herrod | .05 | .02 |
| 179 Clarence Verdin | .07 | .04 |
| 180 Ron Meyer | .05 | .02 |
| 181 Joh Alt | .05 | .02 |
| 182 Steve DeBerg | .10 | .06 |
| 183 Albert Lewis | .05 | .02 |
| 184 Nick Lowery | .07 | .04 |
| 185 Christian Okoye | .12 | .07 |
| 186 Stephone Paige | .07 | .04 |
| 187 Kevin Porter | .05 | .02 |
| 188 Derrick Thomas | .20 | .12 |
| 189 Marty Schottenheimer | .05 | .02 |
| 190 Willie Gault | .07 | .04 |
| 191 Howie Long | .07 | .04 |
| 192 Terry McDaniel | .05 | .02 |
| 193 Jay Schroeder | .10 | .06 |
| 194 Steve Smith | .05 | .02 |
| 195 Greg Townsend | .07 | .04 |
| 196 Lionel Washington | .05 | .02 |
| 197 Steve Wisniewski | .05 | .02 |
| 198 Art Shell | .07 | .04 |
| 199 Henry Ellard | .07 | .04 |
| 200 Jim Everett | .15 | .10 |
| 201 Jerry Gray | .05 | .02 |
| 202 Kevin Greene | .05 | .02 |
| 203 Buford McGee | .05 | .02 |
| 204 Tom Newberry | .05 | .02 |
| 205 Frank Stams | .05 | .02 |
| 206 Alvin Wright | .05 | .02 |
| 207 John Robinson | .05 | .02 |
| 208 Jeff Cross | .05 | .02 |
| 209 Mark Duper | .08 | .05 |
| 210 Dan Marino | .40 | .25 |
| 211a Tim McKyer (Er) | .15 | .10 |
| (No trade stripe) | | |
| 211b Tim McKyer (Cor) | .07 | .04 |
| (Traded stripe) | | |
| 212 John Offerdahl | .07 | .04 |
| 213 Sammie Smith | .08 | .05 |
| 214 Richmond Webb | .05 | .02 |
| 215 Jarvis Williams | .05 | .02 |
| 216 Don Shula | .08 | .05 |
| 217 Darrell Fullington | .05 | .02 |
| 218 Tim Irwin | .05 | .02 |
| 219 Mike Merriweather | .05 | .02 |
| 220 Keith Millard | .07 | .04 |
| 221 Al Noga | .05 | .02 |
| 222 Henry Thomas | .05 | .02 |
| 223 Wade Wilson | .08 | .05 |
| 224 Gary Zimmerman | .05 | .02 |
| 225 Jerry Burns | .05 | .02 |
| 226 Bruce Armstrong | .05 | .02 |
| 227 Marv Cook (R) | .10 | .06 |
| 228 Hart Lee Dykes | .07 | .04 |
| 229 Tommy Hodson | .10 | .06 |
| 230 Ronnie Lippett | .05 | .02 |
| 231 Ed Reynolds | .05 | .02 |
| 232 Chris Singleton | .07 | .04 |
| 233 John Stephens | .08 | .05 |
| 234 Dick MacPherson | .05 | .02 |
| 235 Craig Heyward | .07 | .04 |
| 237 Vaughan Johnson | .07 | .04 |
| 238 Robert Massey | .05 | .02 |
| 239 Brett Maxie | .05 | .02 |
| 240 Rueben Mayes | .05 | .02 |

| | | | |
|---|---|---|---|
| 241 | Pat Swilling | .12 | .07 |
| 242 | Renaldo Turnbull | .07 | .04 |
| 243 | Jim Mora | .05 | .02 |
| 244 | Kyle Clifton | .05 | .02 |
| 245 | Jeff Criswell | .05 | .02 |
| 246 | James Hasty | .05 | .02 |
| 247 | Erik McMillan | .05 | .02 |
| 248 | Scott Mersereau (R) | .07 | .04 |
| 249 | Ken O'Brien | .10 | .06 |
| 250a | Blair Thomas (NFLPA logo) | .50 | .30 |
| 250b | Blair Thomas (No logo) | .25 | .15 |
| 251 | Al Toon | .08 | .05 |
| 252 | Bruce Coslet | .05 | .02 |
| 253 | Eric Allen | .05 | .02 |
| 254 | Fred Barnett | .20 | .12 |
| 255 | Keith Byars | .07 | .04 |
| 256 | Randall Cunningham | .15 | .10 |
| 257 | Seth Joyner | .07 | .04 |
| 258 | Clyde Simmons | .07 | .04 |
| 259 | Jessie Small | .05 | .02 |
| 260 | Andre Waters | .05 | .02 |
| 261 | Rich Kotite | .05 | .02 |
| 262 | Roy Green | .07 | .04 |
| 263 | Ernie Jones | .08 | .05 |
| 264 | Tim McDonald | .05 | .02 |
| 265 | Timm Rosenbach | .12 | .07 |
| 266 | Rod Saddler (R) | .08 | .05 |
| 267 | Luis Sharpe | .05 | .02 |
| 268 | Anthony Thompson | .08 | .05 |
| 269 | Marcus Turner (R) | .08 | .05 |
| 270 | Joe Bugel | .05 | .02 |
| 271 | Gary Anderson | .05 | .02 |
| 272 | Dermontti Dawson | .05 | .02 |
| 273 | Eric Green | .12 | .07 |
| 274 | Merril Hoge | .07 | .04 |
| 275 | Tunch Ilkin | .05 | .02 |
| 276 | David Johnson | .05 | .02 |
| 277 | Louis Lipps | .07 | .04 |
| 278 | Rod Woodson | .08 | .05 |
| 279 | Chuck Noll | .07 | .04 |
| 280 | Martin Bayless | .05 | .02 |
| 281 | Marion Butts | .12 | .07 |
| 282 | Gill Byrd | .05 | .02 |
| 283 | Burt Grossman | .07 | .04 |
| 284 | Courtney Hall | .05 | .02 |
| 285 | Anthony Miller | .15 | .10 |
| 286 | Leslie O'Neal | .07 | .04 |
| 287 | Billy Joe Tolliver | .08 | .05 |
| 288 | Dan Henning | .05 | .02 |
| 289 | Dexter Carter | .08 | .05 |
| 290 | Michael Carter | .05 | .02 |
| 291 | Kevin Fagan | .05 | .02 |
| 292 | Pierce Holt | .05 | .02 |
| 293 | Guy McIntyre | .05 | .02 |
| 294 | Tom Rathman | .08 | .05 |

| | | | |
|---|---|---|---|
| 295 | John Taylor | .15 | .10 |
| 296 | Steve Young | .30 | .18 |
| 297 | George Seifert | .05 | .02 |
| 298 | Brian Blades | .07 | .04 |
| 299 | Jeff Bryant | .05 | .02 |
| 300 | Norm Johnson | .05 | .02 |
| 301 | Tommy Kane | .08 | .05 |
| 302 | Cortez Kennedy | .10 | .06 |
| 303 | Bryan Millard | .05 | .02 |
| 304 | John L. Williams | .05 | .02 |
| 305 | David Wyman | .05 | .02 |
| 306 | Chuck Knox | .05 | .02 |
| 307 | Gary Anderson | .05 | .02 |
| 308 | Reggie Cobb | .10 | .06 |
| 309 | Randy Grimes | .05 | .02 |
| 310 | Harry Hamilton | .05 | .02 |
| 311 | Bruce Hill | .05 | .02 |
| 312 | Eugene Marve | .05 | .02 |
| 313 | Ervin Randle | .05 | .02 |
| 314 | Vinny Testaverde | .10 | .06 |
| 315 | Richard Williamson | .05 | .02 |
| 316 | Earnest Byner | .08 | .05 |
| 317 | Gary Clark | .15 | .10 |
| 318a | Andre Collins (NFLPA logo) | .12 | .07 |
| 318b | Andre Collins (No logo) | .08 | .05 |
| 319 | Darryl Grant | .05 | .02 |
| 320 | Chip Lohmiller | .05 | .02 |
| 321 | Martin Mayhew | .05 | .02 |
| 322 | Mark Rypien | .20 | .12 |
| 323 | Alvin Walton | .05 | .02 |
| 324 | Joe Gibbs | .05 | .02 |
| 325 | Jerry Glaville (Replay) | .05 | .02 |
| 326a | John Elway (Replay) (NFLPA logo) | .12 | .07 |
| 326b | John Elway (Replay) (No logo) | .08 | .05 |
| 327 | Boomer Esiason (Rep) | .08 | .05 |
| 328 | Steve Tasker (Replay) | .05 | .02 |
| 329 | Jerry Rice (Replay) | .12 | .07 |
| 330 | Jeff Rutledge (Replay) | .05 | .02 |
| 331 | Chiefs Defense (Replay) | .05 | .02 |
| 332 | 49ers (Replay) | .05 | .02 |
| 333 | John Taylor (Replay) | .07 | .04 |
| 334 | Randall Cunningham (Replay) | .10 | .06 |
| 335a | Bo Jackson and Barry Sanders (Replay) (NFLPA logo) | .75 | .45 |
| 335b | Bo Jackson and Barry Sanders (Replay) (No logo) | .35 | .20 |
| 336 | Lawrence Taylor (Replay) | .10 | .06 |
| 337 | Warren Moon (Replay) | .10 | .06 |

| | | | |
|---|---|---|---|
| 338 Alan Grant (Replay) | .05 | .02 |
| 339 Todd McNair (Replay) | .05 | .02 |
| 340 Mark Clayton (Replay) | .08 | .05 |
| 341a Jim Kelly (Replay) (NFLPA logo) | .15 | .10 |
| 341b Jim Kelly (Replay) (No logo) | .10 | .06 |
| 342 Matt Bahr (Replay) | .05 | .02 |
| 343 Robert Tisch (News) | .05 | .02 |
| 344 Sam Jankovich (News) | .05 | .02 |
| 345 John Elway (News) | .10 | .06 |
| 346 Bo Jackson (News) | .12 | .07 |
| 347 Teacher Of Year | .05 | .02 |
| 348 Ronnie Lott (News) | .07 | .04 |
| 349 Super Bowl XXV (News) | .07 | .04 |
| 350 Whitney Houston (News) | .25 | .15 |
| 351 U.S. Troops (News) | .07 | .04 |
| 352 Art McNally (OF) | .05 | .02 |
| 353 Dick Jorgensen (OF) | .05 | .02 |
| 354 Jerr Seeman (OF) | .05 | .02 |
| 355 Jim Tunney (OF) | .05 | .02 |
| 356 Gerry Austin (OF) | .05 | .02 |
| 357 Gene Barth (OF) | .05 | .02 |
| 358 Red Cashion (OF) | .05 | .02 |
| 359 Tom Dooley (OF) | .05 | .02 |
| 360 Johnny Grier (OF) | .05 | .02 |
| 361 Pat Haggerty (OF) | .05 | .02 |
| 362 Dale Hamer (OF) | .05 | .02 |
| 363 Dick Hantak (OF) | .05 | .02 |
| 364 Jerry Markbreit (OF) | .05 | .02 |
| 365 Gordon McCarter (OF) | .05 | .02 |
| 366 Bob McElwee (OF) | .05 | .02 |
| 367 Howard Roe (OF) | .05 | .02 |
| 368 Tom White (OF) | .05 | .02 |
| 369 Norm Schachter (OF) | .05 | .02 |
| 370 Warren Moon (Message) | .10 | .06 |
| 371 Boomer Esiason (Message) | .08 | .05 |
| 372 Troy Aikman (Message) | .20 | .12 |
| 373 Carl Banks (Message) | .08 | .05 |
| 374 Jim Everett (Message) | .08 | .05 |
| 375 Anthony Munoz (Message) | .30 | .18 |
| 376 Ray Childress (Message) | .08 | .05 |
| 377 Charles Mann (Message) | .07 | .04 |
| 378 Jackie Slater (Message) | .07 | .04 |
| 379 Jerry Rice (PB) | .20 | .12 |
| 380 Andre Rison (PB) | .12 | .07 |
| 381 Jim Lachey (PB) | .05 | .02 |

| | | | |
|---|---|---|---|
| 382 Jackie Slater (PB) | .05 | .02 |
| 383 Randall McDaniel (PB) | .05 | .02 |
| 384 Mark Bortz (PB) | .05 | .02 |
| 385 Jay Hilgenberg (PB) | .05 | .02 |
| 386 Keith Jackson (PB) | .07 | .04 |
| 387 Joe Montana (PB) | .25 | .15 |
| 388 Barry Sanders (PB) | .25 | .15 |
| 389 Neal Anderson (PB) | .08 | .05 |
| 390 Reggie White (PB) | .08 | .05 |
| 391 Chris Doleman (PB) | .07 | .04 |
| 392 Jerome Brown (PB) | .07 | .04 |
| 393 Charles Haley (PB) | .05 | .02 |
| 394 Lawrence Taylor (PB) | .10 | .06 |
| 395 Pepper Johnson (PB) | .05 | .02 |
| 396 Mike Singletary (PB) | .08 | .05 |
| 397 Darrell Green (PB) | .07 | .04 |
| 398 Carl Lee (PB) | .05 | .02 |
| 399 Joey Browner (PB) | .05 | .02 |
| 400 Ronnie Lott (PB) | .08 | .05 |
| 401 Sean Landeta (PB) | .05 | .02 |
| 402 Morten Andersen (PB) | .05 | .02 |
| 403 Mel Gray (PB) | .05 | .02 |
| 404 Reyna Thompson (PB) | .05 | .02 |
| 405 Jimmy Johnson (PB) | .05 | .02 |
| 406 Andre Reed (PB) | .07 | .04 |
| 407 Anthony Miller (PB) | .07 | .04 |
| 408 Anthony Munoz (PB) | .07 | .04 |
| 409 Bruce Armstrong (PB) | .05 | .02 |
| 410 Bruce Matthews (PB) | .05 | .02 |
| 411 Mike Munchak (PB) | .05 | .02 |
| 412 Kent Hull (PB) | .05 | .02 |
| 413 Rodney Holman (PB) | .05 | .02 |
| 414 Warren Moon (PB) | .10 | .06 |
| 415 Thurman Thomas (PB) | .15 | .10 |
| 416 Marion Butts (PB) | .07 | .04 |
| 417 Bruce Smith (PB) | .07 | .04 |
| 418 Greg Townsend (PB) | .05 | .02 |
| 419 Ray Childress (PB) | .05 | .02 |
| 420 Derrick Thomas (PB) | .08 | .05 |
| 421 Leslie O'Neal (PB) | .05 | .02 |
| 422 John Offerdahl (PB) | .05 | .02 |
| 423 Shane Conlan (PB) | .05 | .02 |
| 424 Rod Woodson (PB) | .07 | .04 |
| 425 Albert Lewis (PB) | .05 | .02 |
| 426 Steve Atwater (PB) | .07 | .04 |
| 427 David Fulcher (PB) | .05 | .02 |
| 428 Rohn Stark (PB) | .05 | .02 |
| 429 Nick Lowery (PB) | .05 | .02 |
| 430 Clarence Verdin (PB) | .05 | .02 |
| 431 Steve Tasker (PB) | .05 | .02 |
| 432 Art Shell (PB) | .05 | .02 |
| 433 Scott Case | .05 | .02 |
| 434 Tory Epps | .05 | .02 |
| 435 Mike Gann | .05 | .02 |
| 436 Brian Jordan | .12 | .07 |

| | | | |
|---|---|---|---|
| 437 Mike Kenn | .05 | .02 |
| 438 John Rade | .05 | .02 |
| 439 Andre Rison | .20 | .12 |
| 440 Mike Rozier | .05 | .02 |
| 441 Jessie Tuggle | .05 | .02 |
| 442 Don Beebe | .07 | .04 |
| 443 John Davis (R) | .07 | .04 |
| 444 James Lofton | .15 | .10 |
| 445 Keith McKeller | .07 | .04 |
| 446 Jamie Mueller | .05 | .02 |
| 447 Scott Norwood | .05 | .02 |
| 448 Frank Reich | .07 | .04 |
| 449 Leon Seals | .05 | .02 |
| 450 Leonard Smith | .05 | .02 |
| 451 Neal Anderson | .12 | .07 |
| 452 Trace Armstrong | .05 | .02 |
| 453 Mark Bortz | .05 | .02 |
| 454 Wendell Davis | .12 | .07 |
| 455 Shaun Gayle | .05 | .02 |
| 456 Jay Hilgenberg | .05 | .02 |
| 457 Steve McMichael | .07 | .04 |
| 458 Mike Singletary | .12 | .07 |
| 459 Donnell Woolford | .05 | .02 |
| 460 Jim Breech | .05 | .02 |
| 461 Eddie Brown | .08 | .05 |
| 462 Barney Bussey (R) | .07 | .04 |
| 463 Bruce Kozerski | .05 | .02 |
| 464 Tim Krumrie | .05 | .02 |
| 465 Bruce Reimers | .05 | .02 |
| 466 Kevin Walker (R) | .10 | .06 |
| 467 Ickey Woods | .05 | .02 |
| 468 Carl Zander | .05 | .02 |
| 469 Mike Baab | .05 | .02 |
| 470 Brian Brennan | .05 | .02 |
| 471 Rob Burnett (R) | .10 | .07 |
| 472 Raymond Clayborn | .05 | .02 |
| 473 Reggie Langhorne | .05 | .02 |
| 474 Kevin Mack | .07 | .04 |
| 475 Anthony Pleasant | .05 | .02 |
| 476 Joe Morris | .07 | .04 |
| 477 Dan Fike | .05 | .02 |
| 478 Ray Horton | .05 | .02 |
| 479 Jim Jeffcoat | .05 | .02 |
| 480 Jimmie Jones | .05 | .02 |
| 481 Kelvin Martin | .08 | .05 |
| 482 Nate Newton | .05 | .02 |
| 483 Danny Noonan | .05 | .02 |
| 484 Jay Novacek | .08 | .05 |
| 485 Emmitt Smith | 1.75 | 1.00 |
| 486 James Washington (R) | .08 | .05 |
| 487 Simon Fletcher | .05 | .02 |
| 488 Ron Holmes | .05 | .02 |
| 489 Mike Horan | .05 | .02 |
| 490 Vance Johnson | .08 | .05 |
| 491 Keith Kartz (R) | .07 | .04 |
| 492 Greg Kragen | .05 | .02 |

| | | | |
|---|---|---|---|
| 493 Ken Lanier | .05 | .02 |
| 494 Warren Powers | .05 | .02 |
| 495 Dennis Smith | .05 | .02 |
| 496 Jeff Campbell | .05 | .02 |
| 497 Ken Dallafior (R) | .07 | .04 |
| 498 Dennis Gibson | .05 | .02 |
| 499 Kevin Glover | .05 | .02 |
| 500 Mel Gray | .05 | .02 |
| 501 Eddie Murray | .05 | .02 |
| 502 Barry Sanders | .75 | .45 |
| 503 Chris Spielman | .05 | .02 |
| 504 William White | .05 | .02 |
| 505 Matt Brock (R) | .08 | .05 |
| 506 Robert Brown | .05 | .02 |
| 507 LeRoy Butler | .05 | .02 |
| 508 James Campen (R) | .07 | .04 |
| 509 Jerry Holmes | .05 | .02 |
| 510 Perry Kemp | .05 | .02 |
| 511 Ken Ruettgers | .05 | .02 |
| 512 Scott Stephen (R) | .08 | .05 |
| 513 Ed West | .05 | .02 |
| 514 Cris Dishman | .12 | .07 |
| 515 Curtis Duncan | .07 | .04 |
| 516 Drew Hill | .08 | .05 |
| 517 Haywood Jeffires | .20 | .12 |
| 518 Sean Jones | .05 | .02 |
| 519 Lamar Lathon | .08 | .05 |
| 520 Don Maggs | .05 | .02 |
| 521 Bubba McDowell | .05 | .02 |
| 522 Johnny Meads | .05 | .02 |
| 523a Chip Banks (Er) | .35 | .20 |
| (No text on back) | | |
| 523b Chip Banks (Cor | .07 | .04 |
| 524 Pat Beach | .05 | .02 |
| 525 Sam Clancy | .05 | .02 |
| 526 Eugene Daniel | .05 | .02 |
| 527 Jon Hand | .05 | .02 |
| 528 Jessie Hester | .05 | .02 |
| 529a Mike Prior (Er) | .35 | .20 |
| (No text on back) | | |
| 529b Mike Prior (Cor) | .07 | .04 |
| 530 Keith Taylor | .05 | .02 |
| 531 Donnell Thompson | .07 | .04 |
| 532 Dino Hackett | .05 | .02 |
| 533 David Lutz (R) | .07 | .04 |
| 534 Chris Martin | .05 | .02 |
| 535 Kevin Ross | .05 | .02 |
| 536 Dan Saleaumua | .05 | .02 |
| 537 Neil Smith | .05 | .02 |
| 538 Percy Snow | .07 | .04 |
| 539 Robb Thomas | .05 | .02 |
| 540 Barry Word | .20 | .12 |
| 541 Marcus Allen | .10 | .06 |
| 542 Eddie Anderson | .05 | .02 |
| 543 Scott Davis | .05 | .02 |
| 544 Mervyn Fernandez | .08 | .05 |
| 545 Ethan Horton | .08 | .05 |

| | | | | | | |
|---|---|---|---|---|---|---|
| 546 | Ronnie Lott | .10 | .06 | 603 | Everson Walls | .05 | .02 |
| 547 | Don Mosebar | .05 | .02 | 604 | Brad Baxter | .12 | .07 |
| 548 | Jerry Robinson | .05 | .02 | 605 | Dennis Byrd | .05 | .02 |
| 549 | Aaron Wallace | .07 | .04 | 606 | Jeff Lageman | .07 | .04 |
| 550 | Flipper Anderson | .08 | .05 | 607 | Pat Leahy | .05 | .02 |
| 551 | Cleveland Gary | .10 | .06 | 608 | Rob Moore | .25 | .15 |
| 552 | Damone Johnson (R) | .08 | .05 | 609 | Joe Mott (R) | .07 | .04 |
| 553 | Duval Love (R) | .08 | .05 | 610 | Tony Stargell | .05 | .02 |
| 554 | Irv Pankey | .05 | .02 | 611 | Brian Washington | .05 | .02 |
| 555 | Mike Piel | .05 | .02 | 612 | Marvin Washington (R) | .08 | .05 |
| 556 | Jackie Slater | .07 | .04 | 613 | David Alexander | .05 | .02 |
| 557 | Michael Stewart | .05 | .02 | 614 | Jerome Brown | .07 | .04 |
| 558 | Pat Terrell | .05 | .02 | 615 | Byron Evans | .05 | .02 |
| 559 | J.B. Brown | .05 | .02 | 616 | Ron Heller | .05 | .02 |
| 560 | Mark Clayton | .12 | .07 | 617 | Wes Hopkins | .05 | .02 |
| 561 | Ferrell Edmunds | .05 | .02 | 618 | Keith Jackson | .15 | .10 |
| 562 | Harry Galbreath | .05 | .02 | 619 | Heath Sherman | .07 | .04 |
| 563 | David Griggs | .05 | .02 | 620 | Reggie White | .12 | .07 |
| 564 | Jim Jensen | .05 | .02 | 621 | Calvin Williams | .12 | .07 |
| 565 | Louis Oliver | .07 | .04 | 622 | Ken Harvey | .05 | .02 |
| 566 | Tony Paige | .05 | .02 | 623 | Eric Hill | .05 | .02 |
| 567 | Keith Sims | .05 | .02 | 624 | Johnny Johnson | .15 | .10 |
| 568 | Joey Browner | .07 | .04 | 625 | Freddie Joe Nunn | .05 | .02 |
| 569 | Anthony Carter | .08 | .05 | 626 | Ricky Proehl | .10 | .06 |
| 570 | Chris Doleman | .08 | .05 | 627 | Tootie Robbins | .05 | .02 |
| 571 | Rich Gannon | .20 | .12 | 628 | Jay Taylor | .05 | .02 |
| 572 | Hassan Jones | .07 | .04 | 629 | Tom Tupa | .08 | .05 |
| 573 | Steve Jordan | .05 | .02 | 630 | Jim Wahler (R) | .07 | .04 |
| 574 | Carl Lee | .05 | .02 | 631 | Bubby Brister | .10 | .06 |
| 575 | Randall McDaniel | .05 | .02 | 632 | Thomas Everett | .05 | .02 |
| 576 | Herschel Walker | .12 | .07 | 633 | Bryan Hinkle | .05 | .02 |
| 577 | Ray Agnew | .05 | .02 | 634 | Carnell Lake | .05 | .02 |
| 578 | Vincent Brown | .05 | .02 | 635 | David Little | .05 | .02 |
| 579 | Irving Fryar | .07 | .04 | 636 | Hardy Nickerson | .05 | .02 |
| 580 | Tim Goad | .05 | .02 | 637 | Gerald Williams | .05 | .02 |
| 581 | Maurice Hurst | .05 | .02 | 638 | Keith Willis | .05 | .02 |
| 582 | Fred Marion | .05 | .02 | 639 | Tim Worley | .07 | .04 |
| 583 | Johnny Rembert | .05 | .02 | 640 | Rod Bernstine | .07 | .04 |
| 584 | Andre Tippett | .07 | .04 | 641 | Frank Cornish | .05 | .02 |
| 585 | Brent Williams | .05 | .02 | 642 | Gary Plummer | .05 | .02 |
| 586 | Morten Andersen | .07 | .04 | 643 | Henry Rolling (R) | .10 | .06 |
| 587 | Toi Cook (R) | .08 | .05 | 644 | Sam Seale (R) | .08 | .05 |
| 588 | Jim Dombrowski | .05 | .02 | 645 | Junior Seau | .20 | .12 |
| 589 | Dalton Hilliard | .08 | .05 | 646 | Billy Ray Smith | .05 | .02 |
| 590 | Rickey Jackson | .07 | .04 | 647 | Broderick Thompson | .05 | .02 |
| 591 | Eric Martin | .08 | .05 | 648 | Derrick Walker (R) | .10 | .06 |
| 592 | Sam Mills | .07 | .04 | 649 | Todd Bowles | .05 | .02 |
| 593 | Bobby Hebert | .15 | .10 | 650 | Don Griffin | .05 | .02 |
| 594 | Steve Walsh | .10 | .06 | 651 | Charles Haley | .07 | .04 |
| 595 | Ottis Anderson | .08 | .05 | 652 | Brent Jones | .07 | .04 |
| 596 | Pepper Johnson | .05 | .02 | 653 | Joe Montana | .60 | .35 |
| 597 | Bob Kratch (R) | .07 | .04 | 654 | Jerry Rice | .40 | .25 |
| 598 | Sean Landeta | .05 | .02 | 655 | Bill Romanowski | .05 | .02 |
| 599 | Doug Riesenberg | .05 | .02 | 656 | Michael Walter | .05 | .02 |
| 600 | William Roberts | .05 | .02 | 657 | Dave Waymer | .05 | .02 |
| 601 | Phil Simms | .12 | .07 | 658 | Jeff Chadwick | .05 | .02 |
| 602 | Lawrence Taylor | .15 | .10 | | | | |

| | | | |
|---|---|---|---|
| 659 | Derrick Fenner | .10 | .06 |
| 660 | Nesby Glasgow | .05 | .02 |
| 661 | Jacob Green | .05 | .02 |
| 662 | Dwayne Harper (R) | .08 | .05 |
| 663 | Andy Heck | .05 | .02 |
| 664 | Dave Krieg | .10 | .06 |
| 665 | Rufus Porter | .05 | .02 |
| 666 | Eugene Robinson | .07 | .04 |
| 667 | Mark Carrier (TB) | .08 | .05 |
| 668 | Steve Christie | .05 | .02 |
| 669 | Reuben Davis | .05 | .02 |
| 670 | Paul Gruber | .05 | .02 |
| 671 | Wayne Haddix | .07 | .04 |
| 672 | Ron Hall | .05 | .02 |
| 673 | Keith McCants | .08 | .05 |
| 674 | Ricky Reynolds | .05 | .02 |
| 675 | Mark Robinson | .05 | .02 |
| 676 | Jeff Bostic | .05 | .02 |
| 677 | Darrell Green | .10 | .06 |
| 678 | Markus Koch | .05 | .02 |
| 679 | Jim Lachey | .07 | .04 |
| 680 | Charles Mann | .05 | .02 |
| 681 | Wilber Marshall | .07 | .04 |
| 682 | Art Monk | .20 | .12 |
| 683 | Gerald Riggs | .08 | .05 |
| 684 | Ricky Sanders | .08 | .05 |
| 685 | Ray Handley (News) | .05 | .02 |
| 686 | NFL Expansion (News) | .05 | .02 |
| 687 | Miami Gets Super Bowl | .05 | .02 |
| 688 | NFL Executive Of Year | .05 | .02 |
| 689 | Five-Millionth Fan at Hall of Fame (News) | .05 | .02 |
| 690 | Sports Illustrated Poll | .05 | .02 |
| 691 | American Bowl London | .05 | .02 |
| 692 | American Bowl Berlin | .05 | .02 |
| 693 | American Bowl Tokyo | .05 | .02 |
| 694 | Joe Ferguson (LG) | .05 | .02 |
| 694a | Russell Maryland (SP) (First Draft Pick) | 2.00 | 1.25 |
| 695 | Carl Hairston (LG) | .05 | .02 |
| 696 | Dan Hampton (LG) | .07 | .04 |
| 697 | Mike Haynes (LG) | .07 | .04 |
| 698 | Marty Lyons (LG) | .05 | .02 |
| 699 | Ozzie Newsome (LG) | .08 | .05 |
| 700 | Scott Studwell (LG) | .05 | .02 |
| 701 | Mike Webster (LG) | .08 | .05 |
| 702 | Dwayne Woodruff (LG) | .05 | .02 |
| 703 | Larry Kennan | .05 | .02 |
| 704 | Stan Gelbaugh (R) (WLAF) | .15 | .10 |
| 705 | John Brantley (R) (WLAF) | .07 | .04 |
| 706 | Danny Lockett (R) (WLAF) | .07 | .04 |
| 707 | Anthony Parker (R) (WLAF) | .07 | .04 |
| 708 | Dan Crossman (R) (WLAF) | .07 | .04 |
| 709 | Eric Wilkerson (R) (WLAF) | .07 | .04 |
| 710 | Judd Garrett (R) (WLAF) | .08 | .05 |
| 711 | Tony Baker (R) (WLAF) | .07 | .04 |
| 712 | Randall Cunningham (Photo Contest) | .08 | .05 |
| 713 | Mark Ingram (Photo Contest) | .05 | .02 |
| 714 | Pete Holohan, Barney Bussey, Carl Carter (Photo Contest) | .05 | .02 |
| 715 | Sterling Sharpe (Photo Contest) | .10 | .06 |
| 716 | Jim Harbaugh (Photo Contest) | .07 | .04 |
| 717 | Anthony Miller, David Fulcher (Photo Contest) | .07 | .04 |
| 718 | Bill Parcells, Lawrence Taylor (Photo Contest) | .08 | .05 |
| 719 | Patriotic Crowd (Photo Contest) | .05 | .02 |
| 720 | Alfredo Roberts (Photo Contest) | .05 | .02 |
| 721 | Ray Bentley (Message) | .05 | .02 |
| 722 | Earnest Byner (Message) | .07 | .04 |
| 723 | Bill Fralic (Message) | .07 | .04 |
| 724 | Joe Jacoby (Message) | .05 | .02 |
| 725 | Howie Long (Message) | .07 | .04 |
| 726 | Dan Marino (Message) | .20 | .12 |
| 727 | Ron Rivera (Message) | .05 | .02 |
| 728 | Mike Singletary (Msg) | .08 | .05 |
| 729 | Cornelius Bennett (Message) | .07 | .04 |
| 730 | Russelll Maryland | .20 | .12 |
| 731 | Eric Turner (R) | .30 | .18 |
| 732 | Bruce Pickens (R) | .20 | .12 |
| 733 | Mike Croel (R) | .35 | .20 |
| 734 | Todd Lyght (R) | .25 | .15 |
| 735 | Eric Swann (R) | .15 | .10 |
| 736 | Charles McRae (R) | .10 | .06 |
| 737 | Antone Davis (R) | .08 | .05 |
| 738 | Stanley Richard (R) | .15 | .10 |
| 739 | Herman Moore (R) | .50 | .30 |
| 740 | Pat Harlow (R) | .08 | .05 |
| 741 | Alvin Harper (R) | .75 | .45 |
| 742 | Mike Pritchard (R) | .50 | .30 |
| 743 | Leonard Russell (R) | .75 | .45 |
| 744 | Huey Richardson (R) | .10 | .06 |

| | | | |
|---|---|---|---|
| 745 Dan McGwire (R) | .75 | .45 |
| 746 Bobby Wilson (R) | .10 | .06 |
| 747 Alfred Williams (R) | .10 | .06 |
| 748 Vinnie Clark (R) | .10 | .06 |
| 749 Kelvin Pritchett (R) | .15 | .10 |
| 750 Harvey Williams (R) | .50 | .30 |
| 751 Stan Thomas (R) | .08 | .05 |
| 752 Randal Hill (R) | .35 | .20 |
| 753 Todd Marinovich (R) | .90 | .60 |
| 754 Ted Washington (R) | .12 | .07 |
| 755 Henry Jones (R) | .25 | .15 |
| 756 Jarrod Bunch (R) | .30 | .18 |
| 757 Mike Dumas (R) | .10 | .06 |
| 758 Ed King (R) | .08 | .05 |
| 759 Reggie Johnson (R) | .15 | .10 |
| 760 Roman Phifer (R) | .10 | .06 |
| 761 Mike Jones (R) | .08 | .05 |
| 762 Brett Favre (R) | 2.00 | 1.25 |
| 763 Browning Nagle (R) | 1.25 | .80 |
| 764 Esera Tuaolo (R) | .08 | .05 |
| 765 George Thornton (R) | .08 | .05 |
| 766 Dixon Edwards (R) | .10 | .06 |
| 767 Darryll Lewis | .08 | .05 |
| 768 Eric Bieniemy (R) | .20 | .12 |
| 769 Shane Curry (R) | .08 | .05 |
| 770 Jerome Henderson (R) | .12 | .07 |
| 771 Wesley Carroll (R) | .35 | .20 |
| 772 Nick Bell (R) | .50 | .30 |
| 773 John Flannery (R) | .10 | .06 |
| 774 Ricky Watters (R) | 1.75 | 1.00 |
| 775 Jeff Graham (R) | .35 | .20 |
| 776 Eric Moten (R) | .08 | .05 |
| 777 Jesse Campbell (R) | .10 | .06 |
| 778 Chris Zorich (R) | .10 | .06 |
| 779 Joe Valerio (R) | .08 | .05 |
| 780 Doug Thomas (R) | .08 | .05 |
| 781 Lamar Rogers (R) | .15 | .10 |
| 782 John Johnson (R) | .08 | .05 |
| 783 Phil Hansen (R) | .12 | .07 |
| 784 Kanavis McGhee (R) | .20 | .12 |
| 785 Calvin Stephens (R) | .08 | .05 |
| 786 James Jones (R) | .08 | .05 |
| 787 Reggie Barrett (R) | .15 | .10 |
| 788 Aeneas Williams (R) | .15 | .10 |
| 789 Aaron Craver (R) | .15 | .10 |
| 790 Keith Traylor (R) | .10 | .06 |
| 791 Godfrey Myles (R) | .08 | .05 |
| 792 Mo Lewis (R) | .15 | .10 |
| 793 James Richard (R) | .07 | .04 |
| 794 Carlos Jenkins (R) | .10 | .06 |
| 795 Lawrence Dawsey (R) | .60 | .35 |
| 796 Don Davey (R) | .08 | .05 |
| 797 Jake Reed (R) | .08 | .05 |
| 798 Dave McCloughan (R) | .08 | .05 |
| 799 Eric Williams (R) | .08 | .05 |
| 800 Steve Jackson (R) | .08 | .05 |
| 801 Bob Dahl (R) | .07 | .04 |

| | | | |
|---|---|---|---|
| 802 Ernie Mills (R) | .35 | .20 |
| 803 David Daniels (R) | .08 | .05 |
| 804 Rob Selby (R) | .08 | .05 |
| 805 Ricky Ervins (R) | .90 | .60 |
| 806 Tim Barnett (R) | .40 | .25 |
| 807 Chris Gardocki (R) | .10 | .06 |
| 808 Kevin Donnalley (R) | .08 | .05 |
| 809 Robert Wilson (R) | .12 | .07 |
| 810 Chuck Webb (R) | .20 | .12 |
| 811 Darryl Wren (R) | .07 | .04 |
| 812 Ed McCaffrey (R) | .35 | .20 |
| 813 Shula's 300th (News) | .07 | .04 |
| 814 Raiders-49ers (News) | .05 | .02 |
| 815 International (News) | .05 | .02 |
| 816 Moe Gardner (R) | .20 | .12 |
| 817 Tim McKyer | .05 | .02 |
| 818 Tom Waddle (R) | .35 | .20 |
| 819 Michael Jackson | .50 | .30 |
| 820 Tony Casillas | .07 | .04 |
| 821 Gaston Green (R) | .20 | .12 |
| 822 Kenny Walker (R) | .40 | .25 |
| 823 Willie Green (R) | .50 | .30 |
| 824 Erik Kramer (R) | .60 | .35 |
| 825 William Fuller | .05 | .02 |
| 826 Allen Pinkett | .05 | .02 |
| 827 Rick Venturi | .05 | .02 |
| 828 Bill Maas | .05 | .02 |
| 829 Jeff Jaeger | .05 | .02 |
| 830 Robert Delpino | .08 | .05 |
| 831 Mark Higgs (R) | .60 | .35 |
| 832 Reggie Roby | .05 | .02 |
| 833 Terry Allen (R) | 1.00 | .70 |
| 834 Cris Carter | .20 | .12 |
| 835 John Randle (R) | .08 | .05 |
| 836 Hugh Millen (R) | .50 | .30 |
| 837 Jon Vaughn (R) | .40 | .25 |
| 838 Gill Fenerty | .07 | .04 |
| 839 Floyd Turner | .05 | .02 |
| 840 Irv Eatman | .05 | .02 |
| 841 Lonnie Yound | .05 | .02 |
| 842 Jim McMahon | .10 | .06 |
| 843 Randal Hill | .30 | .18 |
| 844 Barry Foster (R) | 1.75 | 1.00 |
| 845 Neil O'Donnell (R) | 1.25 | .80 |
| 846 John Friesz (R) | .15 | .10 |
| 847 Broderick Thomas | .08 | .05 |
| 848 Brian Mitchell | .08 | .05 |
| 849 Mike Utley (R) | .60 | .35 |
| 850 Mike Croel (Rookie of the Year) | .25 | .15 |
| ___ Walter Payton | 3.50 | 2.00 |
| ___ Red Grange | 3.50 | 2.00 |
| ___ Pro Set Gazette | .75 | .45 |
| ___ Ottis Anderson SB MVP | .75 | .45 |
| ___ Super Bowl XXVI Art | .75 | .45 |
| ___ Mini Pro Set Gazette | .75 | .45 |

| | | | |
|---|---|---|---|
| ___ | Santa Claus | 1.50 | .90 |
| ___ | Jim Thorpe | 3.00 | 1.75 |
| ___ | Otto Graham | 3.00 | 1.75 |
| ___ | Paul Brown | 2.00 | 1.25 |
| ___ | Lawrence Taylor (Autographed) | 200.00 | 100.00 |

# 1991 Pro Set Platinum

This 315-card set marked Pro Set's first premium card set. The set was issued in two series (1-150) and (151-365). The card fronts feature full color, full-bleed action photos with a small Pro Set Platinum logo in the bottom corner. The horizontal card backs contain another full color action shot along with the player's name, team and position. Key subsets include Special Teams, Platinum Performance (PP) and Platinum Prospects. 10-limited Platinum Collectible cards were randomly distributed in Series II foil packs. These cards, which carry the prefix (PC) are listed at the end of this checklist but are not included in the complete set price below. All cards measure 2-1/2" by 3-1/2".

| | MINT | NR/MT |
|---|---|---|
| Complete Set (315) | 20.00 | 12.50 |
| Commons | .06 | .03 |

| | | | |
|---|---|---|---|
| 1 | Chris Miller | .25 | .15 |
| 2 | Andre Rison | .25 | .15 |
| 3 | Tim Green | .06 | .03 |
| 4 | Jessie Tuggle | .06 | .03 |
| 5 | Thurman Thomas | .75 | .45 |
| 6 | Darryl Talley | .08 | .05 |
| 7 | Kent Hull | .06 | .03 |
| 8 | Bruce Smith | .12 | .07 |
| 9 | Shane Conlan | .08 | .05 |
| 10 | Jim Harbaugh | .15 | .10 |
| 11 | Neal Anderson | .15 | .10 |
| 12 | Mark Bortz | .06 | .03 |
| 13 | Richard Dent | .08 | .05 |
| 14 | Steve McMichael | .08 | .05 |
| 15 | James Brooks | .08 | .05 |
| 16 | Boomer Esiason | .12 | .07 |
| 17 | Tim Krumrie | .06 | .03 |
| 18 | James Francis | .08 | .05 |
| 19 | Lewis Billups | .06 | .03 |
| 20 | Eric Metcalf | .10 | .06 |
| 21 | Kevin Mack | .08 | .05 |
| 22 | Clay Matthews | .06 | .03 |
| 23 | Mike Johnson | .06 | .03 |
| 24 | Troy Aikman | .80 | .50 |
| 25 | Emmitt Smith | 2.00 | 1.25 |
| 26 | Daniel Stubbs | .06 | .03 |
| 27 | Ken Norton | .06 | .03 |
| 28 | John Elway | .25 | .15 |
| 29 | Bobby Humphrey | .10 | .06 |
| 30 | Simon Fletcher | .06 | .03 |
| 31 | Karl Mecklenburg | .08 | .05 |
| 32 | Rodney Peete | .12 | .07 |
| 33 | Barry Sanders | 1.00 | .70 |
| 34 | Michael Cofer | .06 | .03 |
| 35 | Jerry Ball | .06 | .03 |
| 36 | Sterling Sharpe | .25 | .15 |
| 37 | Tony Mandarich | .06 | .03 |
| 38 | Brian Noble | .06 | .03 |
| 39 | Tim Harris | .06 | .03 |
| 40 | Warren Moon | .25 | .15 |
| 41 | Ernest Givins | .15 | .10 |
| 42 | Mike Munchak | .06 | .03 |
| 43 | Sean Jones | .06 | .03 |
| 44 | Ray Childress | .08 | .05 |
| 45 | Jeff George | .50 | .30 |
| 46 | Albert Bentley | .06 | .03 |
| 47 | Duane Bickett | .06 | .03 |
| 48 | Steve DeBerg | .10 | .06 |
| 49 | Christian Okoye | .15 | .10 |
| 50 | Neil Smith | .06 | .03 |
| 51 | Derrick Thomas | .20 | .12 |
| 52 | Willie Gault | .08 | .05 |
| 53 | Don Mosebar | .06 | .03 |
| 54 | Howie Long | .08 | .05 |
| 55 | Greg Townsend | .08 | .05 |
| 56 | Terry McDaniel | .06 | .03 |
| 57 | Jackie Slater | .08 | .05 |
| 58 | Jim Everett | .15 | .10 |

| | | | |
|---|---|---|---|
| 59 Cleveland Gary | .08 | .05 |
| 60 Mike Piel | .06 | .03 |
| 61 Jerry Gray | .06 | .03 |
| 62 Dan Marino | .60 | .35 |
| 63 Sammie Smith | .08 | .05 |
| 64 Richmond Webb | .08 | .05 |
| 65 Louis Oliver | .08 | .05 |
| 66 Ferrell Edmunds | .06 | .03 |
| 67 Jeff Cross | .06 | .03 |
| 68 Wade Wilson | .08 | .05 |
| 69 Chris Doleman | .08 | .05 |
| 70 Joey Browner | .08 | .05 |
| 71 Keith Millard | .08 | .05 |
| 72 John Stephens | .10 | .06 |
| 73 Andre Tippett | .08 | .05 |
| 74 Brent Williams | .06 | .03 |
| 75 Craig Heyward | .08 | .05 |
| 76 Eric Martin | .10 | .06 |
| 77 Pat Swilling | .12 | .07 |
| 78 Sam Mills | .08 | .05 |
| 79 Jeff Hostetler | .20 | .12 |
| 80 Ottis Anderson | .08 | .05 |
| 81 Lawrence Taylor | .20 | .12 |
| 82 Pepper Johnson | .06 | .03 |
| 83 Blair Thomas | .20 | .12 |
| 84 Al Toon | .08 | .05 |
| 85 Ken O'Brien | .10 | .06 |
| 86 Erik McMillan | .06 | .03 |
| 87 Dennis Byrd | .06 | .03 |
| 88 Randall Cunningham | .20 | .12 |
| 89 Fred Barnett | .20 | .12 |
| 90 Seth Joyner | .08 | .05 |
| 91 Reggie White | .12 | .07 |
| 92 Timm Rosenbach | .12 | .07 |
| 93 Johnny Johnson | .20 | .12 |
| 94 Tim McDonald | .06 | .03 |
| 95 Freddie Joe Nunn | .06 | .03 |
| 96 Bubby Brister | .12 | .07 |
| 97 Gary Anderson | .06 | .03 |
| 98 Merril Hoge | .08 | .05 |
| 99 Keith Willis | .06 | .03 |
| 100 Rod Woodson | .10 | .06 |
| 101 Billy Joe Tolliver | .08 | .05 |
| 102 Marion Butts | .15 | .10 |
| 103 Rod Bernstine | .08 | .05 |
| 104 Lee Williams | .06 | .03 |
| 105 Burt Grossman | .08 | .05 |
| 106 Tom Rathman | .08 | .05 |
| 107 John Taylor | .20 | .12 |
| 108 Michael Carter | .06 | .03 |
| 109 Guy McIntyre | .06 | .03 |
| 110 Pierce Holt | .06 | .03 |
| 111 John L. Williams | .08 | .05 |
| 112 Dave Krieg | .10 | .06 |
| 113 Bryan Millard | .06 | .03 |
| 114 Cortez Kennedy | .15 | .10 |
| 115 Derrick Fenner | .15 | .10 |
| 116 Vinny Testaverde | .12 | .07 |
| 117 Reggie Cobb | .20 | .12 |
| 118 Gary Anderson | .06 | .03 |
| 119 Bruce Hill | .06 | .03 |
| 120 Wayne Haddix | .08 | .05 |
| 121 Broderick Thomas | .10 | .06 |
| 122 Keith McCants | .08 | .05 |
| 123 Andre Collins | .06 | .03 |
| 124 Earnest Byner | .08 | .05 |
| 125 Jim Lachey | .08 | .05 |
| 126 Mark Rypien | .20 | .12 |
| 127 Charles Mann | .06 | .03 |
| 128 Nick Lowery | .08 | .05 |
| 129 Chip Lohmiller | .06 | .03 |
| 130 Mike Horan | .06 | .03 |
| 131 Rohn Stark | .06 | .03 |
| 132 Sean Landeta | .06 | .03 |
| 133 Clarence Verdin | .08 | .05 |
| 134 Johnny Bailey | .06 | .03 |
| 135 Herschel Walker | .15 | .10 |
| 136 Bo Jackson (PP) | .35 | .20 |
| 137 Dexter Carter (PP) | .12 | .07 |
| 138 Warren Moon (PP) | .25 | .15 |
| 139 Joe Montana (PP) | .75 | .45 |
| 140 Jerry Rice (PP) | .60 | .35 |
| 141 Deion Sanders (PP) | .25 | .15 |
| 142 Ronnie Lippett (PP) | .06 | .03 |
| 143 Terance Mathis (PP) | .08 | .05 |
| 144 Gaston Green (PP) | .15 | .10 |
| 145 Dean Biasucci (PP) | .06 | .03 |
| 146 Charles Haley (PP) | .08 | .05 |
| 147 Derrick Thomas (PP) | .20 | .12 |
| 148 Lawrence Taylor (PP) | .20 | .12 |
| 149 Art Shell (PP) | .06 | .03 |
| 150 Bill Parcells (PP) | .06 | .03 |
| 151 Steve Broussard | .10 | .06 |
| 152 Darion Conner | .06 | .03 |
| 153 Bill Fralic | .06 | .03 |
| 154 Mike Gann | .06 | .03 |
| 155 Tim McKyer | .06 | .03 |
| 156 Don Beebe | .10 | .06 |
| 157 Cornelius Bennett | .10 | .06 |
| 158 Andre Reed | .20 | .12 |
| 159 Leonard Smith | .06 | .03 |
| 160 Will Wolford | .06 | .03 |
| 161 Mark Carrier (Chi) | .10 | .06 |
| 162 Wendell Davis | .12 | .07 |
| 163 Jay Hilgenberg | .06 | .03 |
| 164 Brad Muster | .08 | .05 |
| 165 Mike Singletary | .12 | .07 |
| 166 Eddie Brown | .08 | .05 |
| 167 David Fulcher | .06 | .03 |
| 168 Rodney Holman | .06 | .03 |
| 169 Anthony Munoz | .10 | .06 |
| 170 Craig Taylor (R) | .08 | .05 |
| 171 Mike Baab | .06 | .03 |
| 172 David Grayson | .06 | .03 |

| # | Player | | |
|---|--------|---|---|
| 173 | Reggie Langhorne | .06 | .03 |
| 174 | Joe Morris | .08 | .05 |
| 175 | Kevin Gogan (R) | .08 | .05 |
| 176 | Jack Del Rio | .06 | .03 |
| 177 | Issiac Holt | .06 | .03 |
| 178 | Michael Irvin | .35 | .20 |
| 179 | Jay Novacek | .08 | .05 |
| 180 | Steve Atwater | .10 | .06 |
| 181 | Mark Jackson | .08 | .05 |
| 182 | Ricky Nattiel | .08 | .05 |
| 183 | Warren Powers | .06 | .03 |
| 184 | Dennis Smith | .06 | .03 |
| 185 | Bennie Blades | .08 | .05 |
| 186 | Lomas Brown | .06 | .03 |
| 187 | Robert Clark | .06 | .03 |
| 188 | Mel Gray | .06 | .03 |
| 189 | Chris Spielman | .06 | .03 |
| 190 | Johnny Holland | .06 | .03 |
| 191 | Don Majkowski | .12 | .07 |
| 192 | Bryce Paup | .06 | .03 |
| 193 | Darrell Thompson | .12 | .07 |
| 194 | Ed West | .06 | .03 |
| 195 | Cris Dishman | .12 | .07 |
| 196 | Drew Hill | .08 | .05 |
| 197 | Bruce Matthews | .06 | .03 |
| 198 | Bubba McDowell | .06 | .03 |
| 199 | Allen Pinkett | .08 | .05 |
| 200 | Bill Brooks | .06 | .03 |
| 201 | Jeff Herrod | .06 | .03 |
| 202 | Anthony Johnson | .06 | .03 |
| 203 | Mike Prior | .06 | .03 |
| 204 | John Alt | .06 | .03 |
| 205 | Stephone Paige | .08 | .05 |
| 206 | Kevin Ross | .06 | .03 |
| 207 | Dan Saleaumua | .06 | .03 |
| 208 | Barry Word | .25 | .15 |
| 209 | Marcus Allen | .12 | .07 |
| 210 | Roger Craig | .10 | .06 |
| 211 | Ronnie Lott | .15 | .10 |
| 212 | Winston Moss | .06 | .03 |
| 213 | Jay Schroeder | .10 | .06 |
| 214 | Robert Delpino | .08 | .05 |
| 215 | Henry Ellard | .08 | .05 |
| 216 | Kevin Greene | .08 | .05 |
| 217 | Tom Newberry | .06 | .03 |
| 218 | Michael Stewart | .06 | .03 |
| 219 | Mark Duper | .10 | .06 |
| 220 | Mark Higgs (R) | .70 | .40 |
| 221 | John Offerdahl | .08 | .05 |
| 222 | Keith Sims | .06 | .03 |
| 223 | Anthony Carter | .10 | .06 |
| 224 | Cris Carter | .20 | .12 |
| 225 | Steve Jordan | .06 | .03 |
| 226 | Randall McDaniel | .06 | .03 |
| 227 | Al Noga | .06 | .03 |
| 228 | Ray Agnew | .06 | .03 |
| 229 | Bruce Armstrong | .06 | .03 |
| 230 | Irving Fryar | .08 | .05 |
| 231 | Greg McMurtry | .12 | .07 |
| 232 | Chris Singleton | .08 | .05 |
| 233 | Morten Andersen | .08 | .05 |
| 234 | Vince Buck | .06 | .03 |
| 235 | Gill Fenerty | .08 | .05 |
| 236 | Rickey Jackson | .08 | .05 |
| 237 | Vaughan Johnson | .08 | .05 |
| 238 | Carl Banks | .08 | .05 |
| 239 | Mark Collins | .06 | .03 |
| 240 | Rodney Hampton | .75 | .45 |
| 241 | David Meggett | .12 | .07 |
| 242 | Bart Oates | .06 | .03 |
| 243 | Kyle Clifton | .06 | .03 |
| 244 | Jeff Lageman | .08 | .05 |
| 245 | Freeman McNeil | .08 | .05 |
| 246 | Rob Moore | .30 | .18 |
| 247 | Eric Allen | .06 | .03 |
| 248 | Keith Byars | .08 | .05 |
| 249 | Keith Jackson | .15 | .10 |
| 250 | Jim McMahon | .10 | .06 |
| 251 | Andre Waters | .06 | .03 |
| 252 | Ken Harvey | .06 | .03 |
| 253 | Ernie Jones | .08 | .05 |
| 254 | Luis Sharpe | .06 | .03 |
| 255 | Anthony Thompson | .10 | .06 |
| 256 | Tom Tupa | .08 | .05 |
| 257 | Eric Green | .15 | .10 |
| 258 | Barry Foster | 1.00 | .70 |
| 259 | Bryan Hinkle | .06 | .03 |
| 260 | Tunch Ilkin | .06 | .03 |
| 261 | Louis Lipps | .07 | .05 |
| 262 | Gill Byrd | .06 | .03 |
| 263 | John Friesz | .15 | .10 |
| 264 | Anthony Miller | .20 | .12 |
| 265 | Junior Seau | .20 | .12 |
| 266 | Ronnie Harmon | .08 | .05 |
| 267 | Harris Barton | .06 | .03 |
| 268 | Todd Bowles | .06 | .03 |
| 269 | Don Griffin | .06 | .03 |
| 270 | Bill Romanowski | .06 | .03 |
| 271 | Steve Young | .45 | .28 |
| 272 | Brian Blades | .08 | .05 |
| 273 | Jacob Green | .06 | .03 |
| 274 | Rufus Porter | .06 | .03 |
| 275 | Eugene Robinson | .06 | .03 |
| 276 | Mark Carrier | .08 | .05 |
| 277 | Reuben Davis | .06 | .03 |
| 278 | Paul Gruber | .06 | .03 |
| 279 | Gary Clark | .20 | .12 |
| 280 | Darrell Green | .12 | .07 |
| 281 | Wilber Marshall | .08 | .05 |
| 282 | Matt Millen | .06 | .03 |
| 283 | Alvin Walton | .06 | .03 |
| 284 | Joe Gibbs | .06 | .03 |
| 285 | Don Shula | .08 | .05 |
| 286 | Larry Brown (R) | .08 | .05 |

| 287 | Mike Croel (R) | .50 | .30 |
| 288 | Antone Davis (R) | .08 | .05 |
| 289 | Ricky Ervins (R) | 1.00 | .70 |
| 290 | Brett Favre (R) | 2.50 | 1.50 |
| 291 | Pat Harlow (R) | .10 | .06 |
| 292 | Michael Jackson (R) | .75 | .45 |
| 293 | Henry Jones (R) | .15 | .10 |
| 294 | Aaron Craver (R) | .15 | .10 |
| 295 | Nick Bell (R) | .75 | .45 |
| 296 | Todd Lyght (R) | .20 | .12 |
| 297 | Todd Marinovich (R) | 1.00 | .70 |
| 298 | Russell Maryland (R) | .35 | .20 |
| 299 | Kanavis McGhee (R) | .20 | .12 |
| 300 | Dan McGwire (R) | .80 | .50 |
| 301 | Charles McRae (R) | .10 | .06 |
| 302 | Eric Moten (R) | .08 | .05 |
| 303 | Jerome Henderson (R) | .12 | .07 |
| 304 | Browning Nagle (R) | 1.25 | .80 |
| 305 | Mike Pritchard (R) | .75 | .45 |
| 306 | Stanley Richard (R) | .15 | .10 |
| 307 | Randal Hill (R) | .50 | .30 |
| 308 | Leonard Russell (R) | .80 | .50 |
| 309 | Eric Swann (R) | .15 | .10 |
| 310 | Phil Hansen (R) | .12 | .07 |
| 311 | Moe Gardner (R) | .15 | .10 |
| 312 | Jon Vaughn (R) | .30 | .18 |
| 313 | Aeneas Williams (R) | .12 | .07 |
| 314 | Alfred Williams (R) | .20 | .12 |
| 315 | Harvey Williams (R) | .50 | .30 |
| PC1 | Bobby Hebert | .40 | .25 |
| PC2 | Art Monk | .80 | .50 |
| PC3 | Kenny Walker | .60 | .35 |
| PC4 | Houston Oilers | .40 | .25 |
| PC5 | Kevin Mack | .40 | .25 |
| PC6 | Neal Anderson | .60 | .35 |
| PC7 | Gaston Green | .60 | .35 |
| PC8 | Barry Sanders | 2.00 | 1.25 |
| PC9 | Emmitt Smith | 4.00 | 2.75 |
| PC10 | Thurman Thomas | 1.75 | 1.00 |

# 1992 Pro Set

This 700-card set was issued in two series (1-400) (401-700) and features full-color action photographs on the fronts with the player's name centered under the photo. A Pro Set logo is printed in the lower right corner. The horizontal card backs consist of a small photo, a brief bio, career highlights and stats. Key subsets include League Leaders (LL), Milestones (M), Innovators, Replays, Newsreel, Play Smart Messages (Msg), Spirit of the Game and Pro Bowl (PB). Six special Ground Force gold foil insert cards were also included in the set. Those cards are listed in the checklist (numbered 86a,105a, 118a, 150a, 206a, and 249a). The set also includes four special collectibles (SP) and a four card limited Emmitt Smith hologram set which are listed at the end of this checklist but are not included in the complete set price below.

| | | MINT | NR/MT |
|---|---|---|---|
| **Complete Set (700)** | | 20.00 | 14.00 |
| **Commons** | | .05 | .02 |
| | | | |
| 1 | Mike Croel | .15 | .10 |
| | (Rookie of the Year) | | |
| 2 | Thurman Thomas | .25 | .15 |
| | (Player of the Year) | | |
| 3 | Wayne Fontes | .05 | .02 |
| | (Coach of the Year) | | |
| 4 | Anthony Munoz | .08 | .05 |
| | (Man of the Year) | | |
| 5 | Steve Young LL | .12 | .07 |
| 6 | Warren Moon LL | .12 | .07 |
| 7 | Emmitt Smith LL | .80 | .50 |
| 8 | Haywood Jeffires LL | .10 | .06 |

| | | | |
|---|---|---|---|
| 9 | Marv Cook LL | .07 | .04 |
| 10 | Michael Irvin LL | .10 | .06 |
| 11 | Thurman Thomas LL | .25 | .15 |
| 12 | Chip Lohmiller LL | .05 | .02 |
| 13 | Barry Sanders LL | .25 | .15 |
| 14 | Reggie Roby LL | .05 | .02 |
| 15 | Mel Gray LL | .05 | .02 |
| 16 | Ronnie Lott LL | .08 | .05 |
| 17 | Pat Swilling LL | .08 | .05 |
| 18 | Reggie White LL | .08 | .05 |
| 19 | Haywood Jeffires (M) | .10 | .06 |
| 20 | Pat Leahy (M) | .05 | .02 |
| 21 | James Lofton (M) | .10 | .06 |
| 22 | Art Monk (M) | .12 | .07 |
| 23 | Don Shula (M) | .07 | .04 |
| 24 | Nick Lowery (M) | .07 | .04 |
| 25 | John Elway (M) | .10 | .06 |
| 26 | Chicage Bears (M) | .05 | .02 |
| 27 | Marcus Allen (M) | .08 | .05 |
| 28 | Terrell Buckley (R) | .60 | .35 |
| 29 | Amp Lee (R) | .50 | .30 |
| 30 | Chris Mims (R) | .20 | .12 |
| 31 | Leon Searcy (R) | .10 | .06 |
| 32 | Jimmy Smith (R) | .25 | .15 |
| 33 | Siran Stacy (R) | .25 | .15 |
| 34 | Pete Gogalak (I) | .05 | .02 |
| 35 | Cowboy Cheerleaders (I) | .10 | .06 |
| 36 | Houston Astrodome (I) | .05 | .02 |
| 37 | Christian Okoye Replay | .08 | .05 |
| 38 | Don Beebe Replay | .07 | .04 |
| 39 | Wendell Davis Replay | .07 | .04 |
| 40 | Don Shula Replay | .07 | .04 |
| 41 | Ronnie Lott Replay | .08 | .05 |
| 42 | Art Monk Replay | .08 | .05 |
| 43 | Thurman Thomas Replay | .20 | .12 |
| 44 | John Stephens Replay | .07 | .04 |
| 45 | Herschel Walker Replay | .07 | .04 |
| 46 | Chris Burkett Replay | .05 | .02 |
| 47 | Colts-Jets Replay | .05 | .02 |
| 48 | Andre Rison Replay | .08 | .05 |
| 49 | Michael Irvin Replay | .10 | .06 |
| 50 | Irving Fryar Replay | .07 | .04 |
| 51 | Bills Replay | .05 | .02 |
| 52 | Kelvin Martin Replay | .07 | .04 |
| 53 | Bruce Coslet Replay | .05 | .02 |
| 54 | Fred Jones Replay | .05 | .02 |
| 55 | Oilers Replay | .05 | .02 |
| 56 | Cowboys Replay | .05 | .02 |
| 57 | Michael Haynes Replay | .08 | .05 |
| 58 | Broncos Replay | .05 | .02 |
| 59 | Thurman Thomas Replay | .20 | .12 |
| 60 | Eric Kramer Replay | .08 | .05 |
| 61 | Darrell Green Replay | .07 | .04 |

| | | | |
|---|---|---|---|
| 62 | AFC Champs Replay | .05 | .02 |
| 63 | NFC Champs Replay | .08 | .05 |
| 64 | Super Bowl Replay | .05 | .02 |
| 65 | Super Bowl Replay | .05 | .02 |
| 66 | Super Bowl Replay | .07 | .04 |
| 67 | Super Bowl Replay | .05 | .02 |
| 68 | Super Bowl Replay | .05 | .02 |
| 69 | Super Bowl Replay | .20 | .12 |
| 70 | Super Bowl Replay | .07 | .04 |
| 71 | Super Bowl Replay | .05 | .02 |
| 72 | Super Bowl Replay | .05 | .02 |
| 73 | Jeff Bostic | .05 | .02 |
| 74 | Earnest Byner | .08 | .05 |
| 75 | Gary Clark | .15 | .10 |
| 76 | Andre Collins | .05 | .02 |
| 77 | Darrell Green | .10 | .06 |
| 78 | Joe Jacoby | .05 | .02 |
| 79 | Jim Lachey | .07 | .04 |
| 80 | Chip Lohmiller | .05 | .02 |
| 81 | Charles Mann | .05 | .02 |
| 82 | Martin Mayhew | .05 | .02 |
| 83 | Matt Millen | .05 | .02 |
| 84 | Brian Mitchell | .07 | .04 |
| 85 | Art Monk | .15 | .10 |
| 86 | Gerald Riggs | .07 | .04 |
| 86a | Gerlad Riggs (Gold) | 1.25 | .80 |
| 87 | Mark Rypien | .20 | .12 |
| 88 | Fred Stokes | .05 | .02 |
| 89 | Bobby Wilson | .05 | .02 |
| 90 | Joe Gibbs | .05 | .02 |
| 91 | Howard Ballard | .05 | .02 |
| 92 | Cornelius Bennett | .10 | .06 |
| 93 | Kenneth Davis | .08 | .05 |
| 94 | Al Edwards | .05 | .02 |
| 95 | Kent Hull | .05 | .02 |
| 96 | Kirby Jackson | .05 | .02 |
| 97 | Mark Kelso | .05 | .02 |
| 98 | James Lofton | .15 | .10 |
| 99 | Keith McKeller | .07 | .04 |
| 100 | Nate Odomes | .05 | .02 |
| 101 | Jim Ritcher | .05 | .02 |
| 102 | Leon Seals | .05 | .02 |
| 103 | Steve Tasker | .05 | .02 |
| 104 | Darryl Talley | .07 | .04 |
| 105 | Thurman Thomas | .50 | .30 |
| 105a | Thurman Thomas (Gold) | 8.50 | 5.50 |
| 106 | Will Wolford | .05 | .02 |
| 107 | Jeff Wright | .05 | .02 |
| 108 | Marv Levy | .05 | .02 |
| 109 | Darion Conner | .05 | .02 |
| 110 | Bill Fralic | .05 | .02 |
| 111 | Moe Gardner | .08 | .05 |
| 112 | Michael Haynes | .20 | .12 |
| 113 | Chris Miller | .20 | .12 |
| 114 | Erric Pegram | .08 | .05 |
| 115 | Bruce Pickens | .10 | .06 |

| | | | |
|---|---|---|---|
| 116 Andre Rison | .20 | .12 |
| 117 Jerry Glanville | .05 | .02 |
| 118 Neal Anderson | .10 | .06 |
| 118a Neal Andserson (Gold) | 3.00 | 1.75 |
| 119 Trace Armstrong | .05 | .02 |
| 120 Wendell Davis | .08 | .05 |
| 121 Richard Dent | .07 | .04 |
| 122 Jay Hilgenberg | .05 | .02 |
| 123 Lemuel Stinson | .05 | .02 |
| 124 Stan Thomas | .05 | .02 |
| 125 Tom Waddle | .12 | .07 |
| 126 Mike Ditka | .08 | .05 |
| 127 James Brooks | .07 | .04 |
| 128 Eddie Brown | .08 | .05 |
| 129 David Fulcher | .05 | .02 |
| 130 Harold Green | .20 | .12 |
| 131 Tim Krumrie | .05 | .02 |
| 132 Anthony Munoz | .10 | .06 |
| 133 Craig Taylor | .05 | .02 |
| 134 Eric Thomas | .05 | .02 |
| 135 David Shula | .08 | .05 |
| 136 Mike Baab | .05 | .02 |
| 137 Brian Brennan | .05 | .02 |
| 138 Michael Jackson | .20 | .12 |
| 139 James Jones | .05 | .02 |
| 140 Ed King | .05 | .02 |
| 141 Clay Matthews | .05 | .02 |
| 142 Eric Metcalf | .08 | .05 |
| 143 Joe Morris | .07 | .04 |
| 144 Bill Belichick | .05 | .02 |
| 145 Steve Beuerlein | .10 | .06 |
| 146 Larry Brown | .05 | .02 |
| 147 Ray Horton | .05 | .02 |
| 148 Ken Norton | .05 | .02 |
| 149 Mike Saxon | .05 | .02 |
| 150 Emmitt Smith | 2.50 | 1.40 |
| 150a Emmitt Smith (GF) | 14.00 | 9.00 |
| 151 Mark Stepnoski | .05 | .02 |
| 152 Alexander Wright | .08 | .05 |
| 153 Jimmy Johnson | .05 | .02 |
| 154 Mike Croel | .15 | .10 |
| 155 John Elway | .20 | .12 |
| 156 Gaston Green | .12 | .07 |
| 157 Wymon Henderson | .05 | .02 |
| 158 Karl Mecklenburg | .07 | .04 |
| 159 Warren Powers | .05 | .02 |
| 160 Steve Sewell | .05 | .02 |
| 161 Doug Widell | .05 | .02 |
| 162 Dan Reeves | .05 | .02 |
| 163 Eric Andolsek | .05 | .02 |
| 164 Jerry Ball | .05 | .02 |
| 165 Bennie Blades | .07 | .04 |
| 166 Ray Crockett | .05 | .02 |
| 167 Willie Green | .20 | .12 |
| 168 Erik Kramer | .20 | .12 |
| 169 Barry Sanders | .75 | .45 |
| 170 Chrs Spielman | .07 | .04 |
| 171 Wayne Fontes | .05 | .02 |
| 172 Vinnie Clark | .05 | .02 |
| 173 Tony Mandarich | .05 | .02 |
| 174 Brian Noble | .05 | .02 |
| 175 Bryce Paup | .05 | .02 |
| 176 Sterling Sharpe | .25 | .15 |
| 177 Darrell Thompson | .08 | .05 |
| 178 Esera Tuaolo | .05 | .02 |
| 179 Ed West | .05 | .02 |
| 180 Mike Holmgren | .07 | .04 |
| 181 Ray Childress | .07 | .04 |
| 182 Cris Dishman | .08 | .05 |
| 183 Curtis Duncan | .07 | .04 |
| 184 William Fuller | .05 | .02 |
| 185 Lamar Lathon | .07 | .04 |
| 186 Warren Moon | .20 | .12 |
| 187 Bo Orlando (R) | .12 | .07 |
| 188 Lorenzo White | .15 | .10 |
| 189 Jack Pardee | .05 | .02 |
| 190 Chip Banks | .05 | .02 |
| 191 Dean Biasucci | .05 | .02 |
| 192 Bill Brooks | .05 | .02 |
| 193 Ray Donaldson | .05 | .02 |
| 194 Jeff Herrod | .05 | .02 |
| 195 Mike Prior | .05 | .02 |
| 196 Mark Vander Poel | .05 | .02 |
| 197 Clarence Verdin | .07 | .04 |
| 198 Ted Marchibroda | .05 | .02 |
| 199 John Alt | .05 | .02 |
| 200 Deron Cherry | .05 | .02 |
| 201 Steve DeBerg | .08 | .05 |
| 202 Nick Lowery | .07 | .04 |
| 203 Neil Smith | .05 | .02 |
| 204 Derrick Thomas | .20 | .12 |
| 205 Joe Valerio | .05 | .02 |
| 206 Barry Word | .15 | .10 |
| 206a Barry Word (Gold) | 4.00 | 2.75 |
| 207 Marty Schottenheimer | .05 | .02 |
| 208 Marcus Allen | .10 | .06 |
| 209 Nick Bell | .35 | .20 |
| 210 Tim Brown | .08 | .05 |
| 211 Howie Long | .07 | .04 |
| 212 Ronnie Lott | .10 | .06 |
| 213 Todd Marinovich | .50 | .30 |
| 214 Greg Townsend | .05 | .02 |
| 215 Steve Wright | .05 | .02 |
| 216 Art Shell | .05 | .02 |
| 217 Flipper Anderson | .08 | .05 |
| 218 Robert Delpino | .07 | .04 |
| 219 Henry Ellard | .07 | .04 |
| 220 Kevin Greene | .05 | .02 |
| 221 Todd Lyght | .15 | .10 |
| 222 Tom Newberry | .05 | .02 |
| 223 Roman Phifer | .07 | .04 |
| 224 Michael Stewart | .05 | .02 |
| 225 Chuck Knox | .05 | .02 |

| | | | |
|---|---|---|---|
| 226 | Aaron Craver | .08 | .05 |
| 227 | Jeff Cross | .05 | .02 |
| 228 | Mark Duper | .08 | .05 |
| 229 | Ferrell Edmunds | .05 | .02 |
| 230 | Jim Jensen | .05 | .02 |
| 231 | Louis Oliver | .07 | .04 |
| 232 | Reggie Roby | .05 | .02 |
| 233 | Sammie Smith | .08 | .05 |
| 234 | Don Shula | .07 | .04 |
| 235 | Joey Browner | .07 | .04 |
| 236 | Anthony Carter | .08 | .05 |
| 237 | Chris Doleman | .08 | .05 |
| 238 | Steve Jordan | .05 | .02 |
| 239 | Kirk Lowdermilk | .05 | .02 |
| 240 | Henry Thomas | .05 | .02 |
| 241 | Herschel Walker | .12 | .07 |
| 242 | Felix Wright | .05 | .02 |
| 243 | Dennis Green | .07 | .04 |
| 244 | Ray Agnew | .05 | .02 |
| 245 | Marv Cook | .07 | .04 |
| 246 | Irving Fryar | .07 | .04 |
| 247 | Pat Harlow | .07 | .04 |
| 248 | Hugh Millen | .15 | .10 |
| 249 | Leonard Russell | .35 | .20 |
| 249a | Leonard Russell | 4.00 | 2.75 |
| | (Gold) | | |
| 250 | Andre Tippett | .07 | .04 |
| 251 | Jon Vaughn | .20 | .12 |
| 252 | Dick MacPherson | .05 | .02 |
| 253 | Morten Andersen | .07 | .04 |
| 254 | Bobby Hebert | .15 | .10 |
| 255 | Joel Hilgenberg | .05 | .02 |
| 256 | Vaughan Johnson | .07 | .04 |
| 257 | Sam Mills | .07 | .04 |
| 258 | Pat Swilling | .12 | .07 |
| 259 | Floyd Turner | .05 | .02 |
| 260 | Steve Walsh | .10 | .06 |
| 261 | Jim Mora | .05 | .02 |
| 262 | Stephen Baker | .05 | .02 |
| 263 | Mark Collins | .05 | .02 |
| 264 | Rodney Hampton | .35 | .20 |
| 265 | Jeff Hostetler | .15 | .10 |
| 266 | Erik Howard | .05 | .02 |
| 267 | Sean Landeta | .05 | .02 |
| 268 | Gary Reasons | .05 | .02 |
| 269 | Everson Walls | .05 | .02 |
| 270 | Ray Handley | .05 | .02 |
| 271 | Louis Aguiar (R) | .08 | .05 |
| 272 | Brad Baxter | .10 | .06 |
| 273 | Chris Burkett | .05 | .02 |
| 274 | Irv Eatman | .05 | .02 |
| 275 | Jeff Lageman | .07 | .04 |
| 276 | Freeman McNeil | .07 | .04 |
| 277 | Rob Moore | .20 | .12 |
| 278 | Lonnie Young | .05 | .02 |
| 279 | Bruce Coslet | .05 | .02 |
| 280 | Jerome Brown | .07 | .04 |
| 281 | Keith Byars | .07 | .04 |
| 282 | Bruce Collie | .05 | .02 |
| 283 | Keith Jackson | .15 | .10 |
| 284 | James Joseph | .10 | .06 |
| 285 | Seth Joyner | .07 | .04 |
| 286 | Andre Waters | .05 | .02 |
| 287 | Reggie White | .12 | .07 |
| 288 | Rich Kotite | .05 | .02 |
| 289 | Rich Camarillo | .05 | .02 |
| 290 | Garth Jax | .05 | .02 |
| 291 | Ernie Jones | .08 | .05 |
| 292 | Tim McDonald | .05 | .02 |
| 293 | Rod Saddler | .05 | .02 |
| 294 | Anthony Thompson | .08 | .05 |
| 295 | Tom Tupa | .07 | .04 |
| 296 | Ron Wolfley | .05 | .02 |
| 297 | Joe Bugel | .05 | .02 |
| 298 | Gary Anderson | .05 | .02 |
| 299 | Jeff Graham | .15 | .10 |
| 300 | Eric Green | .12 | .07 |
| 301 | Bryan Hinkle | .05 | .02 |
| 302 | Tunch Ilkin | .05 | .02 |
| 303 | Louis Lipps | .07 | .04 |
| 304 | Neil O'Donnell | .60 | .35 |
| 305 | Rod Woodson | .10 | .06 |
| 306 | Bill Cowher | .07 | .04 |
| 307 | Eric Bieniemy | .12 | .07 |
| 308 | Marion Butts | .12 | .07 |
| 309 | John Friesz | .10 | .06 |
| 310 | Courtney Hall | .05 | .02 |
| 311 | Ronnie Harmon | .07 | .04 |
| 312 | Henry Rolling | .05 | .02 |
| 313 | Billy Ray Smith | .05 | .02 |
| 314 | George Thornton | .05 | .02 |
| 315 | Bobby Ross | .07 | .04 |
| 316 | Todd Bowles | .05 | .02 |
| 317 | Michael Carter | .05 | .02 |
| 318 | Don Griffin | .05 | .02 |
| 319 | Charles Haley | .07 | .04 |
| 320 | Brent Jones | .08 | .05 |
| 321 | John Taylor | .15 | .10 |
| 322 | Ted Washington | .05 | .02 |
| 323 | Steve Young | .25 | .15 |
| 324 | George Seifert | .05 | .02 |
| 325 | Brian Blades | .07 | .04 |
| 326 | Jacob Green | .05 | .02 |
| 327 | Patrick Hunter | .05 | .02 |
| 328 | Tommy Kane | .08 | .05 |
| 329 | Cortez Kennedy | .12 | .07 |
| 330 | Dave Krieg | .10 | .06 |
| 331 | Rufus Porter | .05 | .02 |
| 332 | John L. Williams | .07 | .04 |
| 333 | Tom Flores | .05 | .02 |
| 334 | Gary Anderson | .05 | .02 |
| 335 | Mark Carrier (TB) | .08 | .05 |
| 336 | Reuben Davis | .05 | .02 |
| 337 | Lawrence Dawsey | .20 | .12 |

| | | | |
|---|---|---|---|
| 338 Keith McCants | .07 | .04 |
| 339 Vinny Testaverde | .12 | .07 |
| 340 Broderick Thomas | .08 | .05 |
| 341 Robert Wilson | .07 | .04 |
| 342 Sam Wyche | .05 | .02 |
| 343 Teacher Of Year (News) | .05 | .02 |
| 344 Instant Replay (News) | .05 | .02 |
| 345 NFL Experience (News) | .05 | .02 |
| 346 Noll Retires (News) | .05 | .02 |
| 347 Isaac Curtis/Tim McGee | .05 | .02 |
| 348 Drew Pearson/Michael Irvin | .12 | .07 |
| 349 Billy Sims/Barry Sanders | .30 | .18 |
| 350 Ken Stabler/Todd Marinovich | .40 | .25 |
| 351 Craig James/Leonard Russell | .25 | .15 |
| 352 Bob Golic (Msg) | .05 | .02 |
| 353 Pat Harlow (Msg) | .05 | .02 |
| 354 Esera Tuaolo (Msg) | .05 | .02 |
| 355 Mark Schlereth (Msg) | .05 | .02 |
| 356 Trace Armstrong (Msg) | .05 | .02 |
| 357 Eric Bieniemy (Msg) | .08 | .05 |
| 358 Bill Romanowski (Msg) | .05 | .02 |
| 359 Irv Eatman (Msg) | .05 | .02 |
| 360 Jonathan Hayes (Msg) | .05 | .02 |
| 361 Falcons (Spirit) | .05 | .02 |
| 362 Bears (Spirit) | .05 | .02 |
| 363 Cowboys (Spirit) | .05 | .02 |
| 364 Lions (Spirit) | .05 | .02 |
| 365 Packers (Spirit) | .05 | .02 |
| 366 Rams (Spirit) | .05 | .02 |
| 367 Vikings (Spirit) | .05 | .02 |
| 368 Saints (Spirit) | .05 | .02 |
| 369 Giants (Spirit) | .05 | .02 |
| 370 Eagles (Spirit) | .05 | .02 |
| 371 Cardinals (Spirit) | .05 | .02 |
| 372 49ers (Spirit) | .05 | .02 |
| 373 Buccaneers (Spirit) | .05 | .02 |
| 374 Redskins (Spirit) | .05 | .02 |
| 375 Steve Atwater (PB) | .07 | .04 |
| 376 Cornelius Bennett (PB) | .08 | .05 |
| 377 Tim Brown (PB) | .07 | .04 |
| 378 Marion Butts (PB) | .08 | .05 |
| 379 Ray Childress (PB) | .07 | .04 |
| 380 Mark Clayton (PB) | .08 | .05 |
| 381 Marv Cook (PB) | .07 | .04 |
| 382 Cris Dishman (PB) | .07 | .04 |
| 383 William Fuller (PB) | .05 | .02 |
| 384 Gaston Green (PB) | .08 | .05 |
| 385 Jeff Jaeger (PB) | .05 | .02 |
| 386 Haywood Jeffires (PB) | .12 | .07 |

| | | | |
|---|---|---|---|
| 387 James Lofton (PB) | .08 | .05 |
| 388 Ronnie Lott (PB) | .08 | .05 |
| 389 Karl Mecklenburg (PB) | .07 | .04 |
| 390 Warren Moon (PB) | .12 | .07 |
| 391 Anthony Munoz (PB) | .07 | .04 |
| 392 Dennis Smith (PB) | .05 | .02 |
| 393 Neil Smith (PB) | .05 | .02 |
| 394 Darryl Talley (PB) | .05 | .02 |
| 395 Derrick Thomas (PB) | .10 | .06 |
| 396 Thurman Thoams (PB) | .20 | .12 |
| 397 Greg Townsend (PB) | .05 | .02 |
| 398 Richmond Webb (PB) | .05 | .02 |
| 399 Rod Woodson (PB) | .08 | .05 |
| 400 Dan Reeves (PB) | .05 | .02 |
| 401 Troy Aikman (PB) | .25 | .15 |
| 402 Eric Allen (PB) | .05 | .02 |
| 403 Bennie Blades (PB) | .07 | .04 |
| 404 Lomas Brown (PB) | .05 | .02 |
| 405 Mark Carrier (PB) | .07 | .04 |
| 406 Gary Clark (PB) | .10 | .06 |
| 407 Mel Gray (PB) | .05 | .02 |
| 408 Darrell Green (PB) | .08 | .05 |
| 409 Michael Irvin (PB) | .15 | .10 |
| 410 Vaughn Johnson (PB) | .05 | .02 |
| 411 Seth Joyner (PB) | .05 | .02 |
| 412 Jim Lachey (PB) | .05 | .02 |
| 413 Chip Lohmiller (PB) | .05 | .02 |
| 414 Charles Mann (PB) | .05 | .02 |
| 415 Chris Miller (PB) | .10 | .06 |
| 416 Sam Mills (PB) | .05 | .02 |
| 417 Bart Oates (PB) | .05 | .02 |
| 418 Jerry Rice (PB) | .20 | .12 |
| 419 Andre Rison (PB) | .10 | .06 |
| 420 Mark Rypien (PB) | .08 | .05 |
| 421 Barry Sanders (PB) | .25 | .15 |
| 422 Deion Sanders (PB) | .08 | .05 |
| 423 Mark Schlereth (PB) | .05 | .02 |
| 424 Mike Singletary (PB) | .08 | .05 |
| 425 Emmitt Smith (PB) | .75 | .40 |
| 426 Pat Swilling (PB) | .07 | .04 |
| 427 Reggie White (PB) | .08 | .05 |
| 428 Rick Bryan | .05 | .02 |
| 429 Tim Green | .05 | .02 |
| 430 Drew Hill | .08 | .05 |
| 431 Norm Johnson | .05 | .02 |
| 432 Keith Jones | .05 | .02 |
| 433 Mike Pritchard | .25 | .15 |
| 434 Deion Sanders | .15 | .10 |
| 435 Tony Smith (R) | .50 | .30 |
| 436 Jessie Tuggle | .05 | .02 |
| 437 Steve Christie | .05 | .02 |
| 438 Shane Conlan | .08 | .05 |
| 439 Matt Darby (R) | .10 | .06 |
| 440 John Fina (R) | .10 | .06 |
| 441 Henry Jones | .07 | .04 |
| 442 Jim Kelly | .50 | .30 |
| 443 Pete Metzelaars | .07 | .04 |

| | | | |
|---|---|---|---|
| 444 | Andre Reed | .15 | .10 |
| 445 | Bruce Smith | .10 | .06 |
| 446 | Troy Auzenne (R) | .10 | .06 |
| 447 | Mark Carrier (Chi) | .08 | .05 |
| 448 | Will Furrer (R) | .30 | .18 |
| 449 | Jim Harbaugh | .10 | .06 |
| 450 | Brad Muster | .07 | .04 |
| 451 | Darren Lewis | .15 | .10 |
| 452 | Mike Singletary | .10 | .06 |
| 453 | Alonzo Spellman (R) | .20 | .12 |
| 454 | Chris Zorich | .08 | .05 |
| 455 | Jim Breech | .05 | .02 |
| 456 | Boomer Esiason | .12 | .07 |
| 457 | Derrick Fenner | .12 | .07 |
| 458 | James Francis | .08 | .05 |
| 459 | David Klingler (R) | 1.25 | .70 |
| 460 | Tim McGee | .08 | .05 |
| 461 | Carl Pickens (R) | .75 | .40 |
| 462 | Alfred Williams | .08 | .05 |
| 463 | Darryl Williams (R) | .25 | .15 |
| 464 | Mark Bavaro | .05 | .02 |
| 465 | Jay Hilgenberg | .05 | .02 |
| 466 | Leroy Hoard | .08 | .05 |
| 467 | Bernie Kosar | .12 | .07 |
| 468 | Michael Dean Perry | .12 | .07 |
| 469 | Todd Philcox (R) | .25 | .15 |
| 470 | Patrick Rowe (R) | .20 | .12 |
| 471 | Tommy Vardell (R) | .75 | .40 |
| 472 | Everson Walls | .05 | .02 |
| 473 | Troy Aikman | .75 | .40 |
| 474 | Kenneth Gant (R) | .12 | .07 |
| 475 | Charles Haley | .07 | .04 |
| 476 | Michael Irvin | .40 | .25 |
| 477 | Robert Jones (R) | .20 | .12 |
| 478 | Russell Maryland | .15 | .10 |
| 479 | Jay Novacek | .12 | .07 |
| 480 | Kevin Smith (R) | .15 | .10 |
| 481 | Tony Tolbert | .05 | .02 |
| 482 | Steve Atwater | .08 | .05 |
| 483 | Shane Dronett (R) | .15 | .10 |
| 484 | Simon Fletcher | .05 | .02 |
| 485 | Greg Lewis | .08 | .05 |
| 486 | Tommy Maddox (R) | 1.00 | .60 |
| 487 | Shannon Sharpe | .07 | .04 |
| 488 | Dennis Smith | .05 | .02 |
| 489 | Sammie Smith | .08 | .05 |
| 490 | Kenny Walker | .08 | .05 |
| 491 | Lomas Brown | .07 | .04 |
| 492 | Mike Farr | .05 | .02 |
| 493 | Mel Gray | .05 | .02 |
| 494 | Jason Hanson (R) | .08 | .05 |
| 495 | Herman Moore | .30 | .18 |
| 496 | Rodney Peete | .12 | .07 |
| 497 | Robert Porcher (R) | .15 | .10 |
| 498 | Kelvin Pritchett | .10 | .06 |
| 499 | Andre Ware | .20 | .12 |
| 500 | Sanjay Beach (R) | .15 | .10 |

| | | | |
|---|---|---|---|
| 501 | Edgar Bennett (R) | .40 | .25 |
| 502 | Lewis Billups | .05 | .02 |
| 503 | Terrell Buckley | .40 | .25 |
| 504 | Ty Detmer | .15 | .10 |
| 505 | Brett Favre | 1.00 | .60 |
| 506 | Johnny Holland | .05 | .02 |
| 507 | Dexter McNabb (R) | .15 | .10 |
| 508 | Vince Workman | .10 | .06 |
| 509 | Cody Carlson | .15 | .10 |
| 510 | Ernest Givens | .15 | .10 |
| 511 | Jerry Gray | .05 | .02 |
| 512 | Haywood Jeffires | .20 | .12 |
| 513 | Bruce Matthews | .07 | .04 |
| 514 | Bubba McDowell | .07 | .04 |
| 515 | Bucky Richardson (R) | .25 | .15 |
| 516 | Webster Slaughter | .10 | .06 |
| 517 | Al Smith | .07 | .04 |
| 518 | Mel Agee | .07 | .04 |
| 519 | Ashley Ambrose (R) | .25 | .15 |
| 520 | Kevin Call | .05 | .02 |
| 521 | Ken Clark | .05 | .02 |
| 522 | Quentin Coryatt (R) | .75 | .40 |
| 523 | Steve Emtman (R) | 1.00 | .60 |
| 524 | Jeff George | .25 | .15 |
| 525 | Jessie Hester | .07 | .04 |
| 526 | Anthony Johnson | .07 | .04 |
| 527 | Tim Barnett | .15 | .10 |
| 528 | Martin Bayless | .05 | .02 |
| 529 | J.J. Birden | .08 | .05 |
| 530 | Dale Carter (R) | .50 | .30 |
| 531 | Dave Krieg | .10 | .06 |
| 532 | Albert Lewis | .05 | .02 |
| 533 | Nick Lowery | .07 | .04 |
| 534 | Christian Okoye | .10 | .06 |
| 535 | Harvey Williams | .20 | .12 |
| 536 | Aundrey Bruce | .05 | .02 |
| 537 | Eric Dickerson | .25 | .15 |
| 538 | Willie Gault | .08 | .05 |
| 539 | Ethan Horton | .07 | .04 |
| 540 | Jeff Jaeger | .05 | .02 |
| 541 | Napoleon McCallum | .05 | .02 |
| 542 | Chester McGlockton (R) | .15 | .10 |
| 543 | Steve Smith | .05 | .02 |
| 544 | Steve Wisniewski | .05 | .02 |
| 545 | Marc Boutte (R) | .12 | .07 |
| 546 | Pat Carter | .05 | .02 |
| 547 | Jim Everett | .12 | .07 |
| 548 | Cleveland Gary | .08 | .05 |
| 549 | Sean Gilbert (R) | .35 | .20 |
| 550 | Steve Israel (R) | .12 | .07 |
| 551 | Todd Kinchen (R) | .40 | .25 |
| 552 | Jackie Slater | .07 | .04 |
| 553 | Tony Zendejas | .05 | .02 |
| 554 | Robert Clark | .05 | .02 |
| 555 | Mark Clayton | .10 | .06 |
| 556 | Marco Coleman (R) | .50 | .30 |

| | | | |
|---|---|---|---|
| 557 Bryan Cox | .15 | .10 |
| 558 Keith Jackson | .15 | .10 |
| 559 Dan Marino | .35 | .20 |
| 560 John Offerdahl | .07 | .04 |
| 561 Troy Vincent (R) | .25 | .15 |
| 562 Richmond Webb | .07 | .04 |
| 563 Terry Allen | .40 | .25 |
| 564 Chris Carter | .15 | .10 |
| 565 Roger Craig | .08 | .05 |
| 566 Rich Gannon | .12 | .07 |
| 567 Hassan Jones | .07 | .04 |
| 568 Randall McDaniel | .05 | .02 |
| 569 Al Noga | .05 | .02 |
| 570 Todd Scott | .05 | .02 |
| 571 Van Waiters | .07 | .04 |
| 572 Bruce Armstrong | .05 | .02 |
| 573 Gene Chilton (R) | .10 | .06 |
| 574 Eugene Chung (R) | .10 | .06 |
| 575 Todd Collins (R) | .10 | .06 |
| 576 Hart Lee Dykes | .05 | .02 |
| 577 David Howard (R) | .10 | .06 |
| 578 Eugene Lockhart | .05 | .02 |
| 579 Greg McMurtry | .08 | .05 |
| 580 Rod Smith (R) | .10 | .06 |
| 581 Gene Atkins | .05 | .02 |
| 582 Vince Buck | .05 | .02 |
| 583 Wesley Carroll | .10 | .06 |
| 584 Jim Dombrowski | .05 | .02 |
| 585 Vaughn Dunbar (R) | .60 | .35 |
| 586 Craig Heyward | .08 | .05 |
| 587 Dalton Hilliard | .08 | .05 |
| 588 Wayne Martin | .05 | .02 |
| 589 Renaldo Turnbull | .05 | .02 |
| 590 Carl Banks | .07 | .04 |
| 591 Derek Brown (R) | .30 | .18 |
| 592 Jarrod Bunch | .10 | .06 |
| 593 Mark Ingram | .07 | .04 |
| 594 Ed McCaffrey | .07 | .04 |
| 595 Phil Simms | .10 | .06 |
| 596 Phillippi Sparks (R) | .10 | .06 |
| 597 Lawrence Taylor | .15 | .10 |
| 598 Lewis Tillman | .05 | .02 |
| 599 Kyle Clifton | .05 | .02 |
| 600 Mo Lewis | .07 | .04 |
| 601 Terance Mathis | .05 | .02 |
| 602 Scott Mersereau | .05 | .02 |
| 603 Johnny Mitchell (R) | .30 | .18 |
| 604 Browning Nagle | .50 | .30 |
| 605 Ken O'Brien | .10 | .06 |
| 606 Al Toon | .08 | .05 |
| 607 Marvin Washington | .07 | .04 |
| 608 Eric Allen | .05 | .02 |
| 609 Fred Barnett | .20 | .12 |
| 610 John Booty | .05 | .02 |
| 611 Randall Cunningham | .15 | .10 |
| 612 Rich Miano | .05 | .02 |
| 613 Clyde Simmons | .07 | .04 |

| | | | |
|---|---|---|---|
| 614 Siran Stacy | .15 | .10 |
| 615 Herschel Walker | .12 | .07 |
| 616 Calvin Williams | .08 | .05 |
| 617 Chris Chandler | .10 | .06 |
| 618 Randal Hill | .20 | .12 |
| 619 Johnny Johnson | .15 | .10 |
| 620 Lorenzo Lynch | .05 | .02 |
| 621 Robert Massey | .05 | .02 |
| 622 Ricky Proehl | .08 | .05 |
| 623 Timm Rosenbach | .10 | .06 |
| 624 Tony Sacca (R) | .25 | .15 |
| 625 Aeneas Williams | .07 | .04 |
| 626 Bubby Brister | .10 | .06 |
| 627 Barry Foster | .60 | .35 |
| 628 Merril Hoge | .08 | .05 |
| 629 David Johnson | .05 | .02 |
| 630 David Little | .05 | .02 |
| 631 Greg Lloyd | .05 | .02 |
| 632 Ernie Mills | .10 | .06 |
| 633 Leon Searcy (R) | .12 | .07 |
| 634 Dwight Stone | .05 | .02 |
| 635 Sam Anno (R) | .08 | .05 |
| 636 Burt Grossman | .08 | .05 |
| 637 Stan Humphries | .30 | .18 |
| 638 Nate Lewis | .12 | .07 |
| 639 Anthony Miller | .15 | .10 |
| 640 Chris Mims | .15 | .10 |
| 641 Marquez Pope (R) | .12 | .07 |
| 642 Stanley Richard | .08 | .05 |
| 643 Junior Seau | .12 | .07 |
| 644 Brian Bollinger (R) | .08 | .05 |
| 645 Steve Bono (R) | .40 | .25 |
| 646 Dexter Carter | .08 | .05 |
| 647 Dana Hall (R) | .12 | .07 |
| 648 Amp Lee | .40 | .25 |
| 649 Joe Montana | .60 | .35 |
| 650 Tom Rathman | .07 | .04 |
| 651 Jerry Rice | .40 | .25 |
| 652 Ricky Watters | .80 | .50 |
| 653 Robert Blackmon | .05 | .02 |
| 654 John Kassy | .05 | .02 |
| 655 Ronnie Lee (R) | .10 | .06 |
| 656 Dan McGwire | .20 | .12 |
| 657 Ray Roberts (R) | .10 | .06 |
| 658 Kelly Stouffer | .10 | .06 |
| 659 Chris Warren | .15 | .10 |
| 660 Tony Woods | .05 | .02 |
| 661 David Wyman | .05 | .02 |
| 662 Reggie Cobb | .15 | .10 |
| 663 Steve DeBerg | .10 | .06 |
| 664 Santana Dotson (R) | .40 | .25 |
| 665 Willie Drewrey | .05 | .02 |
| 666 Paul Gruber | .07 | .04 |
| 667 Ron Hall | .05 | .02 |
| 668 Courtney Hawkins (R) | .20 | .12 |
| 669 Charles McRae | .05 | .02 |
| 670 Ricky Reynolds | .05 | .02 |

| 671 | Monte Coleman | .05 | .02 |
|-----|---------------|-----|-----|
| 672 | Brad Edwards | .05 | .02 |
| 673 | James Geathers | .05 | .02 |
| 674 | Kelly Goodburn | .05 | .02 |
| 675 | Kurt Gouveia | .05 | .02 |
| 676 | Chris Hakel (R) | .20 | .12 |
| 677 | Wilber Marshall | .08 | .05 |
| 678 | Ricky Sanders | .08 | .05 |
| 679 | Mark Schlereth | .07 | .04 |
| 680 | Bills (Spirit) | .05 | .02 |
| 681 | Bengals (Spirit) | .05 | .02 |
| 682 | Browns (Spirit) | .05 | .02 |
| 683 | Broncos (Spirit) | .05 | .02 |
| 684 | Oilers (Spirit) | .05 | .02 |
| 685 | Colts (Spirit) | .05 | .02 |
| 686 | Chiefs (Spirit) | .05 | .02 |
| 687 | Raiders (Spirit) | .05 | .02 |
| 688 | Dolphins (Spirit) | .05 | .02 |
| 689 | Patriots (Spirit) | .05 | .02 |
| 690 | Jets (Spirit) | .05 | .02 |
| 691 | Steelers (Spirit) | .05 | .02 |
| 692 | Chargers (Spirit) | .05 | .02 |
| 693 | Seahawks (Spirit) | .05 | .02 |
| 694 | Stephen Baker (Msg) | .05 | .02 |
| 695 | Hank Williams Jr(News) | .15 | .10 |
| 696 | Three Brothers (News) | .07 | .04 |
| 697 | Japan Bowl (News) | .05 | .02 |
| 698 | Georgia Dome (News) | .05 | .02 |
| 699 | Super Bowl Art | .05 | .02 |
| 700 | SB MVP (Rypien) | .10 | .06 |
| ___ | Santa Claus | .50 | .15 |
| SC1 | Lem Barney (HOF) | .50 | .30 |
| SC2 | Al Davis (HOF) | .75 | .40 |
| SC3 | John Mackey (HOF) | .75 | .40 |
| SC4 | John Riggins (HOF) | .90 | .50 |
| BC1 | Emmitt Smith Holo | 140.00 | 18.00 |
| BC2 | Emmitt Smith Holo | 250.00 | 22.50 |
| BC3 | Emmitt Smith Holo | 365.00 | 28.00 |
| BC4 | Emmitt Smith Holo | 480.00 | 35.00 |

# 1992 Pro Set Gold MVP's

The cards in this 30-card set were distributed in 1992 Pro Set Series I and Series II Jumbo Packs. The cards measure 2-1/2" by 3-1/2". Each card features gold foil stamping on the front and the MVP prefix next to the card numbers on the back.

|  |  | MINT | NR/MT |
|---|---|------|-------|
| **Complete Set (30)** | | 42.00 | 26.00 |
| **Commons** | | .40 | .25 |

| 1 | Thurman Thomas | 5.00 | 3.00 |
|----|------------------|-------|------|
| 2 | Anthony Munoz | .60 | .35 |
| 3 | Clay Matthews | .40 | .25 |
| 4 | John Elway | 1.50 | .90 |
| 5 | Warren Moon | 1.50 | .90 |
| 6 | Bill Brooks | .40 | .25 |
| 7 | Derrick Thomas | 1.50 | .90 |
| 8 | Todd Marinovich | 1.50 | .90 |
| 9 | Mark Higgs | 1.25 | .60 |
| 10 | Leonard Russell | 1.50 | .90 |
| 11 | Rob Moore | 1.00 | .60 |
| 12 | Rod Woodson | .60 | .35 |
| 13 | Marion Butts | 1.00 | .60 |
| 14 | Brian Blades | .40 | .25 |
| 15 | Don Shula | .40 | .25 |
| 16 | Deion Sanders | 1.75 | 1.00 |
| 17 | Neal Anderson | .60 | .35 |
| 18 | Emmitt Smith | 12.00 | 8.00 |
| 19 | Barry Sanders | 6.00 | 3.50 |
| 20 | Brett Favre | 3.50 | 2.00 |
| 21 | Kevin Green | .40 | .25 |
| 22 | Terry Allen | 2.50 | 1.50 |
| 23 | Pat Swilling | .75 | .40 |
| 24 | Rodney Hampton | 2.00 | 1.25 |
| 25 | Randall Cunningham | 1.50 | .90 |
| 26 | Randal Hill | 1.50 | .90 |
| 27 | Jerry Rice | 5.00 | 3.00 |
| 28 | Vinny Testaverde | .50 | .30 |
| 29 | Mark Rypien | 1.25 | .60 |
| 30 | Jimmy Johnson | .40 | .25 |

# 1992 Pro Set Hall Of Fame 2000

The cards in this limited 10-card insert set were distributed randomly in Pro Set foil packs. The cards depict some of the game's elite players who Pro Set projects to be future Hall of Famers. All cards measure 2-1/2" by 3-1/2".

|  |  | MINT | NR/MT |
|---|---|---|---|
| **Complete Set (10)** | | 16.00 | 10.00 |
| **Commons** | | 1.50 | .90 |
| | | | |
| 1 | Marcus Allen | 1.75 | 1.00 |
| 2 | Richard Dent | 1.50 | .90 |
| 3 | Eric Dickerson | 3.00 | 1.75 |
| 4 | Ronnie Lott | 1.75 | 1.00 |
| 5 | Art Monk | 2.50 | 1.50 |
| 6 | Joe Montana | 5.00 | 3.00 |
| 7 | Warren Moon | 3.00 | 1.75 |
| 8 | Anthony Munoz | 1.75 | 1.00 |
| 9 | Mike Singletary | 1.75 | 1.00 |
| 10 | Lawrence Taylor | 2.00 | 1.25 |

# 1992 Pro Set Power

NORM JOHNSON

This 330-card set belongs in the premium category. The card fronts feature full-bleed, full-color action photos with gold foil stamping. The player's name appears across the bottom of the card while a Pro Set Power logo is located in the top corner. The set contains a Rookie Subset (296-330). All cards measure 2-1/2" by 3-1/2".

|  |  | MINT | NR/MT |
|---|---|---|---|
| **Complete Set (330)** | | 34.00 | 20.00 |
| **Commons** | | .10 | .06 |
| | | | |
| 1 | Warren Moon | .35 | .20 |
| 2 | Mike Horan | .10 | .06 |
| 3 | Bobby Hebert | .20 | .12 |
| 4 | Jim Harbaugh | .15 | .10 |
| 5 | Sean Landeta | .10 | .06 |
| 6 | Bubby Brister | .15 | .10 |
| 7 | John Elway | .35 | .20 |
| 8 | Troy Aikman | 1.75 | 1.00 |
| 9 | Rodney Peete | .15 | .10 |
| 10 | Dan McGwire | .35 | .20 |
| 11 | Mark Rypien | .30 | .18 |
| 12 | Randall Cunningham | .30 | .18 |
| 13 | Dan Marino | .75 | .40 |
| 14 | Vinny Testaverde | .15 | .10 |
| 15 | Jeff Hostetler | .15 | .10 |
| 16 | Joe Montana | .80 | .50 |
| 17 | Dave Krieg | .15 | .10 |
| 18 | Jeff Jaeger | .10 | .06 |
| 19 | Bernie Kosar | .20 | .12 |
| 20 | Barry Sanders | 1.75 | 1.00 |
| 21 | Deion Sanders | .30 | .18 |
| 22 | Emmitt Smith | 4.50 | 2.75 |
| 23 | Mel Gray | .10 | .06 |
| 24 | Stanley Richard | .12 | .07 |
| 25 | Brad Muster | .12 | .07 |
| 26 | Rod Woodson | .15 | .10 |
| 27 | Rodney Hampton | .75 | .40 |
| 28 | Darrell Green | .15 | .10 |
| 29 | Barry Foster | 1.50 | .90 |
| 30 | Dave Meggett | .15 | .10 |
| 31 | Lonnie Young | .10 | .06 |
| 32 | Marcus Allen | .15 | .10 |
| 33 | Merril Hoge | .12 | .07 |
| 34 | Thurman Thomas | 1.25 | .70 |
| 35 | Neal Anderson | .15 | .10 |
| 36 | Bennie Blades | .12 | .07 |
| 37 | Pat Terrell | .10 | .06 |
| 38 | Nick Bell | .50 | .30 |
| 39 | Johnny Johnson | .25 | .15 |
| 40 | Bill Bates | .10 | .06 |
| 41 | Keith Byars | .12 | .07 |
| 42 | Ronnie Lott | .15 | .10 |
| 43 | Elvis Patterson | .10 | .06 |
| 44 | Lorenzo White | .25 | .15 |
| 45 | Tony Stargell | .12 | .07 |
| 46 | Tim McDonald | .12 | .07 |
| 47 | Kirby Jackson | .10 | .06 |
| 48 | Lionel Washington | .10 | .06 |

| 49 | Dennis Smith | .10 | .06 |
|---|---|---|---|
| 50 | Mike Singletary | .20 | .12 |
| 51 | Mike Croel | .25 | .15 |
| 52 | Pepper Johnson | .12 | .07 |
| 53 | Vaughn Johnson | .12 | .07 |
| 54 | Chris Spielman | .12 | .07 |
| 55 | Junior Seau | .25 | .15 |
| 56 | Lawrence Taylor | .20 | .12 |
| 57 | Clay Matthews | .10 | .06 |
| 58 | Derrick Thomas | .35 | .20 |
| 59 | Seth Joyner | .12 | .07 |
| 60 | Stan Thomas | .10 | .06 |
| 61 | Nate Newton | .10 | .06 |
| 62 | Matt Brock | .10 | .06 |
| 63 | Gene Chilton (R) | .15 | .10 |
| 64 | Randall McDaniel | .10 | .06 |
| 65 | Max Montoya | .10 | .06 |
| 66 | Joe Jacoby | .12 | .07 |
| 67 | Russell Maryland | .20 | .12 |
| 68 | Ed King | .10 | .06 |
| 69 | Mark Schlereth (R) | .15 | .10 |
| 70 | Charles McRae | .10 | .06 |
| 71 | Charles Mann | .10 | .06 |
| 72 | William Perry | .12 | .07 |
| 73 | Simon Fletcher | .10 | .06 |
| 74 | Paul Gruber | .12 | .07 |
| 75 | Howie Long | .12 | .07 |
| 76 | Steve McMichael | .12 | .07 |
| 77 | Karl Mecklenberg | .12 | .07 |
| 78 | Anthony Munoz | .15 | .10 |
| 79 | Ray Childress | .15 | .10 |
| 80 | Jerry Rice | 1.25 | .70 |
| 81 | Art Monk | .30 | .18 |
| 82 | John Taylor | .15 | .10 |
| 83 | Andre Reed | .25 | .15 |
| 84 | Haywood Jeffires | .30 | .18 |
| 85 | Mark Duper | .12 | .07 |
| 86 | Fred Barnett | .50 | .30 |
| 87 | Tom Waddle | .20 | .12 |
| 88 | Michael Irvin | .75 | .40 |
| 89 | Brian Blades | .12 | .07 |
| 90 | Neil Smith | .12 | .07 |
| 91 | Kevin Greene | .10 | .06 |
| 92 | Reggie White | .25 | .15 |
| 93 | Jerry Ball | .10 | .06 |
| 94 | Charles Haley | .12 | .07 |
| 95 | Richard Dent | .12 | .07 |
| 96 | Clyde Simmons | .12 | .07 |
| 97 | Cornelius Bennett | .20 | .12 |
| 98 | Eric Swann | .12 | .07 |
| 99 | Doug Smith | .10 | .06 |
| 100 | Jim Kelly | 1.00 | .60 |
| 101 | Michael Jackson | .35 | .20 |
| 102 | Steve Christie | .10 | .06 |
| 103 | Timm Rosenbach | .15 | .10 |
| 104 | Brett Favre | 1.75 | 1.00 |
| 105 | Jeff Feagles | .10 | .06 |
| 106 | Kevin Butler | .10 | .06 |
| 107 | Boomer Esiason | .20 | .12 |
| 108 | Steve Young | .60 | .35 |
| 109 | Norm Johnson | .10 | .06 |
| 110 | Jay Schroeder | .15 | .10 |
| 111 | Jeff George | .60 | .35 |
| 112 | Chris Miller | .25 | .15 |
| 113 | Steve Bono (R) | .75 | .40 |
| 114 | Neil O'Donnell | .75 | .40 |
| 115 | David Klingler (R) | 3.50 | 2.00 |
| 116 | Rich Gannon | .20 | .12 |
| 117 | Chris Chandler | .20 | .12 |
| 118 | Stan Gelbaugh | .20 | .12 |
| 119 | Scott Mitchell | .20 | .12 |
| 120 | Mark Carrier | .12 | .07 |
| 121 | Terry Allen | 1.00 | .60 |
| 122 | Tim McKyer | .10 | .06 |
| 123 | Barry Word | .30 | .18 |
| 124 | Freeman McNeil | .12 | .07 |
| 125 | Louis Oliver | .12 | .07 |
| 126 | Jarvis Williams | .10 | .06 |
| 127 | Steve Atwater | .15 | .10 |
| 128 | Cris Dishman | .10 | .06 |
| 129 | Eric Dickerson | .60 | .35 |
| 130 | Brad Baxter | .15 | .10 |
| 131 | Frank Minnifield | .10 | .06 |
| 132 | Ricky Watters | 1.50 | .90 |
| 133 | David Fulcher | .10 | .06 |
| 134 | Herschel Walker | .20 | .12 |
| 135 | Christian Okoye | .15 | .10 |
| 136 | Jerome Henderson | .12 | .07 |
| 137 | Nate Odomes | .10 | .06 |
| 138 | Todd Scott | .10 | .06 |
| 139 | Robert Delpino | .12 | .07 |
| 140 | Gary Anderson | .10 | .06 |
| 141 | Todd Lyght | .20 | .12 |
| 142 | Chris Warren | .20 | .12 |
| 143 | Mike Brim (R) | .15 | .10 |
| 144 | Tom Rathman | .12 | .07 |
| 145 | Dexter McNabb (R) | .35 | .20 |
| 146 | Vince Workman | .20 | .12 |
| 147 | Anthony Johnson | .10 | .06 |
| 148 | Brian Washington | .12 | .07 |
| 149 | David Tate | .10 | .06 |
| 150 | Johnny Holland | .10 | .06 |
| 151 | Monte Coleman | .10 | .06 |
| 152 | Keith McCants | .15 | .10 |
| 153 | Eugene Seale (R) | .15 | .10 |
| 154 | Al Smith | .12 | .07 |
| 155 | Andre Collins | .12 | .07 |
| 156 | Pat Swilling | .20 | .12 |
| 157 | Rickey Jackson | .12 | .07 |
| 158 | Wilbur Marshall | .12 | .07 |
| 159 | Kyle Clifton | .10 | .06 |
| 160 | Fred Stokes | .10 | .06 |
| 161 | Lance Smith | .10 | .06 |
| 162 | Guy McIntyre | .10 | .06 |

| | | | | | | |
|---|---|---|---|---|---|
| 163 | Bill Maas | .10 | .06 | 220 | Kenneth Davis | .20 | .12 |
| 164 | Gerald Perry | .10 | .06 | 221 | Larry Brown | .10 | .06 |
| 165 | Bart Oates | .10 | .06 | 222 | Mark Collins | .12 | .07 |
| 166 | Tony Jones | .10 | .06 | 223 | Vinnie Clark | .10 | .06 |
| 167 | Moe Gardner | .12 | .07 | 224 | Patrick Hunter | .10 | .06 |
| 168 | Joe Wolf | .10 | .06 | 225 | Gaston Green | .20 | .12 |
| 169 | Tim Krumrie | .10 | .06 | 226 | Everson Walls | .10 | .06 |
| 170 | Leonard Marshall | .12 | .07 | 227 | Harold Green | .25 | .15 |
| 171 | Kevin Call | .10 | .06 | 228 | Albert Lewis | .10 | .06 |
| 172 | Keith Kartz | .10 | .06 | 229 | Don Griffin | .10 | .06 |
| 173 | Ron Heller | .10 | .06 | 230 | Lorenzo Lynch | .10 | .06 |
| 174 | Steve Wallace | .10 | .06 | 231 | Brian Mitchell | .15 | .10 |
| 175 | Tony Casillas | .12 | .07 | 232 | Thomas Everett | .12 | .07 |
| 176 | Tim Irwin | .10 | .06 | 233 | Leonard Russell | .40 | .25 |
| 177 | Pat Harlow | .12 | .07 | 234 | Eric Bieniemy | .15 | .10 |
| 178 | Bruce Smith | .20 | .12 | 235 | John L. Williams | .12 | .07 |
| 179 | Jim Lachey | .12 | .07 | 236 | Leroy Hoard | .15 | .10 |
| 180 | Andre Rison | .40 | .25 | 237 | Darren Lewis | .25 | .15 |
| 181 | Michael Haynes | .40 | .25 | 238 | Reggie Cobb | .30 | .18 |
| 182 | Rod Bernstine | .12 | .07 | 239 | Steve Broussard | .15 | .10 |
| 183 | Mark Clayton | .20 | .12 | 240 | Marion Butts | .20 | .12 |
| 184 | Jay Novacek | .20 | .12 | 241 | Mike Pritchard | .40 | .25 |
| 185 | Rob Moore | .25 | .15 | 242 | Dexter Carter | .12 | .07 |
| 186 | Willie Green | .30 | .18 | 243 | Aeneas Williams | .12 | .07 |
| 187 | Ricky Proehl | .15 | .10 | 244 | Bruce Pickens | .15 | .10 |
| 188 | Al Toon | .12 | .07 | 245 | Harvey Williams | .35 | .20 |
| 189 | Webster Slaughter | .15 | .10 | 246 | Bobby Humphrey | .15 | .10 |
| 190 | Tony Bennett | .20 | .12 | 247 | Duane Bickett | .10 | .06 |
| 191 | Jeff Cross | .10 | .06 | 248 | James Francis | .12 | .07 |
| 192 | Michaewl Dean Perry | .20 | .12 | 249 | Broderick Thomas | .12 | .07 |
| 193 | Greg Townsend | .12 | .07 | 250 | Chip Banks | .12 | .07 |
| 194 | Alfred Williams | .10 | .06 | 251 | Bryan Cox | .25 | .15 |
| 195 | William Fuller | .10 | .06 | 252 | Sam Mills | .12 | .07 |
| 196 | Cortez Kennedy | .25 | .15 | 253 | Ken Norton | .12 | .07 |
| 197 | Henry Thomas | .10 | .06 | 254 | Jeff Harrod | .10 | .06 |
| 198 | Esera Tuaolo | .10 | .06 | 255 | John Roper | .10 | .06 |
| 199 | Tim Green | .10 | .06 | 256 | Darryl Talley | .12 | .07 |
| 200 | Keith Jackson | .25 | .15 | 257 | Andre Tippett | .12 | .07 |
| 201 | Don Majkowski | .15 | .10 | 258 | Jeff Lageman | .12 | .07 |
| 202 | Steve Beuerlein | .25 | .15 | 259 | Chris Doleman | .12 | .07 |
| 203 | Hugh Millen | .25 | .15 | 260 | Shane Conlan | .15 | .10 |
| 204 | Browning Nagle | .75 | .40 | 261 | Jessie Tuggle | .10 | .06 |
| 205 | Chip Lohmiller | .10 | .06 | 262 | Eric Hill | .10 | .06 |
| 206 | Phil Simms | .15 | .10 | 263 | Bruce Armstrong | .10 | .06 |
| 207 | Jim Everett | .20 | .12 | 264 | Bill Fralic | .10 | .06 |
| 208 | Erik Kramer | .20 | .12 | 265 | Alvin Harper | .75 | .40 |
| 209 | Todd Marinovich | .60 | .35 | 266 | Bill Brooks | .10 | .06 |
| 210 | Henry Jones | .10 | .06 | 267 | Henry Ellard | .15 | .10 |
| 211 | Dwight Stone | .10 | .06 | 268 | Cris Carter | .20 | .12 |
| 212 | Andre Waters | .10 | .06 | 269 | Irving Fryar | .12 | .07 |
| 213 | Darryl Henley | .10 | .06 | 270 | Lawrence Dawsey | .25 | .15 |
| 214 | Mark Higgs | .35 | .20 | 271 | James Lofton | .25 | .15 |
| 215 | Dalton Hilliard | .15 | .10 | 272 | Ernest Givens | .20 | .12 |
| 216 | Earnest Byner | .15 | .10 | 273 | Terance Mathis | .10 | .06 |
| 217 | Eric Metcalf | .20 | .12 | 274 | Randal Hill | .30 | .18 |
| 218 | Gill Byrd | .12 | .07 | 275 | Eddie Brown | .12 | .07 |
| 219 | Robert Williams (R) | .15 | .10 | 276 | Tim Brown | .15 | .10 |

| | | | |
|---|---|---|---|
| 277 | Anthony Carter | .15 | .10 |
| 278 | Wendell Davis | .20 | .12 |
| 279 | Mark Ingram | .12 | .07 |
| 280 | Anthony Miller | .30 | .18 |
| 281 | Clarence Verdin | .12 | .07 |
| 282 | Willie Anderson | .15 | .10 |
| 283 | Ricky Sanders | .12 | .07 |
| 284 | Steve Jordan | .12 | .07 |
| 285 | Gary Clark | .20 | .12 |
| 286 | Sterling Sharpe | .60 | .35 |
| 287 | Herman Moore | .50 | .30 |
| 288 | Stephen Baker | .12 | .07 |
| 289 | Marv Cook | .12 | .07 |
| 290 | Ernie Jones | .15 | .10 |
| 291 | Eric Green | .20 | .12 |
| 292 | Mervyn Fernandez | .15 | .10 |
| 293 | Greg McMurtry | .12 | .07 |
| 294 | Quinn Early | .10 | .06 |
| 295 | Tim Harris | .12 | .07 |
| 296 | Will Furrer (R) | .50 | .30 |
| 297 | Jason Hanson (R) | .12 | .07 |
| 298 | Chris Hakel (R) | .35 | .20 |
| 299 | Ty Detmer (R) | .30 | .18 |
| 300 | David Klingler | 1.75 | 1.00 |
| 301 | Amp Lee (R) | .80 | .50 |
| 302 | Troy Vincent (R) | .40 | .25 |
| 303 | Kevin Smith (R) | .25 | .15 |
| 304 | Terrell Buckley (R) | 1.25 | .70 |
| 305 | Dana Hall (R) | .25 | .15 |
| 306 | Tony Smith (R) | .80 | .50 |
| 307 | Steve Israel (R) | .20 | .12 |
| 308 | Vaughn Dunbar (R) | .80 | .50 |
| 309 | Ashley Ambrose (R) | .60 | .35 |
| 310 | Edgar Bennett (R) | .75 | .40 |
| 311 | Dale Carter (R) | .90 | .50 |
| 312 | Rodney Culver (R) | .25 | .15 |
| 313 | Matt Darby (R) | .15 | .10 |
| 314 | Tommy Vardell (R) | 1.00 | .60 |
| 315 | Quentin Coryatt (R) | 1.25 | .70 |
| 316 | Robert Jones (R) | .40 | .25 |
| 317 | Joe Bowden (R) | .15 | .10 |
| 318 | Eugene Chung (R) | .15 | .10 |
| 319 | Troy Auzenne (R) | .15 | .10 |
| 320 | Santana Dotson (R) | .60 | .35 |
| 321 | Greg Skrepenak (R) | .15 | .10 |
| 322 | Steve Emtman (R) | 2.50 | 1.40 |
| 323 | Carl Pickens (R) | 1.25 | .70 |
| 324 | Johnny Mitchell (R) | .50 | .30 |
| 325 | Patrick Rowe (R) | .30 | .18 |
| 326 | Alonzo Spellman (R) | .25 | .15 |
| 327 | Robert Porcher (R) | .25 | .15 |
| 328 | Chris Mims (R) | .75 | .40 |
| 329 | Marc Boutte (R) | .15 | .10 |
| 330 | Shane Dronett (R) | .30 | .18 |

# 1992 Pro Set Power Combos

The cards in this 10-card limited insert set were distributed randomly in Pro Set Power foil packs. The cards feature multi-player photos on the fronts with gold foil stamping. All cards measure 2-1/2" by 3-12/".

| | | MINT | NR/MT |
|---|---|---|---|
| **Complete Set (10)** | | 48.00 | 30.00 |
| **Commons** | | 2.50 | 1.50 |

| | | MINT | NR/MT |
|---|---|---|---|
| 1 | Steve Emtman Quentin Coryatt | 7.00 | 4.00 |
| 2 | Barry Word Christian Okoye | 4.50 | 2.75 |
| 3 | Sam Mills Vaughn Johnson | 3.00 | 1.75 |
| 4 | Derrick Thomas Keith McCants | 5.00 | 3.00 |
| 5 | Michael Irvin Emmitt Smith | 24.00 | 15.00 |
| 6 | Jerry Ball Chris Spielman | 3.00 | 1.75 |
| 7 | Gary Clark Art Monk Ricky Sanders | 7.50 | 4.50 |
| 8 | Rod Woodson David Johnson | 3.50 | 2.00 |
| 9 | Bill Fralic Chris Hinton | 2.50 | 1.50 |
| 10 | Irving Fryar Marv Cook | 3.00 | 1.75 |

# 1993 Pro Set Power I

This 200-card set is the first of two series. Card fronts contain full color action shots framed by a silver border. The player's name and team appear in a small box in the bottom corner of the card. A "Power" logo is printed in the top corner. The horizontal card backs feature another full color action shot along with a power rating, stats and 1992 highlights. Random Emmitt Smith hologram insert cards were distributed in foil packs. Those are listed at the end of this checklist. All cards measure 2-1/2" by 3-1/2".

|  | | MINT | NR/MT |
|---|---|---|---|
| Complete Set (200) | | 18.50 | 12.50 |
| Commons | | .12 | .07 |
| 1 | Warren Moon | .35 | .20 |
| 2 | Steve Christie | .12 | .07 |
| 3 | Jim Breech | .12 | .07 |
| 4 | Brett Favre | 1.50 | .90 |
| 5 | Sean Landeta | .12 | .07 |
| 6 | Bubby Brister | .15 | .10 |
| 7 | John Elway | .35 | .20 |
| 8 | Troy Aikman | 1.75 | 1.00 |
| 9 | Rodney Peete | .20 | .12 |
| 10 | Pete Stoyanovich | .12 | .07 |
| 11 | Mark Rypien | .25 | .15 |
| 12 | Jim Kelly | .35 | .20 |
| 13 | Dan Marino | .50 | .30 |
| 14 | Neil O'Donnell | .60 | .35 |
| 15 | David Klingler | 1.50 | .90 |
| 16 | Rich Gannon | .20 | .12 |
| 17 | Dave Krieg | .15 | .10 |
| 18 | Jeff Jaeger | .12 | .07 |
| 19 | Bernie Kosar | .20 | .12 |
| 20 | Barry Sanders | 1.75 | 1.00 |
| 21 | Deion Sanders | .30 | .18 |
| 22 | Emmitt Smith | 4.50 | 2.75 |
| 23 | Barry Word | .25 | .15 |
| 24 | Stanley Richard | .20 | .12 |
| 25 | Louis Oliver | .15 | .10 |
| 26 | Rod Woodson | .20 | .12 |
| 27 | Rodney Hampton | .50 | .30 |
| 28 | Cris Dishman | .15 | .10 |
| 29 | Barry Foster | 1.75 | 1.00 |
| 30 | Dave Meggett | .15 | .10 |
| 31 | Kevin Ross | .12 | .07 |
| 32 | Ricky Watters | 1.75 | 1.00 |
| 33 | Darren Lewis | .20 | .12 |
| 34 | Thurman Thomas | 1.00 | .60 |
| 35 | Rodney Culver | .20 | .12 |
| 36 | Bennie Blades | .15 | .10 |
| 37 | Larry Centers | .12 | .07 |
| 38 | Todd Scott | .12 | .07 |
| 39 | Darren Perry | .12 | .07 |
| 40 | Robert Massey | .12 | .07 |
| 41 | Keith Byars | .15 | .10 |
| 42 | Chris Warren | .25 | .15 |
| 43 | Cleveland Gary | .20 | .12 |
| 44 | Lorenzo White | .25 | .15 |
| 45 | Tony Stargell | .12 | .07 |
| 46 | Bennie Thompson | .12 | .07 |
| 47 | A.J. Johnson | .12 | .07 |
| 48 | Daryl Johnston | .20 | .12 |
| 49 | Dennis Smith | .12 | .07 |
| 50 | Johnny Holland | .12 | .07 |
| 51 | Ken Norton | .20 | .12 |
| 52 | Pepper Johnson | .12 | .07 |
| 53 | Vaughn Johnson | .15 | .10 |
| 54 | Chris Spielman | .12 | .07 |
| 55 | Junior Seau | .25 | .15 |
| 56 | Chris Doleman | .15 | .10 |
| 57 | Rickey Jackson | .15 | .10 |
| 58 | Derrick Thomas | .30 | .18 |
| 59 | Seth Joyner | .15 | .10 |
| 60 | Stan Thomas | .12 | .07 |
| 61 | Nate Newton | .12 | .07 |
| 62 | Matt Brock | .12 | .07 |
| 63 | Mike Munchak | .15 | .10 |
| 64 | Randall McDaniel | .12 | .07 |
| 65 | Ron Hallstrom | .12 | .07 |
| 66 | Andy Heck | .12 | .07 |
| 67 | Russell Maryland | .25 | .15 |
| 68 | Bruce Wilkerson | .12 | .07 |
| 69 | Mark Schlereth | .12 | .07 |
| 70 | John Fina | .12 | .07 |
| 71 | Santana Dotson | .35 | .20 |
| 72 | Don Mosebar | .12 | .07 |
| 73 | Simon Fletcher | .12 | .07 |
| 74 | Paul Gruber | .12 | .07 |
| 75 | Howard Ballard | .12 | .07 |
| 76 | John Alt | .12 | .07 |
| 77 | Carlton Hasselrig | .12 | .07 |
| 78 | Bruce Smith | .25 | .15 |
| 79 | Ray Childress | .20 | .12 |

| | | | |
|---|---|---|---|
| 80 | Jerry Rice | 1.00 | .60 |
| 81 | Art Monk | .30 | .18 |
| 82 | John Taylor | .25 | .15 |
| 83 | Andre Reed | .25 | .15 |
| 84 | Sterling Sharpe | .50 | .30 |
| 85 | Sam Graddy | .15 | .10 |
| 86 | Fred Barnett | .30 | .18 |
| 87 | Ricky Proehl | .25 | .15 |
| 88 | Michael Irvin | 1.25 | .70 |
| 89 | Webster Slaughter | .25 | .15 |
| 90 | Tony Bennett | .15 | .10 |
| 91 | Leslie O'Neal | .20 | .12 |
| 92 | Michael Dean Perry | .15 | .10 |
| 93 | Greg Townsend | .12 | .07 |
| 94 | Anthony Smith | .12 | .07 |
| 95 | Richard Dent | .15 | .10 |
| 96 | Clyde Simmons | .15 | .10 |
| 97 | Cornelius Bennett | .20 | .12 |
| 98 | Eric Swann | .15 | .10 |
| 99 | Cortez Kennedy | .30 | .18 |
| 100 | Power Card | 1.50 | .90 |
| 101 | Michael Jackson | .25 | .15 |
| 102 | Lin Elliott | .12 | .07 |
| 103 | Rohn Stark | .12 | .07 |
| 104 | Jim Harbaugh | .20 | .12 |
| 105 | Greg Davis | .12 | .07 |
| 106 | Mike Cofer | .12 | .07 |
| 107 | Morten Andersen | .15 | .10 |
| 108 | Steve Young | .75 | .45 |
| 109 | Norm Johnson | .12 | .07 |
| 110 | Dan McGwire | .40 | .25 |
| 111 | Jim Everett | .20 | .12 |
| 112 | Randall Cunningham | .30 | .18 |
| 113 | Steve Bono | .30 | .18 |
| 114 | Cody Carlson | .20 | .12 |
| 115 | Jeff Hostetler | .20 | .12 |
| 116 | Rich Camarillo | .12 | .07 |
| 117 | Chris Chandler | .20 | .12 |
| 118 | Stan Gelbaugh | .15 | .10 |
| 119 | Tony Sacca | .25 | .15 |
| 120 | Henry Jones | .12 | .07 |
| 121 | Terry Allen | .80 | .50 |
| 122 | Amp Lee | .75 | .45 |
| 123 | Mel Gray | .12 | .07 |
| 124 | Jon Vaughn | .20 | .12 |
| 125 | Bubba McDowell | .12 | .07 |
| 126 | Aundray McMillian | .12 | .07 |
| 127 | Terrell Buckley | .60 | .35 |
| 128 | Dana Hall | .15 | .10 |
| 129 | Eric Dickerson | .40 | .25 |
| 130 | Martin Bayless | .12 | .07 |
| 131 | Steve Israel | .20 | .12 |
| 132 | Vaughn Dunbar | .70 | .40 |
| 133 | Ronnie Harmon | .25 | .15 |
| 134 | Dale Carter | .60 | .35 |
| 135 | Neal Anderson | .15 | .10 |
| 136 | Merton Hanks | .12 | .07 |
| 137 | James Washington | .12 | .07 |
| 138 | Reggie Rivers | .12 | .07 |
| 139 | Bruce Pickens | .20 | .12 |
| 140 | Gary Anderson | .12 | .07 |
| 141 | Eugene Robinson | .12 | .07 |
| 142 | Charles Mincy | .12 | .07 |
| 143 | Matt Darby | .12 | .07 |
| 144 | Tom Rathman | .15 | .10 |
| 145 | Dexter McNabb | .12 | .07 |
| 146 | Sean Lumpkin | .12 | .07 |
| 147 | Clayton Holmes | .12 | .07 |
| 148 | Wes Hopkins | .12 | .07 |
| 149 | David Tate | .12 | .07 |
| 150 | James Francis | .15 | .10 |
| 151 | Chip Banks | .15 | .10 |
| 152 | Keith McCants | .12 | .07 |
| 153 | Mark Stepnoski | .12 | .07 |
| 154 | Al Smith | .15 | .10 |
| 155 | Robert Jones | .20 | .12 |
| 156 | Lawrence Taylor | .20 | .12 |
| 157 | Clay Matthews | .12 | .07 |
| 158 | Wilber Marshall | .15 | .10 |
| 159 | Mike Johnson | .12 | .07 |
| 160 | Adam Schreiber | .12 | .07 |
| 161 | Tim Grunhard | .12 | .07 |
| 162 | Mark Bortz | .12 | .07 |
| 163 | Gene Chilton | .12 | .07 |
| 164 | Jamie Dukes | .12 | .07 |
| 165 | Bart Oates | .12 | .07 |
| 166 | Kevin Gogan | .12 | .07 |
| 167 | Kent Hull | .12 | .07 |
| 168 | Ed King | .12 | .07 |
| 169 | Eugene Chung | .12 | .07 |
| 170 | Troy Auzenne | .12 | .07 |
| 171 | Charles Mann | .12 | .07 |
| 172 | William Perry | .15 | .10 |
| 173 | Joe Valerio | .12 | .07 |
| 174 | Bruce Matthews | .15 | .10 |
| 175 | Tony Casillas | .15 | .10 |
| 176 | Steve Wisniewski | .12 | .07 |
| 177 | Karl Mecklenburg | .15 | .10 |
| 178 | Richmond Webb | .15 | .10 |
| 179 | Erik Williams | .12 | .07 |
| 180 | Andre Rison | .30 | .18 |
| 181 | Michael Haynes | .40 | .25 |
| 182 | Tim Barnett | .30 | .18 |
| 183 | Anthony Miller | .30 | .18 |
| 184 | Jay Novacek | .25 | .15 |
| 185 | Rob Moore | .25 | .15 |
| 186 | Willie Green | .30 | .18 |
| 187 | Tom Waddle | .25 | .15 |
| 188 | Keith Jackson | .30 | .18 |
| 189 | Steve Tasker | .12 | .07 |
| 190 | Marco Coleman | .40 | .25 |
| 191 | Jeff Wright | .12 | .07 |
| 192 | Burt Grossman | .15 | .10 |
| 193 | Trace Armstrong | .12 | .07 |

| | | | |
|---|---|---|---|
| 194 | Charles Haley | .20 | .12 |
| 195 | Greg Lloyd | .12 | .07 |
| 196 | Marc Boutte | .20 | .12 |
| 197 | Rufus Porter | .12 | .07 |
| 198 | Dennis Gibson | .12 | .07 |
| 199 | Shane Dronett | .12 | .07 |
| 200 | Power Card (Dallas) | 3.50 | 1.75 |
| BC1 | Emmitt Smith Holo I | 40.00 | 28.00 |
| BC2 | Emmitt Smith Holo II | 40.00 | 28.00 |

## 1993 Power I Draft Picks

This limited insert set features the top 1993 NFL draft picks. The cards were distributed randomly in foil packs. All cards measure 2-1/2" by 3-1/2".

| | | MINT | NR/MT |
|---|---|---|---|
| | **Complete Set (30)** | 65.00 | 38.00 |
| | **Commons** | | |
| 1 | Lincoln Kennedy | 2.00 | 1.25 |
| 2 | Thomas Smith | 2.00 | 1.25 |
| 3 | Curtis Conway | 3.50 | 2.00 |
| 4 | John Copeland | 2.00 | 1.25 |
| 5 | Dan Footman | 2.00 | 1.25 |
| 6 | Kevin Williams | 2.50 | 1.50 |
| 7 | Glyn Milburn | 3.50 | 2.00 |
| 8 | Ryan McNeil | 2.50 | 1.50 |
| 9 | George Teague | 2.00 | 1.25 |
| 10 | Michael Barrow | 2.00 | 1.25 |
| 11 | Roosevelt Potts | 3.00 | 1.75 |
| 12 | Jaime Fields | 2.00 | 1.25 |
| 13 | Patrick Bates | 2.00 | 1.25 |
| 14 | Jerome Bettis | 3.50 | 2.00 |
| 15 | O.J. McDuffie | 3.00 | 1.75 |
| 16 | Gino Torretta | 2.50 | 1.50 |
| 17 | Drew Bledsoe | 8.00 | 5.00 |
| 18 | Irv Smith | 2.50 | 1.50 |
| 19 | Marcus Buckley | 2.00 | 1.25 |
| 20 | Coleman Rudolph | 2.00 | 1.25 |
| 21 | Leonard Renfro | 2.00 | 1.25 |
| 22 | Garrison Hearst | 7.00 | 4.00 |
| 23 | Deon Figures | 2.00 | 1.25 |
| 24 | Natrone Means | 3.50 | 2.00 |
| 25 | Todd Kelly | 2.00 | 1.25 |
| 26 | Carlton Gray | 2.00 | 1.25 |
| 27 | Eric Curry | 2.00 | 1.25 |
| 28 | Tom Carter | 2.50 | 1.50 |
| 29 | AFC Stars | 7.50 | 4.50 |
| 30 | NFC Stars | 5.00 | 3.00 |

# SCORE

## 1989 Score

This 330-card set marked Score's entrance into the football card market. The card fronts feature full color action photos with the player's name and position in a horizontal box below the photo. A team helmut is located in the lower right corner. Card backs consist of a full color head shot, the player's personal data and stats. Key subsets include All-Pros (285-309), Speedburners (310-317), Predators (318-325) and Record Breakers (326-329). All cards measure 2-1/2" by 3-1/2".

| | | MINT | NR/MT |
|---|---|---|---|
| | **Complete Set (330)** | 190.00 | 115.00 |
| | **Commons** | .12 | .07 |
| 1 | Joe Montana | 2.50 | 1.50 |
| 2 | Bo Jackson | 1.25 | .80 |
| 3 | Boomer Esiason | .25 | .15 |
| 4 | Roger Craig | .20 | .12 |
| 5 | Ed Too Tall Jones | .15 | .10 |
| 6 | Phil Simms | .35 | .20 |
| 7 | Dan Hampton | .15 | .10 |
| 8 | John Settle (R) | .25 | .15 |
| 9 | Bernie Kosar | .35 | .20 |
| 10 | Al Toon | .25 | .15 |
| 11 | Bubby Brister (R) | 1.25 | .80 |
| 12 | Mark Clayton | .35 | .20 |
| 13 | Dan Marino | 3.50 | 2.00 |
| 14 | Joe Morris | .15 | .10 |
| 15 | Warren Moon | 1.50 | .90 |
| 16 | Chuck Long | .12 | .07 |

| | | | |
|---|---|---|---|
| 17 | Mark Jackson | .20 | .12 |
| 18 | Michael Irvin (R) | 24.00 | 14.00 |
| 19 | Bruce Smith | .25 | .15 |
| 20 | Anthony Carter | .20 | .12 |
| 21 | Charles Haley | .20 | .12 |
| 22 | Dave Duerson | .12 | .07 |
| 23 | Troy Stradford | .12 | .07 |
| 24 | Freeman McNeil | .15 | .10 |
| 25 | Jerry Gray | .12 | .07 |
| 26 | Bill Maas | .12 | .07 |
| 27 | Chris Chandler (R) | .40 | .25 |
| 28 | Tom Newberry | .12 | .07 |
| 29 | Albert Lewis | .15 | .10 |
| 30 | Jay Schroeder | .25 | .15 |
| 31 | Dalton Hilliard | .15 | .10 |
| 32 | Tony Eason | .15 | .10 |
| 33 | Rick Donnelly | .12 | .07 |
| 34 | Hershel Walker | .80 | .50 |
| 35 | Wesley Walker | .15 | .10 |
| 36 | Chris Doleman | .30 | .18 |
| 37 | Pat Swilling | .50 | .30 |
| 38 | Joey Browner | .15 | .10 |
| 39 | Shane Conlan | .20 | .12 |
| 40 | Mike Tomczak | .15 | .10 |
| 41 | Webster Slaughter | .25 | .15 |
| 42 | Ray Donaldson | .12 | .07 |
| 43 | Christian Okoye | 1.00 | .70 |
| 44 | John Bosa | .12 | .07 |
| 45 | Aaron Cox (R) | .25 | .15 |
| 46 | Bobby Hebert | .30 | .18 |
| 47 | Carl Banks | .15 | .10 |
| 48 | Jeff Fuller | .12 | .07 |
| 49 | Gerald Wilhite | .12 | .07 |
| 50 | Mike Singletary | .35 | .20 |
| 51 | Stanley Morgan | .15 | .10 |
| 52 | Mark Bavaro | .15 | .10 |
| 53 | Mickey Shuler | .12 | .07 |
| 54 | Keith Millard | .15 | .10 |
| 55 | Andre Tippett | .15 | .10 |
| 56 | Vance Johnson | .20 | .12 |
| 57 | Bennie Blades (R) | .40 | .25 |
| 58 | Tim Harris | .12 | .07 |
| 59 | Hanford Dixon | .12 | .07 |
| 60 | Chris Miller (R) | 8.50 | 5.50 |
| 61 | Cornelius Bennett | .80 | .50 |
| 62 | Neal Anderson | 2.00 | 1.25 |
| 63 | Ickey Woods (R) | .20 | .12 |
| 64 | Gary Anderson | .15 | .10 |
| 65 | Vaughan Johnson (R) | .80 | .50 |
| 66 | Ronnie Lippett | .12 | .07 |
| 67 | Mike Quick | .15 | .10 |
| 68 | Roy Green | .15 | .10 |
| 69 | Tim Krumrie | .12 | .07 |
| 70 | Mark Malone | .12 | .07 |
| 71 | James Jones | .12 | .07 |
| 72 | Cris Carter (R) | 2.50 | 1.50 |
| 73 | Ricky Nattiel | .15 | .10 |
| 74 | Jim Arnold | .12 | .07 |
| 75 | Randall Cunningham | 1.75 | 1.00 |
| 76 | John L. Williams | .20 | .12 |
| 77 | Paul Gruber (R) | .25 | .15 |
| 78 | Rod Woodson (R) | 1.50 | .90 |
| 79 | Ray Childress | .15 | .10 |
| 80 | Doug Williams | .20 | .12 |
| 81 | Deron Cherry | .15 | .10 |
| 82 | John Offerdahl | .15 | .10 |
| 83 | Louis Lipps | .15 | .10 |
| 84 | Neil Lomax | .20 | .12 |
| 85 | Wade Wilson | .15 | .10 |
| 86 | Tim Brown (R) | 2.50 | 1.50 |
| 87 | Chris Hinton | .12 | .07 |
| 88 | Stump Mitchell | .12 | .07 |
| 89 | Tunch Ilkin (R) | .15 | .10 |
| 90 | Steve Pelluer | .15 | .10 |
| 91 | Brian Noble | .12 | .07 |
| 92 | Reggie White | .70 | .40 |
| 93 | Aundray Bruce (R) | .20 | .12 |
| 94 | Garry James | .12 | .07 |
| 95 | Drew Hill | .25 | .15 |
| 96 | Anthony Munoz | .25 | .15 |
| 97 | James Wilder | .15 | .10 |
| 98 | Dexter Manley | .12 | .07 |
| 99 | Lee Williams | .12 | .07 |
| 100 | Dave Krieg | .25 | .15 |
| 101a | Keith Jackson (R) (Er) (#84 on back) | 3.50 | 2.00 |
| 101b | Keith Jackson (R) (Cor) (#88 on back) | 5.00 | 3.00 |
| 102 | Luis Sharpe | .12 | .07 |
| 103 | Kevin Greene | .15 | .10 |
| 104 | Duane Bickett | .12 | .07 |
| 105 | Mark Rypien (R) | 12.00 | 8.00 |
| 106 | Curt Warner | .20 | .12 |
| 107 | Jacob Green | .12 | .07 |
| 108 | Gary Clark | .75 | .45 |
| 109 | Bruce Matthews (R) | .30 | .18 |
| 110 | Bill Fralic | .12 | .07 |
| 111 | Bill Bates | .12 | .07 |
| 112 | Jeff Bryant | .12 | .07 |
| 113 | Charles Mann | .12 | .07 |
| 114 | Richard Dent | .15 | .10 |
| 115 | Bruce Hill (R) | .30 | .18 |
| 116 | Mark May (R) | .15 | .10 |
| 117 | Mark Collins (R) | .25 | .15 |
| 118 | Ron Holmes | .12 | .07 |
| 119 | Scott Case (R) | .20 | .12 |
| 120 | Tom Rathman | .20 | .12 |
| 121 | Dennis McKinnon | .12 | .07 |
| 122a | Ricky Sanders (Er) (#46 on back) | .30 | .18 |
| 122b | Ricky Sanders (Cor) (#83 on back) | 1.75 | 1.00 |
| 123 | Michael Carter | .12 | .07 |
| 124 | Ozzie Newsome | .30 | .18 |

| | | | |
|---|---|---|---|
| 125 Irving Fryar | .15 | .10 |
| 126a Ron Hall (R)(Er) | .25 | .15 |
| (Wrong Photos) | | |
| 126b Ron Hall (R) (Cor) | 1.25 | .80 |
| 127 Clay Matthews | .12 | .07 |
| 128 Leonard Marshall | .15 | .10 |
| 129 Kevin Mack | .15 | .10 |
| 130 Art Monk | .75 | .45 |
| 131 Garin Veris | .12 | .07 |
| 132 Steve Jordan | .12 | .07 |
| 133 Frank Minnifield | .12 | .07 |
| 134 Eddie Brown | .20 | .12 |
| 135 Stacey Bailey | .12 | .07 |
| 136 Rickey Jackson | .20 | .12 |
| 137 Henry Ellard | .20 | .12 |
| 138 Jim Burt | .12 | .07 |
| 139 Jerome Brown | .15 | .10 |
| 140 Rodney Holman (R) | .30 | .18 |
| 141 Sammy Winder | .12 | .07 |
| 142 Marcus Cotton (R) | .20 | .12 |
| 143 Jim Jeffcoat | .12 | .07 |
| 144 Rueben Mayes | .12 | .07 |
| 145 Jim McMahon | .20 | .12 |
| 146 Reggie Williams | .12 | .07 |
| 147 John Anderson | .12 | .07 |
| 148 Harris Barton (R) | .15 | .10 |
| 149 Phillip Epps | .12 | .07 |
| 150 Jay Hilgenberg | .12 | .07 |
| 151 Earl Ferrell | .12 | .07 |
| 152 Andre Reed | .80 | .50 |
| 153 Dennis Gentry | .12 | .07 |
| 154 Max Montoya | .12 | .07 |
| 155 Darrin Nelson | .15 | .10 |
| 156 Jeff Chadwick | .12 | .07 |
| 157 James Brooks | .15 | .10 |
| 158 Keith Bishop | .12 | .07 |
| 159 Robert Awalt | .12 | .07 |
| 160 Marty Lyons | .12 | .07 |
| 161 Johnny Hector | .15 | .10 |
| 162 Tony Casillas | .30 | .18 |
| 163 Kyle Clifton (R) | .20 | .12 |
| 164 Cody Risien | .12 | .07 |
| 165 Jamie Holland (R) | .15 | .10 |
| 166 Merril Hoge (R) | .60 | .35 |
| 167 Chris Spielman (R) | .75 | .45 |
| 168 Carlos Carson | .12 | .07 |
| 169 Jerry Ball (R) | .50 | .30 |
| 170 Don Majkowski (R) | 1.75 | 1.00 |
| 171 Everson Walls | .12 | .07 |
| 172 Mike Rozier | .15 | .10 |
| 173 Matt Millen | .15 | .10 |
| 174 Karl Mecklenburg | .20 | .12 |
| 175 Paul Palmer | .12 | .07 |
| 176 Brian Blades (R) | 2.00 | 1.25 |
| 177 Brent Fullwood (R) | .15 | .10 |
| 178 Anthony Miller (R) | 5.50 | 3.50 |
| 179 Brian Sochia | .12 | .07 |

| | | | |
|---|---|---|---|
| 180 Stephen Baker (R) | .60 | .35 |
| 181 Jesse Solomon | .12 | .07 |
| 182 John Grimsley | .12 | .07 |
| 183 Timmy Newsome | .12 | .07 |
| 184 Steve Sewell (R) | .20 | .12 |
| 185 Dean Biasucci | .12 | .07 |
| 186 Alonzo Highsmith | .12 | .07 |
| 187 Randy Grimes | .12 | .07 |
| 188a Mark Carrier (R)(Er) | 3.50 | 2.00 |
| (Wrong photo on back) | | |
| 188b Mark Carrier (R)(Cor) | 1.75 | 1.00 |
| 189 Vann McElroy | .12 | .07 |
| 190 Greg Bell | .15 | .10 |
| 191 Quinn Early (R) | .20 | .12 |
| 192 Lawrence Taylor | .75 | .45 |
| 193 Albert Bentley | .12 | .07 |
| 194 Ernest Givins | .40 | .25 |
| 195 Jackie Slater | .15 | .10 |
| 196 Jim Sweeney | .12 | .07 |
| 197 Freddie Joe Nunn | .12 | .07 |
| 198 Keith Byars | .15 | .10 |
| 199 Hardy Nickerson (R) | .20 | .12 |
| 200 Steve Beuerlein (R) | 2.00 | 1.25 |
| 201 Bruce Armstrong (R) | .25 | .15 |
| 202 Lionel Manuel | .12 | .07 |
| 203 J.T. Smith | .12 | .07 |
| 204 Mark Ingram (R) | .50 | .30 |
| 205 Fred Smerlas | .12 | .07 |
| 206 Bryan Hinkle (R) | .15 | .10 |
| 207 Steve McMichael | .15 | .10 |
| 208 Nick Lowery | .15 | .10 |
| 209 Jack Trudeau | .25 | .12 |
| 210 Lornezo Hampton | .12 | .07 |
| 211 Thurman Thomas (R) | 38.00 | 22.00 |
| 212 Steve Young | 2.50 | 1.50 |
| 213 James Lofton | .60 | .35 |
| 214 Jim Covert | .12 | .07 |
| 215 Ronnie Lott | .40 | .25 |
| 216 Stephone Paige | .15 | .10 |
| 217 Mark Duper | .20 | .12 |
| 218a Willie Gault (Er) | .50 | .30 |
| (Wrong photo on front) | | |
| 218b Willie Gault (Cor) | 1.25 | .80 |
| 219 Ken Ruettgers (R) | .15 | .10 |
| 220 Kevin Ross (R) | .25 | .15 |
| 221 Jerry Rice | 4.00 | 2.50 |
| 222 Billy Ray Smith | .12 | .07 |
| 223 Jim Kelly | 3.00 | 2.00 |
| 224 Vinny Testaverde | .25 | .15 |
| 225 Steve Largent | .80 | .50 |
| 226 Warren Williams (R) | .15 | .10 |
| 227 Morten Andersen | .15 | .10 |
| 228 Bill Brooks | .12 | .07 |
| 229 Reggie Langhorne (R) | .25 | .15 |
| 230 Pepper Johnson | .15 | .10 |
| 231 Pat Leahy | .12 | .07 |
| 232 Fred Marion | .12 | .07 |

| | | | |
|---|---|---|---|
| 233 | Gary Zimmerman | .12 | .07 |
| 234 | Marcus Allen | .30 | .18 |
| 235 | Gaston Green (R) | 2.00 | 1.25 |
| 236 | John Stephens (R) | .80 | .50 |
| 237 | Terry Kinard | .12 | .07 |
| 238 | John Taylor (R) | 4.00 | 2.75 |
| 239 | Brian Bosworth | .12 | .07 |
| 240 | Anthony Toney | .15 | .10 |
| 241 | Ken O'Brien | .20 | .12 |
| 242 | Howie Long | .15 | .10 |
| 243 | Doug Flutie | .30 | .18 |
| 244 | Jim Everett | .50 | .30 |
| 245 | Broderick Thomas (R) | 1.50 | .90 |
| 246 | Deion Sanders (R) | 10.00 | 7.00 |
| 247 | Donnell Woolford (R) | .25 | .15 |
| 248 | Wayne Martin (R) | .60 | .35 |
| 249 | David Williams | .12 | .07 |
| 250 | Bill Hawkins (R) | .15 | .10 |
| 251 | Eric Hill (R) | .20 | .12 |
| 252 | Burt Grossman (R) | .35 | .20 |
| 253 | Tracy Rocker (R) | .20 | .12 |
| 254 | Stgeve Wisniewski (R) | .35 | .20 |
| 255 | Jessie Small (R) | .20 | .12 |
| 256 | David Braxton (R) | .12 | .07 |
| 257 | Barry Sanders (R) | 48.00 | 30.00 |
| 258 | Derrick Thomas (R) | 12.00 | 8.50 |
| 259 | Eric Metcalf (R) | 1.75 | 1.00 |
| 260 | Keith DeLong (R) | .20 | .12 |
| 261 | Hart Lee Dykes (R) | .30 | .18 |
| 262 | Sammie Smith (R) | 1.75 | 1.00 |
| 263 | Steve Atwater (R) | 2.00 | 1.25 |
| 264 | Eric Ball (R) | .30 | .18 |
| 265 | Don Beebe (R) | 3.00 | 2.00 |
| 266 | Brian Williams (R) | .12 | .07 |
| 267 | Jeff Lageman (R) | .40 | .25 |
| 268 | Tim Worley (R) | .25 | .15 |
| 269 | Tony Mandarick (R) | .20 | .12 |
| 270 | Troy Aikman (R) | 48.00 | 30.00 |
| 271 | Andy Heck (R) | .15 | .10 |
| 272 | Andre Rison (R) | 12.00 | 8.00 |
| 273 | AFC Championship | .15 | .10 |
| 274 | NFC Championship | .75 | .45 |
| 275 | Super Bowl XXIII | 1.25 | .80 |
| 276 | Rodney Carter | .12 | .07 |
| 277 | Mark Jackson<br>VanceJohnson<br>Ricky Nattiel | .15 | .10 |
| 278 | John L. Williams<br>Curt Warner | .12 | .07 |
| 279 | Joe Montana<br>Jerry Rice | 1.25 | .80 |
| 280 | Roy Green<br>Neil Lomax | .15 | .10 |
| 281 | Randall Cunningham<br>Keith Jackson | .40 | .25 |
| 282 | Chris Doleman<br>Keith Millard | .15 | .10 |
| 283 | Mark Duper<br>Mark Clayton | .20 | .12 |
| 284 | Marcus Allen<br>Bo Jackson | .75 | .45 |
| 285 | Frank Minnifield (AP) | .12 | .07 |
| 286 | Bruce Matthews (AP) | .12 | .07 |
| 287 | Joey Browner (AP) | .15 | .10 |
| 288 | Jay Hilgenberg (AP) | .12 | .07 |
| 289 | Carl Lee (AP) | .12 | .07 |
| 290 | Scott Norwood (AP) | .12 | .07 |
| 291 | John Taylor (AP) | .60 | .35 |
| 292 | Jerry Rice (AP) | 1.00 | .70 |
| 293a | Keith Jackson<br>(AP) (Er) (#84 on back) | .75 | .45 |
| 293b | Keith Jackson (Cor)<br>(#88 on back) | 3.00 | 2.00 |
| 294 | Gary Zimmerman (AP) | .12 | .07 |
| 295 | Lawrence Taylor (AP) | .35 | .20 |
| 296 | Reggie White (AP) | .20 | .12 |
| 297 | Roger Craig (AP) | .15 | .10 |
| 298 | Boomer Esiason (AP) | .15 | .10 |
| 299 | Cornelius Bennett<br>(AP) | .30 | .18 |
| 300 | Mike Horan (AP) | .12 | .07 |
| 301 | Deron Cherry (AP) | .12 | .07 |
| 302 | Tom Newberry (AP) | .12 | .07 |
| 303 | Mike Singletary (AP) | .25 | .15 |
| 304 | Shane Conlan (AP) | .15 | .10 |
| 305a | Tim Brown (AP)(Er)<br>(Wrong photo on front) | .50 | .30 |
| 305b | Tim Brown (AP) (Cor) | 1.75 | 1.00 |
| 306 | Henry Ellard (AP) | .15 | .10 |
| 307 | Bruce Smith (AP) | .15 | .10 |
| 308 | Tim Krumrie (AP) | .12 | .07 |
| 309 | Anthony Munoz (AP) | .15 | .10 |
| 310 | Darrell Green (Speed) | .20 | .12 |
| 311 | Anthony Miller (Speed) | .40 | .25 |
| 312 | Wesley Walker(Speed) | .12 | .07 |
| 313 | Ron Brown (Speed) | .12 | .07 |
| 314 | Bo Jackson (Speed) | .75 | .45 |
| 315 | Philip Epps (Speed) | .12 | .07 |
| 316a | Eric Thomas (Speed)<br>(Er) (#31 on back) | .25 | .15 |
| 316b | Eric Thomas (Speed)<br>(Cor) (#22 on back) | 1.50 | .90 |
| 317 | Herschel Walker (Sp) | .50 | .30 |
| 318 | Jacob Green (Pred) | .12 | .07 |
| 319 | Andre Tippett (Pred) | .12 | .07 |
| 320 | Feddie Joe Nunn<br>(Pred) | .12 | .07 |
| 321 | Reggie White (Pred) | .20 | .12 |
| 322 | Lawrence Taylor<br>(Pred) | .25 | .15 |
| 323 | Greg Townsend (Pred) | .12 | .07 |
| 324 | Tim Harris (Pred) | .12 | .07 |
| 325 | Bruce Smith (Pred) | .15 | .10 |
| 326 | Tony Dorsett (RB) | .25 | .15 |

| | | MINT | NR/MT |
|---|---|---|---|
| 327 | Steve Largent (RB) | .40 | .25 |
| 328 | Tim Brown (RB) | .50 | .30 |
| 329 | Joe Montana (RB) | 1.00 | .70 |
| 330 | Tom Landry | .80 | .50 |

# 1989 Score Supplemental

This 110-card update set contains mostly rookies and players traded just prior to the start of the 1989 season. The cards are identical to the regular Score issue except for the purple borders that frame the full color photos on the card fronts. The card numbers include the letter "S" on the backs. All cards measure 2-1/2" by 3-1/2".

| | | MINT | NR/MT |
|---|---|---|---|
| **Complete Set (110)** | | 26.00 | 16.00 |
| **Commons** | | .07 | .04 |
| | | | |
| 331 | Herschel Walker | .50 | .30 |
| 332 | Allen Pinkett (R) | .25 | .15 |
| 333 | Sterling Sharpe (R) | 15.00 | 10.00 |
| 334 | Alvin Walton (R) | .15 | .10 |
| 335 | Frank Reich (R) | 1.50 | .90 |
| 336 | Jim Thornton (R) | .15 | .10 |
| 337 | David Fulcher | .07 | .04 |
| 338 | Raul Allegre | .07 | .04 |
| 339 | John Elway | .35 | .20 |
| 340 | Michael Cofer | .07 | .04 |
| 341 | Jim Skow | .07 | .04 |
| 342 | Steve DeBerg | .10 | .06 |
| 343 | Mervyn Fernandez (R) | .25 | .15 |
| 344 | Mike Lansford | .07 | .04 |
| 345 | Reggie Roby | .07 | .04 |
| 346 | Raymond Clayborn | .07 | .04 |

| | | MINT | NR/MT |
|---|---|---|---|
| 347 | Lonzell Hill (R) | .12 | .07 |
| 348 | Ottis Anderson | .12 | .07 |
| 349 | Erik McMillan (R) | .25 | .15 |
| 350 | Al Harris (R) | .08 | .05 |
| 351 | Jack Del Rio (R) | .15 | .10 |
| 352 | Gary Anderson | .07 | .04 |
| 353 | Jim McMahon | .12 | .07 |
| 354 | Keena Turner | .08 | .05 |
| 355 | Tony Woods (R) | .12 | .07 |
| 356 | Donald Igwebuike | .07 | .04 |
| 357 | Gerald Riggs | .10 | .06 |
| 358 | Eddie Murray | .07 | .04 |
| 359 | Dino Hackett | .07 | .04 |
| 360 | Brad Muster (R) | .70 | .40 |
| 361 | Paul Palmer | .07 | .04 |
| 362 | Jerry Robinson | .07 | .04 |
| 363 | Simon Fletcher (R) | .60 | .35 |
| 364 | Tommy Kramer | .10 | .06 |
| 365 | Jim Jensen (R) | .10 | .06 |
| 366 | Lorenzo White (R) | 2.50 | 1.50 |
| 367 | Fredd Young | .07 | .04 |
| 368 | Ron Jaworski | .08 | .05 |
| 369 | Mel Owens | .07 | .04 |
| 370 | Dave Waymer | .07 | .04 |
| 371 | Sean Landeta | .07 | .04 |
| 372 | Sam Mills | .10 | .06 |
| 373 | Todd Blackledge | .07 | .04 |
| 374 | Jo Jo Townsell | .07 | .04 |
| 375 | Ron Wolfley | .07 | .04 |
| 376 | Ralf Mojsiejenko | .07 | .04 |
| 377 | Eric Wright | .07 | .04 |
| 378 | Nesby Glasgow | .07 | .04 |
| 379 | Darryl Talley | .08 | .05 |
| 380 | Eric Allen (R) | .25 | .15 |
| 381 | Dennis Smith | .10 | .06 |
| 382 | John Tice | .07 | .04 |
| 383 | Jesse Solomon | .07 | .04 |
| 384 | Bo Jackson | 3.00 | 2.00 |
| | (FB & BB Photo) | | |
| 385 | Mike Merriweather | .07 | .04 |
| 386 | Maurice Carthon | .07 | .04 |
| 387 | Dave Grayson (R) | .10 | .06 |
| 388 | Wilber Marshall | .12 | .07 |
| 389 | David Wyman | .08 | .05 |
| 390 | Thomas Everett (R) | .30 | .18 |
| 391 | Alex Gordon | .07 | .04 |
| 392 | D.J. Dozier | .15 | .10 |
| 393 | Scott Radecic (R) | .08 | .05 |
| 394 | Eric Thomas | .08 | .05 |
| 395 | Mike Gann | .07 | .04 |
| 396 | William Perry | .10 | .06 |
| 397 | Carl Hairston | .07 | .04 |
| 398 | Billy Ard (R) | .10 | .06 |
| 399 | Donnell Thompson | .07 | .04 |
| 400 | Mike Webster | .10 | .06 |
| 401 | Scott Davis (R) | .10 | .06 |
| 402 | Sean Farrell | .07 | .04 |

| | | | |
|---|---|---|---|
| 403 | Mike Golic (R) | .25 | .15 |
| 404 | Mike Kenn | .07 | .04 |
| 405 | Keith Van Horne (R) | .10 | .06 |
| 406 | Bob Golic | .07 | .04 |
| 407 | Neil Smith (R) | 1.00 | .70 |
| 408 | Dermontti Dawson (R) | .12 | .07 |
| 409 | Leslie O'Neal | .35 | .20 |
| 410 | Matt Bahr | .07 | .04 |
| 411 | Guy McIntyre (R) | .15 | .10 |
| 412 | Bryan Millard (R) | .10 | .06 |
| 413 | Joe Jacoby | .08 | .05 |
| 414 | Rob Taylor (R) | .10 | .06 |
| 415 | Tony Zendejas | .07 | .04 |
| 416 | Vai Sikahema | .07 | .04 |
| 417 | Gary Reasons (R) | .15 | .10 |
| 418 | Shawn Collins (R) | .20 | .12 |
| 419 | Mark Green (R) | .08 | .05 |
| 420 | Courtney Hall (R) | .10 | .06 |
| 421 | Bobby Humphrey (R) | 1.75 | 1.00 |
| 422 | Myron Guyton (R) | .10 | .06 |
| 423 | Darryl Ingram (R) | .10 | .06 |
| 424 | Chris Jacke (R) | .08 | .05 |
| 425 | Keith Jones (R) | .08 | .05 |
| 426 | Robert Massey (R) | .15 | .10 |
| 427 | Bubba McDowell (R) | .25 | .15 |
| 428 | Dave Meggett (R) | 1.25 | .80 |
| 429 | Louis Oliver (R) | .30 | .18 |
| 430 | Danny Peebles (R) | .08 | .05 |
| 431 | Rodney Peete (R) | 1.00 | .70 |
| 432 | Jeff Query (R) | .35 | .20 |
| 433 | Timm Rosenbach (R) | 1.50 | .90 |
| 434 | Frank Stams (R) | .10 | .06 |
| 435 | Lawyer Tillman (R) | .20 | .12 |
| 436 | Billy Joe Tolliver (R) | .25 | .15 |
| 437 | Floyd Turner (R) | .40 | .25 |
| 438 | Steve Walsh (R) | .50 | .30 |
| 439 | Joe Wolf (R) | .10 | .06 |
| 440 | Trace Armstrong (R) | .25 | .15 |

# 1990 Score

This set consists of 660-cards and was issued in two series (1-330) and (331-660). Card fronts feature full color action photos with the player's name and team printed in a color bar directly below the photograph. A small Score logo is located in the top right corner. The vertical card backs include a small head shot, the player's personal data and stats. Key subsets include Draft Picks (DP), Hot Guns (HG), Crunch Crew (CC), Ground Force (GF), Rocket Men (RM), All Pros (AP), Record Breakers (RB), Hall of Famers (HOF) and Rookies (R). Five extra cards were included in Score's factory sets. Those cards (numbered B1-B5) depict the final five picks of the 1990 NFL draft and are listed at the end of this checklist. All cards measure 2-1/2" by 3-1/2".

| | | MINT | NR/MT |
|---|---|---|---|
| **Complete Set (660)** | | 10.00 | 6.00 |
| **Commons** | | .04 | .02 |
| | | | |
| 1 | Joe Montana | .50 | .30 |
| 2 | Christian Okoye | .12 | .07 |
| 3 | Mike Singletary | .10 | .06 |
| 4 | Jim Everett | .12 | .07 |
| 5 | Phil Simms | .10 | .06 |
| 6 | Brent Fullwood | .04 | .02 |
| 7 | Bill Fralic | .04 | .02 |
| 8 | Leslie O'Neal | .07 | .04 |
| 9 | John Taylor | .15 | .10 |
| 10 | Bo Jackson | .35 | .20 |
| 11 | John Stephens | .08 | .05 |
| 12 | Art Monk | .20 | .12 |
| 13 | Dan Marino | .35 | .20 |
| 14 | John Settle | .04 | .02 |

| | | | | | | | |
|---|---|---|---|---|---|---|---|
| 15 | Don Majkowski | .10 | .06 | 72 | Skip McClendon | .04 | .02 |
| 16 | Bruce Smith | .10 | .06 | 73 | Jim Covert | .04 | .02 |
| 17 | Brad Muster | .08 | .05 | 74 | Sam Mills | .07 | .04 |
| 18 | Jason Buck | .04 | .02 | 75 | Chris Hinton | .04 | .02 |
| 19 | James Brooks | .07 | .04 | 76 | Irv Eatman | .04 | .02 |
| 20 | Barry Sanders | .75 | .45 | 77 | Bubba Paris | .04 | .02 |
| 21 | Troy Aikman | 1.25 | .80 | 78 | John Elliott | .04 | .02 |
| 22 | Allen Pinkett | .04 | .02 | 79 | Thomas Everett | .04 | .02 |
| 23 | Duane Bickett | .04 | .02 | 80 | Steve Smith | .04 | .02 |
| 24 | Kevin Ross | .04 | .02 | 81 | Jackie Slater | .07 | .04 |
| 25 | John Elway | .20 | .12 | 82 | Kelvin Martin (R) | .20 | .12 |
| 26 | Jeff Query | .08 | .05 | 83 | Jo Jo Townsell | .04 | .02 |
| 27 | Eddie Murray | .04 | .02 | 84 | Jim Jensen | .04 | .02 |
| 28 | Richard Dent | .07 | .04 | 85 | Bobby Humphrey | .12 | .07 |
| 29 | Lorenzo White | .25 | .15 | 86 | Mike Dyal (R) | .07 | .04 |
| 30 | Eric Metcalf | .10 | .06 | 87 | Andre Rison | .20 | .12 |
| 31 | Jeff Dellenbach (R) | .07 | .04 | 88 | Brian Sochia | .04 | .02 |
| 32 | Leon White | .04 | .02 | 89 | Greg Bell | .07 | .04 |
| 33 | Jim Jeffcoat | .04 | .02 | 90 | Dalton Hilliard | .07 | .04 |
| 34 | Herschel Walker | .12 | .07 | 91 | Carl Banks | .07 | .04 |
| 35 | Mike Johnson | .04 | .02 | 92 | Dennis Smith | .04 | .02 |
| 36 | Joe Phillips (R) | .07 | .04 | 93 | Bruce Matthews | .04 | .02 |
| 37 | Willie Gault | .07 | .04 | 94 | Charles Haley | .07 | .04 |
| 38 | Keith Millard | .07 | .04 | 95 | Deion Sanders | .25 | .15 |
| 39 | Fred Marion | .04 | .02 | 96 | Stephone Paige | .07 | .04 |
| 40 | Boomer Esiason | .12 | .07 | 97 | Marion Butts | .12 | .07 |
| 41 | Dermontti Dawson | .04 | .02 | 98 | Howie Long | .07 | .04 |
| 42 | Dino Hackett | .04 | .02 | 99 | Donald Igwebuike | .04 | .02 |
| 43 | Reggie Roby | .04 | .02 | 100 | Roger Craig | .08 | .05 |
| 44 | Roger Vick | .04 | .02 | 101 | Charles Mann | .04 | .02 |
| 45 | Bobby Hebert | .12 | .07 | 102 | Fredd Young | .04 | .02 |
| 46 | Don Beebe | .15 | .10 | 103 | Chris Jacke | .04 | .02 |
| 47 | Neal Anderson | .12 | .07 | 104 | Scott Case | .04 | .02 |
| 48 | Johnny Holland | .04 | .02 | 105 | Warren Moon | .20 | .12 |
| 49 | Bobby Humphery | .04 | .02 | 106 | Clyde Simmons | .07 | .04 |
| 50 | Lawrence Taylor | .15 | .10 | 107 | Steve Atwater | .08 | .05 |
| 51 | Billy Ray Smith | .04 | .02 | 108 | Morten Andersen | .07 | .04 |
| 52 | Robert Perryman | .04 | .02 | 109 | Eugene Marve | .04 | .02 |
| 53 | Gary Anderson | .04 | .02 | 110 | Thurman Thomas | .75 | .45 |
| 54 | Raul Allegre | .04 | .02 | 111 | Carnell Lake | .04 | .02 |
| 55 | Pat Swilling | .12 | .07 | 112 | Jim Kelly | .25 | .15 |
| 56 | Chris Doleman | .07 | .04 | 113 | Stanford Jennings | .04 | .02 |
| 57 | Andre Reed | .12 | .07 | 114 | Jacob Green | .04 | .02 |
| 58 | Seth Joyner | .07 | .04 | 115 | Karl Mecklenburg | .07 | .04 |
| 59 | Bart Oates | .04 | .02 | 116 | Ray Childress | .07 | .04 |
| 60 | Bernie Kosar | .12 | .07 | 117 | Erik McMillan | .04 | .02 |
| 61 | Dave Krieg | .10 | .06 | 118 | Harry Newsome | .04 | .02 |
| 62 | Lars Tate | .04 | .02 | 119 | James Dixon (R) | .07 | .04 |
| 63 | Scott Norwood | .04 | .02 | 120 | Hassan Jones | .07 | .04 |
| 64 | Kyle Clifton | .04 | .02 | 121 | Eric Allen | .04 | .02 |
| 65 | Alan Veingrad | .04 | .02 | 122 | Felix Wright | .04 | .02 |
| 66 | Gerald Riggs | .07 | .04 | 123 | Merril Hoge | .07 | .04 |
| 67 | Tim Worley | .08 | .05 | 124 | Eric Ball | .04 | .02 |
| 68 | Rodney Holman | .04 | .02 | 125 | Flipper Anderson | .08 | .05 |
| 69 | Tony Zendejas | .04 | .02 | 126 | James Jefferson | .04 | .02 |
| 70 | Chris Miller | .25 | .15 | 127 | Tim McDonald | .04 | .02 |
| 71 | Wilber Marshall | .07 | .04 | 128 | Larry Kinnebrew | .04 | .02 |

| | | | |
|---|---|---|---|
| 129 | Mark Collins | .04 | .02 |
| 130 | Ickey Woods | .04 | .02 |
| 131 | Jeff Donaldson | .04 | .02 |
| 132 | Rich Camarillo | .04 | .02 |
| 133 | Melvin Bratton (R) | .07 | .04 |
| 134 | Kevin Butler | .04 | .02 |
| 135 | Albert Bentley | .04 | .02 |
| 136 | Vai Sikahema | .04 | .02 |
| 137 | Todd McNair | .04 | .02 |
| 138 | Alonzo Highsmith | .04 | .02 |
| 139 | Brian Blades | .07 | .04 |
| 140 | Jeff Lageman | .07 | .04 |
| 141 | Eric Thomas | .04 | .02 |
| 142 | Derek Hill | .04 | .02 |
| 143 | Rick Fenney | .04 | .02 |
| 144 | Herman Heard | .04 | .02 |
| 145 | Steve Young | .25 | .15 |
| 146 | Kent Hull | .04 | .02 |
| 147 | Joey Browner | .07 | .04 |
| 148 | Frank Minnifield | .04 | .02 |
| 149 | Robert Massey | .04 | .02 |
| 150 | Dave Meggett | .12 | .07 |
| 151 | Bubba McDowell | .04 | .02 |
| 152 | Rickey Dixon (R) | .10 | .06 |
| 153 | Ray Donaldson | .04 | .02 |
| 154 | Alvin Walton | .04 | .02 |
| 155 | Mike Cofer | .04 | .02 |
| 156 | Darryl Talley | .07 | .04 |
| 157 | A.J. Johnson | .04 | .02 |
| 158 | Jerry Gray | .04 | .02 |
| 159 | Keith Byars | .07 | .04 |
| 160 | Andy Heck | .04 | .02 |
| 161 | Mike Munchak | .04 | .02 |
| 162 | Dennis Gentry | .04 | .02 |
| 163 | Timm Rosenbach | .12 | .07 |
| 164 | Randall McDaniel | .04 | .02 |
| 165 | Pat Leahy | .04 | .02 |
| 166 | Bubby Brister | .10 | .06 |
| 167 | Aundray Bruce | .04 | .02 |
| 168 | Bill Brooks | .04 | .02 |
| 169 | Eddie Anderson | .04 | .02 |
| 170 | Ronnie Lott | .10 | .06 |
| 171 | Jay Hilgenberg | .04 | .02 |
| 172 | Joe Nash | .04 | .02 |
| 173 | Simon Fletcher | .07 | .04 |
| 174 | Shane Conlan | .08 | .05 |
| 175 | Sean Landeta | .04 | .02 |
| 176 | John Alt (R) | .08 | .05 |
| 177 | Clay Matthews | .04 | .02 |
| 178 | Anthony Munoz | .10 | .06 |
| 179 | Pete Holohan | .04 | .02 |
| 180 | Robert Awalt | .04 | .02 |
| 181 | Rohn Stark | .04 | .02 |
| 182 | Vance Johnson | .08 | .05 |
| 183 | David Fulcher | .04 | .02 |
| 184 | Robert Delpino | .08 | .05 |
| 185 | Drew Hill | .08 | .05 |
| 186 | Reggie Langhorne | .07 | .04 |
| 187 | Lonzell Hill | .04 | .02 |
| 188 | Tom Rathman | .08 | .05 |
| 189 | Greg Montgomery | .04 | .02 |
| 190 | Leonard Smith | .04 | .02 |
| 191 | Chris Spielman | .07 | .04 |
| 192 | Tom Newberry | .04 | .02 |
| 193 | Cris Carter | .20 | .12 |
| 194 | Kevin Porter (R) | .12 | .07 |
| 195 | Donnell Thompson | .04 | .02 |
| 196 | Vaughan Johnson | .07 | .04 |
| 197 | Steve McMichael | .07 | .04 |
| 198 | Jim Sweeney | .04 | .02 |
| 199 | Rich Karlis | .04 | .02 |
| 200 | Jerry Rice | .70 | .40 |
| 201 | Dan Hampton | .08 | .05 |
| 202 | Jim Lachey | .07 | .04 |
| 203 | Reggie White | .12 | .07 |
| 204 | Jerry Ball | .04 | .02 |
| 205 | Russ Grimm | .04 | .02 |
| 206 | Tim Green (R) | .08 | .05 |
| 207 | Shawn Collins | .04 | .02 |
| 208a | Ralf Mojsiejenko (Er) (Chargers) | 1.00 | .70 |
| 208b | Ralf Mojsiejenko (Cor) (Redskins) | .04 | .02 |
| 209 | Trace Armstrong | .07 | .04 |
| 210 | Keith Jackson | .12 | .07 |
| 211 | Jamie Holland | .04 | .02 |
| 212 | Mark Clayton | .12 | .07 |
| 213 | Jeff Cross | .04 | .02 |
| 214 | Bob Gagliano | .07 | .04 |
| 215 | Louis Oliver | .07 | .04 |
| 216 | Jim Arnold | .04 | .02 |
| 217 | Robert Clark | .04 | .02 |
| 218 | Gill Byrd | .04 | .02 |
| 219 | Rodney Peete | .12 | .07 |
| 220 | Anthony Miller | .25 | .15 |
| 221 | Steve Grogan | .07 | .04 |
| 222 | Vince Newsome (R) | .10 | .06 |
| 223 | Tom Benson | .04 | .02 |
| 224 | Kevin Murphy | .04 | .02 |
| 225 | Henry Ellard | .07 | .04 |
| 226 | Richard Johson | .04 | .02 |
| 227 | Jim Skow | .04 | .02 |
| 228 | Keith Jones | .04 | .02 |
| 229 | Dave Brown | .04 | .02 |
| 230 | Marcus Allen | .10 | .06 |
| 231 | Steve Walsh | .10 | .06 |
| 232 | Jim Harbaugh (R) | .30 | .18 |
| 233 | Mel Gray | .04 | .02 |
| 234 | David Treadwell | .04 | .02 |
| 235 | John Offerdahl | .07 | .04 |
| 236 | Gary Reasons | .04 | .02 |
| 237 | Tim Krumrie | .04 | .02 |
| 238 | Dave Duerson | .04 | .02 |
| 239 | Gary Clark | .15 | .10 |

| 240 | Mark Jackson | .07 | .04 |
| 241 | Mark Murphy | .04 | .02 |
| 242 | Jerry Holmes | .04 | .02 |
| 243 | Tim McGee | .07 | .04 |
| 244 | Mike Tomczak | .08 | .05 |
| 245 | Sterling Sharpe | .60 | .35 |
| 246 | Bennie Blades | .07 | .04 |
| 247 | Ken Harvey (R) | .12 | .07 |
| 248 | Ron Heller | .04 | .02 |
| 249 | Louis Lipps | .04 | .02 |
| 250 | Wade Wilson | .08 | .05 |
| 251 | Freddie Joe Nunn | .04 | .02 |
| 252 | Jerome Brown | .07 | .04 |
| 253 | Myron Guyton | .04 | .02 |
| 254 | Nate Odomes (R) | .10 | .06 |
| 255 | Rod Woodson | .10 | .06 |
| 256 | Cornelius Bennett | .10 | .06 |
| 257 | Keith Woodside | .04 | .02 |
| 258 | Jeff Uhlenhake | .04 | .02 |
| 259 | Harry Hamilton | .04 | .02 |
| 260 | Mark Bavaro | .07 | .04 |
| 261 | Vinny Testaverde | .12 | .07 |
| 262 | Steve DeBerg | .10 | .06 |
| 263 | Steve Wisniewski | .04 | .02 |
| 264 | Pete Mandley | .04 | .02 |
| 265 | Tim Harris | .04 | .02 |
| 266 | Jack Trudeau | .08 | .05 |
| 267 | Mark Kelso | .04 | .02 |
| 268 | Brian Noble | .04 | .02 |
| 269 | Jessie Tuggle (R) | .10 | .06 |
| 270 | Ken O'Brien | .10 | .06 |
| 271 | David Little | .04 | .02 |
| 272 | Pete Stoyanovich | .04 | .02 |
| 273 | Odessa Turner (R) | .15 | .10 |
| 274 | Anthony Toney | .04 | .02 |
| 275 | Tunch Ilkin | .04 | .02 |
| 276 | Carl Lee | .04 | .02 |
| 277 | Hart Lee Dykes | .07 | .04 |
| 278 | Al Noga | .04 | .02 |
| 279 | Greg Lloyd | .04 | .02 |
| 280 | Billy Joe Tolliver | .10 | .06 |
| 281 | Kirk Lowdermilk | .04 | .02 |
| 282 | Earl Ferrell | .04 | .02 |
| 283 | Eric Sievers (R) | .08 | .04 |
| 284 | Steve Jordan | .04 | .02 |
| 285 | Burt Grossman | .07 | .04 |
| 286 | Johnny Rembert | .04 | .02 |
| 287 | Jeff Jaeger (R) | .07 | .04 |
| 288 | James Hasty | .04 | .02 |
| 289 | Tony Mandarich (R) | .07 | .04 |
| 290 | Chris Singleton (R) | .20 | .12 |
| 291 | Lynn James (R) | .08 | .05 |
| 292 | Andre Ware (R) | .50 | .30 |
| 293 | Ray Agnew (R) | .08 | .05 |
| 294 | Joel Smeenge (R) | .07 | .04 |
| 295 | Marc Spindler (R) | .10 | .06 |
| 296 | Renaldo Turnbull (R) | .15 | .10 |
| 297 | Reggie Rembert (R) | .15 | .10 |
| 298 | Jeff Alm (R) | .08 | .05 |
| 299 | Cortez Kennedy (R) | .75 | .45 |
| 300 | Blair Thomas (R) | .30 | .18 |
| 301 | Pat Terrell (R) | .12 | .07 |
| 302 | Junior Seau (R) | .75 | .45 |
| 303 | M. Elewonibi (R) | .07 | .04 |
| 304 | Tony Bennett (R) | .20 | .12 |
| 305 | Percy Snow (R) | .15 | .10 |
| 306 | Richmond Webb (R) | .15 | .10 |
| 307 | Rodney Hampton (R) | 1.00 | .70 |
| 308 | Barry Foster (R) | 2.50 | 1.50 |
| 309 | John Friesz (R) | .35 | .20 |
| 310 | Ben Smith (R) | .12 | .07 |
| 311 | Joe Montana (HG) | .25 | .15 |
| 312 | Jim Everett (HG) | .08 | .05 |
| 313 | Mark Rypien (HG) | .10 | .06 |
| 314 | Phil Simms (HG) | .08 | .05 |
| 315 | Don Majkowski (HG) | .07 | .04 |
| 316 | Boomer Esiason (HG) | .08 | .05 |
| 317 | Warren Moon (HG) | .20 | .12 |
| 318 | Jim Kelly (HG) | .20 | .12 |
| 319 | Bernie Kosar (HG) | .08 | .05 |
| 320 | Dan Marino (HG) | .25 | .15 |
| 321 | Christian Okoye (GF) | .08 | .05 |
| 322 | Thurman Thomas (GF) | .30 | .18 |
| 323 | James Brooks (GF) | .07 | .04 |
| 324 | Bobby Humphrey (GF) | .07 | .04 |
| 325 | Barry Sanders (GF) | .35 | .20 |
| 326 | Neal Anderson (GF) | .08 | .05 |
| 327 | Dalton Hilliard (GF) | .04 | .02 |
| 328 | Greg Bell (GF) | .04 | .02 |
| 329 | Roger Craig (GF) | .07 | .04 |
| 330 | Bo Jackson (GF) | .25 | .15 |
| 331 | Don Warren | .04 | .02 |
| 332 | Rufus Porter | .04 | .02 |
| 333 | Sammie Smith | .08 | .05 |
| 334 | Lewis Tillman | .04 | .02 |
| 335 | Michael Walter | .04 | .02 |
| 336 | Marc Logan | .04 | .02 |
| 337 | Ron Hallstrom (R) | .07 | .04 |
| 338 | Stanley Morgan | .07 | .04 |
| 339 | Mark Robinson | .04 | .02 |
| 340 | Frank Reich | .12 | .07 |
| 341 | Chip Lohmiller (R) | .08 | .05 |
| 342 | Steve Beuerlein | .10 | .06 |
| 343 | John L. Willims | .07 | .04 |
| 344 | Irving Fryar | .07 | .04 |
| 345 | Anthony Carter | .08 | .05 |
| 346 | Al Toon | .08 | .05 |
| 347 | J.T. Smith | .04 | .02 |
| 348 | Pierce Holt (R) | .15 | .10 |
| 349 | Ferrell Edmunds | .04 | .02 |
| 350 | Mark Rypien | .35 | .20 |
| 351 | Paul Gruber | .04 | .02 |
| 352 | Ernest Givins | .12 | .07 |
| 353 | Ervin Randle | .04 | .02 |

| | | | |
|---|---|---|---|
| 354 | Guy McIntyre | .04 | .02 |
| 355 | Webster Slaughter | .08 | .05 |
| 356 | Reuben Davis (R) | .07 | .04 |
| 357 | Rickey Jackson | .07 | .04 |
| 358 | Earnest Byner | .07 | .04 |
| 359 | Eddie Brown | .08 | .05 |
| 360 | Troy Stradford | .04 | .02 |
| 361 | Pepper Johnson | .04 | .02 |
| 362 | Ravin Caldwell (R) | .07 | .04 |
| 363 | Chris Mohr (R) | .07 | .04 |
| 364 | Jeff Bryant | .04 | .02 |
| 365 | Bruce Collie (R) | .07 | .04 |
| 366 | Courtney Hall | .04 | .02 |
| 367 | Jerry Olsavsky (R) | .07 | .04 |
| 368 | David Galloway | .04 | .02 |
| 369 | Wes Hopkins | .04 | .02 |
| 370 | Johnny Hector | .07 | .04 |
| 371 | Clarence Verdin | .07 | .04 |
| 372 | Nick Lowery | .07 | .04 |
| 373 | Tim Brown | .15 | .10 |
| 374 | Kevin Greene | .04 | .02 |
| 375 | Leonard Marshall | .07 | .04 |
| 376 | Roland James | .04 | .02 |
| 377 | Scott Studwell | .04 | .02 |
| 378 | Jarvis Williams | .04 | .02 |
| 279 | Mike Saxon | .04 | .02 |
| 380 | Kevin Mack | .07 | .04 |
| 381 | Joe Kelly | .04 | .02 |
| 382 | Tom Thayer (R) | .07 | .04 |
| 383 | Roy Green | .07 | .04 |
| 384 | Michael Brooks (R) | .10 | .06 |
| 385 | Michael Cofer | .04 | .02 |
| 386 | Ken Ruettgers | .04 | .02 |
| 387 | Dean Steinkuhler | .04 | .02 |
| 388 | Maurice Carthon | .04 | .02 |
| 389 | Ricky Sanders | .08 | .05 |
| 390 | Winston Moss (R) | .07 | .04 |
| 391 | Tony Woods | .04 | .02 |
| 392 | Keith DeLong | .04 | .02 |
| 393 | David Wyman | .04 | .02 |
| 394 | Vencie Glenn | .04 | .02 |
| 395 | Harris Barton | .04 | .02 |
| 396 | Bryan Hinkle | .04 | .02 |
| 397 | Derek Kennard | .04 | .02 |
| 398 | Heath Sherman (R) | .30 | .18 |
| 399 | Troy Benson | .04 | .02 |
| 400 | Gary Zimmerman | .04 | .02 |
| 401 | Mark Duper | .08 | .05 |
| 402 | Eugene Lockhart | .04 | .02 |
| 403 | Tim Manoa (R) | .07 | .04 |
| 404 | Reggie Williams | .04 | .02 |
| 405 | Mark Bortz (R) | .08 | .05 |
| 406 | Mike Kenn | .04 | .02 |
| 407 | John Grimsley | .04 | .02 |
| 408 | Bill Romanowski (R) | .08 | .05 |
| 409 | Perry Kemp | .04 | .02 |
| 410 | Norm Johnson | .04 | .02 |
| 411 | Broderick Thomas | .10 | .06 |
| 412 | Joe Wolf | .04 | .02 |
| 413 | Andre Waters | .04 | .02 |
| 414 | Jason Staurovsky | .04 | .02 |
| 415 | Eric Martin | .08 | .05 |
| 416 | Joe Prokop | .04 | .02 |
| 417 | Steve Sewell | .04 | .02 |
| 418 | Cedric Jones | .04 | .02 |
| 419 | Alphonso Carreker | .04 | .02 |
| 420 | Keith Willis | .04 | .02 |
| 421 | Bobby Butler | .04 | .02 |
| 422 | John Roper (R) | .07 | .04 |
| 423 | Tim Spencer | .04 | .02 |
| 424 | Jesse Sapolu (R) | .10 | .06 |
| 425 | Ron Wolfley | .04 | .02 |
| 426 | Doug Smith | .04 | .02 |
| 427 | William Howard (R) | .04 | .02 |
| 428 | Keith Van Horne | .04 | .02 |
| 429 | Tony Jordan (R) | .07 | .04 |
| 430 | Mervyn Fernandez | .08 | .05 |
| 431 | Shaun Gayle (R) | .08 | .05 |
| 432 | Ricky Nattiel | .08 | .05 |
| 433 | Albert Lewis | .04 | .02 |
| 434 | Fred Banks (R) | .10 | .06 |
| 435 | Henry Thomas | .04 | .02 |
| 436 | Chet Brooks | .04 | .02 |
| 437 | Mark Ingram | .04 | .02 |
| 438 | Jeff Gossett | .04 | .02 |
| 439 | Mike Wilcher | .04 | .02 |
| 440 | Deron Cherry | .04 | .02 |
| 441 | Mike Rozier | .07 | .04 |
| 442 | Jon Hand | .04 | .02 |
| 443 | Ozzie Newsome | .12 | .07 |
| 444 | Sammy Martin (R) | .07 | .04 |
| 445 | Luis Sharpe | .04 | .02 |
| 446 | Lee Willimas | .04 | .02 |
| 447 | Chris Martin (R) | .07 | .04 |
| 448 | Kevin Fagan (R) | .08 | .05 |
| 449 | Gene Lang | .04 | .02 |
| 450 | Greg Townsend | .07 | .04 |
| 451 | Robert Lyles | .04 | .02 |
| 452 | Eric Hill | .04 | .02 |
| 453 | John Teltschik | .04 | .02 |
| 454 | Vestee Jackson | .04 | .02 |
| 455 | Bruce Reimers | .04 | .02 |
| 456 | Butch Rolle (R) | .08 | .05 |
| 457 | Lawyer Tillman | .07 | .04 |
| 458 | Andre Tippett | .07 | .04 |
| 459 | James Thornton | .04 | .02 |
| 460 | Randy Grimes | .04 | .02 |
| 461 | Larry Roberts | .04 | .02 |
| 462 | Ron Holmes | .04 | .02 |
| 463 | Mike Wise | .04 | .02 |
| 464 | Danny Copeland (R) | .08 | .05 |
| 465 | Bruce Wilkerson (R) | .08 | .05 |
| 466 | Mike Quick | .07 | .04 |
| 467 | Mickey Shuler | .04 | .02 |

| | | | | | | | |
|---|---|---|---|---|---|---|---|
| 468 | Mike Prior | .04 | .02 | 525 | Michael Ball (R) | .08 | .05 |
| 469 | Ron Rivera | .04 | .02 | 526 | Ernie Jones (R) | .20 | .12 |
| 470 | Dean Biasucci | .04 | .02 | 527 | Tony Eason | .07 | .04 |
| 471 | Perry Williams | .04 | .02 | 528 | Ed Reynolds | .04 | .02 |
| 472 | Darren Comeaux | .04 | .02 | 529 | Gary Hogeboom | .04 | .02 |
| 473 | Freeman McNeil | .07 | .04 | 530 | Don Mosebar | .04 | .02 |
| 474 | Tyrone Braxton | .04 | .02 | 531 | Ottis Anderson | .08 | .05 |
| 475 | Jay Schroeder | .12 | .07 | 532 | Bucky Scribner | .04 | .02 |
| 476 | Naz Worthen (R) | .04 | .02 | 533 | Aaron Cox | .04 | .02 |
| 477 | Lionel Washington | .04 | .02 | 534 | Sean Jones | .04 | .02 |
| 478 | Carl Zander | .04 | .02 | 535 | Doug Flutie | .12 | .07 |
| 479 | Bubba Baker | .04 | .02 | 536 | Leo Lewis | .04 | .02 |
| 380 | Mike Merriweather | .04 | .02 | 537 | Art Still | .04 | .02 |
| 481 | Mike Gann | .04 | .02 | 538 | Matt Bahr | .04 | .02 |
| 482 | Brent Williams | .04 | .02 | 539 | Keena Turner | .04 | .02 |
| 483 | Eugene Robinson | .04 | .02 | 540 | Sammy Winder | .04 | .02 |
| 484 | Ray Horton | .04 | .02 | 541 | Mike Webster | .08 | .05 |
| 485 | Bruce Armstrong | .04 | .02 | 542 | Doug Riesenberg (R) | .07 | .04 |
| 486 | John Fourcade | .04 | .02 | 543 | Dan Fike | .04 | .02 |
| 487 | Lewis Billups | .04 | .02 | 544 | Clarence Kay | .04 | .02 |
| 488 | Scott Davis | .04 | .02 | 545 | Jim Burt | .04 | .02 |
| 489 | Ken Sims | .04 | .02 | 546 | Mike Horan | .04 | .02 |
| 490 | Chris Chandler | .12 | .07 | 547 | Al Harris | .04 | .02 |
| 491 | Mark Lee | .04 | .02 | 548 | Maury Buford | .04 | .02 |
| 492 | Johnny Meads | .04 | .02 | 549 | Jerry Robinson | .04 | .02 |
| 493 | Tim Irwin | .04 | .02 | 550 | Tracy Rocker | .04 | .02 |
| 494 | E.J. Junior | .04 | .02 | 551 | Karl Mecklenburg (CC) | .04 | .02 |
| 495 | Hardy Nickerson | .04 | .02 | 552 | Lawrence Taylor (CC) | .15 | .10 |
| 496 | Rob McGovern | .04 | .02 | 553 | Derrick Thomas (CC) | .15 | .10 |
| 497 | Fred Strickland (R) | .10 | .06 | 554 | Mike Singletary (CC) | .08 | .05 |
| 498 | Reggie Rutland (R) | .10 | .06 | 555 | Tim Harris (CC) | .04 | .02 |
| 499 | Mel Owens | .04 | .02 | 556 | Jerry Rice (RM) | .25 | .15 |
| 500 | Derrick Thomas | .30 | .18 | 557 | Art Monk (RM) | .15 | .10 |
| 501 | Jerrol Willimas | .04 | .02 | 558 | Mark Carrier (RM) | .04 | .02 |
| 502 | Maurice Hurst (R) | .10 | .06 | 559 | Andre Reed (RM) | .08 | .05 |
| 503 | Larry Kelm (R) | .08 | .05 | 560 | Sterling Sharpe (RM) | .10 | .06 |
| 504 | Herman Fontenot | .04 | .02 | 561 | Hershel Walker (GF) | .08 | .05 |
| 505 | Pat Beach | .04 | .02 | 562 | Ottis Anderson (GF) | .07 | .04 |
| 506 | Haywoold Jeffires (R) | .80 | .50 | 563 | Randall Cunningham (HG) | .12 | .07 |
| 507 | Neil Smith | .04 | .02 | | | | |
| 508 | Cleveland Gary (R) | .20 | .12 | 564 | John Elway (HG) | .12 | .07 |
| 509 | William Perry | .08 | .05 | 565 | David Fulcher (AP) | .04 | .02 |
| 510 | Michael Carter | .04 | .02 | 566 | Ronnie Lott (AP) | .08 | .05 |
| 511 | Walker Lee Ashley | .04 | .02 | 567 | Jerry Gray (AP) | .04 | .02 |
| 512 | Bob Golic | .04 | .02 | 568 | Albert Lewis (AP) | .04 | .02 |
| 513 | Danny Villa (R) | .08 | .05 | 569 | Karl Mecklenburg (AP) | .04 | .02 |
| 514 | Matt Millen | .07 | .04 | 570 | Mike Singletary (AP) | .08 | .05 |
| 515 | Don Griffin | .04 | .02 | 571 | Lawrence Taylor (AP) | .10 | .06 |
| 516 | Jonathan Hayes | .04 | .02 | 572 | Tim Harris (AP) | .04 | .02 |
| 517 | Gerald Williams (R) | .08 | .05 | 573 | Keith Millard (AP) | .04 | .02 |
| 518 | Scott Fulhage | .04 | .02 | 574 | Reggie White (AP) | .08 | .05 |
| 519 | Irv Pankey | .04 | .02 | 575 | Chris Doleman (AP) | .04 | .02 |
| 520 | Randy Dixon (R) | .07 | .04 | 576 | Dave Meggett (AP) | .08 | .05 |
| 521 | Terry McDaniel | .04 | .02 | 577 | Rod Woodson (AP) | .07 | .04 |
| 522 | Dan Saleaumua | .04 | .02 | 578 | Sean Landeta (AP) | .04 | .02 |
| 523 | Darrin Nelson | .07 | .04 | 579 | Eddie Murray (AP) | .04 | .02 |
| 524 | Leonard Griffin | .04 | .02 | 580 | Barry Sanders (AP) | .35 | .20 |

| | | | |
|---|---|---|---|
| 581 | Christian Okoye (AP) | .08 | .05 |
| 582 | Joe Montana (AP) | .30 | .18 |
| 583 | Jay Hilgenberg (AP) | .04 | .02 |
| 584 | Bruce Matthews (AP) | .04 | .02 |
| 585 | Tom Newberry (AP) | .04 | .02 |
| 586 | Gary Zimmerman (AP) | .04 | .02 |
| 587 | Anthony Munoz (AP) | .07 | .04 |
| 588 | Keith Jackson (AP) | .08 | .05 |
| 589 | Sterling Sharpe (AP) | .25 | .15 |
| 590 | Jerry Rice (AP) | .30 | .18 |
| 591 | Bo Jackson (AP) | .20 | .12 |
| 592 | Steve Largent (RB) | .25 | .15 |
| 593 | Flipper Anderson (RB) | .07 | .04 |
| 594 | Joe Montana (RB) | .30 | .18 |
| 595 | Franco Harris (HOF) | .15 | .10 |
| 596 | Bob St. Clair (HOF) | .07 | .04 |
| 597 | Tom Landry (HOF) | .15 | .10 |
| 598 | Jack Lambert (HOF) | .08 | .05 |
| 599 | Ted Hendricks (HOF) | .08 | .05 |
| 600 | Buck Buckanan (HOF) | .08 | .05 |
| 601 | Bob Griese (HOF) | .15 | .10 |
| 602 | Super Bowl | .10 | .06 |
| 603 | Vince Lombardi | .25 | .15 |
| 604 | Mark Carrier (TB) | .08 | .05 |
| 605 | Randall Cunningham | .20 | .12 |
| 606 | Percy Snow ('90) | .12 | .07 |
| 607 | Andre Ware ('90) | .15 | .10 |
| 608 | Blair Thomas ('90) | .25 | .15 |
| 609 | Eric Green ('90) | .15 | .10 |
| 610 | Reggie Rembert ('90) | .08 | .05 |
| 611 | Richmond Webb ('90) | .08 | .05 |
| 612 | Bern Brostek ('90) | .07 | .04 |
| 613 | James Williams ('90) | .07 | .04 |
| 614 | Mark Carrier ('90) | .15 | .10 |
| 615 | Renaldo Turnbull ('90) | .07 | .04 |
| 616 | Cortez Kennedy ('90) | .20 | .12 |
| 617 | Keith McCants ('90) | .10 | .06 |
| 618 | Anthony Thompson (R) | .20 | .12 |
| 619 | LeRoy Butler (R) | .08 | .05 |
| 620 | Aaron Wallace (R) | .12 | .07 |
| 622 | Keith McCants (R) | .15 | .10 |
| 623 | Jimmie Jones (R) | .12 | .07 |
| 624 | Anthony Johnson (R) | .15 | .10 |
| 625 | Fred Washington (R) | .07 | .04 |
| 626 | Mike Bellamy (R) | .08 | .05 |
| 627 | Mark Carrier (R)(Chi) | .30 | .18 |
| 628 | Harold Green (R) | .70 | .40 |
| 629 | Eric Green (R) | .35 | .20 |
| 630 | Andre Collins (R) | .12 | .07 |
| 631 | Lamar Lathon (R) | .12 | .07 |
| 632 | Terry Wooden (R) | .10 | .06 |
| 633 | Jesse Anderson (R) | .07 | .04 |
| 634 | Jeff George (R) | 1.00 | .70 |
| 635 | Carwell Gardner (R) | .12 | .07 |
| 636 | Darrell Thompson (R) | .20 | .12 |
| 637 | Vince Buck (R) | .12 | .07 |
| 638 | Mike Jones (R) | .08 | .05 |

| | | | |
|---|---|---|---|
| 639 | Charles Arbuckle (R) | .10 | .05 |
| 640 | Dennis Brown (R) | .08 | .05 |
| 641 | James Williams (R) | .08 | .05 |
| 642 | Bern Brostek (R) | .08 | .05 |
| 643 | Darion Conner (R) | .12 | .07 |
| 644 | Mike Fox (R) | .10 | .06 |
| 645 | Cary Conklin (R) | .15 | .10 |
| 646 | Tim Grunhard (R) | .08 | .05 |
| 647 | Ron Cox (R) | .12 | .07 |
| 648 | Keith Sims (R) | .10 | .06 |
| 649 | Alton Montgomery (R) | .10 | .06 |
| 650 | Greg McMurtry (R) | .20 | .12 |
| 651 | Scott Mitchell (R) | .25 | .15 |
| 652 | Tim Ryan (R) | .08 | .05 |
| 653 | Jeff Mills (R) | .15 | .10 |
| 654 | Ricky Proehl (R) | .35 | .20 |
| 655 | Steve Broussard (R) | .20 | .12 |
| 656 | Peter Tom Willis (R) | .30 | .18 |
| 657 | Dexter Carter (R) | .20 | .12 |
| 658 | Tony Casillas | .07 | .04 |
| 659 | Joe Morris | .07 | .04 |
| 660 | Greg Kragen | .04 | .02 |
| B1 | Judd Garrett | .10 | .06 |
| B2 | Matt Stover | .08 | .05 |
| B3 | Ken McMichael | .07 | .04 |
| B4 | Demetrius Davis | .07 | .04 |
| B5 | Elliott Searcy | .07 | .04 |

## 1990 Score Update

This 110-card update set consists of rookies and players who were traded just prior to the 1990 season. Cards feature the same design as the regular Score set except the border colors are purple and blue. The card numbers on the back carry the "T" designation. All cards measure 2-1/2" by 3-1/2".

|  |  | MINT | NR/MT |
|---|---|---|---|
| | Complete Set (110) | 90.00 | 60.00 |
| | Commons | .12 | .07 |
| 1 | Marcus Dupree | .15 | .10 |
| 2 | Jerry Kauric (R) | .12 | .07 |
| 3 | Everson Walls | .12 | .07 |
| 4 | Elliott Smith (R) | .12 | .07 |
| 5 | Donald Evans (R) | .15 | .10 |
| 6 | Jerry Holmes | .12 | .07 |
| 7 | Dan Stryzinski (R) | .15 | .10 |
| 8 | Gerald McNeil | .12 | .07 |
| 9 | Rick Tuten (R) | .15 | .10 |
| 10 | Mickey Shuler | .12 | .07 |
| 11 | Jay Novacek (R) | 2.50 | 1.50 |
| 12 | Eric Williams (R) | .15 | .10 |
| 13 | Stanley Morgan | .15 | .10 |
| 14 | Wayne Haddix (R) | .30 | .18 |
| 15 | Gary Anderson | .15 | .10 |
| 16 | Stan Humphries (R) | 5.00 | 3.00 |
| 17 | Raymond Clayborn | .12 | .07 |
| 18 | Mark Boyer (R) | .12 | .07 |
| 19 | Dave Waymer | .12 | .07 |
| 20 | Andre Rison | 1.50 | .90 |
| 21 | Daniel Stubbs | .12 | .07 |
| 22 | Mike Rozier | .15 | .10 |
| 23 | Damian Johnson (R) | .15 | .10 |
| 24 | Don Smith (R) | .15 | .10 |
| 25 | Max Montoya | .12 | .07 |
| 26 | Terry Kinard | .12 | .07 |
| 27 | Herb Welch (R) | .12 | .07 |
| 28 | Cliff Odom | .12 | .07 |
| 29 | John Kidd (R) | .12 | .07 |
| 30 | Barry Word (R) | 2.50 | 1.50 |
| 31 | Rich Karlis | .12 | .07 |
| 32 | Mike Baab | .12 | .07 |
| 33 | Ronnie Harmon | .15 | .10 |
| 34 | Jeff Donaldson | .12 | .07 |
| 35 | Riki Ellison | .12 | .07 |
| 36 | Steve Walsh | .20 | .12 |
| 37 | Bill Lewis (R) | .15 | .10 |
| 38 | Tim McKyer | .12 | .07 |
| 39 | James Wilder | .12 | .07 |
| 40 | Tony Paige | .12 | .07 |
| 41 | Derrick Fenner (R) | .80 | .50 |
| 42 | Thane Gash (R) | .20 | .12 |
| 43 | Dave Duerson | .12 | .07 |
| 44 | Clarence Weathers (R) | .15 | .10 |
| 45 | Matt Bahr | .12 | .07 |
| 46 | Alonzo Highsmith | .12 | .07 |
| 47 | Joe Kelly | .12 | .07 |
| 48 | Chris Hinton | .12 | .07 |
| 49 | Bobby Humphery | .12 | .07 |
| 50 | Greg Bell | .15 | .10 |
| 51 | Fred Smerlas | .12 | .07 |
| 52 | Walter Stanley | .12 | .07 |
| 53 | Jim Skow | .12 | .07 |
| 54 | Renaldo Turnbull | .15 | .10 |
| 55 | Bern Brostek | .12 | .07 |
| 56 | Charles Wilson (R) | .12 | .07 |
| 57 | Keith McCants | .25 | .15 |
| 58 | Alexander Wright (R) | .40 | .25 |
| 59 | Ian Beckles (R) | .15 | .10 |
| 60 | Eric Davis (R) | .20 | .12 |
| 61 | Chris Singleton | .15 | .10 |
| 62 | Rob Moore (R) | 3.50 | 2.25 |
| 63 | Darion Conner | .15 | .10 |
| 64 | Tim Grunhard | .12 | .07 |
| 65 | Junior Seau | 3.50 | 2.25 |
| 66 | Tony Stargell (R) | .40 | .25 |
| 67 | Anthony Thompson (R) | .60 | .35 |
| 68 | Cortez Kennedy | 3.50 | 2.25 |
| 69 | Darrell Thompson | .70 | .40 |
| 70 | Calvin Williams (R) | 1.25 | .80 |
| 71 | Rodney Hampton | 5.00 | 3.00 |
| 72 | Terry Wooden | .12 | .07 |
| 73 | Leo Goeas (R) | .12 | .07 |
| 74 | Ken Willis (R) | .12 | .07 |
| 75 | Ricky Proehl | 1.00 | .70 |
| 76 | Steve Christie (R) | .30 | .18 |
| 77 | Andre Ware | 1.25 | .80 |
| 78 | Jeff George | 8.00 | 5.00 |
| 79 | Walter Wilson (R) | .12 | .07 |
| 80 | Johnny Bailey (R) | .75 | .45 |
| 81 | Harold Green | 3.00 | 2.00 |
| 82 | Mark Carrier (Chi) | .80 | .50 |
| 83 | Frank Cornish (R) | .15 | .10 |
| 84 | James Williams | .12 | .07 |
| 85 | James Francis (R) | .75 | .45 |
| 86 | Percy Snow | .25 | .15 |
| 87 | Anthony Johnson | .35 | .20 |
| 88 | Tim Ryan | .12 | .07 |
| 89 | Dan Owens (R) | .25 | .15 |
| 90 | Aaron Wallace | .15 | .10 |
| 91 | Steve Broussard | .50 | .30 |
| 92 | Eric Green | 2.50 | 1.50 |
| 93 | Blair Thomas | 1.50 | .90 |
| 94 | Robert Blackmon (R) | .25 | .15 |
| 95 | Alan Grant (R) | .12 | .07 |
| 96 | Andre Collins | .20 | .12 |
| 97 | Dexter Carter | .60 | .35 |
| 98 | Reggie Cobb (R) | 2.50 | 1.50 |
| 99 | Dennis Brown | .12 | .07 |
| 100 | Kenny Davidson (R) | .20 | .12 |
| 101 | Emmitt Smith (R) | 60.00 | 42.00 |
| 102 | Jeff Alm | .12 | .07 |
| 103 | Alton Montgomery | .12 | .07 |
| 104 | Tony Bennett | .25 | .15 |
| 105 | Johnny Johnson (R) | 2.50 | 1.50 |
| 106 | Leroy Hoard (R) | 1.25 | .80 |
| 107 | Ray Agnew | .15 | .10 |
| 108 | Richmond Webb | .60 | .35 |
| 109 | Keith Sims | .12 | .07 |

| | | MINT | NR/MT |
|---|---|---|---|
| 110 | Barry Foster | 15.00 | 10.00 |

# 1991 Score

This 686-card set was issued in two series (1-345) and (346-686). Four bonus cards were issued in Score's factory sets. Those cards are listed at the end of this checklist. All cards measure 2-1/2" by 3-1/2". Card fronts feature full color action photographs with the player's name and position printed in a color bar at the bottom of the card. A team logo is located in the lower left corner. The horizontal card backs contain a full color head shot along with stats and a brief biography. Key subsets include Draft Picks , Dream Team (DT), Team MVP's (MVP), Crunch Crew (CC), Sack Attack (SA), Top Leaders (TL) and Hall of Famers (HOF).

| | | MINT | NR/MT |
|---|---|---|---|
| **Complete Set (686)** | | 12.00 | 8.00 |
| **Commons** | | .04 | .02 |
| 1 | Joe Montana | .50 | .30 |
| 2 | Eric Allen | .04 | .02 |
| 3 | Rohn Stark | .04 | .02 |
| 4 | Frank Reich | .07 | .04 |
| 5 | Derrick Thomas | .20 | .12 |
| 6 | Mike Singletary | .10 | .06 |
| 7 | Boomer Esiason | .10 | .06 |
| 8 | Matt Millen | .07 | .04 |
| 9 | Chris Spielman | .04 | .02 |
| 10 | Gerald McNeil | .04 | .02 |
| 11 | Nick Lowery | .07 | .04 |
| 12 | Randall Cunningham | .15 | .10 |
| 13 | Marion Butts | .12 | .07 |
| 14 | Tim Brown | .10 | .06 |
| 15 | Emmitt Smith | 1.75 | 1.00 |
| 16 | Rich Camarillo | .04 | .02 |
| 17 | Mike Merriweather | .04 | .02 |
| 18 | Derrick Fenner | .10 | .06 |
| 19 | Clay Matthews | .04 | .02 |
| 20 | Barry Sanders | .75 | .45 |
| 21 | James Brooks | .07 | .04 |
| 22 | Alton Montgomery | .04 | .02 |
| 23 | Steve Atwater | .10 | .06 |
| 24 | Ron Morris | .04 | .02 |
| 25 | Brad Muster | .08 | .05 |
| 26 | Andre Rison | .25 | .15 |
| 27 | Brian Brennan | .04 | .02 |
| 28 | Leonard Smith | .04 | .02 |
| 29 | Kevin Butler | .04 | .02 |
| 30 | Tim Harris | .04 | .02 |
| 31 | Jay Novacek | .15 | .10 |
| 32 | Eddie Murray | .04 | .02 |
| 33 | Keith Woodside | .04 | .02 |
| 34 | Ray Crockett (R) | .07 | .04 |
| 35 | Eugene Lockhart | .04 | .02 |
| 36 | Bill Romanowski | .04 | .02 |
| 37 | Eddie Brown | .08 | .05 |
| 38 | Eugene Daniel | .04 | .02 |
| 39 | Scott Fulhage | .04 | .02 |
| 40 | Harold Green | .30 | .18 |
| 41 | Mark Jackson | .07 | .04 |
| 42 | Sterling Sharpe | .25 | .15 |
| 43 | Mel Gray | .04 | .02 |
| 44 | Jerry Holmes | .04 | .02 |
| 45 | Allen Pinkett | .04 | .02 |
| 46 | Warren Powers | .04 | .02 |
| 47 | Rodney Peete | .12 | .07 |
| 48 | Lorenzo White | .12 | .07 |
| 49 | Dan Owens | .04 | .02 |
| 50 | James Francis | .08 | .05 |
| 51 | Ken Norton | .04 | .02 |
| 52 | Ed West | .04 | .02 |
| 53 | Andre Reed | .12 | .07 |
| 54 | John Grimsley | .04 | .02 |
| 55 | Michael Cofer | .04 | .02 |
| 56 | Chris Doleman | .07 | .04 |
| 57 | Pat Swilling | .12 | .07 |
| 58 | Jessie Tuggle | .04 | .02 |
| 59 | Mike Johnson | .04 | .02 |
| 60 | Steve Walsh | .10 | .06 |
| 61 | Sam Mills | .07 | .04 |
| 62 | Don Mosebar | .04 | .02 |
| 63 | Jay Hilgenberg | .04 | .02 |
| 64 | Cleveland Gary | .08 | .05 |
| 65 | Andre Tippett | .07 | .04 |
| 66 | Tom Newberry | .04 | .02 |
| 67 | Maurice Hurst | .04 | .02 |
| 68 | Louis Oliver | .07 | .04 |
| 69 | Fred Marion | .04 | .02 |

| # | Player | | |
|---|--------|------|------|
| 70 | Christian Okoye | .12 | .07 |
| 71 | Marv Cook (R) | .12 | .07 |
| 72 | Darryl Talley | .07 | .04 |
| 73 | Rick Fenney | .04 | .02 |
| 74 | Kelvin Martin | .08 | .05 |
| 75 | Howie Long | .07 | .04 |
| 76 | Steve Wisniewski | .04 | .02 |
| 77 | Karl Mecklenburg | .07 | .04 |
| 78 | Dan Saleaumua | .04 | .02 |
| 79 | Ray Childress | .07 | .04 |
| 80 | Henry Ellard | .07 | .04 |
| 81 | Ernest Givins | .15 | .10 |
| 82 | Ferrell Edmunds | .04 | .02 |
| 83 | Steve Jordan | .04 | .02 |
| 84 | Tony Mandarich | .04 | .02 |
| 85 | Eric Martin | .08 | .05 |
| 86 | Rich Gannon | .20 | .12 |
| 87 | Irving Fryar | .07 | .04 |
| 88 | Tom Rathman | .07 | .04 |
| 89 | Dan Hampton | .07 | .04 |
| 90 | Barry Word | .35 | .20 |
| 91 | Kevin Greene | .04 | .02 |
| 92 | Sean Landeta | .04 | .02 |
| 93 | Trace Armstrong | .04 | .02 |
| 94 | Dennis Byrd | .07 | .04 |
| 95 | Timm Rosenbach | .12 | .07 |
| 96 | Anthony Toney | .04 | .02 |
| 97 | Tim Krumris | .04 | .02 |
| 98 | Jerry Ball | .04 | .02 |
| 99 | Tim Green | .04 | .02 |
| 100 | Bo Jackson | .35 | .20 |
| 101 | Myron Guyton | .04 | .02 |
| 102 | Mike Mularkey | .04 | .02 |
| 103 | Jerry Gray | .04 | .02 |
| 104 | Scott Stephen (R) | .07 | .04 |
| 105 | Anthony Bell | .04 | .02 |
| 106 | Lomas Brown | .04 | .02 |
| 107 | David Little | .04 | .02 |
| 108 | Brad Baxter (R) | .25 | .15 |
| 109 | Freddie Joe Nunn | .04 | .02 |
| 110 | Dave Meggett | .12 | .07 |
| 111 | Mark Rypien | .20 | .12 |
| 112 | Warrem Williams | .04 | .02 |
| 113 | Ron Rivera | .04 | .02 |
| 114 | Terance Mathis (R) | .12 | .07 |
| 115 | Anthony Munoz | .08 | .05 |
| 116 | Jeff Bryant | .04 | .02 |
| 117 | Issiac Holt | .04 | .02 |
| 118 | Steve Sewell | .04 | .02 |
| 119 | Tim Newton (R) | .07 | .04 |
| 120 | Emile Harry | .04 | .02 |
| 121 | Gary Anderson | .04 | .02 |
| 122 | Mark Lee | .04 | .02 |
| 123 | Alfred Anderson | .04 | .02 |
| 124 | Tony Blaylock (R) | .10 | .06 |
| 125 | Earnest Byner | .07 | .04 |
| 126 | Bill Maas | .04 | .02 |
| 127 | Keith Taylor | .04 | .02 |
| 128 | Cliff Odom | .04 | .02 |
| 129 | Bob Golic | .04 | .02 |
| 130 | Bart Oates | .04 | .02 |
| 131 | Jim Arnold | .04 | .02 |
| 132 | Jeff Herrod | .04 | .02 |
| 133 | Bruce Armstrong | .04 | .02 |
| 134 | Craig Heyward | .08 | .05 |
| 135 | Joey Browner | .07 | .04 |
| 136 | Darren Comeaux | .04 | .02 |
| 137 | Pat Beach | .04 | .02 |
| 138 | Dalton Hilliard | .08 | .05 |
| 139 | David Treadwell | .04 | .02 |
| 140 | Gary Anderson | .04 | .02 |
| 141 | Eugene Robinson | .04 | .02 |
| 142 | Scott Case | .04 | .02 |
| 143 | Paul Farren | .04 | .02 |
| 144 | Gill Fenerty | .04 | .02 |
| 145 | Tim Irwin | .04 | .02 |
| 146 | Norm Johnson | .04 | .02 |
| 147 | Willie Gault | .07 | .04 |
| 148 | Clarence Verdin | .07 | .04 |
| 149 | Jeff Uhlenhake | .04 | .02 |
| 150 | Erik McMillan | .04 | .02 |
| 151 | Kevin Ross | .04 | .02 |
| 152 | Pepper Johnson | .04 | .02 |
| 153 | Bryan Hinkle | .04 | .02 |
| 154 | Gary Clark | .15 | .10 |
| 155 | Robert Delpino | .08 | .05 |
| 156 | Doug Smith | .04 | .02 |
| 157 | Chris Martin | .04 | .02 |
| 158 | Ray Berry | .04 | .02 |
| 159 | Steve Christie | .04 | .02 |
| 160 | Don Smith | .04 | .02 |
| 161 | Greg McMurtry | .12 | .07 |
| 162 | Jack Del Rio | .04 | .02 |
| 163 | Floyd Dixon | .04 | .02 |
| 164 | Buford McGee | .04 | .02 |
| 165 | Brett Maxie | .04 | .02 |
| 166 | Morten Andersen | .07 | .04 |
| 167 | Kent Hull | .04 | .02 |
| 168 | Skip McClendon | .04 | .02 |
| 169 | Keith Sims | .04 | .02 |
| 170 | Leonard Marshall | .07 | .04 |
| 171 | Tony Woods | .04 | .02 |
| 172 | Byron Evans | .04 | .02 |
| 173 | Rob Burnett (R) | .15 | .10 |
| 174 | Tory Epps | .04 | .02 |
| 175 | Toi Cook (R) | .08 | .05 |
| 176 | John Elliott | .04 | .02 |
| 177 | Tommie Agee | .04 | .02 |
| 178 | Keith Van Horne | .04 | .02 |
| 179 | Dennis Smith | .04 | .02 |
| 180 | James Lofton | .15 | .10 |
| 181 | Art Monk | .20 | .12 |
| 182 | Anthony Carter | .08 | .05 |
| 183 | Louis Lipps | .07 | .04 |

| 184 | Bruce Hill | .04 | .02 |
|---|---|---|---|
| 185 | Mike Young | .04 | .02 |
| 186 | Eric Green | .15 | .10 |
| 187 | Barney Bussey | .04 | .02 |
| 188 | Curtis Duncan | .07 | .04 |
| 189 | Robert Awalt | .04 | .02 |
| 190 | Johnny Johnson | .20 | .12 |
| 191 | Jeff Cross | .04 | .02 |
| 192 | Keith McKeller | .07 | .04 |
| 193 | Robert Brown | .04 | .02 |
| 194 | Vincent Brown | .04 | .02 |
| 195 | Calvin Williams | .12 | .07 |
| 196 | Sean Jones | .04 | .02 |
| 197 | Willie Drewrey | .04 | .02 |
| 198 | Bubba McDowell | .04 | .02 |
| 199 | Al Noga | .04 | .02 |
| 200 | Ronnie Lott | .10 | .06 |
| 201 | Warren Moon | .20 | .12 |
| 202 | Chris Hinton | .04 | .02 |
| 203 | Jim Sweeney | .04 | .02 |
| 204 | Wayne Haddix | .07 | .04 |
| 205 | Tim Jorden (R) | .07 | .04 |
| 206 | Marvin Allen | .04 | .02 |
| 207 | Jim Morrissey (R) | .07 | .04 |
| 208 | Ben Smith | .04 | .02 |
| 209 | William White | .04 | .02 |
| 210 | Jim Jensen | .04 | .02 |
| 211 | Doug Reed (R) | .07 | .04 |
| 212 | Ethan Horton (R) | .12 | .07 |
| 213 | Chris Jacke | .04 | .02 |
| 214 | Johnny Hector | .07 | .04 |
| 215 | Drew Hill | .08 | .05 |
| 216 | Roy Green | .07 | .04 |
| 217 | Dean Steinkuhler | .04 | .02 |
| 218 | Cedric Mack | .04 | .02 |
| 219 | Chris Miller | .30 | .18 |
| 220 | Keith Byars | .07 | .04 |
| 221 | Lewis Billups | .04 | .02 |
| 222 | Roger Craig | .08 | .05 |
| 223 | Shaun Gayle | .04 | .02 |
| 224 | Mike Rozier | .07 | .04 |
| 225 | Troy Aikman | 1.00 | .70 |
| 226 | Bobby Humphrey | .10 | .06 |
| 227 | Eugene Marve | .04 | .02 |
| 228 | Michael Carter | .04 | .02 |
| 229 | Richard Johnson | .04 | .02 |
| 230 | Billy Joe Tolliver | .10 | .06 |
| 231 | Mark Murphy | .04 | .02 |
| 232 | John L. Williams | .07 | .04 |
| 233 | Ronnie Harmon | .07 | .04 |
| 234 | Thurman Thomas | .60 | .35 |
| 235 | Martin Mayhew | .04 | .02 |
| 236 | Richmond Webb | .07 | .04 |
| 237 | Gerald Riggs | .07 | .04 |
| 238 | Mike Prior | .04 | .02 |
| 239 | Mike Gann | .04 | .02 |
| 240 | Alvin Walton | .04 | .02 |
| 241 | Tim McGee | .07 | .04 |
| 242 | Bruce Matthews | .04 | .02 |
| 243 | Johnny Holland | .04 | .02 |
| 244 | Martin Bayless | .04 | .02 |
| 245 | Eric Metcalf | .10 | .06 |
| 246 | John Alt | .04 | .02 |
| 247 | Max Montoya | .04 | .02 |
| 248 | Rod Bernstine | .07 | .04 |
| 249 | Paul Gruber | .04 | .02 |
| 250 | Charles Haley | .07 | .04 |
| 251 | Scott Norwood | .04 | .02 |
| 252 | Michael Haddix | .07 | .04 |
| 253 | Ricky Sanders | .08 | .05 |
| 254 | Ervin Randle | .04 | .02 |
| 255 | Duane Bickett | .04 | .02 |
| 256 | Mike Munchak | .04 | .02 |
| 257 | Keith Jones | .04 | .02 |
| 258 | Riki Ellison | .04 | .02 |
| 259 | Vince Newsome | .04 | .02 |
| 260 | Lee Williams | .04 | .02 |
| 261 | Steve Smith | .04 | .02 |
| 262 | Sam Clancy | .04 | .02 |
| 263 | Pierce Holt | .04 | .02 |
| 264 | Jim Harbaugh | .15 | .10 |
| 265 | Dino Hackett | .04 | .02 |
| 266 | Andy Heck | .04 | .02 |
| 267 | Leo Goeas | .04 | .02 |
| 268 | Russ Grimm | .04 | .02 |
| 269 | Gill Byrd | .04 | .02 |
| 270 | Neal Anderson | .12 | .07 |
| 271 | Jackie Slater | .07 | .04 |
| 272 | Joe Nash | .04 | .02 |
| 273 | Todd Bowles | .04 | .02 |
| 274 | D.J. Dozier | .08 | .05 |
| 275 | Kevin Fagan | .04 | .02 |
| 276 | Don Warren | .04 | .02 |
| 277 | Jim Jeffcoat | .04 | .02 |
| 278 | Bruce Smith | .12 | .07 |
| 279 | Cortez Kennedy | .20 | .12 |
| 280 | Thane Gash | .04 | .02 |
| 281 | Perry Kemp | .04 | .02 |
| 282 | John Taylor | .15 | .10 |
| 283 | Stephone Paige | .07 | .04 |
| 284 | Paul Skansi | .04 | .02 |
| 285 | Shawn Collins | .04 | .02 |
| 286 | Mervyn Fernandez | .07 | .04 |
| 287 | Daniel Stubbs | .04 | .02 |
| 288 | Chip Lohmiller | .04 | .02 |
| 289 | Brian Blades | .07 | .04 |
| 290 | Mark Carrier (TB) | .07 | .04 |
| 291 | Carl Zander | .04 | .02 |
| 292 | David Wyman | .04 | .02 |
| 293 | Jeff Bostic | .04 | .02 |
| 294 | Irv Pankey | .04 | .02 |
| 295 | Keith Millard | .07 | .04 |
| 296 | Jamie Mueller | .04 | .02 |
| 297 | Bill Fralic | .04 | .02 |

| No. | Player | | |
|---|---|---|---|
| 298 | Wendell Davis | .12 | .07 |
| 299 | Ken Clarke | .04 | .02 |
| 300 | Wymon Henderson | .04 | .02 |
| 301 | Jeff Campbell | .04 | .02 |
| 302 | Cody Carlson (R) | .40 | .25 |
| 303 | Matt Brock (R) | .08 | .05 |
| 304 | Maurice Carthon | .04 | .02 |
| 305 | Scott Mersereau (R) | .10 | .06 |
| 306 | Steve Wright (R) | .08 | .05 |
| 307 | J.B. Brown | .04 | .02 |
| 307 | Ricky Reynolds | .04 | .02 |
| 309 | Darryl Pollard | .04 | .02 |
| 310 | Donald Evans | .04 | .02 |
| 311 | Nick Bell (R) | .60 | .35 |
| 312 | Pat Harlow (R) | .10 | .06 |
| 313 | Dan McGwire (R) | .70 | .40 |
| 314 | Mike Dumas (R) | .12 | .07 |
| 315 | Mike Croel (R) | .35 | .20 |
| 316 | Chris Smith (R) | .08 | .05 |
| 317 | Kenny Walker (R) | .20 | .12 |
| 318 | Todd Lyght (R) | .25 | .15 |
| 319 | Mike Stonebreaker (R) | .08 | .05 |
| 320 | Randall Cunningham | .15 | .10 |
| 321 | Terance Mathis | .07 | .04 |
| 322 | Gaston Green | .10 | .06 |
| 323 | Johnny Bailey | .08 | .05 |
| 324 | Donnie Elder | .04 | .02 |
| 325 | Dwight Stone | .04 | .02 |
| 326 | J.J. Birden (R) | .15 | .10 |
| 327 | Alexander Wright | .08 | .05 |
| 328 | Eric Metcalf | .08 | .05 |
| 329 | Andre Rison (TL) | .12 | .07 |
| 330 | Warren Moon (TL) | .12 | .07 |
| 331 | Steve Tasker (DT) | .04 | .02 |
| 332 | Mel Gray (DT) | .04 | .02 |
| 333 | Nick Lowery (DT) | .04 | .02 |
| 334 | Sean Landeta (DT) | .04 | .02 |
| 335 | David Fulcher (DT) | .04 | .02 |
| 336 | Joey Browner (DT) | .04 | .02 |
| 337 | Albert Lewis (DT) | .04 | .02 |
| 338 | Rod Woodson (DT) | .08 | .05 |
| 339 | Shane Conlan (DT) | .07 | .04 |
| 340 | Pepper Johnson (DT) | .07 | .04 |
| 341 | Chris Spielman (DT) | .04 | .02 |
| 342 | Derrick Thomas (DT) | .12 | .07 |
| 343 | Ray Childress (DT) | .04 | .02 |
| 344 | Reggie White (DT) | .08 | .05 |
| 345 | Bruce Smith (DT) | .08 | .05 |
| 346 | Darrell Green | .10 | .06 |
| 347 | Ray Bentley | .04 | .02 |
| 348 | Herschel Walker | .12 | .07 |
| 349 | Rodney Holman | .04 | .02 |
| 350 | Al Toon | .08 | .05 |
| 351 | Harry Hamilton | .04 | .02 |
| 352 | Albert Lewis | .04 | .02 |
| 353 | Renaldo Turnbull | .07 | .04 |
| 354 | Junior Seau | .20 | .12 |
| 355 | Merril Hoge | .07 | .04 |
| 356 | Shane Conlan | .08 | .05 |
| 357 | Jay Schroeder | .10 | .06 |
| 358 | Steve Broussard | .10 | .06 |
| 359 | Mark Bavaro | .07 | .04 |
| 360 | Jim Lachey | .07 | .04 |
| 361 | Greg Townsend | .07 | .04 |
| 362 | Dave Krieg | .10 | .06 |
| 363 | Jessie Hester | .04 | .02 |
| 364 | Steve Tasker | .04 | .02 |
| 365 | Ron Hall | .04 | .02 |
| 366 | Pat Leahy | .04 | .02 |
| 367 | Jim Everett | .12 | .07 |
| 368 | Felix Wright | .04 | .02 |
| 369 | Ricky Proehl | .12 | .07 |
| 370 | Anthony Miller | .15 | .10 |
| 371 | Keith Jackson | .12 | .07 |
| 372 | Pete Stoyanovich | .04 | .02 |
| 373 | Tommy Kane | .08 | .05 |
| 374 | Richard Johnson | .04 | .02 |
| 375 | Randall McDaniel | .04 | .02 |
| 376 | John Stephens | .08 | .05 |
| 377 | Haywood Jeffieres | .25 | .15 |
| 378 | Rodney Hampton | .35 | .20 |
| 379 | Tim Grunhard | .04 | .02 |
| 380 | Jerry Rice | .40 | .25 |
| 381 | Ken Harvey | .04 | .02 |
| 382 | Vaughan Johnson | .07 | .04 |
| 383 | J.T. Smith | .04 | .02 |
| 384 | Carnell Lake | .04 | .02 |
| 385 | Dan Marino | .40 | .25 |
| 386 | Kyle Clifton | .04 | .02 |
| 387 | Wilber Marshall | .07 | .04 |
| 388 | Pete Holohan | .04 | .02 |
| 389 | Gary Plummer | .04 | .02 |
| 390 | William Perry | .07 | .04 |
| 391 | Mark Robinson | .04 | .02 |
| 392 | Nate Odomes | .04 | .02 |
| 393 | Ickey Woods | .04 | .02 |
| 394 | Reyna Thompson | .04 | .02 |
| 395 | Deion Sanders | .25 | .15 |
| 396 | Harris Barton | .04 | .02 |
| 397 | Sammie Smith | .08 | .05 |
| 398 | Vinny Testaverde | .12 | .07 |
| 399 | Ray Donaldson | .04 | .02 |
| 400 | Tim McKyer | .04 | .02 |
| 401 | Nesby Glasgow | .04 | .02 |
| 402 | Brent Williams | .04 | .02 |
| 403 | Rob Moore | .25 | .15 |
| 404 | Bubby Brister | .10 | .06 |
| 405 | David Fulcher | .04 | .02 |
| 406 | Reggie Cobb | .20 | .12 |
| 407 | Jerome Brown | .07 | .04 |
| 408 | Erik Howard | .04 | .02 |
| 409 | Tony Paige | .04 | .02 |
| 410 | John Elway | .20 | .12 |
| 411 | Charles Mann | .04 | .02 |

| | | | |
|---|---|---|---|
| 412 Luis Sharpe | .04 | .02 |
| 413 Hassan Jones | .07 | .04 |
| 414 Frank Minnifield | .04 | .02 |
| 415 Steve DeBerg | .10 | .06 |
| 416 Mark Carrier (Chi) | .12 | .07 |
| 417 Brian Jordan (R) | .15 | .10 |
| 418 Reggie Langhorne | .07 | .04 |
| 419 Don Majkowski | .12 | .07 |
| 420 Marcus Allen | .10 | .06 |
| 421 Michael Brooks | .04 | .02 |
| 422 Vai Sikahema | .04 | .02 |
| 423 Dermontti Dawson | .04 | .02 |
| 424 Jacob Green | .04 | .02 |
| 425 Flipper Anderson | .08 | .05 |
| 426 Bill Brooks | .04 | .02 |
| 427 Keith McCants | .08 | .05 |
| 428 Ken O'Brien | .10 | .06 |
| 429 Fred Barnett (R) | .30 | .18 |
| 430 Mark Duper | .08 | .05 |
| 431 Mark Kelso | .04 | .02 |
| 432 Leslie O'Neal | .07 | .04 |
| 433 Ottis Anderson | .07 | .04 |
| 434 Jesse Sapolu | .04 | .02 |
| 435 Gary Zimmerman | .04 | .02 |
| 436 Kevin Porter | .04 | .02 |
| 437 Anthony Thompson | .08 | .05 |
| 438 Robert Clark | .04 | .02 |
| 439 Chris Warren (R) | .12 | .07 |
| 440 Gerald Williams | .04 | .02 |
| 441 Jim Skow | .04 | .02 |
| 442 Rick Donnelly | .04 | .02 |
| 443 Guy McIntyre | .04 | .02 |
| 444 Jeff Lageman | .07 | .04 |
| 445 John Offerdahl | .07 | .04 |
| 446 Clyde Simmons | .07 | .04 |
| 447 John Kidd | .04 | .02 |
| 448 Chip Banks | .04 | .02 |
| 449 Johnny Meads | .04 | .02 |
| 450 Rickey Jackson | .07 | .04 |
| 451 Lee Johnson | .04 | .02 |
| 452 Michael Irvin | .35 | .20 |
| 453 Leon Seals | .04 | .02 |
| 454 Darrell Thompson | .10 | .06 |
| 455 Everson Walls | .04 | .02 |
| 456 LeRoy Butler | .04 | .02 |
| 457 Marcus Dupree | .07 | .04 |
| 458 Kirk Lowdermilk | .04 | .02 |
| 459 Chris Singleton | .07 | .04 |
| 460 Seth Joyner | .07 | .04 |
| 461 Rueben Mayes | .04 | .02 |
| 462 Ernie Jones | .08 | .05 |
| 463 Greg Kragen | .04 | .02 |
| 464 Bennie Blades | .07 | .04 |
| 465 Mark Bortz | .04 | .02 |
| 466 Tony Stargell | .04 | .02 |
| 467 Mike Cofer | .04 | .02 |
| 468 Randy Grimes | .04 | .02 |

| | | | |
|---|---|---|---|
| 469 Tim Worley | .08 | .05 |
| 470 Kevin Mack | .07 | .04 |
| 471 Wes Hopkins | .04 | .02 |
| 472 Will Wolford | .04 | .02 |
| 473 Sam Seale (R) | .08 | .05 |
| 474 Jim Ritcher | .04 | .02 |
| 475 Jeff Hostetler | .20 | .12 |
| 476 Mitchell Price | .04 | .02 |
| 477 Ken Lanier | .04 | .02 |
| 478 Naz Worthen | .04 | .02 |
| 479 Ed Reynolds | .04 | .02 |
| 480 Mark Clayton | .12 | .07 |
| 481 Matt Bahr | .04 | .02 |
| 482 Gary Reasons | .04 | .02 |
| 483 Dave Szott (R) | .07 | .04 |
| 484 Barry Foster | .80 | .50 |
| 485 Bruce Reimers | .04 | .02 |
| 486 Dean Biasucci | .04 | .02 |
| 487 Cris Carter | .15 | .10 |
| 488 Albert Bentley | .04 | .02 |
| 489 Robert Massey | .04 | .02 |
| 490 Al Smith | .04 | .02 |
| 491 Greg Lloyd | .04 | .02 |
| 492 Steve McMichael | .07 | .04 |
| 493 Jeff Wright (R) | .08 | .05 |
| 494 Scott Davis | .04 | .02 |
| 495 Freeman McNeil | .07 | .04 |
| 496 Simon Fletcher | .04 | .02 |
| 497 Terry McDaniel | .04 | .02 |
| 498 Heath Sherman | .08 | .05 |
| 499 Jeff Jaeger | .04 | .02 |
| 500 Mark Collins | .04 | .02 |
| 501 Tim Goad | .04 | .02 |
| 502 Jeff George | .40 | .25 |
| 503 Jimmie Jones | .04 | .02 |
| 504 Henry Thomas | .04 | .02 |
| 505 Steve Young | .35 | .20 |
| 506 William Roberts | .04 | .02 |
| 507 Neil Smith | .04 | .02 |
| 508 Mike Saxon | .04 | .02 |
| 509 Johnny Bailey | .07 | .04 |
| 510 Broderick Thomas | .08 | .05 |
| 511 Wade Wilson | .08 | .05 |
| 512 Hart Lee Dykes | .07 | .04 |
| 513 Hardy Nickerson | .04 | .02 |
| 514 Tim McDonald | .04 | .02 |
| 515 Frank Cornish | .04 | .02 |
| 516 Jarvis Williams | .04 | .02 |
| 517 Carl Lee | .04 | .02 |
| 518 Carl Banks | .07 | .04 |
| 519 Mike Golic | .04 | .02 |
| 520 Brian Noble | .04 | .02 |
| 521 James Hasty | .04 | .02 |
| 522 Bubba Paris | .04 | .02 |
| 523 Kevin Walker (R) | .10 | .06 |
| 524 William Fuller | .04 | .02 |
| 525 Eddie Anderson | .04 | .02 |

| | | | |
|---|---|---|---|
| 526 | Roger Ruzek | .04 | .02 |
| 527 | Robert Blackmon | .04 | .02 |
| 528 | Vince Buck | .04 | .02 |
| 529 | Lawrence Taylor | .15 | .10 |
| 530 | Reggie Roby | .04 | .02 |
| 531 | Doug Riesenberg | .04 | .02 |
| 532 | Joe Jacoby | .04 | .02 |
| 533 | Kirby Jackson (R) | .10 | .06 |
| 534 | Robb Thomas | .04 | .02 |
| 535 | Don Griffin | .04 | .02 |
| 536 | Andre Waters | .04 | .02 |
| 537 | Marc Logan | .04 | .02 |
| 538 | James Thornton | .04 | .02 |
| 539 | Ray Agnew | .04 | .02 |
| 540 | Frank Stams | .04 | .02 |
| 541 | Brett Perriman | .07 | .04 |
| 542 | Andre Ware | .20 | .12 |
| 543 | Kevin Haverdink | .04 | .02 |
| 544 | Greg Jackson (R) | .07 | .04 |
| 545 | Tunch Ilkin | .04 | .02 |
| 546 | Dexter Carter | .08 | .05 |
| 547 | Rod Woodson | .10 | .06 |
| 548 | Donnell Woolford | .04 | .02 |
| 549 | Mark Boyer | .04 | .02 |
| 550 | Jeff Query | .08 | .05 |
| 551 | Burt Grossman | .07 | .04 |
| 552 | Mike Kenn | .04 | .02 |
| 553 | Richard Dent | .07 | .04 |
| 554 | Gaston Green | .15 | .10 |
| 555 | Phil Simms | .10 | .06 |
| 556 | Brent Jones | .08 | .05 |
| 557 | Ronnie Lippett | .04 | .02 |
| 558 | Mike Horan | .04 | .02 |
| 559 | Danny Noonan | .04 | .02 |
| 560 | Reggie White | .12 | .07 |
| 561 | Rufus Porter | .04 | .02 |
| 562 | Aaron Wallace | .04 | .02 |
| 563 | Vance Johnson | .08 | .05 |
| 564 | Aaron Craver (R) | .15 | .10 |
| 565 | Russell Maryland (R) | .40 | .25 |
| 566 | Paul Justin (R) | .08 | .05 |
| 567 | Walter Dean (R) | .07 | .04 |
| 568 | Herman Moore (R) | .75 | .45 |
| 569 | Bill Musgrave (R) | .20 | .12 |
| 570 | Rob Carpenter (R) | .20 | .12 |
| 571 | Greg Lewis (R) | .20 | .12 |
| 572 | Ed King (R) | .08 | .05 |
| 573 | Ernie Mills (R) | .35 | .20 |
| 574 | Jake Reed (R) | .10 | .06 |
| 575 | Ricky Watters (R) | 2.50 | 1.50 |
| 576 | Derek Russell (R) | .25 | .15 |
| 577 | Shawn Moore (R) | .25 | .15 |
| 578 | Eric Bieniemy (R) | .25 | .15 |
| 579 | Chris Zorich (R) | .10 | .06 |
| 580 | Scott Miller (R) | .08 | .05 |
| 581 | Jarrod Bunch (R) | .30 | .18 |
| 582 | Ricky Ervins (R) | 1.00 | .70 |
| 583 | Browning Nagle | 1.25 | .80 |
| 584 | Eric Turner (R) | .35 | .20 |
| 585 | Williams Thomas (R) | .08 | .05 |
| 586 | Stanley Richard (R) | .20 | .12 |
| 587 | Adrian Cooper (R) | .12 | .07 |
| 588 | Harvey Williams (R) | .50 | .30 |
| 589 | Alvin Harper (R) | .80 | .50 |
| 590 | John Carney (R) | .07 | .04 |
| 591 | Mark Vander Poel (R) | .10 | .06 |
| 592 | Mike Pritchard (R) | .60 | .35 |
| 593 | Eric Moten (R) | .08 | .05 |
| 594 | Moe Gardner (R) | .20 | .12 |
| 595 | Wesley Carroll (R) | .35 | .20 |
| 596 | Eric Swann (R) | .15 | .10 |
| 597 | Joe Kelly (R) | .07 | .04 |
| 598 | Steve Jackson (R) | .08 | .05 |
| 599 | Kelvin Pritchett (R) | .20 | .12 |
| 600 | Jesse Campbell (R) | .10 | .06 |
| 601 | Darryl Lewis (R) | .20 | .12 |
| 602 | Howard Griffith (R) | .07 | .04 |
| 603 | Blais Bryant (R) | .08 | .05 |
| 604 | Vinnie Clark (R) | .15 | .10 |
| 605 | Mel Agee (R) | .10 | .06 |
| 606 | Bobby Wilson (R) | .10 | .06 |
| 607 | Kevin Donnalley (R) | .08 | .05 |
| 608 | Randal Hill (R) | .50 | .30 |
| 609 | Stan Thomas (R) | .08 | .05 |
| 610 | Mike Heldt (R) | .07 | .04 |
| 611 | Brett Favre (R) | 2.00 | 1.25 |
| 612 | Lawrence Dawsey (R) | .50 | .30 |
| 613 | Dennis Gibson (R) | .04 | .02 |
| 614 | Dean Dingman (R) | .07 | .04 |
| 615 | Bruce Pickens (R) | .20 | .12 |
| 616 | Todd Marinovich (R) | 1.25 | .80 |
| 617 | Gene Atkins | .04 | .02 |
| 618 | Marcus Dupree (Comeback Player) | .07 | .04 |
| 619 | Warren Moon (Man of the Year) | .12 | .07 |
| 620 | Joe Montana (MVP) | .20 | .12 |
| 621 | Neal Anderson (MVP) | .08 | .05 |
| 622 | James Brooks (MVP) | .04 | .02 |
| 623 | Thurman Thomas (MVP) | .20 | .12 |
| 624 | Bobby Humphrey (MVP) | .07 | .04 |
| 625 | Kevin Mack (MVP) | .04 | .02 |
| 626 | Mark Carrier (MVP) | .04 | .02 |
| 627 | Johnny Johnson (MVP) | .08 | .05 |
| 628 | Marion Butts (MVP) | .07 | .04 |
| 629 | Steve DeBerg (MVP) | .07 | .04 |
| 630 | Jeff George (MVP) | .15 | .10 |
| 631 | Troy Aikman (MVP) | .25 | .15 |
| 632 | Dan Marino (MVP) | .20 | .12 |
| 633 | Randall Cunningham (MVP) | .10 | .06 |

| | | | |
|---|---|---|---|
| 634 | Andre Rison (MVP) | .10 | .06 |
| 635 | Pepper Johnson (MVP) | .04 | .02 |
| 636 | Pat Leahy (MVP) | .04 | .02 |
| 637 | Barry Sanders (MVP) | .25 | .15 |
| 638 | Warren Moon (MVP) | .10 | .06 |
| 639 | Sterling Sharpe (MVP) | .10 | .06 |
| 640 | Bruce Armstrong (MVP) | .04 | .02 |
| 641 | Bo Jackson (MVP) | .20 | .12 |
| 642 | Henry Ellard (MVP | .07 | .04 |
| 643 | Earnest Byner (MVP) | .07 | .04 |
| 644 | Pat Swilling (MVP) | .08 | .05 |
| 645 | John L. Williams (MVP) | .04 | .02 |
| 646 | Rod Woodson (MVP) | .07 | .04 |
| 647 | Chris Doleman (MVP) | .04 | .02 |
| 648 | Joey Browner (CC) | .04 | .02 |
| 649 | Erik McMillan (CC) | .04 | .02 |
| 650 | David Fulcher (CC) | .04 | .02 |
| 651 | Ronnie Lott (CC) | .08 | .05 |
| 652 | Louis Oliver (CC) | .04 | .02 |
| 653 | Mark Robinson (CC) | .04 | .02 |
| 654 | Dennis Smith (CC) | .04 | .02 |
| 655 | Reggie White (SA) | .08 | .05 |
| 656 | Charles Haley (SA) | .04 | .02 |
| 657 | Leslie O'Neal (SA) | .04 | .02 |
| 658 | Kevin Greene (SA) | .04 | .02 |
| 659 | Dennis Byrd (SA) | .04 | .02 |
| 660 | Bruce Smith (SA) | .08 | .05 |
| 661 | Derrick Thomas (SA) | .10 | .06 |
| 662 | Steve DeBerg (TL) | .07 | .04 |
| 663 | Barry Sanders (TL) | .30 | .18 |
| 664 | Thurman Thomas (TL) | .25 | .15 |
| 665 | Jerry Rice (TL) | .25 | .15 |
| 666 | Derrick Thomas (TL) | .12 | .07 |
| 667 | Bruce Smith (TL) | .08 | .05 |
| 668 | Mark Carrier (TL) | .07 | .04 |
| 669 | Richard Johnson (TL) | .04 | .02 |
| 670 | Jan Stenerud (HOF) | .07 | .04 |
| 671 | Stan Jones (HOF) | .07 | .04 |
| 672 | John Hannah (HOF) | .07 | .04 |
| 673 | Tex Schramm (HOF) | .07 | .04 |
| 674 | Earl Campbell (HOF) | .15 | .10 |
| 675 | Rookies of the Year | .25 | .15 |
| | Mark Carrier | | |
| | Emmitt Smith | | |
| 676 | Warren Moon (DT) | .12 | .07 |
| 677 | Barry Sanders (DT) | .50 | .30 |
| 678 | Thurman Thomas (DT) | .40 | .25 |
| 679 | Andre Reed (DT) | .12 | .07 |
| 680 | Andre Rison (DT) | .15 | .10 |
| 681 | Keith Jackson (DT) | .08 | .05 |
| 682 | Bruce Armstrong (DT) | .04 | .02 |
| 683 | Jim Lachey (DT) | .04 | .02 |
| 684 | Bruce Matthews (DT) | .04 | .02 |
| 685 | Mike Munchak (DT) | .04 | .02 |
| 686 | Don Mosebar (DT) | .04 | .02 |
| B1 | Jeff Hostetler (SB) | .15 | .10 |

| | | | |
|---|---|---|---|
| B2 | Matt Bahr (SB) | .04 | .02 |
| B3 | Ottis Anderson (SB) | .08 | .05 |
| B4 | Ottis Anderson (SB) | .08 | .05 |

# 1991 Score Update

This 1991 update set contains 110-cards, mostly rookies and traded players. The card fronts are identical to the Score regular edition except for the blue-green colors along the border. The card backs are horizontal and feature a small head shot, personal data and a brief biography. Card nubmerd carry the "T" designation. All cards measure 2-1/2" by 3-1/2".

| | | MINT | NR/MT |
|---|---|---|---|
| **Complete Set (110)** | | 10.00 | 6.50 |
| **Commons** | | .05 | .02 |
| | | | |
| 1 | Ronnie Lott | .10 | .06 |
| 2 | Matt Millen | .07 | .04 |
| 3 | Tim McKyer | .05 | .02 |
| 4 | Vince Newsome | .05 | .02 |
| 5 | Gaston Green | .20 | .12 |
| 6 | Brett Perriman | .07 | .04 |
| 7 | Roger Craig | .08 | .05 |
| 8 | Pete Holohan | .05 | .02 |
| 9 | Tony Zendejas | .05 | .02 |
| 10 | Lee Williams | .05 | .02 |
| 11 | Mike Stonebreaker | .07 | .04 |
| 12 | Felix Wright | .05 | .02 |
| 13 | Lonnie Young | .05 | .02 |
| 14 | Hugh Millen (R) | .40 | .25 |
| 15 | Roy Green | .07 | .04 |
| 16 | Greg Davis (R) | .08 | .05 |
| 17 | Dexter Manley | .05 | .02 |

| | | | |
|---|---|---|---|
| 18 | Ted Washington (R) | .15 | .10 |
| 19 | Norm Johnson | .05 | .02 |
| 20 | Joe Morris | .07 | .04 |
| 21 | Robert Perryman | .05 | .02 |
| 22 | Mike Iaquaniello (R) | .07 | .04 |
| 23 | Gerald Perry (R) | .10 | .06 |
| 24 | Zeke Mowatt | .05 | .02 |
| 25 | Rich Miano (R) | .10 | .06 |
| 26 | Nick Bell | .50 | .30 |
| 27 | Terry Orr (R) | .20 | .12 |
| 28 | Matt Stover | .07 | .04 |
| 29 | Bubba Paris | .05 | .02 |
| 30 | Ron Brown | .07 | .04 |
| 31 | Don Davey (R) | .08 | .05 |
| 32 | Lee Rouson | .05 | .02 |
| 33 | Terry Hoage | .05 | .02 |
| 34 | Tony Covington (R) | .10 | .06 |
| 35 | John Rienstra | .05 | .02 |
| 36 | Charles Dimry (R) | .10 | .06 |
| 37 | Todd Marinovich | 1.25 | .80 |
| 38 | Winston Moss | .05 | .02 |
| 39 | Vestee Jackson | .05 | .02 |
| 40 | Brian Hansen | .05 | .02 |
| 41 | Irv Eatman | .05 | .02 |
| 42 | Jarrod Bunch | .25 | .15 |
| 43 | Kanavis McGhee (R) | .25 | .15 |
| 44 | Vai Sikahema | .05 | .02 |
| 45 | Charles McRae (R) | .08 | .05 |
| 46 | Quinn Early | .07 | .04 |
| 47 | Jeff Faulkner (R) | .08 | .05 |
| 48 | William Frizzell (R) | .08 | .05 |
| 49 | John Booty | .05 | .02 |
| 50 | Tim Harris | .07 | .04 |
| 51 | Derek Russell | .20 | .12 |
| 52 | John Flannery (R) | .10 | .06 |
| 53 | Tim Barnett (R) | .50 | .30 |
| 54 | Alfred Williams (R) | .30 | .18 |
| 55 | Dan McGwire | .60 | .35 |
| 56 | Ernie Mills | .15 | .10 |
| 57 | Stanley Richard | .10 | .06 |
| 58 | Huey Richardson (R) | .10 | .06 |
| 59 | Jerome Henderson (R) | .15 | .10 |
| 60 | Bryan Cox (R) | .35 | .20 |
| 61 | Russell Maryland | .25 | .15 |
| 62 | Reggie Jones (R) | .12 | .07 |
| 63 | Mo Lewis (R) | .15 | .10 |
| 64 | Moe Gardner | .10 | .06 |
| 65 | Wesley Carroll | .25 | .15 |
| 66 | Michael Jackson (R) | .50 | .30 |
| 67 | Shawn Jefferson (R) | .20 | .12 |
| 68 | Chris Zorich | .08 | .05 |
| 69 | Kenny Walker | .20 | .12 |
| 70 | Erric Pegram (R) | .25 | .15 |
| 71 | Alvin Harper | .50 | .30 |
| 72 | Harry Colon (R) | .10 | .06 |
| 73 | Scott Miller (R) | .07 | .04 |
| 74 | Lawrence Dawsey | .30 | .18 |
| 75 | Phil Hansen (R) | .25 | .15 |
| 76 | Roman Phifer (R) | .12 | .07 |
| 77 | Greg Lewis | .20 | .12 |
| 78 | Merton Hanks (R) | .08 | .05 |
| 79 | James Jones (R) | .10 | .06 |
| 80 | Vinnie Clark | .08 | .05 |
| 81 | R.J. Kors (R) | .08 | .05 |
| 82 | Mike Pritchard | .40 | .25 |
| 83 | Stan Thomas | .07 | .04 |
| 84 | Lamar Rogers (R) | .20 | .12 |
| 85 | Eric Williams (R) | .10 | .06 |
| 86 | Keith Traylor (R) | .12 | .07 |
| 87 | Mike Dumas | .08 | .05 |
| 88 | Mel Agee | .08 | .05 |
| 89 | Harvey Williams | .40 | .25 |
| 90 | Todd Lyght | .20 | .12 |
| 91 | Jake Reed | .08 | .05 |
| 92 | Pat Harlow | .07 | .04 |
| 93 | Antone Davis (R) | .10 | .06 |
| 94 | Aeneas Williams (R) | .20 | .12 |
| 95 | Eric Bieniemy | .25 | .15 |
| 96 | John Kasay (R) | .08 | .05 |
| 97 | Robert Wilson | .15 | .10 |
| 98 | Ricky Ervins | 1.25 | .80 |
| 99 | Mike Croel | .25 | .15 |
| 100 | David Lang (R) | .15 | .10 |
| 101 | Esera Tuaolo (R) | .08 | .05 |
| 102 | Randal Hill | .60 | .35 |
| 103 | Jon Vaughn (R) | .40 | .25 |
| 104 | Dave McCloughan (R) | .08 | .05 |
| 105 | David Daniels | .07 | .04 |
| 106 | Eric Moten | .05 | .02 |
| 107 | Anthony Morgan (R) | .35 | .20 |
| 108 | Ed King | .07 | .04 |
| 109 | Leonard Russell (R) | 1.00 | .70 |
| 110 | Aaron Craver | .15 | .10 |

# 1991 Score Pinnacle

This 415-card set marks Score's first premium football card product. The card fronts feature an action photo and a small head shot against a black background framed by a white border. The player's name and position appear in a small box below the action photograph while the team name is located above the action shot. The vertical card backs contain another action shot set against a black background. The backs also feature the player's personal data, stats and a brief bio.  Key subsets include Rookies, who's cards are distinguished by a green background on the fronts, Gamewinners (GW), Head to Head (HH), Idols (ID), Technicians (TECH) and Sidelines (SL). All cards measure 2-1/2" by 3-/2".

|  |  | MINT | NR/MT |
|---|---|---|---|
| **Complete Set (415)** | | 45.00 | 30.00 |
| **Commons** | | .07 | .04 |
| | | | |
| 1 | Warren Moon | .75 | .45 |
| 2 | Morten Andersen | .10 | .06 |
| 3 | Rohn Stark | .07 | .04 |
| 4 | Mark Bortz | .07 | .04 |
| 5 | Mark Higgs (R) | 1.25 | .80 |
| 6 | Troy Aikman | 3.00 | 1.75 |
| 7 | John Elway | .50 | .30 |
| 8 | Neal Anderson | .25 | .15 |
| 9 | Chris Doleman | .10 | .06 |
| 10 | Jay Schroeder | .12 | .07 |
| 11 | Sterling Sharpe | 1.00 | .70 |
| 12 | Steve DeBerg | .12 | .07 |
| 13 | Ronnie Lott | .25 | .15 |
| 14 | Sean Landeta | .07 | .04 |
| 15 | Jim Everett | .20 | .12 |
| 16 | Jim Breech | .07 | .04 |
| 17 | Barry Foster | 1.75 | 1.00 |
| 18 | Mike Merriweather | .07 | .04 |
| 19 | Eric Metcalf | .12 | .07 |
| 20 | Mark Carrier (Chi) | .20 | .12 |
| 21 | James Brooks | .10 | .06 |
| 22 | Nate Odomes | .07 | .04 |
| 23 | Rodney Hampton | 1.25 | .80 |
| 24 | Chris Miller | .40 | .25 |
| 25 | Roger Craig | .15 | .10 |
| 26 | Louis Oliver | .10 | .06 |
| 27 | Allen Pinkett | .10 | .06 |
| 28 | Bubby Brister | .15 | .10 |
| 29 | Reyna Thompson | .07 | .04 |
| 30 | Issiac Holt | .07 | .04 |
| 31 | Steve Broussard | .20 | .12 |
| 32 | Christian Okoye | .25 | .15 |
| 33 | Dave Meggett | .25 | .15 |
| 34 | Andre Reed | .25 | .15 |
| 35 | Shane Conlan | .12 | .07 |
| 36 | Eric Ball | .07 | .04 |
| 37 | Johnny Bailey | .10 | .06 |
| 38 | Don Majkowski | .15 | .10 |
| 39 | Gerald Williams | .07 | .04 |
| 40 | Kevin Mack | .10 | .06 |
| 41 | Jeff Herrod | .07 | .04 |
| 42 | Emmitt Smith | 7.50 | 4.50 |
| 43 | Wendell Davis | .25 | .15 |
| 44 | Lorenzo White | .25 | .15 |
| 45 | Andre Rison | .50 | .30 |
| 46 | Jerry Gray | .07 | .04 |
| 47 | Dennis Smith | .07 | .04 |
| 48 | Gaston Green | .40 | .25 |
| 49 | Dermontti Dawson | .07 | .04 |
| 50 | Jeff Hostetler | .40 | .25 |
| 51 | Nick Lowery | .10 | .06 |
| 52 | Merril Hoge | .10 | .06 |
| 53 | Bobby Hebert | .25 | .15 |
| 54 | Scott Case | .07 | .04 |
| 55 | Jack Del Rio | .07 | .04 |
| 56 | Cornelius Bennett | .25 | .15 |
| 57 | Tony Mandarich | .07 | .04 |
| 58 | Bill Brooks | .07 | .04 |
| 59 | Jessie Tuggle | .07 | .04 |
| 60 | Hugh Millen (R) | .75 | .45 |
| 61 | Tony Bennett | .12 | .07 |
| 62 | Cris Dishman (R) | .20 | .12 |
| 63 | Darryl Henley (R) | .20 | .12 |
| 64 | Duane Bickett | .07 | .04 |
| 65 | Jay Hilgenberg | .07 | .04 |
| 66 | Joe Montana | 1.25 | .80 |
| 67 | Bill Fralic | .07 | .04 |
| 68 | Sam Mills | .10 | .07 |
| 69 | Bruce Armstrong | .07 | .04 |
| 70 | Dan Marino | 1.25 | .80 |

| | | | |
|---|---|---|---|
| 71 | Jim Lachey | .10 | .06 |
| 72 | Rod Woodson | .15 | .10 |
| 73 | Simon Fletcher | .07 | .04 |
| 74 | Bruce Matthews | .07 | .04 |
| 75 | Howie Long | .10 | .06 |
| 76 | John Friesz | .25 | .15 |
| 77 | Karl Mecklenberg | .10 | .06 |
| 78 | John L. Williams | .10 | .06 |
| 79 | Rob Burnett (R) | .20 | .12 |
| 80 | Anthony Carter | .12 | .07 |
| 81 | Henry Ellard | .12 | .07 |
| 82 | Don Beebe | .15 | .10 |
| 83 | Louis Lipps | .10 | .06 |
| 84 | Greg McMurtry | .15 | .10 |
| 85 | Will Wolford | .07 | .04 |
| 86 | Eric Green | .30 | .18 |
| 87 | Irving Fryar | .10 | .06 |
| 88 | John Offerdahl | .10 | .06 |
| 89 | John Alt | .07 | .04 |
| 90 | Tom Tupa | .12 | .07 |
| 91 | Don Mosebar | .07 | .04 |
| 92 | Jeff George | 1.00 | .70 |
| 93 | Vinny Testaverde | .15 | .10 |
| 94 | Greg Townsend | .10 | .06 |
| 95 | Derrick Fenner | .25 | .15 |
| 96 | Brian Mitchell | .10 | .06 |
| 97 | Herschel Walker | .25 | .15 |
| 98 | Ricky Proehl | .20 | .12 |
| 99 | Mark Clayton | .20 | .12 |
| 100 | Derrick Thomas | .35 | .20 |
| 101 | Jim Harbaugh | .25 | .15 |
| 102 | Barry Word | .40 | .25 |
| 103 | Jerry Rice | 1.25 | .80 |
| 104 | Keith Byars | .10 | .06 |
| 105 | Marion Butts | .15 | .10 |
| 106 | Rich Moran | .07 | .04 |
| 107 | Thurman Thomas | 2.00 | 1.25 |
| 108 | Stephon Paige | .10 | .06 |
| 109 | David Johnson (R) | .15 | .10 |
| 110 | Williams Perry | .10 | .06 |
| 111 | Haywood Jeffires | .50 | .30 |
| 112 | Rodney Peete | .20 | .12 |
| 113 | Andy Heck | .07 | .04 |
| 114 | Kevin Ross | .07 | .04 |
| 115 | Michael Carter | .07 | .04 |
| 116 | Tim McKyer | .07 | .04 |
| 117 | Kenneth Davis | .15 | .10 |
| 118 | Richmond Webb | .10 | .06 |
| 119 | Rich Camarillo | .07 | .04 |
| 120 | James Francis | .12 | .07 |
| 121 | Craig Heyward | .10 | .06 |
| 122 | Hardy Nickerson | .07 | .04 |
| 123 | Michael Brooks | .07 | .04 |
| 124 | Fred Barnett | .50 | .30 |
| 125 | Cris Carter | .35 | .20 |
| 126 | Brian Jordan | .20 | .12 |
| 127 | Pat Leahy | .07 | .04 |
| 128 | Kevin Greene | .07 | .04 |
| 129 | Trace Armstrong | .07 | .04 |
| 130 | Eugene Lockhart | .07 | .04 |
| 131 | Albert Lewis | .07 | .04 |
| 132 | Ernie Jones | .15 | .10 |
| 133 | Eric Martin | .12 | .07 |
| 134 | Anthony Thompson | .20 | .12 |
| 135 | Tim Krumrie | .07 | .04 |
| 136 | James Lofton | .35 | .20 |
| 137 | John Taylor | .50 | .30 |
| 138 | Jeff Cross | .07 | .04 |
| 139 | Tommy Kane | .10 | .06 |
| 140 | Robb Thomas | .10 | .06 |
| 141 | Gary Anderson | .07 | .04 |
| 142 | Mark Murphy | .07 | .04 |
| 143 | Rickey Jackson | .10 | .06 |
| 144 | Ken O'Brien | .15 | .10 |
| 145 | Ernest Givins | .35 | .20 |
| 146 | Jessie Hester | .10 | .06 |
| 147 | Deion Sanders | .75 | .45 |
| 148 | Keith Henderson (R) | .25 | .15 |
| 149 | Chris Singleton | .10 | .06 |
| 150 | Rod Bernstine | .12 | .07 |
| 151 | Quinn Early | .10 | .06 |
| 152 | Boomer Esiason | .25 | .15 |
| 153 | Mike Gann | .07 | .04 |
| 154 | Dino Hackett | .07 | .04 |
| 155 | Perry Kemp | .07 | .04 |
| 156 | Mark Ingram | .10 | .06 |
| 157 | Daryl Johnston | .12 | .07 |
| 158 | Eugene Daniel | .07 | .04 |
| 159 | Dalton Hilliard | .10 | .07 |
| 160 | Rufus Porter | .07 | .04 |
| 161 | Tunch Ilkin | .07 | .04 |
| 162 | James Hasty | .07 | .04 |
| 163 | Keith McKeller | .15 | .10 |
| 164 | Heath Sherman | .12 | .07 |
| 165 | Vai Sikahema | .07 | .04 |
| 166 | Pat Terrell | .10 | .06 |
| 167 | Anthony Munoz | .15 | .10 |
| 168 | Brad Edwards (R) | .15 | .10 |
| 169 | Tom Rathman | .12 | .07 |
| 170 | Steve McMichael | .10 | .06 |
| 171 | Vaughan Johnson | .10 | .06 |
| 172 | Nate Lewis (R) | .25 | .15 |
| 173 | Mark Rypien | .75 | .45 |
| 174 | Rob Moore | .60 | .35 |
| 175 | Tim Green | .07 | .04 |
| 176 | Tony Casillas | .10 | .06 |
| 177 | Jon Hand | .07 | .04 |
| 178 | Todd McNair | .07 | .04 |
| 179 | Toi Cook (R) | .12 | .07 |
| 180 | Eddie Brown | .12 | .07 |
| 181 | Mark Jackson | .10 | .06 |
| 182 | Pete Stoyanovich | .07 | .04 |
| 183 | Bryce Paup (R) | .12 | .07 |
| 184 | Anthony Miler | .25 | .15 |

| # | Player | | |
|---|--------|---|---|
| 185 | Dan Saleaumua | .07 | .04 |
| 186 | Guy McIntyre | .07 | .04 |
| 187 | Broderick Thomas | .20 | .12 |
| 188 | Frank Warren | .07 | .04 |
| 189 | Drew Hill | .15 | .10 |
| 190 | Reggie White | .25 | .15 |
| 191 | Chris Hinton | .07 | .04 |
| 192 | David Little | .07 | .04 |
| 193 | David Fulcher | .07 | .04 |
| 194 | Clarence Verdin | .10 | .06 |
| 195 | Junior Seau | .50 | .30 |
| 196 | Blair Thomas | .70 | .40 |
| 197 | Stan Brock | .07 | .04 |
| 198 | Gary Clark | .30 | .18 |
| 199 | Michael Irvin | 1.00 | .70 |
| 200 | Ronnie Harmon | .12 | .07 |
| 201 | Steve Young | 1.00 | .70 |
| 202 | Brian Noble | .07 | .04 |
| 203 | Dan Stryzinski | .07 | .04 |
| 204 | Darryl Talley | .10 | .06 |
| 205 | David Alexander | .07 | .04 |
| 206 | Pat Swilling | .25 | .15 |
| 207 | Gary Plummer | .07 | .04 |
| 208 | Robert Delpino | .10 | .06 |
| 209 | Norm Johnson | .07 | .04 |
| 210 | Mike Singletary | .25 | .15 |
| 211 | Anthony Johnson | .15 | .10 |
| 212 | Eric Allen | .07 | .04 |
| 213 | Gill Fenerty | .10 | .06 |
| 214 | Neil Smith | .07 | .04 |
| 215 | Joe Phillips | .07 | .04 |
| 216 | Ottis Anderson | .12 | .07 |
| 217 | LeRoy Butler | .07 | .04 |
| 218 | Ray Childress | .10 | .06 |
| 219 | Rodney Holman | .10 | .06 |
| 220 | Kevin Fagan | .07 | .04 |
| 221 | Bruce Smith | .20 | .12 |
| 222 | Brad Muster | .12 | .07 |
| 223 | Mike Horan | .07 | .04 |
| 224 | Steve Atwater | .15 | .10 |
| 225 | Rich Gannon | .30 | .18 |
| 226 | Anthony Pleasant | .07 | .04 |
| 227 | Steve Jordan | .07 | .04 |
| 228 | Lomas Brown | .07 | .04 |
| 229 | Jackie Slater | .10 | .06 |
| 230 | Brad Baxter | .25 | .15 |
| 231 | Joe Morris | .10 | .06 |
| 232 | Marcus Allen | .20 | .12 |
| 233 | Chris Warren | .25 | .15 |
| 234 | Johnny Johnson | .40 | .25 |
| 235 | Phil Simms | .20 | .12 |
| 236 | Dave Krieg | .15 | .10 |
| 237 | Jim McMahon | .15 | .10 |
| 238 | Richard Dent | .10 | .06 |
| 239 | John Washington (R) | .10 | .06 |
| 240 | Sammie Smith | .15 | .10 |
| 241 | Brian Brennan | .07 | .04 |
| 242 | Cortez Kennedy | .50 | .30 |
| 243 | Tim McDonald | .07 | .04 |
| 244 | Charles Haley | .10 | .06 |
| 245 | Joey Browner | .10 | .06 |
| 246 | Eddie Murray | .07 | .04 |
| 247 | Bob Golic | .07 | .04 |
| 248 | Myron Guyton | .07 | .04 |
| 249 | Dennis Byd | .10 | .06 |
| 250 | Barry Sanders | 3.00 | 2.00 |
| 251 | Clay Matthews | .07 | .04 |
| 252 | Pepper Johnson | .10 | .06 |
| 253 | Eric Swann (R) | .30 | .18 |
| 254 | Lamar Lathon | .12 | .07 |
| 255 | Andre Tippett | .10 | .06 |
| 256 | Tom Newberry | .07 | .04 |
| 257 | Kyle Clifton | .07 | .04 |
| 258 | Leslie O'Neal | .12 | .07 |
| 259 | Bubba McDowell | .07 | .04 |
| 260 | Scott Davis | .07 | .04 |
| 261 | Wilber Marshall | .10 | .06 |
| 262 | Marv Cook | .15 | .10 |
| 263 | Jeff Lageman | .10 | .06 |
| 264 | Mike Young | .07 | .04 |
| 265 | Gary Zimmerman | .07 | .04 |
| 266 | Mike Munchak | .07 | .04 |
| 267 | David Treadwell | .07 | .04 |
| 268 | Steve Wisniewski | .07 | .04 |
| 269 | Mark Duper | .12 | .07 |
| 270 | Chris Spielman | .10 | .06 |
| 271 | Brett Perriman | .10 | .06 |
| 272 | Lionel Washington | .07 | .04 |
| 273 | Lawrence Taylor | .45 | .28 |
| 274 | Mark Collins | .10 | .06 |
| 275 | Mark Carrier (TB) | .12 | .07 |
| 276 | Paul Gruber | .07 | .04 |
| 277 | Earnest Byner | .12 | .07 |
| 278 | Andre Collins | .10 | .06 |
| 279 | Reggie Cobb | .35 | .20 |
| 280 | Art Monk | .50 | .30 |
| 281 | Henry Jones | .50 | .30 |
| 282 | Mike Pritchard (R) | 1.25 | .80 |
| 283 | Moe Gardner (R) | .35 | .20 |
| 284 | Chris Zorich (R) | .20 | .12 |
| 285 | Keith Traylor (R) | .25 | .15 |
| 286 | Mike Dumas (R) | .20 | .12 |
| 287 | Ed King (R) | .15 | .10 |
| 288 | Russell Maryland (R) | 1.00 | .70 |
| 289 | Alfred Williams (R) | .30 | .18 |
| 290 | Derek Russell (R) | .50 | .30 |
| 291 | Vinnie Clark (R) | .20 | .12 |
| 292 | Mike Croel (R) | 1.00 | .70 |
| 293 | Todd Marinovich (R) | 2.00 | 1.25 |
| 294 | Phil Hansen (R) | .25 | .15 |
| 295 | Aaron Craver (R) | .25 | .15 |
| 296 | Nick Bell (R) | 1.75 | 1.00 |
| 297 | Kenny Walker (R) | .40 | .25 |
| 298 | Roman Phifer (R) | .25 | .15 |

| 299 | Kanavis McGhee (R) | .40 | .25 |
| 300 | Ricky Ervins (R) | 2.50 | 1.50 |
| 301 | Jim Price (R) | .12 | .07 |
| 302 | John Johnson (R) | .20 | .12 |
| 303 | George Thornton (R) | .12 | .07 |
| 304 | Huey Richardson (R) | .15 | .10 |
| 305 | Harry Colon (R) | .15 | .10 |
| 306 | Antone Davis (R) | .15 | .10 |
| 307 | Todd Lyght (R) | .75 | .45 |
| 308 | Bryan Cox (R) | .80 | .50 |
| 309 | Brad Goebel (R) | .40 | .25 |
| 310 | Eric Moten (R) | .15 | .10 |
| 311 | John Kasay (R) | .10 | .06 |
| 312 | Eseara Tuaolo (R) | .15 | .10 |
| 313 | Bobby Wilson (R) | .20 | .12 |
| 314 | Mo Lewis (R) | .40 | .25 |
| 315 | Harvey Williams (R) | 1.25 | .80 |
| 316 | Mike Stonebreaker (R) | .15 | .10 |
| 317 | Charles McRae (R) | .15 | .10 |
| 318 | John Flannery (R) | .15 | .10 |
| 319 | Ted Washington (R) | .25 | .15 |
| 320 | Stanley Richard (R) | .30 | .18 |
| 321 | Browning Nagle (R) | 3.00 | 2.00 |
| 322 | Ed McCaffery (R) | .70 | .40 |
| 323 | Jeff Graham (R) | .60 | .35 |
| 324 | Stan Thomas (R) | .15 | .10 |
| 325 | Lawrence Dawsey (R) | 1.00 | .70 |
| 326 | Eric Bieniemy (R) | .60 | .35 |
| 327 | Tim Barnett (R) | .75 | .45 |
| 328 | Erric Pegram (R) | .50 | .30 |
| 329 | Lamar Rogers (R) | .30 | .18 |
| 330 | Ernie Mills (R) | .50 | .30 |
| 331 | Pat Harlow (R) | .15 | .10 |
| 332 | Greg Lewis (R) | .35 | .20 |
| 333 | Jarrod Bunch (R) | .60 | .35 |
| 334 | Dan McGwire (R) | 1.00 | .70 |
| 335 | Randal Hill (R) | .80 | .50 |
| 336 | Leonard Russell (R) | 1.50 | .90 |
| 337 | Carnell Lake | .07 | .04 |
| 338 | Brian Blades | .10 | .06 |
| 339 | Darrell Green | .20 | .12 |
| 340 | Bobby Humphrey | .20 | .12 |
| 341 | Mervyn Fernandez | .12 | .07 |
| 342 | Ricky Sanders | .15 | .10 |
| 343 | Keith Jackson | .25 | .15 |
| 344 | Carl Banks | .12 | .07 |
| 345 | Gill Byrd | .10 | .06 |
| 346 | Al Toon | .15 | .10 |
| 347 | Stephen Baker | .10 | .06 |
| 348 | Randall Cunningham | .50 | .30 |
| 349 | Flipper Anderson | .15 | .10 |
| 350 | Jay Novacek | .20 | .12 |
| 351 | Steve Young/Bruce Smith (HH) | .25 | .15 |
| 352 | Barry Sanders/Joey Browner (HH) | .50 | .30 |
| 353 | Joe Montana/Mark Carrier (HH) | .50 | .30 |
| 354 | Thurman Thomas/ Lawrence Taylor (HH) | .50 | .30 |
| 355 | Jerry Rice/Darrell Green (HH) | .50 | .30 |
| 356 | Warren Moon (Tech) | .25 | .15 |
| 357 | Anthony Munoz (Tech) | .12 | .07 |
| 358 | Barry Sanders (Tech) | 1.00 | .70 |
| 359 | Jerry Rice (Tech) | .75 | .45 |
| 360 | Joey Browner (Tech) | .10 | .06 |
| 361 | Morten Andersen (Tech.) | .10 | .06 |
| 362 | Sean Landeta (Tech) | .10 | .06 |
| 363 | Thurman Thomas (GW) | .75 | .45 |
| 364 | Emmitt Smith (GW) | 3.50 | 2.00 |
| 365 | Gaston Green (GW) | .20 | .12 |
| 366 | Barry Sanders (GW) | 1.00 | .70 |
| 367 | Christian Okoye (GW) | .12 | .07 |
| 368 | Earnest Byner (GW) | .10 | .06 |
| 369 | Neal Anderson (GW) | .12 | .07 |
| 370 | Herschel Walker (GW) | .15 | .10 |
| 371 | Rodney Hampton (GW) | .50 | .30 |
| 372 | Darryl Talley/Ted Hendricks (ID) | .10 | .06 |
| 373 | Mark Carrier/Ronnie Lott (ID) | .15 | .10 |
| 374 | Jim Breech/Jan Stenerud (ID) | .10 | .06 |
| 375 | Rodney Hampton/Ottis Anderson (ID) | .50 | .30 |
| 376 | Kevin Mack/Earnest Byner (ID) | .12 | .07 |
| 377 | Steve Jordan/Oscar Robertson (ID) | .20 | .12 |
| 378 | Boomer Esiason/Bert Jones (ID) | .15 | .10 |
| 379 | Steve DeBerg/Roman Gabriel (ID) | .12 | .07 |
| 380 | Al Toon/Wesley Walker (ID) | .10 | .06 |
| 381 | Ronnie Lott IDOL Charley Taylor | .07 | .04 |
| 382 | Henry Ellard/Bob Hayes (ID) | .12 | .07 |
| 383 | Troy Aikman/Roger Staubach | 1.00 | .70 |
| 384 | Thurman Thomas/Earl Campbell (ID) | .75 | .40 |
| 385 | Dan Marino/Terry Bradshaw (ID) | .60 | .35 |
| 386 | Howie Long/Joe Green | .15 | .10 |
| 387 | Franco Harris | .12 | .07 |
| 388 | Esera Tuaolo | .10 | .06 |
| 389 | Super Bowl XXVI | .07 | .04 |
| 390 | Charles Mann | .07 | .04 |

| 391 | Kenny Walker (Trib) | .30 | .18 |
|---|---|---|---|
| 392 | Reggie Roby | .07 | .04 |
| 393 | Bruce Pickens (R) | .40 | .25 |
| 394 | Ray Childress (SL) | .08 | .05 |
| 395 | Karl Mecklenburg (SL) | .08 | .05 |
| 396 | Dean Biasucci (SL) | .07 | .04 |
| 397 | John Alt (SL) | .07 | .04 |
| 398 | Marcus Allen (SL) | .15 | .10 |
| 399 | John Offerdahl (SL) | .08 | .05 |
| 400 | Richard Tardits (SL) | .10 | .06 |
| 401 | Al Toon (SL) | .10 | .06 |
| 402 | Joey Browner (SL) | .08 | .05 |
| 403 | Spencer Tillman (SL) | .12 | .07 |
| 404 | Jay Novacek (SL) | .08 | .05 |
| 405 | Stephen Braggs (SL) | .07 | .04 |
| 406 | Mike Tice (SL) | .12 | .07 |
| 407 | Kevin Greene (SL) | .07 | .04 |
| 408 | Reggie White (SL) | .15 | .10 |
| 409 | Brian Noble (SL) | .07 | .04 |
| 410 | Bart Oates (SL) | .07 | .04 |
| 411 | Art Monk (SL) | .15 | .10 |
| 412 | Ron Wolfley (SL) | .07 | .04 |
| 413 | Louis Lipps (SL) | .08 | .05 |
| 414 | Dante Jones (SL) | .10 | .06 |
| 415 | Kenneth Davis (SL) | .08 | .05 |

# 1992 Score

The cards in this 550-card set feature full colors action photos on the front framed by a small red border and a larger dark blue border. The player's name appears in a small green color bar above the photo. His position is printed across the bottom of the card. The backs contain a small head shot, a biography and stats. Key subsets include Draft Picks (476-514), Crunch Crew (CC), Little Big Men (LB), Sack Attack (SA), the 90-

Yard Club (90) and Hall of Famers (HOF). All cards measure 2-1/2" by 3-12".

|  |  | MINT | NR/MT |
|---|---|---|---|
| **Complete Set (550)** | | 16.00 | 10.50 |
| **Commons** | | .04 | .02 |

| 1 | Barry Sanders | .75 | .45 |
|---|---|---|---|
| 2 | Pat Swilling | .12 | .07 |
| 3 | Moe Gardner | .10 | .06 |
| 4 | Steve Young | .25 | .15 |
| 5 | Chris Spielman | .07 | .04 |
| 6 | Richard Dent | .07 | .04 |
| 7 | Anthony Munoz | .12 | .07 |
| 8 | Martin Mayhew | .04 | .02 |
| 9 | Terry McDaniel | .04 | .02 |
| 10 | Thurman Thomas | .60 | .35 |
| 11 | Ricky Sanders | .08 | .05 |
| 12 | Steve Atwater | .08 | .05 |
| 13 | Tony Tolbert | .04 | .02 |
| 14 | Vince Workman | .08 | .05 |
| 15 | Haywood Jeffires | .20 | .12 |
| 16 | Duane Bickett | .04 | .02 |
| 17 | Jeff Uhlenhake | .04 | .02 |
| 18 | Tim McDonald | .04 | .02 |
| 19 | Cris Carter | .20 | .12 |
| 20 | Derrick Thomas | .20 | .12 |
| 21 | Hugh Millen | .20 | .12 |
| 22 | Bart Oates | .04 | .02 |
| 23 | Eugene Robinson | .04 | .02 |
| 24 | Jerrol Williams | .04 | .02 |
| 25 | Reggie White | .12 | .07 |
| 26 | Marion Butts | .12 | .07 |
| 27 | Jim Sweeney | .04 | .02 |
| 28 | Tom Newberry | .04 | .02 |
| 29 | Pete Stoyanovich | .04 | .02 |
| 30 | Ronnie Lott | .10 | .06 |
| 31 | Simon Fletcher | .04 | .02 |
| 32 | Dino Hackett | .04 | .02 |
| 33 | Morten Andersen | .07 | .04 |
| 34 | Clyde Simmons | .07 | .04 |
| 35 | Mark Rypien | .20 | .12 |
| 36 | Greg Montgomery | .04 | .02 |
| 37 | Nate Lewis | .10 | .06 |
| 38 | Henry Ellard | .08 | .05 |
| 39 | Luis Sharpe | .04 | .02 |
| 40 | Michael Irvin | .30 | .18 |
| 41 | Louis Lipps | .07 | .04 |
| 42 | John L. Williams | .07 | .04 |
| 43 | Broderick Thomas | .12 | .07 |
| 44 | Michael Haynes | .25 | .15 |
| 45 | Don Majkowski | .10 | .06 |
| 46 | William Perry | .07 | .04 |
| 47 | David Fulcher | .04 | .02 |
| 48 | Lorenzo White | .15 | .10 |

| # | Player | | |
|---|--------|-----|-----|
| 49 | Clay Matthews | .04 | .02 |
| 50 | Warren Moon | .20 | .12 |
| 51 | Bruce Armstrong | .04 | .02 |
| 52 | Harry Newsome | .04 | .02 |
| 53 | Bill Brooks | .04 | .02 |
| 54 | Greg Townsend | .07 | .04 |
| 55 | Tom Rathman | .08 | .05 |
| 56 | Sean Landeta | .04 | .02 |
| 57 | Kyle Clifton | .04 | .02 |
| 58 | Steve Broussard | .08 | .05 |
| 59 | Mark Carrier (TB) | .08 | .05 |
| 60 | Mel Gray | .04 | .02 |
| 61 | Tim Krumrie | .04 | .02 |
| 62 | Rufus Porter | .04 | .02 |
| 63 | Kevin Mack | .07 | .04 |
| 64 | Todd Bowles | .04 | .02 |
| 65 | Emmitt Smith | 1.75 | 1.00 |
| 66 | Mike Croel | .20 | .12 |
| 67 | Brian Mitchell | .07 | .04 |
| 68 | Bennie Blades | .07 | .04 |
| 69 | Carnell Lake | .04 | .02 |
| 70 | Cornelius Bennett | .12 | .07 |
| 71 | Darrell Thompson | .08 | .05 |
| 72 | Wes Hopkins | .04 | .02 |
| 73 | Jessie Hester | .04 | .02 |
| 74 | Irv Eatman | .04 | .02 |
| 75 | Marv Cook | .08 | .05 |
| 76 | Tim Brown | .10 | .06 |
| 77 | Pepper Johnson | .04 | .02 |
| 78 | Mark Duper | .08 | .05 |
| 79 | Robert Delpino | .07 | .04 |
| 80 | Charles Mann | .04 | .02 |
| 81 | Brian Jordan | .10 | .06 |
| 82 | Wendell Davis | .10 | .06 |
| 83 | Lee Johnson | .04 | .02 |
| 84 | Ricky Reynolds | .04 | .02 |
| 85 | Vaughan Johnson | .07 | .04 |
| 86 | Brian Blades | .07 | .04 |
| 87 | Sam Seale | .04 | .02 |
| 88 | Ed King | .04 | .02 |
| 89 | Gaston Green | .15 | .10 |
| 90 | Christian Okoye | .15 | .10 |
| 91 | Chris Jacke | .04 | .02 |
| 92 | Rohn Stark | .04 | .02 |
| 93 | Kevin Greene | .04 | .02 |
| 94 | Jay Novacek | .08 | .05 |
| 95 | Chip Lohmiller | .04 | .02 |
| 96 | Cris Dishman | .07 | .04 |
| 97 | Ethan Horton | .07 | .04 |
| 98 | Pat Harlow | .04 | .02 |
| 99 | Mark Ingram | .07 | .04 |
| 100 | Mark Carrier (Chi) | .10 | .06 |
| 101 | Deron Cherry | .04 | .02 |
| 102 | Sam Mills | .07 | .04 |
| 103 | Mark Higgs | .25 | .15 |
| 104 | Keith Jackson | .12 | .07 |
| 105 | Steve Tasker | .04 | .02 |
| 106 | Ken Harvey | .04 | .02 |
| 107 | Bryan Hinkle | .04 | .02 |
| 108 | Anthony Carter | .08 | .05 |
| 109 | Johnny Hector | .07 | .04 |
| 110 | Randall McDaniel | .04 | .02 |
| 111 | Johnny Johnson | .20 | .12 |
| 112 | Shane Conlan | .08 | .05 |
| 113 | Ray Horton | .04 | .02 |
| 114 | Sterling Sharpe | .25 | .15 |
| 115 | Guy McIntyre | .04 | .02 |
| 116 | Tom Waddle | .12 | .07 |
| 117 | Albert Lewis | .04 | .02 |
| 118 | Riki Ellison | .04 | .02 |
| 119 | Chris Doleman | .07 | .04 |
| 120 | Andre Rison | .25 | .15 |
| 121 | Bobby Hebert | .12 | .07 |
| 122 | Dan Owens | .04 | .02 |
| 123 | Rodney Hampton | .35 | .20 |
| 124 | Ron Holmes | .04 | .02 |
| 125 | Ernie Jones | .08 | .05 |
| 126 | Michael Carter | .04 | .02 |
| 127 | Reggie Cobb | .20 | .12 |
| 128 | Esera Tuaolo | .04 | .02 |
| 129 | Wilber Marshall | .07 | .04 |
| 130 | Mike Munchak | .04 | .02 |
| 131 | Cortez Kennedy | .15 | .10 |
| 132 | Lamar Lathon | .07 | .04 |
| 133 | Todd Lyght | .12 | .07 |
| 134 | Jeff Feagles | .04 | .02 |
| 135 | Burt Grossman | .07 | .04 |
| 136 | Mike Cofer | .04 | .02 |
| 137 | Frank Warren | .04 | .02 |
| 138 | Jarvis Williams | .04 | .02 |
| 139 | Eddie Brown | .08 | .05 |
| 140 | John Elliott | .04 | .02 |
| 141 | Jim Everett | .12 | .07 |
| 142 | Hardy Nickerson | .04 | .02 |
| 143 | Eddie Murray | .04 | .02 |
| 144 | Andre Tippett | .07 | .04 |
| 145 | Heath Sherman | .07 | .04 |
| 146 | Ronnie Harmon | .07 | .04 |
| 147 | Eric Metcalf | .10 | .06 |
| 148 | Tony Martin | .04 | .02 |
| 149 | Chris Burkett | .04 | .02 |
| 150 | Andre Waters | .04 | .02 |
| 151 | Ray Donaldson | .04 | .02 |
| 152 | Paul Gruber | .04 | .02 |
| 153 | Chris Singleton | .07 | .04 |
| 154 | Clarence Kay | .04 | .02 |
| 155 | Ernest Givins | .15 | .10 |
| 156 | Eric Hill | .04 | .02 |
| 157 | Jesse Sapolu | .04 | .02 |
| 158 | Jack Del Rio | .04 | .02 |
| 159 | Erric Pegram | .10 | .06 |
| 160 | Joey Browner | .07 | .04 |
| 161 | Marcus Allen | .12 | .07 |
| 162 | Eric Moten | .04 | .02 |

| No. | Name | | |
|---|---|---|---|
| 163 | Donnell Thompson | .04 | .02 |
| 164 | Chuck Cecil | .04 | .02 |
| 165 | Matt Millen | .07 | .04 |
| 166 | Barry Foster | .70 | .40 |
| 167 | Kent Hull | .04 | .02 |
| 168 | Tony Jones | .04 | .02 |
| 169 | Mike Prior | .04 | .02 |
| 170 | Neal Anderson | .12 | .07 |
| 171 | Roger Craig | .08 | .05 |
| 172 | Felix Wright | .04 | .02 |
| 173 | James Francis | .08 | .05 |
| 174 | Eugene Lockhart | .04 | .02 |
| 175 | Dalton Hilliard | .07 | .04 |
| 176 | Nick Lowery | .07 | .04 |
| 177 | Tim McKyer | .04 | .02 |
| 178 | Lorenzo White | .15 | .10 |
| 179 | Jeff Hostetler | .15 | .10 |
| 180 | Jerome Brown | .07 | .04 |
| 181 | Ken Norton | .04 | .02 |
| 182 | Flipper Anderson | .08 | .05 |
| 183 | Don Warren | .04 | .02 |
| 184 | Brad Baxter | .08 | .05 |
| 185 | John Taylor | .15 | .10 |
| 186 | Harold Green | .25 | .15 |
| 187 | James Washington | .04 | .02 |
| 188 | Aaron Craver | .08 | .05 |
| 189 | Mike Merriweather | .04 | .02 |
| 190 | Gary Clark | .15 | .10 |
| 191 | Vince Buck | .04 | .02 |
| 192 | Cleveland Gary | .08 | .05 |
| 193 | Dan Saleaumua | .04 | .02 |
| 194 | Gary Zimmerman | .04 | .02 |
| 195 | Richmond Webb | .04 | .02 |
| 196 | Gary Plummer | .04 | .02 |
| 197 | Willie Green | .15 | .10 |
| 198 | Chris Warren | .10 | .06 |
| 199 | Mike Pritchard | .25 | .15 |
| 200 | Art Monk | .20 | .12 |
| 201 | Matt Stover | .04 | .02 |
| 202 | Tim Grunhard | .04 | .02 |
| 203 | Mervyn Fernandez | .08 | .05 |
| 204 | Mark Jackson | .07 | .04 |
| 205 | Freddie Joe Nunn | .04 | .02 |
| 206 | Stan Thomas | .04 | .02 |
| 207 | Keith McKeller | .08 | .05 |
| 208 | Jeff Lageman | .07 | .04 |
| 209 | Kenny Walker | .10 | .06 |
| 210 | Dave Krieg | .10 | .06 |
| 211 | Dean Biasucci | .04 | .02 |
| 212 | Herman Moore | .25 | .15 |
| 213 | Jon Vaughn | .15 | .10 |
| 214 | Howard Cross | .04 | .02 |
| 215 | Greg Davis | .04 | .02 |
| 216 | Bubby Brister | .10 | .06 |
| 217 | John Kasay | .04 | .02 |
| 218 | Ron Hall | .04 | .02 |
| 219 | Mo Lewis | .07 | .04 |
| 220 | Eric Green | .12 | .07 |
| 221 | Scott Case | .04 | .02 |
| 222 | Sean Jones | .04 | .02 |
| 223 | Winston Moss | .04 | .02 |
| 224 | Reggie Langhorne | .04 | .02 |
| 225 | Greg Lewis | .15 | .10 |
| 226 | Todd McNair | .04 | .02 |
| 227 | Rod Bernstine | .07 | .04 |
| 228 | Joe Jacoby | .04 | .02 |
| 229 | Brad Muster | .08 | .05 |
| 230 | Nick Bell | .30 | .18 |
| 231 | Terry Allen | .50 | .30 |
| 232 | Cliff Odom | .04 | .02 |
| 233 | Brian Hansen | .04 | .02 |
| 234 | William Fuller | .04 | .02 |
| 235 | Issiac Holt | .04 | .02 |
| 236 | Dexter Carter | .08 | .05 |
| 237 | Gene Atkins | .04 | .02 |
| 238 | Pat Beach | .04 | .02 |
| 239 | Tim McGee | .07 | .04 |
| 240 | Dermontti Dawson | .04 | .02 |
| 241 | Dan Fike | .04 | .02 |
| 242 | Don Beebe | .10 | .06 |
| 243 | Jeff Bostic | .04 | .02 |
| 244 | Mark Collins | .07 | .04 |
| 245 | Steve Sewell | .04 | .02 |
| 246 | Steve Walsh | .10 | .06 |
| 247 | Erik Kramer | .20 | .12 |
| 248 | Scott Norwood | .04 | .02 |
| 249 | Jesse Solomon | .04 | .02 |
| 250 | Jerry Ball | .04 | .02 |
| 251 | Eugene Daniel | .04 | .02 |
| 252 | Michael Stewart | .04 | .02 |
| 253 | Fred Barnett | .15 | .10 |
| 254 | Rodney Holman | .04 | .02 |
| 255 | Stephen Baker | .07 | .04 |
| 256 | Don Griffin | .04 | .02 |
| 257 | Will Wolford | .04 | .02 |
| 258 | Perry Kemp | .04 | .02 |
| 259 | Leonard Russell | .35 | .20 |
| 260 | Jeff Gossett | .04 | .02 |
| 261 | Dwayne Harper | .04 | .02 |
| 262 | Vinny Testaverde | .10 | .06 |
| 263 | Maurice Hurst | .04 | .02 |
| 264 | Tony Casillas | .07 | .04 |
| 265 | Louis Oliver | .07 | .04 |
| 266 | Jim Morrissey | .04 | .02 |
| 267 | Kenneth Davis | .08 | .05 |
| 268 | John Alt | .04 | .02 |
| 269 | Michael Zordich (R) | .08 | .05 |
| 270 | Brian Brennan | .04 | .02 |
| 271 | Greg Kragen | .04 | .02 |
| 272 | Andre Collins | .04 | .02 |
| 273 | Dave Meggett | .10 | .06 |
| 274 | Scott Fulhage | .04 | .02 |
| 275 | Tony Zendejas | .04 | .02 |
| 276 | Herschel Walker | .12 | .07 |

| | | | | | | | |
|---|---|---|---|---|---|---|---|
| 277 | Keith Henderson | .08 | .05 | 334 | Ray Berry | .04 | .02 |
| 278 | Johnny Bailey | .07 | .04 | 335 | Dennis Smith | .04 | .02 |
| 279 | Vince Newsome | .04 | .02 | 336 | Jeff Herrod | .04 | .02 |
| 280 | Chris Hinton | .04 | .02 | 337 | Tony Mandarich | .04 | .02 |
| 281 | Robert Blackmon | .04 | .02 | 338 | Matt Bahr | .04 | .02 |
| 282 | James Hasty | .04 | .02 | 339 | Mike Saxon | .04 | .02 |
| 283 | John Offerdahl | .07 | .04 | 340 | Bruce Matthews | .04 | .02 |
| 284 | Wesley Carroll | .20 | .12 | 341 | Rickey Jackson | .07 | .04 |
| 285 | Lomas Brown | .04 | .02 | 342 | Eric Allen | .04 | .02 |
| 286 | Neil O'Donnell | .50 | .30 | 343 | Lonnie Young | .04 | .02 |
| 287 | Kevin Porter | .04 | .02 | 344 | Steve McMichael | .07 | .04 |
| 288 | Lionel Washington | .04 | .02 | 345 | Willie Gault | .07 | .04 |
| 289 | Carlton Bailey (R) | .10 | .06 | 346 | Barry Word | .20 | .12 |
| 290 | Leonard Marshall | .07 | .04 | 347 | Rich Camarillo | .04 | .02 |
| 291 | John Carney | .04 | .02 | 348 | Bill Romanowski | .04 | .02 |
| 292 | Bubba McDowell | .04 | .02 | 349 | Jim Lachey | .07 | .04 |
| 293 | Nate Newton | .04 | .02 | 350 | Jim Ritcher | .04 | .02 |
| 294 | Dave Waymer | .04 | .02 | 351 | Irving Fryar | .07 | .04 |
| 295 | Rob Moore | .20 | .12 | 352 | Gary Anderson | .04 | .02 |
| 296 | Earnest Byner | .08 | .05 | 353 | Henry Rolling | .04 | .02 |
| 297 | Jason Staurovsky | .04 | .02 | 354 | Mark Bortz | .04 | .02 |
| 298 | Keith McCants | .08 | .05 | 355 | Mark Clayton | .15 | .10 |
| 299 | Floyd Turner | .04 | .02 | 356 | Keith Woodside | .07 | .04 |
| 300 | Steve Jordan | .04 | .02 | 357 | Jonathan Hayes | .04 | .02 |
| 301 | Nate Odomes | .04 | .02 | 358 | Derrick Fenner | .08 | .05 |
| 302 | Gerald Riggs | .07 | .04 | 359 | Keith Byars | .07 | .04 |
| 303 | Marvin Washington | .04 | .02 | 360 | Drew Hill | .08 | .05 |
| 304 | Anthony Thompson | .08 | .05 | 361 | Harris Barton | .04 | .02 |
| 305 | Steve DeBerg | .10 | .06 | 362 | John Kidd | .04 | .02 |
| 306 | Jim Harbaugh | .12 | .07 | 363 | Aeneas Williams | .07 | .04 |
| 307 | Larry Brown | .04 | .02 | 364 | Brian Washington | .04 | .02 |
| 308 | Roger Ruzek | .04 | .02 | 365 | John Stephens | .08 | .05 |
| 309 | Jessie Tuggle | .04 | .02 | 366 | Norm Johnson | .04 | .02 |
| 310 | Al Smith | .04 | .02 | 367 | Darryl Henley | .04 | .02 |
| 311 | Mark Kelso | .04 | .02 | 368 | William White | .04 | .02 |
| 312 | Lawrence Dawsey | .20 | .12 | 369 | Mark Murphy | .04 | .02 |
| 313 | Steve Bono | .35 | .20 | 370 | Myron Guyton | .04 | .02 |
| 314 | Greg Lloyd | .04 | .02 | 371 | Leon Seals | .04 | .02 |
| 315 | Steve Wisniewski | .04 | .02 | 372 | Rich Gannon | .20 | .12 |
| 316 | Gill Fenerty | .04 | .02 | 373 | Toi Cook | .04 | .02 |
| 317 | Mark Stepnoski | .04 | .02 | 374 | Anthony Johnson | .04 | .02 |
| 318 | Derek Russell | .12 | .07 | 375 | Rod Woodson | .10 | .06 |
| 319 | Chris Martin | .04 | .02 | 376 | Alexander Wright | .08 | .05 |
| 320 | Shaun Gayle | .04 | .02 | 377 | Kevin Butler | .04 | .02 |
| 321 | Bob Golic | .04 | .02 | 378 | Neil Smith | .04 | .02 |
| 322 | Larry Kelm | .04 | .02 | 379 | Gary Anderson | .04 | .02 |
| 323 | Mike Brim (R) | .08 | .05 | 380 | Reggie Roby | .04 | .02 |
| 324 | Tommy Kane | .07 | .04 | 381 | Jeff Bryant | .04 | .02 |
| 325 | Mark Schlereth (R) | .08 | .05 | 382 | Ray Crockett | .04 | .02 |
| 326 | Ray Childress | .07 | .04 | 383 | Richard Johnson | .04 | .02 |
| 327 | Richard Brown | .04 | .02 | 384 | Hassan Jones | .07 | .04 |
| 328 | Vincent Brown | .04 | .02 | 385 | Karl Mecklenburg | .07 | .04 |
| 329 | Mike Farr | .04 | .02 | 386 | Jeff Jaeger | .04 | .02 |
| 330 | Eric Swann | .08 | .05 | 387 | Keith Willis | .04 | .02 |
| 331 | Bill Fralic | .04 | .02 | 388 | Phil Simms | .10 | .06 |
| 332 | Rodney Peete | .15 | .10 | 389 | Kevin Ross | .04 | .02 |
| 333 | Jerry Gray | .04 | .02 | 390 | Chris Miller | .20 | .12 |

| | | | |
|---|---|---|---|
| 391 | Brian Noble | .04 | .02 |
| 392 | Jamie Dukes (R) | .08 | .05 |
| 393 | George Jamison | .04 | .02 |
| 394 | Rickey Dixon | .04 | .02 |
| 395 | Carl Lee | .04 | .02 |
| 396 | Jon Hand | .04 | .02 |
| 397 | Kirby Jackson | .04 | .02 |
| 398 | Pat Terrell | .04 | .02 |
| 399 | Howie Long | .07 | .04 |
| 400 | Mike Young | .04 | .02 |
| 401 | Keith Sims | .04 | .02 |
| 402 | Tommy Barnhardt | .04 | .02 |
| 403 | Greg McMurtry | .08 | .05 |
| 404 | Keith Van Horne | .04 | .02 |
| 405 | Seth Joyner | .07 | .04 |
| 406 | Jim Jeffcoat | .04 | .02 |
| 407 | Courtney Hall | .04 | .02 |
| 408 | Tony Covington | .04 | .02 |
| 409 | Jacob Green | .04 | .02 |
| 410 | Charles Haley | .07 | .04 |
| 411 | Darryl Talley | .07 | .04 |
| 412 | Jeff Cross | .04 | .02 |
| 413 | John Elway | .20 | .12 |
| 414 | Donald Evans | .04 | .02 |
| 415 | Jackie Slater | .07 | .04 |
| 416 | John Friesz | .10 | .06 |
| 417 | Anthony Smith | .04 | .02 |
| 418 | Gill Byrd | .04 | .02 |
| 419 | Willie Drewrey | .04 | .02 |
| 420 | Jay Hilgenberg | .04 | .02 |
| 421 | David Treadwell | .04 | .02 |
| 422 | Curtis Duncan | .07 | .04 |
| 423 | Sammie Smith | .08 | .05 |
| 424 | Henry Thomas | .04 | .02 |
| 425 | James Lofton | .15 | .10 |
| 426 | Fred Marion | .04 | .02 |
| 427 | Bryce Paup | .04 | .02 |
| 428 | Eric Andolsek | .04 | .02 |
| 429 | Reyna Thompson | .04 | .02 |
| 430 | Mike Kenn | .04 | .02 |
| 431 | Bill Maas | .04 | .02 |
| 432 | Quinn Early | .04 | .02 |
| 433 | Everson Walls | .04 | .02 |
| 434 | Jimmie Jones | .04 | .02 |
| 435 | Dwight Stone | .04 | .02 |
| 436 | Harry Colon | .04 | .02 |
| 437 | Don Mosebar | .04 | .02 |
| 438 | Calvin Williams | .10 | .06 |
| 439 | Tom Tupa | .08 | .05 |
| 440 | Darrell Green | .12 | .07 |
| 441 | Eric Thomas | .04 | .02 |
| 442 | Terry Wooden | .04 | .02 |
| 443 | Brett Perriman | .04 | .02 |
| 444 | Todd Marinovich | .50 | .30 |
| 445 | Jim Breech | .04 | .02 |
| 446 | Eddie Anderson | .04 | .02 |
| 447 | Jay Schroeder | .10 | .06 |
| 448 | William Roberts | .04 | .02 |
| 449 | Brad Edwards | .04 | .02 |
| 450 | Tunch Ilkin | .04 | .02 |
| 451 | Joe Ivy | .04 | .02 |
| 452 | Robert Clark | .07 | .04 |
| 453 | Tim Barnett | .15 | .10 |
| 454 | Jarrod Bunch | .12 | .07 |
| 455 | Tim Harris | .04 | .02 |
| 456 | James Brooks | .07 | .04 |
| 457 | Trace Armstrong | .04 | .02 |
| 458 | Michael Brooks | .04 | .02 |
| 459 | Andy Heck | .04 | .02 |
| 460 | Greg Jackson | .04 | .02 |
| 461 | Vance Johnson | .08 | .05 |
| 462 | Kirk Lowdermilk | .04 | .02 |
| 463 | Erik McMillan | .04 | .02 |
| 464 | Scott Mersereau | .04 | .02 |
| 465 | Jeff Wright | .04 | .02 |
| 466 | Mike Tomczak | .08 | .05 |
| 467 | David Alexander | .04 | .02 |
| 468 | Bryan Millard | .04 | .02 |
| 469 | John Randle | .04 | .02 |
| 470 | Joel Hilgenberg | .04 | .02 |
| 471 | Bennie Thompson | .07 | .04 |
| 472 | Freeman McNeil | .07 | .04 |
| 473 | Terry Orr | .10 | .06 |
| 474 | Mike Horan | .04 | .02 |
| 475 | Leroy Hoard | .08 | .05 |
| 476 | Patrick Rowe (R) | .25 | .15 |
| 477 | Siran Stacy (R) | .25 | .15 |
| 478 | Amp Lee (R) | .75 | .45 |
| 479 | Eddie Blake (R) | .12 | .07 |
| 480 | Joe Bowden (R) | .10 | .06 |
| 481 | Roderick Milstead (R) | .08 | .05 |
| 482 | Keith Hamilton (R) | .15 | .10 |
| 483 | Darryl Williams (R) | .20 | .12 |
| 484 | Robert Porcher (R) | .15 | .10 |
| 485 | Ed Cunningham (R) | .08 | .05 |
| 486 | Chris Mims (R) | .30 | .18 |
| 487 | Chris Hakel (R) | .20 | .12 |
| 488 | Jimmy Smith (R) | .15 | .10 |
| 489 | Todd Harrison (R) | .12 | .07 |
| 490 | Edgar Bennett (R) | .40 | .25 |
| 491 | Dexter McNabb (R) | .15 | .10 |
| 492 | Leon Searcy (R) | .10 | .06 |
| 493 | Tommy Vardell (R) | .75 | .45 |
| 494 | Terrell Buckley (R) | .60 | .35 |
| 495 | Kevin Turner (R) | .15 | .10 |
| 496 | Russ Campbell (R) | .08 | .05 |
| 497 | Torrance Small (R) | .12 | .07 |
| 498 | Nate Turner (R) | .10 | .06 |
| 499 | Cornelius Benton (R) | .12 | .07 |
| 500 | Matt Elliott (R) | .07 | .04 |
| 501 | Robert Stewart (R) | .08 | .05 |
| 502 | M. Shamsid-Deen (R) | .07 | .04 |
| 503 | George Williams (R) | .08 | .05 |
| 504 | Pumpy Tudors (R) | .07 | .04 |

| | | | |
|---|---|---|---|
| 505 | Matt LaBounty (R) | .08 | .05 |
| 506 | Darryl Hardy (R) | .10 | .06 |
| 507 | Derrick Moore (R) | .10 | .06 |
| 508 | Willie Clay (R) | .12 | .07 |
| 509 | Bob Whitfield (R) | .10 | .06 |
| 510 | Ricardo McDonald (R) | .12 | .07 |
| 511 | Carlos Huerta (R) | .07 | .04 |
| 512 | Selwyn Jones (R) | .10 | .06 |
| 513 | Steve Gordon (R) | .08 | .05 |
| 514 | Bob Meeks (R) | .07 | .04 |
| 515 | Bennie Blades (CC) | .04 | .02 |
| 516 | Andre Waters (CC) | .04 | .02 |
| 517 | Bubba McDowell (CC) | .04 | .02 |
| 518 | Kevin Porter (CC) | .04 | .02 |
| 519 | Carnell Lake (CC) | .04 | .02 |
| 520 | Leonard Russell (ROY) | .25 | .15 |
| 521 | Mike Croel (ROY) | .15 | .10 |
| 522 | Lawrence Dawsey (ROY) | .15 | .10 |
| 523 | Moe Gardner (ROY) | .08 | .05 |
| 524 | Steve Broussard (LB) | .07 | .04 |
| 525 | Dave Meggett (LB) | .10 | .06 |
| 526 | Darrell Green (LB) | .10 | .06 |
| 527 | Tony Jones (LB) | .04 | .02 |
| 528 | Barry Sanders (LB) | .40 | .25 |
| 529 | Pat Swilling (SA) | .08 | .05 |
| 530 | Reggie White (SA) | .08 | .05 |
| 531 | William Fuller (SA) | .04 | .02 |
| 532 | Simon Fletcher (SA) | .04 | .02 |
| 533 | Derrick Thomas (SA) | .10 | .06 |
| 534 | Mark Rypien (Man of Year) | .12 | .07 |
| 535 | John Mackey (HOF) | .10 | .06 |
| 536 | John Riggins (HOF) | .12 | .07 |
| 537 | Lem Barney (HOF) | .08 | .05 |
| 538 | Shawn McCarthy (90) | .08 | .05 |
| 539 | Al Edwards (90) | .04 | .02 |
| 540 | Alexander Wright (90) | .07 | .04 |
| 541 | Ray Crockett (90) | .04 | .02 |
| 542 | Steve Young (90) | .15 | .10 |
| 543 | Nate Lewis (90) | .07 | .04 |
| 544 | Dexter Carter (90) | .07 | .04 |
| 545 | Reggie Rutland (90) | .04 | .02 |
| 546 | Jon Vaughn (90) | .10 | .06 |
| 547 | Chris Martin (90) | .04 | .02 |
| 548 | Warren Moon (HL) | .15 | .10 |
| 549 | Super Bowl Logo | .04 | .02 |
| 550 | Robb Thomas | .07 | .04 |

# 1992 Score Dream Team

This marks the first time Score issued Dream Team cards as a limited insert. The cards were distributed randomly in Score foil paqcks. The horizontal card fronts feature two images, a close up head shot alongside an action photo. Card backs consist of another photo and brief highlights. Cards measure 3-1/2" by 2-1/2".

| | | MINT | NR/MT |
|---|---|---|---|
| Complete Set (25) | | 52.00 | 36.00 |
| Commons | | 1.25 | .80 |
| 1 | Michael Irvin | 7.50 | 4.50 |
| 2 | Haywood Jeffires | 2.75 | 1.60 |
| 3 | Emmitt Smith | 28.00 | 18.00 |
| 4 | Barry Sanders | 15.00 | 9.00 |
| 5 | Marv Cook | 1.75 | 1.00 |
| 6 | Bart Oates | 1.25 | .80 |
| 7 | Steve Wisniewski | 1.25 | .80 |
| 8 | Randall McDaniel | 1.25 | .80 |
| 9 | Jim Lachey | 1.75 | 1.00 |
| 10 | Lomas Brown | 1.25 | .80 |
| 11 | Reggie White | 2.50 | 1.40 |
| 12 | Clyde Simmons | 1.25 | .80 |
| 13 | Derrick Thomas | 3.50 | 2.00 |
| 14 | Seth Joyner | 1.25 | .80 |
| 15 | Darryl Talley | 1.25 | .80 |
| 16 | Karl Mecklenburg | 1.25 | .80 |
| 17 | Sam Mills | 1.25 | .80 |
| 18 | Darrell Green | 1.75 | 1.00 |
| 19 | Steve Atwater | 1.25 | .80 |
| 20 | Mark Carrier | 1.25 | .80 |
| 21 | Jeff Gossett | 1.25 | .80 |
| 22 | Chip Lohmiller | 1.25 | .80 |
| 23 | Mel Gray | 1.25 | .80 |

| | | MINT | NR/MT |
|---|---|---|---|
| 24 | Steve Tasker | 1.25 | .80 |
| 25 | Mark Rypien | 3.00 | 1.75 |

# 1992 Score Pinnacle

For the second straight year Score produced a premium football set. The 360-card Pinnacle set features full color action photographs on the front with the player's name printed in a color bar below the photo. A team name is located in the border under the players name. Card backs are highlighted by a smaller photo along with a brief bio and stats. Key subsets include Rookies (R), Sidelines (SL), Game Winners (GW), Hall of Famers (HOF) and Idols (ID). All cards measure 2-1/2" by 3-1/2".

| | | MINT | NR/MT |
|---|---|---|---|
| **Complete Set (360)** | | 30.00 | 20.00 |
| **Commons** | | .08 | .05 |
| | | | |
| 1 | Reggie White | .20 | .12 |
| 2 | Eric Green | .15 | .10 |
| 3 | Craig Heyward | .10 | .06 |
| 4 | Phil Simms | .10 | .06 |
| 5 | Pepper Johnson | .08 | .05 |
| 6 | Sean Landeta | .08 | .05 |
| 7 | Dino Hackett | .08 | .05 |
| 8 | Andre Ware | .25 | .15 |
| 9 | Ricky Nattiel | .10 | .06 |
| 10 | Jim Price | .08 | .05 |
| 11 | Jim Ritcher | .08 | .05 |
| 12 | Kelly Stouffer | .12 | .07 |
| 13 | Ray Crockett | .08 | .05 |
| 14 | Steve Tasker | .08 | .05 |
| 15 | Barry Sanders | 2.00 | 1.25 |
| 16 | Pat Swilling | .20 | .12 |
| 17 | Moe Gardner | .12 | .07 |
| 18 | Steve Young | .50 | .30 |
| 19 | Chris Spielman | .10 | .06 |
| 20 | Richard Dent | .10 | .06 |
| 21 | Anthony Munoz | .15 | .10 |
| 22 | Thurman Thomas | 1.50 | .90 |
| 23 | Ricky Sanders | .10 | .06 |
| 24 | Steve Atwater | .15 | .10 |
| 25 | Tony Tolbert | .08 | .05 |
| 26 | Haywood Jeffires | .25 | .15 |
| 27 | Duane Bickett | .08 | .05 |
| 28 | Tim McDonald | .08 | .05 |
| 29 | Cris Carter | .25 | .15 |
| 30 | Derrick Thomas | .25 | .15 |
| 31 | Hugh Millen | .25 | .15 |
| 32 | Bart Oates | .08 | .05 |
| 33 | Darryl Talley | .10 | .06 |
| 34 | Marion Butts | .15 | .10 |
| 35 | Pete Stoyanovich | .08 | .05 |
| 36 | Ronnie Lott | .10 | .06 |
| 37 | Simon Fletcher | .08 | .05 |
| 38 | Morten Andersen | .10 | .06 |
| 39 | Clyde Simmons | .10 | .06 |
| 40 | Mark Rypien | .25 | .15 |
| 41 | Henry Ellard | .10 | .06 |
| 42 | Michael Irvin | .75 | .45 |
| 43 | Louis Lipps | .08 | .05 |
| 44 | John L. Williams | .10 | .06 |
| 45 | Broderick Thomas | .12 | .07 |
| 46 | Don Majkowski | .15 | .10 |
| 47 | William Perry | .10 | .06 |
| 48 | David Fulcher | .08 | .05 |
| 49 | Tony Bennett | .15 | .10 |
| 50 | Clay Matthews | .08 | .05 |
| 51 | Warren Moon | .20 | .12 |
| 52 | Bruce Armstrong | .08 | .05 |
| 53 | Bill Brooks | .08 | .05 |
| 54 | Greg Townsend | .10 | .06 |
| 55 | Steve Broussard | .12 | .07 |
| 56 | Mel Gray | .08 | .05 |
| 57 | Kevin Mack | .10 | .06 |
| 58 | Emmitt Smith | 4.50 | 2.75 |
| 59 | Mike Croel | .15 | .10 |
| 60 | Brian Mitchell | .10 | .06 |
| 61 | Bennie Blades | .10 | .06 |
| 62 | Carnell Lake | .08 | .05 |
| 63 | Cornelius Bennett | .12 | .07 |
| 64 | Darrell Thompson | .10 | .06 |
| 65 | Jessie Hester | .10 | .06 |
| 66 | Marv Cook | .10 | .06 |
| 67 | Tim Brown | .12 | .07 |
| 68 | Mark Duper | .10 | .06 |
| 69 | Robert Delpino | .10 | .06 |
| 70 | Eric Martin | .10 | .06 |
| 71 | Wendell Davis | .12 | .07 |
| 72 | Vaughan Johnson | .10 | .06 |

| | | | |
|---|---|---|---|
| 73 | Brian Blades | .10 | .06 |
| 74 | Ed King | .08 | .05 |
| 75 | Gaston Green | .15 | .10 |
| 76 | Christian Okoye | .15 | .10 |
| 77 | Rohn Stark | .08 | .05 |
| 78 | Kevin Greene | .08 | .05 |
| 79 | Jay Novacek | .20 | .12 |
| 80 | Chip Lohmiller | .08 | .05 |
| 81 | Cris Dishman | .10 | .06 |
| 82 | Ethan Horton | .10 | .06 |
| 83 | Pat Harlow | .08 | .05 |
| 84 | Mark Ingram | .10 | .06 |
| 85 | Mark Carrier | .10 | .06 |
| 86 | Sam Mills | .10 | .06 |
| 87 | Mark Higgs | .25 | .15 |
| 88 | Keith Jackson | .20 | .12 |
| 89 | Gary Anderson | .08 | .05 |
| 90 | Ken Harvey | .08 | .05 |
| 91 | Anthony Carter | .10 | .06 |
| 92 | Randall McDaniel | .08 | .05 |
| 93 | Johnny Johnson | .20 | .12 |
| 94 | Shane Conlan | .10 | .06 |
| 95 | Sterling Sharpe | .25 | .15 |
| 96 | Guy McIntyre | .08 | .05 |
| 97 | Albert Lewis | .08 | .05 |
| 98 | Chris Doleman | .10 | .06 |
| 99 | Andre Rison | .25 | .15 |
| 100 | Bobby Hebert | .12 | .07 |
| 101 | Dan Owens | .08 | .05 |
| 102 | Rodney Hampton | .30 | .18 |
| 103 | Ernie Jones | .10 | .06 |
| 104 | Reggie Cobb | .20 | .12 |
| 105 | Wilber Marshall | .10 | .06 |
| 106 | Mike Munchak | .08 | .05 |
| 107 | Cortez Kennedy | .20 | .12 |
| 108 | Todd Lyght | .15 | .10 |
| 109 | Burt Grossman | .10 | .06 |
| 110 | Ferrell Edmunds | .08 | .05 |
| 111 | Jim Everett | .15 | .10 |
| 112 | Hardy Nickerson | .08 | .05 |
| 113 | Andre Tippett | .10 | .06 |
| 114 | Ronnie Harmon | .10 | .06 |
| 115 | Andre Waters | .08 | .05 |
| 116 | Ernest Givins | .15 | .10 |
| 117 | Eric Hill | .08 | .05 |
| 118 | Erric Pegram | .12 | .07 |
| 119 | Jarrod Bunch | .20 | .12 |
| 120 | Marcus Allen | .15 | .10 |
| 121 | Barry Foster | 1.50 | .90 |
| 122 | Kent Hull | .08 | .05 |
| 123 | Neal Anderson | .15 | .10 |
| 124 | Stephen Braggs | .08 | .05 |
| 125 | Nick Lowery | .10 | .06 |
| 126 | Jeff Hostetler | .20 | .12 |
| 127 | Michael Carter | .08 | .05 |
| 128 | Don Warren | .08 | .05 |
| 129 | Brad Baxter | .12 | .07 |
| 130 | John Taylor | .15 | .10 |
| 131 | Harold Green | .25 | .15 |
| 132 | Mike Merriweather | .08 | .05 |
| 133 | Gary Clark | .20 | .12 |
| 134 | Vince Buck | .08 | .05 |
| 135 | Dan Saleaumua | .08 | .05 |
| 136 | Gary Zimmerman | .08 | .05 |
| 137 | Richmond Webb | .10 | .06 |
| 138 | Art Monk | .25 | .15 |
| 139 | Mervyn Fernandez | .10 | .06 |
| 140 | Mark Jackson | .10 | .06 |
| 141 | Freddie Joe Nunn | .08 | .05 |
| 142 | Jeff Lageman | .10 | .06 |
| 143 | Kenny Walker | .12 | .07 |
| 144 | Mark Carrier | .10 | .06 |
| 145 | Jon Vaughn | .20 | .12 |
| 146 | Greg Davis | .10 | .06 |
| 147 | Bubby Brister | .12 | .07 |
| 148 | Mo Lewis | .12 | .07 |
| 149 | Howie Long | .10 | .06 |
| 150 | Rod Bernstine | .10 | .06 |
| 151 | Nick Bell | .50 | .30 |
| 152 | Terry Allen | .90 | .60 |
| 153 | William Fuller | .08 | .05 |
| 154 | Dexter Carter | .12 | .07 |
| 155 | Gene Atkins | .08 | .05 |
| 156 | Don Beebe | .15 | .10 |
| 157 | Mark Collins | .10 | .06 |
| 158 | Jerry Ball | .10 | .06 |
| 159 | Fred Barnett | .25 | .15 |
| 160 | Rodney Holman | .08 | .05 |
| 161 | Stephen Baker | .10 | .06 |
| 162 | Jeff Graham | .20 | .12 |
| 163 | Leonard Russell | .60 | .35 |
| 164 | Jeff Gossett | .08 | .05 |
| 165 | Vinny Testaverde | .12 | .07 |
| 166 | Maurice Hurst | .08 | .05 |
| 167 | Louis Oliver | .10 | .06 |
| 168 | Jim Morrissey | .08 | .05 |
| 169 | Greg Kragen | .08 | .05 |
| 170 | Andre Collins | .10 | .06 |
| 171 | Dave Meggett | .15 | .10 |
| 172 | Keith Henderson | .12 | .07 |
| 173 | Vince Newsome | .08 | .05 |
| 174 | Chris Hinton | .08 | .05 |
| 175 | James Hasty | .08 | .05 |
| 176 | John Offerdahl | .10 | .06 |
| 177 | Lomas Brown | .08 | .05 |
| 178 | Neil O'Donnell | .60 | .35 |
| 179 | Leonard Marshall | .10 | .06 |
| 180 | Bubba McDowell | .08 | .05 |
| 181 | Herman Moore | .40 | .25 |
| 182 | Rob Moore | .25 | .15 |
| 183 | Earnest Byner | .10 | .06 |
| 184 | Keith McCants | .12 | .07 |
| 185 | Floyd Turner | .08 | .05 |
| 186 | Steve Jordan | .08 | .05 |

| 187 | Nate Odomes | .08 | .05 |
|---|---|---|---|
| 188 | Jeff Herrod | .08 | .05 |
| 189 | Jim Harbaugh | .15 | .10 |
| 190 | Jessie Tuggle | .08 | .05 |
| 191 | Al Smith | .08 | .05 |
| 192 | Lawrence Dawsey | .25 | .15 |
| 193 | Steve Bono | .80 | .50 |
| 194 | Greg Lloyd | .08 | .05 |
| 195 | Steve Wisniewski | .08 | .05 |
| 196 | Larry Kelm | .08 | .05 |
| 197 | Tommy Kane | .10 | .06 |
| 198 | Mark Schlereth | .10 | ..06 |
| 199 | Ray Childress | .10 | .06 |
| 200 | Vincent Brown | .08 | .05 |
| 201 | Rodney Peete | .15 | .10 |
| 202 | Dennis Smith | .08 | .05 |
| 203 | Bruce Matthews | .08 | .05 |
| 204 | Rickey Jackson | .10 | .06 |
| 205 | Eric Allen | .08 | .05 |
| 206 | Rich Camarillo | .08 | .05 |
| 207 | Jim Lachey | .10 | .06 |
| 208 | Kevin Ross | .08 | .05 |
| 209 | Irving Fryer | .10 | .06 |
| 210 | Mark Clayton | .15 | .10 |
| 211 | Keith Byars | .10 | .06 |
| 212 | John Elway | .25 | .15 |
| 213 | Harris Barton | .08 | .05 |
| 214 | Aeneas Williams | .10 | .06 |
| 215 | Rich Gannon | .20 | .12 |
| 216 | Toi Cook | .08 | .05 |
| 217 | Rod Woodson | .12 | .07 |
| 218 | Gary Anderson | .08 | .05 |
| 219 | Reggie Roby | .08 | .05 |
| 220 | Karl Mecklenburg | .10 | .06 |
| 221 | Rufus Porter | .08 | .05 |
| 222 | Jon Hand | .08 | .05 |
| 223 | Tim Barnett | .25 | .15 |
| 224 | Eric Swann | .12 | .07 |
| 225 | Eugene Robinson | .10 | .06 |
| 226 | Mike Young | .08 | .05 |
| 227 | Frank Warren | .08 | .05 |
| 228 | Mike Kenn | .08 | .05 |
| 229 | Tim Green | .08 | .05 |
| 230 | Barry Word | .20 | .12 |
| 231 | Mike Pritchard | .35 | .20 |
| 232 | John Kasay | .08 | .05 |
| 233 | Derek Russell | .15 | .10 |
| 234 | Jim Breech | .08 | .05 |
| 235 | Pierce Holt | .08 | .05 |
| 236 | Tim Krumrie | .08 | .05 |
| 237 | William Roberts | .08 | .05 |
| 238 | Erik Kramer | .20 | .12 |
| 239 | Brett Perriman | .10 | .06 |
| 240 | Reyna Thompson | .08 | .05 |
| 241 | Chris Miller | .25 | .15 |
| 242 | Drew Hill | .10 | .06 |
| 243 | Curtis Duncan | .10 | .06 |
| 244 | Seth Joyner | .10 | .06 |
| 245 | Ken Norton | .08 | .05 |
| 246 | Calvin Williams | .12 | .07 |
| 247 | James Joseph | .12 | .07 |
| 248 | Bennie Thompson (R) | .12 | .07 |
| 249 | Tunch Ilkin | .08 | .05 |
| 250 | Brad Edward | .08 | .05 |
| 251 | Jeff Jaeger | .08 | .05 |
| 252 | Gill Byrd | .10 | .06 |
| 253 | Jeff Feagles | .08 | .05 |
| 254 | Jamie Dukes (R) | .12 | .07 |
| 255 | Greg McMurtry | .15 | .10 |
| 256 | Anthony Johnson | .10 | .06 |
| 257 | Lamar Lathon | .10 | .06 |
| 258 | John Roper | .08 | .05 |
| 259 | Lorenzo White | .20 | .12 |
| 260 | Brian Noble | .08 | .05 |
| 261 | Chris Singleton | .10 | .06 |
| 262 | Todd Marinovich | .70 | .50 |
| 263 | Jay Hilgenberg | .08 | .05 |
| 264 | Kyle Clifton | .08 | .05 |
| 265 | Tony Casillas | .10 | .06 |
| 266 | James Francis | .12 | .07 |
| 267 | Eddie Anderson | .08 | .05 |
| 268 | Tim Harris | .08 | .05 |
| 269 | James Lofton | .15 | .10 |
| 270 | Jay Schroeder | .12 | .07 |
| 271 | Ed West | .08 | .05 |
| 272 | Don Mosebar | .08 | .05 |
| 273 | Jackie Slater | .10 | .06 |
| 274 | Fred McAfee | .20 | .12 |
| 275 | Steve Sewell | .08 | .05 |
| 276 | Charles Mann | .08 | .05 |
| 277 | Ron Hall | .08 | .05 |
| 278 | Darrell Green | .20 | .12 |
| 279 | Jeff Cross | .08 | .05 |
| 280 | Jeff Wright | .08 | .05 |
| 281 | Issiac Holt | .08 | .05 |
| 282 | Dermontti Dawson | .08 | .05 |
| 283 | Michael Haynes | .30 | .18 |
| 284 | Tony Mandarich | .08 | .05 |
| 285 | Leroy Hoard | .12 | .07 |
| 286 | Darryl Henley | .08 | .05 |
| 287 | Tim McGee | .10 | .06 |
| 288 | Willie Gault | .10 | .06 |
| 289 | Dalton Hilliard | .10 | .06 |
| 290 | Tim McKyer | .08 | .05 |
| 291 | Tom Waddle | .12 | .07 |
| 292 | Eric Thomas | .08 | .05 |
| 293 | Herschel Walker | .15 | .10 |
| 294 | Donnell Woolford | .08 | .05 |
| 295 | James Brooks | .10 | .06 |
| 296 | Brad Muster | .12 | .07 |
| 297 | Brent Jones | .10 | .06 |
| 298 | Erik Howard | .08 | .05 |
| 299 | Alvin Harper | .70 | .40 |
| 300 | Joey Browner | .10 | .06 |

| | | | |
|---|---|---|---|
| 301 | Jack Del Rio | .08 | .05 |
| 302 | Cleveland Gary | .10 | .06 |
| 303 | Brett Favre | 2.50 | 1.50 |
| 304 | Freeman McNeil | .10 | .06 |
| 305 | Willie Green | .20 | .12 |
| 306 | Percy Snow | .10 | .06 |
| 307 | Neil Smith | .08 | .05 |
| 308 | Eric Bieniemy | .12 | .07 |
| 309 | Keith Traylor | .10 | .06 |
| 310 | Ernie Mills | .15 | .10 |
| 311 | Will Wolford | .08 | .05 |
| 312 | Robert Young | .08 | .05 |
| 313 | Anthony Smith | .08 | .05 |
| 314 | Robert Porcher (R) | .20 | .12 |
| 315 | Leon Searcy (R) | .12 | .07 |
| 316 | Amp Lee (R) | 1.00 | .70 |
| 317 | Siran Stacy (R) | .35 | .20 |
| 318 | Patrick Rowe (R) | .30 | .18 |
| 319 | Chris Mims (R) | .30 | .18 |
| 320 | Matt Elliott (R) | .10 | .06 |
| 321 | Ricardo McDonald (R) | .12 | .07 |
| 322 | Keith Hamilton (R) | .15 | .10 |
| 323 | Edgar Bennett (R) | .60 | .35 |
| 324 | Chris Hakel (R) | .30 | .18 |
| 325 | Dexter McNabb (R) | .20 | .12 |
| 326 | Roderick Milstead (R) | .12 | .07 |
| 327 | Joe Bowden (R) | .15 | .10 |
| 328 | Brian Bollinger (R) | .15 | .10 |
| 329 | Darryl Williams (R) | .30 | .18 |
| 330 | Tommy Vardell (R) | 1.00 | .70 |
| 331 | Glenn Parker (SL) | .08 | .05 |
| 331 | Mitch Frerotte (SL) | .08 | .05 |
| 332 | Herschel Walker (R) | .10 | .06 |
| 333 | Mike Cofer (SL) | .08 | .05 |
| 334 | Mark Rypien (SL) | .15 | .10 |
| 335 | Andre Rison (SL) | .15 | .10 |
| 336 | Henry Ellard (GW) | .08 | .05 |
| 337 | Rob Moore (GW) | .12 | .07 |
| 338 | Fred Barnett (GW) | .12 | .07 |
| 339 | Mark Clayton (GW) | .12 | .07 |
| 340 | Eric Martin (GW) | .08 | .05 |
| 341 | Irving Fryar (GW) | .08 | .05 |
| 342 | Tim Brown (GW) | .10 | .06 |
| 343 | Sterling Sharpe (GW) | .25 | .15 |
| 344 | Gary Clark (GW) | .10 | .06 |
| 345 | John Mackey (HOF) | .15 | .10 |
| 346 | Lem Barney (HOF) | .10 | .06 |
| 347 | John Riggins (HOF) | .15 | .10 |
| 348 | Marion Butts (ID) | .10 | .06 |
| 349 | Jeff Lageman (ID) | .08 | .05 |
| 350 | Eric Green (ID) | .10 | .06 |
| 352 | Marv Cook (ID) | .08 | .05 |
| 353 | John Elway (ID) | .25 | .15 |
| 354 | Steve Tasker (ID) | .08 | .05 |
| 355 | Nick Lowery (ID) | .08 | .05 |
| 356 | Mark Clayton (ID) | .12 | .07 |
| 357 | Warren Moon (ID) | .12 | .07 |

| | | | |
|---|---|---|---|
| 358 | Eric Metcalf | .15 | .10 |
| 359 | Charles Haley | .10 | .06 |
| 360 | Terrell Buckley (R) | 1.25 | .80 |

# 1992 Score Pinnacle Team 2000

This limited inserts were issued in Score Jumbo Packs and feature players who are projected to become superstars over the next decade. Cards consist of action photos with a Pinnacle Team 2000 logo. All cards measure 2-1/2" by 3-1/2".

| | | MINT | NR/MT |
|---|---|---|---|
| Complete Set (30) | | 12.50 | 8.50 |
| Commons | | .25 | .15 |
| | | | |
| 1 | Todd Marinovich | 1.25 | .80 |
| 2 | Rodney Hampton | 1.25 | .80 |
| 3 | Mike Croel | .30 | .18 |
| 4 | Leonard Russell | .80 | .50 |
| 5 | Herman Moore | .75 | .45 |
| 6 | Rob Moore | .40 | .25 |
| 7 | Jon Vaughn | .30 | .18 |
| 8 | Lamar Lathon | .25 | .15 |
| 9 | Ed King | .25 | .15 |
| 10 | Moe Gardner | .25 | .15 |
| 11 | Barry Foster | 2.00 | 1.25 |
| 12 | Eric Green | .50 | .30 |
| 13 | Kenny Walker | .30 | .18 |
| 14 | Tim Barnett | .40 | .25 |
| 15 | Derrick Thomas | .75 | .45 |
| 16 | Steve Atwater | .25 | .15 |
| 17 | Nick Bell | .50 | .30 |
| 18 | John Friesz | .30 | .18 |
| 19 | Emmitt Smith | 7.50 | 4.50 |
| 20 | Eric Swann | .30 | .18 |
| 21 | Barry Sanders | 3.50 | 2.00 |
| 22 | Mark Carrier | .30 | .18 |
| 23 | Brett Favre | 2.50 | 1.50 |
| 24 | James Francis | .30 | .18 |
| 25 | Lawrence Dawsey | .35 | .20 |
| 26 | Keith McCants | .30 | .18 |
| 27 | Broderick Thomas | .30 | .18 |
| 28 | Mike Pritchard | .80 | .50 |
| 29 | Bruce Pickens | .30 | .18 |
| 30 | Todd Lyght | .30 | .18 |

# 1992 Score Team Pinnacle

These limited inserts were issued randomly in Pinnacle foil packs. Cards feature dual action photos with a Team Pinnacle logo. ALl cards measure 2-1/2" by 3-1/2".

| | | MINT | NR/MT |
|---|---|---|---|
| | Complete Set (13) | 175.00 | 100.00 |
| | Commons | 8.00 | 5.00 |
| | | | |
| 1 | Mark Rypien<br>Ronnie Lott | 14.00 | 10.00 |
| 2 | Barry Sanders<br>Derrick Thomas | 36.00 | 22.00 |
| 3 | Thurman Thomas<br>Pat Swilling | 28.00 | 18.00 |
| 4 | Eric Green<br>Steve Atwater | 10.00 | 6.00 |
| 5 | Haywood Jeffires<br>Darrell Green | 20.00 | 12.00 |
| 6 | Michael Irvin<br>Eric Allen | 24.00 | 16.00 |
| 7 | Bruce Matthews<br>Jerry Ball | 8.00 | 5.00 |
| 8 | Steve Wisniewski<br>Pepper Johnson | 8.00 | 5.00 |
| 9 | Karl Mecklenburg<br>Wiliams Roberts | 8.00 | 5.00 |
| 10 | Jim Lachey<br>William Fuller | 8.00 | 5.00 |
| 11 | Anthony Munoz<br>Reggie White | 12.00 | 7.00 |
| 12 | Mel Gray<br>Steve Tasker | 8.00 | 5.00 |
| 13 | Jeff Jaeger<br>Jeff Gossett | 8.00 | 5.00 |

# 1993 Score

The 1993 Score set contains 440 cards which feature full color game action photoes on the front an personal data, stats and highlights on the card backs. Key subsets include Double Trouble (DT), The 90+ Club (90+) and Highlights (HL). Two limited insert sets were produced (Dream Team) and (Franchise). Those cards were randomly distributed in Score packs. All cards measure 2-1/2" by 3-1/2".

| | | MINT | NR/MT |
|---|---|---|---|
| | Complete Set (440) | 20.00 | 12.50 |
| | Commons | .05 | .02 |
| | | | |
| 1 | Barry Sanders | .75 | .40 |
| 2 | Moe Gardner | .05 | .02 |
| 3 | Ricky Watters | .60 | .35 |
| 4 | Todd Lyght | .07 | .04 |
| 5 | Rodney Hampton | .25 | .15 |
| 6 | Curtis Duncan | .07 | .04 |
| 7 | Barry Word | .15 | .10 |
| 8 | Reggie Cobb | .20 | .12 |
| 9 | Mike Kenn | .05 | .02 |
| 10 | Michael Irvin | .35 | .20 |
| 11 | Bryan Cox | .07 | .04 |
| 12 | Chris Doleman | .07 | .04 |
| 13 | Rod Woodson | .08 | .05 |
| 14 | Emmitt Smith | 1.50 | .90 |
| 15 | Pete Stoyanovich | .05 | .02 |
| 16 | Steve Young | .40 | .25 |
| 17 | Randall McDaniel | .05 | .02 |
| 18 | Cortez Kennedy | .15 | .10 |
| 19 | Mel Gray | .05 | .02 |
| 20 | Barry Foster | .60 | .35 |
| 21 | Tim Brown | .12 | .07 |
| 22 | Todd McNair | .05 | .02 |
| 23 | Anthony Johnson | .07 | .04 |
| 24 | Nate Odomes | .05 | .02 |

| | | | | |
|---|---|---|---|---|
| 25 Brett Favre | .80 | .50 | 82 Greg Kragen | .05 | .02 |
| 26 Jack Del Rio | .05 | .02 | 83 Ricky Reynolds | .05 | .02 |
| 27 Terry McDaniel | .05 | .02 | 84 Hardy Nickerson | .05 | .02 |
| 28 Haywood Jeffires | .20 | .12 | 85 Brian Mitchell | .10 | .06 |
| 29 Jay Novacek | .12 | .07 | 86 Rufus Porter | .05 | .02 |
| 30 Wilber Marshall | .05 | .02 | 87 Greg Jackson | .05 | .02 |
| 31 Richmond Webb | .07 | .04 | 88 Seth Joyner | .07 | .04 |
| 32 Steve Atwater | .07 | .04 | 89 Tim Grunhard | .05 | .02 |
| 33 James Lofton | .15 | .10 | 90 Tim Harris | .05 | .02 |
| 34 Harold Green | .25 | .15 | 91 Sterling Sharpe | .30 | .18 |
| 35 Eric Metcalf | .15 | .10 | 92 Daniel Stubbs | .05 | .02 |
| 36 Bruce Matthews | .05 | .02 | 93 Rob Burnett | .08 | .05 |
| 37 Albert Lewis | .05 | .02 | 94 Rich Camarillo | .05 | .02 |
| 38 Jeff Herrod | .05 | .02 | 95 Al Smith | .07 | .04 |
| 39 Vince Workman | .05 | .02 | 96 Thurman Thomas | .35 | .20 |
| 40 John Elway | .20 | .12 | 97 Morten Andersen | .07 | .04 |
| 41 Brett Perriman | .07 | .04 | 98 Reggie White | .12 | .07 |
| 42 Jon Vaughn | .10 | .06 | 99 Gill Byrd | .05 | .02 |
| 43 Terry Allen | .40 | .25 | 100 Pierce Holt | .05 | .02 |
| 44 Clyde Simmons | .07 | .04 | 101 Tim McGee | .08 | .05 |
| 45 Benny Thompson | .05 | .02 | 102 Rickey Jackson | .07 | .04 |
| 46 Wendell Davis | .10 | .06 | 103 Vince Newsome | .05 | .02 |
| 47 Bobby Hebert | .12 | .07 | 104 Chris Spielman | .05 | .02 |
| 48 John Offerdahl | .07 | .04 | 105 Tim McDonald | .05 | .02 |
| 49 Jeff Graham | .10 | .06 | 106 James Francis | .07 | .04 |
| 50 Steve Wisniewski | .05 | .02 | 107 Andre Tippett | .07 | .04 |
| 51 Louis Oliver | .07 | .04 | 108 Sam Mills | .07 | .04 |
| 52 Rohn Stark | .05 | .02 | 109 Hugh Millen | .12 | .07 |
| 53 Cleveland Gary | .10 | .06 | 110 Brad Baxter | .08 | .05 |
| 54 John Randle | .05 | .02 | 111 Ricky Sanders | .10 | .06 |
| 55 Jim Everett | .12 | .07 | 112 Marion Butts | .12 | .07 |
| 56 Donnell Woolford | .05 | .02 | 113 Fred Barnett | .20 | .12 |
| 57 Pepper Johnson | .05 | .02 | 114 Wade Wilson | .12 | .07 |
| 58 Irving Fryar | .08 | .05 | 115 Dave Meggett | .12 | .07 |
| 59 Greg Townsend | .05 | .02 | 116 Kevin Greene | .05 | .02 |
| 60 Chris Burkett | .05 | .02 | 117 Reggie Langhorne | .05 | .02 |
| 61 Johnny Johnson | .12 | .07 | 118 Simon Fletcher | .05 | .02 |
| 62 Ronnie Harmon | .15 | .10 | 119 Tommy Vardell | .30 | .18 |
| 63 Don Griffin | .05 | .02 | 120 Darion Conner | .05 | .02 |
| 64 Wayne Martin | .07 | .04 | 121 Darren Lewis | .12 | .07 |
| 65 John L. Williams | .08 | .05 | 122 Charles Mann | .05 | .02 |
| 66 Brad Edwards | .05 | .02 | 123 David Fulcher | .05 | .02 |
| 67 Toi Cook | .05 | .02 | 124 Tommy Kane | .08 | .05 |
| 68 Lawrence Dawsey | .15 | .10 | 125 Richard Brown | .05 | .02 |
| 69 Johnny Bailey | .08 | .05 | 126 Nate Lewis | .10 | .06 |
| 70 Mike Brim | .05 | .02 | 127 Tony Tolbert | .05 | .02 |
| 71 Andre Rison | .20 | .12 | 128 Greg Lloyd | .05 | .02 |
| 72 Cornelius Bennett | .08 | .05 | 129 Herman Moore | .20 | .12 |
| 73 Brad Muster | .08 | .05 | 130 Robert Massey | .05 | .02 |
| 74 Broderick Thomas | .07 | .04 | 131 Chris Jacke | .05 | .02 |
| 75 Tom Waddle | .12 | .07 | 132 Keith Byars | .08 | .05 |
| 76 Paul Gruber | .05 | .02 | 133 William Fuller | .05 | .02 |
| 77 Jackie Harris | .05 | .02 | 134 Rob Moore | .12 | .07 |
| 78 Kenneth Davis | .10 | .06 | 135 Duane Bickett | .05 | .02 |
| 79 Norm Johnson | .05 | .02 | 136 Jarrod Bunch | .10 | .06 |
| 80 Jim Jeffcoat | .05 | .02 | 137 Ethan Horton | .07 | .04 |
| 81 Chris Warren | .15 | .10 | 138 Leonard Russell | .20 | .12 |

| | | | |
|---|---|---|---|
| 139 | Darryl Henley | .05 | .02 |
| 140 | Tony Bennett | .07 | .04 |
| 141 | Harry Newsome | .05 | .02 |
| 142 | Kelvin Martin | .08 | .05 |
| 143 | Audrey McMillian | .05 | .02 |
| 144 | Chip Lohmiller | .05 | .02 |
| 145 | Henry Jones | .05 | .02 |
| 146 | Rod Bernstine | .12 | .07 |
| 147 | Darryl Talley | .07 | .04 |
| 148 | Clarence Verdin | .07 | .04 |
| 149 | Derrick Thomas | .15 | .10 |
| 150 | Raleigh McKenzie | .05 | .02 |
| 151 | Phil Hansen | .05 | .02 |
| 152 | Lin Elliott | .05 | .02 |
| 153 | Chip Banks | .05 | .02 |
| 154 | Shannon Sharpe | .05 | .02 |
| 155 | David Williams | .05 | .02 |
| 156 | Gaston Green | .12 | .07 |
| 157 | Trace Armstrong | .05 | .02 |
| 158 | Todd Scott | .05 | .02 |
| 159 | Stan Humphries | .40 | .25 |
| 160 | Christian Okoye | .12 | .07 |
| 161 | Dennis Smith | .05 | .02 |
| 162 | Derek Kennard | .05 | .02 |
| 163 | Melvin Jenkins | .05 | .02 |
| 164 | Tommy Barnhardt | .05 | .02 |
| 165 | Eugene Robinson | .05 | .02 |
| 166 | Tom Rathman | .08 | .05 |
| 167 | Chris Chandler | .12 | .07 |
| 168 | Steve Broussard | .10 | .06 |
| 169 | Wymon Henderson | .05 | .02 |
| 170 | Bryce Paup | .05 | .02 |
| 171 | Kent Hull | .05 | .02 |
| 172 | Willie Davis | .05 | .02 |
| 173 | Richard Dent | .07 | .04 |
| 174 | Rodney Peete | .12 | .07 |
| 175 | Clay Matthews | .05 | .02 |
| 176 | Erik Williams | .05 | .02 |
| 177 | Mike Cofer | .05 | .02 |
| 178 | Mark Kelso | .05 | .02 |
| 179 | Kurt Gouveia | .05 | .02 |
| 180 | Keith McCants | .07 | .04 |
| 181 | Jim Arnold | .05 | .02 |
| 182 | Sean Jones | .05 | .02 |
| 183 | Chuck Cecil | .05 | .02 |
| 184 | Mark Rypien | .15 | .10 |
| 185 | William Perry | .07 | .04 |
| 186 | Mark Jackson | .07 | .04 |
| 187 | Jim Dombrowski | .05 | .02 |
| 188 | Heath Sherman | .08 | .05 |
| 189 | Bubba McDowell | .05 | .02 |
| 190 | Fuad Reveiz | .05 | .02 |
| 191 | Darren Perry | .05 | .02 |
| 192 | Karl Mecklenburg | .07 | .04 |
| 193 | Frank Reich | .12 | .07 |
| 194 | Tony Casillas | .07 | .04 |
| 195 | Jerry Ball | .05 | .02 |
| 196 | Jessie Hester | .07 | .04 |
| 197 | David Lang | .05 | .02 |
| 198 | Sean Landeta | .05 | .02 |
| 199 | Jerry Grey | .05 | .02 |
| 200 | Mark Higgs | .20 | .12 |
| 201 | Bruce Armstrong | .05 | .02 |
| 202 | Vaughn Johnson | .07 | .04 |
| 203 | Calvin Williams | .08 | .05 |
| 204 | Leonard Marshall | .07 | .04 |
| 205 | Mike Munchak | .07 | .04 |
| 206 | Kevin Ross | .05 | .02 |
| 207 | Daryl Johnston | .10 | .06 |
| 208 | Jay Schroeder | .10 | .06 |
| 209 | Mo Lewis | .05 | .02 |
| 210 | Carlton Hasselrig | .05 | .02 |
| 211 | Cris Carter | .15 | .10 |
| 212 | Marv Cook | .08 | .05 |
| 213 | Mark Duper | .10 | .06 |
| 214 | Jackie Slater | .05 | .02 |
| 215 | Mike Prior | .05 | .02 |
| 216 | Warren Moon | .20 | .12 |
| 217 | Mike Saxon | .05 | .02 |
| 218 | Derrick Fenner | .12 | .07 |
| 219 | Brian Washington | .05 | .02 |
| 220 | Jessie Tuggle | .05 | .02 |
| 221 | Jeff Hostetler | .15 | .10 |
| 222 | Deion Sanders | .25 | .15 |
| 223 | Neal Anderson | .10 | .06 |
| 224 | Kevin Mack | .08 | .05 |
| 225 | Tommy Maddox | .75 | .40 |
| 226 | Neil Smith | .07 | .04 |
| 227 | Ronnie Lott | .12 | .07 |
| 228 | Willie Anderson | .10 | .06 |
| 229 | Keith Jackson | .15 | .10 |
| 230 | Pat Swilling | .10 | .06 |
| 231 | Carl Banks | .07 | .04 |
| 232 | Eric Allen | .05 | .02 |
| 233 | Randal Hill | .20 | .12 |
| 234 | Burt Grossman | .07 | .04 |
| 235 | Jerry Rice | .35 | .20 |
| 236 | Santana Dotson | .20 | .12 |
| 237 | Andre Reed | .15 | .10 |
| 238 | Troy Aikman | .75 | .40 |
| 239 | Ray Childress | .08 | .05 |
| 240 | Phil Simms | .12 | .07 |
| 241 | Steve McMichael | .07 | .04 |
| 242 | Browning Nagle | .40 | .25 |
| 243 | Anthony Miller | .20 | .12 |
| 244 | Earnest Byner | .08 | .05 |
| 245 | Jay Hilgenberg | .05 | .02 |
| 246 | Jeff George | .20 | .12 |
| 247 | Marco Coleman | .20 | .12 |
| 248 | Mark Carrier (Chi) | .07 | .04 |
| 249 | Howie Long | .07 | .04 |
| 250 | Ed McCaffrey | .10 | .06 |
| 251 | Jim Kelly | .60 | .35 |
| 252 | Henry Ellard | .10 | .06 |

| | | | |
|---|---|---|---|
| 253 Joe Montana | .50 | .30 |
| 254 Dale Carter | .30 | .18 |
| 255 Boomer Esiason | .12 | .07 |
| 256 Gary Clark | .15 | .10 |
| 257 Carl Pickens | .35 | .20 |
| 258 Dave Krieg | .08 | .05 |
| 259 Russell Maryland | .15 | .10 |
| 260 Randall Cunningham | .20 | .12 |
| 261 Leslie O'Neal | .08 | .05 |
| 262 Vinny Testaverde | .10 | .06 |
| 263 Ricky Ervins | .25 | .15 |
| 264 Chris Mims | .20 | .12 |
| 265 Dan Marino | .60 | .35 |
| 266 Eric Martin | .07 | .04 |
| 267 Bruce Smith | .10 | .06 |
| 268 Jim Harbaugh | .12 | .07 |
| 269 Steve Emtman | .60 | .35 |
| 270 Ricky Proehl | .12 | .07 |
| 271 Vaughn Dunbar | .35 | .20 |
| 272 Junior Seau | .15 | .10 |
| 273 Sean Gilbert | .20 | .12 |
| 274 Jim Lachey | .08 | .05 |
| 275 Dalton Hilliard | .08 | .05 |
| 276 David Klingler | 1.25 | .70 |
| 277 Robert Jones | .20 | .12 |
| 278 David Treadwell | .05 | .02 |
| 279 Tracy Scroggins | .05 | .02 |
| 280 Terrell Buckley | .35 | .20 |
| 281 Quentin Coryatt | .50 | .30 |
| 282 Jason Hanson | .05 | .02 |
| 283 Shane Conlan | .07 | .04 |
| 284 Guy McIntyre | .05 | .02 |
| 285 Gary Zimmerman | .05 | .02 |
| 286 Marty Carter | .05 | .02 |
| 287 Jim Sweeney | .05 | .02 |
| 288 Arthur Marshall | .05 | .02 |
| 289 Eugene Chung | .05 | .02 |
| 290 Mike Pritchard | .20 | .12 |
| 291 Jim Ritcher | .05 | .02 |
| 292 Todd Marinovich | .30 | .18 |
| 293 Courtney Hall | .05 | .02 |
| 294 Mark Collins | .08 | .05 |
| 295 Troy Auzenne | .07 | .04 |
| 296 Aeneas Williams | .10 | .06 |
| 297 Andy Heck | .05 | .02 |
| 298 Shaun Gayle | .05 | .02 |
| 299 Kevin Fagan | .05 | .02 |
| 300 Carnell Lake | .05 | .02 |
| 301 Bernie Kosar | .12 | .07 |
| 302 Maurice Hurst | .05 | .02 |
| 303 Mike Merriweather | .05 | .02 |
| 304 Reggie Roby | .05 | .02 |
| 305 Darryl Williams | .05 | .02 |
| 306 Jerome Bettis (R) | .50 | .30 |
| 307 Curtis Conway (R) | .60 | .35 |
| 308 Drew Bledsoe (R) | 2.50 | 1.50 |
| 309 John Copeland (R) | .25 | .15 |
| 310 Eric Curry (R) | .25 | .15 |
| 311 Lincoln Kennedy (R) | .20 | .12 |
| 312 Dan Williams (R) | .20 | .12 |
| 313 Patrick Bates (R) | .20 | .12 |
| 314 Tom Carter (R) | .20 | .12 |
| 315 Garrison Hearst (R) | 1.75 | 1.00 |
| 316 Joel Hilgenberg | .05 | .02 |
| 317 Harris Barton | .05 | .02 |
| 318 Jeff Lageman | .07 | .04 |
| 319 Charles Mincy | .05 | .02 |
| 320 Ricardo McDonald | .05 | .02 |
| 321 Lorenzo White | .15 | .10 |
| 322 Troy Vincent | .10 | .06 |
| 323 Bennie Blades | .07 | .04 |
| 324 Dana Hall | .05 | .02 |
| 325 Ken Norton | .07 | .04 |
| 326 Will Wolford | .05 | .02 |
| 327 Neil O'Donnell | .40 | .25 |
| 328 Tracy Simien | .05 | .02 |
| 329 Darrell Green | .10 | .06 |
| 330 Kyle Clifton | .05 | .02 |
| 331 Elbert Shelley | .05 | .02 |
| 332 Jeff Wright | .05 | .02 |
| 333 Mike Johnson | .05 | .02 |
| 334 John Gesek | .05 | .02 |
| 335 Michael Brooks | .05 | .02 |
| 336 George Jamison | .05 | .02 |
| 337 Johnny Holland | .05 | .02 |
| 338 Lamar Lathon | .07 | .04 |
| 339 Bern Brostek | .05 | .02 |
| 340 Steve Jordan | .08 | .05 |
| 341 Gene Atkins | .05 | .02 |
| 342 Aaron Wallace | .05 | .02 |
| 343 Adrian Cooper | .07 | .04 |
| 344 Amp Lee | .50 | .30 |
| 345 Vincent Brown | .05 | .02 |
| 346 James Hasty | .05 | .02 |
| 347 Ron Hall | .05 | .02 |
| 348 Matt Elliott | .05 | .02 |
| 349 Tim Krumrie | .05 | .02 |
| 350 Mark Stepnoski | .05 | .02 |
| 351 Matt Stover | .05 | .02 |
| 352 James Washington | .05 | .02 |
| 353 Marc Spindler | .05 | .02 |
| 354 Frank Warren | .05 | .02 |
| 355 Vai Sikahema | .05 | .02 |
| 356 Dan Saleaumua | .05 | .02 |
| 357 Mark Clayton | .12 | .07 |
| 358 Brent Jones | .07 | .04 |
| 359 Andy Harmon | .05 | .02 |
| 360 Anthony Parker | .05 | .02 |
| 361 Chris Hinton | .05 | .02 |
| 362 Greg Montgomery | .05 | .02 |
| 363 Greg McMurtry | .12 | .07 |
| 364 Craig Heyward | .08 | .05 |
| 365 David Johnson | .05 | .02 |
| 366 Bill Romanowski | .05 | .02 |

| 367 | Steve Christie | .05 | .02 |
|---|---|---|---|
| 368 | Art Monk | .15 | .10 |
| 369 | Howard Ballard | .05 | .02 |
| 370 | Andre Collins | .07 | .04 |
| 371 | Alvin Harper | .30 | .18 |
| 372 | Blaise Winter | .05 | .02 |
| 373 | Al Del Greco | .05 | .02 |
| 374 | Eric Green | .08 | .05 |
| 375 | Chris Mohr | .05 | .02 |
| 376 | Tom Newberry | .05 | .02 |
| 377 | Chris Dishman | .05 | .02 |
| 378 | James Geathers | .05 | .02 |
| 379 | Don Mosebar | .05 | .02 |
| 380 | Andre Ware | .15 | .10 |
| 381 | Marvin Washington | .05 | .02 |
| 382 | Bobby Humphrey | .08 | .05 |
| 383 | Marc Logan | .05 | .02 |
| 384 | Lomas Brown | .05 | .02 |
| 385 | Steve Tasker | .05 | .02 |
| 386 | Chris Miller | .15 | .10 |
| 387 | Tony Paige | .05 | .02 |
| 388 | Charles Haley | .08 | .05 |
| 389 | Rich Moran | .05 | .02 |
| 390 | Mike Sherrard | .10 | .06 |
| 391 | Nick Lowery | .07 | .04 |
| 392 | Henry Thomas | .05 | .02 |
| 393 | Keith Sims | .05 | .02 |
| 394 | Thomas Everett | .05 | .02 |
| 395 | Steve Wallace | .05 | .02 |
| 396 | John Carney | .05 | .02 |
| 397 | Tim Johnson | .05 | .02 |
| 398 | Jeff Gossett | .05 | .02 |
| 399 | Anthony Smith | .05 | .02 |
| 400 | Kelvin Pritchett | .12 | .07 |
| 401 | Dermontti Dawson | .05 | .02 |
| 402 | Alfred Williams | .05 | .02 |
| 403 | Michael Haynes | .25 | .15 |
| 404 | Bart Oates | .05 | .02 |
| 405 | Ken Lanier | .05 | .02 |
| 406 | Vencie Glenn | .05 | .02 |
| 407 | John Taylor | .15 | .10 |
| 408 | Nate Newton | .05 | .02 |
| 409 | Mark Carrier | .08 | .05 |
| 410 | Ken Harvey | .05 | .02 |
| 411 | Troy Aikman (HL) | .75 | .40 |
| 412 | Charles Haley (HL) | .07 | .04 |
| 413 | Moon/Jeffires (DT) | .20 | .12 |
| 414 | Jones/Kelso (DT) | .07 | .04 |
| 415 | Jackson/Mills (DT) | .07 | .04 |
| 416 | Simmons/White (DT) | .08 | .05 |
| 417 | Dale Carter (ROY) | .10 | .06 |
| 418 | Carl Pickens (ROY) | .15 | .10 |
| 419 | Vaughn Dunbar(ROY) | .15 | .10 |
| 420 | Santana Dotson (ROY) | .10 | .06 |
| 421 | Steve Emtman (90+) | .25 | .15 |
| 422 | Louis Oliver (90+) | .07 | .04 |
| 423 | Carl Pickens (90+) | .15 | .10 |

| 424 | Eddie Anderson (90+) | .07 | .04 |
|---|---|---|---|
| 425 | Deion Sanders (90+) | .12 | .07 |
| 426 | Jon Vaughn (90+) | .08 | .05 |
| 427 | Darren Lewis (90+) | .08 | .05 |
| 428 | Kevin Ross (90+) | .07 | .04 |
| 429 | David Brandon (90+) | .07 | .04 |
| 430 | Dave Meggett (90+) | .08 | .05 |
| 431 | Jerry Rice (HL) | .20 | .12 |
| 432 | Sterling Sharpe (HL) | .20 | .12 |
| 433 | Art Monk (HL) | .12 | .07 |
| 434 | James Lofton (HL) | .10 | .06 |
| 435 | Lawrence Taylor | .15 | .10 |
| 436 | Bill Walsh (HOF) | .07 | .04 |
| 437 | Chuck Noll (HOF) | .07 | .04 |
| 438 | Dan Fouts (HOF) | .12 | .07 |
| 439 | Larry Little (HOF) | .07 | .04 |
| 440 | Steve Young (MOY) | .12 | .07 |

# 1993 Score
# Dream Team

The cards in this 26-card insert set were randomly distributed in Score foil packs. The set features the top players by position. All cards measure 2-1/2" by 3-1/2".

| | | MINT | NR/MT |
|---|---|---|---|
| **Complete Set (26)** | | 60.00 | 38.00 |
| **Commons** | | 1.25 | .70 |
| 1 | Steve Young | 4.00 | 2.75 |
| 2 | Emmitt Smith | 25.00 | 15.00 |
| 3 | Barry Foster | 12.00 | 8.00 |
| 4 | Sterling Sharpe | 5.00 | 3.00 |
| 5 | Jerry Rice | 7.50 | 4.00 |
| 6 | Keith Jackson | 1.75 | 1.00 |
| 7 | Steve Wallace | 1.25 | .70 |
| 8 | Richmond Webb | 1.25 | .70 |
| 9 | Guy McIntyre | 1.25 | .70 |
| 10 | Carlton Hasselrig | 1.25 | .70 |
| 11 | Bruce Matthews | 1.25 | .70 |
| 12 | Morten Andersen | 1.25 | .70 |
| 13 | Rich Camarillo | 1.25 | .70 |
| 14 | Deion Sanders | 2.50 | 1.50 |
| 15 | Steve Tasker | 1.25 | .70 |

| 16 | Clyde Simmons | 1.25 | .70 |
| 17 | Reggie White | 1.75 | 1.00 |
| 18 | Cortez Kennedy | 1.75 | 1.00 |
| 19 | Rod Woodson | 1.50 | .80 |
| 20 | Terry McDaniel | 1.25 | .70 |
| 21 | Chuck Cecil | 1.25 | .70 |
| 22 | Steve Atwater | 1.50 | .80 |
| 23 | Bryan Cox | 1.25 | .70 |
| 24 | Derrick Thomas | 2.00 | 1.25 |
| 25 | Wilber Marshall | 1.25 | .70 |
| 26 | Sam Mills | 1.25 | .70 |

# SKYBOX

## 1992 SkyBox Impact

This 350-card set is the first football edition produced by Skybox. The card fronts feature full-bleed, full color action shots with the player's last name printed in bold type across the top. A team logo appears in the lower left corner. The vertical card backs include a smaller action shot. stats, bios and career highlights. Key subsets include Team Checklists (CL), High Impact League Leaders (LL), Sudden Impact Hardest Hitters (HH), and Instant Impact Rookies (R). In addition, the set contains limited hologram cards of Jim Kelly and Lawrence Taylor which were randomly placed in the company's foil packs. 2,500 Total Impact gold foil stamped autographed cards of Kelly were also randomly inserted into foil packs. These

limited inserts are included at the end on the checklist but are not factored into the complete set price below. All cards in the set measure 2-1/2" by 3-1/2".

| | | MINT | NR/MT |
|---|---|---|---|
| Complete Set (350) | | 22.50 | 13.50 |
| Commons | | .05 | .02 |

| 1 | Jim Kelly | .60 | .35 |
|---|---|---|---|
| 2 | Andre Rison | .25 | .15 |
| 3 | Michael Dean Perry | .12 | .07 |
| 4 | Herman Moore | .20 | .12 |
| 5 | Fred McAfee (R) | .25 | .15 |
| 6 | Ricky Proehl | .08 | .05 |
| 7 | Jim Everett | .15 | .10 |
| 8 | Mark Carrier (Chi) | .08 | .05 |
| 9 | Eric Martin | .07 | .04 |
| 10 | John Elway | .20 | .12 |
| 11 | Michael Irvin | .35 | .20 |
| 12 | Keith McCants | .07 | .04 |
| 13 | Greg Lloyd | .05 | .02 |
| 14 | Lawrence Taylor | .12 | .07 |
| 15 | Mike Tomczak | .07 | .04 |
| 16 | Cortez Kennedy | .08 | .05 |
| 17 | William Fuller | .05 | .02 |
| 18 | James Lofton | .20 | .12 |
| 19 | Kevin Fagan | .05 | .02 |
| 20 | Bill Brooks | .05 | .02 |
| 21 | Roger Craig | .08 | .05 |
| 22 | Jay Novacek | .12 | .07 |
| 23 | Steve Sewell | .05 | .02 |
| 24 | William Perry | .07 | .04 |
| 25 | Jerry Rice | .40 | .25 |
| 26 | James Joseph | .12 | .07 |
| 27 | Tim Rosenbach | .12 | .07 |
| 28 | Pat Terrell | .07 | .04 |
| 29 | Jon Vaughn | .15 | .10 |
| 30 | Steve Walsh | .10 | .06 |
| 31 | James Hasty | .05 | .02 |
| 32 | Dwight Stone | .05 | .02 |
| 33 | Derrick Fenner | .08 | .05 |
| 34 | Mark Bortz | .05 | .02 |
| 35 | Dan Saleaumua | .05 | .02 |
| 36 | Sammie Smith | .10 | .06 |
| 37 | Antone Davis | .05 | .02 |
| 38 | Steve Young | .35 | .20 |
| 39 | Mike Baab | .05 | .02 |
| 40 | Rick Fenney | .05 | .02 |
| 41 | Chris Hinton | .05 | .02 |
| 42 | Bart Oates | .05 | .02 |
| 43 | Bryan Hinkle | .05 | .02 |
| 44 | James Francis | .08 | .05 |
| 45 | Ray Crockett | .05 | .02 |
| 46 | Eric Dickerson | .20 | .12 |

| | | | |
|---|---|---|---|
| 47 | Hart Lee Dykes | .07 | .04 |
| 48 | Percy Snow | .07 | .04 |
| 49 | Ron Hall | .05 | .02 |
| 50 | Warren Moon | .20 | .12 |
| 51 | Ed West | .05 | .02 |
| 52 | Clarence Verdin | .07 | .04 |
| 53 | Eugene Lockhart | .05 | .02 |
| 54 | Andre Reed | .12 | .07 |
| 55 | Kevin Ross | .05 | .02 |
| 56 | Al Noga | .05 | .02 |
| 57 | Wes Hopkins | .05 | .02 |
| 58 | Rufus Porter | .05 | .02 |
| 59 | Brian Mitchell | .07 | .04 |
| 60 | Reggie Roby | .05 | .02 |
| 61 | Rodney Peete | .10 | .06 |
| 62 | Jeff Herrod | .05 | .02 |
| 63 | Anthony Smith | .05 | .02 |
| 64 | Brad Muster | .08 | .05 |
| 65 | Jessie Tuggle | .05 | .02 |
| 66 | Al Smith | .05 | .02 |
| 67 | Jeff Hostetler | .12 | .07 |
| 68 | John L. Williams | .07 | .04 |
| 69 | Paul Gruber | .05 | .02 |
| 70 | Cornelius Bennett | .12 | .07 |
| 71 | William White | .05 | .02 |
| 72 | Tom Rathman | .08 | .05 |
| 73 | Boomer Esiason | .15 | .10 |
| 74 | Neil Smith | .05 | .02 |
| 75 | Sterling Sharpe | .30 | .18 |
| 76 | James Jones | .05 | .02 |
| 77 | David Treadwell | .05 | .02 |
| 78 | Willie Anderson | .08 | .05 |
| 79 | Eric Allen | .05 | .02 |
| 80 | Joe Jacoby | .05 | .02 |
| 81 | Keith Sims | .05 | .02 |
| 82 | Bubba McDowell | .05 | .02 |
| 83 | Ronnie Lippett | .05 | .02 |
| 84 | Cris Carter | .20 | .12 |
| 85 | Chris Burkett | .05 | .02 |
| 86 | Issiac Holt | .05 | .02 |
| 87 | Duane Bickett | .05 | .02 |
| 88 | Leslie O'Neal | .07 | .04 |
| 89 | Gil Fenerty | .05 | .02 |
| 90 | Pierce Holt | .05 | .02 |
| 91 | Willie Drewrey | .05 | .02 |
| 92 | Brian Blades | .07 | .04 |
| 93 | Tony Martin | .05 | .02 |
| 94 | Jessie Hester | .05 | .02 |
| 95 | John Stephens | .08 | .05 |
| 96 | Keith Willis | .05 | .02 |
| 97 | Vai Sikahema | .05 | .02 |
| 98 | Mark Higgs | .25 | .15 |
| 99 | Steve McMichael | .07 | .04 |
| 100 | Deion sanders | .25 | .15 |
| 101 | Marvin Washington | .05 | .02 |
| 102 | Ken Norton | .05 | .02 |
| 103 | Barry Word | .15 | .10 |
| 104 | Sean Jones | .05 | .02 |
| 105 | Ronnie Harman | .05 | .02 |
| 106 | Donnell Woolford | .05 | .02 |
| 107 | Ray Agnew | .05 | .02 |
| 108 | Lemuel Stinson | .05 | .02 |
| 109 | Dennis Smith | .05 | .02 |
| 110 | Lorenzo White | .15 | .10 |
| 111 | Craig Heyward | .07 | .04 |
| 112 | Jeff Query | .08 | .05 |
| 113 | Gary Plummer | .05 | .02 |
| 114 | John Taylor | .15 | .10 |
| 115 | Rohn Stark | .05 | .02 |
| 116 | Tom Waddle | .12 | .07 |
| 117 | Jeff Cross | .05 | .02 |
| 118 | Tim Green | .05 | .02 |
| 119 | Anthony Munoz | .08 | .05 |
| 120 | Mel Gray | .05 | .02 |
| 121 | Ray Donaldson | .05 | .02 |
| 122 | Dennis Byrd | .05 | .02 |
| 123 | Carnell Lake | .05 | .02 |
| 124 | Broderick Thomas | .08 | .05 |
| 125 | Charles Mann | .05 | .02 |
| 126 | Darion Conner | .07 | .04 |
| 127 | John Roper | .05 | .02 |
| 128 | Jack Del Rio | .05 | .02 |
| 129 | Rickey Dixon | .05 | .02 |
| 130 | Eddie Anderson | .05 | .02 |
| 131 | Steve Broussard | .08 | .05 |
| 132 | Michael Young | .05 | .02 |
| 133 | Lamar Lathan | .07 | .04 |
| 134 | Rickey Jackson | .07 | .04 |
| 135 | Billy Ray Smith | .05 | .02 |
| 136 | Tony Casillas | .07 | .04 |
| 137 | Ickey Woods | .05 | .02 |
| 138 | Ray Childress | .07 | .04 |
| 139 | Vance Johnson | .08 | .05 |
| 140 | Brett Perriman | .08 | .05 |
| 141 | Calvin Williams | .08 | .05 |
| 142 | Dino Hackett | .05 | .02 |
| 143 | Jacob Green | .05 | .02 |
| 144 | Robert Delpino | .07 | .04 |
| 145 | Marv Cook | .05 | .02 |
| 146 | Dwayne Harper | .05 | .02 |
| 147 | Ricky Ervins | .50 | .30 |
| 148 | Kelvin Martin | .08 | .05 |
| 149 | Leroy Hoard | .08 | .05 |
| 150 | Dan Marino | .40 | .25 |
| 151 | Richard Johnson | .05 | .02 |
| 152 | Henry Ellard | .07 | .04 |
| 153 | Al Toon | .08 | .05 |
| 154 | Dermontti Dawson | .05 | .02 |
| 155 | Robert Blackman | .05 | .02 |
| 156 | Howie Long | .07 | .04 |
| 157 | David Fulcher | .05 | .02 |
| 158 | Mike Merriweather | .05 | .02 |
| 159 | Gary Anderson | .05 | .02 |
| 160 | John Friesz | .10 | .06 |

| 161 | Eugene Robinson | .05 | .02 |
| 162 | Brad Baxter | .12 | .07 |
| 163 | Bennie Blades | .07 | .04 |
| 164 | Harold Green | .15 | .10 |
| 165 | Ernest Givins | .10 | .06 |
| 166 | Deron Cherry | .05 | .02 |
| 167 | Carl Banks | .07 | .04 |
| 168 | Keith Jackson | .15 | .10 |
| 169 | Pat Leahy | .05 | .02 |
| 170 | Alvin Harper | .30 | .18 |
| 171 | David Little | .05 | .02 |
| 172 | Anthony Carter | .08 | .05 |
| 173 | Willie Gault | .07 | .04 |
| 174 | Bruce Armstrong | .05 | .02 |
| 175 | Junior Seau | .15 | .10 |
| 176 | Eric Metcalf | .10 | .06 |
| 177 | Tony Mandarich | .05 | .02 |
| 178 | Ernie Jones | .05 | .02 |
| 179 | Albert Bentley | .05 | .02 |
| 180 | Mike Pritchard | .25 | .15 |
| 181 | Bubby Brister | .10 | .06 |
| 182 | Vaughan Johnson | .07 | .04 |
| 183 | Robert Clark | .05 | .02 |
| 184 | Lawrence Dawsey | .15 | .10 |
| 185 | Eric Green | .10 | .06 |
| 186 | Jay Schroeder | .10 | .06 |
| 187 | Andre Tippett | .07 | .04 |
| 188 | Vinny Testaverde | .10 | .06 |
| 189 | Wendell Davis | .12 | .07 |
| 190 | Russell Maryland | .15 | .10 |
| 191 | Chris Singleton | .07 | .04 |
| 192 | Ken O'Brien | .10 | .06 |
| 193 | Merril Hoge | .07 | .04 |
| 194 | Steve Bono (R) | .50 | .30 |
| 195 | Earnest Byner | .07 | .04 |
| 196 | Mike Singletary | .10 | .06 |
| 197 | Gaston Green | .12 | .07 |
| 198 | Mark Carrier (TB) | .07 | .04 |
| 199 | Harvey Williams | .25 | .15 |
| 200 | Randall Cunningham | .20 | .12 |
| 201 | Cris Dishman | .07 | .04 |
| 202 | Greg Townsend | .07 | .04 |
| 203 | Christian Okoye | .10 | .06 |
| 204 | Sam Mills | .07 | .04 |
| 205 | Kyle Clifton | .05 | .02 |
| 206 | Jim Harbaugh | .12 | .07 |
| 207 | Anthony Thompson | .08 | .05 |
| 208 | Rob Moore | .20 | .12 |
| 209 | Irving Fryar | .08 | .05 |
| 210 | Derrick Thomas | .20 | .12 |
| 211 | Chris Miller | .20 | .12 |
| 212 | Doug Smith | .05 | .02 |
| 213 | Michael Haynes | .20 | .12 |
| 214 | Phil Simms | .10 | .06 |
| 215 | Charles Haley | .07 | .04 |
| 216 | Burt Grossman | .07 | .04 |
| 217 | Rod Bernstine | .08 | .05 |
| 218 | Louis Lipps | .07 | .04 |
| 219 | Dan McGwire | .35 | .20 |
| 220 | Ethan Horton | .05 | .02 |
| 221 | Michael Carter | .05 | .02 |
| 222 | Neil O'Donnell | .60 | .35 |
| 223 | Anthony Miller | .15 | .10 |
| 224 | Eric Swann | .08 | .05 |
| 225 | Thurman Thomas | .35 | .20 |
| 226 | Jeff George | .25 | .15 |
| 227 | Joe Montana | .40 | .25 |
| 228 | Leonard Marshall | .05 | .02 |
| 229 | Haywood Jeffires | .20 | .12 |
| 230 | Mark Clayton | .12 | .07 |
| 231 | Chris Doleman | .07 | .04 |
| 232 | Troy Aikman | .75 | .45 |
| 233 | Gary Anderson | .05 | .02 |
| 234 | Pat Swilling | .10 | .06 |
| 235 | Ronnie Lott | .10 | .06 |
| 236 | Brian Jordan | .12 | .07 |
| 237 | Bruce Smith | .10 | .06 |
| 238 | Tony Jones | .05 | .02 |
| 239 | Tim McKyer | .05 | .02 |
| 240 | Gary Clark | .15 | .10 |
| 241 | Mitchell Price | .05 | .02 |
| 242 | John Kasay | .05 | .02 |
| 243 | Stephone Paige | .08 | .05 |
| 244 | Jeff Wright | .05 | .02 |
| 245 | Shannon Sharpe | .08 | .05 |
| 246 | Keith Byars | .08 | .05 |
| 247 | Charles Dimry | .05 | .02 |
| 248 | Steve Smith | .05 | .02 |
| 249 | Erric Pegram | .08 | .05 |
| 250 | Bernie Kosar | .12 | .07 |
| 251 | Peter Tom Willis | .15 | .10 |
| 252 | Mark Ingram | .05 | .02 |
| 253 | Keith McKeller | .05 | .02 |
| 254 | Lewis Billups | .05 | .02 |
| 255 | Alton Montgomery | .05 | .02 |
| 256 | Jimmie Jones | .05 | .02 |
| 257 | Brent Williams | .05 | .02 |
| 258 | Gene Atkins | .05 | .02 |
| 259 | Reggie Rutland | .05 | .02 |
| 260 | Sam Seale | .05 | .02 |
| 261 | Andre Ware | .15 | .10 |
| 262 | Fred Barnett | .15 | .10 |
| 263 | Randal Hill | .15 | .10 |
| 264 | Patrick Hunter | .05 | .02 |
| 265 | Johnny Rembert | .05 | .02 |
| 266 | Monte Coleman | .05 | .02 |
| 267 | Aaron Wallace | .07 | .04 |
| 268 | Ferrell Edmunds | .05 | .02 |
| 269 | Stan Thomas | .05 | .02 |
| 270 | Robb Thomas | .05 | .02 |
| 271 | Martin Bayless | .05 | .02 |
| 272 | Dean Biasucci | .05 | .02 |
| 273 | Keith Henderson | .08 | .05 |
| 274 | Vinnie Clark | .05 | .02 |

| | | | |
|---|---|---|---|
| 275 | Emmitt Smith | 2.50 | 1.50 |
| 276 | Mark Rypien | .25 | .15 |
| 277 | Atlanta (CL) | .08 | .05 |
| 278 | Buffalo (CL) | .20 | .12 |
| 279 | Chicago (CL) | .07 | .04 |
| 280 | Cincinnati (CL) | .05 | .02 |
| 281 | Cleveland (CL) | .07 | .04 |
| 282 | Dallas (CL) | .15 | .10 |
| 283 | Denver (CL) | .10 | .06 |
| 284 | Detroit (CL) | .05 | .02 |
| 285 | Green Bay (CL) | .10 | .06 |
| 286 | Houston (CL) | .10 | .06 |
| 287 | Indianapolis (CL) | .10 | .06 |
| 288 | Kansas City (CL) | .10 | .06 |
| 289 | LA Raiders (CL) | .08 | .05 |
| 290 | LA Rams (CL) | .05 | .02 |
| 291 | Miami (CL) | .20 | .12 |
| 292 | Minnesota (CL) | .08 | .05 |
| 293 | New England (CL) | .05 | .02 |
| 294 | New Orleans (CL) | .05 | .02 |
| 295 | NY Giants (CL) | .08 | .05 |
| 296 | NY Jets (CL) | .08 | .05 |
| 297 | Philadelphia (CL) | .07 | .04 |
| 298 | Phoenix (CL) | .05 | .02 |
| 299 | Pittsburgh (CL) | .05 | .02 |
| 300 | San Diego (CL) | .05 | .02 |
| 301 | San Francisco (CL) | .15 | .10 |
| 302 | Seattle (CL) | .05 | .02 |
| 303 | Tampa Bay (CL) | .05 | .02 |
| 304 | Washington (CL) | .10 | .06 |
| 305 | Jim Kelly (LL) | .20 | .12 |
| 306 | Steve Young (LL) | .15 | .10 |
| 307 | Thurman Thomas (LL) | .15 | .10 |
| 308 | Emmitt Smith (LL) | .80 | .50 |
| 309 | Haywood Jeffires (LL) | .08 | .05 |
| 310 | Michael Irvin (LL) | .15 | .10 |
| 311 | William Fuller (LL) | .05 | .02 |
| 312 | Pat Swilling (LL) | .07 | .04 |
| 313 | Ronnie Lott (LL) | .08 | .05 |
| 314 | Deion sanders (LL) | .10 | .06 |
| 315 | Cornelius Bennett (HH) | .07 | .04 |
| 316 | David Fulcher (HH) | .05 | .02 |
| 317 | Ronnie Lott (HH) | .08 | .05 |
| 318 | Pat Swilling (HH) | .08 | .05 |
| 319 | Lawrence Taylor (HH) | .10 | .06 |
| 320 | Derrick Thomas (HH) | .10 | .06 |
| 321 | Steve Emtman (R) | 1.25 | .80 |
| 322 | Carl Pickens (R) | 1.00 | .70 |
| 323 | David Klingler (R) | 2.50 | 1.50 |
| 324 | Dale Carter (R) | .25 | .15 |
| 325 | Mike Gaddis (R) | .12 | .07 |
| 326 | Quentin Coryatt (R) | .50 | .30 |
| 327 | Darryl Williams (R) | .12 | .07 |
| 328 | Jeremy Lincoln (R) | .08 | .05 |
| 329 | Robert Jones (R) | .25 | .15 |
| 330 | Bucky Richardson (R) | .25 | .15 |
| 331 | Tony Brooks (R) | .20 | .12 |

| | | | |
|---|---|---|---|
| 332 | Alonzo Spellman (R) | .15 | .10 |
| 333 | Robert Brooks (R) | .10 | .06 |
| 334 | Marco Coleman (R) | .30 | .18 |
| 335 | Siran Stacy (R) | .20 | .12 |
| 336 | Tommy Maddox (R) | 1.25 | .80 |
| 337 | Steve Israel (R) | .12 | .07 |
| 338 | Vaughn Dunbar (R) | .75 | .45 |
| 339 | Shane Collins (R) | .15 | .10 |
| 340 | Kevin Smith (R) | .15 | .10 |
| 341 | Chris Mims (R) | .25 | .15 |
| 342 | Chester McGlockton (R) | .12 | .07 |
| 343 | Tracy Scroggins (R) | .10 | .06 |
| 344 | Howard Dinkins (R) | .10 | .06 |
| 345 | Levon Kirkland (R) | .10 | .06 |
| 346 | Terrell Buckley (R) | .60 | .35 |
| 347 | Marquez Pope (R) | .10 | .06 |
| 348 | Phillippi Sparks (R) | .12 | .07 |
| 349 | Joe Bowden (R) | ..10 | .06 |
| 350 | Edgar Bennett (R) | .35 | .20 |
| H1 | Jim Kelly Hologram | 4.00 | 1.75 |
| H2 | Lawrence Taylor Holo | 2.00 | .75 |
| SP1 | Jim Kelly (Total) | 12.00 | 8.00 |
| SP2 | Jim Kelly Autograph | 175.00 | 100.00 |
| SP3 | Jim Kelly/Magic Johnson Autograph | 350.00 | 200.00 |

# 1992 SkyBox
# Major Impact

The 20-cards in this limited insert set were distributed randomly in SkyBox Jumbo Packs. Cards feature full-color action shots on front and measure 2-1/2" by 3-1/2".

|  | MINT | NR/MT |
|---|---|---|
| **Complete Set (20)** | 36.00 | 21.50 |
| **Commons** | .80 | .50 |

| | | MINT | NR/MT |
|---|---|---|---|
| 1 | Cornelius Bennett | 1.25 | .80 |
| 2 | David Fulcher | .80 | .50 |
| 3 | Haywood Jeffries | 2.00 | 1.25 |
| 4 | Ronnie Lott | 1.50 | .90 |
| 5 | Dan Marino | 4.00 | 2.75 |
| 6 | Warren Moon | 2.50 | 1.50 |
| 7 | Christian Okoye | 1.00 | .70 |
| 8 | Andre Reed | 1.25 | .80 |
| 9 | Derrick Thomas | 2.00 | 1.25 |
| 10 | Thurman Thomas | 4.50 | 2.75 |
| 11 | Troy Aikman | 10.00 | 6.50 |
| 12 | Randall Cunningham | 2.50 | 1.50 |
| 13 | Michael Irvin | 4.50 | 2.75 |
| 14 | Jerry Rice | 5.00 | 3.00 |
| 15 | Joe Montana | 4.50 | 2.75 |
| 16 | Mark Rypien | 1.50 | .90 |
| 17 | Deion Sanders | 2.00 | 1.25 |
| 18 | Emmitt Smith | 12.50 | 8.50 |
| 19 | Pat Swilling | 1.00 | .70 |
| 20 | Lawrence Taylor | 1.50 | .90 |

# 1992 SkyBox PrimeTime

The cards in this 360-card premium set feature action photos superimposed over a color background that includes thin vertical lines running across the top portion of the card front. The player's name is printed at the top while the team name appears in a small vertical box at the side. The player's uniform number is printed in bold type in the upper third of the card front. A SkyBox logo is located at the bottom of the card. Key subsets include Team MVP's and Poster Cards (PC). The set also includes two randomly distributed limited bonus cards of Jim Kelly and Steve Emtman which are listed at the end of this checklist. All cards measure 2-1/2" by 3-1/2".

| | | MINT | NR/MT |
|---|---|---|---|
| **Complete Set (360)** | | 45.00 | 28.00 |
| **Commons** | | .10 | .06 |

| | | MINT | NR/MT |
|---|---|---|---|
| 1 | Deion Sanders | .50 | .30 |
| 2 | Shane Collins (R) | .30 | .18 |
| 3 | James Patton (R) | .15 | .10 |
| 4 | Reggie Roby | .10 | .06 |
| 5 | Merril Hoge | .12 | .07 |
| 6 | Vinny Testaverde | .15 | .10 |
| 7 | Boomer Esiason | .15 | .10 |
| 8 | Troy Aikman | 2.00 | 1.25 |
| 9 | Tommy Jeter (R) | .15 | .10 |
| 10 | Brent Williams | .10 | .06 |
| 11 | Mark Rypien | .30 | .18 |
| 12 | Jim Kelly | 1.25 | .80 |
| 13 | Dan Marino | 1.00 | .70 |
| 14 | Bill Cowher (R) | .12 | .07 |
| 15 | Leslie O'Neal | .15 | .10 |
| 16 | Joe Montana | 1.00 | .70 |
| 17 | William Fuller | .12 | .07 |
| 18 | Paul Gruber | .12 | .07 |
| 19 | Bernie Kosar | .15 | .10 |
| 20 | Ricky Jackson | .12 | .07 |
| 21 | Earnest Byner | .12 | .07 |
| 22 | Emmitt Smith | 4.50 | 2.75 |
| 23 | Neal Anderson | .15 | .10 |
| 24 | Greg Lloyd | .10 | .06 |
| 25 | Ronnie Harmon | .15 | .10 |
| 26 | Ray Donaldson | .10 | .06 |
| 27 | Kevin Ross | .10 | .06 |
| 28 | Irving Fryar | .12 | .07 |
| 29 | John L. Williams | .12 | .07 |
| 30 | Chris Hinton | .10 | .06 |
| 31 | Tracy Scoggins | .20 | .12 |
| 32 | Rohn Stark | .10 | .06 |
| 33 | David Fulcher | .10 | .06 |
| 34 | Thurman Thomas | 1.25 | .80 |
| 35 | Christian Okoye | .15 | .10 |
| 36 | Vaughn Dunbar (R) | 1.00 | .70 |
| 37 | Joel Steed (R) | .15 | .10 |
| 38 | James Francis | .12 | .07 |
| 39 | Dermontti Dawson | .10 | .06 |
| 40 | Mark Higgs | .40 | .25 |
| 41 | Flipper Anderson | .15 | .10 |

| No. | Player | | |
|---|---|---|---|
| 42 | Ronnie Lott | .20 | .12 |
| 43 | Jim Everett | .15 | .10 |
| 44 | Burt Grossman | .12 | .07 |
| 45 | Charles Haley | .12 | .07 |
| 46 | Ricky Proehl | .15 | .10 |
| 47 | Marquez Pope (R) | .15 | .10 |
| 48 | David Treadwell | .10 | .06 |
| 49 | William White | .10 | .06 |
| 50 | John Elway | .50 | .30 |
| 51 | Mark Carrier | .12 | .07 |
| 52 | Brian Blades | .12 | .07 |
| 53 | Keith McKellar | .12 | .07 |
| 54 | Art Monk | .35 | .20 |
| 55 | Lamar Latham | .12 | .07 |
| 56 | Pat Swilling | .15 | .10 |
| 57 | Steve Broussard | .12 | .07 |
| 58 | Derrick Thomas | .60 | .35 |
| 59 | Keith Jackson | .25 | .15 |
| 60 | Leonard Marshall | .12 | .07 |
| 61 | Eric Metcalf | .20 | .12 |
| 62 | Andy Heck | .10 | .06 |
| 63 | Mark Carrier | .12 | .07 |
| 64 | Neil O'Donnell | .80 | .50 |
| 65 | Broderick Thomas (MVP) | .10 | .06 |
| 66 | Eric Kramer | .35 | .20 |
| 67 | Joe Montana (PC) | .50 | .30 |
| 68 | Robert Delpino (MVP) | .10 | .06 |
| 69 | Steve Israel (R) | .25 | .15 |
| 70 | Herman Moore | .60 | .35 |
| 71 | Jacob Green | .10 | .06 |
| 72 | Lorenzo White | .20 | .12 |
| 73 | Nick Lowery | .12 | .07 |
| 74 | Eugene Robinson | .10 | .06 |
| 75 | Carl Banks | .12 | .07 |
| 76 | Bruce Smith | .20 | .12 |
| 77 | Mark Rypien | .20 | .12 |
| 78 | Anthony Munoz | .20 | .12 |
| 79 | Clayton Holmes (R) | .20 | .12 |
| 80 | Jerry Rice | 1.00 | .70 |
| 81 | Henry Ellard | .15 | .10 |
| 82 | Tim McGee | .12 | .07 |
| 83 | Al Toon | .12 | .07 |
| 84 | Haywood Jeffires | .50 | .30 |
| 85 | Mike Singletary | .20 | .12 |
| 86 | Thurman Thomas (PC) | .75 | .45 |
| 87 | Jessie Hester | .10 | .06 |
| 88 | Michael Irvin | .80 | .50 |
| 89 | Jack Del Rio | .10 | .06 |
| 90 | Seth Joyner (MVP) | .12 | .07 |
| 91 | Jeff Herrod | .10 | .06 |
| 92 | Michael Dean Perry | .25 | .15 |
| 93 | Louis Oliver | .12 | .07 |
| 94 | Dan McGwire | .50 | .30 |
| 95 | Cris Carter (MVP) | .20 | .12 |
| 96 | Dale Carter (R) | .80 | .50 |
| 97 | Cornelius Bennett | .20 | .12 |
| 98 | Edgar Bennett (R) | .75 | .45 |
| 99 | Steve Young | .80 | .50 |
| 100 | Warren Moon | .50 | .30 |
| 101 | Deion Sanders (MVP) | .20 | .12 |
| 102 | Mel Gray | .10 | .06 |
| 103 | Mark Murphy | .10 | .06 |
| 104 | Jeff George | .75 | .45 |
| 105 | Anthony Miller | .40 | .25 |
| 106 | Tom Rathman | .12 | .07 |
| 107 | Fred McAfee (R) | .40 | .25 |
| 108 | Paul Siever (R) | .15 | .10 |
| 109 | Lemuel Stinson | .10 | .06 |
| 110 | Vance Johnson | .15 | .10 |
| 111 | Jay Schroeder | .15 | .10 |
| 112 | Calvin Williams | .20 | .12 |
| 113 | Cortez Kennedy | .25 | .15 |
| 114 | Quentin Coryatt (R) | 1.25 | .80 |
| 115 | Ronnie Lippett | .10 | .06 |
| 116 | Brad Baxter | .20 | .12 |
| 117 | Bubba McDowell | .10 | .06 |
| 118 | Cris Carter | .25 | .15 |
| 119 | John Stephens | .20 | .12 |
| 120 | James Hasty | .10 | .06 |
| 121 | Bubby Brister | .15 | .10 |
| 122 | Robert Jones (R) | .40 | .25 |
| 123 | Sterling Sharpe | .80 | .50 |
| 124 | Jason Hanson (R) | .15 | .10 |
| 125 | Sam Mills | .15 | .10 |
| 126 | Ernie Jones | .12 | .07 |
| 127 | Chester McGlockton (R) | .25 | .15 |
| 128 | Troy Vincent (R) | .50 | .30 |
| 129 | Chuck Smith (R) | .20 | .12 |
| 130 | Tim McKyer | .10 | .06 |
| 131 | Tom Newberry | .10 | .06 |
| 132 | Leonard Wheeler (R) | .15 | .10 |
| 133 | Patrick Rowe (R) | .40 | .25 |
| 134 | Eric Swann | .15 | .10 |
| 135 | Jeremy Lincoln (R) | .15 | .10 |
| 136 | Brian Noble | .10 | .06 |
| 137 | Allen Pinkett | .15 | .10 |
| 138 | Carl Pickens (R) | 1.00 | .70 |
| 139 | Eric Green | .25 | .15 |
| 140 | Louis Lipps | .12 | .07 |
| 141 | Chris Singleton | .12 | .07 |
| 142 | Gary Clark | .25 | .15 |
| 143 | Tim Green | .12 | .07 |
| 144 | Dennis Green | .15 | .10 |
| 145 | Gary Anderson | .10 | .06 |
| 146 | Mark Clayton | .20 | .12 |
| 147 | Kelvin Martin | .15 | .10 |
| 148 | Mike Holmgren (R) | .15 | .10 |
| 149 | Gaston Green | .20 | .12 |
| 150 | Terrell Buckley (R) | 1.25 | .80 |
| 151 | Robert Brooks (R) | .30 | .18 |
| 152 | Anthony Smith | .15 | .10 |
| 153 | Jay Novacek | .25 | .15 |

| # | Player | | |
|---|--------|---|---|
| 154 | Webster Slaughter | .15 | .10 |
| 155 | John Roper | .10 | .06 |
| 156 | Steve Emtman (R) | 2.50 | 1.50 |
| 157 | Tony Sacca (R) | .60 | .35 |
| 158 | Ray Crockett | .10 | .06 |
| 159 | Jerry Rice (MVP) | .60 | .35 |
| 160 | Alonzo Spellman (R) | .50 | .30 |
| 161 | Deion Sanders (PC) | .40 | .25 |
| 162 | Robert Clark | .10 | .06 |
| 163 | Mark Ingram | .12 | .07 |
| 164 | Ricardo McDonald (R) | .20 | .12 |
| 165 | Emmitt Smith (PC) | 2.50 | 1.50 |
| 166 | Tommy Maddox (R) | 2.50 | 1.50 |
| 167 | Tom Myslinski (R) | .15 | .10 |
| 168 | Tony Bennett (MVP) | .15 | .10 |
| 169 | Ernest Givens | .20 | .12 |
| 170 | Eugene Robinson (MVP) | .10 | .06 |
| 171 | Roger Craig | .12 | .07 |
| 172 | Irving Fryar (MVP) | .12 | .07 |
| 173 | Jeff Herrod (MVP) | .10 | .06 |
| 174 | Chris Mims (R) | .50 | .30 |
| 175 | Bart Oates | .10 | .06 |
| 176 | Michael Irvin (MVP) | .50 | .30 |
| 177 | Lawrence Dawsey | .25 | .15 |
| 178 | Warren Moon (MVP) | .25 | .15 |
| 179 | Timm Rosenbach | .15 | .10 |
| 180 | Bobby Ross (R) | .15 | .10 |
| 181 | Chris Burkett (MVP) | .10 | .06 |
| 182 | Tony Brooks (R) | .35 | .20 |
| 183 | Clarence Verdin | .12 | .07 |
| 184 | Bernie Kosar | .15 | .10 |
| 185 | Eric Martin | .15 | .10 |
| 186 | Jeff Bryant | .10 | .06 |
| 187 | Carnell Lake | .10 | .06 |
| 188 | Darren Woodson (R) | .20 | .12 |
| 189 | Dwayne Harper | .10 | .06 |
| 190 | Bernie Kosar (MVP) | .15 | .10 |
| 191 | Keith Sims | .10 | .06 |
| 192 | Rich Gannon | .20 | .12 |
| 193 | Broderick Thomas | .12 | .07 |
| 194 | Michael Young | .10 | .06 |
| 195 | Cris Dishman | .12 | .07 |
| 196 | Wes Hopkins | .10 | .06 |
| 197 | Christian Okoye | .15 | .10 |
| 198 | David Little | .10 | .06 |
| 199 | Chris Crooms (R) | .15 | .10 |
| 200 | Lawrence Taylor | .20 | .12 |
| 201 | Marc Boutte (R) | .15 | .10 |
| 202 | Mark Carrier | .12 | .07 |
| 203 | Keith McCants | .12 | .07 |
| 204 | Dwayne Sabb (R) | .15 | .10 |
| 205 | Brian Mitchell | .15 | .10 |
| 206 | Keith Byars | .12 | .07 |
| 207 | Jeff Hostetler | .20 | .12 |
| 208 | Percy Snow | .12 | .07 |
| 209 | Lawrence Taylor (MVP) | .20 | .12 |
| 210 | Troy Auzene (R) | .20 | .12 |
| 211 | Warren Moon (PC) | .35 | .20 |
| 212 | Mike Pritchard | .40 | .25 |
| 213 | Eric Dickerson | .60 | .35 |
| 214 | Harvey Williams | .40 | .25 |
| 215 | Phil Simms | .15 | .10 |
| 216 | Sean Lumpkin (R) | .15 | .10 |
| 217 | Marco Coleman (R) | 1.00 | .70 |
| 218 | Phillippi Sparks (R) | .20 | .12 |
| 219 | Gerald Dixon (R) | .15 | .10 |
| 220 | Steve Walsh | .12 | .07 |
| 221 | Russell Maryland | .30 | .18 |
| 222 | Eddie Anderson | .10 | .06 |
| 223 | Shane Dronnett (R) | .30 | .18 |
| 224 | Todd Collins (R) | .15 | .10 |
| 225 | Leon Searcy (R) | .15 | .10 |
| 226 | Andre Rison | .40 | .25 |
| 227 | James Lofton | .25 | .15 |
| 228 | Ken O'Brien | .12 | .07 |
| 229 | Mike Tomczak | .12 | .07 |
| 230 | Nick Bell | .40 | .25 |
| 231 | Ben Smith | .10 | .06 |
| 232 | Wendell Davis (MVP) | .15 | .10 |
| 233 | Craig Thompson (R) | .15 | .10 |
| 234 | Dana Hall (R) | .30 | .18 |
| 235 | Larry Webster (R) | .15 | .10 |
| 236 | Jerry Rice (PC) | .60 | .35 |
| 237 | Rod Bernstine | .15 | .10 |
| 238 | David Klingler (R) | 3.00 | 1.75 |
| 239 | Greg Skrepenak (R) | .20 | .12 |
| 240 | Mark Wheeler (R) | .15 | .10 |
| 241 | Kevin Smith (R) | .40 | .25 |
| 242 | Charles Mann | .10 | .06 |
| 243 | Barry Sanders (MVP) | .35 | .20 |
| 244 | Curtis Whitley | .15 | .10 |
| 245 | Ronnie Harmon (MVP) | .15 | .10 |
| 246 | Brent Jones | .12 | .07 |
| 247 | Robert Harris | .12 | .07 |
| 248 | Ted Marchibroda | .10 | .06 |
| 249 | Willie Gault | .12 | .07 |
| 250 | Siran Stacy (R) | .40 | .25 |
| 251 | Dennis Byrd | .12 | .07 |
| 252 | Corey Harris (R) | .15 | .10 |
| 253 | Al Noga | .10 | .06 |
| 254 | David Shula (R) | .15 | .10 |
| 255 | Rob Moore | .25 | .15 |
| 256 | Marv Cook | .12 | .07 |
| 257 | John Elway (MVP) | .30 | .18 |
| 258 | Harold Green | .30 | .18 |
| 259 | Tom Flores | .12 | .07 |
| 260 | Andre Reed | .25 | .15 |
| 261 | Anthony Thompson | .15 | .10 |
| 262 | Isaac Holt | .10 | .06 |
| 263 | Mike Evans (R) | .15 | .10 |
| 264 | Jimmy Smith (R) | .25 | .15 |
| 265 | Anthony Carter | .15 | .10 |
| 266 | Ashley Ambrose (R) | .30 | .18 |

| | | | |
|---|---|---|---|
| 267 | John Fina (R) | .15 | .10 |
| 268 | Sean Gilbert (R) | .50 | .30 |
| 269 | Ken Norton | .12 | .07 |
| 270 | Barry Word | .30 | .18 |
| 271 | Pat Swilling (MVP) | .15 | .10 |
| 272 | Dan Marino (PC) | .50 | .30 |
| 273 | David Fulcher (MVP) | .10 | .06 |
| 274 | William Perry | .12 | .07 |
| 275 | Ed West | .10 | .06 |
| 276 | Gene Atkins | .10 | .06 |
| 277 | Neal Anderson | .15 | .10 |
| 278 | Dino Hackett | .10 | .06 |
| 279 | Greg Townsend | .12 | .07 |
| 280 | Andre Tippett | .12 | .07 |
| 281 | Darry Williams (R) | .35 | .20 |
| 282 | Kurt Barber (R) | .20 | .12 |
| 283 | Pat Terrell | .10 | .06 |
| 284 | Derrick Thomas (PC) | .25 | .15 |
| 285 | Eddie Robinson (R) | .20 | .12 |
| 286 | Howie Long | .12 | .07 |
| 287 | Tim McDonald | .10 | .06 |
| 288 | Thurman Thomas (MVP) | .50 | .30 |
| 289 | Wendell Davis | .20 | .12 |
| 290 | Jeff Cross | .10 | .06 |
| 291 | Duane Bickett | .10 | .06 |
| 292 | Tony Smith (R) | .75 | .45 |
| 293 | Jerry Ball | .10 | .06 |
| 294 | Jessie Tuggle | .10 | .06 |
| 295 | Chris Burkett | .10 | .06 |
| 296 | Eugene Chung (R) | .15 | .10 |
| 297 | Chris Miller | .40 | .25 |
| 298 | Albert Bentley | .10 | .06 |
| 299 | Richard Johnson | .10 | .06 |
| 300 | Randall Cunningham | .30 | .18 |
| 301 | Courtney Hawkins (R) | .50 | .30 |
| 302 | Ray Childress | .15 | .10 |
| 303 | Rodney Peete | .15 | .10 |
| 304 | Kevin Fagan | .10 | .06 |
| 305 | Ronnie Lott (MVP) | .20 | .12 |
| 306 | Michael Carter | .10 | .06 |
| 307 | Derrick Thomas (MVP) | .25 | .15 |
| 308 | Jarvis Williams | .10 | .06 |
| 309 | Greg Lloyd (MVP) | .10 | .06 |
| 310 | Ethan Horton | .12 | .07 |
| 311 | Rickey Ervins | .80 | .50 |
| 312 | Bennie Blades | .12 | .07 |
| 313 | Troy Aikman (PC) | 1.00 | .70 |
| 314 | Bruce Armstrong | .10 | .06 |
| 315 | Leroy Hoard | .15 | .10 |
| 316 | Gary Anderson | .10 | .06 |
| 317 | Steve McMichael | .12 | .07 |
| 318 | Junior Seau | .30 | .18 |
| 319 | Mark Thomas (R) | .15 | .10 |
| 320 | Fred Barnett | .40 | .25 |
| 321 | Mike Merriweather | .10 | .06 |
| 322 | Keith Willis | .10 | .06 |
| 323 | Brett Perriman | .15 | .10 |
| 324 | Michael Haynes | .60 | .35 |
| 325 | Jim Harbaugh | .15 | .10 |
| 326 | Sammie Smith | .15 | .10 |
| 327 | Robert Delpino | .12 | .07 |
| 328 | Tony Mandarich | .12 | .07 |
| 329 | Mark Bortz | .10 | .06 |
| 330 | Ray Etheridge (R) | .15 | .10 |
| 331 | Jarvis Williams/ Louis Oliver | .12 | .07 |
| 332 | Dan Marino (MVP) | .40 | .25 |
| 333 | Dwight Stone | .10 | .06 |
| 334 | Billy Ray Smith | .10 | .06 |
| 335 | Darion Connor | .10 | .06 |
| 336 | Howard Dinkins (R) | .15 | .10 |
| 337 | Robert Porcher (R) | .30 | .18 |
| 338 | Chris Doleman | .12 | .07 |
| 339 | Alvin Harper | .75 | .45 |
| 340 | John Taylor | .20 | .12 |
| 341 | Ray Agnew | .10 | .06 |
| 342 | Jon Vaughn | .20 | .12 |
| 343 | James Brown (R) | .15 | .10 |
| 344 | Michael Irvin (PC) | .50 | .30 |
| 345 | Neil Smith | .15 | .10 |
| 346 | Vaughn Smith | .10 | .06 |
| 347 | Checklist | .10 | .06 |
| 348 | Checklist | .10 | .06 |
| 349 | Checklist | .10 | .06 |
| 350 | Checklist | .10 | .06 |
| 351 | Checklist | .10 | .06 |
| 352 | Checklist | .10 | .06 |
| 353 | Checklist | .10 | .06 |
| 354 | Checklist | .10 | .06 |
| 355 | Checklist | .10 | .06 |
| 356 | Checklist | .10 | .06 |
| 357 | Checklist | .10 | .06 |
| 358 | Checklist | .10 | .06 |
| 359 | Checklist | .10 | .06 |
| 360 | Checklist | .10 | .06 |
| H1 | Jim Kelly | 8.00 | 5.00 |
| S1 | Steve Emtman | 10.00 | 6.50 |

# 1992 Primetime Poster Cards

These 16 insert cards were distributed randomly in Primetime foil packs. Based on Costacos Brothers Sports Posters, the cards depict players in thematic non-football settings. These cards are the same as the poster cards in the regular edition except for the metallic silver foil borders. All cards measure 2-1/2" by 3-1/2".

|  |  | MINT | NR/MT |
|---|---|---|---|
| **Complete Set (16)** | | 70.00 | 48.00 |
| **Commons** | | 1.50 | .90 |
| | | | |
| 1 | Bernie Kosar | 2.00 | 1.25 |
| 2 | Mark Carrier | 1.50 | .90 |
| 3 | Neal Anderson | 2.00 | 1.25 |
| 4 | Thurman Thomas | 10.00 | 6.00 |
| 5 | Deion Sanders | 5.00 | 3.00 |
| 6 | Joe Montana | 7.50 | 4.50 |
| 7 | Jerry Rice | 10.00 | 6.00 |
| 8 | Louis Oliver | 1.50 | .90 |
| | Jarvis Williams | | |
| 9 | Dan Marino | 7.50 | 4.50 |
| 10 | Derrick Thomas | 4.50 | 2.75 |
| 11 | Christian Okoye | 1.75 | 1.00 |
| 12 | Warren Moon | 5.00 | 3.00 |
| 13 | Michael Irvin | 8.50 | 5.50 |
| 14 | Troy Aikman | 18.00 | 12.00 |
| 15 | Emmitt Smith | 22.00 | 15.00 |
| 16 | Checklist | 2.00 | .25 |

# STAR PICS

## 1991 Star Pics Prospects

This 112-card set is primarily made up of the NFL's top 1991 draft picks. Card fronts feature full color action photos of players wearing their college uniforms. The photos are framed by a thin white inside border and a larger outer border with footballs in the background. Vertical card backs contain a small head shot of the player along with his accomplishments and a scouting report. The set contains two subsets including Flashback (FB), featuring current NFL stars and another devoted to player agents. All cards measure 2-1/2" by 3-1/2".

|  |  | MINT | NR/MT |
|---|---|---|---|
| **Complete Set (112)** | | 8.00 | 5.00 |
| **Commons** | | .05 | .02 |
| | | | |
| 1 | Draft Overview | .05 | .02 |
| 2 | Barry Sanders (FB) | .60 | .35 |
| 3 | Nick Bell | .50 | .30 |
| 4 | Kelvin Pritchett | .20 | .12 |
| 5 | Huey Richardson | .08 | .05 |
| 6 | Mike Croel | .35 | .20 |
| 7 | Paul Justin | .10 | .06 |
| 8 | Ivory Lee Brown | .10 | .06 |
| 9 | Herman Moore | .75 | .45 |
| 10 | Derrick Thomas (FB) | .20 | .12 |
| 11 | Keith Traylor | .10 | .06 |
| 12 | Joe Johnson | .07 | .04 |
| 13 | Dan McGwire | .70 | .40 |

| | | | |
|---|---|---|---|
| 14 | Harvey Williams | .60 | .35 |
| 15 | Eric Moten | .05 | .02 |
| 16 | Steve Zucker (Agt) | .05 | .02 |
| 17 | Randal Hill | .40 | .25 |
| 18 | Browning Nagle | .80 | .50 |
| 19 | Stan Thomas | .07 | .04 |
| 20 | Emmitt Smith (FB) | 1.00 | .70 |
| 21 | Ted Washington | .12 | .07 |
| 22 | Lamar Rogers | .08 | .05 |
| 23 | Kenny Walker | .30 | .18 |
| 24 | Howard Griffith | .08 | .05 |
| 25 | Reggie Johnson | .08 | .05 |
| 26 | Lawrence Dawsey | .50 | .30 |
| 27 | Joe Garten | .05 | .02 |
| 28 | Moe Gardner | .15 | .10 |
| 29 | Michael Stonebreaker | .08 | .05 |
| 30 | Jeff George (FB) | .40 | .25 |
| 31 | Leigh Steinberg (Agt) | .05 | .02 |
| 32 | John Flannery | .08 | .05 |
| 33 | Pat Harlow | .08 | .05 |
| 34 | Kanavis McGhee | .20 | .12 |
| 35 | Mike Dumas | .15 | .10 |
| 36 | Godfrey Myles | .08 | .05 |
| 37 | Shawn Moore | .35 | .20 |
| 38 | Jeff Graham | .40 | .25 |
| 39 | Ricky Watters | .80 | .50 |
| 40 | Andre Ware (FB) | .12 | .07 |
| 41 | Henry Jones | .08 | .05 |
| 42 | Eric Turner | .20 | .12 |
| 43 | Bob Woolf (Agt) | .05 | .02 |
| 44 | Randy Baldwin | .08 | .05 |
| 45 | Mo Lewis | .15 | .10 |
| 46 | Jerry Evans | .08 | .05 |
| 47 | Derek Russell | .20 | .12 |
| 48 | Merton Hanks | .07 | .04 |
| 49 | Kevin Donnalley | .05 | .02 |
| 50 | Troy Aikman (FB) | .75 | .45 |
| 51 | William Thomas | .07 | .04 |
| 52 | Chris Thome | .05 | .02 |
| 53 | Ricky Ervins | 1.25 | .80 |
| 54 | Jake Reed | .08 | .05 |
| 55 | Jerome Henderson | .08 | .05 |
| 56 | Mark Vander Poel | .08 | .05 |
| 57 | Bernard Ellison | .05 | .02 |
| 58 | Jack Mills (Agt) | .05 | .02 |
| 59 | Jarrod Bunch | .30 | .18 |
| 60 | Mark Carrier (FB) | .08 | .05 |
| 61 | Rocen Keeton | .05 | .02 |
| 62 | Louis Riddick | .07 | .04 |
| 63 | Bobby Wilson | .15 | .10 |
| 64 | Steve Jackson | .08 | .05 |
| 65 | Brett Favre | 1.50 | .90 |
| 66 | Ernie Mills | .15 | .10 |
| 67 | Joe Valerio | .05 | .02 |
| 68 | Chris Smith | .10 | .06 |
| 69 | Ralph Cindrich (Agt) | .05 | .02 |
| 70 | Christian Okoye (FB) | .12 | .07 |
| 71 | Charles McRae | .08 | .05 |
| 72 | Jon Vaughn | .30 | .18 |
| 73 | Eric Swann | .15 | .10 |
| 74 | Bill Musgrave | .12 | .07 |
| 75 | Eric Bieniemy | .25 | .15 |
| 76 | Pat Tyrance | .08 | .05 |
| 77 | Vinnie Clark | .12 | .07 |
| 78 | Eugene Williams | .05 | .02 |
| 79 | Rob Carpenter | .20 | .12 |
| 80 | Deion Sanders (FB) | .25 | .15 |
| 81 | Roman Phifer | .08 | .05 |
| 82 | Greg Lewis | .25 | .15 |
| 83 | John Johnson | .08 | .05 |
| 84 | Richard Howell (Agt) | .05 | .02 |
| 85 | Jesse Campbell | .08 | .05 |
| 86 | Stanley Richard | .20 | .12 |
| 87 | Alfred Williams | .15 | .10 |
| 88 | Mike Pritchard | .75 | .45 |
| 89 | Mel Agee | .08 | .05 |
| 90 | Aaron Craver | .15 | .10 |
| 91 | Tim Barnett | .50 | .30 |
| 92 | Wesley Carroll | .40 | .25 |
| 93 | Kevin Scott | .07 | .04 |
| 94 | Darren Lewis | .25 | .15 |
| 95 | Tim Bruton | .12 | .07 |
| 96 | Tim James | .05 | .02 |
| 97 | Darryll Lewis | .20 | .12 |
| 98 | Shawn Jefferson | .20 | .12 |
| 99 | Mitch Donahue | .05 | .02 |
| 100 | Marvin Demoff (Agt) | .05 | .02 |
| 101 | Adrian Cooper | .10 | .06 |
| 102 | Bruce Pickens | .20 | .12 |
| 103 | Scott Zolak | .25 | .15 |
| 104 | Phil Hansen | .08 | .05 |
| 105 | Ed King | .08 | .05 |
| 106 | Mike Jones | .08 | .05 |
| 107 | Alvin Harper | .75 | .45 |
| 108 | Robert Young | .05 | .02 |
| 109 | Offensive Prospects (Bell, Favre, Harper, McRae) | .25 | .15 |
| 110 | Defensive Prospects (Croel, Swann, Turner) | .12 | .07 |
| 111 | Checklist | .05 | .02 |
| 112 | Checklist | .05 | .02 |

# 1992 Star Pics Prospects

Star Pics

This 100-card set includes the cards of the top picks in the 1992 NFL draft plus 5-Flashback cards (FB) and a StarStat subset (SS) that compares the draft picks college stats to the college stats of all-time NFL greats. All cards measure 2-1/2" by 3-1/2". Card fronts contain full color action shots of players in their college uniforms. The photos are framed by a white border. The player's name isn't printed vertically down the right side of the card in a color stripe. Vertical card backs include a small head shot in the lower right corner and a scouting report.

|  |  | MINT | NR/MT |
|---|---|---|---|
| Complete Set (100) |  | 9.00 | 6.00 |
| Commons |  | .05 | .02 |
| 1 | Steve Emtman (SS) | .50 | .30 |
| 2 | Chris Hakel | .12 | .07 |
| 3 | Phillippi Sparks | .12 | .07 |
| 4 | Howard Dinkins | .10 | .06 |
| 5 | Robert Brooks | .10 | .06 |
| 6 | Chris Pederson | .05 | .02 |
| 7 | Bucky Richardson | .15 | .10 |
| 8 | Keith Goganious | .08 | .05 |
| 9 | Robert Porcher | .08 | .05 |
| 10 | Andre Rison (FB) | .25 | .15 |
| 11 | Jason Hanson | .08 | .05 |
| 12 | Tommy Vardell | .70 | .40 |
| 13 | Kurt Barber | .10 | .06 |
| 14 | Bernard Dafney | .08 | .05 |
| 15 | Levon Kirkland | .10 | .06 |
| 16 | Corey Widmer | .08 | .05 |
| 17 | Santana Dotson | .20 | .12 |
| 18 | Chris Holder | .08 | .05 |
| 19 | Elbert Turner | .05 | .02 |
| 20 | Mike Croel (FB) | .15 | .10 |
| 21 | Darren Perry | .08 | .05 |
| 22 | Troy Vincent | .25 | .15 |
| 23 | Quentin Coryatt | .40 | .25 |
| 24 | John Brown III | .07 | .04 |
| 25 | John Ray | .05 | .02 |
| 26 | Vaughn Dunbar | .75 | .45 |
| 27 | Stacey Dillard | .07 | .04 |
| 28 | Alonzo Spellman | .12 | .07 |
| 29 | Darren Woodson | .08 | .05 |
| 30 | Pat Swilling (FB) | .10 | .06 |
| 31 | Eddie Robinson | .12 | .07 |
| 32 | Tyji Armstrong | .08 | .05 |
| 33 | Bill Johnson | .10 | .06 |
| 34 | Eugene Chung | .08 | .05 |
| 35 | Ricardo McDonald | .10 | .06 |
| 36 | Sean Lumpkin | .08 | .05 |
| 37 | Greg Skrepenak | .08 | .05 |
| 38 | Ashley Ambrose | .12 | .07 |
| 39 | Kevin Smith | .12 | .07 |
| 40 | Todd Collins | .08 | .05 |
| 41 | Shane Dronett | .12 | .07 |
| 42 | Ronnie West | .08 | .05 |
| 43 | Darryl Williams | .20 | .12 |
| 44 | Rodney Blackshear | .07 | .04 |
| 45 | Dion Lambert | .07 | .04 |
| 46 | Mike Saunders | .08 | .05 |
| 47 | Keo Coleman | .08 | .05 |
| 48 | Dana Hall | .20 | .12 |
| 49 | Arthur Marshall | .05 | .02 |
| 50 | Leonard Russell (FB) | .40 | .25 |
| 51 | Matt Rodgers | .15 | .10 |
| 52 | Shane Collins | .15 | .10 |
| 53 | Courtney Hawkins | .20 | .12 |
| 54 | Chuck Smith | .12 | .07 |
| 55 | Joe Bowden | .07 | .04 |
| 56 | Gene McGuire | .05 | .02 |
| 57 | Tracy Scroggins | .12 | .07 |
| 58 | Mark D'Onofrio | .12 | .07 |
| 59 | Jimmy Smith | .20 | .12 |
| 60 | Carl Pickens | .75 | .45 |
| 61 | Robert Harris | .08 | .05 |
| 62 | Erick Anderson | .12 | .07 |
| 63 | Doug Rigby | .07 | .04 |
| 64 | Keith Hamilton | .10 | .06 |
| 65 | Vaughn Dunbar (SS) | .40 | .25 |
| 66 | Willie Clay | .15 | .10 |
| 67 | Robert Jones | .20 | .12 |
| 68 | Leon Searcy | .08 | .05 |
| 69 | Elliot Pilton | .05 | .02 |
| 70 | Thurman Thomas (FB) | .60 | .35 |
| 71 | Mark Wheeler | .08 | .05 |
| 72 | Jeremy Lincoln | .08 | .05 |
| 73 | Tony McCoy | .07 | .04 |
| 74 | Charles Davenport | .15 | .10 |

| 75 | Patrick Rowe | .20 | .12 |
|----|--------------|-----|-----|
| 76 | Tommy Jeter | .08 | .05 |
| 77 | Rod Smith | .08 | .05 |
| 78 | Johnny Mitchell | .25 | .15 |
| 79 | Corey Barlow | .08 | .05 |
| 80 | Scottie Graham | .25 | .15 |
| 81 | Mark Bounds | .05 | .02 |
| 82 | Chester McGlockton | .12 | .07 |
| 83 | Ray Roberts | .08 | .05 |
| 84 | Dale Carter | .25 | .15 |
| 85 | James Patton | .08 | .05 |
| 86 | Tyrone Legette | .15 | .10 |
| 87 | Leodis Flowers | .07 | .04 |
| 88 | Rico Smith | .10 | .06 |
| 89 | Kevin Turner | .15 | .10 |
| 90 | Steve Emtman | 1.00 | .70 |
| 91 | Rodney Culver | .20 | .12 |
| 92 | Chris Mims | .20 | .12 |
| 93 | Carlos Snow | .10 | .06 |
| 94 | Corey Harris | .12 | .07 |
| 95 | Nate Williams | .10 | .06 |
| 96 | Timothy Roberts | .07 | .04 |
| 97 | Steve Israel | .10 | .06 |
| 98 | Tony Smith | .15 | .10 |
| 99 | Dwayne Sabb | .07 | .04 |
| 100 | Checklist | .05 | .02 |

# TOPPS

## 1950 Topps Felt Backs

JACKIE JENSEN
All-American Halfback
U. of CALIFORNIA

This 100-card set marked Topps first football effort. Card fronts feature close up portraits while the card backs depict a college pennant and are made out of felt.. Cards with a yellow background are valued at twice the listed price. Cards measure 7/8" by 1-7/16".

|  |  | NR/MT | EX |
|--|--|-------|-----|
| Complete Set (100) | | 3,250.00 | 1,650.00 |
| Commons | | 27.50 | 13.00 |
| Commons (Yellow) | | 55.00 | 26.00 |

| 1 | Lou Allen | 27.50 | 13.00 |
|---|-----------|-------|------|
| 2 | Morris Bailey | 27.50 | 13.00 |
| 3 | George Bell | 27.50 | 13.00 |
| 4 | Lindy Berry | 27.50 | 13.00 |
| 5 | Mike Boldin | 27.50 | 13.00 |
| 6 | Bernie Botula | 27.50 | 13.00 |
| 7 | Bob Bowlby | 27.50 | 13.00 |
| 8 | Bob Bucher | 27.50 | 13.00 |
| 9 | Al Burentt | 27.50 | 13.00 |
| 10 | Don Burson | 27.50 | 13.00 |
| 11 | Paul Campbell | 27.50 | 13.00 |
| 12 | Herb Carey | 27.50 | 13.00 |
| 13 | Bimbo Cecconi | 27.50 | 13.00 |
| 14 | Bill Chauncey | 27.50 | 13.00 |
| 15 | Dick Clark | 27.50 | 13.00 |

| | | | |
|---|---|---|---|
| 16 | Tom Coleman | 27.50 | 13.00 |
| 17 | Billy Conn | 27.50 | 13.00 |
| 18 | John Cox | 27.50 | 13.00 |
| 19 | Lou Creekmur | 38.00 | 18.00 |
| 20 | Glen Davis | 30.00 | 14.50 |
| 21 | Warren Davis | 27.50 | 13.00 |
| 22 | Bob Deuber | 27.50 | 13.00 |
| 23 | Ray Dooney | 27.50 | 13.00 |
| 24 | Tom Dublinski | 27.50 | 13.00 |
| 25 | Jeff Fleischman | 27.50 | 13.00 |
| 26 | Jack Friedland | 27.50 | 13.00 |
| 27 | Bob Fuchs | 27.50 | 13.00 |
| 28 | Arnold Galiffa | 32.00 | 15.00 |
| 29 | Dick Gilman | 27.50 | 13.00 |
| 30 | Frank Gitschier | 27.50 | 13.00 |
| 31 | Gene Glick | 27.50 | 13.00 |
| 32 | Bill Gregus | 27.50 | 13.00 |
| 33 | Harold Hagan | 27.50 | 13.00 |
| 34 | Charles Hall | 27.50 | 13.00 |
| 35 | Leon Hart | 45.00 | 22.00 |
| 36 | Bob Hester | 27.50 | 13.00 |
| 37 | George Hughes | 27.50 | 13.00 |
| 38 | Levi Jackson | 27.50 | 13.00 |
| 39 | Jackie Jensen | 125.00 | 60.00 |
| 40 | Charlie Justice | 80.00 | 38.00 |
| 41 | Gary Kerkorian | 27.50 | 13.00 |
| 42 | Bernie Krueger | 27.50 | 13.00 |
| 43 | Bill Kuhn | 27.50 | 13.00 |
| 44 | Dean Laun | 27.50 | 13.00 |
| 45 | Chet Leach | 27.50 | 13.00 |
| 46 | Bobby Lee | 27.50 | 13.00 |
| 47 | Roger Lehew | 27.50 | 13.00 |
| 48 | Glenn Lippman | 27.50 | 13.00 |
| 49 | Melvin Lyle | 27.50 | 13.00 |
| 50 | Len Makowski | 27.50 | 13.00 |
| 51 | Al Malekoff | 27.50 | 13.00 |
| 52 | Jim Martin | 32.00 | 15.00 |
| 53 | Frank Mataya | 27.50 | 13.00 |
| 54 | Ray Mathews | 30.00 | 14.50 |
| 56 | Frank Miller | 27.50 | 13.00 |
| 57 | John Miller | 27.50 | 13.00 |
| 58 | Ed Modzelewski | 32.00 | 15.00 |
| 59 | Don Mouser | 27.50 | 13.00 |
| 60 | James Murphy | 27.50 | 13.00 |
| 61 | Ray Nagle | 30.00 | 14.50 |
| 62 | Leo Nomellini | 100.00 | 48.00 |
| 63 | James O'Day | 27.50 | 13.00 |
| 64 | Joe Paterno (R) | 375.00 | 175.00 |
| 65 | Andy Pavich | 27.50 | 13.00 |
| 66 | Pete Perini | 27.50 | 13.00 |
| 67 | Jim Powers | 27.50 | 13.00 |
| 68 | Dave Rakestraw | 27.50 | 13.00 |
| 69 | Herb Rich | 27.50 | 13.00 |
| 70 | Fran Rogel | 30.00 | 14.50 |
| 71 | Darrell Royal (R) | 75.00 | 36.00 |
| 72 | Steve Sawie | 27.50 | 13.00 |
| 73 | Nick Sebek | 27.50 | 13.00 |
| 74 | Herb Seidell | 27.50 | 13.00 |
| 75 | Charles Shaw | 27.50 | 13.00 |
| 76 | Emil Sitko | 27.50 | 13.00 |
| 77 | Butch Songin | 30.00 | 14.50 |
| 78 | Mariano Stalloni | 27.50 | 13.00 |
| 79 | Ernie Stautner | 100.00 | 48.00 |
| 80 | Don Stehley | 27.50 | 13.00 |
| 81 | Gil Stevenson | 27.50 | 13.00 |
| 82 | Bishop Strickland | 27.50 | 13.00 |
| 83 | Harry Szulborski | 27.50 | 13.00 |
| 84 | Wally Teninga | 27.50 | 13.00 |
| 85 | Clayton Tonnemaker | 27.50 | 13.00 |
| 86 | Dan Towler | 35.00 | 16.50 |
| 87 | Bert Turek | 27.50 | 13.00 |
| 88 | Harry Ulinski | 27.50 | 13.00 |
| 89 | Leon Van Billingham | 27.50 | 13.00 |
| 90 | Langdon Viracola | 27.50 | 13.00 |
| 91 | Leo Wagner | 27.50 | 13.00 |
| 92 | Doak Walker | 120.00 | 55.00 |
| 93 | Jim Ward | 27.50 | 13.00 |
| 94 | Art Weiner | 27.50 | 13.00 |
| 95 | Dick Weiss | 27.50 | 13.00 |
| 96 | Froggie Williams | 27.50 | 13.00 |
| 97 | Robert Wilson | 27.50 | 13.00 |
| 98 | Roger Wilson | 27.50 | 13.00 |
| 99 | Carl Wren | 27.50 | 13.00 |
| 100 | Pete Zinaich | 27.50 | 13.00 |

# 1955 Topps All-American

"TURK" EDWARDS  Tackle

Composed of some of college footballs legendary stars, this 100-card set features posed player shots on the front with the player's name and position printed across the bottom. A shield type All-American logo is located above the player's name. Card backs contain a small cartoon and highlights. A number of cards were short-printed (SP) and are considered scarce. Cards measure 2-5/8" by 3-5/8".

|  |  | NR/MT | EX |
|---|---|---|---|
| Complete Set (100) | | 3,500.00 | 1,850.00 |
| Commons | | 12.00 | 6.00 |
| Commons (SP) | | 20.00 | 10.00 |

| | | NR/MT | EX |
|---|---|---|---|
| 1 | Herman Hickman(R) | 100.00 | 38.00 |
| 2 | John Kimbrough | 12.00 | 6.00 |
| 3 | Ed Weir | 12.00 | 6.00 |
| 4 | Ernie Pinckert | 12.00 | 6.00 |
| 5 | Bobby grayson | 12.00 | 6.00 |
| 6 | Nile Kinnick(R) | 25.00 | 12.50 |
| 7 | Andy Bershak | 12.00 | 6.00 |
| 8 | George Catego (R) | 12.00 | 6.00 |
| 9 | Tom Hamilton (SP) | 20.00 | 10.00 |
| 10 | Bill Dudley | 25.00 | 12.50 |
| 11 | Bobby Dodd (SP) | 20.00 | 10.00 |
| 12 | Otto Graham | 180.00 | 85.00 |
| 13 | Aaron Rosenberg | 12.00 | 6.00 |
| 14 | Gaynell Tinsley | 15.00 | 7.50 |
| 15 | Ed Kaw (SP) | 20.00 | 10.00 |
| 16 | Knute Rockne | 250.00 | 110.00 |
| 17 | Bob Reynolds | 12.00 | 6.00 |
| 18 | Pudge Heffelfinger | 20.00 | 10.00 |
| 19 | Bruce Smith | 12.00 | 6.00 |
| 20 | Sammy Baugh | 150.00 | 70.00 |
| 21A | Whizzer White (Er) | 30.00 | 14.00 |
| 21B | Whizzer White (Cor) | 40.00 | 18.50 |
| 22 | Brick Muller | 12.00 | 6.00 |
| 23 | Dick Kazmaier (R) | 16.00 | 8.00 |
| 24 | Ken Strong | 18.00 | 9.00 |
| 25 | Casimir Myslinski | 20.00 | 10.00 |
| 26 | Larry Kelley (SP) | 20.00 | 10.00 |
| 27 | Red Grange | 275.00 | 130.00 |
| 28 | Mel Hein (R) (SP) | 24.00 | 12.00 |
| 29 | Leo Nomellini (SP) | 30.00 | 14.00 |
| 30 | Wes E. Fesler | 12.00 | 6.00 |
| 31 | George Sauer Sr. (R) | 15.00 | 7.50 |
| 32 | Hank Foldberg | 12.00 | 6.00 |
| 33 | Bob Higgins | 12.00 | 6.00 |
| 34 | Davey O'Brien (R) | 25.00 | 12.50 |
| 35 | Tom Harmon (R) (SP) | 38.00 | 18.00 |
| 36 | Turk Edwards (SP) | 25.00 | 12.50 |
| 37 | Jim Thorpe | 350.00 | 160.00 |
| 38 | Amos Alonzo Stagg (R) | 38.00 | 18.00 |
| 39 | Jerome Holland (R) | 14.00 | 7.00 |
| 40 | Donn Moomaw | 12.00 | 6.00 |
| 41 | Joseph Alexander (SP) | 20.00 | 10.00 |
| 42 | J. Edward Tryon (SP) | 20.00 | 10.00 |
| 43 | Georgie Savitsky | 12.00 | 6.00 |
| 44 | Ed Garbisch | 12.00 | 6.00 |
| 45 | Elmer Oliphant | 12.00 | 6.00 |
| 46 | Arnold Lassman | 12.00 | 6.00 |
| 47 | Bo McMillan | 12.00 | 6.00 |
| 48 | Ed Widseth | 12.00 | 6.00 |
| 49 | Don Zimmerman | 12.00 | 6.00 |
| 50 | Ken Kavanaugh | 16.00 | 8.00 |
| 51 | Duane Purvis (SP) | 20.00 | 10.00 |
| 52 | John Lujack | 30.00 | 14.00 |
| 53 | John Green | 12.00 | 6.00 |
| 54 | Edwin Dooley (SP) | 20.00 | 10.00 |
| 55 | Frank Merritt (SP) | 20.00 | 10.00 |
| 56 | Ernie Nevers (R) | 40.00 | 19.00 |
| 57 | Vic Hanson (SP) | 24.00 | 12.00 |
| 58 | Ed Franco | 12.00 | 6.00 |
| 59 | Doc Blanchard (R) | 40.00 | 19.00 |
| 60 | Dan Hill | 12.00 | 6.00 |
| 61 | Charles Brickley (SP) | 20.00 | 10.00 |
| 62 | Harry Newman | 12.00 | 6.00 |
| 63 | Charlie Justice | 16.00 | 8.00 |
| 64 | Benny Friedman (SP) | 12.00 | 6.00 |
| 65 | Joe Donchess (SP) | 20.00 | 10.00 |
| 66 | Bruiser Kinard (R) | 18.00 | 9.00 |
| 67 | Frankie Albert | 18.00 | 9.00 |
| 68 | Four Horsemen | 450.00 | 200.00 |
| 69 | Frank Sinkwich | 16.00 | 8.00 |
| 70 | Bill Daddio | 12.00 | 6.00 |
| 71 | Bob Wilson | 12.00 | 6.00 |
| 72 | Chub Peabody | 12.00 | 6.00 |
| 73 | Paul Governali | 12.00 | 6.00 |
| 74 | Gene McEver | 12.00 | 6.00 |
| 75 | Hugh Gallarneau | 12.00 | 6.00 |
| 76 | Angelo Bertelli (R) | 16.00 | 8.00 |
| 77 | Bowden Wyatt (SP) | 20.00 | 10.00 |
| 78 | Jay Berwanger (R) | 24.00 | 12.00 |
| 79 | Pug Lund | 12.00 | 6.00 |
| 80 | Bennie Oosterbaan | 12.00 | 6.00 |
| 81 | Cotton Warburton | 12.00 | 6.00 |
| 82 | Alex Wojciechowicz | 20.00 | 10.00 |
| 83 | Ted Coy (SP) | 20.00 | 10.00 |
| 84 | Ace Parker (R)(SP) | 36.00 | 18.00 |
| 85 | Sid Luckman | 75.00 | 36.00 |
| 86 | Albie Booth (SP) | 20.00 | 10.00 |
| 87 | Adolph Schultz (SP) | 20.00 | 10.00 |
| 88 | Ralph Kercheval | 12.00 | 6.00 |
| 89 | Marshall Goldberg | 12.00 | 6.00 |
| 90 | Charlie O'Rourke | 12.00 | 6.00 |
| 91 | Bob Odell | 12.00 | 6.00 |
| 92 | Biggie Munn | 12.00 | 6.00 |
| 93 | Willie Heston (SP) | 20.00 | 10.00 |
| 94 | Joe Bernard (SP) | 20.00 | 10.00 |
| 95 | Red Cagle (SP) | 20.00 | 10.00 |
| 96 | Bill Hollenback (SP) | 20.00 | 10.00 |

| | | NR/MT | EX |
|---|---|---|---|
| 97 | Don Hutson (R)(SP) | 125.00 | 60.00 |
| 98 | Beattie Feathers (SP) | 30.00 | 14.00 |
| 99 | Don Whitmire (SP) | 20.00 | 10.00 |
| 100 | Fats Henry (R)(SP) | 175.00 | 60.00 |

## 1956 Topps

This 120-card set represents Topps first NFL set. The fronts feature posed portrait shots over a plain background. The player's name, position and team are found in a horizontal box at the bottom of the card. The horizontal card backs contain a brief paragraph of copy, a cartoon and statistics. Some short prints exist in this set and are indicated by the initials (SP). All cards measure 2-5/8" by 3-5/8".

| | | NR/MT | EX |
|---|---|---|---|
| **Complete Set (120)** | | 1,775.00 | 850.00 |
| **Commons** | | 5.00 | 2.25 |
| | | | |
| 1 | Jack Carson (SP) | 50.00 | 15.00 |
| 2 | Gordon Soltau | 5.00 | 2.25 |
| 3 | Frank Varrichione | 5.00 | 2.25 |
| 4 | Eddie Bell | 5.00 | 2.25 |
| 5 | Alex Webster (R) | 12.00 | 5.00 |
| 6 | Norm Van Brocklin | 28.00 | 12.50 |
| 7 | Packers Team | 12.00 | 5.00 |
| 8 | Lou Creekmur | 5.00 | 2.25 |
| 9 | Lou Groza | 25.00 | 10.00 |
| 10 | Tom Bienemann(R) | 12.00 | 5.00 |
| 11 | George Blanda | 70.00 | 32.00 |
| 12 | Alan Ameche | 10.00 | 4.00 |
| 13 | Vic Janowicz (SP) | 12.00 | 5.00 |
| 14 | Dick Moegle | 5.00 | 2.25 |
| 15 | Fran Rogel | 5.00 | 2.25 |
| 16 | Harold Giancanelli | 5.00 | 2.25 |
| 17 | Emlen Tunnell | 12.00 | 5.00 |
| 18 | Tank Younger | 7.50 | 3.50 |
| 19 | Bill Howton | 7.50 | 3.50 |
| 20 | Jack Christiansen | 12.00 | 5.00 |
| 21 | Darrell Brewster | 5.00 | 2.25 |
| 22 | Cardinals Team (SP) | 75.00 | 35.00 |
| 23 | Ed Brown | 7.50 | 3.50 |
| 24 | Joe Campanella | 5.00 | 2.25 |
| 25 | Leon Heath (SP) | 10.00 | 4.00 |
| 26 | 49er's Team | 12.00 | 5.00 |
| 27 | Dick Flanagan | 5.00 | 2.25 |
| 28 | Chuck Bednarik | 18.00 | 8.00 |
| 29 | Kyle Rote | 10.00 | 4.00 |
| 30 | Les Richter | 7.00 | 3.00 |
| 31 | Howard Ferguson | 5.00 | 2.25 |
| 32 | Dorne Dibble | 5.00 | 2.25 |
| 33 | Kenny Konz | 5.00 | 2.25 |
| 34 | Dave Mann (SP) | 10.00 | 4.00 |
| 35 | Rick Casares | 7.50 | 3.50 |
| 36 | Art Donovan | 16.00 | 7.00 |
| 37 | Chuck Drazenovich | 10.00 | 4.00 |
| 38 | Joe Arenas | 5.00 | 2.25 |
| 39 | Lynn Chandnois | 5.00 | 2.25 |
| 40 | Eagles Team | 12.00 | 5.00 |
| 41 | Roosevelt Brown (R) | 35.00 | 16.00 |
| 42 | Tom Fears | 12.00 | 5.00 |
| 43 | Gary Knafelc | 5.00 | 2.25 |
| 44 | Joe Schmidt (R) | 48.00 | 22.00 |
| 45 | Browns Team | 12.00 | 5.00 |
| 46 | Len Teeuws (R)(SP) | 15.00 | 6.50 |
| 47 | Bill George (R) | 36.00 | 16.50 |
| 48 | Colts Team | 12.00 | 5.00 |
| 49 | Eddie LeBaron (SP) | 18.00 | 8.00 |
| 50 | Hugh McElhenny | 18.00 | 8.00 |
| 51 | Ted Marchibroda | 7.50 | 3.50 |
| 52 | Adrian Burk | 5.00 | 2.25 |
| 53 | Frank Gifford | 175.00 | 80.00 |
| 54 | Charley Toogood | 5.00 | 2.25 |
| 55 | Tobin Rote | 7.50 | 3.50 |
| 56 | Bill Stits | 5.00 | 2.25 |
| 57 | Don Colo | 5.00 | 2.25 |
| 58 | Ollie Matson (SP) | 36.00 | 16.50 |
| 59 | Harlon Hill | 7.00 | 3.00 |
| 60 | Lenny Moore (R) | 75.00 | 35.00 |
| 61 | Redskins Team (SP) | 75.00 | 35.00 |
| 62 | Billy Wilson | 5.00 | 2.25 |
| 63 | Steelers Team | 12.00 | 5.00 |
| 64 | Bob Pellegrini | 5.00 | 2.25 |
| 65 | Ken MacAfee | 5.00 | 2.25 |
| 66 | Willard Sherman | 5.00 | 2.25 |
| 67 | Roger Zatkoff | 5.00 | 2.25 |
| 68 | Dave Middleton | 5.00 | 2.25 |
| 69 | Ray Renfro | 7.00 | 3.00 |
| 70 | Don Stonesifer (SP) | 12.00 | 5.00 |
| 71 | Stan Jones (R) | 28.00 | 12.50 |
| 72 | Jim Mutscheller | 5.00 | 2.25 |
| 73 | Volney Peters (R) | 10.00 | 4.00 |

| | | | |
|---|---|---|---|
| 74 | Leo Nomellini | 15.00 | 6.50 |
| 75 | Ray Mathews | 5.00 | 2.25 |
| 76 | Dick Bielski | 5.00 | 2.25 |
| 77 | Charley Conerly | 28.00 | 12.50 |
| 78 | Elroy Hirsch | 18.00 | 8.00 |
| 79 | Bill Forester (R) | 7.00 | 3.00 |
| 80 | Jim Doran | 5.00 | 2.25 |
| 81 | Fred Morrison | 5.00 | 2.25 |
| 82 | Jack Simmons (SP) | 12.00 | 5.00 |
| 83 | Bill McColl | 5.00 | 2.25 |
| 84 | Bert Rechichar | 5.00 | 2.25 |
| 85 | Joe Scudero (SP) | 10.00 | 4.00 |
| 86 | Y.A. Tittle | 36.00 | 16.50 |
| 87 | Ernie Stautner | 12.00 | 5.00 |
| 88 | Norm Willey | 5.00 | 2.25 |
| 89 | Bob Schnelker | 7.00 | 3.00 |
| 90 | Dan Towler | 5.00 | 2.25 |
| 91 | John Martinkovic | 5.00 | 2.25 |
| 92 | Lions Team | 12.00 | 5.00 |
| 93 | George Ratterman | 7.00 | 3.00 |
| 94 | Chuck Ulrich | 12.00 | 5.00 |
| 95 | Bobby Watkins | 5.00 | 2.25 |
| 96 | Buddy Young | 7.50 | 3.50 |
| 97 | Billy Wells (SP) | 10.00 | 4.00 |
| 98 | Bob Toneff | 5.00 | 2.25 |
| 99 | Bill McPeak | 5.00 | 2.25 |
| 100 | Bobby Thomason | 5.00 | 2.25 |
| 101 | Roosevelt Grier (R) | 28.00 | 12.50 |
| 102 | Ron Walker | 5.00 | 2.25 |
| 103 | Bobby Dillon | 5.00 | 2.25 |
| 104 | Leon Hart | 7.50 | 3.50 |
| 105 | Mike McCormack | 12.00 | 5.00 |
| 106 | John Olszewski (SP) | 12.00 | 5.00 |
| 107 | Bill Wightkin | 5.00 | 2.25 |
| 108 | George Shaw (R) | 7.50 | 3.50 |
| 109 | Dale Atkeson (SP) | 10.00 | 4.00 |
| 110 | Joe Perry | 18.00 | 8.00 |
| 111 | Dale Dodrill | 5.00 | 2.25 |
| 112 | Tom Scott | 5.00 | 2.25 |
| 113 | Giants Team | 12.00 | 5.00 |
| 114 | Los Angeles Rams | 12.00 | 5.00 |
| 115 | Al Carmichael | 5.00 | 2.25 |
| 116 | Bobby Layne | 35.00 | 16.00 |
| 117 | Ed Modzelewski | 5.00 | 2.25 |
| 118 | Lamar McHan (R) (SP) | 15.00 | 6.50 |
| 119 | Bears Team | 12.00 | 5.00 |
| 120 | Billy Vessels (R) | 30.00 | 12.50 |
| ___ | Checklist Card | 340.00 | 75.00 |

# 1957 Topps

This set includes 154-cards and an unnumbered checklist card. The horizontal card fronts contain a close-up head shot and an action shot. The card backs feature the player's personal data and stats on the left side and a cartoon on the right side. The high numbered cards are not as plentiful as the lower numbers. All cards measure 2-1/2" by 3-1/2".

| | | NR/MT | EX |
|---|---|---|---|
| **Complete Set (155)** | | 3,350.00 | 1,550.00 |
| **Commons (1-88)** | | 4.00 | 2.00 |
| **Commons (89-154)** | | 6.00 | 3.00 |
| | | | |
| 1 | Eddie LeBaron | 40.00 | 12.00 |
| 2 | Pete Retzlaff (R) | 7.50 | 3.75 |
| 3 | Mike McCormack | 7.50 | 3.75 |
| 4 | Lou Baldacci | 4.00 | 2.00 |
| 5 | Gino Marchetti | 12.50 | 6.25 |
| 6 | Leo Nomellini | 12.50 | 6.25 |
| 7 | Bobby Watkins | 4.00 | 2.00 |
| 8 | Dave Middleton | 4.00 | 2.00 |
| 9 | Bobby Dillon | 4.00 | 2.00 |
| 10 | Les Richter | 4.00 | 2.00 |
| 11 | Roosevelt Brown | 12.50 | 6.50 |
| 12 | Lavern Torgeson | 4.00 | 2.00 |
| 13 | Dick Bielski | 4.00 | 2.00 |
| 14 | Pat Summerall | 10.00 | 5.00 |
| 15 | Jack Butler (R) | 5.00 | 2.50 |
| 16 | John Henry Johnson | 12.50 | 6.50 |
| 17 | Art Spinney | 4.00 | 2.00 |
| 18 | Bob St. Clair | 10.00 | 5.00 |
| 19 | Perry Jeter | 4.00 | 2.00 |
| 20 | Lou Creekmur | 4.00 | 2.00 |
| 21 | Dave Hanner | 4.00 | 2.00 |
| 22 | Norm Van Brocklin | 24.00 | 12.00 |
| 23 | Don Chandler (R) | 8.00 | 4.00 |
| 24 | Al Dorow | 4.00 | 2.00 |

| | | | |
|---|---|---|---|
| 25 | Tom Scott | 4.00 | 2.00 |
| 26 | Ollie Matson | 15.00 | 7.50 |
| 27 | Fran Rogel | 4.00 | 2.00 |
| 28 | Lou Groza | 20.00 | 10.00 |
| 29 | Billy Vessels | 5.00 | 2.50 |
| 30 | Y.A. Tittle | 42.00 | 21.00 |
| 41 | George Blanda | 55.00 | 27.50 |
| 32 | Bobby Layne | 35.00 | 17.50 |
| 33 | Bill Howton | 4.50 | 2.25 |
| 34 | Bill Wade | 5.00 | 2.50 |
| 35 | Emlen Tunnell | 10.00 | 5.00 |
| 36 | Leo Elter | 4.00 | 2.00 |
| 37 | Clarence Peaks (R) | 4.50 | 2.25 |
| 38 | Don Stonesifer | 4.00 | 2.00 |
| 39 | George Tarasovic | 4.00 | 2.00 |
| 40 | Darrell Brewster | 4.00 | 2.00 |
| 41 | Bert Rechichar | 4.00 | 2.00 |
| 42 | Billy Wilson | 4.00 | 2.00 |
| 43 | Ed Brown | 4.50 | 2.25 |
| 44 | Gene Gedman | 4.00 | 2.00 |
| 45 | Gary Knafelc | 4.00 | 2.00 |
| 46 | Elroy Hirsch | 14.00 | 7.00 |
| 47 | Don Heinrich | 5.00 | 2.50 |
| 48 | Gene Brito | 4.00 | 2.00 |
| 49 | Chuck Bednarik | 15.00 | 7.50 |
| 50 | Dave Mann | 4.00 | 2.00 |
| 51 | Bill McPeak | 4.00 | 2.00 |
| 52 | Kenny Konz | 4.00 | 2.00 |
| 53 | Alan Ameche | 8.50 | 4.25 |
| 54 | Gordon Soltau | 4.00 | 2.00 |
| 55 | Rick Casares | 4.50 | 2.25 |
| 56 | Charlie Ane | 4.00 | 2.00 |
| 57 | Al Carmichael | 4.00 | 2.00 |
| 58A | Willard Sherman (Er) (No team name) | 15.00 | 7.50 |
| 58B | Willard Sherman (Cor) | 4.00 | 2.00 |
| 59 | Kyle Rote | 8.00 | 4.00 |
| 60 | Chuck Drazenovich | 4.00 | 2.00 |
| 61 | Bobby Walston | 4.00 | 2.00 |
| 62 | John Olszewski | 4.00 | 2.00 |
| 63 | Ray Mathews | 4.00 | 2.00 |
| 64 | Maurice Bassett | 4.00 | 2.00 |
| 65 | Art Donovan | 12.00 | 6.00 |
| 66 | Joe Arenas | 4.00 | 2.00 |
| 67 | Harlon Hill | 4.00 | 2.00 |
| 68 | Yale Lary | 8.50 | 4.25 |
| 69 | Bill Forester | 4.00 | 2.00 |
| 70 | Bob Boyd | 4.00 | 2.00 |
| 71 | Andy Robustelli | 12.50 | 6.25 |
| 72 | Sam Baker (R) | 6.50 | 3.25 |
| 73 | Bob Pellegrini | 4.00 | 2.00 |
| 74 | Leo Sanford | 4.00 | 2.00 |
| 75 | Sid Watson | 4.00 | 2.00 |
| 76 | Ray Renfro | 4.50 | 2.25 |
| 77 | Carl Taseff | 4.00 | 2.00 |
| 78 | Clyde Conner | 4.00 | 2.00 |
| 79 | J.C. Caroline | 4.00 | 2.00 |
| 80 | Howard Cassady (R) | 12.00 | 6.00 |
| 81 | Tobin Rote | 4.50 | 2.25 |
| 82 | Ron Waller | 4.00 | 2.00 |
| 83 | Jim Patton (R) | 4.50 | 2.25 |
| 84 | Volney Peters | 4.00 | 2.00 |
| 85 | Dick Lane (R) | 40.00 | 20.00 |
| 86 | Royce Womble | 4.00 | 2.00 |
| 87 | Duane Putnam | 4.00 | 2.00 |
| 88 | Frank Gifford | 125.00 | 62.50 |
| 89 | Steve Meilinger | 6.00 | 3.00 |
| 90 | Buck Lansford | 6.00 | 3.00 |
| 91 | Lindon Crow | 6.00 | 3.00 |
| 92 | Ernie Stautner | 12.00 | 6.00 |
| 93 | Preston Carpenter (R) | 7.50 | 3.75 |
| 94 | Raymond Berry (R) | 85.00 | 42.50 |
| 95 | Hugh McElhenny | 16.00 | 8.00 |
| 96 | Stan Jones | 12.00 | 6.00 |
| 97 | Dorne Dibble | 6.00 | 3.00 |
| 98 | Joe Scudero | 6.00 | 3.00 |
| 99 | Eddie Bell | 6.00 | 3.00 |
| 100 | Joe Childress | 6.00 | 3.00 |
| 101 | Elbert Nickel | 6.00 | 3.00 |
| 102 | Walt Michaels | 7.50 | 3.75 |
| 103 | Jim Mutscheller | 6.00 | 3.00 |
| 104 | Earl Morrall (R) | 28.00 | 14.00 |
| 105 | Larry Strickland | 6.00 | 3.00 |
| 106 | Jack Christiansen | 12.00 | 6.00 |
| 107 | Fred Cone | 6.00 | 3.00 |
| 108 | Bud McFadin (R) | 7.00 | 3.50 |
| 109 | Charley Conerly | 35.00 | 17.50 |
| 110 | Tom Runnels | 6.00 | 3.00 |
| 111 | Ken Keller | 6.00 | 3.00 |
| 112 | James Root | 6.00 | 3.00 |
| 113 | Ted Marchibroda | 7.00 | 3.50 |
| 114 | Don Paul | 6.00 | 3.00 |
| 115 | George Shaw | 6.50 | 3.25 |
| 116 | Dick Moegle | 6.00 | 3.00 |
| 117 | Don Bingham | 6.00 | 3.00 |
| 118 | Leon Hart | 8.50 | 4.25 |
| 119 | Bart Starr | 550.00 | 275.00 |
| 120 | Paul Miller | 6.00 | 3.00 |
| 121 | Alex Webster | 8.50 | 4.25 |
| 122 | Ray Wietecha | 6.00 | 3.00 |
| 123 | Johnny Carson | 6.00 | 3.00 |
| 124 | Tommy McDonald (R) | 12.00 | 6.00 |
| 125 | Jerry Tubbs (R) | 8.50 | 4.25 |
| 126 | Jack Scarbath | 6.00 | 3.00 |
| 127 | Ed Modzelewski | 6.00 | 3.00 |
| 128 | Lenny Moore | 30.00 | 15.00 |
| 129 | Joe Perry | 20.00 | 10.00 |
| 130 | Bill Wightkin | 6.00 | 3.00 |
| 131 | Jim Doran | 6.00 | 3.00 |
| 132 | Howard Ferguson | 6.00 | 3.00 |
| 133 | Tom Wilson | 6.00 | 3.00 |

| | | NR/MT | EX |
|---|---|---|---|
| 134 | Dick James | 6.00 | 3.00 |
| 135 | Jimmy Harris | 6.00 | 3.00 |
| 136 | Chuck Ulrich | 6.00 | 3.00 |
| 137 | Lynn Chandnois | 6.00 | 3.00 |
| 138 | John Unitas | 700.00 | 350.00 |
| 139 | Jim Ridlon | 6.00 | 3.00 |
| 140 | Zeke Bratkowski | 8.00 | 4.00 |
| 141 | Ray Krouse | 6.00 | 3.00 |
| 142 | John Martinkovic | 6.00 | 3.00 |
| 143 | Jim Cason | 6.00 | 3.00 |
| 144 | Ken MacAfee | 6.50 | 3.25 |
| 145 | Sid Youngelman | 6.00 | 3.00 |
| 146 | Paul Larson | 6.00 | 3.00 |
| 147 | Len Ford | 10.00 | 5.00 |
| 148 | Bob Toneff | 6.00 | 3.00 |
| 149 | Ronnie Knox | 6.00 | 3.00 |
| 150 | Jim David (R) | 7.50 | 3.25 |
| 151 | Paul Hornung (R) | 550.00 | 275.00 |
| 152 | Tank Younger | 7.50 | 3.25 |
| 153 | Bill Svoboda | 6.00 | 3.00 |
| 154 | Fred Morrison | 38.00 | 10.00 |
| ___ | Checklist | 475.00 | 110.00 |

## 1958 Topps

JIM RINGO (CENTER) GREEN BAY PACKERS

The cards in this 132-card set feature posed action shots inside an oval border on the card fronts. The player's name, team and position are printed below the photo. Card backs are horizontal and include personal data, highlights and a trivia question. All cards measure 2-1/2" by 3-1/2".

| | NR/MT | EX |
|---|---|---|
| **Complete Set (132)** | 1,400.00 | 700.00 |
| **Commons** | 2.50 | 1.25 |

| | | NR/MT | EX |
|---|---|---|---|
| 1 | Gene Flipski (R) | 18.00 | 4.00 |
| 2 | Bobby Layne | 25.00 | 12.50 |
| 3 | Joe Schmidt | 8.50 | 4.25 |
| 4 | Bill Barnes | 2.50 | 1.25 |
| 5 | Milt Plum (R) | 7.00 | 3.50 |
| 6 | Bill Howton | 3.00 | 1.50 |
| 7 | Howard Cassady | 4.50 | 2.25 |
| 8 | Jim Dooley | 2.50 | 1.25 |
| 9 | Browns Team | 6.00 | 3.00 |
| 10 | Lenny Moore | 15.00 | 7.50 |
| 11 | Darrell Brewster | 2.50 | 1.25 |
| 12 | Alan Ameche | 5.00 | 2.50 |
| 13 | Jim David | 2.50 | 1.25 |
| 14 | Jim Mutscheller | 2.50 | 1.25 |
| 15 | Andy Robustelli | 10.00 | 5.00 |
| 16 | Gino Marchetti | 10.00 | 5.00 |
| 17 | Ray Renfro | 2.50 | 1.25 |
| 18 | Yale Lary | 8.00 | 4.00 |
| 19 | Gary Glick | 2.50 | 1.25 |
| 20 | Jon Arnett (R) | 7.00 | 3.50 |
| 21 | Bob Boyd | 2.50 | 1.25 |
| 22 | John Unitas | 250.00 | 125.00 |
| 23 | Zeke Bratkowski | 3.50 | 1.75 |
| 24 | Sid Youngelman | 2.50 | 1.25 |
| 25 | Leo Elter | 2.50 | 1.25 |
| 26 | Kenny Konz | 2.50 | 1.25 |
| 27 | Redskins Team | 6.00 | 3.00 |
| 28 | Carl Brettschneider | 2.50 | 1.25 |
| 29 | Bears Team | 6.00 | 3.00 |
| 30 | Alex Webster | 3.50 | 1.75 |
| 31 | Al Carmichael | 2.50 | 1.25 |
| 32 | Bobby Dillon | 2.50 | 1.25 |
| 33 | Steve Meilinger | 2.50 | 1.25 |
| 34 | Sam Baker | 2.50 | 1.25 |
| 35 | Chuck Bednarik | 12.00 | 6.00 |
| 36 | Vic Zucco | 2.50 | 1.25 |
| 37 | George Tarasovic | 2.50 | 1.25 |
| 38 | Bill Wade | 3.50 | 1.75 |
| 39 | Dick Stanfel | 2.50 | 1.25 |
| 40 | Jerry Norton | 2.50 | 1.25 |
| 41 | 49er's Team | 6.00 | 3.00 |
| 42 | Emlen Tunnell | 8.00 | 4.00 |
| 43 | Jim Doran | 2.50 | 1.25 |
| 44 | Ted Marchibroda | 3.00 | 1.50 |
| 45 | Chet Hanulak | 2.50 | 1.25 |
| 46 | Dale Dodrill | 2.50 | 1.25 |
| 47 | Johnny Carson | 2.50 | 1.25 |
| 48 | Dick Deschaine | 2.50 | 1.25 |
| 49 | Billy Wells | 2.50 | 1.25 |
| 50 | Larry Morris | 2.50 | 1.25 |
| 51 | Jack McClaren | 2.50 | 1.25 |
| 52 | Lou Groza | 22.00 | 11.00 |
| 53 | Rick Casares | 3.00 | 1.50 |
| 54 | Don Chandler | 3.00 | 1.50 |
| 55 | Duane Putnam | 2.50 | 1.25 |
| 56 | Gary Knafelc | 2.50 | 1.25 |
| 57 | Earl Morrall | 7.50 | 3.75 |

| | | | |
|---|---|---|---|
| 58 | Ron Kramer (R) | 4.50 | 2.25 |
| 59 | Mike McCormack | 7.00 | 3.50 |
| 60 | Gern Nagler | 2.50 | 1.25 |
| 61 | Giants Team Card | 6.00 | 3.00 |
| 62 | Jim Brown (R) | 500.00 | 250.00 |
| 63 | Joe Marconi (R) | 3.00 | 1.50 |
| 64 | R.C. Owens (R) | 4.50 | 2.25 |
| 65 | Jimmy Carr (R) | 3.50 | 1.75 |
| 66 | Bart Starr | 140.00 | 70.00 |
| 67 | Tom Wilson | 2.50 | 1.25 |
| 68 | Lamar McHan | 2.50 | 1.25 |
| 69 | Cardinals Team | 6.00 | 3.00 |
| 70 | Jack Christiansen | 8.00 | 4.00 |
| 71 | Don McIlhenny | 2.50 | 1.25 |
| 72 | Ron Waller | 2.50 | 1.25 |
| 73 | Frank Gifford | 80.00 | 40.00 |
| 74 | Bert Rechichar | 2.50 | 1.25 |
| 75 | John Henry Johnson | 8.50 | 4.25 |
| 76 | Jack Butler | 2.50 | 1.25 |
| 77 | Frank Varrichione | 2.50 | 1.25 |
| 78 | Ray Mathews | 2.50 | 1.25 |
| 79 | Marv Matuszak | 2.50 | 1.25 |
| 80 | Harlon Hill | 2.50 | 1.25 |
| 81 | Lou Creekmur | 2.50 | 1.25 |
| 82 | Woodley Lewis | 2.50 | 1.25 |
| 83 | Don Heinrich | 3.00 | 1.50 |
| 84 | Charley Conerly | 16.00 | 8.00 |
| 85 | Rams Team | 6.00 | 3.00 |
| 86 | Y.A. Tittle | 32.00 | 16.00 |
| 87 | Bobby Walston | 2.50 | 1.25 |
| 88 | Earl Putman | 2.50 | 1.25 |
| 89 | Leo Nomellini | 8.50 | 4.25 |
| 90 | Sonny Jurgensen(R) | 120.00 | 60.00 |
| 91 | Don Paul | 2.50 | 1.25 |
| 92 | Paige Cothren | 2.50 | 1.25 |
| 93 | Joe Perry | 12.50 | 6.25 |
| 94 | Tobin Rote | 3.50 | 1.75 |
| 95 | Billy Wilson | 2.50 | 1.25 |
| 96 | Packers Team | 6.00 | 3.00 |
| 97 | Lavern Torgeson | 2.50 | 1.25 |
| 98 | Milt Davis | 2.50 | 1.25 |
| 99 | Larry Strickland | 2.50 | 1.25 |
| 100 | Matt Hazeltine (R) | 3.50 | 1.75 |
| 101 | Walt Yowarski | 2.50 | 1.25 |
| 102 | Roosevelt Brown | 8.50 | 4.25 |
| 103 | Jim Ringo | 8.50 | 4.25 |
| 104 | Joe Krupa | 2.50 | 1.25 |
| 105 | Les Richter | 2.50 | 1.25 |
| 106 | Art Donovan | 8.50 | 4.25 |
| 107 | John Olszewski | 2.50 | 1.25 |
| 108 | Ken Keller | 2.50 | 1.25 |
| 109 | Eagles Team | 6.00 | 3.00 |
| 110 | Colts Team | 6.00 | 3.00 |
| 111 | Dick Bielski | 2.50 | 1.25 |
| 112 | Eddie LeBaron | 3.50 | 1.75 |
| 113 | Gene Brito | 2.50 | 1.25 |
| 114 | Willie Galimore (R) | 10.00 | 5.00 |
| 115 | Lions Team | 6.00 | 3.00 |
| 116 | Steelers Team | 6.00 | 3.00 |
| 117 | L.G. Dupre | 2.50 | 1.25 |
| 118 | Babe Parilli | 4.00 | 2.00 |
| 119 | Bill George | 8.50 | 4.25 |
| 120 | Raymond Berry | 22.00 | 11.00 |
| 121 | Jim Podoley | 2.50 | 1.25 |
| 122 | Hugh McElhenny | 10.00 | 5.00 |
| 123 | Ed Brown | 3.50 | 1.75 |
| 124 | Dick Moegle | 2.50 | 1.25 |
| 125 | Tom Scott | 2.50 | 1.25 |
| 126 | Tommy McDonald | 3.50 | 1.75 |
| 127 | Ollie Matson | 10.00 | 5.00 |
| 128 | Preston Carpenter | 2.50 | 1.25 |
| 129 | George Blanda | 38.00 | 19.00 |
| 130 | Gordon Soltau | 2.50 | 1.25 |
| 131 | Dick Nolan (R) | 3.50 | 1.75 |
| 132 | Don Bosseler (R) | 15.00 | 5.00 |

# 1959 Topps

SAM HUFF
LINEBACKER   NEW YORK GIANTS

This 176-card set features posed photographs framed by white borders on the card fronts with the player's name, position and team printed across the bottom border. Card backs are vertical and contain personal data, brief copy and a trivia question. The set was issued in two series. All cards measure 2-1/2" by 3-1/2".

| | NR/MT | EX |
|---|---|---|
| Complete Set (176) | 1,100.00 | 575.00 |
| Commons (1-88) | 2.00 | 1.00 |
| Commons (89-176) | 1.50 | .75 |
| | | |
| 1   Johnny Unitas | 125.00 | 60.00 |

| | | | |
|---|---|---:|---:|
| 2 | Gene Brito | 2.00 | 1.00 |
| 3 | Lions Team | | |
| 4 | Max McGee (R) | 7.50 | 3.75 |
| 5 | Hugh McElhenny | 8.00 | 4.00 |
| 6 | Joe Schmidt | 7.00 | 3.50 |
| 7 | Kyle Rote | 3.50 | 1.75 |
| 8 | Clarence Peaks | 2.00 | 1.00 |
| 9 | Steelers Pennant | 2.50 | 1.25 |
| 10 | Jim Brown | 190.00 | 95.00 |
| 11 | Ray Mathews | 2.00 | 1.00 |
| 12 | Bobby Dillon | 2.00 | 1.00 |
| 13 | Joe Childress | 2.00 | 1.00 |
| 14 | Terry Barr | 2.50 | 1.25 |
| 15 | Del Shofner (R) | 5.00 | 2.50 |
| 16 | Bob Pellegrini | 2.00 | 1.00 |
| 17 | Colts Team | 5.00 | 2.50 |
| 18 | Preston Carpenter | 2.00 | 1.00 |
| 19 | Leo Nomellini | 7.50 | 3.75 |
| 20 | Frank Gifford | 60.00 | 30.00 |
| 21 | Charlie Ane | 2.00 | 1.00 |
| 22 | Jack Butler | 2.00 | 1.00 |
| 23 | Bart Starr | 55.00 | 27.50 |
| 24 | Cardinals Pennant | 2.50 | 1.25 |
| 25 | Bill Barnes | 2.00 | 1.00 |
| 26 | Walt Michaels | 2.50 | 1.25 |
| 27 | Clyde Conner | 2.00 | 1.00 |
| 28 | Paige Cothren | 2.00 | 1.00 |
| 29 | Roosevelt Grier | 5.00 | 2.50 |
| 30 | Alan Ameche | 4.50 | 2.25 |
| 31 | Eagles Team | 5.00 | 2.50 |
| 32 | Dick Nolan | 2.00 | 1.00 |
| 33 | R.C. Owens | 2.00 | 1.00 |
| 34 | Dale Dodrill | 2.00 | 1.00 |
| 35 | Gene Gedman | 2.00 | 1.00 |
| 36 | Gene Lipscomb (R) | 7.50 | 3.75 |
| 37 | Ray Renfro | 2.50 | 1.25 |
| 38 | Browns Pennant | 2.50 | 1.25 |
| 39 | Bill Forester | 2.00 | 1.00 |
| 40 | Bobby Layne | 22.00 | 11.00 |
| 41 | Pat Summerall | 5.00 | 2.50 |
| 42 | Jerry Mertens | 2.00 | 1.00 |
| 43 | Steve Myhra | 2.00 | 1.00 |
| 44 | John Henry Johnson | 7.50 | 3.75 |
| 45 | Woody Lewis | 2.00 | 1.00 |
| 46 | Packers Team | 5.00 | 2.50 |
| 47 | Don Owens | 2.00 | 1.00 |
| 48 | Ed Beatty | 2.00 | 1.00 |
| 49 | Don Chandler | 2.50 | 1.25 |
| 50 | Ollie Matson | 7.50 | 3.75 |
| 51 | Sam Huff (R) | 55.00 | 27.50 |
| 52 | Tom Miner | 2.00 | 1.00 |
| 53 | Giants Pennant | 2.50 | 1.25 |
| 54 | Kenny Konz | 2.00 | 1.00 |
| 55 | Raymond Berry | 7.50 | 3.75 |
| 56 | Howard Ferguson | 2.00 | 1.00 |
| 57 | Chuck Ulrich | 2.00 | 1.00 |
| 58 | Bob St. Clair | 5.00 | 2.50 |
| 59 | Don Burroughs (R) | 2.50 | 1.25 |
| 60 | Lou Groza | 10.00 | 5.00 |
| 61 | 49er's Team | 5.00 | 2.50 |
| 62 | Andy Nelson | 2.00 | 1.00 |
| 63 | Hal Bradley | 2.00 | 1.00 |
| 64 | Dave Hanner | 2.00 | 1.00 |
| 65 | Charley Conerly | 14.00 | 7.00 |
| 66 | Gene Cronin | 2.00 | 1.00 |
| 67 | Duane Putnam | 2.00 | 1.00 |
| 68 | Colts Pennant | 2.50 | 1.25 |
| 69 | Ernie Stautner | 6.00 | 3.00 |
| 70 | Jon Arnett | 2.50 | 1.25 |
| 71 | Ken Panfil | 2.00 | 1.00 |
| 72 | Matt Hazeltine | 2.00 | 1.00 |
| 73 | Harley Sewell | 2.00 | 1.00 |
| 74 | Mike McCormack | 4.50 | 2.25 |
| 75 | Jim Ringo | 5.00 | 2.50 |
| 76 | Rams Team | 5.00 | 2.50 |
| 77 | Bob Gain | 2.00 | 1.00 |
| 78 | Buzz Nutter | 2.00 | 1.00 |
| 79 | Jerry Norton | 2.00 | 1.00 |
| 80 | Joe Perry | 8.50 | 4.25 |
| 81 | Carl Brettschneider | 2.00 | 1.00 |
| 82 | Paul Hornung | 60.00 | 30.00 |
| 83 | Eagles Pennant | 2.50 | 1.25 |
| 84 | Les Richter | 2.00 | 1.00 |
| 85 | Howard Cassady | 2.50 | 1.25 |
| 86 | Art Donovan | 5.00 | 2.50 |
| 87 | Jim Patton | 2.00 | 1.00 |
| 88 | Pete Retzlaff | 2.50 | 1.25 |
| 89 | Jim Mutscheller | 1.50 | .75 |
| 90 | Zeke Bratkowski | 2.50 | 1.25 |
| 91 | Redskins Team | 3.50 | 1.75 |
| 92 | Art Hunter | 1.50 | .75 |
| 93 | Gern Nagler | 1.50 | .75 |
| 94 | Chuck Weber | 1.50 | .75 |
| 95 | Lew Carpenter | 1.50 | .75 |
| 96 | Stan Jones | 4.50 | 2.25 |
| 97 | Ralph Guglielmi | 1.50 | .75 |
| 98 | Packers Pennant | 1.75 | .85 |
| 99 | Ray Wietecha | 1.50 | .75 |
| 100 | Lenny Moore | 8.50 | 4.25 |
| 101 | Jim Ray Smith (R) | 2.50 | 1.25 |
| 102 | Abe Woodson (R) | 2.50 | 1.25 |
| 103 | Alex Karras (R) | 70.00 | 35.00 |
| 104 | Bears Team | 3.50 | 1.75 |
| 105 | John David Crow (R) | 8.00 | 4.00 |
| 106 | Joe Fortunato (R) | 3.00 | 1.50 |
| 107 | Babe Parilli | 3.50 | 1.75 |
| 108 | Proverb Jacobs | 1.50 | .75 |
| 109 | Gino Marchetti | 6.00 | 3.00 |
| 110 | Bill Wade | 2.00 | 1.00 |
| 111 | 49er's Pennant | 1.75 | .85 |
| 112 | Karl Rubke | 1.50 | .75 |
| 113 | Dave Middleton | 1.50 | .75 |
| 114 | Roosevelt Brown | 7.00 | 3.50 |
| 115 | John Olszewski | 1.50 | .75 |

| | | NR/MT | EX |
|---|---|---|---|
| 116 | Jerry Kramer (R) | 24.00 | 12.00 |
| 117 | King Hill (R) | 3.00 | 1.50 |
| 118 | Cardinals Team | 3.50 | 1.75 |
| 119 | Frank Varrichione | 1.50 | .75 |
| 120 | Rick Casares | 1.50 | .75 |
| 121 | George Strugar | 1.50 | .75 |
| 122 | Bill Glass (R) | 2.00 | 1.00 |
| 123 | Don Bosseler | 1.50 | .75 |
| 124 | John Reger | 1.50 | .75 |
| 125 | Jim Ninowski (R) | 2.00 | 1.00 |
| 126 | Rams Pennant | 1.75 | .86 |
| 127 | Willard Sherman | 1.50 | .75 |
| 128 | Bob Schnelker | 1.50 | .75 |
| 129 | Ollie Spencer | 1.50 | .75 |
| 130 | Y.A. Tittle | 30.00 | 15.00 |
| 131 | Yale Lary | 7.00 | 3.50 |
| 132 | Jim Parker (R) | 25.00 | 12.50 |
| 133 | Giants Team | 3.50 | 1.75 |
| 134 | Jim Schrader | 1.50 | .75 |
| 135 | M.C. Reynolds | 1.50 | .75 |
| 136 | Mike Sandusky | 1.50 | .75 |
| 137 | Ed Brown | 2.00 | 1.00 |
| 138 | Al Barry | 1.50 | .75 |
| 139 | Lions Pennant | 1.75 | .85 |
| 140 | Bobby Mitchell (R) | 38.00 | 19.00 |
| 141 | Larry Morris | 1.50 | .75 |
| 142 | Jim Phillips (R) | 1.75 | .85 |
| 143 | Jim David | 1.50 | .75 |
| 144 | Joe Krupa | 1.50 | .75 |
| 145 | Willie Galimore | 2.50 | 1.25 |
| 146 | Steelers Team | 3.50 | 1.75 |
| 147 | Andy Robustelli | 7.00 | 3.50 |
| 148 | Billy Wilson | 1.50 | .75 |
| 149 | Leo Sanford | 1.50 | .75 |
| 150 | Eddie LeBaron | 3.00 | 1.50 |
| 151 | Bill McColl | 1.50 | .75 |
| 152 | Buck Lansford | 1.50 | .75 |
| 153 | Bears Pennant | 1.75 | .85 |
| 154 | Leo Sugar | 1.50 | .75 |
| 155 | Jim Taylor (R) | 24.00 | 12.50 |
| 156 | Lindon Crow | 1.50 | .75 |
| 157 | Jack McClairen | 1.50 | .75 |
| 158 | Vince Costello (R) | 1.75 | .85 |
| 159 | Stan Wallace | 1.50 | .75 |
| 160 | Mel Triplett (R) | 2.00 | 1.00 |
| 161 | Browns Team | 3.50 | 1.75 |
| 162 | Dan Currie | 1.50 | .75 |
| 163 | L.G. Dupre | 1.50 | .75 |
| 164 | John Morrow | 1.50 | .75 |
| 165 | Jim Podoley | 1.50 | .75 |
| 166 | Bruce Bosley (R) | 1.75 | .85 |
| 167 | Harlon Hill | 1.50 | .75 |
| 168 | Redskins Pennant | 1.75 | .85 |
| 169 | Junior Wren | 1.50 | .75 |
| 170 | Tobin Rote | 2.00 | 1.00 |
| 171 | Art Spinney | 1.50 | .75 |
| 172 | Chuck Drazenovich | 1.50 | .75 |
| 173 | Bobby Joe Conrad (R) | 4.00 | 2.00 |
| 174 | Jesse Richardson | 1.50 | .75 |
| 175 | Sam Baker | 1.50 | .75 |
| 176 | Tom Tracy (R) | 8.50 | 2.50 |

# 1960 Topps

This 132-card set consists of posed shots on the card fronts with the player's name, team and position located in a small football-shaped design in the bottom corner of the card. The vertical card backs contain personal data, statistics and a Football Funnies trivia question. Checklists are included on the back of the team cards. All cards measure 2-1/2" by 3-1/2".

| | | NR/MT | EX |
|---|---|---|---|
| | Complete Set (132) | 725.00 | 360.00 |
| | Commons | 1.75 | .85 |
| | | | |
| 1 | John Unitas | 110.00 | 50.00 |
| 2 | Alan Ameche | 3.50 | 1.75 |
| 3 | Lenny Moore | 7.50 | 3.75 |
| 4 | Raymond Berry | 5.00 | 2.50 |
| 5 | Jim Parker | 5.00 | 2.50 |
| 6 | George Preas (R) | 1.75 | .85 |
| 7 | Art Spinney | 1.75 | .85 |
| 8 | Bill Pellington (R) | 1.75 | .85 |
| 9 | John Sample (R) | 2.50 | 1.25 |
| 10 | Gene Lipscomb | 3.50 | 1.75 |
| 11 | Colts Team | 4.50 | 2.25 |
| 12 | Ed Brown | 1.75 | .85 |
| 13 | Rick Casares | 1.75 | .85 |
| 14 | Willie Galimore | 2.50 | 1.25 |
| 15 | Jim Dooley | 1.75 | .85 |

| | | | |
|---|---|---|---|
| 16 | Harlon Hill | 1.75 | .85 |
| 17 | Stan Jones | 4.00 | 2.00 |
| 18 | Bill George | 4.00 | 2.00 |
| 19 | Erich Barnes (R) | 3.00 | 1.50 |
| 20 | Doug Atkins | 6.00 | 3.00 |
| 21 | Bears Team | 4.50 | 2.25 |
| 22 | Milt Plum | 2.50 | 1.25 |
| 23 | Jim Brown | 90.00 | 45.00 |
| 24 | Sam Baker | 1.75 | .85 |
| 25 | Bobby Mitchell | 10.00 | 5.00 |
| 26 | Ray Renfro | 2.00 | 1.00 |
| 27 | Bill Howton | 1.75 | .85 |
| 28 | Jim Ray Smith | 1.75 | .85 |
| 29 | Jim Shofner (R) | 3.50 | 1.75 |
| 30 | Bob Gain | 1.75 | .85 |
| 31 | Browns Team | 4.50 | 2.25 |
| 32 | Don Heinrich | 2.00 | 1.00 |
| 33 | Ed Modzelewski | 1.75 | .85 |
| 34 | Fred Cone | 1.75 | .85 |
| 35 | L.G. Dupre | 1.75 | .85 |
| 36 | Dick Bielski | 1.75 | .85 |
| 37 | Charlie Ane | 1.75 | .85 |
| 38 | Jerry Tubbs | 2.00 | 1.00 |
| 39 | Doyle Nix | 1.75 | .85 |
| 40 | Ray Krouse | 1.75 | .85 |
| 41 | Earl Morrall | 4.50 | 2.25 |
| 42 | Howard Cassady | 2.50 | 1.25 |
| 43 | Dave Middleton | 1.75 | .85 |
| 44 | Jim Gibbons (R) | 2.00 | 1.00 |
| 45 | Darris McCord | 1.75 | .85 |
| 46 | Joe Schmidt | 5.00 | 2.50 |
| 47 | Terry Barr | 1.75 | .85 |
| 48 | Yale Lary | 4.50 | 2.25 |
| 49 | Gil Mains | 1.75 | .85 |
| 50 | Lions Team | 4.50 | 2.25 |
| 51 | Bart Starr | 45.00 | 22.50 |
| 52 | Jim Taylor (Er) (Wrong Photo) | 8.00 | 4.00 |
| 53 | Lew Carpenter | 1.75 | .85 |
| 54 | Paul Hornung | 40.00 | 20.00 |
| 55 | Max McGee | 3.50 | 1.75 |
| 56 | Forrest Gregg (R) | 26.00 | 13.00 |
| 57 | Jim Ringo | 4.00 | 2.00 |
| 58 | Bill Forester | 1.75 | .85 |
| 59 | Dave Hanner | 1.75 | .85 |
| 60 | Packers Team | 4.50 | 2.25 |
| 61 | Bill Wade | 2.00 | 1.00 |
| 62 | Frank Ryan (R) | 7.50 | 3.75 |
| 63 | Ollie Matson | 7.00 | 3.50 |
| 64 | Jon Arnett | 2.00 | 1.00 |
| 65 | Del Schofner | 2.00 | 1.00 |
| 66 | Jim Phillips | 1.75 | .85 |
| 67 | Art Hunter | 1.75 | .85 |
| 68 | Les richter | 1.75 | .85 |
| 69 | Lou Michaels | 2.50 | 1.25 |
| 70 | John Baker | 1.75 | .85 |
| 71 | Rams Team | 4.50 | 2.25 |
| 72 | Charley Conerly | 12.00 | 6.00 |
| 73 | Mel Tripeltt | 1.75 | .85 |
| 74 | Frank Gifford | 55.00 | 27.50 |
| 75 | Alex Webster | 2.50 | 1.25 |
| 76 | Bob Schnelker | 1.75 | .85 |
| 77 | Pat Summerall | 4.00 | 2.00 |
| 78 | Roosevelt Brown | 5.00 | 2.50 |
| 79 | Jim Patton | 1.75 | .85 |
| 80 | Sam Huff | 12.00 | 6.00 |
| 81 | Andy Robustelli | 5.00 | 2.50 |
| 82 | Giants Team | 4.50 | 2.25 |
| 83 | Clarence Peaks | 1.75 | .85 |
| 84 | Bill Barnes | 1.75 | .85 |
| 85 | Pete Retzlaff | 1.75 | .85 |
| 86 | Bobby Walston | 1.75 | .85 |
| 87 | Chuck Bednarik | 5.00 | 2.50 |
| 88 | Bob Pellegrini | 1.75 | .85 |
| 89 | Tom Brookshier (R) | 4.00 | 2.00 |
| 90 | Marion Campbell | 2.00 | 1.00 |
| 91 | Jesse Richardson | 1.75 | .85 |
| 92 | Philadelphia Eagles | 4.50 | 2.25 |
| 93 | Bobby Layne | 25.00 | 12.50 |
| 94 | John Henry Johnson | 6.00 | 3.00 |
| 95 | Tom Tracy | 1.75 | .85 |
| 96 | Preston Carpenter | 1.75 | .85 |
| 97 | Frank Varrichione | 1.75 | .85 |
| 98 | John Nisby | 1.75 | .85 |
| 99 | Dean Derby | 1.75 | .85 |
| 100 | George Tarasovic | 1.75 | .85 |
| 101 | Ernie Stautner | 4.50 | 2.25 |
| 102 | Steelers Team | 4.50 | 2.25 |
| 103 | King Hill | 2.00 | 1.00 |
| 104 | Mal Hammack | 1.75 | .85 |
| 105 | John David Crow | 3.00 | 1.50 |
| 106 | Bobby Joe Conrad | 2.00 | 1.00 |
| 107 | Woodley Lewis | 1.75 | .85 |
| 108 | Don Gillis | 1.75 | .85 |
| 109 | Carl Brettschneider | 1.75 | .85 |
| 110 | Leo Sugar | 1.75 | .85 |
| 111 | Frank Fuller | 1.75 | .85 |
| 112 | Cardinals Team | 4.50 | 2.25 |
| 113 | Y.A. Tittle | 28.00 | 14.00 |
| 114 | Joe Perry | 7.00 | 3.50 |
| 115 | J.D. Smith (R) | 2.00 | 1.00 |
| 116 | Hugh McElhenny | 6.00 | 3.00 |
| 117 | Billy Wilson | 1.75 | .85 |
| 118 | Bob St. Clair | 4.00 | 2.00 |
| 119 | Matt Hazeltine | 1.75 | .85 |
| 120 | Abe Woodson | 1.75 | .85 |
| 121 | Leo Nomellini | 6.00 | 3.00 |
| 122 | 49ers Team | 4.50 | 2.25 |
| 123 | Ralph Guglielmi | 1.75 | .85 |
| 124 | Don Bosseler | 1.75 | .85 |
| 125 | John Olszewski | 1.75 | .85 |
| 126 | Bill Anderson | 1.75 | .85 |
| 127 | Joe Walton (R) | 3.50 | 1.75 |
| 128 | Jim Schrader | 1.75 | .85 |

| 129 | Ralph Felton | 1.75 | .85 |
|---|---|---|---|
| 130 | Gary Glick | 1.75 | .85 |
| 131 | Bob Toneff | 1.75 | .85 |
| 132 | Redskins Team | 20.00 | 5.00 |

# 1961 Topps

JIM TAYLOR

At 198-cards this marks Topps largest football set to date. The set includes both NFL players (1-132) and AFL players (133-198). The card fronts consist of posed photos framed by a white border. The player's name, team and position appear in a box under the picture. The horizontal card backs contain personal data and stats on the left side and a scratch-off game called "Make-A-Photo" on the right side. All cards measure 2-1/2" by 3-1/2".

|  |  | NR/MT | EX |
|---|---|---|---|
| Complete Set (198) | | 1,150.00 | 600.00 |
| Commons (1-132) | | 1.25 | .60 |
| Commons (133-198) | | 1.75 | .85 |
| | | | |
| 1 | Johnny Unitas | 100.00 | 40.00 |
| 2 | Lenny Moore | 6.50 | 3.25 |
| 3 | Alan Ameche | 3.00 | 1.50 |
| 4 | Raymond Berry | 5.00 | 2.50 |
| 5 | Jim Mutscheller | 1.25 | .60 |
| 6 | Jim Parker | 4.00 | 2.00 |
| 7 | Gino Marchetti | 5.00 | 2.50 |
| 8 | Gene Lipscomb | 3.00 | 1.50 |
| 9 | Colts Team | 4.50 | 2.25 |
| 10 | Bill Wade | 1.75 | .85 |
| 11 | Johnny Morris (R) | 5.00 | 2.50 |
| 12 | Rick Casares | 1.50 | .75 |

| 13 | Harlon Hill | 1.25 | .60 |
|---|---|---|---|
| 14 | Stan Jones | 3.50 | 1.75 |
| 15 | Doug Atkins | 6.50 | 3.25 |
| 16 | Bill George | 3.50 | 1.75 |
| 17 | J.C. Caroline | 1.25 | .60 |
| 18 | Bears Team | 4.50 | 2.25 |
| 19 | Eddie LeBaron (Big time football comes to Texas) | 3.50 | 1.75 |
| 20 | Eddie LeBaron | 3.00 | 1.50 |
| 21 | Don McIlhenny | 1.25 | .60 |
| 22 | L.G. Dupre | 1.25 | .60 |
| 23 | Jim Duran | 1.25 | .60 |
| 24 | Bill Howton | 1.75 | .85 |
| 25 | Buzz Guy (R) | 1.50 | .75 |
| 26 | Jack Patera (R) | 1.75 | .85 |
| 27 | Tom Frankhauser (R) | 1.50 | .75 |
| 28 | Cowboys Team | 6.00 | 3.00 |
| 29 | Jim Ninowski | 1.50 | .75 |
| 30 | Dan Lewis (R) | 2.00 | 1.00 |
| 31 | Nick Pietrosante (R) | 3.50 | 1.75 |
| 32 | Gail Cogdill (R) | 2.00 | 1.00 |
| 33 | Jim Gibbons | 1.25 | .60 |
| 34 | Jim Martin | 1.25 | .60 |
| 35 | Alex Karras | 28.00 | 14.00 |
| 36 | Joe Schmidt | 5.00 | 2.50 |
| 37 | Lions Team | 4.50 | 2.25 |
| 38 | Paul Hornung (Scoring Record) | 8.50 | 4.25 |
| 39 | Bart Starr | 35.00 | 17.50 |
| 40 | Paul Hornung | 28.00 | 14.00 |
| 41 | Jim Taylor | 22.00 | 11.00 |
| 42 | Max McGee | 2.50 | 1.25 |
| 43 | Boyd Dowler (R) | 4.00 | 2.00 |
| 44 | Jim Ringo | 4.00 | 2.00 |
| 45 | Henry Jordan (R) | 4.00 | 2.00 |
| 46 | Bill Forester | 1.25 | .60 |
| 47 | Packers Team | 4.50 | 2.25 |
| 48 | Frank Ryan | 3.50 | 1.75 |
| 49 | Jon Arnett | 1.75 | .85 |
| 50 | Ollie Matson | 6.00 | 3.00 |
| 51 | Jim Phillips | 1.25 | .60 |
| 52 | Del Shofner | 1.75 | .85 |
| 53 | Art Hunter | 1.25 | .60 |
| 54 | Gene Brito | 1.25 | .60 |
| 55 | Lindon Crow | 1.25 | .60 |
| 56 | Rams Team | 4.50 | 2.25 |
| 57 | Johnny Unitas (25 TD passes) | 15.00 | 7.50 |
| 58 | Y.A. Tittle | 20.00 | 10.00 |
| 59 | John Brodie (R) | 50.00 | 25.00 |
| 60 | J.D. Smith | 1.25 | .60 |
| 61 | R.C. Owens | 1.50 | .75 |
| 62 | Clyde Conner | 1.25 | .60 |
| 63 | Bob St. Clair | 4.00 | 2.00 |
| 64 | Leo Nomellini | 5.00 | 2.50 |
| 65 | Abe Woodson | 1.25 | .60 |

| | | | |
|---|---|---|---|
| 66 | 49ers Team | 4.50 | 2.25 |
| 67 | Checklist Card | 38.00 | 5.00 |
| 68 | Milt Plum | 2.00 | 1.00 |
| 69 | Ray Renfro | 1.50 | .75 |
| 70 | Bobby Mitchell | 6.50 | 3.25 |
| 71 | Jim Brown | 90.00 | 45.00 |
| 72 | Mike McCormack | 3.00 | 1.50 |
| 73 | Jim Ray Smith | 1.25 | .60 |
| 74 | Sam Baker | 1.50 | .75 |
| 75 | Walt Michaels | 1.75 | .85 |
| 76 | Browns Team | 4.50 | 2.25 |
| 77 | Jim Brown | 30.00 | 15.00 |
| | (1,257 Yards) | | |
| 78 | George Shaw | 1.50 | .75 |
| 79 | Hugh McElhenny | 6.50 | 3.25 |
| 80 | Clancy Osborne | 1.25 | .60 |
| 81 | Dave Middleton | 1.25 | .60 |
| 82 | Frank Youso | 1.25 | .60 |
| 83 | Don Joyce | 1.25 | .60 |
| 84 | Ed Culpepper | 1.25 | .60 |
| 85 | Charley Conerly | 10.00 | 5.00 |
| 86 | Mel Triplett | 1.25 | .60 |
| 87 | Kyle Rote | 3.50 | 1.75 |
| 88 | Roosevelt Brown | 5.00 | 2.50 |
| 89 | Ray Wietecha | 1.25 | .60 |
| 90 | Andy Robustelli | 6.00 | 3.00 |
| 91 | Sam Huff | 8.50 | 4.25 |
| 92 | Jim Patton | 1.25 | .60 |
| 93 | Giants Team | 4.50 | 2.25 |
| 94 | Charley Conerly | 5.00 | 2.50 |
| | (13 Year) | | |
| 95 | Sonny Jurgensen | 26.00 | 13.00 |
| 96 | Tommy McDonald | 2.00 | 1.00 |
| 97 | Bill Barnes | 1.25 | .60 |
| 98 | Bobby Walston | 1.25 | .60 |
| 99 | Pete Retzlaff | 1.50 | .75 |
| 100 | Jim McCusker | 1.25 | .60 |
| 101 | Chuck Bednarik | 6.00 | 3.00 |
| 102 | Tom Brookshier | 3.00 | 1.50 |
| 103 | Eagles Team | 4.50 | 2.25 |
| 104 | Bobby Layne | 22.00 | 11.00 |
| 105 | John Henry Johnson | 6.50 | 3.25 |
| 106 | Tom Tracy | 1.50 | .75 |
| 107 | Buddy Dial (R) | 3.50 | 1.75 |
| 108 | Jimmy Orr (R) | 4.00 | 2.00 |
| 109 | Mike Sandusky | 1.25 | .60 |
| 110 | John Reger | 1.25 | .60 |
| 111 | Junior Wren | 1.25 | .60 |
| 112 | Steelers Team | 4.50 | 2.25 |
| 113 | Bobby Layne | 6.00 | 3.00 |
| | (NewPassing Record) | | |
| 114 | John Roach | 1.25 | .60 |
| 115 | Sam Etcheverry | 1.75 | .85 |
| 116 | John David Crow | 2.50 | 1.25 |
| 117 | Mal Hammack | 1.25 | .60 |
| 118 | Sonny Randle (R) | 3.00 | 1.50 |
| 119 | Leo Sugar | 1.25 | .60 |

| | | | |
|---|---|---|---|
| 120 | Jerry Norton | 1.25 | .60 |
| 121 | Cardinals Team | 4.50 | 2.25 |
| 122 | Checklist Card | 38.00 | 5.00 |
| 123 | Ralph Guglielmi | 1.50 | .75 |
| 124 | Dick James | 1.25 | .60 |
| 125 | Don Bosseler | 1.25 | .60 |
| 126 | Joe Walton | 2.00 | 1.00 |
| 127 | Bill Anderson | 1.25 | .60 |
| 128 | Vince Promuto (R) | 1.75 | .85 |
| 129 | Bob Toneff | 1.25 | .60 |
| 130 | John Paluck | 1.25 | .60 |
| 131 | Redskins Team | 4.50 | 2.25 |
| 132 | Milt Plum | 2.50 | 1.25 |
| | (Wins Passing Title) | | |
| 133 | Abner Haynes | 5.00 | 2.50 |
| 134 | Mel Branch | 2.50 | 1.25 |
| 135 | Jerry Cornelison | 1.75 | .85 |
| 136 | Bill Krisher | 1.75 | .85 |
| 137 | Paul Miller | 1.75 | .85 |
| 138 | Jack Spikes | 2.50 | 1.25 |
| 139 | Johnny Robinson (R) | 5.00 | 2.50 |
| 140 | Cotton Davidson (R) | 4.50 | 2.25 |
| 141 | Dave Smith | 1.75 | .85 |
| 142 | Bill Groman | 2.00 | 1.00 |
| 143 | Rich Michael | 1.75 | .85 |
| 144 | Mike Dukes | 1.75 | .85 |
| 145 | George Blanda | 28.00 | 14.00 |
| 146 | Billy Cannon | 4.50 | 2.25 |
| 147 | Dennit Morris | 1.75 | .85 |
| 148 | Jacky Lee | 2.00 | 1.00 |
| 149 | Al Dorow | 1.75 | .85 |
| 150 | Don Maynard (R) | 55.00 | 27.50 |
| 151 | Art Powell (R) | 4.00 | 2.00 |
| 152 | Sid Youngelman | 1.75 | .85 |
| 153 | Bob Mischak | 1.75 | .85 |
| 154 | Larry Grantham | 2.50 | 1.25 |
| 155 | Tom Saidock | 1.75 | .85 |
| 156 | Roger Donnahoo | 1.75 | .85 |
| 157 | Laverne Torczon | 1.75 | .85 |
| 158 | Archie Matsos (R) | 2.00 | 1.00 |
| 159 | Elbert Dubenion | 2.50 | 1.25 |
| 160 | Wray Carlton (R) | 2.50 | 1.25 |
| 161 | Rich McCabe | 1.75 | .85 |
| 162 | Ken Rice | 1.75 | .85 |
| 163 | Art Baker | 1.75 | .85 |
| 164 | Tom Rychlec | 1.75 | .85 |
| 165 | Mack Yoho | 1.75 | .85 |
| 166 | Jack Kemp | 125.00 | 60.00 |
| 167 | Paul Lowe | 4.00 | 2.00 |
| 168 | Ron Mix | 8.00 | 4.00 |
| 169 | Paul Maguire | 3.00 | 1.50 |
| 170 | Volney Peters | 1.75 | .85 |
| 171 | Ernie Wright | 1.75 | .85 |
| 172 | Ron Nary | 1.75 | .85 |
| 173 | Dave Kocourek | 1.75 | .85 |
| 174 | Jim Colclough | 1.75 | .85 |
| 175 | Babe Parilli | 3.50 | 1.75 |

| | | NR/MT | EX |
|---|---|---|---|
| 176 | Billy Lott (R) | 2.50 | 1.25 |
| 177 | Fred Bruney | 1.75 | .85 |
| 178 | Ross O'Hanley | 1.75 | .85 |
| 179 | Walt Cudzik | 1.75 | .85 |
| 180 | Charley Leo | 1.75 | .85 |
| 181 | Bob Dee | 1.75 | .85 |
| 182 | Jim Otto (R) | 36.00 | 18.00 |
| 183 | Eddie Macon | 1.75 | .85 |
| 184 | Dick Christy | 1.75 | .85 |
| 185 | Alan Miller | 1.75 | .85 |
| 186 | Tom Flores (R) | 12.50 | 6.25 |
| 187 | Joe Cannavino | 1.75 | .85 |
| 188 | Don Manoukian | 1.75 | .85 |
| 189 | Bob Coolbaugh | 1.75 | .85 |
| 190 | Lionel Taylor (R) | 8.50 | 4.25 |
| 191 | Bud McFadin | 1.75 | .85 |
| 192 | Goose Gonsoulin (R) | 2.50 | 1.25 |
| 193 | Frank Tripucka | 3.50 | 1.75 |
| 194 | Gene Mingo (R) | 2.50 | 1.25 |
| 195 | Eldon Danenhauer (R) | 2.00 | 1.00 |
| 196 | Bob McNamara | 1.75 | .85 |
| 197 | Dave Rolle | 1.75 | .85 |
| 198 | Checklist Card | 85.00 | 10.00 |

# 1962 Topps

The cards in this 176-card set feature horizontal card fronts and vertical card backs. The fronts contain a large color photo of the player and a smaller black and white football action shot framed by a black border. The player's name, team and position appear under the smaller photo.  The backs consist of personal data, stats, a small cartoon and a football trivia question. There are a number of short prints in the set (SP) that are more difficult to locate than the rest of the cards in the set. All cards measure 2-1/2" by 3-1/2".

| | | NR/MT | EX |
|---|---|---|---|
| **Complete Set (176)** | | 1,750.00 | 875.00 |
| **Commons** | | 2.50 | 1.25 |
| **Commons (SP)** | | 5.00 | 2.50 |
| 1 | John Unitas | 125.00 | 50.00 |
| 2 | Lenny Moore | 6.50 | 3.25 |
| 3 | Alex Hawkins (R)(SP) | 6.00 | 3.00 |
| 4 | Joe Perry | 6.00 | 3.00 |
| 5 | Raymond Berry (SP) | 15.00 | 7.50 |
| 6 | Steve Myhra | 2.50 | 1.25 |
| 7 | Tom Gilburg (SP) | 5.00 | 2.50 |
| 8 | Gino Marchetti | 6.00 | 3.00 |
| 9 | Bill Pellington | 2.50 | 1.25 |
| 10 | Andy Nelson | 2.50 | 1.25 |
| 11 | Wendell Harris (SP) | 5.00 | 2.50 |
| 12 | Colts Team | 4.50 | 2.25 |
| 13 | Bill Wade (SP) | 5.00 | 2.50 |
| 14 | Willie Galimore | 3.50 | 1.75 |
| 15 | Johnny Morris (SP) | 5.00 | 2.50 |
| 16 | Rick Casares | 2.50 | 1.25 |
| 17 | Mike Ditka (R) | 125.00 | 60.00 |
| 18 | Stan Jones | 3.50 | 1.75 |
| 19 | Roger LeClerc | 2.50 | 1.25 |
| 20 | Angelo Coia | 2.50 | 1.25 |
| 21 | Doug Atkins | 6.00 | 3.00 |
| 22 | Bill George | 4.50 | 2.25 |
| 23 | Richie Petibon (R) | 7.50 | 3.75 |
| 24 | Ron Bull (R)(SP) | 6.00 | 3.00 |
| 25 | Bears Team | 4.50 | 2.25 |
| 26 | Howard Cassady | 3.00 | 1.50 |
| 27 | Ray Renfro (SP) | 5.00 | 2.50 |
| 28 | Jim Brown | 125.00 | 60.00 |
| 29 | Rich Kreitling | 2.50 | 1.25 |
| 30 | Jim Ray Smith | 2.50 | 1.25 |
| 31 | John Morrow | 2.50 | 1.25 |
| 32 | Lou Groza | 8.00 | 4.00 |
| 33 | Bob Gain | 2.50 | 1.25 |
| 34 | Bernie Parrish | 2.50 | 1.25 |
| 35 | Jim Shofner | 2.50 | 1.25 |
| 36 | Ernie Davis (R)(SP) | 50.00 | 25.00 |
| 37 | Browns Team | 4.50 | 2.25 |
| 38 | Eddie LeBaron | 3.00 | 1.50 |
| 39 | Don Meredith (R) | 70.00 | 35.00 |
| 40 | J.W. Lockett (SP) | 5.00 | 2.50 |
| 41 | Don Perkins (R) | 5.00 | 2.50 |
| 42 | Bill Howton | 2.50 | 1.25 |
| 43 | Dick Bielski | 2.50 | 1.25 |
| 44 | Mike Connelly | 2.50 | 1.25 |
| 45 | Jerry Tubbs (SP) | 5.00 | 2.50 |
| 46 | Don Bishop (SP) | 5.00 | 2.50 |
| 47 | Dick Moegle | 2.50 | 1.25 |

| # | Player | Price 1 | Price 2 |
|---|--------|---------|---------|
| 48 | Bobby Plummer (SP) | 5.00 | 2.50 |
| 49 | Cowboys Team | 8.00 | 4.00 |
| 50 | Milt Plum | 3.50 | 1.75 |
| 51 | Dan Lewis | 2.50 | 1.25 |
| 52 | Nick Pietrosante (SP) | 6.50 | 3.25 |
| 53 | Gail Cogdill | 2.50 | 1.25 |
| 54 | Jim Gibbons | 2.50 | 1.25 |
| 55 | Jim Martin | 2.50 | 1.25 |
| 56 | Yale Lary | 4.00 | 2.00 |
| 57 | Darris McCord | 2.50 | 1.25 |
| 58 | Alex Karras | 15.00 | 7.50 |
| 59 | Joe Schmidt | 6.00 | 3.00 |
| 60 | Dick Lane | 6.00 | 3.00 |
| 61 | John Lomakoski (SP) | 5.00 | 2.50 |
| 62 | Lions Team (SP) | 10.00 | 5.00 |
| 63 | Bart Starr (SP) | 45.00 | 22.50 |
| 64 | Paul Hornung (SP) | 40.00 | 20.00 |
| 65 | Tom Moore (SP) | 5.00 | 2.50 |
| 66 | Jim Taylor (SP) | 28.00 | 14.00 |
| 67 | Max McGee (SP) | 6.00 | 3.00 |
| 68 | Jim Ringo (SP) | 10.00 | 5.00 |
| 69 | Fuzzy Thurston (R) | 8.50 | 4.25 |
| 70 | Forrest Gregg | 5.00 | 2.50 |
| 71 | Boyd Dowler | 2.50 | 1.25 |
| 72 | Henry Jordan (SP) | 5.00 | 2.50 |
| 73 | Bill Forester (SP) | 5.00 | 2.50 |
| 74 | Earl Gros (SP) | 5.00 | 2.50 |
| 75 | Packers Team (SP) | 18.00 | 9.00 |
| 76 | Checklist (SP) | 60.00 | 10.00 |
| 77 | Zeke Bratkowski (SP) | 6.00 | 3.00 |
| 78 | Jon Arnett (SP) | 6.00 | 3.00 |
| 79 | Ollie Matson (SP) | 16.00 | 8.00 |
| 80 | Dick Bass (SP) | 7.50 | 3.75 |
| 81 | Jim Phillips | 2.50 | 1.25 |
| 82 | Carroll Dale (R) | 3.00 | 1.50 |
| 83 | Frank Varrichione | 2.50 | 1.25 |
| 84 | Art Hunter | 2.50 | 1.25 |
| 85 | Danny Villanueva | 2.50 | 1.25 |
| 86 | Les Richter (SP) | 5.00 | 2.50 |
| 87 | Lindon Crow | 2.50 | 1.25 |
| 88 | Roman Gabriel (R) | 45.00 | 22.50 |
| 89 | Rams Team (SP) | 12.00 | 6.00 |
| 90 | Fran Tarkenton (R) | 400.00 | 200.00 |
| 91 | Jerry Reichow (SP) | 5.00 | 2.50 |
| 92 | Hugh McElhenny (SP) | 12.50 | 6.25 |
| 93 | Mel Triplett (SP) | 5.00 | 2.50 |
| 94 | Tommy Mason (R) (SP) | 6.00 | 3.00 |
| 95 | Dave Middleton (SP) | 5.00 | 2.50 |
| 96 | Frank Youso (SP) | 5.00 | 2.50 |
| 97 | Mike Mercer (SP) | 5.00 | 2.50 |
| 98 | Rip Hawkins (SP) | 5.00 | 2.50 |
| 99 | Cliff Livingston (SP) | 5.00 | 2.50 |
| 100 | Roy Winston (R)(SP) | 6.00 | 3.00 |
| 101 | Vikings Team (SP) | 12.00 | 6.00 |
| 102 | Y.A. Tittle | 24.00 | 12.00 |
| 103 | Joe Walton | 3.00 | 1.50 |
| 104 | Frank Gifford | 55.00 | 27.50 |
| 105 | Alex Webster | 3.00 | 1.50 |
| 106 | Del Shofner | 3.00 | 1.50 |
| 107 | Don Chandler | 3.00 | 1.50 |
| 108 | Andy Robustelli | 5.00 | 2.50 |
| 109 | Jim Katcavage (R) | 3.50 | 1.75 |
| 110 | Sam Huff (SP) | 15.00 | 7.50 |
| 111 | Erich Barnes | 2.50 | 1.25 |
| 112 | Jim Patton | 2.50 | 1.25 |
| 113 | Jerry Hillebrand (SP) | 5.00 | 2.50 |
| 114 | Giants Team | 4.50 | 2.25 |
| 115 | Sonny Jurgensen | 26.00 | 13.00 |
| 116 | Tommy McDonald | 3.00 | 1.50 |
| 117 | Ted Dean (SP) | 5.00 | 2.50 |
| 118 | Clarence Peaks | 2.50 | 1.25 |
| 119 | Bobby Walston | 2.50 | 1.25 |
| 120 | Pete Retzlaff (SP) | 5.00 | 2.50 |
| 121 | Jim Schrader (SP) | 5.00 | 2.50 |
| 122 | J.D. Smith | 2.50 | 1.25 |
| 123 | King Hill | 3.00 | 1.50 |
| 124 | Maxie Baughan | 3.00 | 1.50 |
| 125 | Pete Case (SP) | 5.00 | 2.50 |
| 126 | Eagles Team | 4.50 | 2.25 |
| 127 | Bobby Layne | 24.00 | 12.00 |
| 128 | Tom Tracy | 2.50 | 1.25 |
| 129 | John Henry Johnson | 6.00 | 3.00 |
| 130 | Buddy Dial (SP) | 5.00 | 2.50 |
| 131 | Preston Carpenter | 2.50 | 1.25 |
| 132 | Lou Michaels (SP) | 5.00 | 2.50 |
| 133 | Gene Lipscomb (SP) | 6.00 | 3.00 |
| 134 | Ernie Stautner (SP) | 10.00 | 5.00 |
| 135 | John Reger (SP) | 5.00 | 2.50 |
| 136 | Myron Pottios (R) | 3.00 | 1.50 |
| 137 | Bob Ferguson (R)(SP) | 6.00 | 3.00 |
| 138 | Steelers Team (SP) | 10.00 | 5.00 |
| 139 | Sam Etcheverry | 2.50 | 1.25 |
| 140 | John David Crow (SP) | 6.00 | 3.00 |
| 141 | Bobby Joe Conrad (SP) | 5.00 | 2.50 |
| 142 | Prentice Gautt (R)(SP) | 5.00 | 2.50 |
| 143 | Frank Mestnick | 2.50 | 1.25 |
| 144 | Sonny Randle | 2.50 | 1.25 |
| 145 | Gerry Perry | 2.50 | 1.25 |
| 146 | Jerry Norton | 2.50 | 1.25 |
| 147 | Jimmy Hill | 2.50 | 1.25 |
| 148 | Bill Stacy | 2.50 | 1.25 |
| 149 | Fate Echols (SP) | 5.00 | 2.50 |
| 150 | Cardinals Team | 4.50 | 2.25 |
| 151 | Bill Kilmer (R) | 20.00 | 10.00 |
| 152 | John Brodie | 18.00 | 9.00 |
| 153 | J.D. Smith | 2.50 | 1.25 |
| 154 | C.R. Roberts (SP) | 5.00 | 2.50 |
| 155 | Monty Stickles | 2.50 | 1.25 |
| 156 | Clyde Conner | 2.50 | 1.25 |
| 157 | Bob St.Clair | 5.00 | 2.50 |
| 158 | Tommy Davis (R) | 2.50 | 1.25 |

| | | NR/MT | EX |
|---|---|---|---|
| 159 | Leo Nomellini | 6.00 | 3.00 |
| 160 | Matt Hazeltine | 2.50 | 1.25 |
| 161 | Abe Woodson | 2.50 | 1.25 |
| 162 | Dave Baker | 2.50 | 1.25 |
| 163 | 49ers Team | 4.50 | 2.25 |
| 164 | Norm Snead (R) | 18.00 | 9.00 |
| 165 | Dick James | 2.50 | 1.25 |
| 166 | Bobby Mitchell | 5.00 | 2.50 |
| 167 | Sam Horner | 2.50 | 1.25 |
| 168 | Bill Barnes | 2.50 | 1.25 |
| 169 | Bill Anderson | 2.50 | 1.25 |
| 170 | Fred Dugan | 2.50 | 1.25 |
| 171 | John Aveni (SP) | 5.00 | 2.50 |
| 172 | Bob Toneff | 2.50 | 1.25 |
| 173 | Jim Kerr | 2.50 | 1.25 |
| 174 | Leroy Jackson (SP) | 5.00 | 2.50 |
| 175 | Redskins Team | 4.50 | 2.25 |
| 176 | Checklist | 90.00 | 15.00 |

## 1963 Topps

This 170-card set consists of mostly posed photos on the front with the player's name, team and position printed in a small box across the bottom of the card. The vertical card backs feature personal data, stats and a small drawing containing a football trivia question. The set includes a number short-prints that are more scarce than the other cards in the set. All cards measure 2-1/2" by 3-1/2".

| | NR/MT | EX |
|---|---|---|
| Complete Set (170) | 1,325.00 | 650.00 |
| Commons | 2.00 | 1.00 |
| Commons (SP) | 4.00 | 2.00 |

| | | NR/MT | EX |
|---|---|---|---|
| 1 | John Unitas | 110.00 | 45.00 |
| 2 | Lenny Moore | 6.50 | 3.25 |
| 3 | Jimmy Orr | 2.50 | 1.25 |
| 4 | Raymond Berry | 5.00 | 2.50 |
| 5 | Jim Parker | 5.00 | 2.50 |
| 6 | Alex Sandusky | 2.00 | 1.00 |
| 7 | Dick Szymanski | 2.00 | 1.00 |
| 8 | Gino Marchetti | 4.50 | 2.25 |
| 9 | Billy Ray Smith (R) | 3.00 | 1.50 |
| 10 | Bill Pellington | 2.00 | 1.00 |
| 11 | Bob Boyd (R) | 2.50 | 1.25 |
| 12 | Colts Team (SP) | 8.50 | 4.25 |
| 13 | Frank Ryan (SP) | 6.00 | 3.00 |
| 14 | Jim Brown (SP) | 140.00 | 70.00 |
| 15 | Ray Renfro (SP) | 4.50 | 2.25 |
| 16 | Rich Kreitling (SP) | 4.00 | 2.00 |
| 17 | Mike McCormack (SP) | 7.00 | 3.50 |
| 18 | Jim Ray Smith (SP) | 4.00 | 2.00 |
| 19 | Lou Groza (SP) | 15.00 | 7.50 |
| 20 | Bill Glass (SP) | 4.00 | 2.00 |
| 21 | Galen Fiss (SP) | 4.00 | 2.00 |
| 22 | Don Fleming (SP) | 4.00 | 2.00 |
| 23 | Bob Gain (SP) | 4.00 | 2.00 |
| 24 | Browns Team (SP) | 8.50 | 4.25 |
| 25 | Milt Plum | 2.50 | 1.25 |
| 26 | Dan Lewis | 2.00 | 1.00 |
| 27 | Nick Pietrosante | 2.50 | 1.25 |
| 28 | Gail Cogdill | 2.00 | 1.00 |
| 29 | Harley Sewell | 2.00 | 1.00 |
| 30 | Jim Gibbons | 2.00 | 1.00 |
| 31 | Carl Brettschneider | 2.00 | 1.00 |
| 32 | Dick Lane | 5.00 | 2.50 |
| 33 | Yale Lary | 4.00 | 2.00 |
| 34 | Roger Brown (R) | 3.50 | 1.75 |
| 35 | Joe Schmidt | 5.00 | 2.50 |
| 36 | Lions Team (SP) | 8.50 | 4.25 |
| 37 | Roman Gabriel | 7.00 | 3.50 |
| 38 | Zeke Bratkowski | 2.50 | 1.25 |
| 39 | Dick Bass | 2.50 | 1.25 |
| 40 | Jon Arnett | 2.50 | 1.25 |
| 41 | Jim Phillips | 2.00 | 1.00 |
| 42 | Frank Varrichione | 2.00 | 1.00 |
| 43 | Danny Villanueva | 2.00 | 1.00 |
| 44 | Deacon Jones (R) | 50.00 | 25.00 |
| 45 | Lindon Crow | 2.00 | 1.00 |
| 46 | Marlin McKeever (R) | 2.50 | 1.25 |
| 47 | Ed Meador (R) | 2.50 | 1.25 |
| 48 | Rams Team | 3.50 | 1.75 |
| 49 | Y.A. Tittle (SP) | 24.00 | 12.00 |
| 50 | Del Shofner (SP) | 4.50 | 2.25 |
| 51 | Alex Webster (SP) | 4.50 | 2.25 |
| 52 | Phil King (SP) | 4.00 | 2.00 |
| 53 | Jack Stroud (SP) | 4.00 | 2.00 |
| 54 | Darrell Dess (SP) | 4.00 | 2.00 |
| 55 | Jim Katcavage (SP) | 4.50 | 2.25 |
| 56 | Rossevelt Grier (SP) | 8.50 | 4.25 |
| 57 | Erich Barnes (SP) | 4.50 | 2.25 |

| | | | |
|---|---|---|---|
| 58 | Jim Patton (SP) | 4.00 | 2.00 |
| 59 | Sam Huff (SP) | 10.00 | 5.00 |
| 60 | Giants Team | 3.50 | 1.75 |
| 61 | Bill Wade | 2.50 | 1.25 |
| 62 | Mike Ditka | 40.00 | 20.00 |
| 63 | Johnny Morris | 2.00 | 1.00 |
| 64 | Roger LeClerc | 2.00 | 1.00 |
| 65 | Roger Davis | 2.00 | 1.00 |
| 66 | Joe Marconi | 2.00 | 1.00 |
| 67 | Herman Lee | 2.00 | 1.00 |
| 68 | Doug Atkins | 5.50 | 2.75 |
| 69 | Joe Fortunato | 2.00 | 1.00 |
| 70 | Bill George | 5.00 | 2.50 |
| 71 | Richie Petitbon | 3.50 | 1.75 |
| 72 | Bears Team (SP) | 8.50 | 4.25 |
| 73 | Eddie LeBaron (SP) | 4.50 | 2.25 |
| 74 | Don Meredith (SP) | 50.00 | 25.00 |
| 75 | Don Perkins (SP) | 5.00 | 2.50 |
| 76 | Amos Marsh (SP) | 4.00 | 2.00 |
| 77 | Bill Howton (SP) | 4.50 | 2.25 |
| 78 | Andy Cvercko (SP) | 4.00 | 2.00 |
| 79 | Sam Baker (SP) | 4.00 | 2.00 |
| 80 | Jerry Tubbs (SP) | 5.00 | 2.50 |
| 81 | Don Bishop (SP) | 4.00 | 2.00 |
| 82 | Bob Lilly (R) (SP) | 95.00 | 45.00 |
| 83 | Jerry Norton (SP) | 4.00 | 2.00 |
| 84 | Cowboys Team (SP) | 12.50 | 6.25 |
| 85 | Checklist Card | 25.00 | 12.50 |
| 86 | Bart Starr | 28.00 | 14.00 |
| 87 | Jim Taylor | 12.50 | 6.25 |
| 88 | Boyd Dowler | 2.50 | 1.25 |
| 89 | Forrest Gregg | 5.00 | 2.50 |
| 90 | Fuzzy Thurston | 2.50 | 1.25 |
| 91 | Jim Ringo | 5.00 | 2.50 |
| 92 | Ron Kramer | 2.50 | 1.25 |
| 93 | Henry Jordan | 2.50 | 1.25 |
| 94 | Bill Forester | 2.00 | 1.00 |
| 95 | Willie Wood (R) | 28.00 | 14.00 |
| 96 | Ray Nitschke (R) | 65.00 | 37.50 |
| 97 | Packers Team | 3.50 | 1.75 |
| 98 | Fran Tarkenton | 100.00 | 50.00 |
| 99 | Tommy Mason | 2.50 | 1.25 |
| 100 | Mel Triplett | 2.00 | 1.00 |
| 101 | Jerry Reichow | 2.00 | 1.00 |
| 102 | Frank Youso | 2.00 | 1.00 |
| 103 | Hugh McElhenny | 6.00 | 3.00 |
| 104 | Gerry Huth | 2.00 | 1.00 |
| 105 | Ed Sharockman | 2.00 | 1.00 |
| 106 | Rip Hawkins | 2.00 | 1.00 |
| 107 | Jim Marshall (R) | 24.00 | 12.00 |
| 108 | Jim Prestel | 2.00 | 1.00 |
| 109 | Vikings Team | 3.50 | 1.75 |
| 110 | Sonny Jurgensen (SP) | 25.00 | 12.50 |
| 111 | Tim Brown (R) (SP) | 7.50 | 3.50 |
| 112 | Tommy McDonald (SP) | 5.00 | 2.50 |
| 113 | Clarence Peaks (SP) | 4.00 | 2.00 |
| 114 | Pete Retzlaff (SP) | 4.00 | 2.00 |
| 115 | Jim Schrader (SP) | 4.00 | 2.00 |
| 116 | Jim McCusker (SP) | 4.00 | 2.00 |
| 117 | Don Burroughs (SP) | 4.00 | 2.00 |
| 118 | Maxie Baughan (SP) | 5.00 | 2.50 |
| 119 | Riley Gunnels (SP) | 4.00 | 2.00 |
| 120 | Jimmy Carr (SP) | 4.00 | 2.00 |
| 121 | Eagles Team (SP) | 8.50 | 4.25 |
| 122 | Ed Brown (SP) | 4.50 | 2.25 |
| 123 | John Henry Johnson (SP) | 10.00 | 5.00 |
| 124 | Buddy Dial (SP) | 5.00 | 2.50 |
| 125 | Red Mack (SP) | 4.00 | 2.00 |
| 126 | Preston Carpenter (SP) | 4.00 | 2.00 |
| 127 | Ray Lemek (SP) | 4.00 | 2.00 |
| 128 | Buzz Nutter (SP) | 4.00 | 2.00 |
| 129 | Ernie Stautner (SP) | 8.50 | 4.25 |
| 130 | Lou Michaels (SP) | 4.50 | 2.25 |
| 131 | Clendon Thomas (R) (SP) | 5.00 | 2.50 |
| 132 | Tom Bettis (SP) | 4.00 | 2.00 |
| 133 | Steelers Team (SP) | 8.50 | 4.25 |
| 134 | John Brodie | 10.00 | 5.00 |
| 135 | J.D. Smith | 2.00 | 1.00 |
| 136 | Bill Kilmer | 6.50 | 3.25 |
| 137 | Bernie Casey (R) | 3.50 | 1.75 |
| 138 | Tommy Davis | 2.00 | 1.00 |
| 139 | Ted Connolly | 2.00 | 1.00 |
| 140 | Bob St. Clair | 5.00 | 2.50 |
| 141 | Abe Woodson | 2.00 | 1.00 |
| 142 | Matt Hazeltine | 2.00 | 1.00 |
| 143 | Leo Nomellini | 6.00 | 3.00 |
| 144 | Dan Colchico | 2.00 | 1.00 |
| 145 | 49ers Team (R) | 8.50 | 4.25 |
| 146 | Charlie Johnson (R) | 7.50 | 3.75 |
| 147 | John David Crow | 3.00 | 1.50 |
| 148 | Bobby Joe Conrad | 2.50 | 1.25 |
| 149 | Sonny Randle | 2.50 | 1.25 |
| 150 | Prentice Gautt | 2.00 | 1.00 |
| 151 | Taz Anderson | 2.00 | 1.00 |
| 152 | Ernie McMillan (R) | 3.00 | 1.50 |
| 153 | Jimmy Hill | 2.00 | 1.00 |
| 154 | Bill Koman | 2.00 | 1.00 |
| 155 | Larry Wilson (R) | 26.00 | 13.00 |
| 156 | Don Owens | 2.00 | 1.00 |
| 157 | Cardinals Team (SP) | 8.50 | 4.25 |
| 158 | Norm Snead (SP) | 7.00 | 3.50 |
| 159 | Bobby Mitchell (SP) | 10.00 | 5.00 |
| 160 | Bill Barnes (SP) | 4.00 | 2.00 |
| 161 | Fred Dugan (SP) | 4.00 | 2.00 |
| 162 | Don Bosseler (SP) | 4.00 | 2.00 |
| 163 | John Nisby (SP) | 4.00 | 2.00 |
| 164 | Riley Mattson (SP) | 4.00 | 2.00 |
| 165 | Bob Toneff (SP) | 4.00 | 2.00 |
| 166 | Rod Breedlove (SP) | 4.00 | 2.00 |

| | | NR/MT | EX |
|---|---|---|---|
| 167 | Dick James (SP) | 4.00 | 2.00 |
| 168 | Claude Crabb (SP) | 4.00 | 2.00 |
| 169 | Redskins Team (SP) | 8.50 | 4.25 |
| 170 | Checklist Card | 55.00 | 7.50 |

# 1964 Topps

This 176-card set consists of players from the American Football League. The card fronts feature mostly posed photos framed by small stars and white borders. The player's name, team and position appear in a small box across the bottom of the card. The horizontal card backs include personal data, stats and a small cartoon with a football trivia question. Numerous short-prints (SP) exist in this set and are indicated in the checklist. All cards measure 2-1/2" by 3-1/2".

| | | NR/MT | EX |
|---|---|---|---|
| **Complete Set (176)** | | 1,500.00 | 750.00 |
| **Commons** | | 2.50 | 1.25 |
| **Commons (SP)** | | 6.50 | 3.25 |
| | | | |
| 1 | Tommy Addison (SP) | 35.00 | 7.50 |
| 2 | Houston Antwine (R) | 3.00 | 1.50 |
| 3 | Nick Buoniconti | 10.00 | 5.00 |
| 4 | Ron Burton (SP) | 6.50 | 3.25 |
| 5 | Gino Cappelletti | 5.00 | 2.50 |
| 6 | Jim Colclough (SP) | 6.50 | 3.25 |
| 7 | Bob Dee (SP) | 6.50 | 3.25 |
| 8 | Larry Eisenhauer (R) | 3.00 | 1.50 |
| 9 | Dick Felt (SP) | 6.50 | 3.25 |
| 10 | Larry Garron | 2.50 | 1.25 |
| 11 | Art Graham | 2.50 | 1.25 |
| 12 | Ron Hall | 2.50 | 1.25 |
| 13 | Charles Long | 2.50 | 1.25 |
| 14 | Don McKinnon | 2.50 | 1.25 |
| 15 | Don Oakes (SP) | 6.50 | 3.25 |
| 16 | Ross O'Hanley (SP) | 6.50 | 3.25 |
| 17 | Babe Parilli (SP) | 8.00 | 4.00 |
| 18 | Jesse Richardson (SP) | 6.50 | 3.25 |
| 19 | Jack Rudolph (SP) | 6.50 | 3.25 |
| 20 | Don Webb (R) | 3.00 | 1.50 |
| 21 | Patriots Team | 6.00 | 3.00 |
| 22 | Ray Abbruzzesse | 2.50 | 1.25 |
| 23 | Stew Barber (R) | 3.00 | 1.50 |
| 24 | Dave Behrman | 2.50 | 1.25 |
| 25 | Al Bemiller | 2.50 | 1.25 |
| 26 | Elbert Dubenion (SP) | 7.00 | 3.50 |
| 27 | Jim Dunaway (R)(SP) | 7.50 | 3.50 |
| 28 | Booker Edgerson (SP) | 6.50 | 3.25 |
| 29 | Cookie Gilchrist (SP) | 8.50 | 4.25 |
| 30 | Jack Kemp (SP) | 125.00 | 60.00 |
| 31 | Daryle Lamonica (R) | 50.00 | 25.00 |
| 32 | Bill Miller | 2.50 | 1.25 |
| 33 | Herb Paterra (R) | 3.00 | 1.50 |
| 34 | Ken Rice (SP) | 6.50 | 3.25 |
| 35 | Ed Rutkowski | 2.50 | 1.25 |
| 36 | George Saimes (R) | 3.50 | 1.75 |
| 37 | Tom Sestak | 2.50 | 1.25 |
| 38 | Billy Shaw (SP) | 6.50 | 3.25 |
| 39 | Mike Stratton (R) | 2.50 | 1.25 |
| 40 | Gene Sykes | 2.50 | 1.25 |
| 41 | John Tracey (SP) | 6.50 | 3.25 |
| 42 | Sid Youngelman (SP) | 6.50 | 3.25 |
| 43 | Bills Team | 6.00 | 3.00 |
| 44 | Eldon Danenhauer (SP) | 6.50 | 3.26 |
| 45 | Jim Fraser (SP) | 6.50 | 3.25 |
| 46 | Chuck Gavin (SP) | 6.50 | 3.25 |
| 47 | Goose Gonsoulin (SP) | 6.50 | 3.25 |
| 48 | Ernie Barnes (R) | 3.50 | 1.75 |
| 49 | Tom Janik | 2.50 | 1.25 |
| 50 | Billy Joe (R) | 3.00 | 1.50 |
| 51 | Ike Lassiter (R) | 3.50 | 1.75 |
| 52 | John McCormick (SP) | 6.50 | 3.25 |
| 53 | Bud McFadin (SP) | 6.50 | 3.25 |
| 54 | Gene Mingo (SP) | 6.50 | 3.25 |
| 55 | Charlie Mitchell | 2.50 | 1.25 |
| 56 | John Nocera (SP) | 6.50 | 3.25 |
| 57 | Tom Nomina | 2.50 | 1.25 |
| 58 | Harold Olson (SP) | 6.50 | 3.25 |
| 59 | Bob Scarpitto | 2.50 | 1.25 |
| 60 | John Sklopan | 2.50 | 1.25 |
| 61 | Mickey Slaughter | 2.50 | 1.25 |
| 62 | Don Stone | 2.50 | 1.25 |
| 63 | Jerry Sturn | 2.50 | 1.25 |
| 64 | Lionel Taylor (SP) | 10.00 | 5.00 |
| 65 | Broncos Team | 12.00 | 6.00 |

| | | | |
|---|---|---|---|
| 66 | Scott Appleton (R) | 4.50 | 2.25 |
| 67 | Tony Banfield (SP) | 6.50 | 3.25 |
| 68 | George Blanda (SP) | 70.00 | 35.00 |
| 69 | Billy Cannon | 5.00 | 2.50 |
| 70 | Doug Cline (SP) | 6.50 | 3.25 |
| 71 | Gary Cutsinger (SP) | 6.50 | 3.25 |
| 72 | Willard Dewveall (SP) | 6.50 | 3.25 |
| 73 | Don Floyd (SP) | 6.50 | 3.25 |
| 74 | Freddy Glick (SP) | 6.50 | 3.25 |
| 75 | Charlie Hennigan (SP) | 8.50 | 4.25 |
| 76 | Ed Husmann (SP) | 6.50 | 3.25 |
| 77 | Bobby Jancik (SP) | 6.50 | 3.25 |
| 78 | Jacky Lee (SP) | 7.00 | 3.50 |
| 79 | Bob McLeod (SP) | 6.50 | 3.25 |
| 80 | Rich Michael (SP) | 6.50 | 3.25 |
| 81 | Larry Onesti (R) | 3.00 | 1.50 |
| 82 | Checklist Card | 30.00 | 12.00 |
| 83 | Bob Schmidt (SP) | 6.50 | 3.25 |
| 84 | Walt Suggs (SP) | 6.50 | 3.25 |
| 85 | Bob Talamini (SP) | 6.50 | 3.25 |
| 86 | Charley Tolar (SP) | 7.50 | 3.75 |
| 87 | Don Trull (R) | 3.50 | 1.75 |
| 88 | Oilers Team | 6.00 | 3.00 |
| 89 | Fred Arbanas | 3.50 | 1.75 |
| 90 | Bobby Bell (R) | 30.00 | 15.00 |
| 91 | Mel Branch (SP) | 7.50 | 3.75 |
| 92 | Buck Buchanan (SP) | 32.00 | 16.00 |
| 93 | Ed Budde (R) | 6.00 | 3.00 |
| 94 | Chris Burford (SP) | 6.50 | 3.25 |
| 95 | Walt Corey (R) | 3.50 | 1.75 |
| 96 | Len Dawson (SP) | 75.00 | 32.50 |
| 97 | Dave Grayson (R) | 3.50 | 1.75 |
| 98 | Abner Haynes | 5.00 | 2.50 |
| 99 | Sherrill Headrick (SP) | 6.50 | 3.25 |
| 100 | E.J. Holub (R) | 4.50 | 2.25 |
| 101 | Bobby Hunt | 2.50 | 1.25 |
| 102 | Frank Jackson (SP) | 6.50 | 3.25 |
| 103 | Curtis McClinton | 2.50 | 1.25 |
| 104 | Jerry Mays (SP) | 6.50 | 3.25 |
| 105 | Johnny Robinson (SP) | 7.50 | 3.75 |
| 106 | Jack Spikes (SP) | 6.50 | 3.25 |
| 107 | Smokey Stover (SP) | 6.50 | 3.75 |
| 108 | Jim Tyrer (R) | 6.00 | 3.00 |
| 109 | Duane Wood (R) | 6.50 | 3.25 |
| 110 | Chiefs Team | 6.00 | 3.00 |
| 111 | Dick Christy (SP) | 6.50 | 3.25 |
| 112 | Dan Ficca (SP) | 6.50 | 3.25 |
| 113 | Larry Grantham | 3.50 | 1.75 |
| 114 | Curley Johnson (R) (SP) | 7.50 | 3.75 |
| 115 | Gene Heeter | 2.50 | 1.25 |
| 116 | Jack Klotz | 2.50 | 1.25 |
| 117 | Pete Liske (R) | 3.50 | 1.75 |
| 118 | Bob McAdam | 2.50 | 1.25 |
| 119 | Dee Mackey (SP) | 6.50 | 3.25 |
| 120 | Bill Mathis (SP) | 6.50 | 3.25 |
| 121 | Don Maynard | 24.00 | 12.00 |
| 122 | Dainard Paulson (SP) | 6.50 | 3.25 |
| 123 | Gerry Philbin | 3.50 | 1.75 |
| 124 | Mark Smolinski (SP) | 6.50 | 3.25 |
| 125 | Matt Snell (R) | 14.00 | 7.00 |
| 126 | Mike Taliaferro | 2.50 | 1.25 |
| 127 | Bake Turner (R)(SP) | 7.50 | 3.75 |
| 128 | Jeff Ware | 2.50 | 1.25 |
| 129 | Clyde Washington | 2.50 | 1.25 |
| 130 | Dick Wood (R) | 3.00 | 1.50 |
| 131 | Jets Team | 6.00 | 3.00 |
| 132 | Dalva Allen (SP) | 6.50 | 3.25 |
| 133 | Dan Birdwell | 2.50 | 1.25 |
| 134 | Dave Costa (R) | 3.50 | 1.75 |
| 135 | Dobie Craig | 2.50 | 1.25 |
| 136 | Clem Daniels | 4.00 | 2.00 |
| 137 | Cotton Davidson (SP) | 7.00 | 3.50 |
| 138 | Claude Gibson | 2.50 | 1.25 |
| 139 | Tom Flores (SP) | 10.00 | 5.00 |
| 140 | Wayne Hawkins (SP) | 6.50 | 3.25 |
| 141 | Ken Herock | 2.50 | 1.25 |
| 142 | Jon Jelacic (SP) | 6.50 | 3.25 |
| 143 | Joe Krakoski | 2.50 | 1.25 |
| 144 | Archie Matsos (SP) | 6.50 | 3.25 |
| 145 | Mike Mercer | 2.50 | 1.25 |
| 146 | Alan Miller (SP) | 6.50 | 3.25 |
| 147 | Bob Mischak (SP) | 6.50 | 3.25 |
| 148 | Jim Otto (SP) | 18.00 | 9.00 |
| 149 | Clancy Osborne (SP) | 6.50 | 3.25 |
| 150 | Art Powell (SP) | 8.50 | 4.25 |
| 151 | Bo Roberson | 2.50 | 1.25 |
| 152 | Fred Williamson (SP) | 7.50 | 3.75 |
| 153 | Raiders Team | 6.00 | 3.00 |
| 154 | Chuck Allen (SP) | 6.50 | 3.25 |
| 155 | Lance Alworth | 36.00 | 18.00 |
| 156 | George Blair | 2.50 | 1.25 |
| 157 | Earl Faison | 2.50 | 1.25 |
| 158 | Sam Gruneisen | 2.50 | 1.25 |
| 159 | John Hadl (R) | 24.00 | 12.00 |
| 160 | Dick Harris (SP) | 6.50 | 3.25 |
| 161 | Emil Karas (SP) | 6.50 | 3.25 |
| 162 | Dave Kocourek (SP) | 6.50 | 3.25 |
| 163 | Ernie Ladd | 5.00 | 2.50 |
| 164 | Keith Lincoln | 5.00 | 2.50 |
| 165 | Paul Lowe (SP) | 7.50 | 3.75 |
| 166 | Charles McNeil (R) | 3.50 | 1.75 |
| 167 | Jacque MacKinnon (SP) | 6.50 | 3.25 |
| 168 | Ron Mix (SP) | 12.50 | 6.25 |
| 169 | Don Norton (SP) | 6.50 | 3.25 |
| 170 | Don Rogers (SP) | 6.50 | 3.25 |
| 171 | Tobin Rote (SP) | 7.00 | 3.50 |
| 172 | Henry Schmidt (SP) | 6.50 | 3.25 |
| 173 | Bud Whitehead | 2.50 | 1.25 |
| 174 | Ernie Wright (SP) | 6.50 | 3.25 |
| 175 | Chargers Team | 6.00 | 3.00 |
| 176 | Checklist (SP) | 110.00 | 15.00 |

# 1965 Topps

JIM OTTO    center

For the second straight year Topps issued a set containing only American Football League players. The set is noteworthy for the unusual size of the cards (2-1/2" by 4-11/16") and the Joe Namath rookie card.  Card fronts consist of mostly posed photographs framed by a white border. The player's name and position are location across the bottom. The team name is printed in large letters across the top. The horizontal card backs contain personal data, a brief paragraph of copy and statistics on the left side and an illustration describing one of the highlights from the player's career on the right side. The set contains numerous short-prints (SP) which are indicated in the checklist.

|  |  | NR/MT | EX |
|---|---|---|---|
| **Complete Set (176)** | | 3,800.00 | 1,900.00 |
| **Commons** | | 5.00 | 2.50 |
| **Commons (SP)** | | 10.00 | 5.00 |
| 1 | Tommy Addison (SP) | 40.00 | 8.50 |
| 2 | Houston Antwine (SP) | 10.00 | 5.00 |
| 3 | Nick Buoniconti (SP) | 18.00 | 9.00 |
| 4 | Ron Burton (SP) | 10.00 | 5.00 |
| 5 | Gino Cappelletti (SP) | 15.00 | 7.50 |
| 6 | Jim Colclough | 5.00 | 2.50 |
| 7 | Bob Dee (SP) | 10.00 | 5.00 |
| 8 | Larry Eisenhauer | 5.00 | 2.50 |
| 9 | J.D. Garrett | 5.00 | 2.50 |
| 10 | Larry Garron | 5.00 | 2.50 |
| 11 | Art Graham (SP) | 10.00 | 5.00 |
| 12 | Ron Hall | 5.00 | 2.50 |
| 13 | Charles Long | 5.00 | 2.50 |
| 14 | Jon Morris (R) | 7.00 | 3.50 |
| 15 | Bill Neighbors (SP) | 10.00 | 5.00 |
| 16 | Ross O'Hanley | 5.00 | 2.50 |
| 17 | Babe Parilli (SP) | 12.50 | 6.25 |
| 18 | Tony Romero (SP) | 10.00 | 5.00 |
| 19 | Jack Rudolph (SP) | 10.00 | 5.00 |
| 20 | Bob Schmidt | 5.00 | 2.50 |
| 21 | Don Webb (SP) | 10.00 | 5.00 |
| 22 | Jim Whalen (SP) | 10.00 | 5.00 |
| 23 | Stew Barber | 5.00 | 2.50 |
| 24 | Glenn Bass (SP) | 10.00 | 5.00 |
| 25 | Al Bemiller (SP) | 10.00 | 5.00 |
| 26 | Wray Carlton (SP) | 10.00 | 5.00 |
| 27 | Tom Day | 5.00 | 2.50 |
| 28 | Elbert Dubenion (SP) | 12.00 | 6.00 |
| 29 | Jim Dunaway | 5.00 | 2.50 |
| 30 | Pete Gogolak (R) (SP) | 14.00 | 7.00 |
| 31 | Dick Hudson (SP) | 10.00 | 5.00 |
| 32 | Harry Jacobs (SP) | 10.00 | 5.00 |
| 33 | Billy Joe (SP) | 10.00 | 5.00 |
| 34 | Tom Keating (R)(SP) | 12.00 | 6.00 |
| 35 | Jack Kemp (SP) | 240.00 | 120.00 |
| 36 | Daryle Lamonica (SP) | 25.00 | 12.50 |
| 37 | Paul Maguire (SP) | 12.00 | 6.00 |
| 38 | Ron McDole (R)(SP) | 12.50 | 6.25 |
| 39 | George Saimes (SP) | 10.00 | 5.00 |
| 40 | Tom Sestak (R)(SP) | 10.00 | 5.00 |
| 41 | Billy Shaw (SP) | 10.00 | 5.00 |
| 42 | Mike Stratton (SP) | 10.00 | 5.00 |
| 43 | John Tracey (SP) | 10.00 | 5.00 |
| 44 | Ernie Warlick | 5.00 | 2.50 |
| 45 | Odell Barry | 5.00 | 2.50 |
| 46 | Willie Brown(R)(SP) | 50.00 | 25.00 |
| 47 | Garry Bussell (SP) | 10.00 | 5.00 |
| 48 | Eldon Danenhauer (SP) | 10.00 | 5.00 |
| 49 | Al Denson (SP) | 10.00 | 5.00 |
| 50 | Hewritt Dixon(R)(SP) | 15.00 | 7.50 |
| 51 | Cookie Gilchrist (SP) | 20.00 | 10.00 |
| 52 | Goose Gonsoulin (SP) | 12.00 | 6.00 |
| 53 | Abner Haynes (SP) | 16.00 | 8.00 |
| 54 | Jerry Hopkins (SP) | 10.00 | 5.00 |
| 55 | Ray Jacobs (SP) | 10.00 | 5.00 |
| 56 | Jacky Lee (SP) | 12.00 | 6.00 |
| 57 | John McCormick (SP) | 5.00 | 2.50 |
| 58 | Bob McCullough (SP) | 10.00 | 5.00 |
| 59 | John McGeever | 5.00 | 2.50 |
| 60 | Charlie Mitchell (SP) | 10.00 | 5.00 |
| 61 | Jim Perkins (SP) | 10.00 | 5.00 |
| 62 | Bob Scarpitto (SP) | 10.00 | 5.00 |

| | | | |
|---|---|---|---|
| 63 | Mickey Slaughter(SP) | 10.00 | 5.00 |
| 64 | Jerry Sturm (SP) | 10.00 | 5.00 |
| 65 | Lionel Taylor (SP) | 18.00 | 9.00 |
| 66 | Scott Appleton (SP) | 12.00 | 6.00 |
| 67 | Johnny Baker (SP) | 10.00 | 5.00 |
| 68 | Sonny Bishop (SP) | 10.00 | 5.00 |
| 69 | George Blanda (SP) | 100.00 | 50.00 |
| 70 | Sid Blanks (SP) | 10.00 | 5.00 |
| 71 | Ode Burrell (SP) | 10.00 | 5.00 |
| 72 | Doug Cline (SP) | 10.00 | 5.00 |
| 73 | Willard Dewveall | 5.00 | 2.50 |
| 74 | Larry Elkins (SP) | 7.00 | 3.50 |
| 75 | Don Floyd (SP) | 10.00 | 5.00 |
| 76 | Freddy Glick | 5.00 | 2.50 |
| 77 | Tom Goode (SP) | 10.00 | 5.00 |
| 78 | Charlie Hennigan (SP) | 15.00 | 7.50 |
| 79 | Ed Husmann | 5.00 | 2.50 |
| 80 | Bobby Jancik (SP) | 10.00 | 5.00 |
| 81 | Bud McFadin (SP) | 10.00 | 5.00 |
| 82 | Bob McLeod (SP) | 10.00 | 5.00 |
| 83 | Jim Norton (SP) | 10.00 | 5.00 |
| 84 | Walt Suggs | 5.00 | 2.50 |
| 85 | Bob Talamini | 5.00 | 2.50 |
| 86 | Charley Tolar (SP) | 12.00 | 6.00 |
| 87 | Checklist 1-88 (SP) | 125.00 | 15.00 |
| 88 | Don Trull (SP) | 10.00 | 5.00 |
| 89 | Fred Arbanas (SP) | 12.00 | 6.00 |
| 90 | Pete Beathard (R) (SP) | 18.00 | 9.00 |
| 91 | Bobby Bell (SP) | 25.00 | 12.50 |
| 92 | Mel Branch (SP) | 10.00 | 5.00 |
| 93 | Tommy Brooker (SP) | 10.00 | 5.00 |
| 94 | Buck Buchanan (SP) | 25.00 | 12.50 |
| 95 | Ed Budde (SP) | 12.50 | 6.25 |
| 96 | Chris Burford (SP) | 10.00 | 5.00 |
| 97 | Walt Corey | 5.00 | 2.50 |
| 98 | Jerry Cornelison | 5.00 | 2.50 |
| 99 | Len Dawson (SP) | 75.00 | 37.50 |
| 100 | Jon Gilliam (SP) | 10.00 | 5.00 |
| 101 | Sherrill Headrick(SP) | 10.00 | 5.00 |
| 102 | Dave Hill (SP) | 10.00 | 5.00 |
| 103 | E.J. Holub (SP) | 12.50 | 6.25 |
| 104 | Bobby Hunt (SP) | 10.00 | 5.00 |
| 105 | Frank Jackson (SP) | 10.00 | 5.00 |
| 106 | Jerry Mays | 6.00 | 3.00 |
| 107 | Curtis McClinton(SP) | 12.00 | 6.00 |
| 108 | Bobby Ply (SP) | 10.00 | 5.00 |
| 109 | Johnny Robinson (SP) | 12.50 | 6.25 |
| 110 | Jim Tyrer (SP) | 10.00 | 5.00 |
| 111 | Bill Baird (SP) | 10.00 | 5.00 |
| 112 | Ralph Baker (R)(SP) | 12.00 | 6.00 |
| 113 | Sam DeLuca (SP) | 10.00 | 5.00 |
| 114 | Larry Grantham(SP) | 12.00 | 6.00 |
| 115 | Gene Heeter (SP) | 10.00 | 5.00 |
| 116 | Winston Hill (R)(SP) | 15.00 | 7.50 |
| 117 | John Huarte (R)(SP) | 22.00 | 11.00 |
| 118 | Cosmo Iacavazzi (SP) | 10.00 | 5.00 |
| 119 | Curley Johnson (SP) | 10.00 | 5.00 |
| 120 | Dee Mackey | 5.00 | 2.50 |
| 121 | Don Maynard | 38.00 | 19.00 |
| 122 | Joe Namath (R) (SP) | 1,650.00 | 750.00 |
| 123 | Dainard Paulson | 5.00 | 2.50 |
| 124 | Gerry Philbin (SP) | 10.00 | 5.00 |
| 125 | Sherman Plunkett (R) | 14.00 | 7.00 |
| 126 | Mark Smolinski | 5.00 | 2.50 |
| 127 | Matt Snell (SP) | 18.00 | 9.00 |
| 128 | Mike Taliaferro (SP) | 10.00 | 5.00 |
| 129 | Bake Turner (SP) | 10.00 | 5.00 |
| 130 | Clyde Washington (SP) | 10.00 | 5.00 |
| 131 | Verlon Biggs (R)(SP) | 14.00 | 7.00 |
| 132 | Dalva Allen | 5.00 | 2.50 |
| 133 | Fred Biletnikoff (R) (SP) | 165.00 | 82.50 |
| 134 | Billy Cannon (SP) | 16.00 | 8.00 |
| 135 | Dave Costa (SP) | 10.00 | 5.00 |
| 136 | Clem Daniels (SP) | 14.00 | 7.00 |
| 137 | Ben Davidson (R) (SP) | 35.00 | 17.50 |
| 138 | Cotton Davidson (SP) | 12.00 | 6.00 |
| 139 | Tom Flores (SP) | 20.00 | 10.00 |
| 140 | Claude Gibson | 5.00 | 2.50 |
| 141 | Wayne Hawkins | 5.00 | 2.50 |
| 142 | Archie Matsos (SP) | 10.00 | 5.00 |
| 143 | Mike Mercer (SP) | 10.00 | 5.00 |
| 144 | Bob Mischak (SP) | 10.00 | 5.00 |
| 145 | Jim Otto | 24.00 | 12.00 |
| 146 | Art Powell (SP) | 15.00 | 7.50 |
| 147 | Warren Powers (SP) | 10.00 | 5.00 |
| 148 | Ken Rice (SP) | 10.00 | 5.00 |
| 149 | Bo Roberson (SP) | 10.00 | 5.00 |
| 150 | Harry Schuh (R) | 7.00 | 3.50 |
| 151 | Larry Todd (SP) | 10.00 | 5.00 |
| 152 | Fred Williamson (SP) | 15.00 | 7.50 |
| 153 | J.R. Williamson | 5.00 | 2.50 |
| 154 | Chuck Allen | 5.00 | 2.50 |
| 155 | Lance Alworth | 50.00 | 25.00 |
| 156 | Frank Buncom | 5.00 | 2.50 |
| 157 | Steve DeLong (R) (SP) | 12.50 | 6.25 |
| 158 | Earl Faison (SP) | 10.00 | 5.00 |
| 159 | Kenny Graham (SP) | 10.00 | 5.00 |
| 160 | George Gross (SP) | 10.00 | 5.00 |
| 161 | John Hadl (SP) | 18.50 | 9.25 |
| 162 | Emil Karas (SP) | 10.00 | 5.00 |
| 163 | Dave Kocourek (SP) | 10.00 | 5.00 |
| 164 | Ernie Ladd (SP) | 15.00 | 7.50 |

| | | NR/MT | EX |
|---|---|---|---|
| 165 | Keith Lincoln (SP) | 15.00 | 7.50 |
| 166 | Paul Lowe (SP) | 12.50 | 6.25 |
| 167 | Jacque McKinnon | 5.00 | 2.50 |
| 168 | Ron Mix | 18.00 | 9.00 |
| 169 | Don Norton (SP) | 10.00 | 5.00 |
| 170 | Bob Petrich | 5.00 | 2.50 |
| 171 | Rick Redman (SP) | 10.00 | 5.00 |
| 172 | Pat Shea | 5.00 | 2.50 |
| 173 | Walt Sweeney (R) (SP) | 16.00 | 8.00 |
| 174 | Dick Westmoreland(R) | 6.50 | 3.25 |
| 175 | Ernie Wright (SP) | 10.00 | 5.00 |
| 176 | Checklist 89-176 | 225.00 | 25.00 |

# 1966 Topps

LEN DAWSON

This standard-size card set once again features players from the American Football League. The horizontal card fronts consist of posed player photos with the player's name, team and position printed in the lower right corner. The card backs contain a team logo, personal data, a brief highlight, stats and a small cartoon. Cards measure 2-1/2" by 3-1/2".

| | | NR/MT | EX |
|---|---|---|---|
| **Complete Set (132)** | | 1,425.00 | 375.00 |
| **Commons** | | 3.00 | 1.50 |
| | | | |
| 1 | Tommy Addison | 24.00 | 4.50 |
| 2 | Houston Antwine | 3.00 | 1.50 |
| 3 | Nick Buoniconti | 7.50 | 3.75 |
| 4 | Gino Cappelletti | 4.00 | 2.00 |
| 5 | Bob Dee | 3.00 | 1.50 |
| 6 | Larry Garron | 3.00 | 1.50 |
| 7 | Art Graham | 3.00 | 1.50 |

| | | NR/MT | EX |
|---|---|---|---|
| 8 | Ron Hall | 3.00 | 1.50 |
| 9 | Charles Long | 3.00 | 1.50 |
| 10 | Jon Morris | 3.00 | 1.50 |
| 11 | Don Oakes | 3.00 | 1.50 |
| 12 | Babe Parilli | 4.00 | 2.00 |
| 13 | Don Webb | 3.00 | 1.50 |
| 14 | Jim Whalen | 3.00 | 1.50 |
| 15 | Funny Ring CL | 375.00 | 75.00 |
| 16 | Steve Barber | 3.00 | 1.50 |
| 17 | Glenn Bass | 3.00 | 1.50 |
| 18 | Dave Behrman | 3.00 | 1.50 |
| 19 | Al Bemiller | 3.00 | 1.50 |
| 20 | Butch Byrd (R) | 3.50 | 1.75 |
| 21 | Wray Carlton | 3.50 | 1.75 |
| 22 | Tom Day | 3.00 | 1.50 |
| 23 | Elbert Dubenion | 3.50 | 1.75 |
| 24 | Jim Dunaway | 3.00 | 1.50 |
| 25 | Dick Hudson | 3.00 | 1.50 |
| 26 | Jack Kemp | 125.00 | 62.50 |
| 27 | Daryle Lamonica | 7.50 | 3.75 |
| 28 | Tom Sestak | 3.00 | 1.50 |
| 29 | Billy Shaw | 3.00 | 1.50 |
| 30 | Mike Stratton | 3.00 | 1.50 |
| 31 | Eldon Danenhauer | 3.00 | 1.50 |
| 32 | Cookie Gilchrist | 6.00 | 3.00 |
| 33 | Goose Gonsoulin | 3.00 | 1.50 |
| 34 | Wendell Hayes (R) | 4.50 | 2.25 |
| 35 | Abner Haynes | 5.00 | 2.50 |
| 36 | Jerry Hopkins | 3.00 | 1.50 |
| 37 | Ray Jacobs | 3.00 | 1.50 |
| 38 | Charlie Janerette | 3.00 | 1.50 |
| 39 | Ray Kubala | 3.00 | 1.50 |
| 40 | John McCormick | 3.00 | 1.50 |
| 41 | Leroy Moore | 3.00 | 1.50 |
| 42 | Bob Scarpitto | 3.00 | 1.50 |
| 43 | Mickey Slaughter | 3.00 | 1.50 |
| 44 | Jerry Sturm | 3.00 | 1.50 |
| 45 | Lionel Taylor | 6.00 | 3.00 |
| 46 | Scott Appleton | 3.50 | 1.75 |
| 47 | Johnny Baker | 3.00 | 1.50 |
| 48 | George Blanda | 42.00 | 21.00 |
| 49 | Sid Blanks | 3.00 | 1.50 |
| 50 | Danny Brabham | 3.00 | 1.50 |
| 51 | Ode Burrell | 3.00 | 1.50 |
| 52 | Gary Cutsinger | 3.00 | 1.50 |
| 53 | Larry Elkins | 3.00 | 1.50 |
| 54 | Don Floyd | 3.00 | 1.50 |
| 55 | Willie Frazier (R) | 4.50 | 2.25 |
| 56 | Freddy Glick | 3.00 | 1.50 |
| 57 | Charlie Hennigan | 4.00 | 2.00 |
| 58 | Bobby Jancik | 3.00 | 1.50 |
| 59 | Rich Michael | 3.00 | 1.50 |
| 60 | Don Trull | 3.00 | 1.50 |
| 61 | Checklist | 35.00 | 5.00 |
| 62 | Fred Arbanas | 3.50 | 1.75 |
| 63 | Pete Beathard | 4.00 | 2.00 |
| 64 | Bobby Bell | 7.50 | 3.75 |

| | | | |
|---|---|---|---|
| 65 | Ed Budde | 3.50 | 1.75 |
| 66 | Chris Burford | 3.00 | 1.50 |
| 67 | Len Dawson | 22.00 | 11.00 |
| 68 | Jon Gilliam | 3.00 | 1.50 |
| 69 | Sherrill Headrick | 3.00 | 1.50 |
| 70 | E.J. Holub | 4.00 | 2.00 |
| 71 | Bobby Hunt | 3.00 | 1.50 |
| 72 | Curtis McClinton | 3.50 | 1.75 |
| 73 | Jerry Mays | 4.00 | 2.00 |
| 74 | Johnny Robinson | 4.00 | 2.00 |
| 75 | Otis Taylor (R) | 12.50 | 6.25 |
| 76 | Tom Erlandson | 3.00 | 1.50 |
| 77 | Norm Evans (R) | 4.00 | 2.00 |
| 78 | Tom Goode | 3.00 | 1.50 |
| 79 | Mike Hudock | 3.00 | 1.50 |
| 80 | Frank Jackson | 3.00 | 1.50 |
| 81 | Billy Joe | 3.00 | 1.50 |
| 82 | Dave Kocourek | 3.00 | 1.50 |
| 83 | Bo Roberson | 3.00 | 1.50 |
| 84 | Jack Spikes | 3.50 | 1.75 |
| 85 | Jim Warren (R) | 3.50 | 1.75 |
| 86 | Willie West (R) | 3.50 | 1.75 |
| 87 | Dick Westmoreland | 3.00 | 1.50 |
| 88 | Eddie Wilson | 3.00 | 1.50 |
| 89 | Dick Wood | 3.00 | 1.50 |
| 90 | Verlon Biggs | 3.50 | 1.75 |
| 91 | Sam DeLuca | 3.00 | 1.50 |
| 92 | Winston Hill | 3.00 | 1.50 |
| 93 | Dee Mackey | 3.00 | 1.50 |
| 94 | Bill Mathis | 3.00 | 1.50 |
| 95 | Don Maynard | 18.50 | 9.25 |
| 96 | Joe Namath | 295.00 | 145.00 |
| 97 | Dainard Paulson | 3.00 | 1.50 |
| 98 | Gerry Philbin | 3.00 | 1.50 |
| 99 | Sherman Plunkett | 3.00 | 1.50 |
| 100 | Paul Rochester | 3.00 | 1.50 |
| 101 | George Sauer Jr. (R) | 7.50 | 3.75 |
| 102 | Matt Snell | 6.50 | 3.25 |
| 103 | Jim Turner (R) | 5.00 | 2.50 |
| 104 | Fred Biletnikoff | 50.00 | 25.00 |
| 105 | Bill Budness | 3.00 | 1.50 |
| 106 | Billy Cannon | 4.50 | 2.25 |
| 107 | Clem Daniels | 4.50 | 2.25 |
| 108 | Ben Davidson | 6.50 | 3.25 |
| 109 | Cotton Davidson | 3.50 | 1.75 |
| 110 | Claude Gibson | 3.00 | 1.50 |
| 111 | Wayne Hawkins | 3.00 | 1.50 |
| 112 | Ken Herock | 3.00 | 1.50 |
| 113 | Bob Mischak | 3.00 | 1.50 |
| 114 | Gus Otto | 3.00 | 1.50 |
| 115 | Jim Otto | 15.00 | 7.50 |
| 116 | Art Powell | 4.50 | 2.25 |
| 117 | Harry Schuh | 3.00 | 1.50 |
| 118 | Chuck Allen | 3.00 | 1.50 |
| 119 | Lance Alworth | 28.00 | 14.00 |
| 120 | Frank Buncom | 3.00 | 1.50 |
| 121 | Steve DeLong | 3.00 | 1.50 |

| | | | |
|---|---|---|---|
| 122 | John Farris | 3.00 | 1.50 |
| 123 | Kenny Graham | 3.00 | 1.50 |
| 124 | Sam Gruniesen | 3.00 | 1.50 |
| 125 | John Hadl | 8.50 | 4.25 |
| 126 | Walt Sweeney | 3.50 | 1.75 |
| 127 | Keith Lincoln | 4.50 | 2.25 |
| 128 | Ron Mix | 8.00 | 4.00 |
| 129 | Don Norton | 3.00 | 1.50 |
| 130 | Pat Shea | 3.00 | 1.50 |
| 131 | Ernie Wright | 3.00 | 1.50 |
| 132 | Checklist | 85.00 | 10.00 |

## 1967 Topps

This 132-card set consists of players from the American Football League. The card fronts feature player photos inside an oval border with the team name printed in the top corners of the border. The player's name and position appear in a horizontal box across the bottom of the card. The vertical card backs contain personal data, stats, a brief biographical sketch and a trivia question. All cards measure 2-1/2" by 3-1/2".

| | | NR/MT | EX |
|---|---|---|---|
| Complete Set (132) | | 575.00 | 285.00 |
| Commons | | 1.50 | .75 |
| | | | |
| 1 | John Huarte | 8.50 | 2.50 |
| 2 | Babe Parilli | 2.50 | 1.25 |
| 3 | Gino Cappelletti | 2.50 | 1.25 |
| 4 | Larry Garron | 1.50 | .75 |
| 5 | Tommy Addison | 1.50 | .75 |
| 6 | Jon Morris | 1.50 | .75 |
| 7 | Houston Antwine | 1.50 | .75 |

| | | | | | | | | |
|---|---|---|---|---|---|---|---|
| 8 | Don Oakes | 1.50 | .75 | 65 | Johnny Robinson | 2.50 | 1.25 |
| 9 | Larry Eisenhauer | 1.50 | .75 | 66 | E.J. Holub | 2.50 | 1.25 |
| 10 | Jim Hunt | 1.50 | .75 | 67 | Jerry Mays | 2.00 | 1.00 |
| 11 | Jim Whalen | 1.50 | .75 | 68 | Jim Tyrer | 1.50 | .75 |
| 12 | Art Graham | 1.50 | .75 | 69 | Bobby Bell | 6.00 | 3.00 |
| 13 | Nick Buoniconti | 4.00 | 2.00 | 70 | Fred Arbanas | 1.75 | .85 |
| 14 | Bob Dee | 1.50 | .75 | 71 | Buck Buchanan | 6.00 | 3.00 |
| 15 | Keith Lincoln | 3.00 | 1.50 | 72 | Chris Burford | 1.50 | .75 |
| 16 | Tom Flores | 4.00 | 2.00 | 73 | Otis Taylor | 4.50 | 2.25 |
| 17 | Art Powell | 3.00 | 1.50 | 74 | Cookie Gilchrist | 4.00 | 2.00 |
| 18 | Stew Barber | 1.50 | .75 | 75 | Earl Faison | 1.50 | .75 |
| 19 | Wray Carlton | 1.50 | .75 | 76 | George Wilson | 1.50 | .75 |
| 20 | Elbert Dubenion | 2.00 | 1.00 | 77 | Rick Norton | 1.50 | .75 |
| 21 | Jim Dunaway | 1.50 | .75 | 78 | Frank Jackson | 1.50 | .75 |
| 22 | Dick Hudson | 1.50 | .75 | 79 | Joe Auer | 1.50 | .75 |
| 23 | Harry Jacobs | 1.50 | .75 | 80 | Willie West | 1.50 | .75 |
| 24 | Jack Kemp | 75.00 | 37.50 | 81 | Jim Warren | 1.50 | .75 |
| 25 | Ron McDole | 1.50 | .75 | 82 | Wahoo McDaniel (R) | 12.50 | 6.25 |
| 26 | George Saimes | 1.50 | .75 | 83 | Ernie Park | 1.50 | .75 |
| 27 | Tom Sestak | 1.50 | .75 | 84 | Bill Neighbors | 1.50 | .75 |
| 28 | Billy Shaw | 1.50 | .75 | 85 | Norm Evans | 1.50 | .75 |
| 29 | Mike Stratton | 1.50 | .75 | 86 | Tom Nomina | 1.50 | .75 |
| 30 | Nemiah Wilson (R) | 2.50 | 1.25 | 87 | Rich Zecher | 1.50 | .75 |
| 31 | John McCormick | 1.50 | .75 | 88 | Dave Kocourek | 1.50 | .75 |
| 32 | Rex Mirich | 1.50 | .75 | 89 | Bill Baird | 1.50 | .75 |
| 33 | Dave Costa | 1.50 | .75 | 90 | Ralph Baker | 1.50 | .75 |
| 34 | Goose Gonsoulin | 1.50 | .75 | 91 | Verlon Biggs | 1.75 | .85 |
| 35 | Abner Haynes | 3.50 | 1.75 | 92 | Sam DeLuca | 1.50 | .75 |
| 36 | Wendell Hayes | 1.50 | .75 | 93 | Larry Grantham | 2.00 | 1.00 |
| 37 | Archie Matsos | 1.50 | .75 | 94 | Jim Harris | 1.50 | .75 |
| 38 | John Bramlett | 1.50 | .75 | 95 | Winston Hill | 1.50 | .75 |
| 39 | Jerry Sturm | 1.50 | .75 | 96 | Bill Mathis | 1.50 | .75 |
| 40 | Max Leetzow | 1.50 | .75 | 97 | Don Maynard | 18.00 | 9.00 |
| 41 | Bob Scarpitto | 1.50 | .75 | 98 | Joe Namath | 160.00 | 80.00 |
| 42 | Lionel Taylor | 3.50 | 1.75 | 99 | Gerry Philbin | 1.50 | .75 |
| 43 | Al Denson | 1.50 | .75 | 100 | Paul Rochester | 1.50 | .75 |
| 44 | Miller Farr | 1.50 | .75 | 101 | George Sauer Jr. | 3.00 | 1.50 |
| 45 | Don Trull | 1.50 | .75 | 102 | Matt Snell | 4.00 | 2.00 |
| 46 | Jacky Lee | 1.50 | .75 | 103 | Daryle Lamonica | 5.00 | 2.50 |
| 47 | Bobby Jancik | 1.50 | .75 | 104 | Glenn Bass | 1.50 | .75 |
| 48 | Ode Burrell | 1.50 | .75 | 105 | Jim Otto | 6.50 | 3.25 |
| 49 | Larry Elkins | 1.50 | .75 | 106 | Fred Biletnikoff | 18.50 | 9.25 |
| 50 | W.K. Hicks | 1.50 | .75 | 107 | Cotton Davidson | 2.00 | 1.00 |
| 51 | Sid Blanks | 1.50 | .75 | 108 | Larry Todd | 1.50 | .75 |
| 52 | Jim Norton | 1.50 | .75 | 109 | Billy Cannon | 3.00 | 1.50 |
| 53 | Bobby Maples (R) | 2.00 | 1.00 | 110 | Clem Daniels | 2.50 | 1.25 |
| 54 | Bob Talamini | 1.50 | .75 | 111 | Dave Grayson | 1.50 | .75 |
| 55 | Walt Suggs | 1.50 | .75 | 112 | Kent McCloughan | 1.50 | .75 |
| 56 | Gary Cutsinger | 1.50 | .75 | 113 | Bob Svihus | 1.50 | .75 |
| 57 | Danny Brabham | 1.50 | .75 | 114 | Ike Lassiter | 1.50 | .75 |
| 58 | Ernie Ladd | 3.50 | 1.75 | 115 | Harry Schuh | 1.50 | .75 |
| 59 | Checklist | 24.00 | 4.00 | 116 | Ben Davidson | 4.50 | 2.25 |
| 60 | Pete Beathard | 2.50 | 1.50 | 117 | Tom Day | 1.50 | .75 |
| 61 | Len Dawson | 24.00 | 12.00 | 118 | Scott Appleton | 1.75 | .85 |
| 62 | Bobby Hunt | 1.50 | .75 | 119 | Steve Tensi (R) | 2.00 | 1.00 |
| 63 | Bert Coan | 1.50 | .75 | 120 | John Hadl | 5.00 | 2.50 |
| 64 | Curtis McClinton | 1.50 | .75 | 121 | Paul Lowe | 2.50 | 1.25 |

| 122 | Jim Allison | 1.50 | .75 |
| 123 | Lance Alworth | 20.00 | 10.00 |
| 124 | Jacque MacKinnon | 1.50 | .75 |
| 125 | Ron Mix | 6.00 | 3.00 |
| 126 | Bob Petrich | 1.50 | .75 |
| 127 | Howard Kindig | 1.50 | .75 |
| 128 | Steve DeLong | 1.50 | .75 |
| 129 | Chuck Allen | 1.50 | .75 |
| 130 | Frank Buncom | 1.50 | .75 |
| 131 | Speedy Duncan (R) | 2.50 | 1.25 |
| 132 | Checklist | 45.00 | 7.50 |

# 1968 Topps

DON MEREDITH
DALLAS COWBOYS

In 1968 Topps expanded their football set and included NFL players along with AFC players. The card fronts feature mostly posed photos framed by a white border. The player's name, team and position are printed in a small multi-colored oval below the photo. Card backs are vertical and contain personal data, stats and a brief paragraph of copy. Most card backs feature a rub-off game at the bottom of the card. Others feature part of a 10-card puzzle of either Len Dawson or Bart Starr. The high numbered cards (133-219) are more scare that the other cards. All cards measure 2-1/2" by 3-1/2".

|  |  | NR/MT | EX |
|---|---|---|---|
| **Complete Set (219)** | | 625.00 | 310.00 |
| **Commons (1-132)** | | .75 | .35 |
| **Commons (133-219)** | | 1.00 | .50 |
| 1 | Bart Starr | 38.00 | 15.00 |
| 2 | Dick Bass | 1.00 | .50 |

| 3 | Grady Alderman | .75 | .35 |
| 4 | Obert Logan | .75 | .35 |
| 5 | Ernie Koy (R ) | 1.00 | .50 |
| 6 | Don Hultz | .75 | .35 |
| 7 | Earl Gros | .75 | .35 |
| 8 | Jim Bakken | 1.25 | .60 |
| 9 | George Mira | 1.00 | .50 |
| 10 | Carl Kammerer | .75 | .35 |
| 11 | Willie Frazier | .75 | .35 |
| 12 | Kent McCloughan | .75 | .35 |
| 13 | George Sauer Jr. | 1.50 | .75 |
| 14 | Jack Clancy | .75 | .35 |
| 15 | Jim Tyrer | .75 | .35 |
| 16 | Bobby Maples | .75 | .35 |
| 17 | Bo Hickey | .75 | .35 |
| 18 | Frank Buncom | .75 | .35 |
| 19 | Keith Lincoln | 1.25 | .60 |
| 20 | Jim Whalen | .75 | .35 |
| 21 | Junior Coffey | .75 | .35 |
| 22 | Billy Ray Smith | .75 | .35 |
| 23 | Johnny Morris | 1.25 | .60 |
| 24 | Ernie Green | .90 | .45 |
| 25 | Don Meredith | 24.00 | 12.00 |
| 26 | Wayne Walker | .90 | .45 |
| 27 | Carroll Dale | .90 | .45 |
| 28 | Bernie Casey | 1.00 | .50 |
| 29 | Dave Osborn (R) | 1.75 | .85 |
| 30 | Ray Poage | .75 | .35 |
| 31 | Homer Jones | .75 | .35 |
| 32 | Sam Baker | .75 | .35 |
| 33 | Bill Saul | .75 | .35 |
| 34 | Ken Willard | 1.00 | .50 |
| 35 | Bobby Mitchell | 4.50 | 2.25 |
| 36 | Gary Garrison (R) | 1.00 | .50 |
| 37 | Billy Cannon | 2.00 | 1.00 |
| 38 | Ralph Baker | .75 | .35 |
| 39 | Howard Twilley (R) | 2.50 | 1.25 |
| 40 | Wendell Hayes | .90 | .45 |
| 41 | Jim Norton | .75 | .35 |
| 42 | Tom Beer | .75 | .35 |
| 43 | Chris Burford | .75 | .35 |
| 44 | Stew Barber | .75 | .35 |
| 45 | Leroy Mitchell | .75 | .35 |
| 46 | Dan Grimm | .75 | .35 |
| 47 | Jerry Logan | .75 | .35 |
| 48 | Andy Livingston | .75 | .35 |
| 49 | Paul Warfield | 8.00 | 4.00 |
| 50 | Don Perkins | 1.25 | .60 |
| 51 | Ron Kramer | .90 | .45 |
| 52 | Bob Jeter (R) | 1.00 | .50 |
| 53 | Les Josephson (R) | 1.75 | .85 |
| 54 | Bobby Walden | .75 | .35 |
| 55 | Checklist | 8.50 | .75 |
| 56 | Walter Roberts | .75 | .35 |
| 57 | Henry Carr | .75 | .35 |
| 58 | Gary Ballman | .75 | .35 |
| 59 | J.R. Wilburn | .75 | .35 |

| 60 | Jim Hart (R) | 8.50 | 4.25 |
|----|-------------|------|------|
| 61 | Jim Johnson | .75 | .35 |
| 62 | Chris Hanburger | 1.75 | .85 |
| 63 | John Hadl | 3.50 | 1.75 |
| 64 | Hewritt Dixon | .90 | .45 |
| 65 | Joe Namath | 90.00 | 45.00 |
| 66 | Jim Warren | .75 | .35 |
| 67 | Curtis McClinton | .75 | .35 |
| 68 | Bob Talamini | .75 | .35 |
| 69 | Steve Tensi | .75 | .35 |
| 70 | Dick Van Raaphorst | .75 | .35 |
| 71 | Art Powell | 1.25 | .60 |
| 72 | Jim Nance (R) | 4.50 | 2.25 |
| 73 | Bob Riggle | .75 | .35 |
| 74 | John Mackey | 4.50 | 2.25 |
| 75 | Gale Sayers | 85.00 | 42.50 |
| 76 | Gene Hickerson | .75 | .35 |
| 77 | Dan Reeves | 4.00 | 2.00 |
| 78 | Tom Nowatzke | .75 | .35 |
| 79 | Elijah Pitts | .90 | .45 |
| 80 | Lamar Lundy | .90 | .45 |
| 81 | Paul Flatley | .75 | .35 |
| 82 | Dave Whitsell | .75 | .35 |
| 83 | Spider Lockhart | .75 | .35 |
| 84 | Dave Lloyd | .75 | .35 |
| 85 | Roy Jefferson | 1.00 | .50 |
| 86 | Jackie Smith | 1.75 | .85 |
| 87 | John David Crow | 1.50 | .75 |
| 88 | Sonny Jurgensen | 8.50 | 4.25 |
| 89 | Ron Mix | 3.50 | 1.75 |
| 90 | Clem Daniels | 1.00 | .50 |
| 91 | Cornell Gordon | .75 | .35 |
| 92 | Tom Goode | .75 | .35 |
| 93 | Bobby Bell | 4.50 | 2.25 |
| 94 | Walt Suggs | .75 | .35 |
| 95 | Eric Crabtree | .75 | .35 |
| 96 | Sherrill Headrick | .75 | .35 |
| 97 | Wray Carlton | .75 | .35 |
| 98 | Gino Cappelletti | 1.50 | .75 |
| 99 | Tommy McDonald | 1.00 | .50 |
| 100 | John Unitas | 32.00 | 16.00 |
| 101 | Richie Petitbon | .90 | .45 |
| 102 | Erich Barnes | .90 | .45 |
| 103 | Bob Hayes | 2.50 | 1.25 |
| 104 | Milt Plum | 1.00 | .50 |
| 105 | Boyd Dowler | .90 | .45 |
| 106 | Ed Meador | .75 | .35 |
| 107 | Fred Cox | .90 | .45 |
| 108 | Steve Stonebreaker (R) | 1.25 | .60 |
| 109 | Aaron Thomas | .75 | .35 |
| 110 | Norm Snead | 2.50 | 1.25 |
| 111 | Paul Martha (R) | 1.25 | .60 |
| 112 | Jerry Stovall | .90 | .45 |
| 113 | Kay McFarland | .75 | .35 |
| 114 | Pat Richter | .90 | .45 |
| 115 | Rick Redman | .75 | .35 |
| 116 | Tom Keating | .75 | .35 |
| 117 | Matt Snell | 3.00 | 1.50 |
| 118 | Dick Westmoreland | .75 | .35 |
| 119 | Jerry Mays | .75 | .35 |
| 120 | Sid Blanks | .75 | .35 |
| 121 | Al Denson | .75 | .35 |
| 122 | Bobby Hunt | .75 | .35 |
| 123 | Mike Mercer | .75 | .35 |
| 124 | Nick Buoniconti | 3.00 | 1.50 |
| 125 | Ron Vanderkelen (R) | 1.00 | .50 |
| 126 | Ordell Braase | .75 | .35 |
| 127 | Dick Butkus | 38.00 | 19.00 |
| 128 | Gary Collins | 1.00 | .50 |
| 129 | Mel Renfro | 1.75 | .85 |
| 130 | Alex Karras | 5.00 | 2.50 |
| 131 | Herb Adderley | 3.50 | 1.75 |
| 132 | Roman Gabriel | 3.50 | 1.75 |
| 133 | Bill Brown | 1.25 | .60 |
| 134 | Kent Kramer | 1.00 | .50 |
| 135 | Tucker Frederickson | 1.25 | .60 |
| 136 | Nate Ramsey | 1.00 | .50 |
| 137 | Marv Woodson | 1.00 | .50 |
| 138 | Ken Gray | 1.00 | .50 |
| 139 | John Brodie | 6.50 | 3.25 |
| 140 | Jerry Smith | 1.00 | .50 |
| 141 | Brad Hubbert | 1.00 | .50 |
| 142 | George Blanda | 24.00 | 12.00 |
| 143 | Pete Lammons (R) | 1.25 | .60 |
| 144 | Doug Moreau | 1.00 | .50 |
| 145 | E.J. Holub | 1.25 | .60 |
| 146 | Ode Burrell | 1.00 | .50 |
| 147 | Bob Scarpitto | 1.00 | .50 |
| 148 | Andre White | 1.00 | .50 |
| 149 | Jack Kemp | 36.00 | 18.00 |
| 150 | Art Graham | 1.00 | .50 |
| 151 | Tommy Nobis | 3.50 | 1.75 |
| 152 | Willie Richardson (R) | 1.50 | .75 |
| 153 | Jack Concannon | 1.25 | .60 |
| 154 | Bill Glass | 1.25 | .60 |
| 155 | Craig Morton (R) | 8.50 | 4.25 |
| 156 | Pat Studstill | 1.25 | .60 |
| 157 | Ray Nitschke | 4.50 | 2.25 |
| 158 | Roger Brown | 1.25 | .60 |
| 159 | Joe Kapp | 4.50 | 2.25 |
| 160 | Jim Taylor | 8.00 | 4.00 |
| 161 | Fran Tarkenton | 28.00 | 14.00 |
| 162 | Mike Ditka | 8.00 | 4.00 |
| 163 | Andy Russell (R) | 4.00 | 2.00 |
| 164 | Larry Wilson | 3.00 | 1.75 |
| 165 | Tommy Davis | 1.00 | .50 |
| 166 | Paul Krause | 2.50 | 1.25 |
| 167 | Speedy Duncan | 1.00 | .50 |
| 168 | Fred Biletnikoff | 8.50 | 4.25 |
| 169 | Don Maynard | 8.50 | 4.25 |
| 170 | Frank Emanuel | 1.00 | .50 |
| 171 | Len Dawson | 9.00 | 4.50 |
| 172 | Miller Farr | 1.00 | .50 |

| 173 | Floyd Little (R) | 12.50 | 6.25 |
|---|---|---|---|
| 174 | Lonnie Wright | 1.00 | .50 |
| 175 | Paul Costa | 1.00 | .50 |
| 176 | Don Trull | 1.00 | .50 |
| 177 | Jerry Simmons | 1.00 | .50 |
| 178 | Tom Matte | 1.25 | .60 |
| 179 | Bennie McRae | 1.00 | .50 |
| 180 | Jim Kanicki | 1.00 | .50 |
| 181 | Bob Lilly | 6.00 | 3.00 |
| 182 | Tom Watkins | 1.00 | .50 |
| 183 | Jim Grabowski (R) | 3.00 | 1.50 |
| 184 | Jack Snow (R) | 3.50 | 1.75 |
| 185 | Gary Cuozzo (R) | 1.50 | .75 |
| 186 | Bill Kilmer | 3.50 | 1.75 |
| 187 | Jim Katcavage | 1.25 | .60 |
| 188 | Floyd Peters | 1.00 | .50 |
| 189 | Bill Nelsen | 1.25 | .60 |
| 190 | Bobby Joe Conrad | 1.25 | .60 |
| 191 | Kermit Alexander | 1.25 | .60 |
| 192 | Charley Taylor | 7.50 | 3.75 |
| 193 | Lance Alworth | 9.00 | 4.50 |
| 194 | Daryle Lamonica | 3.50 | 1.75 |
| 195 | Al Atkinson | 1.00 | .50 |
| 196 | Bob Griese | 95.00 | 48.00 |
| 197 | Buck Buchanan | 4.50 | 2.25 |
| 198 | Pete Beathard | 1.25 | .60 |
| 199 | Nemiah Wilson | 1.00 | .50 |
| 200 | Ernie Wright | 1.00 | .50 |
| 201 | George Saimes | 1.00 | .50 |
| 202 | John Charles | 1.00 | .50 |
| 203 | Randy Johnson | 1.25 | .60 |
| 204 | Tony Lorick | 1.00 | .50 |
| 205 | Dick Evey | 1.00 | .50 |
| 206 | Leroy Kelly | 6.00 | 3.00 |
| 207 | Lee Roy Jordan | 3.00 | 1.50 |
| 208 | Jim Gibbons | 1.00 | .50 |
| 209 | Donny Anderson (R) | 3.50 | 1.75 |
| 210 | Maxie Baughan | 1.25 | .60 |
| 211 | Joe Morrison | 1.50 | .75 |
| 212 | Jim Snowden | 1.00 | .50 |
| 213 | Lenny Lyles | 1.00 | .50 |
| 214 | Bobby Joe Green | 1.00 | .50 |
| 215 | Frank Ryan | 2.00 | 1.00 |
| 216 | Cornell Green | 1.25 | .60 |
| 217 | Karl Sweetan | 1.25 | .60 |
| 218 | Dave Williams | 1.00 | .50 |
| 219A | Checklist (Blue) | 20.00 | 3.50 |
| 219B | Checklist (Green) | 16.00 | 2.00 |

# 1969 Topps

Bob
LILLY
DALLAS COWBOYS • DEF TACKLE

At 263-cards, this set is Topps' largest football edition to date. The set is notable because of two different designs on the card fronts. Series I (1-132) features a borderless design with full color photos on the front. A team logo appears in the bottom corner of the photo while the player's name, team and position appear in a white box at the bottom of the card. The cards in Series II (133-263) feature white borders around full color photos. The horizontal card backs in both series are the same with personal data, a brief paragraph of copy and a small cartoon. All cards measure 2-1/2" by 3-1/2".

|  | NR/MT | EX |
|---|---|---|
| **Complete Set (263)** | 550.00 | 275.00 |
| **Commons (1-132)** | .75 | .35 |
| **Commons (133-263)** | 1.00 | .50 |

| 1 | Leroy Kelly | 6.50 | 2.00 |
|---|---|---|---|
| 2 | Paul Flatley | .75 | .35 |
| 3 | Jim Cadile | .75 | .35 |
| 4 | Erich Barnes | .75 | .35 |
| 5 | Willie Richardson | .75 | .35 |
| 6 | Bob Hayes | 2.00 | 1.00 |
| 7 | Bob Jeter | .75 | .35 |
| 8 | Jim Colclough | .75 | .35 |
| 9 | Sherrill Headrick | .75 | .35 |
| 10 | Jim Dunaway | .75 | .35 |
| 11 | Bill Munson | 1.00 | .50 |
| 12 | Jack Pardee | 2.50 | 1.25 |
| 13 | Jim Lindsey | .75 | .35 |
| 14 | Dave Whitsell | .75 | .35 |
| 15 | Tucker Frederickson | .75 | .35 |
| 16 | Alvin Haymond | .75 | .35 |
| 17 | Andy Russell | 1.00 | .50 |

| 18 | Tom Beer | .75 | .35 |
|---|---|---|---|
| 19 | Bobby Maples | .75 | .35 |
| 20 | Len Dawson | 7.00 | 3.50 |
| 21 | Willis Crenshaw | .75 | .35 |
| 22 | Tommy Davis | .75 | .35 |
| 23 | Rickie Harris | .75 | .35 |
| 24 | Jerry Simmons | .75 | .35 |
| 25 | John Unitas | 32.00 | 16.00 |
| 26 | Brian Piccolo | 55.00 | 27.50 |
| 27 | Bob Matheson | .75 | .35 |
| 28 | Howard Twilley | 1.00 | .50 |
| 29 | Jim Turner | .75 | .35 |
| 30 | Pete Banaszak (R) | 2.00 | 1.00 |
| 31 | Lance Rentzel (R) | 1.50 | .75 |
| 32 | Bill Triplett | .75 | .35 |
| 33 | Boyd Dowler | .90 | .45 |
| 34 | Merlin Olsen | 6.50 | 3.25 |
| 35 | Joe Kapp | 1.25 | .60 |
| 36 | Dan Abramowicz (R) | 2.50 | 1.25 |
| 37 | Spider Lockhart | .75 | .35 |
| 38 | Tom Day | .75 | .35 |
| 39 | Art Graham | .75 | .35 |
| 40 | Bob Cappadona | .75 | .35 |
| 41 | Gary Ballman | .75 | .35 |
| 42 | Clendon Thomas | .75 | .35 |
| 43 | Jackie Smith | 1.00 | .50 |
| 44 | Dave Wilcox (R) | 1.00 | .50 |
| 45 | Jerry Smith | .75 | .35 |
| 46 | Dan Grimm | .75 | .35 |
| 47 | Tom Matte | 1.25 | .60 |
| 48 | John Stofa | .75 | .35 |
| 49 | Rex Mirich | .75 | .35 |
| 50 | Miller Farr | .75 | .35 |
| 51 | Gale Sayers | 70.00 | 35.00 |
| 52 | Bill Nelsen | 1.25 | .60 |
| 53 | Bob Lilly | 5.00 | 2.50 |
| 54 | Wayne Walker | .90 | .45 |
| 55 | Ray Nitschke | 4.50 | 2.25 |
| 56 | Ed Meador | .75 | .35 |
| 57 | Lonnie Warwick | .75 | .35 |
| 58 | Wendell Hayes | .75 | .35 |
| 59 | Dick Anderson (R) | 2.50 | 1.25 |
| 60 | Don Maynard | 5.00 | 2.50 |
| 61 | Tony Lorick | .75 | .35 |
| 62 | Pete Gogolak | .90 | .45 |
| 63 | Nate Ramsey | .75 | .35 |
| 64 | Dick Shiner (R) | .75 | .45 |
| 65 | Larry Wilson | 3.00 | 1.50 |
| 66 | Ken Willard | 1.00 | .50 |
| 67 | Charley Taylor | 5.00 | 2.50 |
| 68 | Billy Cannon | 1.50 | .75 |
| 69 | Lance Alworth | 6.00 | 3.00 |
| 70 | Jim Nance | 1.50 | .75 |
| 71 | Nick Rassas | .75 | .35 |
| 72 | Lenny Lyles | .75 | .35 |
| 73 | Bennie McRae | .75 | .35 |
| 74 | Bill Glass | .90 | .45 |
| 75 | Don Meredith | 24.00 | 12.00 |
| 76 | Dick LeBeau | 1.00 | .50 |
| 77 | Carroll Dale | .75 | .35 |
| 78 | Ron McDole | .75 | .35 |
| 79 | Charley King | .75 | .35 |
| 80 | Checklist 1-132 | 8.00 | .75 |
| 81 | Dick Bass | 1.00 | .50 |
| 82 | Roy Winston | .75 | .45 |
| 83 | Don McCall | .75 | .35 |
| 84 | Jim Katcavage | .90 | .45 |
| 85 | Norm Snead | 2.00 | 1.00 |
| 86 | Earl Gros | .75 | .35 |
| 87 | Don Brumm | .75 | .35 |
| 88 | Sonny Bishop | .75 | .35 |
| 89 | Fred Arbanas | .75 | .35 |
| 90 | Karl Noonan | .75 | .35 |
| 91 | Dick Witcher | .75 | .35 |
| 92 | Vince Promuto | .75 | .35 |
| 93 | Tommy Nobis | 2.50 | 1.25 |
| 94 | Jerry Hill | .75 | .35 |
| 95 | Ed O'Bradovich (R) | .90 | .45 |
| 96 | Ernie Kellerman | .75 | .35 |
| 97 | Chuck Howley | 1.00 | .50 |
| 98 | Hewritt Dixon | .90 | .45 |
| 99 | Ron Mix | 3.50 | 1.75 |
| 100 | Joe Namath | 65.00 | 37.50 |
| 101 | Billy Gambrell | .75 | .35 |
| 102 | Elijah Pitts | .90 | .45 |
| 103 | Billy Truax (R) | .75 | .45 |
| 104 | Ed Sharockman | .75 | .35 |
| 105 | Doug Atkins | 3.50 | 1.75 |
| 106 | Greg Larson | .75 | .35 |
| 107 | Israel Lang | .75 | .35 |
| 108 | Houston Antwine | .75 | .35 |
| 109 | Paul Guidry | .75 | .35 |
| 110 | Al Denson | .75 | .35 |
| 111 | Roy Jefferson | .90 | .45 |
| 112 | Chuck Latourette | .75 | .35 |
| 113 | Jim Johnson | .75 | .35 |
| 114 | Bobby Mitchell | 4.00 | 2.00 |
| 115 | Randy Johnson | .75 | .35 |
| 116 | Lou Michaels | .90 | .45 |
| 117 | Rudy Kuechenberg | .75 | .35 |
| 118 | Walt Suggs | .75 | .35 |
| 119 | Goldie Sellers | .75 | .35 |
| 120 | Larry Csonka (R) | 75.00 | 37.50 |
| 121 | Jim Houston | .75 | .35 |
| 122 | Craig Baynham | .75 | .35 |
| 123 | Alex Karras | 5.00 | 2.50 |
| 124 | Jim Grabowski | .75 | .35 |
| 125 | Roman Gabriel | 3.00 | 1.50 |
| 126 | Larry Bowie | .75 | .35 |
| 127 | Dave Parks | 1.00 | .50 |
| 128 | Ben Davidson | 3.50 | 1.50 |
| 129 | Steve DeLong | .75 | .35 |
| 130 | Fred Hill | .75 | .35 |
| 131 | Ernie Koy | .75 | .35 |

| | | | |
|---|---|---|---|
| 132 | Checklist 133-263 | 8.00 | .75 |
| 133 | Dick Hoak | .90 | .45 |
| 134 | Larry Stallings (R) | 1.75 | .85 |
| 135 | Clifton McNeil (R) | 1.50 | .75 |
| 136 | Walter Rock | 1.00 | .50 |
| 137 | Billy Lothridge | 1.00 | .50 |
| 138 | Bob Vogel | 1.00 | .50 |
| 139 | Dick Butkus | 20.00 | 10.00 |
| 140 | Frank Ryan | 2.00 | 1.00 |
| 141 | Larry Garron | 1.00 | .50 |
| 142 | George Saimes | 1.00 | .50 |
| 143 | Frank Buncom | 1.00 | .50 |
| 144 | Don Perkins | 1.50 | .75 |
| 145 | Johnny Robinson | 1.25 | .60 |
| 146 | Lee Roy Caffey | 1.00 | .50 |
| 147 | Bernie Casey | 1.25 | .60 |
| 148 | Billy Martin | 1.00 | .50 |
| 149 | Gene Howard | 1.00 | .50 |
| 150 | Fran Tarkenton | 28.00 | 14.00 |
| 151 | Eric Crabtree | 1.00 | .50 |
| 152 | W.K. Hicks | 1.00 | .50 |
| 153 | Bobby Bell | 4.00 | 2.00 |
| 154 | Sam Baker | 1.00 | .50 |
| 155 | Marv Woodson | 1.00 | .50 |
| 156 | Dave Williams | 1.00 | .50 |
| 157 | Bruce Bosley | 1.00 | .50 |
| 158 | Carl Kammerer | 1.00 | .50 |
| 159 | Jim Burson | 1.00 | .50 |
| 160 | Roy Hilton | 1.00 | .50 |
| 161 | Bob Griese | 24.00 | 12.00 |
| 162 | Bob Talamini | 1.00 | .50 |
| 163 | Jim Otto | 4.00 | 2.00 |
| 164 | Ron Bull | 1.25 | .60 |
| 165 | Walter Johnson (R) | 1.00 | .50 |
| 166 | Lee Roy Jordan | 3.00 | 1.50 |
| 167 | Mike Lucci | 1.00 | .50 |
| 168 | Willie Wood | 4.00 | 2.00 |
| 169 | Maxie Baughan | 1.25 | .60 |
| 170 | Bill Brown | 1.50 | .75 |
| 171 | John Hadl | 3.00 | 1.50 |
| 172 | Gino Cappelletti | 1.50 | .75 |
| 173 | George Byrd | 1.00 | .50 |
| 174 | Steve Stonebreaker | 1.00 | .50 |
| 175 | Joe Morrison | 1.25 | .60 |
| 176 | Joe Scarpati | 1.00 | .50 |
| 177 | Bobby Walden | 1.00 | .50 |
| 178 | Roy Shivers | 1.00 | .50 |
| 179 | Kermit Alexander | 1.25 | .60 |
| 180 | Pat Richter | 1.25 | .60 |
| 181 | Pete Perreault | 1.00 | .50 |
| 182 | Pete Duranko | 1.00 | .50 |
| 183 | Leroy Mitchell | 1.00 | .50 |
| 184 | Jim Simon | 1.00 | .50 |
| 185 | Billy Ray Smith | 1.00 | .50 |
| 186 | Jack Concannon | 1.25 | .60 |
| 187 | Ben Davis | 1.00 | .50 |
| 188 | Mike Clark | 1.00 | .50 |
| 189 | Jim Gibbons | 1.00 | .50 |
| 190 | Dave Robinson | 1.00 | .50 |
| 191 | Otis Taylor | 2.50 | 1.25 |
| 192 | Nick Buoniconti | 2.00 | 1.00 |
| 193 | Matt Snell | 2.50 | 1.25 |
| 194 | Bruce Gossett | 1.00 | .50 |
| 195 | Mick Tingelhoff | 1.25 | .60 |
| 196 | Earl Leggett | 1.00 | .50 |
| 197 | Pete Case | 1.00 | .50 |
| 198 | Tom Woodeshick (R) | 1.25 | .60 |
| 199 | Ken Kortas | 1.00 | .50 |
| 200 | Jim Hart | 3.50 | 1.75 |
| 201 | Fred Biletnikoff | 6.50 | 3.25 |
| 202 | Jacque MacKinnon | 1.00 | .50 |
| 203 | Jim Whalen | 1.00 | .50 |
| 204 | Matt Hazeltine | 1.00 | .50 |
| 205 | Charlie Gogolak | 1.00 | .50 |
| 206 | Ray Ogden | 1.00 | .50 |
| 207 | John Mackey | 3.50 | 1.75 |
| 208 | Roosevelt Taylor | 1.00 | .50 |
| 209 | Gene Hickerson | 1.00 | .50 |
| 210 | Dave Edwards (R) | 1.00 | .50 |
| 211 | Tom Sestak | 1.00 | .50 |
| 212 | Ernie Wright | 1.00 | .50 |
| 213 | Dave Costa | 1.00 | .50 |
| 214 | Tom Vaughn | 1.00 | .50 |
| 215 | Bart Starr | 28.00 | 14.00 |
| 216 | Les Josephson | 1.00 | .50 |
| 217 | Fred Cox | 1.00 | .50 |
| 218 | Mike Tilleman | 1.00 | .50 |
| 219 | Darrell Dess | 1.00 | .50 |
| 220 | Dave Lloyd | 1.00 | .50 |
| 221 | Pete Beathard | 1.00 | .50 |
| 222 | Buck Buchanan | 4.00 | 2.00 |
| 223 | Frank Emanuel | 1.00 | .50 |
| 224 | Paul Martha | 1.00 | .50 |
| 225 | Johnny Roland | 1.75 | .85 |
| 226 | Gary Lewis | 1.00 | .50 |
| 227 | Sonny Jurgensen | 8.50 | 4.25 |
| 228 | Jim Butler | 1.00 | .50 |
| 229 | Mike Curtis (R) | 3.00 | 1.50 |
| 230 | Richie Petitbon | 1.25 | .60 |
| 231 | George Sauer Jr. | 1.25 | .60 |
| 232 | George Blanda | 24.00 | 12.00 |
| 233 | Gary Garrison | 1.00 | .50 |
| 234 | Gary Collins | 1.00 | .50 |
| 235 | Craig Morton | 3.50 | 1.75 |
| 236 | Tom Nowatzke | 1.00 | .50 |
| 237 | Donny Anderson | 1.25 | .60 |
| 238 | Deacon Jones | 4.50 | 2.25 |
| 239 | Grady Alderman | 1.00 | .50 |
| 240 | Bill Kilmer | 3.50 | 1.75 |
| 241 | Mike Taliaferro | 1.00 | .50 |
| 242 | Stew Barber | 1.00 | .50 |
| 243 | Bobby Hunt | 1.00 | .50 |
| 244 | Homer Jones | 1.00 | .50 |
| 245 | Bob Brown | 1.00 | .50 |

| | | NR/MT | EX |
|---|---|---|---|
| 246 | Bill Asbury | 1.00 | .50 |
| 247 | Charlie Johnson | 2.00 | 1.00 |
| 248 | Chris Hanburger | 1.25 | .60 |
| 249 | John Brodie | 5.00 | 2.50 |
| 250 | Earl Morrall | 3.00 | 1.50 |
| 251 | Floyd Little | 3.50 | 1.75 |
| 252 | Jerrel Wilson (R) | 1.25 | .60 |
| 253 | Jim Keyes | 1.00 | .50 |
| 254 | Mel Renfro | 1.75 | .85 |
| 255 | Herb Adderley | 3.50 | 1.75 |
| 256 | Jack Snow | 1.25 | .60 |
| 257 | Charlie Durkee | 1.00 | .50 |
| 258 | Charlie Harper | 1.00 | .50 |
| 259 | J.R. Wilburn | 1.00 | .50 |
| 260 | Charlie Krueger | 1.00 | .50 |
| 261 | Pete Jacques | 1.00 | .50 |
| 262 | Gerry Philbin | 1.00 | .50 |
| 263 | Daryle Lamonica | 12.50 | 3.50 |

# 1970 Topps

This 263-card set features mostly posed photos on the card fronts. The photos are located inside an oval frame. The player's name and team appear in a small pennant below the photo. His position is located in a small football in the lower right corner of the card. The horizontal backs include personal data, a brief highlight and a small cartoon. All cards measure 2-1/2" by 3-1/2".

| | NR/MT | EX |
|---|---|---|
| Complete Set (263) | 480.00 | 240.00 |
| Commons (1-132) | .50 | .25 |
| Commons (133-263) | .75 | .35 |

| | | NR/MT | EX |
|---|---|---|---|
| 1 | Len Dawson | 15.00 | 6.00 |
| 2 | Doug Hart | .50 | .25 |
| 3 | Verlon Biggs | .50 | .25 |
| 4 | Ralph Neely (R) | .80 | .40 |
| 5 | Harmon Wages | .50 | .25 |
| 6 | Dan Conners | .50 | .25 |
| 7 | Gino Cappelletti | 1.25 | .60 |
| 8 | Erich Barnes | .50 | .25 |
| 9 | Checklist 1-132 | 7.50 | .75 |
| 10 | Bob Griese | 10.00 | 5.00 |
| 11 | Ed Flanagan | .50 | .25 |
| 12 | George Seals | .50 | .25 |
| 13 | Harry Jacobs | .50 | .25 |
| 14 | Mike Haffner | .50 | .25 |
| 15 | Bob Vogel | .50 | .25 |
| 16 | Bill Peterson | .50 | .25 |
| 17 | Spider Lockhart | .50 | .25 |
| 18 | Billy Truax | .50 | .25 |
| 19 | Jim Beirne | .50 | .25 |
| 20 | Leroy Kelly | 3.00 | 1.50 |
| 21 | Dave Lloyd | .50 | .25 |
| 22 | Mike Tilleman | .50 | .25 |
| 23 | Gary Garrison | .50 | .25 |
| 24 | Larry Brown (R) | 5.00 | 2.50 |
| 25 | Jan Stenerud (R) | 10.00 | 5.00 |
| 26 | Rolf Krueger | .50 | .25 |
| 27 | Roland Lakes | .50 | .25 |
| 28 | Dick Hoak | .50 | .25 |
| 29 | Gene Washington (R) | .80 | .40 |
| 30 | Bart Starr | 20.00 | 10.00 |
| 31 | Dave Grayson | .50 | .25 |
| 32 | Jerry Rush | .50 | .25 |
| 33 | Len St. Jean | .50 | .25 |
| 34 | Randy Edmunds | .50 | .25 |
| 35 | Matt Snell | 1.50 | .75 |
| 36 | Paul Costa | .50 | .25 |
| 37 | Mike Pyle | .50 | .25 |
| 38 | Roy Hilton | .50 | .25 |
| 39 | Steve Tensi | .50 | .25 |
| 40 | Tommy Nobis | 1.50 | .75 |
| 41 | Pete Case | .50 | .25 |
| 42 | Andy Rice | .50 | .25 |
| 43 | Elvin Bethea (R) | 2.50 | 1.25 |
| 44 | Jack Snow | .80 | .40 |
| 45 | Mel Renfro | 1.25 | .60 |
| 46 | Andy Livingston | .50 | .25 |
| 47 | Gary Ballman | .50 | .25 |
| 48 | Bob DeMarco | .50 | .25 |
| 49 | Steve DeLong | .50 | .25 |
| 50 | Daryle Lamonica | 4.50 | 2.25 |
| 51 | Jim Lynch (R) | 1.00 | .50 |
| 52 | Mel Farr (R) | 1.25 | .60 |
| 53 | Bob Long | .50 | .25 |
| 54 | John Elliott | .50 | .25 |
| 55 | Ray Nitschke | 3.50 | 1.75 |
| 56 | Jim Shorter | .50 | .25 |
| 57 | Dave Wilcox | .50 | .25 |

| 58 | Eric Crabtree | .50 | .25 |
|---|---|---|---|
| 59 | Alan Page (R) | 28.00 | 14.00 |
| 60 | Jim Nance | 1.00 | .50 |
| 61 | Glen Ray Hines | .50 | .25 |
| 62 | John Mackey | 4.50 | 2.25 |
| 63 | Ron McDole | .50 | .25 |
| 64 | Tom Beier | .50 | .25 |
| 65 | Bill Nelsen | .75 | .35 |
| 66 | Paul Flatley | .50 | .25 |
| 67 | Sam Brunelli | .50 | .25 |
| 68 | Jack Pardee | 1.50 | .75 |
| 69 | Brig Owens | .50 | .25 |
| 70 | Gale Sayers | 48.00 | 24.00 |
| 71 | Lee Roy Jordan | 1.50 | .75 |
| 72 | Harold Jackson (R) | 5.00 | 2.50 |
| 73 | John Hadl | 3.00 | 1.50 |
| 74 | Dave Parks | .75 | .35 |
| 75 | Lem Barney (R) | 12.50 | 6.25 |
| 76 | Johnny Roland | .75 | .35 |
| 77 | Ed Budde | .50 | .25 |
| 78 | Ben McGee | .50 | .25 |
| 79 | Ken Bowman | .50 | .25 |
| 80 | Fran Tarkenton | 24.00 | 12.00 |
| 81 | Gene Washington (R) | 3.50 | 1.75 |
| 82 | Larry Grantham | .50 | .25 |
| 83 | Bill Brown | .75 | .45 |
| 84 | John Charles | .50 | .25 |
| 85 | Fred Biletnikoff | 5.00 | 2.50 |
| 86 | Royce Berry | .50 | .25 |
| 87 | Bob Lilly | 5.00 | 2.50 |
| 88 | Earl Morrall | 2.50 | 1.25 |
| 89 | Jerry LeVias (R) | .80 | .40 |
| 90 | O.J. Simpson (R) | 175.00 | 85.00 |
| 91 | Mike Howell | .50 | .25 |
| 92 | Ken Gray | .50 | .25 |
| 93 | Chris Hanburger | .80 | .40 |
| 94 | Larry Seiple (R) | 1.00 | .50 |
| 95 | Rich Jackson (R) | .75 | .35 |
| 96 | Marty Freitas | .50 | .25 |
| 97 | Dick Post (R) | .75 | .35 |
| 98 | Ben Hawkins | .50 | .25 |
| 99 | Ken Reaves | .50 | .25 |
| 100 | Roman Gabriel | 3.00 | 1.50 |
| 101 | Dave Rowe | .50 | .25 |
| 102 | Dave Robinson | .50 | .25 |
| 103 | Otis Taylor | 2.00 | 1.00 |
| 104 | Jim Turner | .50 | .25 |
| 105 | Joe Morrison | .80 | .50 |
| 106 | Dick Evey | .50 | .25 |
| 107 | Ray Mansfield | .50 | .25 |
| 108 | Grady Alderman | .50 | .25 |
| 109 | Bruce Gossett | .50 | .25 |
| 110 | Bob Trumpy (R) | 7.50 | 3.75 |
| 111 | Jim Hunt | .50 | .25 |
| 112 | Larry Stallings | .80 | .50 |
| 113 | Lance Rentzel | .80 | .50 |
| 114 | Bubba Smith (R) | 22.00 | 11.00 |
| 115 | Norm Snead | 1.75 | .85 |
| 116 | Jim Otto | 3.50 | 1.75 |
| 117 | Bo Scott | .75 | .35 |
| 118 | Rick Redman | .50 | .25 |
| 119 | George Byrd | .50 | .25 |
| 120 | George Webster (R) | 1.75 | .85 |
| 121 | Chuck Walton | .50 | .25 |
| 122 | Dave Costa | .50 | .25 |
| 123 | Al Dodd | .50 | .25 |
| 124 | Len Hauss | .50 | .25 |
| 125 | Deacon Jones | 4.00 | 2.00 |
| 126 | Randy Johnson | .75 | .35 |
| 127 | Ralph Heck | .50 | .25 |
| 128 | Emerson Boozer (R) | 3.00 | 1.50 |
| 129 | Johnny Robinson | .50 | .25 |
| 130 | John Brodie | 6.50 | 3.25 |
| 131 | Gale Gillingham | .75 | .35 |
| 132 | Checklist 133-263 | 7.50 | .75 |
| 133 | Chuck Walker | .75 | .35 |
| 134 | Bennie McRae | .75 | .35 |
| 135 | Paul Warfield | 6.50 | 3.25 |
| 136 | Dan Darragh | .75 | .35 |
| 137 | Paul Robinson | 1.00 | .50 |
| 138 | Ed Philpott | .75 | .35 |
| 139 | Craig Morton | 2.00 | 1.00 |
| 140 | Tom Dempsey (R) | 3.50 | 1.75 |
| 141 | Al Nelson | .75 | .35 |
| 142 | Tom Matte | 1.00 | .50 |
| 143 | Dick Schafrath | .75 | .35 |
| 144 | Willie Brown | 4.50 | 2.25 |
| 145 | Charley Taylor | 6.00 | 3.00 |
| 146 | John Huard | .75 | .35 |
| 147 | Dave Osborn | .90 | .45 |
| 148 | Gene Mingo | .75 | .35 |
| 149 | Larry Hand | .75 | .35 |
| 150 | Joe Namath | 60.00 | 30.00 |
| 151 | Tom Mack (R) | 5.00 | 2.50 |
| 152 | Kenny Graham | .75 | .35 |
| 153 | Don Herrmann | .75 | .35 |
| 154 | Bobby Bell | 4.00 | 2.00 |
| 155 | Hoyle Granger | .75 | .35 |
| 156 | Claude Humphrey (R) | 1.50 | .75 |
| 157 | Clifton McNeil | .75 | .35 |
| 158 | Mick Tingelhoff | 1.00 | .50 |
| 159 | Don Horn (R) | 1.25 | .60 |
| 160 | Larry Wilson | 3.50 | 1.75 |
| 161 | Tom Neville | .75 | .35 |
| 162 | Larry Csonka | 20.00 | 10.00 |
| 163 | Doug Buffone (R) | 1.00 | .50 |
| 164 | Cornell Green | 1.00 | .50 |
| 165 | Haven Moses (R) | 2.00 | 1.00 |
| 166 | Bill Kilmer | 3.00 | 1.50 |
| 167 | Tim Rossovich (R) | 1.00 | .50 |
| 168 | Bill Bergey (R) | 4.50 | 2.25 |
| 169 | Gary Collins | .90 | .45 |
| 170 | Floyd Little | 3.00 | 1.50 |
| 171 | Tom Keating | .75 | .35 |

| | | | |
|---|---|---|---|
| 172 | Pat Fischer | .75 | .35 |
| 173 | Walt Sweeney | .75 | .35 |
| 174 | Greg Larson | .75 | .35 |
| 175 | Carl Eller | 3.50 | 1.75 |
| 176 | George Sauer Jr. | 1.25 | .60 |
| 177 | Jim Hart | 3.50 | 1.75 |
| 178 | Bob Brown | .90 | .45 |
| 179 | Mike Garrett (R) | 3.50 | 1.75 |
| 180 | John Unitas | 30.00 | 15.00 |
| 181 | Tom Regner | .75 | .35 |
| 182 | Bob Jeter | .75 | .35 |
| 183 | Gail Cogdill | .75 | .35 |
| 184 | Earl Gros | .75 | .35 |
| 185 | Dennis Partee | .75 | .35 |
| 186 | Charlie Krueger | .75 | .35 |
| 187 | Martin Baccaglio | .75 | .35 |
| 188 | Charles Long | .75 | .35 |
| 189 | Bob Hayes | 2.00 | 1.00 |
| 190 | Dick Butkus | 16.00 | 8.00 |
| 191 | Al Bemiller | .75 | .35 |
| 192 | Dick Westmoreland | .75 | .35 |
| 193 | Joe Scarpati | .75 | .35 |
| 194 | Ron Snidow | .75 | .35 |
| 195 | Earl McCullouch (R) | 1.25 | .60 |
| 196 | Jake Kupp | .75 | .35 |
| 197 | Bob Lurtsema | .75 | .35 |
| 198 | Mike Current | .75 | .35 |
| 199 | Charlie Smith | .75 | .35 |
| 200 | Sonny Jurgensen | 7.50 | 3.75 |
| 201 | Mike Curtis | 1.25 | .60 |
| 202 | Aaron Brown | .75 | .35 |
| 203 | Richie Petitbon | .90 | .45 |
| 204 | Walt Suggs | .75 | .35 |
| 205 | Roy Jefferson | .90 | .45 |
| 206 | Russ Washington (R) | 1.00 | .50 |
| 207 | Woody Peoples (R) | .90 | .45 |
| 208 | Dave Williams | .75 | .35 |
| 209 | John Zook (R) | 1.00 | .50 |
| 210 | Tom Woodeshick | .75 | .35 |
| 211 | Howard Fest | .75 | .35 |
| 212 | Jack Concannon | .90 | .45 |
| 213 | Jim Marshall | 3.50 | 1.75 |
| 214 | Jon Morris | .75 | .35 |
| 215 | Dan Abramowicz | 1.00 | .50 |
| 216 | Paul Martha | .75 | .35 |
| 217 | Ken Willard | 1.25 | .60 |
| 218 | Walter Rock | .75 | .35 |
| 219 | Garland Boyette | .75 | .35 |
| 220 | Buck Buchanan | 4.00 | 2.00 |
| 221 | Bill Munson | 1.00 | .50 |
| 222 | David Lee | .75 | .35 |
| 223 | Karl Noonan | .75 | .35 |
| 224 | Harry Schuh | .75 | .35 |
| 225 | Jackie Smith | 1.25 | .60 |
| 226 | Gerry Philbin | .75 | .35 |
| 227 | Ernie Koy | .75 | .35 |
| 228 | Chuck Howley | 1.00 | .50 |
| 229 | Billy Shaw | .75 | .35 |
| 230 | Jerry Hillebrand | .75 | .35 |
| 231 | Bill Thompson (R) | 1.25 | .60 |
| 232 | Carroll Dale | .75 | .35 |
| 233 | Gene Hickerson | .75 | .35 |
| 234 | Jim Butler | .75 | .35 |
| 235 | Greg Cook (R) | 1.50 | .75 |
| 236 | Lee Roy Caffey | .75 | .35 |
| 237 | Merlin Olsen | 5.00 | 2.50 |
| 238 | Fred Cox | .90 | .45 |
| 239 | Nate Ramsey | .75 | .35 |
| 240 | Lance Alworth | 5.00 | 2.50 |
| 241 | Chuck Hinton | .75 | .35 |
| 242 | Jerry Smith | .75 | .35 |
| 243 | Tony Baker | .75 | .35 |
| 244 | Nick Buoniconti | 2.50 | 1.25 |
| 245 | Jim Johnson | .75 | .35 |
| 246 | Willie Richardson | .75 | .35 |
| 247 | Fred Dryer (R) | 15.00 | 7.50 |
| 248 | Bobby Maples | .75 | .35 |
| 249 | Alex Karras | 5.00 | 2.50 |
| 250 | Joe Kapp | 1.25 | .60 |
| 251 | Ben Davidson | 3.50 | 1.75 |
| 252 | Mike Stratton | .75 | .35 |
| 253 | Les Josephson | .75 | .35 |
| 254 | Don Maynard | 5.00 | 2.50 |
| 255 | Houston Antwine | .75 | .35 |
| 256 | Mac Percival (R) | .75 | .35 |
| 257 | George Goeddeke | .75 | .35 |
| 258 | Homer Jones | .75 | .35 |
| 259 | Bob Berry | .75 | .35 |
| 260 | Calvin Hill (R) | 5.00 | 2.50 |
| 261 | Willie Wood | 3.50 | 1.75 |
| 262 | Ed Weisacosky | .75 | .35 |
| 263 | Jim Tyrer | 3.00 | .50 |

# 1971 Topps

This 263-card set features mostly posed photos on the card fronts. The photos are framed by red borders for AFC players and blue borders for NFC players. The player's name is printed across the top and the team name appears in large bold type across the bottom. Card backs contain personal data, a brief paragraph of copy and a box for statistics. All cards measure 2-1/2" by 3-1/2".

|  |  | NR/MT | EX |
|---|---|---|---|
| **Complete Set (263)** | | 540.00 | 270.00 |
| **Commons (1-132)** | | .50 | .25 |
| **Commons (133-263)** | | .75 | .35 |
| 1 | John Unitas | 35.00 | 12.00 |
| 2 | Jim Butler | .50 | .25 |
| 3 | Marty Schottenheimer (R) | 7.50 | 3.75 |
| 4 | Joe O'Donnell | .50 | .25 |
| 5 | Tom Dempsey | .80 | .50 |
| 6 | Chuck Allen | .50 | .25 |
| 7 | Ernie Kellerman | .50 | .25 |
| 8 | Walt Garrison (R) | 1.75 | .85 |
| 9 | Bill Van Heusen | .50 | .25 |
| 10 | Lance Alworth | 4.50 | 2.25 |
| 11 | Greg Landry (R) | 3.50 | 1.75 |
| 12 | Larry Krause | .50 | .25 |
| 13 | Buck Buchanan | 3.50 | 1.75 |
| 14 | Roy Gerela (R) | .90 | .45 |
| 15 | Clifton McNeil | .50 | .25 |
| 16 | Bob Brown | .75 | .35 |
| 17 | Lloyd Mumphord | .50 | .25 |
| 18 | Gary Cuozzo | .75 | .35 |
| 19 | Don Maynard | 4.50 | 2.25 |
| 20 | Larry Wilson | 2.00 | 1.00 |
| 21 | Charlie Smith | .50 | .25 |
| 22 | Ken Avery | .50 | .25 |
| 23 | Billy Walik | .50 | .25 |
| 24 | Jim Johnson | .50 | .25 |
| 25 | Dick Butkus | 10.00 | 5.00 |
| 26 | Charley Taylor | 4.00 | 2.00 |
| 27 | Checklist 1-132 | 8.50 | 1.00 |
| 28 | Lionel Aldridge (R) | 1.25 | .60 |
| 29 | Billy Lothridge | .50 | .25 |
| 30 | Terry Hanratty (R) | 1.75 | .85 |
| 31 | Lee Roy Jordan | 1.50 | .75 |
| 32 | Rick Volk (R) | .75 | .35 |
| 33 | Howard Kindig | .50 | .25 |
| 34 | Carl Garrett (R) | .75 | .35 |
| 35 | Bobby Bell | 3.00 | 1.50 |
| 36 | Gene Hickerson | .50 | .25 |
| 37 | Dave Parks | .75 | .35 |
| 38 | Paul Martha | .50 | .25 |
| 39 | George Blanda | 14.00 | 7.00 |
| 40 | Tom Woodeshick | .50 | .25 |
| 41 | Alex Karras | 4.00 | 2.00 |
| 42 | Rick Redman | .50 | .25 |
| 43 | Zeke Moore | .50 | .25 |
| 44 | Jack Snow | .75 | .35 |
| 45 | Larry Csonka | 7.50 | 3.75 |
| 46 | Karl Kassulke | .50 | .25 |
| 47 | Jim Hart | 2.00 | 1.00 |
| 48 | Al Atkinson | .50 | .25 |
| 49 | Horst Muhlmann (R) | .50 | .25 |
| 50 | Sonny Jurgensen | 7.00 | 3.50 |
| 51 | Ron Johnson (R) | 2.50 | 1.25 |
| 52 | Cas Banaszek | .50 | .25 |
| 53 | Bubba Smith | 5.00 | 2.50 |
| 54 | Bobby Douglass (R) | 1.75 | .85 |
| 55 | Willie Wood | 3.00 | 1.50 |
| 56 | Bake Turner | .50 | .25 |
| 57 | Mike Morgan | .50 | .25 |
| 58 | George Byrd | .50 | .25 |
| 59 | Don Horn | .50 | .25 |
| 60 | Tommy Nobis | 1.50 | .75 |
| 61 | Jan Stenerud | 2.50 | 1.25 |
| 62 | Altie Taylor (R) | .75 | .35 |
| 63 | Gary Pettigrew | .50 | .25 |
| 64 | Spike Jones | .50 | .25 |
| 65 | Duane Thomas (R) | 2.50 | 1.25 |
| 66 | Marty Domres (R) | .75 | .35 |
| 67 | Dick Anderson | .75 | .35 |
| 68 | Ken Iman | .50 | .25 |
| 69 | Miller Farr | .50 | .25 |
| 70 | Daryle Lamonica | 3.00 | 1.50 |
| 71 | Alan Page | 7.00 | 3.50 |
| 72 | Pat Matson | .50 | .25 |
| 73 | Emerson Boozer | 1.25 | .60 |
| 74 | Pat Fischer | .50 | .25 |
| 75 | Gary Collins | .75 | .35 |
| 76 | John Fuqua (R) | 1.00 | .50 |
| 77 | Bruce Gossett | .50 | .25 |

| No. | Player | | |
|---|---|---|---|
| 78 | Ed O'Bradovich | .50 | .25 |
| 79 | Bob Tucker (R) | .75 | .35 |
| 80 | Mike Curtis | .75 | .35 |
| 81 | Rich Jackson | .50 | .25 |
| 82 | Tom Janik | .50 | .25 |
| 83 | Gale Gillingham | .50 | .25 |
| 84 | Jim Mitchell | .50 | .25 |
| 85 | Charlie Johnson | 1.75 | .85 |
| 86 | Ed Chandler | .50 | .25 |
| 87 | Cyril Pinder | .50 | .25 |
| 88 | Johnny Robinson | .50 | .25 |
| 89 | Ralph Neely | .50 | .25 |
| 90 | Dan Abramowicz | .75 | .35 |
| 91 | Mercury Morris (R) | 3.50 | 1.75 |
| 92 | Steve DeLong | .50 | .25 |
| 93 | Larry Stallings | .50 | .25 |
| 94 | Tom Mack | 1.50 | .75 |
| 95 | Hewritt Dixon | .75 | .35 |
| 96 | Fred Cox | .50 | .25 |
| 97 | Chris Hanburger | .75 | .35 |
| 98 | Gerry Philbin | .50 | .25 |
| 99 | Ernie Wright | .50 | .25 |
| 100 | John Brodie | 5.00 | 2.50 |
| 101 | Tucker Frederickson | .75 | .35 |
| 102 | Bobby Walden | .50 | .25 |
| 103 | Dick Gordon | .50 | .25 |
| 104 | Walter Johnson | .50 | .25 |
| 105 | Mike Lucci | .75 | .35 |
| 106 | Checklist 133-263 | 7.50 | .75 |
| 107 | Ron Berger | .50 | .25 |
| 108 | Dan Sullivan | .50 | .25 |
| 109 | George Kunz (R) | 1.75 | .85 |
| 110 | Floyd Little | 2.50 | 1.25 |
| 111 | Zeke Bratkowski | 1.00 | .50 |
| 112 | Haven Moses | .75 | .35 |
| 113 | Ken Houston (R) | 18.00 | 9.00 |
| 114 | Willie Lanier (R) | 20.00 | 10.00 |
| 115 | Larry Brown | 2.00 | 1.00 |
| 116 | Tom Rossovich | .50 | .25 |
| 117 | Errol Linden | .50 | .25 |
| 118 | Mel Renfro | 1.25 | .60 |
| 119 | Mike Garrett | 1.50 | .75 |
| 120 | Fran Tarkenton | 22.00 | 11.00 |
| 121 | Garo Yepremian (R) | 2.00 | 1.00 |
| 122 | Glen Condren | .50 | .25 |
| 123 | Johnny Roland | .75 | .35 |
| 124 | Dave Herman | .50 | .25 |
| 125 | Merlin Olsen | 3.50 | 1.75 |
| 126 | Doug Buffone | .50 | .25 |
| 127 | Earl McCullouch | .50 | .25 |
| 128 | Spider Lockhart | .50 | .25 |
| 129 | Ken Willard | .75 | .35 |
| 130 | Gene Washington | .75 | .35 |
| 131 | Mike Phipps (R) | 1.75 | .85 |
| 132 | Andy Russell | .75 | .35 |
| 133 | Ray Nitschke | 4.50 | 2.25 |
| 134 | Jerry Logan | .75 | .35 |
| 135 | MacArthur Lane (R) | 1.50 | .75 |
| 136 | Jim Turner | .75 | .35 |
| 137 | Kent McCloughan | .75 | .35 |
| 138 | Paul Guidry | .75 | .35 |
| 139 | Otis Taylor | 2.00 | 1.00 |
| 140 | Virgil Carter (R) | 1.25 | .60 |
| 141 | Joe Dawkins | .75 | .35 |
| 142 | Steve Preece | .75 | .35 |
| 143 | Mike Bragg (R) | 1.00 | .50 |
| 144 | Bob Lilly | 4.00 | 2.00 |
| 145 | Joe Kapp | 1.25 | .60 |
| 146 | Al Dodd | .75 | .35 |
| 147 | Nick Buoniconti | 1.75 | .85 |
| 148 | Speedy Duncan | .75 | .35 |
| 149 | Cedric Hardman (R) | 1.00 | .50 |
| 150 | Gale Sayers | 36.00 | 18.00 |
| 151 | Jim Otto | 4.00 | 2.00 |
| 152 | Billy Truax | .75 | .35 |
| 153 | John Elliott | .75 | .35 |
| 154 | Dick LeBeau | .90 | .45 |
| 155 | Bill Bergey | 1.75 | .85 |
| 156 | Terry Bradshaw (R) | 150.00 | 75.00 |
| 157 | Leroy Kelly | 2.00 | 1.00 |
| 158 | Paul Krause | 1.50 | .75 |
| 159 | Ted Vactor | .75 | .35 |
| 160 | Bob Griese | 8.50 | 4.25 |
| 161 | Ernie McMillan | .75 | .35 |
| 162 | Donny Anderson | 1.50 | .75 |
| 163 | John Pitts | .75 | .35 |
| 164 | Dave Costa | .75 | .35 |
| 165 | Gene Washington | 1.25 | .60 |
| 166 | John Zook | .75 | .35 |
| 167 | Pete Gogolak | .90 | .45 |
| 168 | Erich Barnes | .75 | .35 |
| 169 | Alvin Reed | .75 | .35 |
| 170 | Jim Nance | 1.25 | .60 |
| 171 | Craig Morton | 2.00 | 1.00 |
| 172 | Gary Garrison | .75 | .35 |
| 173 | Joe Scarpati | .75 | .35 |
| 174 | Adrian Young | .75 | .35 |
| 175 | John Mackey | 3.00 | 1.50 |
| 176 | Mac Percival | .75 | .35 |
| 177 | Preston Pearson (R) | 2.50 | 1.25 |
| 178 | Fred Biletnikoff | 4.50 | 2.25 |
| 179 | Mike Battle (R) | .90 | .45 |
| 180 | Len Dawson | 6.50 | 3.25 |
| 181 | Les Josephson | .75 | .35 |
| 182 | Royce Berry | .75 | .35 |
| 183 | Herman Weaver | .75 | .35 |
| 184 | Norm Snead | 2.00 | 1.00 |
| 185 | Sam Brunelli | .75 | .35 |
| 186 | Jim Kiick (R) | 3.00 | 1.50 |
| 187 | Austin Denney | .75 | .35 |
| 188 | Roger Wehrli (R) | 2.00 | 1.00 |
| 189 | Dave Wilcox | .75 | .35 |
| 190 | Bob Hayes | 1.75 | .85 |
| 191 | Joe Morrison | 1.00 | .50 |

| | | | |
|---|---|---|---|
| 192 | Manny Sistrunk | .75 | .35 |
| 193 | Don Cockroft (R) | 1.00 | .50 |
| 194 | Lee Bouggess | .75 | .35 |
| 195 | Bob Berry | .75 | .35 |
| 196 | Ron Sellers | .90 | .45 |
| 197 | George Webster | .75 | .35 |
| 198 | Hoyle Granger | .75 | .35 |
| 199 | Bob Vogel | .75 | .35 |
| 200 | Bart Starr | 24.00 | 12.00 |
| 201 | Mike Mercer | .75 | .35 |
| 202 | Dave Smith | .75 | .35 |
| 203 | Lee Roy Caffey | .75 | .35 |
| 204 | Mick Tingelhoff | .90 | .45 |
| 205 | Matt Snell | 1.50 | .75 |
| 206 | Jim Tyrer | .75 | .35 |
| 207 | Willie Brown | 3.50 | 1.75 |
| 208 | Bob Johnson (R) | .90 | .45 |
| 209 | Deacon Jones | 4.50 | 2.25 |
| 210 | Charlie Sanders (R) | 3.50 | 1.75 |
| 211 | Jake Scott (R) | 3.00 | 1.50 |
| 212 | Bob Anderson (R) | 1.50 | .75 |
| 213 | Charlie Krueger | .75 | .35 |
| 214 | Jim Bakken | .90 | .45 |
| 215 | Harold Jackson | 3.00 | 1.50 |
| 216 | Bill Brundige | .75 | .35 |
| 217 | Calvin Hill | 2.50 | 1.25 |
| 218 | Claude Humphrey | .75 | .35 |
| 219 | Glen Ray Hines | .75 | .35 |
| 220 | Bill Nelsen | 1.00 | .50 |
| 221 | Roy Hilton | .75 | .35 |
| 222 | Don Herrmann | .75 | .35 |
| 223 | John Bramlett | .75 | .35 |
| 224 | Ken Ellis | .75 | .35 |
| 225 | Dave Osborn | .90 | .45 |
| 226 | Edd Hargett (R) | .90 | .45 |
| 227 | Gene Mingo | .75 | .35 |
| 228 | Larry Grantham | .75 | .35 |
| 229 | Dick Post | .75 | .35 |
| 230 | Roman Gabriel | 3.00 | 1.50 |
| 231 | Mike Eischeid | .75 | .35 |
| 232 | Jim Lynch | .75 | .35 |
| 233 | Lemar Parrish (R) | 2.50 | 1.25 |
| 234 | Cecil Turner | .75 | .35 |
| 235 | Dennis Shaw (R) | .90 | .45 |
| 236 | Mel Farr | 1.00 | .50 |
| 237 | Curt Knight | .75 | .35 |
| 238 | Chuck Howley | .90 | .45 |
| 239 | Bruce Taylor (R) | .75 | .35 |
| 240 | Jerry LeVias | .75 | .35 |
| 241 | Bob Lurtsema | .75 | .35 |
| 242 | Earl Morrall | 2.50 | 1.25 |
| 243 | Kermit Alexander | .90 | .45 |
| 244 | Jackie Smith | 1.00 | .50 |
| 245 | Joe Greene (R) | 48.00 | 24.00 |
| 246 | Harmon Wages | .75 | .35 |
| 247 | Errol Mann | .75 | .35 |
| 248 | Mike McCoy | .75 | .35 |

| | | | |
|---|---|---|---|
| 249 | Milt Morin (R) | .75 | .35 |
| 250 | Joe Namath | 55.00 | 27.50 |
| 251 | Jackie Burkett (R) | .75 | .35 |
| 252 | Steve Chomyszak | .75 | .35 |
| 253 | Ed Sharockman | .75 | .35 |
| 254 | Robert Holmes (R) | .75 | .35 |
| 255 | John Hadl | 2.50 | 1.25 |
| 256 | Cornell Gordon | .75 | .35 |
| 257 | Mark Moseley (R) | 4.50 | 2.25 |
| 258 | Gus Otto | .75 | .35 |
| 259 | Mike Taliaferro | .75 | .35 |
| 260 | O.J. Simpson | 50.00 | 25.00 |
| 261 | Paul Warfield | 4.50 | 2.25 |
| 262 | Jack Concannon | .90 | .35 |
| 263 | Tom Matte | 2.50 | .75 |

# 1972 Topps

This 351-card set marks Topps largest football edition to date. The cards consists of full color photos on the front framed by a thin color line and a white border. The team name is printed in bold letters above the photo. The player's name and position appear across the bottom of the photo. The horizontal card backs include personal data, a brief highlight and statistics. The cards in the high number series (264-351) are considered scarce and very difficult to find in near-mint condition. The set features several subsets including League Leaders (1-8), In-Action (IA) and All-Pros (AP). All cards measure 2-1/2" by 3-1/2".

| | NR/MT | EX |
|---|---|---|
| **Complete Set (351)** | 2,175.00 | 1,050.00 |
| **Commons (1-132)** | .40 | .20 |
| **Commons 133-263)** | .60 | .30 |
| **Commons (264-351)** | 15.00 | 7.50 |

| | | | |
|---|---|--:|--:|
| 1 | AFC Rushing Leaders (Little, Csonka, Hubbard) | 3.00 | 1.00 |
| 2 | NFC Rushing Leaders (Brockington, Owens Ellison) | .80 | .40 |
| 3 | AFC Passing Leaders (Griese, Dawson Carter) | 2.50 | 1.25 |
| 4 | NFC Passing Leaders (Staubach, Landry Kilmer) | 3.50 | 1.75 |
| 5 | AFC Receiving Leaders (Biletnikoff, Taylor, Vataha) | 1.00 | .50 |
| 6 | NFC Receiving Leaders (Tucker, Kwalick Jackson, Jefferson) | .75 | .35 |
| 7 | AFC Scoring Leaders (Yepremian, O'Brien, Stenerud) | 1.00 | .50 |
| 8 | NFC Scoring Leaders (Knight, Mann Gossett) | .75 | .35 |
| 9 | Jim Kiick | .75 | .45 |
| 10 | Otis Taylor | 1.25 | .60 |
| 11 | Bobby Joe Green | .40 | .20 |
| 12 | Ken Ellis | .40 | .20 |
| 13 | John Riggins | 28.00 | 14.00 |
| 14 | Dave Parks | .50 | .25 |
| 15 | John Hadl | 1.75 | .85 |
| 16 | Ron Hornsby | .40 | .20 |
| 17 | Chip Myers (R) | .50 | .25 |
| 18 | Bill Kilmer | 1.75 | .85 |
| 19 | Fred Hoaglin | .40 | .20 |
| 20 | Carl Eller | 1.75 | .85 |
| 21 | Steve Zabel | .40 | .20 |
| 22 | Vic Washington (R) | .80 | .40 |
| 23 | Len St.Jean | .40 | .20 |
| 24 | Bill Thompson | .40 | .20 |
| 25 | Steve Owens (R) | 2.50 | 1.25 |
| 26 | Ken Burrough (R) | 2.00 | 1.00 |
| 27 | Mike Clark | .40 | .20 |
| 28 | Willie Brown | 3.50 | 1.75 |
| 29 | Checklist 1-132 | 6.00 | .75 |
| 30 | Marlin Briscoe (R) | .75 | .35 |
| 31 | Jerry Logan | .40 | .20 |
| 32 | Donny Anderson | .75 | .35 |
| 33 | Rich McGeorge | .40 | .20 |
| 34 | Charlie Durkee | .40 | .20 |
| 35 | Willie Lanier | 4.50 | 2.25 |
| 36 | Chris Farasopoulos (R) | .60 | .30 |
| 37 | Ron Shanklin (R) | .60 | .30 |
| 38 | Forrest Blue (R) | .75 | .35 |
| 39 | Ken Reaves | .40 | .20 |
| 40 | Roman Gabriel | 2.50 | 1.25 |
| 41 | Mac Percival | .40 | .20 |
| 42 | Lem Barney | 3.00 | 1.50 |
| 43 | Nick Buoniconti | 1.75 | .85 |
| 44 | Charlie Gogolak | .50 | .25 |
| 45 | Bill Bradley (R) | .80 | .40 |
| 46 | Joe Jones | .40 | .20 |
| 47 | Dave Williams | .40 | .20 |
| 48 | Pete Athas | .40 | .20 |
| 49 | Virgil Carter | .75 | .35 |
| 50 | Floyd Little | 2.50 | 1.25 |
| 51 | Curt Knight | .40 | .20 |
| 52 | Bobby Maples | .40 | .20 |
| 53 | Charlie West (R) | .50 | .25 |
| 54 | Marv Hubbard (R) | 1.50 | .75 |
| 55 | Archie Manning (R) | 14.00 | 7.00 |
| 56 | Jim O'Brien (R) | .80 | .40 |
| 57 | Wayne Patrick | .40 | .20 |
| 58 | Ken Bowman | .40 | .20 |
| 59 | Roger Wehrli | .40 | .20 |
| 60 | Charlie Sanders | .80 | .40 |
| 61 | Jan Stenerud | 2.00 | 1.00 |
| 62 | Willie Ellison | .60 | .30 |
| 63 | Walt Sweeney | .40 | .20 |
| 64 | Ron Smith | .40 | .20 |
| 65 | Jim Plunkett (R) | 20.00 | 10.00 |
| 66 | Herb Adderley | 3.00 | 1.50 |
| 67 | Mike Reid (R) | 3.00 | 1.50 |
| 68 | Richard Caster (R) | 1.50 | .75 |
| 69 | Dave Wilcox | .40 | .20 |
| 70 | Leroy Kelly | 2.00 | 1.00 |
| 71 | Bob Lee (R) | .80 | .40 |
| 72 | Verlon Biggs | .40 | .20 |
| 73 | Henry Allison | .40 | .20 |
| 74 | Steve Ramsey | .40 | .20 |
| 75 | Claude Humphrey | .40 | .20 |
| 76 | Bob Grim (R) | .80 | .40 |
| 77 | John Fuqua | .60 | .30 |
| 78 | Ken Houston | 4.00 | 2.00 |
| 79 | Checklist 133-263 | 6.00 | .75 |
| 80 | Bob Griese | 7.50 | 3.75 |
| 81 | Lance Rentzel | .60 | .30 |
| 82 | Ed Podolak (R) | 1.50 | .75 |
| 83 | Ike Hill | .40 | .20 |
| 84 | George Farmer | .40 | .20 |
| 85 | John Brockington (R) | 3.00 | 1.50 |
| 86 | Jim Otto | 3.00 | 1.50 |
| 87 | Richard Neal | .40 | .20 |
| 88 | Jim Hart | 2.00 | 1.00 |
| 89 | Bob Babich | .40 | .20 |
| 90 | Gene Washington | .75 | .35 |
| 91 | John Zook | .40 | .20 |
| 92 | Bobby Duhon | .40 | .20 |
| 93 | Ted Hendricks (R) | 20.00 | 10.00 |
| 94 | Rockne Freitas | .40 | .20 |
| 95 | Larry Brown | 1.25 | .60 |

| | | | |
|---|---|---|---|
| 96 | Mike Phipps | 1.25 | .60 |
| 97 | Julius Adams (R) | .75 | .45 |
| 98 | Dick Anderson | .60 | .30 |
| 99 | Fred Willis | .40 | .20 |
| 100 | Joe Namath | 45.00 | 22.50 |
| 101 | L.C. Greenwood (R) | 12.50 | 6.25 |
| 102 | Mark Nordquist | .40 | .20 |
| 103 | Robert Holmes | .40 | .20 |
| 104 | Ron Yary (R) | 3.50 | 1.75 |
| 105 | Bob Hayes | 1.50 | .75 |
| 106 | Lyle Alzado (R) | 14.00 | 7.00 |
| 107 | Bob Berry | .40 | .20 |
| 108 | Phil Villapiano (R) | 1.25 | .60 |
| 109 | Dave Elmendorf | .40 | .20 |
| 110 | Gale Sayers | 28.00 | 14.00 |
| 111 | Jim Tyrer | .40 | .20 |
| 112 | Mel Gray (R) | 2.50 | 1.25 |
| 113 | Gerry Philbin | .40 | .20 |
| 114 | Bob James | .40 | .20 |
| 115 | Garo Yepremian | .60 | .30 |
| 116 | Dave Robinson | .40 | .20 |
| 117 | Jeff Queen | .40 | .20 |
| 118 | Norm Snead | 1.50 | .75 |
| 119 | Jim Nance (IA) | .75 | .35 |
| 120 | Terry Bradshaw (IA) | 12.00 | 6.00 |
| 121 | Jim Kiick (IA) | .60 | .30 |
| 122 | Roger Staubach (IA) | 16.00 | 8.00 |
| 123 | Bo Scott (IA) | .40 | .20 |
| 124 | John Brodie (IA) | 2.00 | 1.00 |
| 125 | Rick Volk (IA) | .40 | .20 |
| 126 | John Riggins (IA) | 5.00 | 2.50 |
| 127 | Bubba Smith (IA) | 1.25 | .60 |
| 128 | Roman Gabriel (IA) | 1.25 | .60 |
| 129 | Calvin Hill (IA) | .75 | .35 |
| 130 | Bill Nelsen (IA) | .60 | .30 |
| 131 | Tom Matte (IA) | .60 | .30 |
| 132 | Bob Griese (IA) | 3.00 | 1.50 |
| 133 | AFC Semi-Final | 1.25 | .60 |
| 134 | NFC Semi-Final | 1.00 | .50 |
| 135 | AFC Semi-Final | 1.00 | .50 |
| 136 | NFC Semi-Final | 1.00 | .50 |
| 137 | AFC Championship | 2.00 | 1.00 |
| 138 | NFC Championship | 1.75 | .85 |
| 139 | Super Bowl | 4.50 | 2.25 |
| 140 | Larry Csonka | 6.50 | 3.25 |
| 141 | Rick Volk | .60 | .30 |
| 142 | Roy Jefferson | .75 | .35 |
| 143 | Raymond Chester (R) | 1.50 | .75 |
| 144 | Bobby Douglass | .75 | .35 |
| 145 | Bob Lilly | 4.00 | 2.00 |
| 146 | Harold Jackson | 2.00 | 1.00 |
| 147 | Pete Gogolak | .75 | .35 |
| 148 | Art Malone | .60 | .30 |
| 149 | Ed Flanagan | .60 | .30 |
| 150 | Terry Bradshaw | 38.00 | 19.00 |
| 151 | MacArthur Lane | .75 | .35 |
| 152 | Jack Snow | .75 | .35 |
| 153 | Al Beauchamp | .60 | .30 |
| 154 | Bob Anderson | .60 | .30 |
| 155 | Ted Kwalick (R) | 1.25 | .60 |
| 156 | Dan Pastorini (R) | 2.00 | 1.00 |
| 157 | Emmitt Thomas (R) | 1.25 | .60 |
| 158 | Randy Vataha (R) | 1.75 | .85 |
| 159 | Al Atkinson | .60 | .30 |
| 160 | O.J. Simpson | 35.00 | 17.50 |
| 161 | Jackie Smith | .90 | .45 |
| 162 | Ernie Kellerman | .60 | .30 |
| 163 | Dennis Partee | .60 | .30 |
| 164 | Jake Kupp | .60 | .30 |
| 165 | John Unitas | 26.00 | 13.00 |
| 166 | Clint Jones (R) | .75 | .35 |
| 167 | Paul Warfield | 4.50 | 2.25 |
| 168 | Ron McDole | .60 | .30 |
| 169 | Daryle Lamonica | 2.50 | 1.25 |
| 170 | Dick Butkus | 8.50 | 4.25 |
| 171 | Jim Butler | .60 | .30 |
| 172 | Mike McCoy | .60 | .30 |
| 173 | Dave Smith | .60 | .30 |
| 174 | Greg Landry | 1.50 | .75 |
| 175 | Tom Dempsey | .75 | .35 |
| 176 | John Charles | .60 | .30 |
| 177 | Bobby Bell | 3.00 | 1.50 |
| 178 | Don Horn | .60 | .30 |
| 179 | Bob Trumpy | 1.25 | .60 |
| 180 | Duane Thomas | 1.50 | .75 |
| 181 | Merlin Olsen | 3.50 | 1.75 |
| 182 | Dave Herman | .60 | .30 |
| 183 | Jim Nance | .90 | .45 |
| 184 | Pete Beathard | .80 | .40 |
| 185 | Bob Tucker | .60 | .30 |
| 186 | Gene Upshaw (R) | 15.00 | 7.50 |
| 187 | Bo Scott | .60 | .30 |
| 188 | J.D. Hill (R) | .90 | .45 |
| 189 | Bruce Gossett | .60 | .30 |
| 190 | Bubba Smith | 3.00 | 1.50 |
| 191 | Edd Hargett | .60 | .30 |
| 192 | Gary Garrison | .60 | .30 |
| 193 | Jake Scott | 1.00 | .50 |
| 194 | Fred Cox | .60 | .30 |
| 195 | Sonny Jurgensen | 4.50 | 2.25 |
| 196 | Greg Brezina (R) | .75 | .35 |
| 197 | Ed O'Bradovich | .60 | .30 |
| 198 | John Rowser | .60 | .30 |
| 199 | Altie Taylor | .60 | .30 |
| 200 | Roger Staubach (R) | 135.00 | 65.00 |
| 201 | Leroy Keyes (R) | 1.50 | .75 |
| 202 | Garland Boyette | .60 | .30 |
| 203 | Tom Beer | .60 | .30 |
| 204 | Buck Buchanan | 3.50 | 1.75 |
| 205 | Larry Wilson | 2.00 | 1.00 |
| 206 | Scott Hunter (R) | 1.00 | .50 |
| 207 | Ron Johnson | .80 | .40 |
| 208 | Sam Brunelli | .60 | .30 |
| 209 | Deacon Jones | 3.50 | 1.75 |

| | | | |
|---|---|---|---|
| 210 | Fred Biletnikoff | 4.00 | 2.00 |
| 211 | Bill Nelsen | .75 | .35 |
| 212 | George Nock | .60 | .30 |
| 213 | Dan Abramowicz | .75 | .35 |
| 214 | Irv Goode | .60 | .30 |
| 215 | Isiah Robertson (R) | 1.50 | .75 |
| 216 | Tom Matte | .80 | .50 |
| 217 | Pat Fischer | .60 | .30 |
| 218 | Gene Washington | .75 | .35 |
| 219 | Paul Robinson | .60 | .30 |
| 220 | John Brodie | 3.50 | 1.75 |
| 221 | Manny Fernandez (R) | 1.25 | .60 |
| 222 | Errol Mann | .60 | .30 |
| 223 | Dick Gordon | .60 | .30 |
| 224 | Calvin Hill | 1.50 | .75 |
| 225 | Fran Tarkenton | 22.00 | 11.00 |
| 226 | Jim Turner | .60 | .30 |
| 227 | Jim Mitchell | .60 | .30 |
| 228 | Pete Liske | .60 | .30 |
| 229 | Carl Garrett | .60 | .30 |
| 230 | Joe Greene | 12.00 | 6.00 |
| 231 | Gale Gillingham | .60 | .30 |
| 232 | Norm Bulaich (R) | 1.25 | .60 |
| 233 | Spider Lockhart | .60 | .30 |
| 234 | Ken Willard | .75 | .35 |
| 235 | George Blanda | 10.00 | 5.00 |
| 236 | Wayne Mulligan | .60 | .30 |
| 237 | Dave Lewis | .60 | .30 |
| 238 | Dennis Shaw | .60 | .30 |
| 239 | Fair Hooker (R) | .75 | .35 |
| 240 | Larry Little (R) | 7.50 | 3.75 |
| 241 | Mike Garrett | 1.00 | .50 |
| 242 | Glen Ray Hines | .60 | .30 |
| 243 | Myron Pottios | .60 | .30 |
| 244 | Charlie Joiner (R) | 24.00 | 12.00 |
| 245 | Len Dawson | 4.50 | 2.25 |
| 246 | W.K. Hicks | .60 | .30 |
| 247 | Les Josephson | .60 | .30 |
| 248 | Lance Alworth | 4.50 | 2.25 |
| 249 | Frank Nunley | .60 | .30 |
| 250 | Mel Farr (IA) | .60 | .30 |
| 251 | Johnny Unitas (IA) | 8.50 | 4.25 |
| 252 | George Farmer (IA) | .60 | .30 |
| 253 | Duane Thomas (IA) | .75 | .35 |
| 254 | John Hadl (IA) | 1.25 | .60 |
| 255 | Vic Washington (IA) | .60 | .30 |
| 256 | Don Horn (IA) | .60 | .30 |
| 257 | L.C. Greenwood (IA) | 2.50 | 1.25 |
| 258 | Bob Lee (IA) | .60 | .30 |
| 259 | Larry Csonka (IA) | 3.50 | 1.75 |
| 260 | Mike McCoy (IA) | .60 | .30 |
| 261 | Greg Landry (IA) | .75 | .35 |
| 262 | Ray May (IA) | .60 | .30 |
| 263 | Bobby Douglass (IA) | .60 | .30 |
| 264 | Charlie Sanders (AP) | 15.00 | 7.50 |
| 265 | Ron Yary (AP) | 20.00 | 10.00 |
| 266 | Rayfield Wright (AP) | 15.00 | 7.50 |
| 267 | Larry Little (AP) | 18.50 | 9.25 |
| 268 | John Niland (AP) | 15.00 | 7.50 |
| 269 | Forrest Blue (AP) | 15.00 | 7.50 |
| 270 | Otis Taylor (AP) | 18.00 | 9.00 |
| 271 | Paul Warfield (AP) | 32.00 | 16.00 |
| 272 | Bob Griese (AP) | 38.00 | 19.00 |
| 273 | John Brockington (AP) | 16.00 | 8.00 |
| 274 | Floyd Little (AP) | 20.00 | 10.00 |
| 275 | Garo Yepremian (AP) | 15.00 | 7.50 |
| 276 | Jerrel Wilson (AP) | 15.00 | 7.50 |
| 277 | Carl Eller (AP) | 20.00 | 10.00 |
| 278 | Bubba Smith (AP) | 22.00 | 11.00 |
| 279 | Alan Page (AP) | 28.00 | 14.00 |
| 280 | Bob Lilly (AP) | 35.00 | 17.50 |
| 281 | Ted Hendricks (AP) | 35.00 | 17.50 |
| 282 | Dave Wilcox (AP) | 15.00 | 7.50 |
| 283 | Willie Lanier (AP) | 25.00 | 12.50 |
| 284 | Jim Johnson (AP) | 15.00 | 7.50 |
| 285 | Willie Brown (AP) | 25.00 | 12.50 |
| 286 | Bill Bradley (AP) | 15.00 | 7.50 |
| 287 | Ken Houston (AP | 25.00 | 12.50 |
| 288 | Mel Farr | 15.00 | 7.50 |
| 289 | Kermit Alexander | 15.00 | 7.50 |
| 290 | John Gilliam (R) | 16.00 | 8.00 |
| 291 | Steve Spurrier (R) | 40.00 | 20.00 |
| 292 | Walter Johnson | 15.00 | 7.50 |
| 293 | Jack Pardee | 16.00 | 8.00 |
| 294 | Checklist 264-351 | 48.00 | 10.00 |
| 295 | Winston Hill | 15.00 | 7.50 |
| 296 | Hugo Hollas | 15.00 | 7.50 |
| 297 | Ray May (R) | 16.00 | 8.00 |
| 298 | Jim Bakken | 15.00 | 7.50 |
| 299 | Larry Carwell | 15.00 | 7.50 |
| 300 | Alan Page | 28.00 | 14.00 |
| 301 | Walt Garrison | 16.00 | 8.00 |
| 302 | Mike Lucci | 16.00 | 8.00 |
| 303 | Nemiah Wilson | 15.00 | 7.50 |
| 304 | Carroll Dale | 15.00 | 7.50 |
| 305 | Jim Kanicki | 15.00 | 7.50 |
| 306 | Preston Pearson | 16.00 | 8.00 |
| 307 | Lemar Parrish | 16.00 | 8.00 |
| 308 | Earl Morrall | 18.00 | 9.00 |
| 309 | Tommy Nobis | 20.00 | 10.00 |
| 310 | Rich Jackson | 15.00 | 7.50 |
| 311 | Doug Cunningham | 15.00 | 7.50 |
| 312 | Jim Marsalis | 15.00 | 7.50 |
| 313 | Jim Beirne | 15.00 | 7.50 |
| 314 | Tom McNeill | 15.00 | 7.50 |
| 315 | Milt Morin | 15.00 | 7.50 |
| 316 | Rayfield Wright (R) | 18.50 | 9.25 |
| 317 | Jerry LeVias | 15.00 | 7.50 |
| 318 | Travis Williams (R) | 22.00 | 11.00 |
| 319 | Ed Chandler | 15.00 | 7.50 |
| 320 | Bob Wallace | 15.00 | 7.50 |
| 321 | Delles Howell | 15.00 | 7.50 |

| | | | |
|---|---|---|---|
| 322 | Emerson Boozer | 18.00 | 9.00 |
| 323 | George Atkinson | 16.00 | 8.00 |
| 324 | Mike Montler | 15.00 | 7.50 |
| 325 | Randy Johnson | 15.00 | 7.50 |
| 326 | Mike Curtis | 16.00 | 8.00 |
| 327 | Miller Farr | 15.00 | 7.50 |
| 328 | Horst Muhlmann | 15.00 | 7.50 |
| 329 | John Niland (R) | 18.50 | 9.25 |
| 330 | Andy Russell | 15.00 | 7.50 |
| 331 | Mercury Morris | 20.00 | 10.00 |
| 332 | Jim Johnson | 15.00 | 7.50 |
| 333 | Jerrel Wilson | 15.00 | 7.50 |
| 334 | Charley Taylor | 26.00 | 13.00 |
| 335 | Dick LeBeau | 16.00 | 8.00 |
| 336 | Jim Marshall | 20.00 | 10.00 |
| 337 | Tom Mack | 18.50 | 9.25 |
| 338 | Steve Spurrier (IA) | 22.00 | 11.00 |
| 339 | Floyd Little (IA) | 20.00 | 10.00 |
| 340 | Len Dawson (IA) | 35.00 | 17.50 |
| 341 | Dick Butkus (IA) | 40.00 | 20.00 |
| 342 | Larry Brown (IA) | 20.00 | 10.00 |
| 343 | Joe Namath (IA) | 275.00 | 135.00 |
| 344 | Jim Turner (IA) | 15.00 | 7.50 |
| 345 | Doug Cunningham (IA) | 15.00 | 7.50 |
| 346 | Edd Hargett (IA) | 15.00 | 7.50 |
| 347 | Steve Owens (IA) | 16.00 | 8.00 |
| 348 | George Blanda (IA) | 42.00 | 21.00 |
| 349 | Ed Podolak (IA) | 15.00 | 7.50 |
| 350 | Rich Jackson (IA) | 15.00 | 7.50 |
| 351 | Ken Willard (IA) | 32.00 | 10.00 |

# 1973 Topps

LYLE
ALZADO

DEFENSIVE END
BRONCOS

In 1973 Topps increased the size of
their football set to 528-cards. The card
fronts feature color photos on a white
card stock. A multi-colored pennant-type
stripe appears at the top and bottom of
the left side of the card. The player's
name is printed above the photo while his
position and team appear below the
photo. Card backs are vertical and
contain personal data, a brief highlight,
stats and a cartoon with a trivia question.
Subsets include League Leaders (1-6),
Playoffs (133-139) and Childhood cards
(267-269) that depict players when they
were kids. All cards measure 2-1/2" by 3-
1/2".

| | | NR/MT | EX |
|---|---|---|---|
| **Complete Set (528)** | | 455.00 | 225.00 |
| **Commons** | | .35 | .18 |
| | | | |
| 1 | Rushing Leaders | 4.50 | 2.25 |
| | (Brown, Simpson) | | |
| 2 | Passing Leaders | .75 | .35 |
| | (Snead, Morrall) | | |
| 3 | Receiving Leaders | 1.00 | .50 |
| | (Jackson, Biletnikoff) | | |
| 4 | Scoring Leaders | .40 | .20 |
| | (Marcol, Howfield) | | |
| 5 | Interception Leaders | .40 | .20 |
| | (Bradley, Sensibaugh) | | |
| 6 | Punting Leaders | .40 | .20 |
| | (Chapple, Wilson) | | |
| 7 | Bob Trumpy | 1.00 | .50 |
| 8 | Mel Tom | .35 | .18 |
| 9 | Clarence Ellis | .35 | .18 |
| 10 | John Niland | .35 | .18 |
| 11 | Randy Jackson | .35 | .18 |
| 12 | Greg Landry | 1.25 | .60 |
| 13 | Cid Edwards | .35 | .18 |
| 14 | Phil Olsen | .35 | .18 |
| 15 | Terry Bradshaw | 18.00 | 9.00 |
| 16 | Al Cowlings | .35 | .18 |
| 17 | Walker Gillette (R) | .40 | .20 |
| 18 | Bob Adkins | .35 | .18 |
| 19 | Diron Talbert (R) | 1.25 | .60 |
| 20 | Jim Johnson | .35 | .18 |
| 21 | Howard Twilley | .50 | .30 |
| 22 | Dick Enderle | .35 | .18 |
| 23 | Wayne Coleman | .35 | .18 |
| 24 | John Schmitt | .35 | .18 |
| 25 | George Blanda | 8.00 | 4.00 |
| 26 | Milt Morin | .35 | .18 |
| 27 | Mike Current | .35 | .18 |
| 28 | Rex Kern (R) | .50 | .25 |
| 29 | MacArthur Lane | .50 | .25 |
| 30 | Alan Page | 3.50 | 1.75 |
| 31 | Randy Vataha | .50 | .25 |
| 32 | Jim Keaney | .35 | .18 |
| 33 | Steve Smith | .35 | .18 |
| 34 | Ken Anderson (R) | 24.00 | 12.00 |

| No. | Player | | |
|---|---|---|---|
| 35 | Calvin Hill | .80 | .40 |
| 36 | Andy Maurer | .35 | .18 |
| 37 | Joe Taylor | .35 | .18 |
| 38 | Deacon Jones | 3.00 | 1.50 |
| 39 | Mike Weger | .35 | .18 |
| 40 | Roy Gerela | .35 | .18 |
| 41 | Les Josephson | .35 | .18 |
| 42 | Dave Washington | .35 | .18 |
| 43 | Bill Curry (R) | 1.00 | .50 |
| 44 | Fred Heron | .35 | .18 |
| 45 | John Brodie | 3.50 | 1.75 |
| 46 | Roy Winston | .35 | .18 |
| 47 | Mike Bragg | .35 | .18 |
| 48 | Mercury Morris | 1.00 | .50 |
| 49 | Jim Files | .35 | .18 |
| 50 | Gene Upshaw | 3.50 | 1.75 |
| 51 | Hugo Hollas | .35 | .18 |
| 52 | Rod Sherman | .35 | .18 |
| 53 | Ron Snidow | .35 | .18 |
| 54 | Steve Tannen (R) | .40 | .20 |
| 55 | Jim Carter | .35 | .18 |
| 56 | Lydell Mitchell (R) | 2.50 | 1.25 |
| 57 | Jack Rudnay (R) | .50 | .25 |
| 58 | Hal Hagen | .35 | .18 |
| 59 | Tom Dempsey | .40 | .20 |
| 60 | Fran Tarkenton | 15.00 | 7.50 |
| 61 | Lance Alworth | 3.50 | 1.75 |
| 62 | Vern Holland | .35 | .18 |
| 63 | Steve DeLong | .35 | .18 |
| 64 | Art Malone | .35 | .18 |
| 65 | Isiah Robertson | .50 | .25 |
| 66 | Jerry Rush | .35 | .18 |
| 67 | Bryant Salter | .35 | .18 |
| 68 | Checklist 1-132 | 3.50 | .50 |
| 69 | J.D. Hill | .50 | .25 |
| 70 | Forrest Blue | .40 | .20 |
| 71 | Myron Pottios | .35 | .18 |
| 72 | Norm Thompson (R) | .50 | .25 |
| 73 | Paul Robinson | .35 | .18 |
| 74 | Larry Grantham | .35 | .18 |
| 75 | Manny Fernandez | .35 | .18 |
| 76 | Kent Nix | .35 | .18 |
| 77 | Art Shell (R) | 25.00 | 12.50 |
| 78 | George Saimes | .35 | .18 |
| 79 | Don Cockroft | .50 | .25 |
| 80 | Bob Tucker | .35 | .18 |
| 81 | Don McCauley (R) | .75 | .35 |
| 82 | Bob Brown | .35 | .18 |
| 83 | Larry Carwell | .35 | .18 |
| 84 | Mo Moorman | .35 | .18 |
| 85 | John Gilliam | .35 | .18 |
| 86 | Wade Key | .35 | .18 |
| 87 | Ross Brupbacher | .35 | .18 |
| 88 | Dave Lewis | .35 | .18 |
| 89 | Franco Harris (R) | 65.00 | 32.50 |
| 90 | Tom Mack | .80 | .40 |
| 91 | Mike Tilleman | .35 | .18 |
| 92 | Carl Mauck | .35 | .18 |
| 93 | Larry Hand | .35 | .18 |
| 94 | Dave Foley | .35 | .18 |
| 95 | Frank Nunley | .35 | .18 |
| 96 | John Charles | .35 | .18 |
| 97 | Jim Bakken | .40 | .20 |
| 98 | Pat Fischer | .35 | .18 |
| 99 | Randy Rasmussen | .35 | .18 |
| 100 | Larry Csonka | 4.00 | 2.00 |
| 101 | Mike Siani (R) | .75 | .35 |
| 102 | Tom Roussel | .35 | .18 |
| 103 | Clarence Scott (R) | .50 | .25 |
| 104 | Charlie Johnson | 1.00 | .50 |
| 105 | Rick Volk | .35 | .18 |
| 106 | Willie Young | .35 | .18 |
| 107 | Emmitt Thomas | .35 | .18 |
| 108 | Jon Morris | .35 | .18 |
| 109 | Clarence Williams | .35 | .18 |
| 110 | Rayfield Wright | .35 | .18 |
| 111 | Norm Bulaich | .35 | .18 |
| 112 | Mike Eischeid | .35 | .18 |
| 113 | Speedy Thomas | .35 | .18 |
| 114 | Glen Holloway | .35 | .18 |
| 115 | Jack Ham (R) | 22.00 | 11.00 |
| 116 | Jim Nettle | .35 | .18 |
| 117 | Errol Mann | .35 | .18 |
| 118 | John Mackey | 2.50 | 1.25 |
| 119 | George Knuz | .35 | .18 |
| 120 | Bob James | .35 | .18 |
| 121 | Garland Boyette | .35 | .18 |
| 122 | Mel Phillips | .35 | .18 |
| 123 | Johnny Roland | .60 | .30 |
| 124 | Doug Swift | .35 | .18 |
| 125 | Archie Manning | 3.00 | 1.50 |
| 126 | Dave Herman | .35 | .18 |
| 127 | Carleton Oats | .35 | .18 |
| 128 | Bill Van Heusen | .35 | .18 |
| 129 | Rich Jackson | .35 | .18 |
| 130 | Len Hauss | .35 | .18 |
| 131 | Billy Parks (R) | .50 | .25 |
| 132 | Ray May | .35 | .18 |
| 133 | NFC Semi-Final | 2.50 | 1.25 |
| 134 | AFC Semi-Final | .75 | .35 |
| 135 | NFC Semi-Final | .75 | .35 |
| 136 | AFC Semi-Final | 2.50 | 1.25 |
| 137 | NFC Title Game | 1.00 | .50 |
| 138 | AFC Title Game | .75 | .35 |
| 139 | Super Bowl | 1.50 | .75 |
| 140 | Dwight White (R) | 2.50 | 1.25 |
| 141 | Jim Marsalis | .35 | .18 |
| 142 | Doug Van Horn | .35 | .18 |
| 143 | Al Matthews | .35 | .18 |
| 144 | Bob Windsor | .35 | .18 |
| 145 | Dave Hampton (R) | .75 | .35 |
| 146 | Horst Muhlmann | .35 | .18 |
| 147 | Wally Hilgenberg (R) | 1.00 | .50 |
| 148 | Ron Smith | .35 | .18 |

| | | | |
|---|---|---|---|
| 149 | Coy Bacon (R) | 1.00 | .50 |
| 150 | Winston Hill | .35 | .18 |
| 151 | Ron Jessie (R) | 1.00 | .50 |
| 152 | Ken Iman | .35 | .18 |
| 153 | Ron Saul | .35 | .18 |
| 154 | Jim Braxton (R) | .60 | .30 |
| 155 | Bubba Smith | 3.00 | 1.50 |
| 156 | Gary Cuozzo | .50 | .25 |
| 157 | Charlie Krueger | .35 | .18 |
| 158 | Tim Foley (R) | .75 | .35 |
| 159 | Lee Roy Jordan | 1.50 | .75 |
| 160 | Bob Brown | .35 | .18 |
| 161 | Margene Adkins | .35 | .18 |
| 162 | Ron Widby | .35 | .18 |
| 163 | Jim Houston | .35 | .18 |
| 164 | Joe Dawkins | .35 | .18 |
| 165 | L.C. Greenwood | 2.50 | 1.25 |
| 166 | Richmond Flowers (R) | .60 | .30 |
| 167 | Curley Culp (R) | 2.00 | 1.00 |
| 168 | Len St.Jean | .35 | .18 |
| 169 | Walter Rock | .35 | .18 |
| 170 | Bill Bradley | .40 | .20 |
| 171 | Ken Riley (R) | 1.50 | .75 |
| 172 | Rich Coady | .35 | .18 |
| 173 | Don Hansen | .35 | .18 |
| 174 | Lionel Aldridge | .35 | .18 |
| 175 | Don Maynard | 3.50 | 1.75 |
| 176 | Dave Osborn | .50 | .25 |
| 177 | Jim Bailey | .35 | .18 |
| 178 | John Pitts | .35 | .18 |
| 179 | Dave Parks | .50 | .25 |
| 180 | Chester Marcol (R) | .60 | .30 |
| 181 | Len Rohde | .35 | .18 |
| 182 | Jeff Staggs | .35 | .18 |
| 183 | Gene Hickerson | .35 | .18 |
| 184 | Charlie Evans | .35 | .18 |
| 185 | Mel Renfro | 1.00 | .50 |
| 186 | Marvin Upshaw | .35 | .18 |
| 187 | George Atkinson | .35 | .18 |
| 188 | Norm Evans | .35 | .18 |
| 189 | Steve Ramsey | .35 | .18 |
| 190 | Dave Chapple | .35 | .18 |
| 191 | Gerry Mullins | .35 | .18 |
| 192 | John Didion | .35 | .18 |
| 193 | Bob Gladieux | .35 | .18 |
| 194 | Don Hultz | .35 | .18 |
| 195 | Mike Lucci | .50 | .25 |
| 196 | Hohn Wilbur | .35 | .18 |
| 197 | George Farmer | .35 | .18 |
| 198 | Tommy Casanova (R) | .80 | .50 |
| 199 | Russ Washington | .35 | .18 |
| 200 | Claude Humphrey | .50 | .25 |
| 201 | Pat Hughes | .35 | .18 |
| 202 | Zeke Moore | .35 | .18 |
| 203 | Chip Glass | .35 | .18 |
| 204 | Glenn Ressler | .35 | .18 |
| 205 | Willie Ellison | .35 | .18 |
| 206 | John Leypoldt | .35 | .18 |
| 207 | Johnny Fuller | .35 | .18 |
| 208 | Bill Hayhoe | .35 | .18 |
| 209 | Ed Bell | .35 | .18 |
| 210 | Willie Brown | 2.50 | 1.25 |
| 211 | Carl Eller | 2.00 | 1.00 |
| 212 | Mark Nordquist | .35 | .18 |
| 213 | Larry Willingham | .35 | .18 |
| 214 | Nick Buoniconti | 1.50 | .75 |
| 215 | John Hadl | 1.75 | .85 |
| 216 | Jethro Pugh (R) | 1.00 | .50 |
| 217 | Leroy Mitchell | .35 | .18 |
| 218 | Billy Newsome | .35 | .18 |
| 219 | John McMakin | .35 | .18 |
| 220 | Larry Brown | 1.25 | .60 |
| 221 | Clarence Scott | .35 | .18 |
| 222 | Paul Naumoff | .35 | .18 |
| 223 | Ted Fritsch | .35 | .18 |
| 224 | Checklist 133-264 | 3.50 | .50 |
| 225 | Dan Pastorini | 1.00 | .50 |
| 226 | Joe Beauchamp | .35 | .18 |
| 227 | Pat Matson | .35 | .18 |
| 228 | Tony McGee | .35 | .18 |
| 229 | Mike Phipps | .75 | .35 |
| 230 | Harold Jackson | 1.25 | .60 |
| 231 | Willie Williams | .35 | .18 |
| 232 | Spike Jones | .35 | .18 |
| 233 | Jim Tyrer | .35 | .18 |
| 234 | Roy Hilton | .35 | .18 |
| 235 | Phil Villapiano | .40 | .20 |
| 236 | Charley Taylor | 2.50 | 1.25 |
| 237 | Malcolm Snider | .35 | .18 |
| 238 | Vic Washington | .35 | .18 |
| 239 | Grady Alderman | .35 | .18 |
| 240 | Dick Anderson | .40 | .20 |
| 241 | Ron Yankowski | .35 | .18 |
| 242 | Billy Masters | .35 | .18 |
| 243 | Herb Adderley | 2.50 | 1.25 |
| 244 | David Ray | .35 | .18 |
| 245 | John Riggins | 7.00 | 3.50 |
| 246 | Mike Wagner (R) | 1.25 | .60 |
| 247 | Don Morrison | .35 | .18 |
| 248 | Earl McCullouch | .35 | .18 |
| 249 | Dennis Wirgowski | .35 | .18 |
| 250 | Chris Hanburger | .50 | .25 |
| 251 | Pat Sullivan (R) | 2.50 | 1.25 |
| 252 | Walt Sweeney | .35 | .18 |
| 253 | Willie Alexander | .35 | .18 |
| 254 | Doug Dressler | .35 | .18 |
| 255 | Walter Johnson | .35 | .18 |
| 256 | Ron Hornsby | .35 | .18 |
| 257 | Ben Hawkins | .35 | .18 |
| 258 | Donnie Green | .35 | .18 |
| 259 | Fred Hoaglin | .35 | .18 |
| 260 | Jerrel Wilson | .35 | .18 |
| 261 | Horace Jones | .35 | .18 |
| 262 | Woody Peoples | .35 | .18 |

| 263 | Jim Hill | .35 | .18 |
| 264 | John Fuqua | .50 | .25 |
| 265 | Donny Anderson (Child) | .50 | .25 |
| 266 | Roman Gabriel (Child) | .75 | .35 |
| 267 | Mike Garrett (Child) | .50 | .25 |
| 268 | Rufus Mayes (R) | .50 | .25 |
| 269 | Chip Myrtle | .35 | .18 |
| 270 | Bill Stanfill (R) | .75 | .35 |
| 271 | Clint Jones | .35 | .18 |
| 272 | Miller Farr | .35 | .18 |
| 273 | Harry Schuh | .35 | .18 |
| 274 | Bob Hayes | 1.25 | .60 |
| 275 | Bobby Douglass | .50 | .25 |
| 276 | Gus Hollomon | .35 | .18 |
| 277 | Del Williams | .35 | .18 |
| 278 | Julius Adams | .35 | .18 |
| 279 | Herman Weaver | .35 | .18 |
| 280 | Joe Greene | 4.00 | 2.00 |
| 281 | Wes Chesson | .35 | .18 |
| 282 | Charlie Harraway | .35 | .18 |
| 283 | Paul Guidry | .35 | .18 |
| 284 | Terry Owens (R) | .40 | .20 |
| 285 | Jan Stenerud | 1.25 | .60 |
| 286 | Pete Athas | .35 | .18 |
| 287 | Dale Lindsey | .35 | .18 |
| 288 | Jack Tatum (R) | 4.00 | 2.00 |
| 289 | Floyd Little | 1.75 | .85 |
| 290 | Bob Johnson | .35 | .18 |
| 291 | Tommy Hart (R) | .40 | .20 |
| 292 | Tom Mitchell | .35 | .18 |
| 293 | Walt Patulski (R) | .60 | .30 |
| 294 | Jim Skaggs | .35 | .18 |
| 295 | Bob Griese | 5.00 | 2.50 |
| 296 | Mike McCoy | .35 | .18 |
| 297 | Mel Gray | .75 | .35 |
| 298 | Bobby Bryant | .35 | .18 |
| 299 | Blaine Nye (R) | .40 | .20 |
| 300 | Dick Butkus | 7.00 | 3.50 |
| 301 | Charlie Cowan | .35 | .18 |
| 302 | Mark Lomas | .35 | .18 |
| 303 | Josh Ashton | .35 | .18 |
| 304 | Happy Feller | .35 | .18 |
| 305 | Ron Shanklin | .35 | .18 |
| 306 | Wayne Rasmussen | .35 | .18 |
| 307 | Jerry Smith | .35 | .18 |
| 308 | Ken Reaves | .35 | .18 |
| 309 | Ron East | .35 | .18 |
| 310 | Otis Taylor | 1.00 | .50 |
| 311 | John Garlington | .35 | .18 |
| 312 | Lyle Alzado | 3.50 | 1.75 |
| 313 | Remi Prudhomme | .35 | .18 |
| 314 | Cornelius Johnson | .35 | .18 |
| 315 | Lemar Parrish | .40 | .20 |
| 316 | Jim Kiick | .75 | .35 |
| 317 | Steve Zabel | .35 | .18 |
| 318 | Alden Roche | .35 | .18 |
| 319 | Tom Blanchard | .35 | .18 |
| 320 | Fred Biletnikoff | 4.00 | 2.00 |
| 321 | Ralph Neely | .35 | .18 |
| 322 | Dan Dierdorf (R) | 12.00 | 6.00 |
| 323 | Richard Caster | .50 | .25 |
| 324 | Gene Howard | .35 | .18 |
| 325 | Elvin Bethea | .40 | .20 |
| 326 | Carl Garrett | .35 | .18 |
| 327 | Ron Billingsley | .35 | .18 |
| 328 | Charlie West | .35 | .18 |
| 329 | Tom Neville | .35 | .18 |
| 330 | Ted Kwalick | .40 | .20 |
| 331 | Rudy Redmond | .35 | .18 |
| 332 | Henry Davis | .35 | .18 |
| 333 | John Zook | .35 | .18 |
| 334 | Jim Turner | .35 | .18 |
| 335 | Len Dawson | 4.00 | 2.00 |
| 336 | Bob Chandler (R) | .90 | .45 |
| 337 | Al Beauchamp | .35 | .18 |
| 338 | Tom Matte | .50 | .25 |
| 339 | Paul Laaveg | .35 | .18 |
| 340 | Ken Ellis | .35 | .18 |
| 341 | Jim Langer (R) | 14.00 | 7.00 |
| 342 | Ron Porter | .35 | .18 |
| 343 | Jack Youngblood (R) | 12.50 | 6.25 |
| 344 | Cornell Green | .35 | .18 |
| 345 | Marv Hubbard | .75 | .35 |
| 346 | Bruce Taylor | .35 | .18 |
| 347 | Sam Havrilak | .35 | .18 |
| 348 | Walt Sumner | .35 | .18 |
| 349 | Steve O'Neal | .35 | .18 |
| 350 | Ron Johnson | .50 | .25 |
| 351 | Rockne Freitas | .35 | .18 |
| 352 | Larry Stallings | .35 | .18 |
| 353 | Jim Cadile | .35 | .18 |
| 354 | Ken Burrough | .75 | .35 |
| 355 | Jim Plunkett | 4.00 | 2.00 |
| 356 | Dave Long | .35 | .18 |
| 357 | Ralph Anderson | .35 | .18 |
| 358 | Checklist 265-396 | 3.50 | .50 |
| 359 | Gene Washington | .40 | .20 |
| 360 | Dave Wilcox | .50 | .25 |
| 361 | Paul Smith (R) | .40 | .20 |
| 362 | Alvin Wyatt | .35 | .18 |
| 363 | Charlie Smith | .35 | .18 |
| 364 | Royce Berry | .35 | .18 |
| 365 | Dave Elmendorf | .35 | .18 |
| 366 | Scott Hunter | .40 | .20 |
| 367 | Bob Kuechenberg (R) | 2.00 | 1.00 |
| 368 | Pete Gogolak | .40 | .20 |
| 369 | Dave Edwards | .35 | .18 |
| 370 | Lem Barney | 2.50 | 1.25 |
| 371 | Verlon Biggs | .35 | .18 |
| 372 | John Reaves (R) | .50 | .25 |
| 373 | Ed Podolak | .50 | .25 |
| 374 | Chris Farasopoulos | .35 | .18 |
| 375 | Gary Garrison | .35 | .18 |

| | | | |
|---|---|---|---|
| 376 Tom Funchess | .35 | .18 |
| 377 Bobby Joe Green | .35 | .18 |
| 378 Don Brumm | .35 | .18 |
| 379 Jim O'Brien | .35 | .18 |
| 380 Paul Krause | .80 | .50 |
| 381 Leroy Kelly | 1.25 | .60 |
| 382 Ray Mansfield | .35 | .18 |
| 383 Dan Abramowicz | .50 | .25 |
| 384 John Outlaw (R) | .40 | .20 |
| 385 Tommy Nobis | 1.25 | .60 |
| 386 Tom Domres | .35 | .18 |
| 387 Ken Willard | .50 | .25 |
| 388 Mike Stratton | .35 | .18 |
| 389 Fred Dryer | 3.00 | 1.50 |
| 390 Jake Scott | .40 | .20 |
| 391 Rich Houston | .35 | .18 |
| 392 Virgil Carter | .40 | .20 |
| 393 Tody Smith | .35 | .18 |
| 394 Ernie Calloway | .35 | .18 |
| 395 Charlie Sanders | .50 | .25 |
| 396 Fred Willis | .35 | .18 |
| 397 Curt Knight | .35 | .18 |
| 398 Nemiah Wilson | .35 | .18 |
| 399 Carroll Dale | .35 | .18 |
| 400 Joe Namath | 30.00 | 15.00 |
| 401 Wayne Mulligan | .35 | .18 |
| 402 Jim Harrison | .35 | .18 |
| 403 Tim Rossovich | .35 | .18 |
| 404 David Lee | .35 | .18 |
| 405 Frank Pitts | .35 | .18 |
| 406 Jim Marshall | 1.50 | .75 |
| 407 Bob Brown | .35 | .18 |
| 408 John Rowser | .35 | .18 |
| 409 Mike Montler | .35 | .18 |
| 410 Willie Lanier | 2.50 | 1.25 |
| 411 Bill Bell | .35 | .18 |
| 412 Cedric Hardman | .35 | .18 |
| 413 Bob Anderson | .35 | .18 |
| 414 Earl Morrall | 1.50 | .75 |
| 415 Ken Houston | 2.50 | 1.25 |
| 416 Jack Snow | .50 | .25 |
| 417 Dick Cunningham | .35 | .18 |
| 418 Greg Larson | .35 | .18 |
| 419 Mike Bass | .35 | .18 |
| 420 Mike Reid | 1.75 | .85 |
| 421 Walt Garrison | .50 | .25 |
| 422 Pete Liske | .35 | .18 |
| 423 Jim Yarbrough | .35 | .18 |
| 424 Rich McGeorge | .35 | .18 |
| 425 Bobby Howfield | .35 | .18 |
| 426 Pete Banaszak | .50 | .25 |
| 427 Willie Holman | .35 | .18 |
| 428 Dale Hackbart | .35 | .18 |
| 429 Fair Hooker | .35 | .18 |
| 430 Ted Hendricks | 4.50 | 2.25 |
| 431 Mike Garrett | .50 | .25 |
| 432 Glen Ray Hines | .35 | .18 |

| | | | |
|---|---|---|---|
| 433 Fred Cox | .35 | .18 |
| 434 Bobby Walden | .35 | .18 |
| 435 Bobby Bell | 2.50 | 1.25 |
| 436 Dave Rowe | .35 | .18 |
| 437 Bob Berry | .35 | .18 |
| 438 Bill Thompson | .35 | .18 |
| 439 Jim Beirne | .35 | .18 |
| 440 Larry Little | 2.50 | 1.25 |
| 441 Rocky Thompson | .35 | .18 |
| 442 Brig Owens | .35 | .18 |
| 443 Richard Neal | .35 | .18 |
| 444 Al Nelson | .35 | .18 |
| 445 Chip Myers | .35 | .18 |
| 446 Ken Bowman | .35 | .18 |
| 447 Jim Purnell | .35 | .18 |
| 448 Altie Taylor | .35 | .18 |
| 449 Linzy Cole | .35 | .18 |
| 450 Bob Lilly | 3.50 | 1.75 |
| 451 Charlie Ford | .35 | .18 |
| 452 Milt Sunde | .35 | .18 |
| 453 Doug Wyatt | .35 | .18 |
| 454 Don Nottingham (R) | .75 | .35 |
| 455 John Unitas | 20.00 | 10.00 |
| 456 Frank Lewis (R) | 1.00 | .50 |
| 457 Roger Wehrli | .35 | .18 |
| 458 Jim Cheyunski | .35 | .18 |
| 459 Jerry Sherk (R) | .90 | .45 |
| 460 Gene Washington | .50 | .25 |
| 461 Jim Otto | 2.50 | 1.25 |
| 462 Ed Budde | .35 | .18 |
| 463 Jim Mitchell | .35 | .18 |
| 464 Emerson Boozer | .75 | .35 |
| 465 Garo Yepremian | .40 | .20 |
| 466 Pete Duranko | .35 | .18 |
| 467 Charlie Joiner | 4.50 | 2.25 |
| 468 Spider Lockhart | .35 | .18 |
| 469 Marty Domres | .40 | .20 |
| 470 John Brockington | .80 | .40 |
| 471 Ed Flanagan | .35 | .18 |
| 472 Roy Jefferson | .50 | .25 |
| 473 Julian Fagan | .35 | .18 |
| 474 Bill Brown | .50 | .25 |
| 475 Roger Staubach | 30.00 | 15.00 |
| 476 Jan White | .35 | .18 |
| 477 Pat Holmes | .35 | .18 |
| 478 Bob DeMarco | .35 | .18 |
| 479 Merlin Olsen | 3.50 | 1.75 |
| 480 Andy Russell | .40 | .20 |
| 481 Steve Spurrier | 2.00 | 1.00 |
| 482 Nate Ramsey | .35 | .18 |
| 483 Dennis Partee | .35 | .18 |
| 484 Jerry Simmons | .35 | .18 |
| 485 Donny Anderson | .60 | .30 |
| 486 Ralph Baker | .35 | .18 |
| 487 Ken Stabler (R) | 28.00 | 14.00 |
| 488 Ernie McMillan | .35 | .18 |
| 489 Ken Burrow | .35 | .18 |

| | | NR/MT | EX |
|---|---|---|---|
| 490 | Jack Gregory | .35 | .18 |
| 491 | Larry Seiple | .35 | .18 |
| 492 | Mick Tingelhoff | .50 | .25 |
| 493 | Craig Morton | 1.50 | .75 |
| 494 | Cecil Turner | .35 | .18 |
| 495 | Steve Owens | .75 | .35 |
| 496 | Rickie Harris | .35 | .18 |
| 497 | Buck Buchanan | 2.50 | 1.25 |
| 498 | Checklist 397-528 | 4.00 | .75 |
| 499 | Bill Kilmer | 1.50 | .75 |
| 500 | O.J. Simpson | 25.00 | 12.50 |
| 501 | Bruce Gossett | .35 | .18 |
| 502 | Art Thoms | .35 | .18 |
| 503 | Larry Kaminski | .35 | .18 |
| 504 | Larry Smith | .35 | .18 |
| 505 | Bruce Van Dyke | .35 | .18 |
| 506 | Alvin Reed | .35 | .18 |
| 507 | Delles Howell | .35 | .18 |
| 508 | Leroy Keyes | .60 | .30 |
| 509 | Bo Scott | .35 | .18 |
| 510 | Ron Yary | .75 | .35 |
| 511 | Paul Warfield | 3.50 | 1.75 |
| 512 | Mac Percival | .35 | .18 |
| 513 | Essex Johnson | .35 | .18 |
| 514 | Jackie Smith | .50 | .25 |
| 515 | Norm Snead | 1.00 | .50 |
| 516 | Charlie Stukes | .35 | .18 |
| 517 | Reggie Rucker (R) | 1.25 | .60 |
| 518 | Bill Sandeman | .35 | .18 |
| 519 | Mel Farr | .50 | .25 |
| 520 | Raymond Chester | .50 | .25 |
| 521 | Fred Carr (R) | .50 | .25 |
| 522 | Jerry LeVias | .40 | .20 |
| 523 | Jim Strong | .35 | .18 |
| 524 | Ron McDole | .35 | .18 |
| 525 | Dennis Shaw | .40 | .20 |
| 526 | Dave Manders | .35 | .18 |
| 527 | Skip Vanderbundt | .35 | .18 |
| 528 | Mike Sensibaugh (R) | 1.00 | .30 |

# 1974 Topps

This 528-card set features mostly posed color photos on the card fronts framed by a thin inside border and a white outside border. The player's name and position appear in two small boxes below the photo. The team name is printed in larger type in a box across the bottom of the card. The vertical card backs contain personal data and a brief description of the player. The bottom third of the card back features part of a table top football game. Key subsets include League Leaders (328-333), All-Pros (AP)(121-144) and Playoffs (460-463). All cards measure 2-1/2" by 3-1/2".

| | | NR/MT | EX |
|---|---|---|---|
| **Complete Set (528)** | | 325.00 | 165.00 |
| **Commons** | | .30 | .15 |
| | | | |
| 1 | O.J. Simpson | 22.00 | 8.50 |
| 2 | Blaine Nye | .30 | .15 |
| 3 | Don Hansen | .30 | .15 |
| 4 | Ken Bowman | .30 | .15 |
| 5 | Carl Eller | 1.50 | .75 |
| 6 | Jerry Smith | .30 | .15 |
| 7 | Ed Podolak | .40 | .20 |
| 8 | Mel Gray | .40 | .20 |
| 9 | Pat Matson | .30 | .15 |
| 10 | Floyd Little | 1.50 | .75 |
| 11 | Frank Pitts | .30 | .15 |
| 12 | Vern Den Herder (R) | .50 | .25 |
| 13 | John Fuqua | .40 | .20 |
| 14 | Jack Tatum | 1.75 | .85 |
| 15 | Winston Hill | .30 | .15 |
| 16 | John Beasley | .30 | .15 |
| 17 | David Lee | .30 | .15 |

| No. | Player | | |
|---|---|---|---|
| 18 | Rich Coady | .30 | .15 |
| 19 | Ken Willard | .50 | .30 |
| 20 | Coy Bacon | .30 | .15 |
| 21 | Ben Hawkins | .30 | .15 |
| 22 | Paul Guidry | .30 | .15 |
| 23 | Norm Snead | 1.00 | .50 |
| 24 | Jim Yarbrough | .30 | .15 |
| 25 | Jack Reynolds (R) | 1.75 | .85 |
| 26 | Josh Ashton | .30 | .15 |
| 27 | Donnie Green | .30 | .15 |
| 28 | Bob Hayes | .80 | .40 |
| 29 | John Zook | .30 | .15 |
| 30 | Bobby Bryant | .30 | .15 |
| 31 | Scott Hunter | .40 | .20 |
| 32 | Dan Dierdorf | 2.50 | 1.25 |
| 33 | Curt Knight | .30 | .15 |
| 34 | Elmo Wright (R) | .60 | .30 |
| 35 | Essex Johnson | .30 | .15 |
| 36 | Walt Sumner | .30 | .15 |
| 37 | Marv Montgomery | .30 | .15 |
| 38 | Tim Foley | .40 | .20 |
| 39 | Mike Siani | .30 | .15 |
| 40 | Joe Greene | 4.00 | 2.00 |
| 41 | Bobby Howfield | .30 | .15 |
| 42 | Del Williams | .30 | .15 |
| 43 | Don McCauley | .30 | .15 |
| 44 | Randy Jackson | .30 | .15 |
| 45 | Ron Smith | .30 | .15 |
| 46 | Gene Washington | .50 | .25 |
| 47 | Po James (R) | .40 | .20 |
| 48 | Solomon Freelon | .30 | .15 |
| 49 | Bob Windsor | .30 | .15 |
| 50 | John Hadl | 1.50 | .75 |
| 51 | Greg Larson | .30 | .15 |
| 52 | Steve Owens | .50 | .25 |
| 53 | Jim Cheyunski | .30 | .15 |
| 54 | Rayfield Wright | .30 | .15 |
| 55 | Dave Hampton | .30 | .15 |
| 56 | Ron Widby | .30 | .15 |
| 57 | Milt Sunde | .30 | .15 |
| 58 | Bill Kilmer | 1.50 | .75 |
| 59 | Bobby Bell | 2.00 | 1.00 |
| 60 | Jim Bakken | .30 | .15 |
| 61 | Rufus Mayes | .30 | .15 |
| 62 | Vic Washington | .30 | .15 |
| 63 | Gene Washington | .30 | .15 |
| 64 | Clarence Scott | .30 | .15 |
| 65 | Gene Upshaw | 2.00 | 1.00 |
| 66 | Larry Seiple | .30 | .15 |
| 67 | John McMakin | .30 | .15 |
| 68 | Ralph Baker | .30 | .15 |
| 69 | Lydell Mitchell | .80 | .40 |
| 70 | Archie Manning | 1.75 | .85 |
| 71 | George Farmer | .30 | .15 |
| 72 | Ron East | .30 | .15 |
| 73 | Al Nelson | .30 | .15 |
| 74 | Pat Hughes | .30 | .15 |
| 75 | Fred Willis | .30 | .15 |
| 76 | Larry Walton | .30 | .15 |
| 77 | Tom Neville | .30 | .15 |
| 78 | Ted Kwalick | .40 | .20 |
| 79 | Walt Patulski | .30 | .15 |
| 80 | John Niland | .30 | .15 |
| 81 | Ted Fritsch | .30 | .15 |
| 82 | Paul Krause | .80 | .50 |
| 83 | Jack Snow | .40 | .20 |
| 84 | Mike Bass | .30 | .15 |
| 85 | Jim Tyrer | .30 | .15 |
| 86 | Ron Yankowski | .30 | .15 |
| 87 | Mike Phipps | .50 | .25 |
| 88 | Al Beauchamp | .30 | .15 |
| 89 | Riley Odoms (R) | 1.75 | .85 |
| 90 | MacArthur Lane | .50 | .25 |
| 91 | Art Thomas | .30 | .15 |
| 92 | Marlin Briscoe | .40 | .20 |
| 93 | Bruce Van Dyke | .30 | .15 |
| 94 | Tom Myers (R) | .40 | .20 |
| 95 | Calvin Hill | .80 | .40 |
| 96 | Bruce Laird | .30 | .15 |
| 97 | Tony McGee | .30 | .15 |
| 98 | Len Rohde | .30 | .15 |
| 99 | Tom McNeill | .30 | .15 |
| 100 | Delles Howell | .30 | .15 |
| 101 | Gary Garrison | .30 | .15 |
| 102 | Dan Goich | .30 | .15 |
| 103 | Len St.Jean | .30 | .15 |
| 104 | Zeke Moore | .30 | .15 |
| 105 | Ahmad Rashed (R) | 16.00 | 8.00 |
| 106 | Mel Renfro | .90 | .45 |
| 107 | Jim Mitchell | .30 | .15 |
| 108 | Ed Budde | .30 | .15 |
| 109 | Harry Schuh | .30 | .15 |
| 110 | Greg Pruitt (R) | 2.50 | 1.25 |
| 111 | Ed Flanigan | .30 | .15 |
| 112 | Larry Stallings | .30 | .15 |
| 113 | Chuck Foreman (R) | 3.50 | 1.75 |
| 114 | Royce Berry | .30 | .15 |
| 115 | Gale Gillingham | .30 | .15 |
| 116 | Charlie Johnson | .90 | .45 |
| 117 | Checklist 1-132 | 3.00 | .50 |
| 118 | Bill Butler | .30 | .15 |
| 119 | Roy Jefferson | .40 | .20 |
| 120 | Bobby Douglass | .40 | .20 |
| 121 | Harold Carmichael (R) | 15.00 | 7.50 |
| 122 | George Kunz (AP) | .35 | .18 |
| 123 | Larry Little (AP) | 1.50 | .75 |
| 124 | Forrest Blue (AP) | .40 | .20 |
| 125 | Ron Yary (AP) | .75 | .35 |
| 126 | Tom Mack (AP) | .60 | .30 |
| 127 | Bob Tucker (AP) | .40 | .20 |
| 128 | Paul Warfield (AP) | 3.00 | 1.50 |
| 129 | Fran Tarkenton (AP) | 10.00 | 5.00 |
| 130 | O.J. Simpson (AP) | 18.00 | 9.00 |

| | | | |
|---|---|---|---|
| 131 Larry Csonka (AP) | 3.50 | 1.75 | |
| 132 Bruce Gossett (AP) | .30 | .15 | |
| 133 Bill Stanfill (AP) | .30 | .15 | |
| 134 Alan Page (AP) | 2.50 | 1.25 | |
| 135 Paul Smith (AP) | .30 | .15 | |
| 136 Claude Humphrey (AP) | .40 | .20 | |
| 137 Jack Ham (AP) | 4.00 | 2.00 | |
| 138 Lee Roy Jordan (AP) | 1.00 | .50 | |
| 139 Phil Villapiano (AP) | .40 | .20 | |
| 140 Ken Ellis (AP) | .30 | .15 | |
| 141 Willie Brown (AP) | 1.75 | .85 | |
| 142 Dick Anderson (AP) | .40 | .20 | |
| 143 Bill Bradley (AP) | .40 | .20 | |
| 144 Jerrel Wilson (AP) | .35 | .18 | |
| 145 Reggie Rucker | .50 | .25 | |
| 146 Marty Domres | .40 | .20 | |
| 147 Bob Kowalkowski | .30 | .15 | |
| 148 John Matuszak (R) | 3.50 | 1.75 | |
| 149 Mike Adamle (R) | .75 | .35 | |
| 150 John Unitas | 18.50 | 9.25 | |
| 151 Charlie Ford | .30 | .15 | |
| 152 Bob Klein (R) | .40 | .20 | |
| 153 Jim Merlo | .30 | .15 | |
| 154 Willie Young | .30 | .15 | |
| 155 Donny Anderson | .60 | .30 | |
| 156 Brig Owens | .30 | .15 | |
| 157 Bruce Jarvis | .30 | .15 | |
| 158 Ron Carpenter | .30 | .15 | |
| 159 Don Cockroft | .40 | .20 | |
| 160 Tommy Nobis | 1.00 | .50 | |
| 161 Craig Morton | 1.25 | .60 | |
| 162 Jon Staggers | .30 | .15 | |
| 163 Mike Eischeid | .30 | .15 | |
| 164 Jerry Sisemore (R) | .75 | .35 | |
| 165 Cedric Hardman | .30 | .15 | |
| 166 Bill Thompson | .30 | .15 | |
| 167 Jim Lynch | .30 | .15 | |
| 168 Bob Moore | .30 | .15 | |
| 169 Glen Edwards | .30 | .15 | |
| 170 Mercury Morris | 1.00 | .50 | |
| 171 Julius Adams | .30 | .15 | |
| 172 Cotton Speyrer | .30 | .15 | |
| 173 Bill Munson | .60 | .30 | |
| 174 Benny Johnson | .30 | .15 | |
| 175 Burgess Owens (R) | .60 | .30 | |
| 176 Cid Edwards | .30 | .15 | |
| 177 Doug Buffone | .30 | .15 | |
| 178 Charlie Cowan | .30 | .15 | |
| 179 Bob Newland | .30 | .15 | |
| 180 Ron Johnson | .50 | .25 | |
| 181 Bob Rowe | .30 | .15 | |
| 182 Len Hauss | .30 | .15 | |
| 183 Joe DeLamielleure (R) | 1.25 | .60 | |
| 184 Sherman White (R) | .50 | .25 | |
| 185 Fair Hooker | .30 | .15 | |
| 186 Nick Mike-Mayer | .30 | .15 | |
| 187 Ralph Neely | .30 | .15 | |
| 188 Rich McGeorge | .30 | .15 | |
| 189 Ed Marinaro (R) | 3.50 | 1.75 | |
| 190 Dave Wilcox | .30 | .15 | |
| 191 Joe Owens | .30 | .15 | |
| 192 Bill Van Heusen | .30 | .15 | |
| 193 Jim Kearney | .30 | .15 | |
| 194 Otis Sistrunk (R) | 1.50 | .75 | |
| 195 Ron Shanklin | .30 | .15 | |
| 196 Bill Lenkaitis | .30 | .15 | |
| 197 Tom Drougas | .30 | .15 | |
| 198 Larry Hand | .30 | .15 | |
| 199 Mack Alston | .30 | .15 | |
| 200 Bob Griese | 5.00 | 2.50 | |
| 201 Earlie Thomas | .30 | .15 | |
| 202 Carl Gerbach | .30 | .15 | |
| 203 Jim Harrison | .30 | .15 | |
| 204 Jake Kupp | .30 | .15 | |
| 205 Merlin Olsen | 3.50 | 1.75 | |
| 206 Spider Lockhart | .30 | .15 | |
| 207 Walker Gillette | .30 | .15 | |
| 208 Verlon Biggs | .30 | .15 | |
| 209 Bob James | .30 | .15 | |
| 210 Bob Trumpy | .90 | .45 | |
| 211 Jerry Sherk | .30 | .15 | |
| 212 Andy Maurer | .30 | .15 | |
| 213 Fred Carr | .30 | .15 | |
| 214 Mick Tingelhoff | .75 | .35 | |
| 215 Steve Spurrier | 1.25 | .60 | |
| 216 Richard Harris | .30 | .15 | |
| 217 Charlie Greer | .30 | .15 | |
| 218 Buck Buchanan | 2.00 | 1.00 | |
| 219 Ray Guy (R) | 7.50 | 3.75 | |
| 220 Franco Harris | 20.00 | 10.00 | |
| 221 Darryl Stingley (R) | 1.75 | .85 | |
| 222 Rex Kern | .40 | .20 | |
| 223 Toni Fritsch (R) | .40 | .20 | |
| 224 Levi Johnson | .30 | .15 | |
| 225 Bob Kuechenberg | .60 | .30 | |
| 226 Elvin Bethea | .35 | .18 | |
| 227 Al Woodall (R) | .40 | .20 | |
| 228 Terry Owens | .30 | .15 | |
| 229 Bivian Lee | .30 | .15 | |
| 230 Dick Butkus | 6.00 | 3.00 | |
| 231 Jim Bertelsen (R) | .50 | .25 | |
| 232 John Mendenhall (R) | .50 | .25 | |
| 233 Conrad Dobler (R) | 2.00 | 1.00 | |
| 234 J.D. Hill | .35 | .18 | |
| 235 Ken Houston | 1.75 | .85 | |
| 236 Dave Lewis | .30 | .15 | |
| 237 John Garlington | .30 | .15 | |
| 238 Bill Sandeman | .30 | .15 | |
| 239 Alden Roche | .30 | .15 | |
| 240 John Gilliam | .30 | .15 | |
| 241 Bruce Taylor | .30 | .15 | |
| 242 Vern Winfield | .30 | .15 | |
| 243 Bobby Maples | .30 | .15 | |

| | | | |
|---|---|---|---|
| 244 | Wendell Hayes | .40 | .20 |
| 245 | George Blanda | 8.00 | 4.00 |
| 246 | Dwight White | .40 | .20 |
| 247 | Sandy Durko | .30 | .15 |
| 248 | Tom Mitchell | .30 | .15 |
| 249 | Chuck Walton | .30 | .15 |
| 250 | Bob Lilly | 3.50 | 1.75 |
| 251 | Doug Swift | .30 | .15 |
| 252 | Lynn Dickey (R) | 3.00 | 1.50 |
| 253 | Jerome Barkum (R) | 1.00 | .50 |
| 254 | Clint Jones | .30 | .15 |
| 255 | Billy Newsome | .30 | .15 |
| 256 | Bob Asher | .30 | .15 |
| 257 | Joe Scibelli (R) | .50 | .25 |
| 258 | Tom Blanchard | .30 | .15 |
| 259 | Norm Thompson | .30 | .15 |
| 260 | Larry Brown | .75 | .35 |
| 261 | Paul Seymour | .30 | .15 |
| 262 | Checklist 133-264 | 3.00 | .50 |
| 263 | Doug Dieken (R) | .50 | .25 |
| 264 | Lemar Parrish | .35 | .18 |
| 265 | Bob Lee | .40 | .20 |
| 266 | Bob Brown | .30 | .15 |
| 267 | Roy Winston | .30 | .15 |
| 268 | Randy Beisler | .30 | .15 |
| 269 | Joe Dawkins | .30 | .15 |
| 270 | Tom Dempsey | .40 | .20 |
| 271 | Jack Rudnay | .30 | .15 |
| 272 | Art Shell | 5.00 | 2.50 |
| 273 | Mike Wagner | .40 | .20 |
| 274 | Rick Cash | .30 | .15 |
| 275 | Greg Landry | .80 | .50 |
| 276 | Glenn Ressler | .30 | .15 |
| 277 | Billy Joe DuPree (R) | 2.50 | 1.25 |
| 278 | Norm Evans | .30 | .15 |
| 279 | Billy Parks | .40 | .20 |
| 280 | John Riggins | 7.00 | 3.50 |
| 281 | Lionel Aldridge | .30 | .15 |
| 282 | Steve O'Neal | .30 | .15 |
| 283 | Craig Clemons | .30 | .15 |
| 284 | Willie Williams | .30 | .15 |
| 285 | Isiah Robertson | .40 | .20 |
| 286 | Dennis Shaw | .35 | .18 |
| 287 | Bill Brundige | .30 | .15 |
| 288 | John Leypoldt | .30 | .15 |
| 289 | John DeMarie | .30 | .15 |
| 290 | Mike Reid | .90 | .45 |
| 291 | Greg Brezina | .30 | .15 |
| 292 | Willie Buchanon (R) | 1.75 | .85 |
| 293 | Dave Osborn | .40 | .20 |
| 294 | Mel Phillips | .30 | .15 |
| 295 | Haven Moses | .50 | .25 |
| 296 | Wade Key | .30 | .15 |
| 297 | Marvin Upshaw | .30 | .15 |
| 298 | Ray Mansfield | .30 | .15 |
| 299 | Edgar Chandler | .30 | .15 |
| 300 | Marv Hubbard | .60 | .30 |
| 301 | Herman Weaver | .30 | .15 |
| 302 | Jim Bailey | .30 | .15 |
| 303 | D.D. Lewis (R) | 1.25 | .60 |
| 304 | Ken Burrough | .50 | .25 |
| 305 | Jake Scott | .40 | .20 |
| 306 | Randy Rasmussen | .30 | .15 |
| 307 | Pettis Norman | .30 | .15 |
| 308 | Carl Johnson | .30 | .15 |
| 309 | Joe Taylor | .30 | .15 |
| 310 | Pete Gogolak | .40 | .20 |
| 311 | Tony Baker | .30 | .15 |
| 312 | John Richardson | .30 | .15 |
| 313 | Dave Robinson | .30 | .15 |
| 314 | Reggie McKenzie (R) | 2.00 | 1.00 |
| 315 | Isaac Curtis (R) | 2.50 | 1.25 |
| 316 | Thom Darden | .30 | .15 |
| 317 | Ken Reaves | .30 | .15 |
| 318 | Malcolm Snider | .30 | .15 |
| 319 | Jeff Siemon (R) | 1.25 | .60 |
| 320 | Dan Abramowicz | .40 | .20 |
| 321 | Lyle Alzado | 2.50 | 1.25 |
| 322 | John Reaves | .40 | .20 |
| 323 | Morris Stroud | .30 | .15 |
| 324 | Boobby Walden | .30 | .15 |
| 325 | Randy Vataha | .40 | .20 |
| 326 | Nemiah Wilson | .30 | .15 |
| 327 | Paul Naumoff | .30 | .15 |
| 328 | Rushing Leaders (Simpson, Brockington) | 3.00 | 1.50 |
| 329 | Passing Leaders (Stabler, Staubach) | 3.00 | 1.50 |
| 330 | Receiving Leaders (Willis, Carmichael) | 1.00 | .50 |
| 331 | Scoring Leaders (Gerela, Ray) | .35 | .18 |
| 332 | Interception Leaders (Anderson, Wagner Bryant) | .40 | .20 |
| 333 | Punting Leaders (Wilson, Wittum) | .35 | .18 |
| 334 | Dennis Nelson | .30 | .15 |
| 335 | Walt Garrison | .60 | .30 |
| 336 | Tody Smith | .30 | .15 |
| 337 | Ed Bell | .30 | .15 |
| 338 | Bryant Salter | .30 | .15 |
| 339 | Wayne Colman | .30 | .15 |
| 340 | Garo Yepremian | .35 | .18 |
| 341 | Bob Newton | .30 | .15 |
| 342 | Vince Clements (R) | .60 | .30 |
| 343 | Ken Iman | .30 | .15 |
| 344 | Jim Tolbert | .30 | .15 |
| 345 | Chris Hanburger | .50 | .25 |
| 346 | Dave Foley | .30 | .15 |
| 347 | Tommy Casanova | .50 | .25 |
| 348 | John James | .30 | .15 |
| 349 | Clarence Williams | .30 | .15 |
| 350 | Leroy Kelly | 1.25 | .60 |

| No. | Player | | |
|-----|--------|------|------|
| 351 | Stu Voigt (R) | .75 | .35 |
| 352 | Skip Vanderbundt | .30 | .15 |
| 353 | Pete Duranko | .30 | .15 |
| 354 | John Outlaw | .30 | .15 |
| 355 | Jan Stenerud | 1.50 | .75 |
| 356 | Barry Pearson | .30 | .15 |
| 357 | Brian Dowling (R) | .50 | .25 |
| 358 | Dan Conners | .30 | .15 |
| 359 | Bob Bell | .30 | .15 |
| 360 | Rick Volk | .30 | .15 |
| 361 | Pat Toomay | .30 | .15 |
| 362 | Bob Gresham | .30 | .15 |
| 363 | John Schmitt | .30 | .15 |
| 364 | Mel Rogers | .30 | .15 |
| 365 | Manny Fernandez | .30 | .15 |
| 366 | Ernie Jackson | .30 | .15 |
| 367 | Gary Huff (R) | .90 | .45 |
| 368 | Bob Grim | .30 | .15 |
| 369 | Ernie McMillan | .30 | .15 |
| 370 | Dave Elmendorf | .30 | .15 |
| 371 | Mike Bragg | .30 | .15 |
| 372 | John Skorupan | .30 | .15 |
| 373 | Howard Fest | .30 | .15 |
| 374 | Jerry Tagge (R) | .80 | .40 |
| 375 | Art Malone | .30 | .15 |
| 376 | Bob Babich | .30 | .15 |
| 377 | Jim Marshall | 1.25 | .60 |
| 378 | Bob Hoskinsk | .30 | .15 |
| 379 | Don Zimmerman | .30 | .15 |
| 380 | Ray May | .30 | .15 |
| 381 | Emmitt Thomas | .30 | .15 |
| 382 | Terry Hanratty | .50 | .25 |
| 383 | John Hannah (R) | 15.00 | 7.50 |
| 384 | George Atkinson | .30 | .15 |
| 385 | Ted Hendricks | 2.50 | 1.25 |
| 386 | Jim O'Brien | .30 | .15 |
| 387 | Jethro Pugh | .40 | .20 |
| 388 | Elbert Drungo | .30 | .15 |
| 389 | Richard Caster | .50 | .25 |
| 390 | Deacon Jones | 2.50 | 1.25 |
| 391 | Checklist 265-396 | 3.00 | .50 |
| 392 | Jess Phillips | .30 | .15 |
| 393 | Garry Lyle | .30 | .15 |
| 394 | Jim Files | .30 | .15 |
| 395 | Jim Hart | 1.50 | .75 |
| 396 | Dave Chapple | .30 | .15 |
| 397 | Jim Langer | 2.50 | 1.25 |
| 398 | John Wilbur | .30 | .15 |
| 399 | Dwight Harrison | .30 | .15 |
| 400 | John Brockington | .90 | .45 |
| 401 | Ken Anderson | 5.00 | 2.50 |
| 402 | Mike Tilleman | .30 | .15 |
| 403 | Charlie Hall | .30 | .15 |
| 404 | Tommy Hart | .30 | .15 |
| 405 | Norm Bulaich | .40 | .20 |
| 406 | Jim Turner | .30 | .15 |
| 407 | Mo Moorman | .30 | .15 |
| 408 | Ralph Anderson | .30 | .15 |
| 409 | Jim Otto | 2.50 | 1.25 |
| 410 | Andy Russell | .40 | .20 |
| 411 | Glenn Doughty | .30 | .15 |
| 412 | Altie Taylor | .30 | .15 |
| 413 | Marv Bateman | .30 | .15 |
| 414 | Willie Alexander | .30 | .15 |
| 415 | Bill Zapalac | .30 | .15 |
| 416 | Russ Washington | .30 | .15 |
| 417 | Joe Federspiel | .30 | .15 |
| 418 | Craig Cotton | .30 | .15 |
| 419 | Randy Johnson | .30 | .15 |
| 420 | Harold Jackson | 1.00 | .50 |
| 421 | Roger Wehrli | .30 | .15 |
| 422 | Charlie Harraway | .30 | .15 |
| 423 | Spike Jones | .30 | .15 |
| 424 | Bob Johnson | .30 | .15 |
| 425 | Mike McCoy | .30 | .15 |
| 426 | Dennis Havig | .30 | .15 |
| 427 | Bob McKay | .30 | .15 |
| 428 | Steve Zabel | .30 | .15 |
| 429 | Horace Jones | .30 | .15 |
| 430 | Jim Johnson | .30 | .15 |
| 431 | Roy Gerela | .30 | .15 |
| 432 | Tom Graham | .30 | .15 |
| 433 | Curley Culp | .60 | .30 |
| 434 | Ken Mendenhall | .30 | .15 |
| 435 | Jim Plunkett | 2.00 | 1.00 |
| 436 | Julian Fagan | .30 | .15 |
| 437 | Mike Garrett | .50 | .25 |
| 438 | Bobby Joe Green | .30 | .15 |
| 439 | Jack Gregory | .30 | .15 |
| 440 | Charlie Sanders | .40 | .20 |
| 441 | Bill Curry | .50 | .25 |
| 442 | Bob Pollard | .30 | .15 |
| 443 | David Ray | .30 | .15 |
| 444 | Terry Metcalf (R) | 3.50 | 1.75 |
| 445 | Pat Fischer | .35 | .18 |
| 446 | Bob Chandler | .35 | .18 |
| 447 | Bill Bergey | .80 | .40 |
| 448 | Walter Johnson | .30 | .15 |
| 449 | Charley Young (R) | 1.25 | .60 |
| 450 | Chester Marcol | .35 | .18 |
| 451 | Ken Stabler | 8.00 | 4.00 |
| 452 | Preston Pearson | .60 | .30 |
| 453 | Mike Current | .30 | .15 |
| 454 | Ron Bolton | .30 | .15 |
| 455 | Mark Lomas | .30 | .15 |
| 456 | Raymond Chester | .75 | .35 |
| 457 | Jerry LeVias | .35 | .18 |
| 458 | Skip Butler | .30 | .15 |
| 459 | Mike Livingston (R) | .50 | .25 |
| 460 | AFC Semi-Finals | 1.00 | .50 |
| 461 | NFC Semi-Finals | 2.50 | 1.25 |
| 462 | League Championships | 1.75 | .85 |
| 463 | Super Bowl | 1.75 | .85 |

| | | | |
|---|---|---|---|
| 464 | Wayne Mulligan | .30 | .15 |
| 465 | Horst Muhlmann | .30 | .15 |
| 466 | Milt Morin | .30 | .15 |
| 467 | Don Parish | .30 | .15 |
| 468 | Richard Neal | .30 | .15 |
| 469 | Ron Jessie | .40 | .20 |
| 470 | Terry Bradshaw | 12.50 | 6.25 |
| 471 | Fred Dryer | 2.50 | 1.25 |
| 472 | Jim Carter | .30 | .15 |
| 473 | Ken Burrow | .30 | .15 |
| 474 | Wally Chambers (R) | .75 | .35 |
| 475 | Dan Pastorini | .80 | .40 |
| 476 | Don Morrison | .30 | .15 |
| 477 | Carl Mauck | .30 | .15 |
| 478 | Larry Cole (R) | .50 | .25 |
| 479 | Jim Kiick | .60 | .30 |
| 480 | Willie Lanier | 2.50 | 1.25 |
| 481 | Don Herrmann | .30 | .15 |
| 482 | George Hunt | .30 | .15 |
| 483 | Bob Howard | .30 | .15 |
| 484 | Myron Pottios | .30 | .15 |
| 485 | Jackie Smith | .40 | .20 |
| 486 | Vern Holland | .30 | .15 |
| 487 | Jim Braxton | .30 | .15 |
| 488 | Joe Reed | .30 | .15 |
| 489 | Wally Hilgenberg | .30 | .15 |
| 490 | Fred Biletnikoff | 3.00 | 1.50 |
| 491 | Bob DeMarco | .30 | .15 |
| 492 | Mark Nordquist | .30 | .15 |
| 493 | Larry Brooks | .30 | .15 |
| 494 | Pete Athas | .30 | .15 |
| 495 | Emerson Boozer | .60 | .30 |
| 496 | L.C. Greenwood | 1.50 | .75 |
| 497 | Rockne Freitas | .30 | .15 |
| 498 | Checklist 397-528 | 3.00 | .50 |
| 499 | Joe Schmiesing | .30 | .15 |
| 500 | Roger Staubach | 24.00 | 12.00 |
| 501 | Al Cowlings | .30 | .15 |
| 502 | Sam Cunningham (R) | 1.50 | .75 |
| 503 | Dennis Partee | .30 | .15 |
| 504 | John Didion | .30 | .15 |
| 505 | Nick Buoniconti | 1.25 | .60 |
| 506 | Carl Garrett | .30 | .15 |
| 507 | Doug Van Horn | .30 | .15 |
| 508 | Jamie Rivers | .30 | .15 |
| 509 | Jack Youngblood | 2.50 | 1.50 |
| 510 | Charley Taylor | 2.50 | 1.50 |
| 511 | Ken Riley | .50 | .25 |
| 512 | Joe Ferguson (R) | 2.50 | 1.25 |
| 513 | Bill Lueck | .30 | .15 |
| 514 | Ray Brown | .30 | .15 |
| 515 | Fred Cox | .30 | .15 |
| 516 | Joe Jones | .30 | .15 |
| 517 | Larry Schreiber | .30 | .15 |
| 518 | Dennis Wirgowski | .30 | .15 |
| 519 | Leroy Mitchell | .30 | .15 |
| 520 | Otis Taylor | .80 | .50 |

| | | | |
|---|---|---|---|
| 521 | Henry Davis | .30 | .15 |
| 522 | Bruce Barnes | .30 | .15 |
| 523 | Charlie Smith | .30 | .15 |
| 524 | Bert Jones (R) | 3.50 | 1.75 |
| 525 | Lem Barney | 2.00 | 1.00 |
| 526 | John Fitzgerald | .30 | .15 |
| 527 | Tom Funchess | .30 | .15 |
| 528 | Steve Tannen | .60 | .20 |

# 1975 Topps

This 528-card set is made up mostly of posed color photos on the card fronts. The player's name is centered at the bottom of the card. The team name appears in a small pennant design in the lower left corner while the player's position is printed on the side of a small helmet in the lower right corner. The vertical card backs contain personal data and highlights. Subsets include League Leaders (1-6), All-Pros (AP)(201-225), Record Breakers (RB)(351-356) and Highlights (HL)(452-460). All cards measure 2-1/2" by 3-1/2".

| | | NR/MT | EX |
|---|---|---|---|
| | Complete Set (528) | 310.00 | 155.00 |
| | Commons | .25 | .12 |
| | | | |
| 1 | Rushing Leaders (McCutcheon, Armstrong) | 1.50 | .50 |
| 2 | Passing Leaders (Jurgensen, Anderson) | 1.25 | .60 |

| | | | |
|---|---|---|---|
| 3 | Receiving Leaders (Young, Mitchell) | .40 | .20 |
| 4 | Scoring Leaders (Marcol, Gerela) | .30 | .15 |
| 5 | Interception Leaders (Ray Brown, Emmitt Thomas) | .40 | .20 |
| 6 | Punting Leaders (Blanchard, Guy) | .50 | .25 |
| 7 | George Blanda (Black Jersey) | 5.00 | 2.50 |
| 8 | Geroge Blanda (White Jersey) | 5.00 | 2.50 |
| 9 | Ralph Baker | .25 | .12 |
| 10 | Don Woods | .25 | .12 |
| 11 | Bob Asher | .25 | .12 |
| 12 | Mel Blount (R) | 20.00 | 10.00 |
| 13 | Sam Cunningham | .75 | .35 |
| 14 | Jackie Smith | .35 | .18 |
| 15 | Greg Landry | .75 | .35 |
| 16 | Buck Buchanan | 1.75 | .85 |
| 17 | Haven Moses | .40 | .20 |
| 18 | Clarence Ellis | .25 | .12 |
| 19 | Jim Carter | .25 | .12 |
| 20 | Charley Taylor | 2.00 | 1.00 |
| 21 | Jess Phillips | .25 | .12 |
| 22 | Larry Seiple | .25 | .12 |
| 23 | Doug Dieken | .25 | .12 |
| 24 | Ron Saul | .25 | .12 |
| 25 | Isaac Curtis | .75 | .35 |
| 26 | Gary Larsen (R) | .60 | .30 |
| 27 | Bruce Jarvis | .25 | .12 |
| 28 | Steve Zabel | .25 | .12 |
| 29 | John Mendenhall | .25 | .12 |
| 30 | Rick Volk | .25 | .12 |
| 31 | Checklist 1-132 | 2.25 | .25 |
| 32 | Dan Abramowicz | .40 | .20 |
| 33 | Bubba Smith | 1.75 | .85 |
| 34 | David Ray | .25 | .12 |
| 35 | Dan Dierdorf | 1.50 | .75 |
| 36 | Randy Rasmussen | .25 | .12 |
| 37 | Bob Howard | .25 | .12 |
| 38 | Gary Huff | .35 | .18 |
| 39 | Rocky Bleier (R) | 6.00 | 3.00 |
| 40 | Mel Gray | .35 | .18 |
| 41 | Tony McGee | .25 | .12 |
| 42 | Larry Hand | .25 | .12 |
| 43 | Wendell Hayes | .25 | .12 |
| 44 | Doug Wilkerson (R) | .50 | .25 |
| 45 | Paul Smith | .25 | .12 |
| 46 | Dave Robinson | .25 | .12 |
| 47 | Bivian Lee | .25 | .12 |
| 48 | Jim Mandich (R) | .60 | .30 |
| 49 | Greg Pruitt | 1.00 | .50 |
| 50 | Dan Pastorini | .80 | .40 |
| 51 | Ron Pritchard | .25 | .12 |
| 52 | Dan Conners | .25 | .12 |
| 53 | Fred Cox | .25 | .12 |
| 54 | Tony Greene | .25 | .12 |
| 55 | Craig Morton | 1.25 | .60 |
| 56 | Jerry Sisemore | .40 | .20 |
| 57 | Glenn Doughty | .25 | .12 |
| 58 | Larry Schreiber | .25 | .12 |
| 59 | Charlie Waters (R) | 2.50 | 1.25 |
| 60 | Jack Youngblood | 1.00 | .50 |
| 61 | Bill Lenkaitis | .25 | .12 |
| 62 | Greg Brezina (R) | .40 | .20 |
| 63 | Bob Pollard | .25 | .12 |
| 64 | Mack Alston | .25 | .12 |
| 65 | Drew Pearson (R) | 6.00 | 3.00 |
| 66 | Charlie Stukes | .25 | .12 |
| 67 | Emerson Boozer | .50 | .25 |
| 68 | Dennis Partee | .25 | .12 |
| 69 | Bob Newton | .25 | .12 |
| 70 | Jack Tatum | .75 | .35 |
| 71 | Frank Lewis | .40 | .20 |
| 72 | Bob Young | .25 | .12 |
| 73 | Julius Adams | .25 | .12 |
| 74 | Paul Naumoff | .25 | .12 |
| 75 | Otis Taylor | .80 | .40 |
| 76 | Dave Hampton | .25 | .12 |
| 77 | Mike Current | .25 | .12 |
| 78 | Brig Owens | .25 | .12 |
| 79 | Bobby Scott | .25 | .12 |
| 80 | Harold Carmichael | 2.50 | 1.25 |
| 81 | Bill Stanfill | .25 | .12 |
| 82 | Bob Babich | .25 | .12 |
| 83 | Vic Washington | .25 | .12 |
| 84 | Mick Tingelhoff | .40 | .20 |
| 85 | Bob Trumpy | .75 | .35 |
| 86 | Earl Edwards | .25 | .12 |
| 87 | Ron Hornsby | .25 | .12 |
| 88 | Don McCauley | .25 | .12 |
| 89 | Jim Johnson | .25 | .12 |
| 90 | Andy Russell | .35 | .18 |
| 91 | Cornell Green | .30 | .15 |
| 92 | Charlie Cowan | .25 | .12 |
| 93 | Jon Staggers | .25 | .12 |
| 94 | Billy Newsome | .25 | .12 |
| 95 | Willie Brown | 1.75 | .85 |
| 96 | Carl Mauck | .25 | .12 |
| 97 | Doug Buffone | .25 | .12 |
| 98 | Preston Pearson | .75 | .35 |
| 99 | Jim Bakken | .25 | .12 |
| 100 | Bob Griese | 4.50 | 2.25 |
| 101 | Bob Windsor | .25 | .12 |
| 102 | Rockne Freitas | .25 | .12 |
| 103 | Jim Marsalis | .25 | .12 |
| 104 | Bill Thompson | .25 | .12 |
| 105 | Ken Burrow | .25 | .12 |
| 106 | Diron Talbert | .40 | .20 |
| 107 | Joe Federspiel | .25 | .12 |
| 108 | Norm Bulaich | .35 | .18 |
| 109 | Bob DeMarco | .25 | .12 |

| No. | Player | | |
|---|---|---|---|
| 110 | Tom Wittum | .25 | .12 |
| 111 | Larry Hefner | .25 | .12 |
| 112 | Tody Smith | .25 | .12 |
| 113 | Stu Voigt | .25 | .12 |
| 114 | Horst Muhlmann | .25 | .12 |
| 115 | Ahmad Rashad | 3.50 | 1.75 |
| 116 | Joe Dawkins | .25 | .12 |
| 117 | George Kunz | .25 | .12 |
| 118 | D.D. Lewis | .35 | .18 |
| 119 | Levi Johnson | .25 | .12 |
| 120 | Len Dawson | 3.50 | 1.75 |
| 121 | Jim Bertelsen | .25 | .12 |
| 122 | Ed Bell | .25 | .12 |
| 123 | Art Thoms | .25 | .12 |
| 124 | Joe Beauchamp | .25 | .12 |
| 125 | Jack Ham | 3.00 | 1.50 |
| 126 | Carl Garrett | .25 | .12 |
| 127 | Roger Finnie | .25 | .12 |
| 128 | Howard Twilley | .40 | .20 |
| 129 | Bruce Barnes | .25 | .12 |
| 130 | Nate Wright | .25 | .12 |
| 131 | Jerry Tagge | .35 | .18 |
| 132 | Floyd Little | 1.00 | .50 |
| 133 | John Zook | .25 | .12 |
| 134 | Len Hauss | .25 | .12 |
| 135 | Archie Manning | 1.50 | .75 |
| 136 | Po James | .25 | .12 |
| 137 | Walt Sumner | .25 | .12 |
| 138 | Randy Beisler | .25 | .12 |
| 139 | Willie Alexander | .25 | .12 |
| 140 | Garo Yepremian | .30 | .15 |
| 141 | Chip Myers | .25 | .12 |
| 142 | Jim Braxton | .25 | .12 |
| 143 | Doug Van Horn | .25 | .12 |
| 144 | Stan White | .25 | .12 |
| 145 | Roger Staubach | 18.00 | 9.00 |
| 146 | Herman Weaver | .25 | .12 |
| 147 | Marvin Upshaw | .25 | .12 |
| 148 | Bob Klein | .25 | .12 |
| 149 | Earlie Thomas | .25 | .12 |
| 150 | John Brockington | .75 | .35 |
| 151 | Mike Siani | .25 | .12 |
| 152 | Sam Davis | .25 | .12 |
| 153 | Mike Wagner | .35 | .18 |
| 154 | Larry Stallings | .25 | .12 |
| 155 | Wally Chambers | .40 | .20 |
| 156 | Randy Vataha | .35 | .18 |
| 157 | Jim Marshall | 1.25 | .60 |
| 158 | Jim Turner | .25 | .12 |
| 159 | Walt Sweeney | .25 | .12 |
| 160 | Ken Anderson | 3.00 | 1.50 |
| 161 | Ray Brown | .25 | .12 |
| 162 | John Didion | .25 | .12 |
| 163 | Tom Dempsey | .30 | .15 |
| 164 | Clarence Scott | .25 | .12 |
| 165 | Gene Washington | .35 | .18 |
| 166 | Willie Rogers | .25 | .12 |
| 167 | Doug Swift | .25 | .12 |
| 168 | Rufus Mayes | .25 | .12 |
| 169 | Marv Bateman | .25 | .12 |
| 170 | Lydell Mitchell | .60 | .30 |
| 171 | Ron Smith | .25 | .12 |
| 172 | Bill Munson | .50 | .25 |
| 173 | Bob Grim | .25 | .12 |
| 174 | Ed Budde | .25 | .12 |
| 175 | Bob Lilly | 3.00 | 1.50 |
| 176 | Jim Youngblood (R) | .80 | .40 |
| 177 | Steve Tannen | .25 | .12 |
| 178 | Rich McGeorge | .25 | .12 |
| 179 | Jim Tyrer | .25 | .12 |
| 180 | Forrest Blue | .25 | .12 |
| 181 | Jerry LeVias | .25 | .12 |
| 182 | Joe Gilliam (R) | .80 | .40 |
| 183 | Jim Otis (R) | .75 | .35 |
| 184 | Mel Tom | .25 | .12 |
| 185 | Paul Seymour | .25 | .12 |
| 186 | George Webster | .25 | .12 |
| 187 | Pete Duranko | .25 | .12 |
| 188 | Essex Johnson | .25 | .12 |
| 189 | Bob Lee | .35 | .18 |
| 190 | Gene Upshaw | 1.50 | .75 |
| 191 | Tom Myers | .25 | .12 |
| 192 | Don Zimmerman | .25 | .12 |
| 193 | John Garlington | .25 | .12 |
| 194 | Skip Butler | .25 | .12 |
| 195 | Tom Mitchell | .25 | .12 |
| 196 | Jim Langer | 1.50 | .75 |
| 197 | Ron Carpenter | .25 | .12 |
| 198 | Dave Foley | .25 | .12 |
| 199 | Bert Jones | 1.50 | .75 |
| 200 | Larry Brown | .75 | .35 |
| 201 | All Pro Receivers<br>Charley Taylor<br>Fred Biletnikoff | 1.75 | .85 |
| 202 | All Pro Tackles<br>Rayfield Wright<br>Russ Washington | .35 | .18 |
| 203 | All Pro Guards<br>Tom Mack<br>Larry Little | .60 | .30 |
| 204 | All Pro Centers<br>Jeff Van Note<br>Jack Rudnay | .35 | .18 |
| 205 | All Pro Guards<br>Gale Gillingham<br>John Hannah | .80 | .40 |
| 206 | All Pro Tackles<br>Dan Dierdorf<br>Winston Hill | .50 | .25 |
| 207 | All Pro Tight Ends<br>Charley Young<br>Riley Odoms | .40 | .20 |
| 208 | All Pro Quarterbacks<br>Fran Tarkenton | 3.00 | 1.50 |

|  | | | |
|---|---|---|---|
| | Ken Stabler | | |
| 209 | All Pro Backs | 2.50 | 1.25 |
| | Lawrence McCutcheon | | |
| | O.J. Simpson | | |
| 210 | All Pro Backs | .60 | .30 |
| | Terry Metcalf | | |
| | Otis Armstrong | | |
| 211 | All Pro Receivers | .50 | .25 |
| | Mel Gray | | |
| | Isaac Curtis | | |
| 212 | All Pro Kickers | .35 | .18 |
| | Chester Marcol | | |
| | Roy Gerela | | |
| 213 | All Pro Ends | .50 | .25 |
| | Jack Youngblood | | |
| | Elvin Bethea | | |
| 214 | All Pro Tackles | .60 | .30 |
| | Alan Page | | |
| | Otis Sistrunk | | |
| 215 | All Pro Tackles | .75 | .35 |
| | Merlin Olsen | | |
| | Mike Reid | | |
| 216 | All Pro Ends | .50 | .25 |
| | Carl Eller | | |
| | Lyle Alzado | | |
| 217 | All Pro Linebackers | .75 | .35 |
| | Ted Hendricks | | |
| | Phil Villapiano | | |
| 218 | All Pro Linebackers | .80 | .40 |
| | Lee Roy Jordan | | |
| | Willie Lanier | | |
| 219 | All Pro Linebackers | .50 | .25 |
| | Isiah Robertson | | |
| | Andy Russell | | |
| 220 | All Pro Cornerbacks | .35 | .18 |
| | Nate Wright | | |
| | Emmitt Thomas | | |
| 221 | All Pro Cornerbacks | .35 | .18 |
| | Willie Buchanon | | |
| | Lemar Parrish | | |
| 222 | All Pro Safeties | .75 | .35 |
| | Ken Houston | | |
| | Dick Anderson | | |
| 223 | All Pro Safeties | .60 | .30 |
| | Cliff Harris | | |
| | Jack Tatum | | |
| 224 | All Pro Punters | .50 | .25 |
| | Tom Wittum | | |
| | Ray Guy | | |
| 225 | All Pro Returners | .50 | .25 |
| | Terry Metcalf | | |
| | Greg Pruitt | | |
| 226 | Ted Kwalick | .35 | .18 |
| 227 | Spider Lockhart | .25 | .12 |
| 228 | Mike Livingston | .25 | .12 |
| 229 | Larry Cole | .25 | .12 |
| 230 | Gary Garrison | .25 | .12 |
| 231 | Larry Brooks | .25 | .12 |
| 232 | Bobby Howfield | .25 | .12 |
| 233 | Fred Carr | .25 | .12 |
| 234 | Norm Evans | .25 | .12 |
| 235 | Dwight White | .40 | .20 |
| 236 | Conrad Dobler | .60 | .30 |
| 237 | Garry Lyle | .25 | .12 |
| 238 | Darryl Stingley | .60 | .30 |
| 239 | Tom Graham | .25 | .12 |
| 240 | Chuck Foreman | 1.25 | .60 |
| 241 | Ken Riley | .35 | .18 |
| 242 | Don Morrison | .25 | .12 |
| 243 | Lynn Dickey | .75 | .35 |
| 244 | Don Cockroft | .35 | .18 |
| 245 | Claude Humphrey | .35 | .18 |
| 246 | John Skorupan | .25 | .12 |
| 247 | Raymond Chester | .60 | .30 |
| 248 | Cas Banaszek | .25 | .12 |
| 249 | Art Malone | .25 | .12 |
| 250 | Ed Flanagan | .25 | .12 |
| 251 | Checklist 133-264 | 2.25 | .25 |
| 252 | Nemiah Wilson | .25 | .12 |
| 253 | Ron Jessie | .40 | .20 |
| 254 | Jim Lynch | .25 | .12 |
| 255 | Bob Tucker | .25 | .12 |
| 256 | Terry Owens | .25 | .12 |
| 257 | John Fitzgerald | .25 | .12 |
| 258 | Jack Snow | .35 | .18 |
| 259 | Garry Puetz | .25 | .12 |
| 260 | Mike Phipps | .50 | .25 |
| 261 | Al Matthews | .25 | .12 |
| 262 | Bob Kuechenberg | .40 | .20 |
| 263 | Ron Yankowski | .25 | .12 |
| 264 | Ron Shanklin | .25 | .12 |
| 265 | Bobby Douglass | .40 | .20 |
| 266 | Josh Ashton | .25 | .12 |
| 267 | Bill Van Heusen | .25 | .12 |
| 268 | Jeff Siemon | .50 | .25 |
| 269 | Bob Newland | .25 | .12 |
| 270 | Gale Gillingham | .25 | .12 |
| 271 | Zeke Moore | .25 | .12 |
| 272 | Mike Tilleman | .25 | .12 |
| 273 | John Leypoldt | .25 | .12 |
| 274 | Ken Mendenhall | .25 | .12 |
| 275 | Norm Snead | 1.00 | .50 |
| 276 | Bill Bradley | .30 | .15 |
| 277 | Jerry Smith | .25 | .12 |
| 278 | Clarence Davis | .25 | .12 |
| 279 | Jim Yarbrough | .25 | .12 |
| 280 | Lemar Parrish | .30 | .15 |
| 281 | Bobby Bell | 1.75 | .85 |
| 282 | Lynn Swan (R) | 30.00 | 15.00 |
| 283 | John Hicks (R) | .35 | .18 |
| 284 | Coy Bacon | .25 | .12 |
| 285 | Lee Roy Jordan | .90 | .45 |
| 286 | Willie Buchanon | .35 | .18 |
| 287 | Al Woodall | .25 | .12 |

| 288 | Reggie Rucker | .40 | .20 |
| --- | --- | --- | --- |
| 289 | John Schmitt | .25 | .12 |
| 290 | Carl Eller | 1.25 | .60 |
| 291 | Jake Scott | .35 | .18 |
| 292 | Donny Anderson | .40 | .20 |
| 293 | Charley Wade | .25 | .12 |
| 294 | John Tanner | .25 | .12 |
| 295 | Charlie Johnson | .60 | .30 |
| 296 | Tom Blanchard | .25 | .12 |
| 297 | Curley Culp | .50 | .25 |
| 298 | Jeff Van Note (R) | 1.25 | .60 |
| 299 | Bob James | .25 | .12 |
| 300 | Franco Harris | 12.00 | 6.00 |
| 301 | Tim Berra (R) | .40 | .20 |
| 302 | Bruce Gossett | .25 | .12 |
| 303 | Verlon Biggs | .25 | .12 |
| 304 | Bob Kowalkowski | .25 | .12 |
| 305 | Marv Hubbard | .60 | .30 |
| 306 | Ken Avery | .25 | .12 |
| 307 | Mike Adamle | .50 | .25 |
| 308 | Don Herrmann | .25 | .12 |
| 309 | Chris Fletcher | .25 | .12 |
| 310 | Roman Gabriel | 1.50 | .75 |
| 311 | Billy Joe DuPree | .80 | .40 |
| 312 | Fred Dryer | 2.00 | 1.00 |
| 313 | John Riggins | 5.00 | 2.50 |
| 314 | Bob McKay | .25 | .12 |
| 315 | Ted Hendricks | 1.75 | .85 |
| 316 | Bobby Bryant | .25 | .12 |
| 317 | Don Nottingham | .25 | .12 |
| 318 | John Hannah | 3.00 | 1.50 |
| 319 | Rich Coady | .25 | .12 |
| 320 | Phil Villapiano | .35 | .18 |
| 321 | Jim Plunkett | 1.75 | .85 |
| 322 | Lyle Alzado | 1.25 | .60 |
| 323 | Ernie Jackson | .25 | .12 |
| 324 | Billy Parks | .25 | .12 |
| 325 | Willie Lanier | 1.75 | .85 |
| 326 | John James | .25 | .12 |
| 327 | Joe Ferguson | 1.00 | .50 |
| 328 | Ernie Holmes (R) | 1.25 | .60 |
| 329 | Bruce Laird | .25 | .12 |
| 330 | Chester Marcol | .25 | .12 |
| 331 | Dave Wilcox | .25 | .12 |
| 332 | Pat Fischer | .30 | .15 |
| 333 | Steve Owens | .35 | .18 |
| 334 | Royce Berry | .25 | .12 |
| 335 | Russ Washington | .25 | .12 |
| 336 | Walker Gillette | .25 | .12 |
| 337 | Mark Nordquist | .25 | .12 |
| 338 | James Harris (R) | 1.25 | .60 |
| 339 | Warren Koegel | .25 | .12 |
| 340 | Emmitt Thomas | .35 | .18 |
| 341 | Walt Garrison | .40 | .20 |
| 342 | Thom Darden | .25 | .12 |
| 343 | Mike Eischeid | .25 | .12 |
| 344 | Ernie McMillan | .25 | .12 |
| 345 | Nick Buoniconti | 1.25 | .60 |
| 346 | George Farmer | .25 | .12 |
| 347 | Sam Adams | .25 | .12 |
| 348 | Larry Cipa | .25 | .12 |
| 349 | Bob Moore | .25 | .12 |
| 350 | Otis Armstrong (R) | 4.50 | 2.25 |
| 351 | George Blanda (RB) | 1.50 | .75 |
| 352 | Fred Cox (RB) | .25 | .12 |
| 353 | Tom Dempsey (RB) | .35 | .18 |
| 354 | Ken Houston (RB) | .75 | .35 |
| 355 | O.J. Simpson (RB) | 4.00 | 2.00 |
| 356 | Ron Smith (RB) | .35 | .18 |
| 357 | Bob Atkins | .25 | .12 |
| 358 | Pat Sullivan | .75 | .35 |
| 359 | Joe DeLamielleure | .50 | .25 |
| 360 | Lawrence McCutcheon | 3.00 | 1.50 |
| 361 | David Lee | .25 | .12 |
| 362 | Mike McCoy | .25 | .12 |
| 363 | Skip Vanderbundt | .25 | .12 |
| 364 | Mark Moseley | .50 | .25 |
| 365 | Lem Barney | 1.25 | .60 |
| 366 | Doug Dresslet | .25 | .12 |
| 367 | Dan Fouts (R) | 75.00 | 35.00 |
| 368 | Bob Hyland | .25 | .12 |
| 369 | John Outlaw | .25 | .12 |
| 370 | Roy Gerela | .25 | .12 |
| 371 | Isiah Robertson | .30 | .15 |
| 372 | Jerome Barkum | .35 | .18 |
| 373 | Ed Podolak | .35 | .18 |
| 374 | Milt Morin | .25 | .12 |
| 375 | John Niland | .25 | .12 |
| 376 | Checklist 265-396 | 2.25 | .25 |
| 377 | Ken Iman | .25 | .12 |
| 378 | Manny Fernandez | .25 | .12 |
| 379 | Dave Gallagher | .25 | .12 |
| 380 | Ken Stabler | 4.50 | 2.25 |
| 381 | Mack Herron (R) | .40 | .20 |
| 382 | Bill McClard | .25 | .12 |
| 383 | Ray May | .25 | .12 |
| 384 | Don Hansen | .25 | .12 |
| 385 | Elvin Bethea | .40 | .20 |
| 386 | Joe Scibelli | .25 | .12 |
| 387 | Neal Craig | .25 | .12 |
| 388 | Marty Domres | .30 | .15 |
| 389 | Ken Ellis | .25 | .12 |
| 390 | Charley Young | .35 | .18 |
| 391 | Tommy Hart | .25 | .12 |
| 392 | Moses Denson | .25 | .12 |
| 393 | Larry Walton | .25 | .12 |
| 394 | Dave Green | .25 | .12 |
| 395 | Ron Johnson | .40 | .20 |
| 396 | Ed Bradley | .25 | .12 |
| 397 | J.T. Thomas | .25 | .12 |
| 398 | Jim Bailey | .25 | .12 |
| 399 | Barry Pearson | .25 | .12 |
| 400 | Fran Tarkenton | 9.50 | 4.75 |
| 401 | Jack Rudnay | .25 | .12 |

| | | | |
|---|---|---|---|
| 402 Rayfield Wright | .25 | .12 |
| 403 Roger Wehrli | .25 | .12 |
| 404 Vern Den Herder | .25 | .12 |
| 405 Fred Biletnikoff | 2.50 | 1.25 |
| 406 Ken Grandberry | .25 | .12 |
| 407 Bob Adams | .25 | .12 |
| 408 Jim Merlo | .25 | .12 |
| 409 John Pitts | .25 | .12 |
| 410 Dave Osborn | .35 | .18 |
| 411 Dennis Havig | .25 | .12 |
| 412 Bob Johnson | .25 | .12 |
| 413 Ken Burrough | .40 | .20 |
| 414 Jim Cheyunski | .25 | .12 |
| 415 MacArthur Lane | .40 | .20 |
| 416 Joe Theismann (R) | 22.00 | 11.00 |
| 417 Mike Boryla (R) | .35 | .18 |
| 418 Bruce Taylor | .25 | .12 |
| 419 Chris Hanburger | .40 | .20 |
| 420 Tom Mack | .60 | .30 |
| 421 Errol Mann | .25 | .12 |
| 422 Jack Gregory | .25 | .12 |
| 423 Harrison Davis | .25 | .12 |
| 424 Bugess Owens | .25 | .12 |
| 425 Joe Greene | 3.00 | 1.50 |
| 426 Morris Stroud | .25 | .12 |
| 427 John DeMarie | .25 | .12 |
| 428 Mel Renfro | .75 | .35 |
| 429 Cid Edwards | .25 | .12 |
| 430 Mike Reid | .80 | .40 |
| 431 Jack Mildren (R) | .40 | .20 |
| 432 Jerry Simmons | .25 | .12 |
| 433 Ron Yary | .40 | .20 |
| 434 Howard Stevens | .25 | .12 |
| 435 Ray Guy | 1.50 | .75 |
| 436 Tommy Nobis | .80 | .40 |
| 437 Solomon Freelon | .25 | .12 |
| 438 J.D. Hill | .30 | .15 |
| 439 Toni Linhart | .25 | .12 |
| 440 Dick Anderson | .35 | .18 |
| 441 Guy Morriss | .25 | .12 |
| 442 Bob Hoskins | .25 | .12 |
| 443 John Hadl | 1.25 | .60 |
| 444 Roy Jefferson | .40 | .20 |
| 445 Charlie Sanders | .40 | .20 |
| 446 Pat Curran | .25 | .12 |
| 447 David Knight | .25 | .12 |
| 448 Bob Brown | .25 | .12 |
| 449 Pete Gogolak | .30 | .15 |
| 450 Terry Metcalf | .75 | .35 |
| 451 Bill Bergey | .60 | .30 |
| 452 Dan Abramowicz (HL) | .35 | .18 |
| 453 Otis Armstrong (HL) | .75 | .35 |
| 454 Cliff Branch (HL) | 1.00 | .50 |
| 455 John James (HL) | .35 | .18 |
| 456 Lydell Mitchell (HL) | .40 | .20 |
| 457 Lemar Parrish (HL) | .35 | .18 |
| 458 Ken Stabler (HL) | 1.50 | .75 |
| 459 Lynn Swann (HL) | 4.00 | 2.00 |
| 460 Emmitt Thomas (HL) | .35 | .18 |
| 461 Terry Bradshaw | 10.00 | 5.00 |
| 462 Jerrel Wilson | .25 | .12 |
| 463 Walter Johnson | .25 | .12 |
| 464 Golden Richards (R) | .50 | .25 |
| 465 Tommy Casanova | .30 | .15 |
| 466 Randy Jackson | .25 | .12 |
| 467 Ron Bolton | .25 | .12 |
| 468 Joe Owens | .25 | .12 |
| 469 Wally Hilgenberg | .25 | .12 |
| 470 Riley Odoms | .40 | .20 |
| 471 Otis Sistrunk | .35 | .18 |
| 472 Eddie Ray | .25 | .12 |
| 473 Reggie McKenzie | .50 | .25 |
| 474 Elbert Drungo | .25 | .12 |
| 475 Mercury Morris | .90 | .45 |
| 476 Dan Dickel | .25 | .12 |
| 477 Merritt Kersey | .25 | .12 |
| 478 Mike Holmes | .25 | .12 |
| 479 Clarence Williams | .25 | .12 |
| 480 Bill Kilmer | 1.50 | .75 |
| 481 Altie Taylor | .25 | .12 |
| 482 Dave Elmendorf | .25 | .12 |
| 483 Bob Rowe | .25 | .12 |
| 484 Pete Athas | .25 | .12 |
| 485 Winston Hill | .25 | .12 |
| 486 Bo Matthews | .25 | .12 |
| 487 Earl Thomas | .25 | .12 |
| 488 Jan Stenerud | 1.00 | .50 |
| 489 Steve Holden | .25 | .12 |
| 490 Cliff Harris (R) | 2.50 | 1.25 |
| 491 Boobie Clark (R) | .50 | .25 |
| 492 Joe Taylor | .25 | .12 |
| 493 Tom Neville | .25 | .12 |
| 494 Wayne Colman | .25 | .12 |
| 495 Jim Mitchell | .25 | .12 |
| 496 Paul Krause | .40 | .20 |
| 497 Jim Otto | 1.75 | .85 |
| 498 John Rowser | .25 | .12 |
| 499 Larry Little | 1.50 | .75 |
| 500 O.J. Simpson | 14.00 | 7.00 |
| 501 John Dutton (R) | 1.00 | .50 |
| 502 Pat Hughes | .25 | .12 |
| 503 Malcolm Snider | .25 | .12 |
| 504 Fred Willis | .25 | .12 |
| 505 Harold Jackson | 1.00 | .50 |
| 506 Mike Bragg | .25 | .12 |
| 507 Jerry Sherk | .25 | .12 |
| 508 Mirro Roder | .25 | .12 |
| 509 Tom Sullivan | .25 | .12 |
| 510 Jim Hart | 1.25 | .60 |
| 511 Cedric Hardman | .25 | .12 |
| 512 Blaine Nye | .25 | .12 |
| 513 Elmo Wright | .25 | .12 |
| 514 Herb Orvis | .25 | .12 |
| 515 Richard Caster | .40 | .20 |

| | | NR/MT | EX |
|---|---|---|---|
| 516 | Doug Kotar (R) | .40 | .20 |
| 517 | Checklist 397-528 | 2.25 | .25 |
| 518 | Jesse Freitas | .25 | .12 |
| 519 | Ken Houston | 1.75 | .85 |
| 520 | Alan Page | 2.00 | 1.00 |
| 521 | Tim Foley | .40 | .20 |
| 522 | Bill Olds | .25 | .12 |
| 523 | Bobby Maples | .25 | .12 |
| 524 | Cliff Branch (R) | 6.50 | 3.25 |
| 525 | Merlin Olsen | 2.50 | 1.25 |
| 526 | AFC Champs | 2.00 | 1.00 |
| 527 | NFC Champs | 1.00 | .50 |
| 528 | Super Bowl IX | 3.50 | 1.75 |

# 1976 Topps

The cards in this 528-card set feature color photos on the fronts framed by a thin inside border around the picture and a wider white outside border. The player's name and position appear in the lower corner while the team name is located inside a football design in the opposite corner. The flip side contains personal data, highlights and a cartoon with a trivia question. Subsets include Record Breakers (RB), League Leaders (201-206) and Playoffs (331-333). The set also includes 26 Team Checklist cards. All cards measure 2-1/2" by 3-1/2".

| | | NR/MT | EX |
|---|---|---|---|
| **Complete Set (528)** | | 410.00 | 200.00 |
| **Commons** | | .25 | .12 |
| | | | |
| 1 | George Blanda (RB) | 6.50 | 3.00 |

| | | NR/MT | EX |
|---|---|---|---|
| 2 | Neal Colzie (RB) | .30 | .15 |
| 3 | Chuck Foreman (RB) | .40 | .20 |
| 4 | Jim Marshall (RB) | .40 | .20 |
| 5 | Terry Metcalf (RB) | .40 | .20 |
| 6 | O.J. Simpson (RB) | 3.50 | 1.75 |
| 7 | Fran Tarkenton (RB) | 3.00 | 1.50 |
| 8 | Charley Taylor (RB) | .75 | .35 |
| 9 | Ernie Holmes | .40 | .20 |
| 10 | Ken Anderson | 2.00 | 1.00 |
| 11 | Bobby Bryant | .25 | .12 |
| 12 | Jerry Smith | .25 | .12 |
| 13 | David Lee | .25 | .12 |
| 14 | Robert Newhouse (R) | 1.50 | .75 |
| 15 | Vern Den Herder | .25 | .12 |
| 16 | John Hannah | 2.00 | 1.00 |
| 17 | J.D. Hill | .25 | .12 |
| 18 | James Harris | .50 | .25 |
| 19 | Willie Buchanon | .30 | .15 |
| 20 | Charley Young | .30 | .15 |
| 21 | Jim Yarbrough | .25 | .12 |
| 22 | Ronnie Coleman | .25 | .12 |
| 23 | Don Cockroft | .30 | .15 |
| 24 | Willie Lanier | 1.25 | .60 |
| 25 | Fred Biletnikoff | 2.50 | 1.25 |
| 26 | Ron Yankowski | .25 | .12 |
| 27 | Spider Lockhart | .25 | .12 |
| 28 | Bob Johnson | .25 | .12 |
| 29 | J.T. Thomas | .25 | .12 |
| 30 | Ron Yary | .35 | .18 |
| 31 | Brad Dusek (R) | .35 | .18 |
| 32 | Raymond Chester | .40 | .20 |
| 33 | Larry Little | 1.25 | .60 |
| 34 | Pat Leahy (R) | 1.50 | .75 |
| 35 | Steve Bartkowski (R) | 3.00 | 1.50 |
| 36 | Tom Myers | .25 | .12 |
| 37 | Bill Van Heusen | .25 | .12 |
| 38 | Russ Washington | .25 | .12 |
| 39 | Tom Sullivan | .25 | .12 |
| 40 | Curley Culp | .30 | .15 |
| 41 | Johnnie Gray | .25 | .12 |
| 42 | Bob Klein | .25 | .12 |
| 43 | Lem Barney | 1.25 | .60 |
| 44 | Harvey Martin (R) | 3.00 | 1.50 |
| 45 | Reggie Rucker | .30 | .15 |
| 46 | Neil Clabo | .25 | .12 |
| 47 | Ray Hamilton (R) | .35 | .18 |
| 48 | Joe Ferguson | .80 | .40 |
| 49 | Ed Podolak | .30 | .15 |
| 50 | Ray Guy | 1.00 | .50 |
| 51 | Glen Edwards | .25 | .12 |
| 52 | Jim LeClair | .30 | .15 |
| 53 | Mike Barnes | .25 | .12 |
| 54 | Nat Moore (R) | 2.00 | 1.00 |
| 55 | Bill Kilmer | 1.25 | .60 |
| 56 | Larry Stallings | .25 | .12 |
| 57 | Jack Gregory | .25 | .12 |
| 58 | Steve Mike-Meyer | .25 | .12 |

| | | | |
|---|---|---|---|
| 59 | Virgil Livers | .25 | .12 |
| 60 | Jerry Sherk | .30 | .15 |
| 61 | Guy Morriss | .25 | .12 |
| 62 | Barty Smith | .25 | .12 |
| 63 | Jerome Barkum | .25 | .12 |
| 64 | Ira Gordon | .25 | .12 |
| 65 | Paul Krause | .40 | .20 |
| 66 | John McMakin | .25 | .12 |
| 67 | Checklist 1-132 | 2.00 | .25 |
| 68 | Charlie Johnson | .60 | .30 |
| 69 | Tommy Nobis | .60 | .30 |
| 70 | Lydell Mitchell | .50 | .25 |
| 71 | Vern Holland | .25 | .12 |
| 72 | Tim Foley | .30 | .15 |
| 73 | Golden Richards | .25 | .12 |
| 74 | Bryant Salter | .25 | .12 |
| 75 | Terry Bradshaw | 7.50 | 3.75 |
| 76 | Ted Hendricks | 1.50 | .75 |
| 77 | Rich Saul (R) | .40 | .20 |
| 78 | John Smith | .25 | .12 |
| 79 | Altie Taylor | .25 | .12 |
| 80 | Cedric Hardman | .30 | .15 |
| 81 | Ken Payne | .25 | .12 |
| 82 | Zeke Moore | .25 | .12 |
| 83 | Alvin Maxson | .25 | .12 |
| 84 | Wally Hilgenberg | .25 | .12 |
| 85 | John Niland | .25 | .12 |
| 86 | Mike Sensibaugh | .25 | .12 |
| 87 | Ron Johnson | .35 | .18 |
| 88 | Winston Hill | .25 | .12 |
| 89 | Charlie Joiner | 2.00 | 1.00 |
| 90 | Roger Wehrli | .25 | .12 |
| 91 | Mike Bragg | .25 | .12 |
| 92 | Dan Dickel | .25 | .12 |
| 93 | Earl Morrall | 1.25 | .60 |
| 94 | Pat Toomay | .25 | .12 |
| 95 | Gary Garrison | .25 | .12 |
| 96 | Ken Geddes | .25 | .12 |
| 97 | Mike Current | .25 | .12 |
| 98 | Bob Avelini (R) | .50 | .25 |
| 99 | Dave Pureifory (R) | .35 | .18 |
| 100 | Franco Harris | 6.50 | 3.25 |
| 101 | Randy Logan | .25 | .12 |
| 102 | John Fitzgerald | .25 | .12 |
| 103 | Gregg Bingham (R) | .40 | .20 |
| 104 | Jim Plunkett | 1.25 | .60 |
| 105 | Carl Eller | 1.25 | .60 |
| 106 | Larry Walton | .25 | .12 |
| 107 | Clarence Scott | .25 | .12 |
| 108 | Skip Vanderbundt | .25 | .12 |
| 109 | Boobie Clark | .35 | .18 |
| 110 | Tom Mack | .60 | .30 |
| 111 | Bruce Laird | .25 | .12 |
| 112 | Dave Dalby (R) | .35 | .18 |
| 113 | John Leypoldt | .25 | .12 |
| 114 | Barry Pearson | .25 | .12 |
| 115 | Larry Brown | .50 | .25 |
| 116 | Jackie Smith | .60 | .30 |
| 117 | Pat Hughes | .25 | .12 |
| 118 | Al Woodall | .25 | .12 |
| 119 | John Zook | .25 | .12 |
| 120 | Jake Scott | .30 | .15 |
| 121 | Rich Glover | .25 | .12 |
| 122 | Ernie Jackson | .25 | .12 |
| 123 | Otis Armstrong | .75 | .35 |
| 124 | Bob Grim | .25 | .12 |
| 125 | Jeff Siemon | .25 | .12 |
| 126 | Harold Hart | .25 | .12 |
| 127 | John DeMarie | .25 | .12 |
| 128 | Dan Fouts | 22.00 | 11.00 |
| 129 | Jim Kearney | .25 | .12 |
| 130 | John Dutton | .35 | .18 |
| 131 | Calvin Hill | .50 | .25 |
| 132 | Toni Fritsch | .25 | .12 |
| 133 | Ron Jessie | .30 | .15 |
| 134 | Don Nottington | .35 | .18 |
| 135 | Lemar Parrish | .30 | .15 |
| 136 | Russ Francis (R) | 2.50 | 1.25 |
| 137 | Joe Reed | .25 | .12 |
| 138 | C.L. Whittington | .25 | .12 |
| 139 | Otis Sistrunk | .30 | .15 |
| 140 | Lynn Swann | 6.50 | 3.25 |
| 141 | Jim Carter | .25 | .12 |
| 142 | Mike Montler | .25 | .12 |
| 143 | Walter Johnson | .25 | .12 |
| 144 | Doug Kotar | .25 | .12 |
| 145 | Roman Gabriel | 1.25 | .60 |
| 146 | Billy Newsome | .25 | .12 |
| 147 | Ed Bradley | .25 | .12 |
| 148 | Walter Payton (R) | 200.00 | 100.00 |
| 149 | Johnny Fuller | .25 | .12 |
| 150 | Alan Page | 1.50 | .75 |
| 151 | Frank Grant | .25 | .12 |
| 152 | Dave Green | .25 | .12 |
| 153 | Nelson Munsey | .25 | .12 |
| 154 | Jim Mandich | .25 | .12 |
| 155 | Lawrence McCutcheon | .75 | .35 |
| 156 | Steve Ramsey | .25 | .12 |
| 157 | Ed Flanagan | .25 | .12 |
| 158 | Randy White (R) | 24.00 | 12.00 |
| 159 | Gerry Mullins | .25 | .12 |
| 160 | Jan Stenerud | 1.00 | .50 |
| 161 | Steve Odom | .25 | .12 |
| 162 | Roger Finnie | .25 | .12 |
| 163 | Norm Snead | .80 | .40 |
| 164 | Jeff Van Note | .30 | .15 |
| 165 | Bill Bergey | .50 | .25 |
| 166 | Allen Carter | .25 | .12 |
| 167 | Steve Holden | .25 | .12 |
| 168 | Sherman White | .25 | .12 |
| 169 | Bob Berry | .25 | .12 |
| 170 | Ken Houston | 1.25 | .60 |
| 171 | Bill Olds | .25 | .12 |
| 172 | Larry Seiple | .25 | .12 |

| 173 | Cliff Branch | 1.50 | .75 |
|---|---|---|---|
| 174 | Reggie McKenzie | .35 | .18 |
| 175 | Dan Pastorini | .75 | .35 |
| 176 | Paul Naumoff | .25 | .12 |
| 177 | Checklist 133-264 | 2.00 | .25 |
| 178 | Durwood Keeton | .25 | .12 |
| 179 | Earl Thomas | .25 | .12 |
| 180 | L.C. Greenwood | .80 | .40 |
| 181 | John Outlaw | .25 | .12 |
| 182 | Frank Nunley | .25 | .12 |
| 183 | Dave Jennings (R) | .60 | .30 |
| 184 | MacArthur Lane | .40 | .20 |
| 185 | Chester Marcol | .25 | .12 |
| 186 | J.J. Jones | .25 | .12 |
| 187 | Tom DeLeone | .25 | .12 |
| 188 | Steve Zabel | .25 | .12 |
| 189 | Ken Johnson | .25 | .12 |
| 190 | Rayfield Wright | .25 | .12 |
| 191 | Brent McClanahan | .25 | .12 |
| 192 | Pat Fischer | .30 | .18 |
| 193 | Roger Carr (R) | .60 | .30 |
| 194 | Manny Fernandez | .25 | .12 |
| 195 | Roy Gerela | .25 | .12 |
| 196 | Dave Elmendorf | .25 | .12 |
| 197 | Bob Kowalkowski | .25 | .12 |
| 198 | Phil Villapiano | .30 | .15 |
| 199 | Will Wynn | .25 | .12 |
| 200 | Terry Metcalf | .60 | .30 |
| 201 | Passing Leaders | 2.00 | 1.00 |
| | Ken Anderson | | |
| | Fran Tarkenton | | |
| 202 | Receiving Leaders | .50 | .25 |
| | Reggie Rucker | | |
| | Lydell Mitchell | | |
| | Chuck Foreman | | |
| 203 | Rushing Leaders | 1.75 | .85 |
| | O.J. Simpson | | |
| | Jim Otis | | |
| 204 | Scoring Leaders | 2.00 | 1.00 |
| | O.J. Simpson | | |
| | Chuck Foreman | | |
| 205 | Interception Leaders | .60 | .30 |
| | Mel Blount | | |
| | Paul Krause | | |
| 206 | Punting Leaders | .40 | .20 |
| | Ray Guy | | |
| | Herman Weaver | | |
| 207 | Ken Ellis | .25 | .12 |
| 208 | Ron Saul | .25 | .12 |
| 209 | Toni Linhart | .25 | .12 |
| 210 | Jim Langer | 1.25 | .60 |
| 211 | Jeff Wright | .25 | .12 |
| 212 | Moses Denson | .25 | .12 |
| 213 | Earl Edwards | .25 | .12 |
| 214 | Walker Gillette | .25 | .12 |
| 215 | Bob Trumpy | .60 | .30 |
| 216 | Emmitt Thomas | .25 | .12 |

| 217 | Lyle Alzado | 1.25 | .60 |
|---|---|---|---|
| 218 | Carl Garrett | .25 | .12 |
| 219 | Van Green | .25 | .12 |
| 220 | Jack Lambert (R) | 24.00 | 12.00 |
| 221 | Spike Jones | .25 | .12 |
| 222 | John Hadl | 1.00 | .50 |
| 223 | Billy Johnson (R) | 2.50 | 1.25 |
| 224 | Tony McGee | .25 | .12 |
| 225 | Preston Pearson | .60 | .30 |
| 226 | Isiah Robertson | .25 | .12 |
| 227 | Errol Mann | .25 | .12 |
| 228 | Paul Seal | .25 | .12 |
| 229 | Roland Harper (R) | .60 | .30 |
| 230 | Ed White (R) | .75 | .35 |
| 231 | Joe Theismann | 6.50 | 3.25 |
| 232 | Jim Cheyunski | .25 | .12 |
| 233 | Bill Stanfill | .25 | .12 |
| 234 | Marv Hubbard | .40 | .20 |
| 235 | Tommy Casanova | .30 | .15 |
| 236 | Bob Hyland | .25 | .12 |
| 237 | Jesse Freitas | .25 | .12 |
| 238 | Norm Thompson | .25 | .12 |
| 239 | Charlie Smith | .25 | .12 |
| 240 | John James | .25 | .12 |
| 241 | Alden Roche | .25 | .12 |
| 242 | Gordon Jolley | .25 | .12 |
| 243 | Larry Ely | .25 | .12 |
| 244 | Richard Caster | .30 | .15 |
| 245 | Joe Greene | 3.00 | 1.50 |
| 246 | Larry Schreiber | .25 | .12 |
| 247 | Terry Schmidt | .25 | .12 |
| 248 | Jerrel Wilsosn | .25 | .12 |
| 249 | Marty Domres | .25 | .12 |
| 250 | Isaac Curtis | .50 | .25 |
| 251 | Harold McLinton | .25 | .12 |
| 252 | Fred Dryer | 2.00 | 1.00 |
| 253 | Bill Lenkaitis | .25 | .12 |
| 254 | Don Hardeman | .25 | .12 |
| 255 | Bob Griese | 3.50 | 1.75 |
| 256 | Oscar Roan (R) | .30 | .15 |
| 257 | Randy Gradishar (R) | 4.00 | 2.00 |
| 258 | Bob Thomas (R) | .35 | .18 |
| 259 | Joe Owens | .25 | .12 |
| 260 | Cliff Harris | .75 | .35 |
| 261 | Frank Lewis | .35 | .18 |
| 262 | Mike McCoy | .25 | .12 |
| 263 | Rickey Young (R) | .60 | .30 |
| 264 | Brian Kelley | .25 | .12 |
| 265 | Charlie Sanders | .35 | .18 |
| 266 | Jim Hart | 1.00 | .50 |
| 267 | Greg Gantt | .25 | .12 |
| 268 | John Ward | .25 | .12 |
| 269 | Al Beauchamp | .25 | .12 |
| 270 | Jack Tatum | .50 | .25 |
| 271 | Jim Lash | .25 | .12 |
| 272 | Diron Talbert | .30 | .15 |
| 273 | Checklist 265-396 | 2.00 | .25 |

| | | | |
|---|---|---|---|
| 274 Steve Spurrier | 1.25 | .60 |
| 275 Greg Pruitt | .75 | .35 |
| 276 Jim Mitchell | .25 | .12 |
| 277 Jack Rudnay | .25 | .12 |
| 278 Freddie Solomon (R) | 1.25 | .60 |
| 279 Frank LeMaster | .25 | .12 |
| 280 Wally Chambers | .30 | .15 |
| 281 Mike Collier | .25 | .12 |
| 282 Clarence Williams | .25 | .12 |
| 283 Mitch Hoopes | .25 | .12 |
| 284 Ron Bolton | .25 | .12 |
| 285 Harold Jackson | .80 | .40 |
| 286 Greg Landry | .75 | .35 |
| 287 Tony Greene | .25 | .12 |
| 288 Howard Stevens | .25 | .12 |
| 289 Roy Jefferson | .35 | .18 |
| 290 Jim Bakken | .25 | .12 |
| 291 Doug Sutherland (R) | .35 | .18 |
| 292 Marvin Cobb | .25 | .12 |
| 293 Mack Alston | .25 | .12 |
| 294 Rod McNeil | .25 | .12 |
| 295 Gene Upshaw | 1.25 | .60 |
| 296 Dave Gallagher | .25 | .12 |
| 297 Larry Ball | .25 | .12 |
| 298 Ron Howard | .25 | .12 |
| 299 Don Strock (R) | 1.25 | .60 |
| 300 O.J. Simpson | 10.00 | 5.00 |
| 301 Ray Mansfield | .25 | .12 |
| 302 Larry Marshall | .25 | .12 |
| 303 Dick Himes | .25 | .12 |
| 304 Ray Wersching (R) | .40 | .20 |
| 305 John Riggins | 4.50 | 2.25 |
| 306 Bob Parsons | .25 | .12 |
| 307 Ray Brown | .25 | .12 |
| 308 Len Dawson | 2.50 | 1.25 |
| 309 Andy Maurer | .25 | .12 |
| 310 Jack Youngblood | 1.00 | .50 |
| 311 Essex Johnson | .25 | .12 |
| 312 Stan White | .25 | .12 |
| 313 Drew Pearson | 1.50 | .75 |
| 314 Rockne Freitas | .25 | .12 |
| 315 Mercury Morris | .75 | .35 |
| 316 Willie Alexander | .25 | .12 |
| 317 Paul Warfield | 2.00 | 1.00 |
| 318 Bob Chandler | .25 | .12 |
| 319 Bobby Walden | .25 | .12 |
| 320 Riley Odoms | .35 | .18 |
| 321 Mike Boryla | .25 | .12 |
| 322 Bruce Van Dyke | .25 | .12 |
| 323 Pete Banaszak | .35 | .18 |
| 324 Darryl Stingley | .35 | .18 |
| 325 John Mendenhall | .25 | .12 |
| 326 Dan Dierdorf | 1.25 | .60 |
| 327 Bruce Taylor | .25 | .12 |
| 328 Don McCauley | .30 | .15 |
| 329 John Reaves | .35 | .18 |
| 330 Chris Hanburger | .40 | .20 |
| 331 NFC Champions | 2.50 | 1.25 |
| 332 AFC Champions | 2.00 | 1.00 |
| 333 Super Bowl X | 2.50 | 1.25 |
| 334 Godwin Turk | .25 | .12 |
| 335 Dick Anderson | .25 | .12 |
| 336 Woody Green | .25 | .12 |
| 337 Pat Curran | .25 | .12 |
| 338 Council Rudolph | .25 | .12 |
| 339 Joe Lavender | .25 | .12 |
| 340 John Gilliam | .25 | .12 |
| 341 Steve Furness (R) | .35 | .18 |
| 342 D.D. Lewis | .30 | .15 |
| 343 Duane Carrell | .25 | .12 |
| 344 Jon Morris | .25 | .12 |
| 345 John Brockington | .40 | .20 |
| 346 Mike Phipps | .40 | .20 |
| 347 Lyle Blackwood (R) | .50 | .25 |
| 348 Julius Adams | .25 | .12 |
| 349 Terry Hermeling | .25 | .12 |
| 350 Rolland Lawrence (R) | .30 | .15 |
| 351 Glenn Doughty | .25 | .12 |
| 352 Doug Swift | .25 | .12 |
| 353 Mike Strachan | .25 | .12 |
| 354 Craig Morton | 1.00 | .50 |
| 355 George Blanda | 6.50 | 3.25 |
| 356 Garry Puetz | .25 | .12 |
| 357 Carl Mauck | .25 | .12 |
| 358 Walt Patulski | .25 | .12 |
| 359 Stu Voigt | .25 | .12 |
| 360 Fred Carr | .30 | .15 |
| 361 Po James | .25 | .12 |
| 362 Otis Taylor | .75 | .35 |
| 363 Jeff West | .25 | .12 |
| 364 Gary Huff | .35 | .18 |
| 365 Dwight White | .50 | .25 |
| 366 Dan Ryczek | .25 | .12 |
| 367 Jon Keyworth (R) | .35 | .18 |
| 368 Mel Renfro | .50 | .25 |
| 369 Bruce Coslet (R) | 2.50 | 1.25 |
| 370 Len Hauss | .30 | .15 |
| 371 Rick Volk | .25 | .12 |
| 372 Howard Twilley | .30 | .15 |
| 373 Cullen Bryant (R) | .75 | .35 |
| 374 Bob Babich | .25 | .12 |
| 375 Herman Weaver | .25 | .12 |
| 376 Steve Grogan (R) | 6.00 | 3.00 |
| 377 Bubba Smith | 1.25 | .60 |
| 378 Burgess Owens | .25 | .12 |
| 379 Alvin Matthews | .25 | .12 |
| 380 Art Shell | 1.75 | .85 |
| 381 Larry Brown | .25 | .12 |
| 382 Horst Muhlmann | .25 | .12 |
| 383 Ahmad Rashad | 2.00 | 1.00 |
| 384 Bobby Maples | .25 | .12 |
| 385 Jim Marshall | 1.00 | .50 |
| 386 Joe Dawkins | .25 | .12 |
| 387 Dennis Partee | .25 | .12 |

| | | | |
|---|---|---|---|
| 388 Eddie McMillan | .25 | .12 |
| 389 Randy Johnson | .35 | .18 |
| 390 Bob Kuechenberg | .35 | .18 |
| 391 Rufus Mayes | .25 | .12 |
| 392 Lloyd Mumphord | .25 | .12 |
| 393 Ike Harris | .25 | .12 |
| 394 Dave Hampton | .25 | .12 |
| 395 Roger Staubach | 14.00 | 7.00 |
| 396 Doug Buffone | .25 | .12 |
| 397 Howard Fest | .25 | .12 |
| 398 Wayne Mulligan | .25 | .12 |
| 399 Bill Bradley | .30 | .15 |
| 400 Chuck Foreman | .75 | .35 |
| 401 Jack Snow | .30 | .15 |
| 402 Bob Howard | .25 | .12 |
| 403 John Matuszak | .80 | .40 |
| 404 Bill Munson | .35 | .18 |
| 405 Andy Russell | .30 | .15 |
| 406 Skip Butler | .25 | .12 |
| 407 Hugh McKinnis | .25 | .12 |
| 408 Bob Penchion | .25 | .12 |
| 409 Mike Bass | .25 | .12 |
| 410 George Kunz | .30 | .15 |
| 411 Ron Pritchard | .25 | .12 |
| 412 Barry Smith | .25 | .12 |
| 413 Norm Bulaich | .25 | .12 |
| 414 Marv Bateman | .25 | .12 |
| 415 Ken Stabler | 3.00 | 1.50 |
| 416 Conrad Dobler | .40 | .20 |
| 417 Bob Tucker | .25 | .12 |
| 418 Gene Washington | .30 | .15 |
| 419 Ed Marinaro | .75 | .35 |
| 420 Jack Ham | 3.50 | 1.75 |
| 421 Jim Turner | .25 | .12 |
| 422 Chris Flethcer | .25 | .12 |
| 423 Carl Barzilauskas | .25 | .12 |
| 424 Robert Brazile (R) | 2.50 | 1.25 |
| 425 Harold Carmichael | 1.25 | .60 |
| 426 Ron Jaworski (R) | 3.00 | 1.50 |
| 427 Ed Too Tall Jones (R) | 12.50 | 6.25 |
| 428 Larry McCarren | .25 | .12 |
| 429 Mike Thomas (R) | .40 | .20 |
| 430 Joe DeLamielleure | .30 | .15 |
| 431 Tom Blanchard | .25 | .12 |
| 432 Ron Carpenter | .25 | .12 |
| 433 Levi Johnson | .25 | .12 |
| 434 Sam Cunningham | .50 | .25 |
| 435 Garo Yepremian | .30 | .15 |
| 436 Mike Livingston | .25 | .12 |
| 437 Larry Csonka | 3.00 | 1.50 |
| 438 Doug Dieken | .25 | .12 |
| 439 Bill Lueck | .25 | .12 |
| 440 Tom MacLeod | .25 | .12 |
| 441 Mick Tingelhoff | .30 | .15 |
| 442 Terry Hanratty | .35 | .18 |
| 443 Mike Siani | .25 | .12 |
| 444 Dwight Harrison | .25 | .12 |
| 445 Jim Otis | .40 | .20 |
| 446 Jack Reynolds | .50 | .25 |
| 447 Jean Fugett (R) | .35 | .18 |
| 448 Dave Beverly | .25 | .12 |
| 449 Bernard Jackson (R) | .60 | .30 |
| 450 Charley Taylor | 2.00 | 1.00 |
| 451 Falcons (CL) | 1.25 | .25 |
| 452 Colts (CL) | 1.25 | .25 |
| 453 Bills (CL) | 1.25 | .25 |
| 454 Bears (CL) | 1.25 | .25 |
| 455 Bengals (CL) | 1.25 | .25 |
| 456 Browns (CL) | 1.25 | .25 |
| 457 Cowboys (CL) | 1.25 | .25 |
| 458 Broncos (CL) | 1.25 | .25 |
| 459 Lions (CL) | 1.25 | .25 |
| 460 Packers (CL) | 1.25 | .25 |
| 461 Oilers (CL) | 1.25 | .25 |
| 462 Chiefs (CL) | 1.25 | .25 |
| 463 Rams (CL) | 1.25 | .25 |
| 464 Dolphins (CL) | 1.25 | .25 |
| 465 Vikings (CL) | 1.25 | .25 |
| 466 Patriots (CL) | 1.25 | .25 |
| 467 Saints (CL) | 1.25 | .25 |
| 468 Giants (CL) | 1.25 | .25 |
| 469 Jets (CL) | 1.25 | .25 |
| 470 Raiders (CL) | 1.25 | .25 |
| 471 Eagles (CL) | 1.25 | .25 |
| 472 Steelers (CL) | 1.25 | .25 |
| 473 Cardinals (CL) | 1.25 | .25 |
| 474 Chargers (CL) | 1.25 | .25 |
| 475 49ers (CL) | 1.25 | .25 |
| 476 Seahawks (CL) | 1.25 | .25 |
| 477 Buccaneers (CL) | 1.25 | .25 |
| 478 Redskins (CL) | 1.25 | .25 |
| 479 Fred Cox | .25 | .12 |
| 480 Mel Blount | 4.00 | 2.00 |
| 481 John Bunting | .25 | .12 |
| 482 Ken Mendenhall | .25 | .12 |
| 483 Will Harrell | .25 | .12 |
| 484 Marlin Briscoe | .35 | .18 |
| 485 Archie Manning | 1.00 | .50 |
| 486 Tody Smith | .25 | .12 |
| 487 George Hunt | .25 | .12 |
| 488 Roscoe Word | .25 | .12 |
| 489 Paul Seymour | .25 | .12 |
| 490 Lee Roy Jordan | .80 | .40 |
| 491 Chip Myers | .25 | .12 |
| 492 Norm Evans | .25 | .12 |
| 493 Jim Bertelsen | .25 | .12 |
| 494 Mark Moseley | .35 | .18 |
| 495 George Buehler | .25 | .12 |
| 496 Charlie Hall | .25 | .12 |
| 497 Marvin Upshaw | .25 | .12 |
| 498 Tom Banks (R) | .40 | .20 |
| 499 Randy Vataha | .30 | .15 |
| 500 Fran Tarkenton | 8.50 | 4.25 |
| 501 Mike Wagner | .30 | .15 |

| 502 | Art Malone | .30 | .15 |
|---|---|---|---|
| 503 | Fred Cook (R) | .30 | .15 |
| 504 | Rich McGeorge | .25 | .12 |
| 505 | Ken Burrough | .35 | .18 |
| 506 | Nick Mike-Meyer | .25 | .12 |
| 507 | Checklist 397-528 | 2.00 | .25 |
| 508 | Steve Owens | .35 | .18 |
| 509 | Brad Van Pelt (R) | .80 | .40 |
| 510 | Ken Riley | .35 | .18 |
| 511 | Art Thomas | .25 | .12 |
| 512 | Ed Bell | .25 | .12 |
| 513 | Tom Wittum | .25 | .12 |
| 514 | Jim Braxston | .25 | .12 |
| 515 | Nick Buoniconti | .80 | .40 |
| 516 | Brian Sipe (R) | 3.00 | 1.50 |
| 517 | Jim Lynch | .25 | .12 |
| 518 | Prentice McCray | .25 | .12 |
| 519 | Tom Dempsey | .30 | .15 |
| 520 | Mel Gray | .30 | .15 |
| 521 | Nate Wright | .25 | .12 |
| 522 | Rocky Bleier | 1.50 | .75 |
| 523 | Dennis Johnson | .25 | .12 |
| 524 | Jerry Sisemore | .30 | .15 |
| 525 | Bert Jones | 1.25 | .60 |
| 526 | Perry Smith | .25 | .12 |
| 527 | Blaine Nye | .25 | .12 |
| 528 | Bob Moore | .40 | .15 |

# 1977 Topps

This 528-card set features mostly action photos framed by thin inside border and a larger white border on the outside. The team name appears in a pennant-type design at the top of the card. The player's position is located in a small football within the pennant. His name appears in a box above the photograph. The vertical card backs include personal data and statistics. Key subsets include League Leaders (1-6), Record Breakers (RB) and Playoffs (526-528). The set includes 28 team checklist cards. All cards measure 2-1/2" by 3-1/2".

| | | NR/MT | EX |
|---|---|---|---|
| **Complete Set (528)** | | 270.00 | 140.00 |
| **Commons** | | .12 | .06 |

| 1 | Passing Leaders | 2.00 | .90 |
|---|---|---|---|
| | James Harris | | |
| | Ken Stabler | | |
| 2 | Receiving Leaders | .50 | .25 |
| | Drew Pearson | | |
| | MacArthur Lane | | |
| 3 | Rushing Leaders | 7.50 | 3.75 |
| | Walter Payton | | |
| | O.J. Simpson | | |
| 4 | Scoring Leaders | .20 | .10 |
| | Mark Moseley | | |
| | Toni Linhart | | |
| 5 | Interception Leaders | .20 | .15 |
| | Monte Jackson | | |
| | Ken Riley | | |
| 6 | Punting Leaders | .20 | .15 |
| | John James | | |
| | Marv Bateman | | |
| 7 | Mike Phipps | .35 | .18 |
| 8 | Rick Volk | .12 | .06 |
| 9 | Steve Furness | .12 | .06 |
| 10 | Isaac Curtis | .35 | .18 |
| 11 | Nate Wright | .12 | .06 |
| 12 | Jean Fugett | .12 | .06 |
| 13 | Ken Mendenhall | .12 | .06 |
| 14 | Sam Adams | .12 | .06 |
| 15 | Charlie Waters | .50 | .25 |
| 16 | Bill Stanfill | .12 | .06 |
| 17 | John Holland | .12 | .06 |
| 18 | Pat Haden (R) | 2.00 | 1.00 |
| 19 | Bob Young | .12 | .06 |
| 20 | Wally Chambers | .20 | .10 |
| 21 | Lawrence Gaines | .12 | .06 |
| 22 | Larry McCarren | .12 | .06 |
| 23 | Horst Muhlmann | .12 | .06 |
| 24 | Phil Villapiano | .20 | .12 |
| 25 | Greg Pruitt | .50 | .25 |
| 26 | Ron Howard | .12 | .06 |
| 27 | Craig Morton | .80 | .40 |
| 28 | Rufus Mayes | .12 | .06 |
| 29 | Lee Roy Selmon (R) | 3.50 | 1.75 |
| 30 | Ed White | .20 | .10 |
| 31 | Harold McLinton | .12 | .06 |
| 32 | Glenn Doughty | .12 | .06 |
| 33 | Bob Kuechenberg | .25 | .12 |

| | | | |
|---|---|---|---|
| 34 | Duane Carrell | .12 | .06 |
| 35 | Riley Odoms | .25 | .12 |
| 36 | Bobby Scott | .25 | .12 |
| 37 | Nick Mike-Mayer | .12 | .06 |
| 38 | Bill Lenkaitis | .12 | .06 |
| 39 | Roland Harper | .25 | .12 |
| 40 | Tommy Hart | .15 | .08 |
| 41 | Mike Sensibaugh | .12 | .06 |
| 42 | Rusty Jackson | .12 | .06 |
| 43 | Levi Johnson | .12 | .06 |
| 44 | Mike McCoy | .12 | .06 |
| 45 | Roger Staubach | 10.00 | 5.00 |
| 46 | Fred Cox | .12 | .06 |
| 47 | Bob Babich | .12 | .06 |
| 48 | Reggie McKenzie | .25 | .12 |
| 49 | Dave Jennings | .12 | .06 |
| 50 | Mike Haynes (R) | 4.50 | 2.25 |
| 51 | Larry Brown | .12 | .06 |
| 52 | Marvin Cobb | .12 | .06 |
| 53 | Fred Cook | .12 | .06 |
| 54 | Freddie Solomon | .40 | .20 |
| 55 | John Riggins | 3.00 | 1.50 |
| 56 | John Bunting | .12 | .06 |
| 57 | Ray Wersching | .12 | .06 |
| 58 | Mike Livingston | .12 | .06 |
| 59 | Billy Johnson | .75 | .35 |
| 60 | Mike Wagner | .25 | .12 |
| 61 | Waymond Bryant (R) | .20 | .10 |
| 62 | Jim Otis | .25 | .12 |
| 63 | Ed Galligher | .12 | .06 |
| 64 | Randy Vataha | .25 | .12 |
| 65 | Jim Zorn (R) | 2.50 | 1.25 |
| 66 | Jon Keyworth | .20 | .10 |
| 67 | Checklist 1-132 | 1.25 | .25 |
| 68 | Henry Childs | .12 | .06 |
| 69 | Thom Darden | .12 | .06 |
| 70 | George Kunz | .20 | .10 |
| 71 | Lenvil Elliott | .12 | .06 |
| 72 | Curtis Johnson | .12 | .06 |
| 73 | Doug Van Horn | .12 | .06 |
| 74 | Joe Theismann | 3.00 | 1.50 |
| 75 | Dwight White | .30 | .15 |
| 76 | Scott Laidlaw | .12 | .06 |
| 77 | Monte Johnson (R) | .20 | .10 |
| 78 | Dave Beverly | .12 | .06 |
| 79 | Jim Mitchell | .12 | .06 |
| 80 | Jack Youngblood | .75 | .35 |
| 81 | Mel Gray | .25 | .12 |
| 82 | Dwight Harrison | .12 | .06 |
| 83 | John Hadl | .75 | .35 |
| 84 | Matt Blair (R) | 1.50 | .75 |
| 85 | Charlie Sanders | .20 | .10 |
| 86 | Noah Jackson | .12 | .06 |
| 87 | Ed Marinaro | .60 | .30 |
| 88 | Bob Howard | .12 | .06 |
| 89 | John McDaniel | .12 | .06 |
| 90 | Dan Dierdorf | 1.25 | .60 |
| 91 | Mark Moseley | .25 | .12 |
| 92 | Cleo Miller | .12 | .06 |
| 93 | Andre Tillman | .12 | .06 |
| 94 | Bruce Taylor | .12 | .06 |
| 95 | Bert Jones | .90 | .45 |
| 96 | Anthony Davis (R) | 1.25 | .60 |
| 97 | Don Goode | .12 | .06 |
| 98 | Ray Rhodes (R) | .20 | .10 |
| 99 | Mike Webster (R) | 8.00 | 4.00 |
| 100 | O.J. Simpson | 9.00 | 4.50 |
| 101 | Doug Plank (R) | .75 | .35 |
| 102 | Efren Herrera (R) | .12 | .06 |
| 103 | Charlie Smith | .12 | .06 |
| 104 | Carlos Brown (R) | .15 | .08 |
| 105 | Jim Marshall | .80 | .40 |
| 106 | Paul Naufoff | .12 | .06 |
| 107 | Walter White | .12 | .06 |
| 108 | John Cappelletti (R) | 2.00 | 1.00 |
| 109 | Chip Myers | .12 | .06 |
| 110 | Ken Stabler | 2.50 | 1.25 |
| 111 | Joe Ehrmann | .12 | .06 |
| 112 | Rick Engles | .12 | .06 |
| 113 | Jack Dolbin (R) | .20 | .10 |
| 114 | Ron Bolton | .12 | .06 |
| 115 | Mike Thomas | .15 | .08 |
| 116 | Mike Fuller | .12 | .06 |
| 117 | John Hill | .12 | .06 |
| 118 | Richard Todd (R) | 1.25 | .60 |
| 119 | Duriel Harris (R) | .35 | .18 |
| 120 | John James | .12 | .06 |
| 121 | Lionel Antoine | .12 | .06 |
| 122 | John Skorupan | .12 | .06 |
| 123 | Skip Butler | .12 | .06 |
| 124 | Bob Tucker | .12 | .06 |
| 125 | Paul Krause | .40 | .20 |
| 126 | Dave Hampton | .12 | .06 |
| 127 | Tom Wittum | .12 | .06 |
| 128 | Gary Huff | .25 | .12 |
| 129 | Emmitt Thomas | .12 | .06 |
| 130 | Drew Pearson | 1.25 | .60 |
| 131 | Ron Saul | .12 | .06 |
| 132 | Steve Niehaus | .12 | .06 |
| 133 | Fred Carr | .12 | .06 |
| 134 | Norm Bulaich | .20 | .10 |
| 135 | Bob Trumpy | .40 | .20 |
| 136 | Greg Landry | .60 | .30 |
| 137 | George Buehler | .12 | .06 |
| 138 | Reggie Rucker | .25 | .12 |
| 139 | Julius Adams | .12 | .06 |
| 140 | Jack Ham | 2.00 | 1.00 |
| 141 | Wayne Morris (R) | .20 | .10 |
| 142 | Marv Bateman | .12 | .06 |
| 143 | Bobby Maples | .12 | .06 |
| 144 | Harold Carmichael | 1.25 | .60 |
| 145 | Bob Avellini | .25 | .12 |
| 146 | Harry Carson (R) | 5.50 | 2.75 |
| 147 | Lawrence Pillers | .12 | .06 |

| 148 | Ed Williams | .12 | .06 |
| 149 | Dan Pastorini | .60 | .30 |
| 150 | Ron Yary | .20 | .10 |
| 151 | Joe Lavender | .12 | .06 |
| 152 | Pat McInally (R) | .75 | .35 |
| 153 | Lloyd Mumphord | .12 | .06 |
| 154 | Cullen Bryant | .35 | .18 |
| 155 | Willie Lanier | 1.25 | .60 |
| 156 | Gene Washington | .20 | .10 |
| 157 | Scott Hunter | .25 | .12 |
| 158 | Jim Merlo | .12 | .06 |
| 159 | Randy Grossman | .12 | .06 |
| 160 | Blaine Nye | .12 | .06 |
| 161 | Ike Harris | .12 | .06 |
| 162 | Doug Dieken | .12 | .06 |
| 163 | Guy Morriss | .12 | .06 |
| 164 | Bob Parsons | .12 | .06 |
| 165 | Steve Grogan | 1.50 | .75 |
| 166 | John Brockington | .40 | .20 |
| 167 | Charlie Joiner | 1.50 | .75 |
| 168 | Ron Carpenter | .12 | .06 |
| 169 | Jeff Wright | .12 | .06 |
| 170 | Chris Hanburger | .30 | .15 |
| 171 | Roosevelt Leaks (R) | .35 | .18 |
| 172 | Larry Little | .60 | .30 |
| 173 | John Matuszak | .30 | .15 |
| 174 | Joe Ferguson | .75 | .35 |
| 175 | Brad Van Pelt | .35 | .18 |
| 176 | Dexter Bussey (R) | .40 | .20 |
| 177 | Steve Largent (R) | 70.00 | 35.00 |
| 178 | Dewey Selmon (R) | .30 | .15 |
| 179 | Randy Gradishar | .75 | .35 |
| 180 | Mel Blount | 1.75 | .85 |
| 181 | Dan Neal | .12 | .06 |
| 182 | Rich Szaro | .12 | .06 |
| 183 | Mike Boryla | .15 | .08 |
| 184 | Steve Jones | .12 | .06 |
| 185 | Paul Warfield | 1.75 | .85 |
| 186 | Greg Buttle (R) | .40 | .20 |
| 187 | Rich McGeorge | .12 | .06 |
| 188 | Leon Gray (R) | .40 | .20 |
| 189 | John Shinners | .12 | .06 |
| 190 | Toni Linhart | .12 | .06 |
| 191 | Robert Miller | .12 | .06 |
| 192 | Jake Scott | .25 | .12 |
| 193 | Jon Morris | .12 | .06 |
| 194 | Randy Crowder | .12 | .06 |
| 195 | Lynn Swann | 4.50 | 2.25 |
| 196 | Marsh White (R) | .12 | .06 |
| 197 | Rod Perry (R) | .20 | .10 |
| 198 | Willie Hall | .12 | .06 |
| 199 | Mike Hartenstine | .12 | .06 |
| 200 | Jim Bakken | .20 | .10 |
| 201 | Falcons (CL) | .80 | .15 |
| 202 | Colts (CL) | .80 | .15 |
| 203 | Bills (CL) | .80 | .15 |
| 204 | Bears (CL) | .80 | .15 |
| 205 | Bengals (CL) | .80 | .15 |
| 206 | Browns (CL) | .80 | .15 |
| 207 | Cowboys (CL) | .80 | .15 |
| 208 | Broncos (CL) | .80 | .15 |
| 209 | Lions (CL) | .80 | .15 |
| 210 | Packers (CL) | .80 | .15 |
| 211 | Oilers (CL) | .80 | .15 |
| 212 | Chiefs (CL) | .80 | .15 |
| 213 | Rams (CL) | .80 | .15 |
| 214 | Dolphins (CL) | .80 | .15 |
| 215 | Vikings (CL) | .80 | .15 |
| 216 | Patriots (CL) | .80 | .15 |
| 217 | Saints (CL) | .80 | .15 |
| 218 | Giants (CL) | .80 | .15 |
| 219 | Jets (CL) | .80 | .15 |
| 220 | Raiders (CL) | .80 | .15 |
| 221 | Eagles (CL) | .80 | .15 |
| 222 | Steelers (CL) | .80 | .15 |
| 223 | Cardinals (CL) | .80 | .15 |
| 224 | Chargers (CL) | .80 | .15 |
| 225 | 49ers (CL) | .80 | .15 |
| 226 | Seahawks (CL) | .80 | .15 |
| 227 | Buccaneers (CL) | .80 | .15 |
| 228 | Redskins (CL) | .80 | .15 |
| 229 | Sam Cunningham | .40 | .20 |
| 230 | Alan Page | 1.50 | .75 |
| 231 | Eddie Brown | .12 | .06 |
| 232 | Stan White | .12 | .06 |
| 233 | Vern den Herder | .12 | .06 |
| 234 | Clarence Davis | .12 | .06 |
| 235 | Ken Anderson | 1.75 | .85 |
| 236 | Karl Chandler | .12 | .06 |
| 237 | Will Harrell | .12 | .06 |
| 238 | Clarence Scott | .12 | .06 |
| 239 | Bo Rather (R) | .20 | .10 |
| 240 | Robert Brazile | .35 | .18 |
| 241 | Bob Bell | .12 | .06 |
| 242 | Rolland Lawrence | .12 | .06 |
| 243 | Tom Sullivan | .12 | .06 |
| 244 | Larry Brunson | .12 | .06 |
| 245 | Terry Bradshaw | 5.50 | 2.75 |
| 246 | Rich Saul | .12 | .06 |
| 247 | Cleveland Elam | .12 | .06 |
| 248 | Don Woods | .12 | .06 |
| 249 | Bruce Laird | .12 | .06 |
| 250 | Coy Bacon | .12 | .06 |
| 251 | Russ Francis | .50 | .25 |
| 252 | Jim Braxton | .12 | .06 |
| 253 | Perry Smith | .12 | .06 |
| 254 | Jerome Barkum | .20 | .10 |
| 255 | Garo Yepremian | .20 | .10 |
| 256 | Checklist 133-264 | 1.25 | .25 |
| 257 | Tony Galbreath (R) | .50 | .25 |
| 258 | Troy Archer (R) | .25 | .12 |
| 259 | Brian Sipe | .90 | .45 |
| 260 | Billy Joe DuPree | .40 | .20 |
| 261 | Bobby Walden | .12 | .06 |

| | | | | | | |
|---|---|---|---|---|---|---|
| 262 | Larry Marshall | .12 | .06 | | | |
| 263 | Ted Fritsch | .12 | .06 | | | |
| 264 | Larry Hand | .12 | .06 | | | |
| 265 | Tom Mack | .30 | .15 | | | |
| 266 | Ed Bradley | .12 | .06 | | | |
| 267 | Pat Leahy | .50 | .25 | | | |
| 268 | Louis Carter | .12 | .06 | | | |
| 269 | Archie Griffin (R) | 3.50 | 1.75 | | | |
| 270 | Art Shell | 1.25 | .60 | | | |
| 271 | Stu Voigt | .12 | .06 | | | |
| 272 | Prentice McCray | .12 | .06 | | | |
| 273 | MacArthur Lane | .35 | .18 | | | |
| 274 | Dan Fouts | 10.00 | 5.00 | | | |
| 275 | Charley Young | .20 | .10 | | | |
| 276 | Wilbur Jackson (R) | .60 | .30 | | | |
| 277 | John Hicks | .12 | .06 | | | |
| 278 | Nat Moore | .75 | .35 | | | |
| 279 | Virgil Livers | .12 | .06 | | | |
| 280 | Curley Culp | .30 | .15 | | | |
| 281 | Rocky Bleier | .80 | .40 | | | |
| 282 | John Zook | .12 | .06 | | | |
| 283 | Tom DeLeone | .12 | .06 | | | |
| 284 | Danny White (R) | 3.50 | 1.75 | | | |
| 285 | Otis Armstrong | .40 | .20 | | | |
| 286 | Larry Walton | .12 | .06 | | | |
| 287 | Jim Carter | .12 | .06 | | | |
| 288 | Don McCauley | .15 | .08 | | | |
| 289 | Frank Grant | .12 | .06 | | | |
| 290 | Roger Wehrli | .20 | .10 | | | |
| 291 | Mick Tingelhoff | .25 | .12 | | | |
| 292 | Bernard Jackson | .12 | .06 | | | |
| 293 | Tom Owen (R) | .25 | .12 | | | |
| 294 | Mike Esposito | .12 | .06 | | | |
| 295 | Fred Biletnikoff | 2.50 | 1.25 | | | |
| 296 | Revie Sorey | .12 | .06 | | | |
| 297 | John McMakin | .12 | .06 | | | |
| 298 | Dan Ryczek | .12 | .06 | | | |
| 299 | Wayne Moore | .12 | .06 | | | |
| 300 | Franco Harris | 4.50 | 2.25 | | | |
| 301 | Rick Upchurch (R) | 1.25 | .60 | | | |
| 302 | Jim Stienke | .12 | .06 | | | |
| 303 | Charlie Davis | .12 | .06 | | | |
| 304 | Don Cockroft | .15 | .08 | | | |
| 305 | Ken Burrough | .35 | .18 | | | |
| 306 | Clark Gaines | .12 | .06 | | | |
| 307 | Bobby Douglass | .25 | .12 | | | |
| 308 | Ralph Perretta | .12 | .06 | | | |
| 309 | Wally Hilgenberg | .12 | .06 | | | |
| 310 | Monte Jackson (R) | .40 | .20 | | | |
| 311 | Chris Barr (R) | .40 | .20 | | | |
| 312 | Jim Cheyunski | .12 | .06 | | | |
| 313 | Mike Patrick | .12 | .06 | | | |
| 314 | Ed Too Tall Jones | 3.00 | 1.50 | | | |
| 315 | Bill Bradley | .20 | .10 | | | |
| 316 | Benny Malone | .12 | .06 | | | |
| 317 | Paul Seymour | .12 | .06 | | | |
| 318 | Jim Laslavic | .12 | .06 | | | |
| 319 | Frank Lewis | .25 | .12 |
| 320 | Ray Guy | .60 | .30 |
| 321 | Allan Ellis | .12 | .06 |
| 322 | Conrad Dobler | .20 | .10 |
| 323 | Chester Marcol | .12 | .06 |
| 324 | Doug Kotar | .12 | .06 |
| 325 | Lemar Parrish | .20 | .10 |
| 326 | Steve Holden | .12 | .06 |
| 327 | Jeff Van Note | .20 | .10 |
| 328 | Howard Stevens | .12 | .06 |
| 329 | Brad Dusek | .12 | .06 |
| 330 | Joe DeLamielleure | .20 | .10 |
| 331 | Jim Plunkett | 1.00 | .50 |
| 332 | Checklist 265-396 | 1.25 | .25 |
| 333 | Lou Piccone | .12 | .06 |
| 334 | Ray Hamilton | .12 | .06 |
| 335 | Jan Stenerud | .80 | .40 |
| 336 | Jeris White | .12 | .06 |
| 337 | Sherman Smith (R) | .30 | .15 |
| 338 | Dave Green | .12 | .06 |
| 339 | Terry Schmidt | .12 | .06 |
| 340 | Sammie White (R) | .80 | .40 |
| 341 | Jon Kolb (R) | .20 | .10 |
| 342 | Randy White | 4.50 | 2.25 |
| 343 | Bob Klein | .12 | .06 |
| 344 | Bob Kowalkowski | .12 | .06 |
| 345 | Terry Metcalf | .50 | .25 |
| 346 | Joe Danelo | .12 | .06 |
| 347 | Ken Payne | .12 | .06 |
| 348 | Neal Craig | .12 | .06 |
| 349 | Dennis Johnson | .12 | .06 |
| 350 | Bill Bergey | .40 | .20 |
| 351 | Raymond Chester | .25 | .12 |
| 352 | Bob Matheson | .15 | .08 |
| 353 | Mike Kadish | .12 | .06 |
| 354 | Mark Van Eeghen (R) | .60 | .30 |
| 355 | L.C. Greenwood | .80 | .40 |
| 356 | Sam Hunt | .12 | .06 |
| 357 | Darrell Austin | .12 | .06 |
| 358 | Jim Turner | .12 | .06 |
| 359 | Ahmad Rashad | 1.50 | .75 |
| 360 | Walter Payton | 42.00 | 21.00 |
| 361 | Mark Arneson | .12 | .06 |
| 362 | Jerrel Wilson | .12 | .06 |
| 363 | Steve Bartkowski | .90 | .45 |
| 364 | John Watson | .12 | .06 |
| 365 | Ken Riley | .20 | .10 |
| 366 | Gregg Bingham | .12 | .06 |
| 367 | Golden Richards | .12 | .06 |
| 368 | Clyde Powers | .12 | .06 |
| 369 | Diron Talbert | .20 | .10 |
| 370 | Lydell Mitchell | .30 | .15 |
| 371 | Bob Jackson | .12 | .06 |
| 372 | Jim Mandich | .12 | .06 |
| 373 | Frank LeMaster | .12 | .06 |
| 374 | Benny Ricardo | .12 | .06 |
| 375 | Lawrence McCutcheon | .50 | .25 |

| 376 | Lynn Dickey | .60 | .30 |
| 377 | Phil Wise | .12 | .06 |
| 378 | Tony McGee | .12 | .06 |
| 379 | Norm Thompson | .12 | .06 |
| 380 | Dave Casper (R) | 3.50 | 1.75 |
| 381 | Glen Edwards | .12 | .06 |
| 382 | Bob Thomas | .12 | .06 |
| 383 | Bob Chandler | .12 | .06 |
| 384 | Rickey Young | .12 | .06 |
| 385 | Carl Eller | 1.00 | .50 |
| 386 | Lyle Alzado | .80 | .40 |
| 387 | John Leypoldt | .12 | .06 |
| 388 | Gordon Bell | .12 | .06 |
| 389 | Mike Bragg | .12 | .06 |
| 390 | Jim Langer | 1.00 | .50 |
| 391 | Vern Holland | .12 | .06 |
| 392 | Nelson Munsey | .12 | .06 |
| 393 | Mack Mitchell | .12 | .06 |
| 394 | Tony Adams | .12 | .06 |
| 395 | Preston Pearson | .30 | .15 |
| 396 | Emanuel Zanders | .12 | .06 |
| 397 | Vince Papale | .12 | .06 |
| 398 | Joe Fields (R) | .30 | .15 |
| 399 | Craig Clemons | .12 | .06 |
| 400 | Fran Tarkenton | 7.00 | 3.50 |
| 401 | Andy Johnson | .12 | .06 |
| 402 | Willie Buchanon | .20 | .10 |
| 403 | Pat Curran | .12 | .06 |
| 404 | Ray Jarvis | .12 | .06 |
| 405 | Joe Greene | 2.50 | 1.25 |
| 406 | Bill Simpson | .12 | .06 |
| 407 | Ronnie Coleman | .12 | .06 |
| 408 | J.K. McKay (R) | .25 | .12 |
| 409 | Pat Fischer | .20 | .10 |
| 410 | John Dutton | .20 | .10 |
| 411 | Boobie Clark | .25 | .12 |
| 412 | Pat Tilley (R) | .75 | .35 |
| 413 | Don Strock | .40 | .20 |
| 414 | Brian Kelley | .12 | .06 |
| 415 | Gene Upshaw | 1.00 | .50 |
| 416 | Mike Montler | .12 | .06 |
| 417 | Checklist 397-528 | 1.25 | .25 |
| 418 | John Gilliam | .12 | .06 |
| 419 | Brent McClanahan | .12 | .06 |
| 420 | Jerry Sherk | .20 | .10 |
| 421 | Roy Gerela | .12 | .06 |
| 422 | Tim Fox | .12 | .06 |
| 423 | John Ebersole | .12 | .06 |
| 424 | James Scott | .12 | .06 |
| 425 | Delvin Williams (R) | .60 | .30 |
| 426 | Spike Jones | .12 | .06 |
| 427 | Harvey Martin | 1.00 | .50 |
| 428 | Don Herrmann | .12 | .06 |
| 429 | Calvin Hill | .60 | .30 |
| 430 | Isiah Robertson | .20 | .10 |
| 431 | Tony Greene | .12 | .06 |
| 432 | Bob Johnson | .12 | .06 |
| 433 | Lem Barney | 1.00 | .50 |
| 434 | Eric Torkelson | .12 | .06 |
| 435 | John Mendenhall | .12 | .06 |
| 436 | Larry Seiple | .12 | .06 |
| 437 | Art Kuehn | .12 | .06 |
| 438 | John Vella | .12 | .06 |
| 439 | Greg Latta | .12 | .06 |
| 440 | Roger Carr | .25 | .12 |
| 441 | Doug Sutherland | .12 | .06 |
| 442 | Mike Kruczek (R) | .25 | .12 |
| 443 | Steve Zabel | .12 | .06 |
| 444 | Mike Pruitt (R) | 1.25 | .60 |
| 445 | Harold Jackson | .75 | .35 |
| 446 | George Jakowenko | .12 | .06 |
| 447 | John Fitzgerald | .12 | .06 |
| 448 | Carey Joyce | .12 | .06 |
| 449 | Jim LeClair | .12 | .06 |
| 450 | Ken Houston | 1.25 | .60 |
| 451 | Steve Grogan (RB) | .30 | .15 |
| 452 | Jim Marshall (RB) | .40 | .20 |
| 453 | O.J. Simpson (RB) | 3.50 | 1.75 |
| 454 | Frank Tarkenton (RB) | 3.50 | 1.75 |
| 455 | Jim Zorn (RB) | .30 | .15 |
| 456 | Robert Pratt | .12 | .06 |
| 457 | Walker Gillette | .12 | .06 |
| 458 | Charlie Hall | .12 | .06 |
| 459 | Robert Newhouse | .30 | .15 |
| 460 | John Hannah | 1.00 | .50 |
| 461 | Ken Reaves | .12 | .06 |
| 462 | Herman Weaver | .12 | .06 |
| 463 | James Harris | .50 | .25 |
| 464 | Howard Twilley | .25 | .12 |
| 465 | Jeff Siemon | .15 | .08 |
| 466 | John Outlaw | .12 | .06 |
| 467 | Chuck Muncie (R) | 1.25 | .60 |
| 468 | Bob Moore | .12 | .06 |
| 469 | Robert Woods | .12 | .06 |
| 470 | Cliff Branch | 1.00 | .50 |
| 471 | Johnnie Gray | .12 | .06 |
| 472 | Don Hardeman | .12 | .06 |
| 473 | Steve Ramsey | .12 | .06 |
| 474 | Steve Mike Mayer | .12 | .06 |
| 475 | Gary Garrison | .12 | .06 |
| 476 | Walter Johnson | .12 | .06 |
| 477 | Neil Clabo | .12 | .06 |
| 478 | Len Hauss | .12 | .06 |
| 479 | Darryl Stingley | .25 | .12 |
| 480 | Jack Lambert | 4.50 | 2.25 |
| 481 | Mike Adamle | .20 | .10 |
| 482 | David Lee | .12 | .06 |
| 483 | Tom Mullen | .12 | .06 |
| 484 | Claude Humphrey | .20 | .10 |
| 485 | Jim Hart | .75 | .35 |
| 486 | Bobby Thompson | .12 | .06 |
| 487 | Jack Rudnay | .12 | .06 |
| 488 | Rich Sowells | .12 | .06 |
| 489 | Reuben Gant | .12 | .06 |

| 490 | Cliff Harris | .50 | .25 |
|---|---|---|---|
| 491 | Bob Brown | .12 | .06 |
| 492 | Don Nottingham | .20 | .10 |
| 493 | Ron Jessie | .20 | .10 |
| 494 | Otis Sistrunk | .12 | .06 |
| 495 | Bill Kilmer | 1.00 | .50 |
| 496 | Oscar Roan | .12 | .06 |
| 497 | Bill Van Heusen | .12 | .06 |
| 498 | Randy Logan | .12 | .06 |
| 499 | John Smith | .12 | .06 |
| 500 | Chuck Foreman | .75 | .35 |
| 501 | J.T. Thomas | .12 | .06 |
| 502 | Steve Schubert | .12 | .06 |
| 503 | Mike Barnes | .12 | .06 |
| 504 | J.V. Cain | .12 | .06 |
| 505 | Larry Csonka | 2.50 | 1.25 |
| 506 | Elvin Bethea | .25 | .12 |
| 507 | Ray Easterling | .12 | .06 |
| 508 | Joe Reed (R) | .20 | .10 |
| 509 | Steve Odom (R) | .20 | .10 |
| 510 | Tommy Casanova | .20 | .10 |
| 511 | Dave Dalby | .12 | .06 |
| 512 | Richard Caster | .25 | .12 |
| 513 | Fred Dryer | 1.50 | .75 |
| 514 | Jeff Kinney | .20 | .10 |
| 515 | Bob Griese | 3.00 | 1.50 |
| 516 | Butch Johnson (R) | .80 | .40 |
| 517 | Gerald Irons | .12 | .06 |
| 518 | Don Calhoun | .12 | .06 |
| 519 | Jack Gregory | .12 | .06 |
| 520 | Tom Banks | .20 | .10 |
| 521 | Bobby Bryant | .12 | .06 |
| 522 | Reggie Harrison | .12 | .06 |
| 523 | Terry Hermeling | .12 | .06 |
| 524 | David Taylor | .12 | .06 |
| 525 | Brian Baschnagel (R) | .35 | .18 |
| 526 | AFC Championship | .60 | .30 |
| 527 | NFC Championship | .50 | .25 |
| 528 | Super Bowl XI | 1.50 | .50 |

# 1978 Topps

The 528 cards in this set feature color photos on the fronts with the player's name and position printed in a box across the top of the card. Team names appear in a color bar along the side border. The card backs include personal data, statistics and a short paragraph of copy devoted to highlights. Key subsets include Highlights (HL), Playoffs (166-168) and Team Leaders (TL). The Team Leaders subset includes individual team checklists on the back. All cards measure 2-1/2" by 3-1/2".

| | | NR/MT | EX |
|---|---|---|---|
| **Complete Set (528)** | | 150.00 | 70.00 |
| **Commons** | | .10 | .05 |
| | | | |
| 1 | Gary Huff (HL) | .50 | .10 |
| 2 | Craig Morton (HL) | .30 | .15 |
| 3 | Walter Payton (HL) | 4.00 | 2.00 |
| 4 | O.J. Simpson (HL) | 3.00 | 1.50 |
| 5 | Fran Tarkenton (HL) | 2.00 | 1.00 |
| 6 | Bob Thomas (HL) | .15 | .08 |
| 7 | Joe Pisarcik (R) | .25 | .12 |
| 8 | Skip Thomas | .10 | .05 |
| 9 | Roosevelt Leaks | .20 | .10 |
| 10 | Ken Houston | 1.00 | .50 |
| 11 | Tom Blanchard | .10 | .05 |
| 12 | Jim Turner | .10 | .05 |
| 13 | Tom DeLeone | .10 | .05 |
| 14 | Jim LeClair | .10 | .05 |
| 15 | Bob Avellini | .20 | .10 |
| 16 | Tony McGee | .10 | .05 |
| 17 | James Harris | .30 | .15 |
| 18 | Terry Nelson | .10 | .05 |
| 19 | Rocky Bleier | .75 | .35 |

| | | | |
|---|---|---|---|
| 20 | Joe DeLamielleure | .15 | .08 |
| 21 | Richard Caster | .20 | .10 |
| 22 | A.J. Duhe (R) | .75 | .35 |
| 23 | John Outlaw | .10 | .05 |
| 24 | Danny White | .90 | .45 |
| 25 | Larry Csonka | 2.00 | 1.00 |
| 26 | David Hill | .10 | .05 |
| 27 | Mark Arneson | .10 | .05 |
| 28 | Jack Tatum | .30 | .15 |
| 29 | Norm Thompson | .10 | .05 |
| 30 | Sammie White | .35 | .18 |
| 31 | Dennis Johnson | .10 | .05 |
| 32 | Robin Earl | .10 | .05 |
| 33 | Don Cockroft | .10 | .05 |
| 34 | Bob Johnson | .10 | .05 |
| 35 | John Hannah | 1.00 | .50 |
| 36 | Scott Hunter | .15 | .08 |
| 37 | Ken Burrough | .20 | .10 |
| 38 | Wilbur Jackson | .15 | .08 |
| 39 | Rich McGeorge | .10 | .05 |
| 40 | Lyle Alzado | .80 | .40 |
| 41 | John Ebersole | .10 | .05 |
| 42 | Gary Green (R) | .20 | .10 |
| 43 | Art Kuehn | .10 | .05 |
| 44 | Glen Edwards | .10 | .05 |
| 45 | Lawrence McCutcheon | .30 | .15 |
| 46 | Duriel Harris | .10 | .05 |
| 47 | Rich Szaro | .10 | .05 |
| 48 | Mike Washington | .10 | .05 |
| 49 | Stan White | .10 | .05 |
| 50 | Dave Casper | .80 | .40 |
| 51 | Len Hauss | .10 | .05 |
| 52 | James Scott | .10 | .05 |
| 53 | Brian Sipe | .75 | .35 |
| 54 | Gary Shirk | .10 | .05 |
| 55 | Archie Griffin | .75 | .35 |
| 56 | Mike Patrick | .10 | .05 |
| 57 | Mario Clark | .10 | .05 |
| 58 | Jeff Siemon | .10 | .05 |
| 59 | Steve Mike Mayer | .10 | .05 |
| 60 | Randy White | 3.00 | 1.50 |
| 61 | Darrell Austin | .10 | .05 |
| 62 | Tom Sullivan | .10 | .05 |
| 63 | Johnny Rodgers (R) | 2.00 | 1.00 |
| 64 | Ken Reaves | .10 | .05 |
| 65 | Terry Bradshaw | 4.50 | 2.25 |
| 66 | Fred Steinfort | .10 | .05 |
| 67 | Curley Culp | .20 | .10 |
| 68 | Ted Hendricks | .90 | .45 |
| 69 | Raymond Chester | .15 | .08 |
| 70 | Jim Langer | .75 | .35 |
| 71 | Calvin Hill | .30 | .15 |
| 72 | Mike Hartenstine | .10 | .05 |
| 73 | Gerald Irons | .10 | .05 |
| 74 | Billy Brooks | .25 | .12 |
| 75 | John Mendenahll | .10 | .05 |
| 76 | Andy Johnson | .10 | .05 |
| 77 | Tom Wittum | .10 | .05 |
| 78 | Lynn Dickey | .40 | .20 |
| 79 | Carl Eller | .75 | .35 |
| 80 | Tom Mack | .30 | .15 |
| 81 | Clark Gaines | .10 | .05 |
| 82 | Lem Barney | .80 | .40 |
| 83 | Mike Montler | .10 | .05 |
| 84 | Jon Kolb | .10 | .05 |
| 85 | Bob Chandler | .10 | .05 |
| 86 | Robert Newhouse | .20 | .10 |
| 87 | Frank LeMaster | .10 | .05 |
| 88 | Jeff West | .10 | .05 |
| 89 | Lyle Blackwood | .15 | .08 |
| 90 | Gene Upshaw | .75 | .35 |
| 91 | Frank Grant | .10 | .05 |
| 92 | Tom Hicks | .10 | .05 |
| 93 | Mike Pruitt | .40 | .20 |
| 94 | Chris Bahr | .10 | .05 |
| 95 | Russ Francis | .30 | .15 |
| 96 | Norris Thomas | .10 | .05 |
| 97 | Gary Barbaro (R) | .40 | .20 |
| 98 | Jim Merlo | .10 | .05 |
| 99 | Karl Chandler | .10 | .05 |
| 100 | Fran Tarkenton | 5.50 | 2.75 |
| 101 | Abdul Salaam | .10 | .05 |
| 102 | Marv Kellum | .10 | .05 |
| 103 | Herman Weaver | .10 | .05 |
| 104 | Roy Gerela | .10 | .05 |
| 105 | Harold Jackson | .50 | .25 |
| 106 | Dewey Selmon | .15 | .08 |
| 107 | Checklist 1-132 | .80 | .10 |
| 108 | Clarence Davis | .10 | .05 |
| 109 | Robert Pratt | .10 | .05 |
| 110 | Harvey Martin | .60 | .30 |
| 111 | Brad Dusek | .10 | .05 |
| 112 | Greg Latta | .10 | .05 |
| 113 | Tony Peters | .10 | .05 |
| 114 | Jim Braxton | .10 | .05 |
| 115 | Ken Riley | .15 | .08 |
| 116 | Steve Nelson | .10 | .05 |
| 117 | Rick Upchurch | .25 | .12 |
| 118 | Spike Jones | .10 | .05 |
| 119 | Doug Kotar | .10 | .05 |
| 120 | Bob Griese | 2.50 | 1.25 |
| 121 | Burgess Owens | .10 | .05 |
| 122 | Rolf Benirschke (R) | .35 | .18 |
| 123 | Haskel Stanback (R) | .20 | .10 |
| 124 | J.T. Thomas | .10 | .05 |
| 125 | Ahmad Rashad | 1.00 | .50 |
| 126 | Rick Kane | .10 | .05 |
| 127 | Elvin Bethea | .20 | .10 |
| 128 | Dave Dalby | .10 | .05 |
| 129 | Mike Barnes | .10 | .05 |
| 130 | Isiah Robertson | .15 | .08 |
| 131 | Jim Plunkett | .50 | .25 |
| 132 | Allan Ellis | .10 | .05 |
| 133 | Mike Bragg | .10 | .05 |

| 124 | Bob Jackson | .10 | .05 |
| 135 | Coy Bacon | .10 | .05 |
| 136 | John Smith | .10 | .05 |
| 137 | Chuck Muncie | .50 | .25 |
| 138 | Johnnie Gray | .10 | .05 |
| 139 | Jimmy Robinson | .10 | .05 |
| 140 | Tom Banks | .15 | .08 |
| 141 | Marvin Powell (R) | .40 | .20 |
| 142 | Jerrel Wilson | .10 | .05 |
| 143 | Ron Howard | .10 | .05 |
| 144 | Rob Lytle (R) | .25 | .12 |
| 145 | L.C. Greenwood | .75 | .35 |
| 146 | Morris Owens | .10 | .05 |
| 147 | Joe Reed | .10 | .05 |
| 148 | Mike Kadish | .10 | .05 |
| 149 | Phil Villapiano | .15 | .08 |
| 150 | Lydell Mitchell | .30 | .15 |
| 151 | Randy Logan | .10 | .05 |
| 152 | Mike Williams | .10 | .05 |
| 153 | Jeff Van Note | .15 | .08 |
| 154 | Steve Schubert | .10 | .05 |
| 155 | Bill Kilmer | .80 | .40 |
| 156 | Boobie Clark | .15 | .08 |
| 157 | Charlie Hall | .10 | .05 |
| 158 | Raymond Clayborn (R) | .50 | .25 |
| 159 | Jack Gregory | .10 | .05 |
| 160 | Cliff Harris | .30 | .15 |
| 161 | Joe Fields | .10 | .05 |
| 162 | Don Nottingham | .10 | .05 |
| 163 | Ed White | .10 | .05 |
| 164 | Toni Fritsch | .10 | .05 |
| 165 | Jack Lambert | 2.50 | 1.25 |
| 166 | NFC Championship | 1.25 | .60 |
| 167 | AFC Championship | .50 | .25 |
| 168 | Super Bowl XII | 2.00 | 1.00 |
| 169 | Neal Colzie (R) | .25 | .12 |
| 170 | Cleveland Elam | .10 | .05 |
| 171 | David Lee | .10 | .05 |
| 172 | Jim Otis | .25 | .12 |
| 173 | Archie Manning | .80 | .40 |
| 174 | Jim Carter | .10 | .05 |
| 175 | Jean Fugett | .10 | .05 |
| 176 | Willie Parker | .10 | .05 |
| 177 | Haven Moses | .15 | .08 |
| 178 | Horace King | .10 | .05 |
| 179 | Bob Thomas | .10 | .05 |
| 180 | Monte Jackson | .10 | .05 |
| 181 | Steve Zabel | .10 | .05 |
| 182 | John Fitzgerald | .10 | .05 |
| 183 | Mike Livingston | .10 | .05 |
| 184 | Larry Poole | .10 | .05 |
| 185 | Isaac Curtis | .25 | .12 |
| 186 | Chuck Ramsey | .10 | .05 |
| 187 | Bob Klein | .10 | .05 |
| 188 | Ray Rhodes | .10 | .05 |
| 189 | Otis Sistrunk | .10 | .05 |
| 190 | Bill Bergey | .25 | .12 |
| 191 | Sherman Smith | .10 | .05 |
| 192 | Dave Green | .10 | .05 |
| 193 | Carl Mauck | .10 | .05 |
| 194 | Reggie Harrison | .10 | .05 |
| 195 | Roger Carr | .15 | .08 |
| 196 | Steve Bartkowski | .80 | .40 |
| 197 | Ray Wersching | .10 | .05 |
| 198 | Willie Buchanon | .15 | .08 |
| 199 | Neil Clabo | .10 | .05 |
| 200 | Walter Payton | 25.00 | 12.50 |
| 201 | Sam Adams | .10 | .05 |
| 202 | Larry Gordon | .10 | .05 |
| 203 | Pat Tilley | .10 | .05 |
| 204 | Mack Mithcell | .10 | .05 |
| 205 | Ken Anderson | 1.25 | .60 |
| 206 | Scott Dierking | .10 | .05 |
| 207 | Jack Rudnay | .10 | .05 |
| 208 | Jim Stienke | .10 | .05 |
| 209 | Bill Simpson | .10 | .05 |
| 210 | Errol Mann | .10 | .05 |
| 211 | Bucky Dilts | .10 | .05 |
| 212 | Reuben Gant | .10 | .05 |
| 213 | Thomas Henderson (R) | .40 | .20 |
| 214 | Steve Furness | .10 | .05 |
| 215 | John Riggins | 2.00 | 1.00 |
| 216 | Keith Krepfle (R) | .20 | .10 |
| 217 | Fred Dean (R) | 1.00 | .50 |
| 218 | Emanuel Zanders | .10 | .05 |
| 219 | Don Testerman | .10 | .05 |
| 220 | George Kunz | .10 | .05 |
| 221 | Darryl Stingley | .20 | .10 |
| 222 | Ken Sanders | .10 | .05 |
| 223 | Gary Huff | .30 | .15 |
| 224 | Gregg Bingham | .15 | .08 |
| 225 | Jerry Sherk | .15 | .08 |
| 226 | Doug Plank | .20 | .10 |
| 227 | Ed Taylor | .10 | .05 |
| 228 | Emery Moorehead | .10 | .05 |
| 229 | Reggie Williams (R) | 2.00 | 1.00 |
| 230 | Claude Humphrey | .15 | .08 |
| 231 | Randy Cross (R) | 1.00 | .50 |
| 232 | Jim Hart | .60 | .30 |
| 233 | Bobby Bryant | .10 | .05 |
| 234 | Larry Brown | .10 | .05 |
| 235 | Mark Van Eeghen | .20 | .10 |
| 236 | Terry Hermeling | .10 | .05 |
| 237 | Steve Odom | .10 | .05 |
| 238 | Jan Stenerud | .60 | .30 |
| 239 | Andre Tillman | .10 | .05 |
| 240 | Tom Jackson (R) | 2.00 | 1.00 |
| 241 | Ken Mendenhall | .10 | .05 |
| 242 | Tim Fox | .10 | .05 |
| 243 | Don Herrmann | .10 | .05 |
| 244 | Eddie McMillan | .10 | .05 |
| 245 | Greg Pruitt | .40 | .20 |
| 246 | J.K. McKay | .10 | .05 |

| # | Player | | |
|---|--------|---|---|
| 247 | Larry Keller | .10 | .05 |
| 248 | Dave Jennings | .10 | .05 |
| 249 | Bo Harris | .10 | .05 |
| 250 | Revie Sorey | .10 | .05 |
| 251 | Tony Greene | .10 | .05 |
| 252 | Butch Johnson | .25 | .12 |
| 253 | Paul Naumoff | .10 | .05 |
| 254 | Ricky Young | .10 | .05 |
| 255 | Dwight White | .25 | .12 |
| 256 | Joe Lavender | .10 | .05 |
| 257 | Checklist 133-264 | .80 | .10 |
| 258 | Ronnie Coleman | .10 | .05 |
| 259 | Charlie Smith | .10 | .05 |
| 260 | Ray Guy | .50 | .25 |
| 261 | David Taylor | .10 | .05 |
| 262 | Bill Lenkaitis | .10 | .05 |
| 263 | Jim Mitchell | .10 | .05 |
| 264 | Delvin Williams | .10 | .05 |
| 265 | Jack Youngblood | .60 | .30 |
| 266 | Chuck Crist | .10 | .05 |
| 267 | Richard Todd | .50 | .25 |
| 268 | Dave Logan (R) | .25 | .12 |
| 269 | Rufus Mayes | .10 | .05 |
| 270 | Brad Van Pelt | .15 | .08 |
| 271 | Chester Marcol | .10 | .05 |
| 272 | J.V. Cain | .10 | .05 |
| 273 | Larry Seiple | .10 | .05 |
| 274 | Brent McClanahan | .10 | .05 |
| 275 | Mike Wagner | .15 | .08 |
| 276 | Diron Talbert | .15 | .08 |
| 277 | Brian Baschnagel | .10 | .05 |
| 278 | Ed Podolak | .15 | .08 |
| 279 | Don Goode | .10 | .05 |
| 280 | John Dutton | .15 | .08 |
| 281 | Don Calhoun | .10 | .05 |
| 282 | Monte Johnson | .10 | .05 |
| 283 | Ron Jessie | .15 | .08 |
| 284 | Jon Morris | .10 | .05 |
| 285 | Riley Odoms | .15 | .08 |
| 286 | Marv Bateman | .10 | .05 |
| 287 | Joe Klecko (R) | 2.50 | 1.25 |
| 288 | Oliver Davis | .10 | .05 |
| 289 | John McDaniel | .10 | .05 |
| 290 | Roger Staubach | 7.50 | 3.75 |
| 291 | Brian Kelley | .10 | .05 |
| 292 | Mike Hogan | .10 | .05 |
| 293 | John Leypoldt | .10 | .05 |
| 294 | Jack Novak | .10 | .05 |
| 295 | Joe Greene | 1.50 | .75 |
| 296 | John Hill | .10 | .05 |
| 297 | Danny Buggs | .10 | .05 |
| 298 | Ted Albrecht | .10 | .05 |
| 299 | Nelson Munsey | .10 | .05 |
| 300 | Chuck Foreman | .60 | .30 |
| 301 | Dan Pastorini | .40 | .20 |
| 302 | Tommy Hart | .10 | .05 |
| 303 | Dave Beverly | .10 | .05 |
| 304 | Tony Reed (R) | .20 | .10 |
| 305 | Cliff Branch | .75 | .35 |
| 306 | Clarence Duren | .10 | .05 |
| 307 | Randy Rasmussen | .10 | .05 |
| 308 | Oscar Roan | .10 | .05 |
| 309 | Lenvil Elliott | .10 | .05 |
| 310 | Dan Dierdorf | .60 | .30 |
| 311 | Johnny Perkins | .10 | .05 |
| 312 | Rafael Septien (R) | .20 | .10 |
| 313 | Terry Beeson | .10 | .05 |
| 314 | Lee Roy Selmon | .80 | .40 |
| 315 | Tony Dorsett (R) | 40.00 | 20.00 |
| 316 | Greg Landry | .35 | .18 |
| 317 | Jake Scott | .15 | .08 |
| 318 | Dan Peiffer | .10 | .05 |
| 319 | John Bunting | .10 | .05 |
| 320 | John Stallworth (R) | 12.00 | 6.00 |
| 321 | Bob Howard | .10 | .05 |
| 322 | Larry Little | .50 | .25 |
| 323 | Reggie McKenzie | .15 | .08 |
| 324 | Duane Carrell | .10 | .05 |
| 325 | Ed Simonini | .10 | .05 |
| 326 | John Vella | .10 | .05 |
| 327 | Wesley Walker (R) | 2.50 | 1.25 |
| 328 | Jon Keyworth | .10 | .05 |
| 329 | Ron Bolton | .10 | .05 |
| 330 | Tommy Casanova | .10 | .05 |
| 331 | Passing Leaders | 3.00 | 1.50 |
| | Bob Griese | | |
| | Roger Staubach | | |
| 332 | Receiving Leaders | .80 | .40 |
| | Lydell Mitchell | | |
| | Ahmad Rashad | | |
| 333 | Rushing Leaders | 2.50 | 1.25 |
| | Mark Van Eeghen | | |
| | Walter Payton | | |
| 334 | Scoring Leaders | 2.50 | 1.25 |
| | Errol Mann | | |
| | Walter Payton | | |
| 335 | Interception Leaders | .20 | .10 |
| | Lyle Blackwood | | |
| | Rolland Lawrence | | |
| 336 | Punting Leaders | .40 | .20 |
| | Ray Guy | | |
| | Tom Blanchard | | |
| 337 | Robert Brazile | .20 | .10 |
| 338 | Charlie Joiner | 1.25 | .60 |
| 339 | Joe Ferguson | .40 | .20 |
| 340 | Bill Thompson | .10 | .05 |
| 341 | Sam Cunningham | .20 | .10 |
| 342 | Curtis Johnson | .10 | .05 |
| 343 | Jim Marshall | .75 | .35 |
| 344 | Charlie Sanders | .10 | .05 |
| 345 | Willie Hall | .10 | .05 |
| 346 | Pat Haden | .50 | .25 |
| 347 | Jim Bakken | .10 | .05 |
| 348 | Bruce Taylor | .10 | .05 |

| No. | Player | | |
|---|---|---|---|
| 349 | Barty Smith | .10 | .05 |
| 350 | Drew Pearson | .75 | .35 |
| 351 | Mike Webster | 2.00 | 1.00 |
| 352 | Bobby Hammond | .10 | .05 |
| 353 | Dave Mays | .10 | .05 |
| 354 | Pat McInally | .20 | .10 |
| 355 | Toni Linhart | .10 | .05 |
| 356 | Larry Hand | .10 | .05 |
| 357 | Ted Fritsch | .10 | .05 |
| 358 | Larry Marshall | .10 | .05 |
| 359 | Waymond Bryant | .10 | .05 |
| 360 | Louie Kelcher (R) | .35 | .18 |
| 361 | Stanley Morgan (R) | 6.50 | 3.25 |
| 362 | Bruce Harper (R) | .20 | .10 |
| 363 | Bernard Jackson | .10 | .05 |
| 364 | Walter White | .10 | .05 |
| 365 | Ken Stabler | 1.75 | .85 |
| 366 | Fred Dryer | .80 | .50 |
| 367 | Ike Harris | .10 | .05 |
| 368 | Norm Bulaich | .10 | .05 |
| 369 | Merv Krakau | .10 | .05 |
| 370 | John James | .10 | .05 |
| 371 | Bennie Cunningham (R) | .35 | .18 |
| 372 | Doug Van Horn | .10 | .05 |
| 373 | Thom Darden | .10 | .05 |
| 374 | Eddie Edwards (R) | .20 | .10 |
| 375 | Mike Thomas | .10 | .05 |
| 376 | Fred Cook | .10 | .05 |
| 377 | Mike Phipps | .25 | .12 |
| 378 | Paul Krause | .20 | .10 |
| 379 | Harold Carmichael | .80 | .40 |
| 380 | Mike Haynes | .80 | .40 |
| 381 | Wayne Morris | .10 | .05 |
| 382 | Greg Buttle | .10 | .05 |
| 383 | Jim Zorn | .75 | .35 |
| 384 | Jack Dolbin | .10 | .05 |
| 385 | Charlie Waters | .35 | .18 |
| 386 | Dan Ryczek | .10 | .05 |
| 387 | Joe Washington (R) | 1.25 | .60 |
| 388 | Checklist 265-396 | .80 | .10 |
| 389 | James Hunter | .10 | .05 |
| 390 | Billy Johnson | .30 | .15 |
| 391 | Jim Allen | .10 | .05 |
| 392 | George Buehler | .10 | .05 |
| 393 | Harry Carson | 1.25 | .60 |
| 394 | Cleo Miller | .10 | .05 |
| 395 | Gary Burley | .10 | .05 |
| 396 | Mark Moseley | .15 | .08 |
| 397 | Virgil Livers | .10 | .05 |
| 398 | Joe Ehrmann | .10 | .05 |
| 399 | Freddie Solomon | .15 | .08 |
| 400 | O.J. Simpson | 6.50 | 3.25 |
| 401 | Julius Adams | .10 | .05 |
| 402 | Artimus Parker | .10 | .05 |
| 403 | Gene Washington | .15 | .08 |
| 404 | Herman Edwards | .10 | .05 |
| 405 | Craig Morton | .60 | .30 |
| 406 | Alan Page | 1.25 | .60 |
| 407 | Larry McCarren | .10 | .05 |
| 408 | Tony Galbreath | .15 | .08 |
| 409 | Roman Gabriel | .60 | .30 |
| 410 | Efren Herrera | .10 | .05 |
| 411 | Jim Smith (R) | .30 | .15 |
| 412 | Bill Bryant | .10 | .05 |
| 413 | Doug Dieken | .10 | .05 |
| 414 | Marvin Cobb | .10 | .05 |
| 415 | Fred Biletnikoff | 1.75 | .85 |
| 416 | Joe Theismann | 2.00 | 1.00 |
| 417 | Roland Harper | .15 | .08 |
| 418 | Derrel Luce | .10 | .05 |
| 419 | Ralph Perretta | .10 | .05 |
| 420 | Louis Wright (R) | .75 | .35 |
| 421 | Prentice McCray | .10 | .05 |
| 422 | Garry Puetz | .10 | .05 |
| 423 | Alfred Jenkins (R) | .40 | .20 |
| 424 | Paul Seymour | .10 | .05 |
| 425 | Garo Yepremian | .15 | .08 |
| 426 | Emmitt Thomas | .10 | .05 |
| 427 | Dexter Bussey | .10 | .05 |
| 428 | John Sanders | .10 | .05 |
| 429 | Ed Too Tall Jones | 1.75 | .85 |
| 430 | Ron Yary | .15 | .08 |
| 431 | Frank Lewis | .10 | .05 |
| 432 | Jerry Golsteyn | .10 | .05 |
| 433 | Clarence Scott | .10 | .05 |
| 434 | Pete Johnson (R) | .60 | .30 |
| 435 | Charley Young | .10 | .05 |
| 436 | Harold McLinton | .10 | .05 |
| 437 | Noah Jackson | .10 | .05 |
| 438 | Bruce Laird | .10 | .05 |
| 439 | John Matuszak | .25 | .12 |
| 440 | Nat Moore | .40 | .20 |
| 441 | Leon Gray | .10 | .05 |
| 442 | Jerome Barkum | .10 | .05 |
| 443 | Steve Largent | 18.50 | 9.25 |
| 444 | John Zook | .10 | .05 |
| 445 | Preston Pearson | .35 | .18 |
| 446 | Conrad Dobler | .15 | .08 |
| 447 | Wilbur Summers | .10 | .05 |
| 448 | Lou Piccone | .10 | .05 |
| 449 | Ron Jaworski | .50 | .25 |
| 450 | Jack Ham | 1.25 | .60 |
| 451 | Mick Tingelhof | .15 | .08 |
| 452 | Clyde Powers | .10 | .05 |
| 453 | John Cappelletti | .25 | .12 |
| 454 | Dick Ambrose | .10 | .05 |
| 455 | Lemar Parrish | .10 | .05 |
| 456 | Ron Saul | .10 | .05 |
| 457 | Bob Parsons | .10 | .05 |
| 458 | Glenn Doughty | .10 | .05 |
| 459 | Don Woods | .10 | .05 |
| 460 | Art Shell | 1.00 | .50 |
| 461 | Sam Hunt | .10 | .05 |

| | | |
|---|---|---|
| 462 Lawrence Pillers | .10 | .05 |
| 463 Henry Childs | .10 | .05 |
| 464 Roger Wehrli | .10 | .05 |
| 465 Otis Armstrong | .25 | .12 |
| 466 Bob Baumhower (R) | .60 | .30 |
| 467 Ray Jarvis | .10 | .05 |
| 468 Guy Morriss | .10 | .05 |
| 469 Matt Blair | .25 | .12 |
| 470 Billy Joe DuPree | .25 | .12 |
| 471 Roland Hooks | .10 | .05 |
| 472 Joe Danelo | .10 | .05 |
| 473 Reggie Rucker | .15 | .08 |
| 474 Vern Holland | .10 | .05 |
| 475 Mel Blount | 1.00 | .50 |
| 476 Eddie Brown | .10 | .05 |
| 477 Bo Rather | .10 | .05 |
| 478 Don McCauley | .15 | .08 |
| 479 Glen Walker | .10 | .05 |
| 480 Randy Gradishar | .60 | .30 |
| 481 Dave Rowe | .10 | .05 |
| 482 Pat Leahy | .25 | .12 |
| 483 Mike Fuller | .10 | .05 |
| 484 David Lewis | .10 | .05 |
| 485 Steve Grogan | .75 | .35 |
| 486 Mel Gray | .15 | .08 |
| 487 Eddie Payton (R) | .25 | .12 |
| 488 Checklist 397-528 | .80 | .10 |
| 489 Stu Voigt | .10 | .05 |
| 490 Rolland Lawrence | .10 | .05 |
| 491 Nick Mike-Mayer | .10 | .05 |
| 492 Troy Archer | .10 | .05 |
| 493 Benny Malone | .10 | .05 |
| 494 Golden Richards | .10 | .05 |
| 495 Chris Hanburger | .25 | .12 |
| 496 Dwight Harrison | .10 | .05 |
| 497 Gary Fencik (R) | 1.00 | .50 |
| 498 Rich Saul | .10 | .05 |
| 499 Dan Fouts | 7.50 | 3.75 |
| 500 Franco Harris | 2.00 | 1.00 |
| 501 Falcons (TL) | .40 | .20 |
| 502 Colts (TL) | .40 | .20 |
| 503 Bills (TL) | .80 | .40 |
| 504 Bears (TL) | 1.25 | .60 |
| 505 Bengals (TL) | .50 | .25 |
| 506 Browns (TL) | .50 | .25 |
| 507 Cowboys (TL) | 1.50 | .75 |
| 508 Broncos (TL) | .40 | .20 |
| 509 Lions (TL) | .40 | .20 |
| 510 Packers (TL) | .40 | .20 |
| 511 Oilers (TL) | .40 | .20 |
| 512 Chiefs (TL) | .40 | .20 |
| 513 Rams (TL) | .60 | .30 |
| 514 Dolphins (TL) | .40 | .20 |
| 515 Vikings (TL) | .50 | .25 |
| 516 Patriots (TL) | .50 | .25 |
| 517 Saints (TL) | .40 | .20 |
| 518 Giants (TL) | .40 | .20 |
| 519 Jets (TL) | .40 | .20 |
| 520 Rainders (TL) | .50 | .25 |
| 521 Eagles (TL) | .50 | .25 |
| 522 Steelers (TL) | 1.25 | .60 |
| 523 Cardinals (TL) | .40 | .20 |
| 524 Chargers (TL) | .50 | .25 |
| 525 49ers (TL) | .40 | .20 |
| 526 Seahawks (TL) | 1.00 | .50 |
| 527 Buccaneers (TL) | .40 | .20 |
| 528 Redskins (TL) | .60 | .25 |

# 1979 Topps

This 528-card set features full color photos on the card fronts with the player's name and team name stacked across the top border. The player's position is located in a small football deisgn in the top corner of the card. The backs are vertical and include personal data, stats and a brief highlight. Key subsets consist of League Leaders (1-6), Playoffs (166-168), Record Breakers (RB)(331-336) and Team Leaders (TL) which feature multi-player photos on the card fronts with team checklists on the back. All cards measure 2-1/2' by 3-1/2".

| | NR/MT | EX |
|---|---|---|
| Complete Set (528) | 130.00 | 65.00 |
| Commons | .08 | .04 |
| 1 Passing Leaders Roger Staubach Terry Bradshaw | 5.00 | 2.00 |
| 2 Receiving Leaders Rickey Young Steve Largent | .60 | .30 |

| | | | |
|---|---|---|---|
| 3 | Rushing Leaders | 6.50 | 3.25 |
| | Walter Payton | | |
| | Earl Campbell | | |
| 4 | Scoring Leaders | .10 | .05 |
| | Frank Corral | | |
| | Pat Leahy | | |
| 5 | Interception Leaders | .20 | .10 |
| | Willie Buchanon | | |
| | Ken Stone | | |
| | Thom Darden | | |
| 6 | Punting Leaders | .10 | .05 |
| | Tom Skladany | | |
| | Pat Leahy | | |
| 7 | Johnny Perkins | .08 | .04 |
| 8 | Charles Phillips | .08 | .04 |
| 9 | Derrel Luce | .08 | .04 |
| 10 | John Riggins | 1.75 | .85 |
| 11 | Chester Marcol | .08 | .04 |
| 12 | Bernard Jackson | .08 | .04 |
| 13 | Dave Logan | .08 | .04 |
| 14 | Bo Harris | .08 | .04 |
| 15 | Alan Page | .75 | .35 |
| 16 | John Smith | .08 | .04 |
| 17 | Dwight McDonald | .08 | .04 |
| 18 | John Cappelletti | .25 | .12 |
| 19 | Steelers (TL) | .90 | .45 |
| 20 | Bill Bergey | .20 | .10 |
| 21 | Jerome Barkum | .10 | .05 |
| 22 | Larry Csonka | 1.50 | .75 |
| 23 | Joe Ferguson | .25 | .12 |
| 24 | Ed Too Tall Jones | 1.25 | .60 |
| 25 | Dave Jennings | .08 | .04 |
| 26 | Horace King | .08 | .04 |
| 27 | Steve Little | .08 | .04 |
| 28 | Morris Bradshaw | .08 | .04 |
| 29 | Joe Ehrmann | .08 | .04 |
| 30 | Ahmad Rashad | .60 | .35 |
| 31 | Joe Lavender | .08 | .04 |
| 32 | Dan Neal | .08 | .04 |
| 33 | Johnny Evans | .08 | .04 |
| 34 | Pete Johnson | .15 | .08 |
| 35 | Mike Haynes | .40 | .20 |
| 36 | Tim Mazzetti | .08 | .04 |
| 37 | Mike Barber (R) | .20 | .10 |
| 38 | 49ers (TL) | .90 | .45 |
| 39 | Bill Gregory | .08 | .04 |
| 40 | Randy Gradishar | .40 | .20 |
| 41 | Richard Todd | .30 | .15 |
| 42 | Henry Marshall | .08 | .04 |
| 43 | John Hill | .08 | .04 |
| 44 | Sidney Thornton | .08 | .04 |
| 45 | Ron Jessie | .10 | .05 |
| 46 | Bob Baumhower | .12 | .06 |
| 47 | Johnnie Gray | .08 | .04 |
| 48 | Doug Williams (R) | 1.50 | .75 |
| 49 | Don McCauley | .12 | .06 |
| 50 | Ray Guy | .30 | .15 |

| | | | |
|---|---|---|---|
| 51 | Bob Klein | .08 | .04 |
| 52 | Golden Richards | .08 | .04 |
| 53 | Mark Miller | .08 | .04 |
| 54 | John Sanders | .08 | .04 |
| 55 | Gary Burley | .08 | .04 |
| 56 | Steve Nelson | .08 | .04 |
| 57 | Bills (TL) | .40 | .20 |
| 58 | Bobby Bryant | .08 | .04 |
| 59 | Rick Kane | .08 | .04 |
| 60 | Larry Little | .75 | .35 |
| 61 | Ted Fritsch | .08 | .04 |
| 62 | Larry Mallory | .08 | .04 |
| 63 | Marvin Powell | .10 | .05 |
| 64 | Jim Hart | .50 | .25 |
| 65 | Joe Greene | 1.50 | .75 |
| 66 | Walter White | .08 | .04 |
| 67 | Gregg Bingham | .08 | .04 |
| 68 | Errol Mann | .08 | .04 |
| 69 | Bruce Laird | .08 | .04 |
| 70 | Drew Pearson | .75 | .35 |
| 71 | Steve Bartkowski | .75 | .35 |
| 72 | Ted Albrecht | .08 | .04 |
| 73 | Charlie Hall | .08 | .04 |
| 74 | Pat McInally | .12 | .06 |
| 75 | Bubba Baker (R) | .60 | .30 |
| 76 | Patriots (TL) | .50 | .25 |
| 77 | Steve DeBerg (R) | 5.00 | 2.50 |
| 78 | John Yarno | .08 | .04 |
| 79 | Stu Voigt | .08 | .04 |
| 80 | Frank Corral | .08 | .04 |
| 81 | Troy Archer | .08 | .04 |
| 82 | Bruce Harper | .08 | .04 |
| 83 | Tom Jackson | .60 | .30 |
| 84 | Larry Brown | .08 | .04 |
| 85 | Wilbert Montgomery(R) | .90 | .45 |
| 86 | Butch Johnson | .15 | .08 |
| 87 | Mike Kadish | .08 | .04 |
| 88 | Ralph Perretta | .08 | .04 |
| 89 | David Lee | .08 | .04 |
| 90 | Mark Van Eeghen | .15 | .08 |
| 91 | John McDaniel | .08 | .04 |
| 92 | Gary Fencik | .15 | .08 |
| 93 | Mack Mitchell | .08 | .04 |
| 94 | Bengals (TL) | .40 | .20 |
| 95 | Steve Grogan | .50 | .25 |
| 96 | Garo Yepremian | .10 | .05 |
| 97 | Barty Smith | .08 | .04 |
| 98 | Frank Reed | .08 | .04 |
| 99 | Jim Clark | .08 | .04 |
| 100 | Chuck Foreman | .60 | .30 |
| 101 | Joe Klecko | .60 | .30 |
| 102 | Pat Tilley | .08 | .04 |
| 103 | Conrad Dobler | .12 | .06 |
| 104 | Craig Colquitt (R) | .12 | .06 |
| 105 | Dan Pastorini | .35 | .18 |
| 106 | Rod Perry | .10 | .05 |
| 107 | Nick Mike-Mayer | .08 | .04 |

| | | | |
|---|---|---|---|
| 108 | John Matuszak | .15 | .08 |
| 109 | David Taylor | .08 | .04 |
| 110 | Billy Joe Dupree | .15 | .08 |
| 111 | Harold McLinton | .08 | .04 |
| 112 | Virgil Livers | .08 | .04 |
| 113 | Browns (TL) | .40 | .20 |
| 114 | Checklist 1-132 | .75 | .10 |
| 115 | Ken Anderson | 1.25 | .60 |
| 116 | Bill Lenkaitis | .08 | .04 |
| 117 | Bucky Dilts | .08 | .04 |
| 118 | Tony Greene | .08 | .04 |
| 119 | Bobby Hammond | .08 | .04 |
| 120 | Nat Moore | .25 | .12 |
| 121 | Pat Leahy | .15 | .08 |
| 122 | James Harris | .15 | .08 |
| 123 | Lee Roy Selmon | .40 | .20 |
| 124 | Bennie Cunningham | .12 | .06 |
| 125 | Matt Blair | .12 | .06 |
| 126 | Jim Allen | .08 | .04 |
| 127 | Alfred Jenkins | .15 | .08 |
| 128 | Arthur Whittington (R) | .12 | .06 |
| 129 | Norm Thompson | .08 | .04 |
| 130 | Pat Haden | .50 | .25 |
| 131 | Freddie Solomon | .12 | .06 |
| 132 | Bears (TL) | 1.00 | .50 |
| 133 | Mark Moseley | .15 | .08 |
| 134 | Cleo Miller | .08 | .04 |
| 135 | Ross Browner (R) | .30 | .15 |
| 136 | Don Calhoun | .08 | .04 |
| 137 | David Whitehurst (R) | .20 | .10 |
| 138 | Terry Beeson | .08 | .04 |
| 139 | Ken Stone | .08 | .04 |
| 140 | Brad Van Pelt | .12 | .06 |
| 141 | Wesley Walker | .75 | .35 |
| 142 | Jan Stenerud | .40 | .20 |
| 143 | Henry Childs | .08 | .04 |
| 144 | Otis Armstrong | .30 | .15 |
| 145 | Dwight White | .15 | .08 |
| 146 | Steve Wilson | .08 | .04 |
| 147 | Tom Skladany (R) | .12 | .06 |
| 148 | Lou Piccone | .08 | .04 |
| 149 | Monte Johnson | .08 | .04 |
| 150 | Joe Washington | .25 | .12 |
| 151 | Eagles (TL) | .50 | .25 |
| 152 | Fred Dean | .20 | .10 |
| 153 | Rolland Lawrence | .08 | .04 |
| 154 | Brian Baschnagel | .10 | .05 |
| 155 | Joe Theismann | 1.50 | .75 |
| 156 | Marvin Cobb | .08 | .04 |
| 157 | Dick Ambrose | .08 | .04 |
| 158 | Mike Patrick | .08 | .04 |
| 159 | Gary Shirk | .08 | .04 |
| 160 | Tony Dorsett | 9.00 | 4.50 |
| 161 | Greg Buttle | .10 | .05 |
| 162 | A.J. Duhe | .15 | .08 |
| 163 | Mick Tingelhoff | .12 | .06 |
| 164 | Ken Burrough | .15 | .08 |
| 165 | Mike Wagner | .12 | .06 |
| 166 | AFC Championship | .80 | .50 |
| 167 | NFC Championship | .40 | .20 |
| 168 | Super Bowl XIII | 1.00 | .50 |
| 169 | Raiders (TL) | .75 | .35 |
| 170 | O.J. Simpson | 6.00 | 3.00 |
| 171 | Doug Nettles | .08 | .04 |
| 172 | Dan Dierdorf | .35 | .18 |
| 173 | Dave Beverly | .08 | .04 |
| 174 | Jim Zorn | .40 | .20 |
| 175 | Mike Thomas | .08 | .04 |
| 176 | John Outlaw | .08 | .04 |
| 177 | Jim Turner | .08 | .04 |
| 178 | Freddie Scott | .08 | .04 |
| 179 | Mike Phipps | .25 | .12 |
| 180 | Jack Youngblood | .75 | .35 |
| 181 | Sam Hunt | .08 | .04 |
| 182 | Tony Hill (R) | 1.25 | .60 |
| 183 | Gary Barbaro (R) | .15 | .08 |
| 184 | Archie Griffin | .40 | .20 |
| 185 | Jerry Sherk | .08 | .04 |
| 186 | Bobby Jackson | .08 | .04 |
| 187 | Don Woods | .08 | .04 |
| 188 | Giants (TL) | .40 | .20 |
| 189 | Raymond Chester | .15 | .08 |
| 190 | Joe DeLamielleure | .12 | .06 |
| 191 | Tony Galbreath | .15 | .08 |
| 192 | Robert Brazile | .12 | .06 |
| 193 | Neil O'Donoghue | .08 | .04 |
| 194 | Mike Webster | .90 | .45 |
| 195 | Ed Simonini | .08 | .04 |
| 196 | Benny Malone | .08 | .04 |
| 197 | Tom Wittum | .08 | .04 |
| 198 | Steve Largent | 8.00 | 4.00 |
| 199 | Tommy Hart | .08 | .04 |
| 200 | Fran Tarkenton | 4.50 | 2.25 |
| 201 | Leon Gray | .12 | .06 |
| 202 | Leroy Harris | .08 | .04 |
| 203 | Eric Williams | .08 | .04 |
| 204 | Thom Darden | .10 | .05 |
| 205 | Ken Riley | .12 | .06 |
| 206 | Clark Gaines | .08 | .04 |
| 207 | Chiefs (TL) | .40 | .20 |
| 208 | Joe Danelo | .08 | .04 |
| 209 | Glen Walker | .08 | .04 |
| 210 | Art Shell | .60 | .30 |
| 211 | Jon Keyworth | .10 | .05 |
| 212 | Herman Edwards | .08 | .04 |
| 213 | John Fitzgerald | .08 | .04 |
| 214 | Jim Smith | .08 | .04 |
| 215 | Coy Bacon | .08 | .04 |
| 216 | Dennis Johnson | .08 | .04 |
| 217 | John Jefferson (R) | 1.75 | .85 |
| 218 | Gary Weaver | .08 | .04 |
| 219 | Tom Blanchard | .08 | .04 |
| 220 | Bert Jones | .60 | .30 |
| 221 | Stanley Morgan | 1.75 | .85 |

| | | | |
|---|---|---|---|
| 222 James Hunter | .08 | .04 |
| 223 Jim O'Bradovich | .08 | .04 |
| 224 Carl Mauck | .08 | .04 |
| 225 Chris Bahr | .08 | .04 |
| 226 Jets (TL) | .50 | .25 |
| 227 Roland Harper | .15 | .08 |
| 228 Randy Dean | .08 | .04 |
| 229 Bob Jackson | .08 | .04 |
| 230 Sammie White | .15 | .08 |
| 231 Mike Dawson | .08 | .04 |
| 232 Checklist 133-264 | .75 | .10 |
| 233 Ken MacAfee | .12 | .06 |
| 234 Jon Kolb | .10 | .05 |
| 235 Willie Hall | .08 | .04 |
| 236 Ron Saul | .08 | .04 |
| 237 Haskel Stanback | .12 | .06 |
| 238 Zenon Andrusyshyn | .08 | .04 |
| 239 Norris Thomas | .08 | .04 |
| 240 Rick Upchurch | .20 | .10 |
| 241 Robert Pratt | .08 | .04 |
| 242 Julius Adams | .08 | .04 |
| 243 Rich McGeorge | .08 | .04 |
| 244 Seahawks (TL) | .80 | .40 |
| 245 Blair Bush (R) | .20 | .10 |
| 246 Billy Johnson | .25 | .12 |
| 247 Randy Rasmussen | .08 | .04 |
| 248 Brian Kelley | .08 | .04 |
| 249 Mike Pruitt | .25 | .12 |
| 250 Harold Carmichael | .75 | .35 |
| 251 Mike Hartenstine | .08 | .04 |
| 252 Robert Newhouse | .25 | .12 |
| 253 Gary Danielson (R) | .25 | .12 |
| 254 Mike Fuller | .08 | .04 |
| 255 L.C.Greenwood | .60 | .30 |
| 256 Lemar Parrish | .10 | .05 |
| 257 Ike Harris | .08 | .04 |
| 258 Ricky Bell (R) | 1.25 | .60 |
| 259 Willie Parker | .08 | .04 |
| 260 Gene Upshaw | .75 | .35 |
| 261 Glenn Doughty | .08 | .04 |
| 262 Steve Zabel | .08 | .04 |
| 263 Falcons (TL) | .40 | .20 |
| 264 Ray Wersching | .08 | .04 |
| 265 Lawrence McCutcheon | .25 | .12 |
| 266 Willie Buchanon | .15 | .08 |
| 267 Matt Robinson | .08 | .04 |
| 268 Reggie Rucker | .12 | .06 |
| 269 Doug Van Horn | .08 | .04 |
| 270 Lydell Mitchell | .20 | .10 |
| 271 Vern Holland | .08 | .04 |
| 272 Eason Ramson | .08 | .04 |
| 273 Steve Towle | .08 | .04 |
| 274 Jim Marshall | .60 | .30 |
| 275 Mel Blount | .90 | .45 |
| 276 Bob Kuziel | .08 | .04 |
| 277 James Scott | .08 | .04 |
| 278 Tony Reed | .08 | .04 |
| 279 Dave Green | .08 | .04 |
| 280 Toni Linhart | .08 | .04 |
| 281 Andy Johnson | .08 | .04 |
| 282 Rams (TL) | .40 | .20 |
| 283 Phil Villapiano | .15 | .08 |
| 284 Dexter Bussey | .08 | .04 |
| 285 Craig Morton | .50 | .25 |
| 286 Guy Morriss | .08 | .04 |
| 287 Lawrence Pillers | .08 | .04 |
| 288 Gerald Irons | .08 | .04 |
| 289 Scott Perry | .08 | .04 |
| 290 Randy White | 1.50 | .75 |
| 291 Jack Gregory | .08 | .04 |
| 292 Bob Chandler | .08 | .04 |
| 293 Rich Szaro | .08 | .04 |
| 294 Sherman Smith | .15 | .08 |
| 295 Tom Banks | .12 | .06 |
| 296 Revie Sorey | .10 | .05 |
| 297 Ricky Thompson | .08 | .04 |
| 298 Ron Yary | .15 | .08 |
| 299 Lyle Blackwood | .10 | .05 |
| 300 Franco Harris | 2.50 | 1.25 |
| 301 Oilers (TL) | 2.00 | 1.00 |
| 302 Scott Bull | .12 | .06 |
| 303 Dewey Selmon | .12 | .06 |
| 304 Jack Rudnay | .08 | .04 |
| 305 Fred Biletnikoff | 1.25 | .60 |
| 306 Jeff West | .08 | .04 |
| 307 Shafer Suggs | .08 | .04 |
| 308 Ozzie Newsome (R) | 25.00 | 12.50 |
| 309 Boobie Clark | .15 | .08 |
| 310 James Lofton (R) | 38.00 | 19.00 |
| 311 Joe Pisarcik | .12 | .06 |
| 312 Bill Simpson | .08 | .04 |
| 313 Haven Moses | .15 | .08 |
| 314 Jim Merlo | .08 | .04 |
| 315 Preston Pearson | .15 | .08 |
| 316 Larry Tearry | .08 | .04 |
| 317 Tom Dempsey | .08 | .04 |
| 318 Greg Latta | .08 | .04 |
| 319 Redskins (TL) | .80 | .40 |
| 320 Jack Ham | 1.25 | .60 |
| 321 Harold Jackson | .50 | .25 |
| 322 George Roberts | .08 | .04 |
| 323 Ron Jaworski | .50 | .25 |
| 324 Jim Otis | .15 | .08 |
| 325 Roger Carr | .10 | .05 |
| 326 Jack Tatum | .20 | .10 |
| 327 Derrick Gaffney | .08 | .04 |
| 328 Reggie Willaims | .30 | .15 |
| 329 Doug Dieken | .08 | .04 |
| 330 Efren Herrera | .08 | .04 |
| 331 Earl Campbell (RB) | 6.00 | 3.00 |
| 332 Tony Galbreath (RB) | .15 | .08 |
| 333 Bruce Harper (RB) | .12 | .06 |
| 334 John James (RB) | .10 | .05 |
| 335 Walter Payton (RB) | 3.50 | 1.75 |

| | | | |
|---|---|---|---|
| 336 | Rickey Young (RB) | .12 | .06 |
| 337 | Jeff Van Note | .12 | .06 |
| 338 | Chargers (TL) | .60 | .30 |
| 339 | Stan Walters (R) | .15 | .08 |
| 340 | Louis Wright | .15 | .08 |
| 341 | Horace Ivory | .08 | .04 |
| 342 | Andre Tillman | .08 | .04 |
| 343 | Greg Coleman (R) | .12 | .06 |
| 344 | Doug English (R) | .60 | .30 |
| 345 | Ted Hendricks | .75 | .35 |
| 346 | Rich Saul | .08 | .04 |
| 347 | Mel Gray | .12 | .06 |
| 348 | Toni Fritsch | .08 | .04 |
| 349 | Cornell Webster | .08 | .04 |
| 350 | Ken Houston | .75 | .35 |
| 351 | Ron Johnson | .08 | .04 |
| 352 | Doug Kotar | .08 | .04 |
| 353 | Brian Sipe | .50 | .25 |
| 354 | Billy Brooks | .15 | .08 |
| 355 | John Dutton | .12 | .06 |
| 356 | Don Goode | .08 | .04 |
| 357 | Lions (TL) | .40 | .20 |
| 358 | Reuben Gant | .08 | .04 |
| 359 | Bob Parsons | .08 | .04 |
| 360 | Cliff Harris | .25 | .12 |
| 361 | Raymond Clayborn | .15 | .08 |
| 362 | Scott Dierking | .08 | .04 |
| 363 | Bill Bryan | .08 | .04 |
| 364 | Mike Livingston | .08 | .04 |
| 365 | Otis Sistrunk | .08 | .04 |
| 366 | Charley Young | .08 | .04 |
| 367 | Keith Wortman | .08 | .04 |
| 368 | Checklist 265-396 | .75 | .10 |
| 369 | Mike Michel | .08 | .04 |
| 370 | Delvin Williiams | .12 | .06 |
| 371 | Steve Furness | .08 | .04 |
| 372 | Emery Moorehead | .08 | .04 |
| 373 | Clarence Scott | .08 | .04 |
| 374 | Rufus Mayes | .08 | .04 |
| 375 | Chris Hanburger | .20 | .10 |
| 376 | Colts (TL) | .40 | .20 |
| 377 | Bob Avellini | .15 | .08 |
| 378 | Jeff Siemon | .08 | .04 |
| 379 | Roland Hooks | .08 | .04 |
| 380 | Russ Francis | .15 | .08 |
| 381 | Roger Wehrli | .08 | .04 |
| 382 | Joe Fields | .10 | .05 |
| 383 | Archie Manning | .50 | .25 |
| 384 | Rob Lytle | .08 | .04 |
| 385 | Thomas Henderson | .12 | .06 |
| 386 | Morris Owens | .08 | .04 |
| 387 | Dan Fouts | 4.50 | 2.25 |
| 388 | Chuck Crist | .08 | .04 |
| 389 | Ed O'Neil | .08 | .04 |
| 390 | Earl Campbell (R) | 36.00 | 18.00 |
| 391 | Randy Grossman | .08 | .04 |
| 392 | Monte Jackson | .08 | .04 |
| 393 | John Mendenhall | .08 | .04 |
| 394 | Dolphins (TL) | .40 | .20 |
| 395 | Isaac Curtis | .20 | .10 |
| 396 | Mike Bragg | .08 | .04 |
| 397 | Doug Plank | .08 | .04 |
| 398 | Mike Barnes | .08 | .04 |
| 399 | Calvin Hill | .15 | .08 |
| 400 | Roger Staubach | 5.00 | 2.50 |
| 401 | Doug Beaudoin | .08 | .04 |
| 402 | Chuck Ramsey | .08 | .04 |
| 403 | Mike Hogan | .08 | .04 |
| 404 | Mario Clark | .08 | .04 |
| 405 | Riley Odoms | .12 | .06 |
| 406 | Carl Eller | .60 | .30 |
| 407 | Packers (TL) | 1.75 | .85 |
| 408 | Mark Arneson | .08 | .04 |
| 409 | Vince Ferragamo (R) | .90 | .45 |
| 410 | Cleveland Elam | .08 | .04 |
| 411 | Donnie Shell (R) | 1.75 | .85 |
| 412 | Ray Rhodes | .08 | .04 |
| 413 | Don Cockroft | .08 | .04 |
| 414 | Don Bass | .08 | .04 |
| 415 | Cliff Branch | .50 | .25 |
| 416 | Diron Talbert | .10 | .05 |
| 417 | Tom Hicks | .08 | .04 |
| 418 | Roosevelt Leaks | .12 | .06 |
| 419 | Charlie Joiner | .90 | .45 |
| 420 | Lyle Alzado | .50 | .25 |
| 421 | Sam Cunningham | .15 | .08 |
| 422 | Larry Keller | .08 | .04 |
| 423 | Jim Mitchell | .08 | .04 |
| 424 | Randy Logan | .08 | .04 |
| 425 | Jim Langer | .50 | .25 |
| 426 | Gary Green | .08 | .04 |
| 427 | Luther Blue | .08 | .04 |
| 428 | Dennis Johnson | .08 | .04 |
| 429 | Danny White | .80 | .40 |
| 430 | Roy Gerela | .08 | .04 |
| 431 | Jimmy Robinson | .08 | .04 |
| 432 | Vikings (TL) | .50 | .25 |
| 433 | Oliver Davis | .08 | .04 |
| 434 | Lenvil Elliott | .08 | .04 |
| 435 | Willie Miller | .08 | .04 |
| 436 | Brad Dusek | .08 | .04 |
| 437 | Bob Thomas | .08 | .04 |
| 438 | Ken Mendenhall | .08 | .04 |
| 439 | Clarence Davis | .12 | .06 |
| 440 | Bob Griese | 2.00 | 1.00 |
| 441 | Tony McGee | .08 | .04 |
| 442 | Ed Taylor | .08 | .04 |
| 443 | Ron Howard | .08 | .04 |
| 444 | Wayne Morris | .08 | .04 |
| 445 | Charlie Waters | .25 | .12 |
| 446 | Rick Danmeier | .08 | .04 |
| 447 | Paul Naumoff | .08 | .04 |
| 448 | Keith Krepfle | .08 | .04 |
| 449 | Rusty Jackson | .08 | .04 |

| | | | |
|---|---|---|---|
| 450 | John Stallworth | 2.50 | 1.25 |
| 451 | Saints (TL) | .40 | .20 |
| 452 | Ron Mikolajczyk | .08 | .04 |
| 453 | Fred Dryer | .80 | .40 |
| 454 | Jim LeClair | .08 | .04 |
| 455 | Greg Pruitt | .30 | .15 |
| 456 | Jake Scott | .12 | .06 |
| 457 | Steve Schubert | .08 | .04 |
| 458 | George Kunz | .08 | .04 |
| 459 | Mike Williams | .08 | .04 |
| 460 | Dave Casper | .15 | .08 |
| 461 | Sam Adams | .08 | .04 |
| 462 | Abdul Salaam | .08 | .04 |
| 463 | Terdell Middleton (R) | .15 | .08 |
| 464 | Mike Wood | .08 | .04 |
| 465 | Bill Thompson | .08 | .04 |
| 466 | Larry Gordon | .08 | .04 |
| 467 | Benny Ricardo | .08 | .04 |
| 468 | Reggie McKenzie | .12 | .06 |
| 469 | Cowboys (TL) | .90 | .45 |
| 470 | Rickey Young | .08 | .04 |
| 471 | Charlie Smith | .08 | .04 |
| 472 | Al Dixon | .08 | .04 |
| 473 | Tom DeLeone | .08 | .04 |
| 474 | Louis Breeden | .08 | .04 |
| 475 | Jack Lambert | 1.25 | .60 |
| 476 | Terry Hermeling | .08 | .04 |
| 477 | J.K. McKay | .08 | .04 |
| 478 | Stan White | .08 | .04 |
| 479 | Terry Nelson | .08 | .04 |
| 480 | Walter Payton | 10.00 | 5.00 |
| 481 | Dave Dalby | .08 | .04 |
| 482 | Burgess Owens | .08 | .04 |
| 483 | Rolf Benirschke | .08 | .04 |
| 484 | Jack Dolbin | .08 | .04 |
| 485 | John Hannah | .60 | .30 |
| 486 | Checklist 397-528 | .75 | .10 |
| 487 | Greg Landry | .35 | .18 |
| 488 | Cardinals (TL) | .40 | .20 |
| 489 | Paul Krause | .12 | .06 |
| 490 | John James | .08 | .04 |
| 491 | Merv Krakau | .08 | .04 |
| 492 | Dan Doornik | .08 | .04 |
| 493 | Curtis Johnson | .08 | .04 |
| 494 | Rafael Septien | .08 | .04 |
| 495 | Jean Fugett | .08 | .04 |
| 496 | Frank LeMaster | .08 | .04 |
| 497 | Allan Ellis | .08 | .04 |
| 498 | Bill Waddy (R) | .20 | .10 |
| 499 | Hank Bauer (R) | .15 | .08 |
| 500 | Terry Bradshaw | 3.50 | 1.75 |
| 501 | Larry McCarren | .08 | .04 |
| 502 | Fred Cook | .08 | .04 |
| 503 | Chuck Muncie | .30 | .15 |
| 504 | Herman Weaver | .08 | .04 |
| 505 | Eddie Edwards | .08 | .04 |
| 506 | Tony Peters | .08 | .04 |

| | | | |
|---|---|---|---|
| 507 | Broncos (TL) | .40 | .20 |
| 508 | Jimbo Elrod | .08 | .04 |
| 509 | David Hill | .08 | .04 |
| 510 | Harvey Martin | .30 | .15 |
| 511 | Terry Miller (R) | .20 | .10 |
| 512 | June Jones (R) | .15 | .08 |
| 513 | Randy Cross | .20 | .10 |
| 514 | Duriel Harris | .12 | .06 |
| 515 | Harry Carson | .80 | .40 |
| 516 | Tim Fox | .08 | .04 |
| 517 | John Zook | .08 | .04 |
| 518 | Bob Tucker | .08 | .04 |
| 519 | Kevin Long | .08 | .04 |
| 520 | Ken Stabler | 1.50 | .75 |
| 521 | John Bunting | .08 | .04 |
| 522 | Rocky Bleier | .40 | .20 |
| 523 | Noah Jackson | .08 | .04 |
| 524 | Cliff Parsley | .08 | .04 |
| 525 | Louie Kelcher | .12 | .06 |
| 526 | Buccaneers (TL) | .50 | .25 |
| 527 | Bob Brudzinski | .08 | .04 |
| 528 | Danny Buggs | .12 | .04 |

# 1980 Topps

JOHN JEFFERSON

This 528-card set features full color photos on the card fronts framed by a white border. The player's name appears across the bottom of the card in a small oval superimposed over a football. The team name is located above the name within the football and the player's position is printed below the name on the football. The horizontal card backs contain personal data, stats and a football fact. Key subsets include Record Breakers (RB). League Leaders (331-336), Playoffs (492-494) and Team Leaders (TL) which include multi-photos on the fronts and team checklists on the backs. All cards measure 2-1/2" by 3-1/2".

| | | MINT | NR/MT |
|---|---|---|---|
| | **Complete Set (528)** | 85.00 | 50.00 |
| | **Commons** | .08 | .05 |

| | | | |
|---|---|---|---|
| 1 | Otis Anderson (RB) | 1.25 | .70 |
| 2 | Harold Carmichael (RB) | .15 | .08 |
| 3 | Dan Fouts (RB) | 1.00 | .60 |
| 4 | Paul Krause (RB) | .10 | .06 |
| 5 | Rick Upchurch (RB) | .10 | .06 |
| 6 | Garo Yepremian (RB) | .10 | .06 |
| 7 | Harold Jackson | .25 | .15 |
| 8 | Mike Williams | .08 | .05 |
| 9 | Calvin Hill | .12 | .07 |
| 10 | Jack Ham | .75 | .40 |
| 11 | Dan Melville | .08 | .05 |
| 12 | Matt Robinson | .08 | .05 |
| 13 | Billy Campfield | .08 | .05 |
| 14 | Phil Tabor | .08 | .05 |
| 15 | Randy Hughes ER | .08 | .05 |
| 16 | Andre Tillman | .08 | .05 |
| 17 | Isaac Curtis | .15 | .08 |
| 18 | Charley Hannah | .08 | .05 |
| 19 | Redskins (TL) | .30 | .18 |
| 20 | Jim Zorn | .35 | .20 |
| 21 | Brian Baschnagel | .10 | .06 |
| 22 | Jon Keyworth | .08 | .05 |
| 23 | Phil Villapiano | .12 | .07 |
| 24 | Richard Osborne | .08 | .05 |
| 25 | Rich Saul | .08 | .05 |
| 26 | Doug Beaudoin | .08 | .05 |
| 27 | Cleveland Elam | .08 | .05 |
| 28 | Charlie Joiner | .80 | .50 |
| 29 | Dick Ambrose | .08 | .05 |
| 30 | Mike Reinfeldt (R) | .20 | .12 |
| 31 | Matt Bahr (R) | 1.25 | .70 |
| 32 | Keith Krepfle | .08 | .05 |
| 33 | Herbert Scott | .08 | .05 |
| 34 | Doug Kotar | .08 | .05 |
| 35 | Bob Griese | 1.75 | 1.00 |
| 36 | Jerry Butler (R) | .75 | .40 |
| 37 | Rolland Lawrence | .08 | .05 |
| 38 | Gary Weaver | .08 | .05 |
| 39 | Chiefs (TL) | .30 | .18 |
| 40 | Chuck Muncie | .15 | .08 |
| 41 | Mike Hartenstine | .08 | .05 |
| 42 | Sammie White | .12 | .07 |
| 43 | Ken Clark | .08 | .05 |
| 44 | Clarence Harmon | .08 | .05 |
| 45 | Bert Jones | .50 | .28 |
| 46 | Mike Washington | .08 | .05 |
| 47 | Joe Fields | .10 | .06 |
| 48 | Mike Wood | .08 | .05 |
| 49 | Oliver Davis | .08 | .05 |
| 50 | Stan Walters | .08 | .05 |
| 51 | Riley Odoms | .12 | .07 |
| 52 | Steve Pisarkiewicz | .12 | .07 |
| 53 | Tony Hill | .25 | .15 |
| 54 | Scott Perry | .08 | .05 |
| 55 | George Martin (R) | .35 | .20 |
| 56 | George Roberts | .08 | .05 |
| 57 | Seahawks (TL) | .75 | .40 |
| 58 | Billy Johnson | .20 | .12 |
| 59 | Reuben Gant | .08 | .05 |
| 60 | Dennis Harrah (R) | .20 | .12 |
| 61 | Rocky Bleier | .30 | .18 |
| 62 | Sam Hunt | .08 | .05 |
| 63 | Allan Ellis | .08 | .05 |
| 64 | Ricky Thompson | .08 | .05 |
| 65 | Ken Stabler | .80 | .45 |
| 66 | Dexter Bussey | .08 | .05 |
| 67 | Ken Mendenhall | .08 | .05 |
| 68 | Woodrow Lowe | .08 | .05 |
| 69 | Thom Darden | .08 | .05 |
| 70 | Randy White | 1.25 | .70 |
| 71 | Ken MacAfee | .10 | .06 |
| 72 | Ron Jaworski | .35 | .20 |
| 73 | William Andrews (R) | .60 | .35 |
| 74 | Jimmy Robinson | .08 | .05 |
| 75 | Roger Wehrli | .08 | .05 |
| 76 | Dolphins (TL) | .40 | .22 |
| 77 | Jack Rudnay | .08 | .05 |
| 78 | James Lofton | 8.50 | 4.50 |
| 79 | Robert Brazile | .12 | .07 |
| 80 | Russ Francis | .12 | .07 |
| 81 | Ricky Bell | .25 | .15 |
| 82 | Bob Avellini | .12 | .07 |
| 83 | Bobby Jackson | .08 | .05 |
| 84 | Mike Bragg | .08 | .05 |
| 85 | Cliff Branch | .50 | .28 |
| 86 | Blair Bush | .08 | .05 |
| 87 | Sherman Smith | .08 | .05 |
| 88 | Glen Edwards | .08 | .05 |
| 89 | Don Cockroft | .08 | .05 |
| 90 | Louis Wright | .10 | .06 |
| 91 | Randy Grossman | .08 | .05 |
| 92 | Carl Hairston (R) | .50 | .28 |
| 93 | Archie Manning | .40 | .22 |
| 94 | Giants (TL) | .25 | .15 |
| 95 | Preston Pearson | .15 | .08 |
| 96 | Rusty Chambers | .08 | .05 |
| 97 | Greg Coleman | .08 | .05 |
| 98 | Charley Young | .08 | .05 |
| 99 | Matt Cavanaugh (R) | .30 | .18 |
| 100 | Jesse Baker | .08 | .05 |
| 101 | Doug Plank | .08 | .05 |
| 102 | Checklist 1-132 | .50 | .08 |
| 103 | Luther Bradley (R) | .15 | .08 |
| 104 | Bob Kuziel | .08 | .05 |
| 105 | Craig Morton | .50 | .28 |

| | | | |
|---|---|---|---|
| 106 | Sherman White | .08 | .05 |
| 107 | Jim Breech (R) | .50 | .28 |
| 108 | Hank Bauer | .08 | .05 |
| 109 | Tom Blanchard | .08 | .05 |
| 110 | Ozzie Newsome | 5.00 | 2.75 |
| 111 | Steve Furness | .08 | .05 |
| 112 | Frank LeMaster | .08 | .05 |
| 113 | Cowboys (TL) | .60 | .35 |
| 114 | Doug Van Horn | .08 | .05 |
| 115 | Delvin Williams | .12 | .07 |
| 116 | Lyle Blackwood | .08 | .05 |
| 117 | Derrick Gaffney | .08 | .05 |
| 118 | Cornell Webster | .08 | .05 |
| 119 | Sam Cunningham | .12 | .07 |
| 120 | Jim Youngblood | .10 | .06 |
| 121 | Bob Thomas | .08 | .05 |
| 122 | Jack Thompson (R) | .20 | .12 |
| 123 | Randy Cross | .10 | .06 |
| 124 | Karl Lorch | .08 | .05 |
| 125 | Mel Gray | .12 | .07 |
| 126 | John James | .08 | .05 |
| 127 | Terdell Middleton | .08 | .05 |
| 128 | Leroy Jones | .08 | .05 |
| 129 | Tom DeLeone | .08 | .05 |
| 130 | John Stallworth | .90 | .50 |
| 131 | Jimmie Giles (R) | .30 | .18 |
| 132 | Eagles (TL) | .25 | .15 |
| 133 | Gary Green | .10 | .06 |
| 134 | John Dutton | .12 | .07 |
| 135 | Harry Carson | .50 | .28 |
| 136 | Bob Kuechenberg | .10 | .06 |
| 137 | Ike Harris | .08 | .05 |
| 138 | Tommy Kramer (R) | .80 | .50 |
| 139 | Sam Adams | .08 | .05 |
| 140 | Doug English | .15 | .08 |
| 141 | Steve Schubert | .08 | .05 |
| 142 | Rusty Jackson | .08 | .05 |
| 143 | Reese McCall | .08 | .05 |
| 144 | Scott Dierking | .08 | .05 |
| 145 | Ken Houston | .75 | .40 |
| 146 | Bob Martin | .08 | .05 |
| 147 | Sam McCullum | .10 | .06 |
| 148 | Tom Banks | .10 | .06 |
| 149 | Willie Buchanon | .10 | .06 |
| 150 | Greg Pruitt | .20 | .12 |
| 151 | Broncos (TL) | .25 | .15 |
| 152 | Don Smith | .08 | .05 |
| 153 | Pete Johnson | .15 | .08 |
| 154 | Charlie Smith | .08 | .05 |
| 155 | Mel Blount | .75 | .40 |
| 156 | John Mendenhall | .08 | .05 |
| 157 | Danny White | .50 | .28 |
| 158 | Jimmy Cefalo (R) | .30 | .18 |
| 159 | Richard Bishop | .08 | .05 |
| 160 | Walter Payton | 10.00 | 6.00 |
| 161 | Dave Dalby | .08 | .05 |
| 162 | Preston Dennard | .08 | .05 |
| 163 | Johnnie Gray | .08 | .05 |
| 164 | Russell Erxleben | .08 | .05 |
| 165 | Toni Fritsch | .08 | .05 |
| 166 | Terry Hermeling | .08 | .05 |
| 167 | Roland Hooks | .08 | .05 |
| 168 | Roger Carr | .08 | .05 |
| 169 | Chargers (TL) | .25 | .15 |
| 170 | Otis Anderson (R) | 10.00 | 6.00 |
| 171 | Brian Sipe | .40 | .22 |
| 172 | Leonard Thompson | .08 | .05 |
| 173 | Tony Reed | .08 | .05 |
| 174 | Bob Tucker | .08 | .05 |
| 175 | Joe Greene | 1.00 | .60 |
| 176 | Jack Dolbin | .08 | .05 |
| 177 | Chuck Ramsey | .08 | .05 |
| 178 | Paul Hofer | .10 | .06 |
| 179 | Randy Logan | .08 | .05 |
| 180 | David Lewis | .08 | .05 |
| 181 | Duriel Harris | .08 | .05 |
| 182 | June Jones | .08 | .05 |
| 183 | Larry McCarren | .08 | .05 |
| 184 | Ken Johnson | .08 | .05 |
| 185 | Charlie Waters | .15 | .08 |
| 186 | Noah Jackson | .08 | .05 |
| 187 | Reggie Williams | .25 | .15 |
| 188 | Patriots (TL) | .25 | .15 |
| 189 | Carl Eller | .50 | .28 |
| 190 | Ed White | .10 | .06 |
| 191 | Mario Clark | .08 | .05 |
| 192 | Roosevelt Leaks | .12 | .07 |
| 193 | Ted McKnight | .08 | .05 |
| 194 | Danny Buggs | .08 | .05 |
| 195 | Lester Hayes (R) | 1.75 | 1.00 |
| 196 | Clarence Scott | .08 | .05 |
| 197 | Saints (TL) | .30 | .18 |
| 198 | Richard Caster | .12 | .07 |
| 199 | Louie Giammona | .08 | .05 |
| 200 | Terry Bradshaw | 2.75 | 1.50 |
| 201 | Ed Newman | .08 | .05 |
| 202 | Fred Dryer | .75 | .40 |
| 203 | Dennis Franks | .08 | .05 |
| 204 | Bob Breunig (R) | .30 | .18 |
| 205 | Alan Page | .80 | .45 |
| 206 | Earnest Gray (R) | .15 | .08 |
| 207 | Vikings (TL) | .25 | .15 |
| 208 | Horace Ivory | .08 | .05 |
| 209 | Isaac Hagins | .08 | .05 |
| 210 | Gary Johnson | .10 | .06 |
| 211 | Kevin Long | .08 | .05 |
| 212 | Bill Thompson | .08 | .05 |
| 213 | Don Bass | .08 | .05 |
| 214 | George Starke (R) | .15 | .08 |
| 215 | Efren Herrera | .08 | .05 |
| 216 | Theo Bell | .08 | .05 |
| 217 | Monte Jackson | .08 | .05 |
| 218 | Reggie McKenzie | .12 | .07 |
| 219 | Bucky Dilts | .08 | .05 |

| | | | |
|---|---|---|---|
| 220 | Lyle Alzado | .40 | .22 |
| 221 | Tim Foley | .10 | .06 |
| 222 | Mark Arneson | .08 | .05 |
| 223 | Fred Quillan | .08 | .05 |
| 224 | Benny Ricardo | .08 | .05 |
| 225 | Phil Simms (R) | 15.00 | 8.00 |
| 226 | Bears (TL) | 1.00 | .60 |
| 227 | Max Runager | .08 | .05 |
| 228 | Barty Smith | .08 | .05 |
| 229 | Jay Saldi | .08 | .05 |
| 230 | John Hannah | .40 | .22 |
| 231 | Tim Wilson | .10 | .06 |
| 232 | Jeff Van Note | .10 | .06 |
| 233 | Henry Marshall | .08 | .05 |
| 234 | Diron Talbert | .10 | .06 |
| 235 | Garo Yepremian | .10 | .06 |
| 236 | Larry Brown | .08 | .05 |
| 237 | Clarence Williams | .08 | .05 |
| 238 | Burgess Owens | .08 | .05 |
| 239 | Vince Ferragamo | .30 | .18 |
| 240 | Rickey Young | .08 | .05 |
| 241 | Dave Logan | .08 | .05 |
| 242 | Larry Gordon | .08 | .05 |
| 243 | Terry Miller | .08 | .05 |
| 244 | Colts (TL) | .25 | .15 |
| 245 | Steve DeBerg | 1.25 | .70 |
| 246 | Checklist 133-264 | .50 | .08 |
| 247 | Greg Latta | .08 | .05 |
| 248 | Raymond Clayborn | .12 | .07 |
| 249 | Jim Clark | .08 | .05 |
| 250 | Drew Pearson | .40 | .22 |
| 251 | John Bunting | .08 | .05 |
| 252 | Rob Lytle | .08 | .05 |
| 253 | Jim Hart | .40 | .22 |
| 254 | John McDaniel | .08 | .05 |
| 255 | Dave Pear | .08 | .05 |
| 256 | Donnie Shell | .40 | .22 |
| 257 | Dan Doornink | .08 | .05 |
| 258 | Wallace Francis (R) | .20 | .12 |
| 259 | Dave Beverly | .08 | .05 |
| 260 | Lee Roy Selmon | .25 | .15 |
| 261 | Doug Dieken | .08 | .05 |
| 262 | Gary Davis | .08 | .05 |
| 263 | Bob Rush | .08 | .05 |
| 264 | Bills (TL) | .25 | .15 |
| 265 | Greg Landry | .35 | .20 |
| 266 | Jan Stenerud | .40 | .22 |
| 267 | Tom Hicks | .08 | .05 |
| 268 | Pat McInally | .12 | .07 |
| 269 | Tim Fox | .08 | .05 |
| 270 | Harvey Martin | .25 | .15 |
| 271 | Dan Lloyd | .08 | .05 |
| 272 | Mike Barber | .10 | .06 |
| 273 | Wendell Tyler (R) | .50 | .28 |
| 274 | Jeff Komlo | .08 | .05 |
| 275 | Wes Chandler (R) | 1.50 | .80 |
| 276 | Brad Dusek | .08 | .05 |
| 277 | Charlie Johnson | .08 | .05 |
| 278 | Dennis Swilley (R) | .12 | .07 |
| 279 | Johnny Evans | .08 | .05 |
| 280 | Jack Lambert | 1.25 | .70 |
| 281 | Vern Den Herder | .08 | .05 |
| 282 | Buccaneers (TL) | .25 | .15 |
| 283 | Bob Klein | .08 | .05 |
| 284 | Jim Turner | .08 | .05 |
| 285 | Marvin Powell | .12 | .07 |
| 286 | Aaron Kyle | .08 | .05 |
| 287 | Dan Neal | .08 | .05 |
| 288 | Wayne Morris | .08 | .05 |
| 289 | Steve Bartkowski | .40 | .22 |
| 290 | Dave Jennings | .08 | .05 |
| 291 | John Smith | .08 | .05 |
| 292 | Bill Gregory | .08 | .05 |
| 293 | Frank Lewis | .12 | .07 |
| 294 | Fred Cook | .08 | .05 |
| 295 | David Hill | .08 | .05 |
| 296 | Wade Key | .08 | .05 |
| 297 | Sidney Thornton | .08 | .05 |
| 298 | Charlie Hall | .08 | .05 |
| 299 | Joe Lavender | .08 | .05 |
| 300 | Tom Rafferty (R) | .15 | .08 |
| 301 | Mike Renfro (R) | .30 | .18 |
| 302 | Wilbur Jackson | .12 | .07 |
| 303 | Packers (TL) | .60 | .35 |
| 304 | Henry Childs | .08 | .05 |
| 305 | Russ Washington | .08 | .05 |
| 306 | Jim LeClair | .08 | .05 |
| 307 | Tommy Hart | .08 | .05 |
| 308 | Gary Barbaro (R) | .15 | .08 |
| 309 | Billy Taylor | .08 | .05 |
| 310 | Ray Guy | .30 | .18 |
| 311 | Don Hasselbeck | .08 | .05 |
| 312 | Doug Williams | .75 | .40 |
| 313 | Nick Mike-Mayer | .08 | .05 |
| 314 | Don McCauley | .10 | .06 |
| 315 | Wesley Walker | .40 | .22 |
| 316 | Dan Dierdorf | .40 | .22 |
| 317 | Dave Brown (R) | .30 | .18 |
| 318 | Leroy Harris | .08 | .05 |
| 319 | Steelers (TL) | .60 | .35 |
| 320 | Mark Moseley | .12 | .07 |
| 321 | Mark Dennard | .08 | .05 |
| 322 | Terry Nelson | .08 | .05 |
| 323 | Tom Jackson | .40 | .22 |
| 324 | Rick Kane | .08 | .05 |
| 325 | Jerry Sherk | .08 | .05 |
| 326 | Ray Preston | .08 | .05 |
| 327 | Golden Richards | .08 | .05 |
| 328 | Randy Dean | .08 | .05 |
| 329 | Rick Danmeier | .08 | .05 |
| 330 | Tony Dorsett | 5.50 | 3.00 |
| 331 | Passing Leaders | 2.50 | 1.40 |
| | Dan Fouts | | |
| | Roger Staubach | | |

| | | | |
|---|---|---|---|
| 332 | Receiving Leaders | .25 | .15 |
| | Joe Washington | | |
| | Ahmad Rashad | | |
| 333 | Sacks Leaders | .12 | .07 |
| | Jesse Baker | | |
| | Bubba Baker | | |
| 334 | Scoring Leaders | .12 | .07 |
| | John Smith | | |
| | Mark Moseley | | |
| 335 | Interception Leaders | .12 | .07 |
| | Mike Reinfeldt | | |
| | Lemar Parrish | | |
| 336 | Punting Leaders | .10 | .06 |
| | Bob Grupp | | |
| | Dave Jennings | | |
| 337 | Freddie Solomon | .10 | .06 |
| 338 | Bengals (TL) | .25 | .15 |
| 339 | Ken Stone | .08 | .05 |
| 340 | Greg Buttle | .10 | .06 |
| 341 | Bob Baumhower | .10 | .06 |
| 342 | Billy Waddy | .08 | .05 |
| 343 | Cliff Parsley | .08 | .05 |
| 344 | Walter White | .08 | .05 |
| 345 | Mike Thomas | .08 | .05 |
| 346 | Neil O'Donoghue | .08 | .05 |
| 347 | Freddie Scott | .08 | .05 |
| 348 | Joe Ferguson | .30 | .18 |
| 349 | Doug Nettles | .08 | .05 |
| 350 | Mike Webster | .50 | .28 |
| 351 | Ron Saul | .08 | .05 |
| 352 | Julius Adams | .08 | .05 |
| 353 | Rafael Septien | .08 | .05 |
| 354 | Cleo Miller | .08 | .05 |
| 355 | Keith Simpson | .08 | .05 |
| 356 | Johnny Perkins | .08 | .05 |
| 357 | Jerry Sisemore | .08 | .05 |
| 358 | Arthur Whittington | .08 | .05 |
| 359 | Cardinals (TL) | .50 | .28 |
| 360 | Rick Upchurch | .15 | .08 |
| 361 | Kim Bokamper (R) | .15 | .08 |
| 362 | Roland Harper | .12 | .07 |
| 363 | Pat Leahy | .12 | .07 |
| 364 | Louis Breeden | .08 | .05 |
| 365 | John Jefferson | .50 | .28 |
| 366 | Jerry Eckwood | .08 | .05 |
| 367 | David Whitehurst | .12 | .07 |
| 368 | Willie Parker | .08 | .05 |
| 369 | Ed Simonini | .08 | .05 |
| 370 | Jack Youngblood | .50 | .28 |
| 371 | Don Warren (R) | 1.00 | .60 |
| 372 | Andy Johnson | .08 | .05 |
| 373 | D.D. Lewis | .10 | .06 |
| 374 | Beasley Reece (R) | .12 | .07 |
| 375 | L.C. Greenwood | .40 | .22 |
| 376 | Browns (TL) | .25 | .15 |
| 377 | Herman Edwards | .08 | .05 |
| 378 | Rob Carpenter (R) | .20 | .12 |
| 379 | Herman Weaver | .08 | .05 |
| 380 | Gary Fencik | .15 | .08 |
| 381 | Don Strock | .20 | .12 |
| 382 | Art Shell | .60 | .35 |
| 383 | Tim Mazzetti | .08 | .05 |
| 384 | Bruce Harper | .08 | .05 |
| 385 | Bubba Baker | .12 | .07 |
| 386 | Conrad Dobler | .12 | .07 |
| 387 | Stu Voigt | .08 | .05 |
| 388 | Ken Anderson | .80 | .45 |
| 389 | Pat Tilley | .08 | .05 |
| 390 | John Riggins | 1.25 | .70 |
| 391 | Checklist 265-396 | .50 | .08 |
| 392 | Fred Dean | .15 | .08 |
| 393 | Benny Barnes (R) | .15 | .08 |
| 394 | Rams (TL) | .25 | .15 |
| 395 | Brad Van Pelt | .08 | .05 |
| 396 | Eddie Hare | .08 | .05 |
| 397 | John Sciarra (R) | .15 | .08 |
| 398 | Bob Jackson | .08 | .05 |
| 399 | John Yarno | .08 | .05 |
| 400 | Franco Harris | 2.00 | 1.20 |
| 401 | Ray Wersching | .08 | .05 |
| 402 | Virgil Livers | .08 | .05 |
| 403 | Raynond Chester | .15 | .08 |
| 404 | Leon Gray | .12 | .07 |
| 405 | Richard Todd | .25 | .15 |
| 406 | Larry Little | .40 | .22 |
| 407 | Ted Fritsch | .08 | .05 |
| 408 | Larry Mucker | .08 | .05 |
| 409 | Jim Allen | .08 | .05 |
| 410 | Randy Gradishar | .25 | .15 |
| 411 | Falcons (TL) | .25 | .15 |
| 412 | Louie Kelcher | .10 | .06 |
| 413 | Robert Newhouse | .20 | .12 |
| 414 | Gary Shirk | .08 | .05 |
| 415 | Mike Haynes | .20 | .12 |
| 416 | Craig Colquitt | .08 | .05 |
| 417 | Lou Piccone | .08 | .05 |
| 418 | Clay Matthews (R) | 2.50 | 1.40 |
| 419 | Marvin Cobb | .08 | .05 |
| 420 | Harold Carmichael | .50 | .28 |
| 421 | Uwe Von Schamann (R) | .15 | .08 |
| 422 | Mike Phipps | .25 | .15 |
| 423 | Nolan Cromwell (R) | 1.25 | .70 |
| 424 | Glenn Doughty | .08 | .05 |
| 425 | Bob Young | .10 | .06 |
| 426 | Tony Galbreath | .15 | .08 |
| 427 | Luke Prestridge | .08 | .05 |
| 428 | Terry Beeson | .08 | .05 |
| 429 | Jack Tatum | .25 | .15 |
| 430 | Lemar Parrish | .10 | .06 |
| 431 | Chester Marcol | .08 | .05 |
| 432 | Oilers (TL) | .25 | .15 |
| 433 | John Fitzgerald | .08 | .05 |
| 434 | Gary Jeter (R) | .30 | .18 |

| | | | | | | | |
|---|---|---|---|---|---|---|---|
| 435 | Steve Grogan | .40 | .22 | 492 | AFC Championship | .25 | .15 |
| 436 | Jon Kolb | .08 | .05 | 493 | NFC Championship | .25 | .15 |
| 437 | Jim O'Bradovich | .08 | .05 | 494 | Super Bowl XIV | .40 | .22 |
| 438 | Gerald Irons | .08 | .05 | 495 | Dwight White | .15 | .08 |
| 439 | Jeff West | .08 | .05 | 496 | Haven Moses | .15 | .08 |
| 440 | Wilbert Montgomery | .40 | .22 | 497 | Guy Morriss | .08 | .05 |
| 441 | Norris Thomas | .08 | .05 | 498 | Dewey Selmon | .10 | .06 |
| 442 | James Scott | .08 | .05 | 499 | Dave Butz (R) | 1.25 | .70 |
| 443 | Curtis Brown | .08 | .05 | 500 | Chuck Foreman | .30 | .18 |
| 444 | Ken Fantetti | .08 | .05 | 501 | Chris Bahr | .08 | .05 |
| 445 | Pat Haden | .30 | .18 | 502 | Mark Miller | .08 | .05 |
| 446 | Carl Mauck | .08 | .05 | 503 | Tony Greene | .08 | .05 |
| 447 | Bruce Laird | .08 | .05 | 504 | Brian Kelley | .08 | .05 |
| 448 | Otis Armstrong | .20 | .12 | 505 | Joe Washington | .20 | .12 |
| 449 | Gene Upshaw | .60 | .35 | 506 | Butch Johnson | .15 | .08 |
| 450 | Steve Largent | 4.50 | 2.50 | 507 | Jets (TL) | .25 | .15 |
| 451 | Benny Malone | .08 | .05 | 508 | Steve Little | .08 | .05 |
| 452 | Steve Nelson | .08 | .05 | 509 | Checklist 397-528 | .50 | .08 |
| 453 | Mark Cotney | .08 | .05 | 510 | Mark Van Eeghen | .12 | .07 |
| 454 | Joe Danelo | .08 | .05 | 511 | Gary Danielson | .12 | .07 |
| 455 | Billy Joe DuPree | .15 | .08 | 512 | Manu Tuiasosopo (R) | .12 | .07 |
| 456 | Ron Johnson | .08 | .05 | 513 | Paul Coffman (R) | .20 | .12 |
| 457 | Archie Griffin | .25 | .15 | 514 | Cullen Bryant | .12 | .07 |
| 458 | Reggie Rucker | .15 | .08 | 515 | Nat Moore | .20 | .12 |
| 459 | Claude Humphrey | .10 | .06 | 516 | Bill Lenkaitis | .08 | .05 |
| 460 | Lydell Mitchell | .20 | .12 | 517 | Lynn Cain (R) | .20 | .12 |
| 461 | Steve Towle | .08 | .05 | 518 | Gregg Bingham | .08 | .05 |
| 462 | Revie Sorey | .08 | .05 | 519 | Ted Albrecht | .08 | .05 |
| 463 | Tom Skladany | .08 | .05 | 520 | Dan Fouts | 3.00 | 1.75 |
| 464 | Clark Gaines | .08 | .05 | 521 | Bernard Jackson | .08 | .05 |
| 465 | Frank Corral | .08 | .05 | 522 | Coy Bacon | .08 | .05 |
| 466 | Steve Fuller (R) | .20 | .12 | 523 | Tony Franklin (R) | .15 | .08 |
| 467 | Ahmad Rashad | .60 | .35 | 524 | Bo Harris | .08 | .05 |
| 468 | Raiders (TL) | .30 | .18 | 525 | Bob Grupp | .08 | .05 |
| 469 | Brian Peets | .08 | .05 | 526 | 49ers (TL) | .25 | .15 |
| 470 | Pat Donovan (R) | .12 | .07 | 527 | Steve Wilson | .08 | .05 |
| 471 | Ken Burrough | .12 | .07 | 528 | Bennie Cunningham | .10 | .06 |
| 472 | Don Calhoun | .08 | .05 | | | | |
| 473 | Bill Bryan | .08 | .05 | | | | |
| 474 | Terry Jackson | .08 | .05 | | | | |
| 475 | Joe Theismann | 1.25 | .70 | | | | |
| 476 | Jim Smith | .08 | .05 | | | | |
| 477 | Joe DeLamielleure | .10 | .06 | | | | |
| 478 | Mike Pruitt | .20 | .12 | | | | |
| 479 | Steve Mike-Mayer | .08 | .05 | | | | |
| 480 | Bill Bergey | .15 | .08 | | | | |
| 481 | Mike Fuller | .08 | .05 | | | | |
| 482 | Bob Parsons | .08 | .05 | | | | |
| 483 | Billy Brooks | .15 | .08 | | | | |
| 484 | Jerome Barkum | .12 | .07 | | | | |
| 485 | Larry Csonka | 1.25 | .70 | | | | |
| 486 | John Hill | .08 | .05 | | | | |
| 487 | Mike Dawson | .08 | .05 | | | | |
| 488 | Lions (TL) | .25 | .15 | | | | |
| 489 | Ted Hendricks | .60 | .35 | | | | |
| 490 | Dan Pastorini | .25 | .15 | | | | |
| 491 | Stanley Morgan | .75 | .40 | | | | |

# 1981 Topps

The cards in this 528-card set consist of full color photos on the fronts framed by a white border. The player's name, team and position appear below the photograph while the Topps logo is printed in an upper corner of the card. The backs feature personal data, statistics and a brief biography of the player. Subsets include League Leaders (1-6), Record Breakers (RB)(331-336), Playoffs (492-494) and Super Action (SA). Team Leader cards (TL) are also included in the set and include multi-photos on the front and team checklists on the back. All cards measure 2-1/2" by 3-1/2".

|   |   | MINT | NR/MT |
|---|---|---|---|
| **Complete Set (528)** | | 265.00 | 150.00 |
| **Commons** | | .07 | .04 |
| | | | |
| 1 | Passing Leaders | .40 | .22 |
| | Ron Jaworski | | |
| | Brian Sipe | | |
| 2 | Receiving Leaders | .40 | .22 |
| | Earl Cooper | | |
| | Kellen Winslow | | |
| 3 | Sack Leaders | .10 | .06 |
| | Bubba Baker | | |
| | Gary Johnson | | |
| 4 | Scoring Leaders | .10 | .06 |
| | Ed Murray | | |
| | John Smith | | |
| 5 | Interception Leaders | .12 | .07 |
| | Nolan Cromwell | | |
| | Lester Hayes | | |
| 6 | Punting Leaders | .10 | .06 |
| | Dave Jennings | | |
| | Luke Prestridge | | |
| 7 | Don Calhoun | .07 | .04 |
| 8 | Jack Tatum | .10 | .06 |
| 9 | Reggie Rucker | .10 | .06 |
| 10 | Mike Webster | .40 | .22 |
| 11 | Vince Evans (R) | .75 | .40 |
| 12 | Ottis Anderson (SA) | .75 | .40 |
| 13 | Leroy Harris | .07 | .04 |
| 14 | Gordon King | .07 | .04 |
| 15 | Harvey Martin | .25 | .15 |
| 16 | Johnny "Lam" Jones (R) | .25 | .15 |
| 17 | Ken Greene | .07 | .04 |
| 18 | Frank Lewis | .10 | .06 |
| 19 | Seahawks (TL) | .30 | .18 |
| 20 | Lester Hayes | .25 | .15 |
| 21 | Uwe Von Schamann | .07 | .04 |
| 22 | Joe Washington | .15 | .08 |
| 23 | Louie Kelcher | .10 | .06 |
| 24 | Willie Miller | .07 | .04 |
| 25 | Steve Grogan | .30 | .18 |
| 26 | John Hill | .07 | .04 |
| 27 | Stan White | .07 | .04 |
| 28 | William Andrews (SA) | .15 | .08 |
| 29 | Clarence Scott | .07 | .04 |
| 30 | Leon Gray | .10 | .06 |
| 31 | Craig Colquitt | .07 | .04 |
| 32 | Doug Williams | .50 | .28 |
| 33 | Bob Breunig | .10 | .06 |
| 34 | Billy Taylor | .07 | .04 |
| 35 | Harold Carmichael | .40 | .22 |
| 36 | Ray Wersching | .07 | .04 |
| 37 | Dennis Johnson | .07 | .04 |
| 38 | Archie Griffin | .20 | .12 |
| 39 | Rams (TL) | .15 | .08 |
| 40 | Gary Fencik | .12 | .07 |
| 41 | Lynn Dickey | .20 | .12 |
| 42 | Steve Bartkowski (SA) | .20 | .12 |
| 43 | Art Shell | .60 | .35 |
| 44 | Wilbur Jackson | .12 | .07 |
| 45 | Frank Corral | .07 | .04 |
| 46 | Ted McKnight | .07 | .04 |
| 47 | Joe Klecko | .25 | .15 |
| 48 | Dan Doornink | .07 | .04 |
| 49 | Doug Dieken | .07 | .04 |
| 50 | Jerry Robinson (R) | .75 | .40 |
| 51 | Wallace Francis | .07 | .04 |
| 52 | Dave Preston | .07 | .04 |
| 53 | Jay Saldi | .07 | .04 |
| 54 | Rush Brown | .07 | .04 |
| 55 | Phil Simms | 3.00 | 2.00 |
| 56 | Nick Mike-Mayer | .07 | .04 |
| 57 | Redskins (TL) | 1.50 | .80 |
| 58 | Mike Renfro | .10 | .06 |
| 59 | Ted Brown | .07 | .04 |
| 60 | Steve Nelson | .07 | .04 |
| 61 | Sidney Thornton | .07 | .04 |
| 62 | Kent Hill | .10 | .06 |

| # | Player | | |
|---|--------|------|------|
| 63 | Don Bessillieu | .07 | .04 |
| 64 | Fred Cook | .07 | .04 |
| 65 | Raymond Chester | .12 | .07 |
| 66 | Rick Kane | .07 | .04 |
| 67 | Mike Fuller | .07 | .04 |
| 68 | Dewey Selmon | .10 | .06 |
| 69 | Charles White (R) | 1.00 | .60 |
| 70 | Jeff Van Note | .10 | .06 |
| 71 | Robert Newhouse | .15 | .08 |
| 72 | Roynell Young (R) | .25 | .15 |
| 73 | Lynn Cain (SA) | .10 | .06 |
| 74 | Mike Friede | .07 | .04 |
| 75 | Earl Cooper (R) | .25 | .15 |
| 76 | Saints (TL) | .15 | .08 |
| 77 | Rick Danmeier | .07 | .04 |
| 78 | Darrol Ray (R) | .10 | .06 |
| 79 | Gregg Bingham | .10 | .06 |
| 80 | John Hannah | .50 | .28 |
| 81 | Jack Thompson | .12 | .07 |
| 82 | Rick Upchurch | .12 | .07 |
| 83 | Mike Butler | .07 | .04 |
| 84 | Don Warren | .20 | .12 |
| 85 | Mark Van Eeghen | .15 | .07 |
| 86 | J.T. Smith (R) | 1.25 | .70 |
| 87 | Herman Weaver | .07 | .04 |
| 88 | Terry Bradshaw (SA) | 1.25 | .70 |
| 89 | Charlie Hall | .07 | .04 |
| 90 | Donnie Shell | .25 | .15 |
| 91 | Ike Harris | .07 | .04 |
| 92 | Charlie Johnson | .07 | .04 |
| 93 | Rickey Watts | .07 | .04 |
| 94 | Patriots (TL) | .15 | .08 |
| 95 | Drew Pearson | .25 | .15 |
| 96 | Neil O'Donoghue | .07 | .04 |
| 97 | Conrad Dobler | .10 | .06 |
| 98 | Jewerl Thomas | .07 | .04 |
| 99 | Mike Barber | .07 | .04 |
| 100 | Billy Sims (R) | 1.75 | 1.00 |
| 101 | Vern Den Herder | .07 | .04 |
| 102 | Greg Landry | .30 | .18 |
| 103 | Joe Cribbs (SA) | .15 | .08 |
| 104 | Mark Murphy (R) | .30 | .18 |
| 105 | Chuck Muncie | .20 | .12 |
| 106 | Alfred Jackson | .12 | .07 |
| 107 | Chris Bahr | .07 | .04 |
| 108 | Gordon Jones (R) | .15 | .08 |
| 109 | Willie Harper (R) | .20 | .12 |
| 110 | Dave Jennings | .07 | .04 |
| 111 | Bennie Cunningham | .12 | .07 |
| 112 | Jerry Sisemore | .07 | .04 |
| 113 | Browns (TL) | .15 | .08 |
| 114 | Rickey Young | .07 | .04 |
| 115 | Ken Anderson | .60 | .35 |
| 116 | Randy Gradishar | .25 | .15 |
| 117 | Eddie Lee Ivery (R) | .30 | .18 |
| 118 | Wesley Walker | .30 | .18 |
| 119 | Chuck Foreman | .20 | .12 |
| 120 | Nolan Cromwell | .25 | .15 |
| 121 | Curtis Dickey (SA) | .15 | .08 |
| 122 | Wayne Morris | .07 | .04 |
| 123 | Greg Stemrick | .07 | .04 |
| 124 | Coy Bacon | .07 | .04 |
| 125 | Jim Zorn | .25 | .15 |
| 126 | Henry Childs | .07 | .04 |
| 127 | Checklist 1-132 | .40 | .05 |
| 128 | Len Walterscheid | .07 | .04 |
| 129 | Johnny Evans | .07 | .04 |
| 130 | Gary Barbaro | .10 | .06 |
| 131 | Jim Smith | .07 | .04 |
| 132 | Jets (TL) | .15 | .08 |
| 133 | Curtis Brown | .07 | .04 |
| 134 | D.D. Lewis | .10 | .06 |
| 135 | Jim Plunkett | .50 | .28 |
| 136 | Nat Moore | .15 | .08 |
| 137 | Don McCauley | .10 | .06 |
| 138 | Tony Dorsett (SA) | 1.00 | .60 |
| 139 | Julius Adams | .07 | .04 |
| 140 | Ahmad Rashad | .40 | .22 |
| 141 | Rich Saul | .07 | .04 |
| 142 | Ken Fantetti | .07 | .04 |
| 143 | Kenny Johnson | .07 | .04 |
| 144 | Clark Gaines | .07 | .04 |
| 145 | Mark Moseley | .07 | .04 |
| 146 | Vernon Perry (R) | .15 | .08 |
| 147 | Jerry Eckwood (R) | .15 | .08 |
| 148 | Freddie Solomon | .10 | .06 |
| 149 | Jerry Sherk | .07 | .04 |
| 150 | Kellen Winslow (R) | 9.00 | 5.00 |
| 151 | Packers (TL) | .75 | .40 |
| 152 | Ross Browner | .12 | .07 |
| 153 | Dan Fouts (SA) | 1.00 | .60 |
| 154 | Woody Peoples | .07 | .04 |
| 155 | Jack Lambert | 1.00 | .60 |
| 156 | Mike Dennis | .07 | .04 |
| 157 | Rafael Septien | .07 | .04 |
| 158 | Archie Manning | .40 | .22 |
| 159 | Don Hasselbeck | .07 | .04 |
| 160 | Alan Page | .60 | .35 |
| 161 | Arthur Whittington | .07 | .04 |
| 162 | Billy Waddy | .07 | .04 |
| 163 | Horace Belton | .07 | .04 |
| 164 | Luke Prestridge | .07 | .04 |
| 165 | Joe Theismann | 1.25 | .70 |
| 166 | Morris Towns | .07 | .04 |
| 167 | Dave Brown | .15 | .08 |
| 168 | Ezra Johnson | .07 | .04 |
| 169 | Buccaneers (TL) | .20 | .12 |
| 170 | Joe DeLamielleure | .10 | .06 |
| 171 | Earnest Gray (SA) | .10 | .06 |
| 172 | Mike Thomas | .07 | .04 |
| 173 | Jim Haslett | .07 | .04 |
| 174 | David Woodley (R) | .40 | .22 |
| 175 | Bubba Baker | .10 | .06 |
| 176 | Nesby Glasgow (R) | .20 | .12 |

| | | | |
|---|---|---|---|
| 177 | Pat Leahy | .07 | .04 |
| 178 | Tom Brahaney | .07 | .04 |
| 179 | Herman Edwards | .07 | .04 |
| 180 | Junior Miller (R) | .20 | .12 |
| 181 | Richard Wood (R) | .30 | .18 |
| 182 | Lenvil Elliott | .07 | .04 |
| 183 | Sammie White | .12 | .07 |
| 184 | Russell Erxleben | .07 | .04 |
| 185 | Ed Too Tall Jones | .75 | .40 |
| 186 | Ray Guy (SA) | .15 | .08 |
| 187 | Haven Moses | .10 | .06 |
| 188 | Giants (TL) | .15 | .08 |
| 189 | David Whitehurst | .10 | .06 |
| 190 | John Jefferson | .15 | .08 |
| 191 | Terry Beeson | .07 | .04 |
| 192 | Dan Ross (R) | .40 | .22 |
| 193 | Dave Williams | .07 | .04 |
| 194 | Art Monk (R) | 55.00 | 28.00 |
| 195 | Roger Wehrli | .07 | .04 |
| 196 | Ricky Feacher | .07 | .04 |
| 197 | Dolphins (TL) | .15 | .08 |
| 198 | Carl Roaches (R) | .12 | .07 |
| 199 | Billy Campfield | .07 | .04 |
| 200 | Ted Hendricks | .60 | .35 |
| 201 | Fred Smerlas (R) | 1.00 | .60 |
| 202 | Walter Payton (SA) | 2.75 | 1.50 |
| 203 | Luther Bradley | .07 | .04 |
| 204 | Herbert Scott | .07 | .04 |
| 205 | Jack Youngblood | .30 | .18 |
| 206 | Danny Pittman | .07 | .04 |
| 207 | Oilers (TL) | .15 | .08 |
| 208 | Vagas Ferguson (R) | .15 | .08 |
| 209 | Mark Dennard | .07 | .04 |
| 210 | Lemar Parrish | .07 | .04 |
| 211 | Bruce Harper | .07 | .04 |
| 212 | Ed Simonini | .07 | .04 |
| 213 | Nick Lowery (R) | 3.00 | 1.75 |
| 214 | Kevin House (R) | .25 | .15 |
| 215 | Mike Kenn (R) | 1.00 | .60 |
| 216 | Joe Montana (R) | 185.00 | 95.00 |
| 217 | Joe Senser (R) | .12 | .07 |
| 218 | Lester Hayes (SA) | .12 | .07 |
| 219 | Gene Upshaw | .60 | .35 |
| 220 | Franco Harris | 1.25 | .70 |
| 221 | Ron Bolton | .07 | .04 |
| 222 | Charles Alexander (R) | .20 | .12 |
| 223 | Matt Robinson | .07 | .04 |
| 224 | Ray Oldham | .07 | .04 |
| 225 | George Martin | .10 | .06 |
| 226 | Bills (TL) | .15 | .08 |
| 227 | Tony Franklin | .07 | .04 |
| 228 | George Cumby | .07 | .04 |
| 229 | Butch Johnson | .15 | .08 |
| 230 | Mike Haynes | .15 | .08 |
| 231 | Rob Carpenter | .10 | .06 |
| 232 | Steve Fuller | .12 | .07 |
| 233 | John Sawyer | .07 | .04 |
| 234 | Kenny King (SA) | .12 | .07 |
| 235 | Jack Ham | .75 | .40 |
| 236 | Jimmy Rogers | .07 | .04 |
| 237 | Bob Parsons | .07 | .04 |
| 238 | Marty Lyons (R) | .60 | .35 |
| 239 | Pat Tilley | .10 | .06 |
| 240 | Dennis Harrah | .10 | .06 |
| 241 | Thom Darden | .07 | .04 |
| 242 | Rolf Benirschke | .07 | .04 |
| 243 | Gerald Small | .07 | .04 |
| 244 | Falcons (TL) | .15 | .08 |
| 245 | Roger Carr | .07 | .04 |
| 246 | Sherman White | .07 | .04 |
| 247 | Ted Brown | .10 | .06 |
| 248 | Matt Cavanaugh | .20 | .12 |
| 249 | John Dutton | .10 | .06 |
| 250 | Bill Bergey | .12 | .07 |
| 251 | Jim Allen | .07 | .04 |
| 252 | Mike Nelms (SA) | .10 | .06 |
| 253 | Tom Blanchard | .07 | .04 |
| 254 | Ricky Thompson | .07 | .04 |
| 255 | John Matuszak | .12 | .07 |
| 256 | Randy Grossman | .07 | .04 |
| 257 | Ray Griffin | .07 | .04 |
| 258 | Lynn Cain | .10 | .06 |
| 259 | Checklist 133-264 | .40 | .05 |
| 260 | Mike Pruitt | .15 | .08 |
| 261 | Chris Ward | .07 | .04 |
| 262 | Fred Steinfort | .07 | .04 |
| 263 | James Owens | .07 | .04 |
| 264 | Bears (TL) | 1.25 | .70 |
| 265 | Dan Fouts | 3.00 | 1.75 |
| 266 | Arnold Morgado | .07 | .04 |
| 267 | John Jefferson (SA) | .12 | .07 |
| 268 | Bill Lenkaitis | .07 | .04 |
| 269 | James Jones | .07 | .04 |
| 270 | Brad Van Pelt | .07 | .04 |
| 271 | Steve Largent | 3.00 | 1.75 |
| 272 | Elvin Bethea | .10 | .06 |
| 273 | Cullen Bryant | .12 | .07 |
| 274 | Gary Danielson | .15 | .08 |
| 275 | Tony Galbreath | .10 | .06 |
| 276 | Dave Butz | .25 | .15 |
| 277 | Steve Mike-Mayer | .07 | .04 |
| 278 | Ron Johnson | .07 | .04 |
| 279 | Tom DeLeone | .07 | .04 |
| 280 | Ron Jaworski | .25 | .15 |
| 281 | Mel Gray | .10 | .06 |
| 282 | Chargers (TL) | .15 | .08 |
| 283 | Mark Brammer | .07 | .04 |
| 284 | Alfred Jenkins (SA) | .10 | .06 |
| 285 | Greg Buttle | .10 | .06 |
| 286 | Randy Hughes | .07 | .04 |
| 287 | Delvin Williams | .10 | .06 |
| 288 | Brian Baschnagel | .10 | .06 |
| 289 | Gary Jeter | .07 | .04 |
| 290 | Stanley Morgan | .75 | .40 |

| # | Player | | |
|---|--------|------|------|
| 291 | Gerry Ellis | .07 | .04 |
| 292 | Al Richardson | .07 | .04 |
| 293 | Jimmie Giles | .10 | .06 |
| 294 | Dave Jennings (SA) | .10 | .06 |
| 295 | Wilbert Montgomery | .25 | .15 |
| 296 | Dave Pureifory | .07 | .04 |
| 297 | Greg Hawthorne | .07 | .04 |
| 298 | Dick Ambrose | .07 | .04 |
| 299 | Terry Hermeling | .07 | .04 |
| 300 | Danny White | .50 | .28 |
| 301 | Ken Burrough | .12 | .07 |
| 302 | Paul Hofer | .07 | .04 |
| 303 | Broncos (TL) | .15 | .08 |
| 304 | Eddie Payton | .10 | .06 |
| 305 | Isaac Curtis | .15 | .08 |
| 306 | Benny Ricardo | .07 | .04 |
| 307 | Riley Odoms | .10 | .06 |
| 308 | Bob Chandler | .07 | .04 |
| 309 | Larry Heater | .07 | .04 |
| 310 | Art Still (R) | .60 | .35 |
| 311 | Harold Jackson | .25 | .15 |
| 312 | Charlie Joiner (SA) | .40 | .22 |
| 313 | Jeff Nixon | .07 | .04 |
| 314 | Aundra Thompson (R) | .12 | .07 |
| 315 | Richard Todd | .25 | .15 |
| 316 | Dan Hampton (R) | 10.00 | 6.00 |
| 317 | Doug Marsh | .07 | .04 |
| 318 | Louie Giammona | .07 | .04 |
| 319 | 49ers (TL) | .35 | .20 |
| 320 | Manu Tuiasosopo | .07 | .04 |
| 321 | Rich Milot | .07 | .04 |
| 322 | Mike Guman | .07 | .04 |
| 323 | Bob Kuechenberg | .10 | .06 |
| 324 | Tom Skladany | .07 | .04 |
| 325 | Dave Logan | .07 | .04 |
| 326 | Bruce Laird | .07 | .04 |
| 327 | James Jones (SA) | .10 | .06 |
| 328 | Joe Danelo | .07 | .04 |
| 329 | Kenny King (R) | .40 | .22 |
| 330 | Pat Donovan | .07 | .04 |
| 331 | Earl Cooper RB | .15 | .08 |
| 332 | John Jefferson RB | .15 | .08 |
| 333 | Kenny King RB | .15 | .08 |
| 334 | Rod Martin RB | .12 | .07 |
| 335 | Jim Plunkett RB | .20 | .12 |
| 336 | Bill Thompson RB | .10 | .06 |
| 337 | John Cappelletti | .15 | .08 |
| 338 | Lions (TL) | .30 | .18 |
| 339 | Don Smith | .07 | .04 |
| 340 | Rod Perry | .10 | .06 |
| 341 | David Lewis | .07 | .04 |
| 342 | Mark Gastineau (R) | 1.25 | .70 |
| 343 | Steve Largent (SA) | 2.00 | 1.10 |
| 344 | Charley Young | .07 | .04 |
| 345 | Toni Fritsch | .07 | .04 |
| 346 | Matt Blair | .10 | .06 |
| 347 | Don Bass | .07 | .04 |
| 348 | Jim Jensen (R) | .30 | .18 |
| 349 | Karl Lorch | .07 | .04 |
| 350 | Brian Sipe | .30 | .18 |
| 351 | Theo Bell | .07 | .04 |
| 352 | Sam Adams | .07 | .04 |
| 353 | Paul Coffman | .07 | .04 |
| 354 | Eric Harris | .07 | .04 |
| 355 | Tony Hill | .20 | .12 |
| 356 | J.T. Turner | .07 | .04 |
| 357 | Frank LeMaster | .07 | .04 |
| 358 | Jim Jodat | .07 | .04 |
| 359 | Raiders (TL) | .30 | .18 |
| 360 | Joe Cribbs (R) | .80 | .45 |
| 361 | James Lofton (SA) | 2.00 | 1.10 |
| 362 | Dexter Bussey | .07 | .04 |
| 363 | Bobby Jackson | .07 | .04 |
| 364 | Steve DeBerg | .80 | .45 |
| 365 | Ottis Anderson | 2.00 | 1.10 |
| 366 | Tom Myers | .07 | .04 |
| 367 | John James | .07 | .04 |
| 368 | Reese McCall | .07 | .04 |
| 369 | Jack Reynolds | .15 | .08 |
| 370 | Gary Johnson | .10 | .06 |
| 371 | Jimmy Cefalo | .10 | .06 |
| 372 | Horace Ivory | .07 | .04 |
| 373 | Garo Yepremian | .10 | .06 |
| 374 | Brian Kelley | .07 | .04 |
| 375 | Terry Bradshaw | 2.75 | 1.50 |
| 376 | Cowboys (TL) | .60 | .35 |
| 377 | Randy Logan | .07 | .04 |
| 378 | Tim Wilson | .07 | .04 |
| 379 | Archie Manning (SA) | .20 | .12 |
| 380 | Revie Sorey | .07 | .04 |
| 381 | Randy Holloway | .07 | .04 |
| 382 | Henry Lawrence | .07 | .04 |
| 383 | Pat McInally | .10 | .06 |
| 384 | Kevin Long | .07 | .04 |
| 385 | Louis Wright | .10 | .06 |
| 386 | Leonard Thompson | .07 | .04 |
| 387 | Jan Stenerud | .30 | .18 |
| 388 | Raymond Butler (R) | .30 | .18 |
| 389 | Checklist 265-396 | .40 | .05 |
| 390 | Steve Bartkowski | .30 | .18 |
| 391 | Clarence Harmon | .07 | .04 |
| 392 | Wilbert Montgomery | .15 | .08 |
| 393 | Billy Joe DuPree | .12 | .07 |
| 394 | Chiefs (TL) | .15 | .08 |
| 395 | Earnest Gray | .10 | .06 |
| 396 | Ray Hamilton | .07 | .04 |
| 397 | Brenard Wilson | .07 | .04 |
| 398 | Calvin Hill | .12 | .07 |
| 399 | Robin Cole | .07 | .04 |
| 400 | Walter Payton | 5.50 | 3.00 |
| 401 | Jim Hart | .30 | .18 |
| 402 | Ron Yary | .12 | .07 |
| 403 | Cliff Branch | .40 | .22 |
| 404 | Roland Hooks | .07 | .04 |

| | | | |
|---|---|---|---|
| 405 | Ken Stabler | .80 | .45 |
| 406 | Chuck Ramsey | .07 | .04 |
| 407 | Mike Nelms (R) | .15 | .08 |
| 408 | Ron Jaworski (SA) | .12 | .07 |
| 409 | James Hunter | .07 | .04 |
| 410 | Lee Roy Selmon | .20 | .12 |
| 411 | Colts (TL) | .15 | .08 |
| 412 | Henry Marshall | .07 | .04 |
| 413 | Preston Pearson | .15 | .08 |
| 414 | Richard Bishop | .07 | .04 |
| 415 | Greg Pruitt | .20 | .12 |
| 416 | Matt Bahr | .12 | .07 |
| 417 | Tom Mullady | .07 | .04 |
| 418 | Glen Edwards | .07 | .04 |
| 419 | Sam McCullum | .10 | .06 |
| 420 | Stan Walters | .07 | .04 |
| 421 | George Roberts | .07 | .04 |
| 422 | Dwight Clark (R) | 3.50 | 2.00 |
| 423 | Pat Thomas (R) | .15 | .08 |
| 424 | Bruce Harper | .07 | .04 |
| 425 | Craig Morton | .30 | .18 |
| 426 | Derrick Gaffney | .07 | .04 |
| 427 | Pete Johnson | .12 | .07 |
| 428 | Wes Chandler | .40 | .22 |
| 429 | Burgess Owens | .07 | .04 |
| 430 | James Lofton | 5.00 | 2.75 |
| 431 | Tony Reed | .07 | .04 |
| 432 | Vikings (TL) | .20 | .12 |
| 433 | Ron Springs (R) | .20 | .12 |
| 434 | Tim Fox | .07 | .04 |
| 435 | Ozzie Newsome | 2.75 | 1.50 |
| 436 | Steve Furness | .07 | .04 |
| 437 | Will Lewis | .07 | .04 |
| 438 | Mike Hartenstine | .07 | .04 |
| 439 | John Bunting | .07 | .04 |
| 440 | Ed Murray (R) | .75 | .40 |
| 441 | Mike Pruitt (SA) | .12 | .07 |
| 442 | Larry Swider | .07 | .04 |
| 443 | Steve Freeman | .07 | .04 |
| 444 | Bruce Hardy (R) | .10 | .06 |
| 445 | Pat Haden | .25 | .15 |
| 446 | Curtis Dickey (R) | .30 | .18 |
| 447 | Doug Wilkerson | .07 | .04 |
| 448 | Alfred Jenkins | .12 | .07 |
| 449 | Dave Dalby | .07 | .04 |
| 450 | Robert Brazile | .10 | .06 |
| 451 | Bobby Hammond | .07 | .04 |
| 452 | Raymond Clayborn | .10 | .06 |
| 453 | Jim Miller | .07 | .04 |
| 454 | Roy Simmons | .07 | .04 |
| 455 | Charlie Waters | .12 | .07 |
| 456 | Ricky Bell | .15 | .08 |
| 457 | Ahmad Rashad (SA) | .20 | .12 |
| 458 | Don Cockroft | .07 | .04 |
| 459 | Keith Krepfle | .07 | .04 |
| 460 | Marvin Powell | .10 | .06 |
| 461 | Tommy Kramer | .30 | .18 |
| 462 | Jim LeClair | .07 | .04 |
| 463 | Freddie Scott | .07 | .04 |
| 464 | Rob Lytle | .07 | .04 |
| 465 | Johnnie Gray | .07 | .04 |
| 466 | Doug France (R) | .20 | .12 |
| 467 | Carlos Carson (R) | .35 | .20 |
| 468 | Cardinals (TL) | .15 | .08 |
| 469 | Efren Herrera | .07 | .04 |
| 470 | Randy White | .90 | .50 |
| 471 | Richard Caster | .12 | .07 |
| 472 | Andy Johnson | .07 | .04 |
| 473 | Billy Sims (SA) | .40 | .22 |
| 474 | Joe Lavender | .07 | .04 |
| 475 | Harry Carson | .40 | .22 |
| 476 | John Stallworth | .50 | .28 |
| 477 | Bob Thomas | .07 | .04 |
| 478 | Keith Wright | .07 | .04 |
| 479 | Ken Stone | .07 | .04 |
| 480 | Carl Hairston | .10 | .06 |
| 481 | Reggie McKenzie | .12 | .07 |
| 482 | Bob Griese | 1.50 | .80 |
| 483 | Mike Bragg | .07 | .04 |
| 484 | Scott Dierking | .07 | .04 |
| 485 | David Hill | .07 | .04 |
| 486 | Brian Sipe (SA) | .15 | .08 |
| 487 | Rod Martin (R) | .30 | .18 |
| 488 | Bengals (TL) | .15 | .08 |
| 489 | Preston Dennard | .07 | .04 |
| 490 | John Smith | .07 | .04 |
| 491 | Mike Reinfeldt | .07 | .04 |
| 492 | NFC Championship | .20 | .12 |
| 493 | AFC Championship | .25 | .15 |
| 494 | Super Bowl XV | .50 | .28 |
| 495 | Joe Greene | 1.00 | .60 |
| 496 | Charlie Joiner | .80 | .45 |
| 497 | Rolland Lawrence | .07 | .04 |
| 498 | Bubba Baker (SA) | .10 | .06 |
| 499 | Brad Dusek | .07 | .04 |
| 500 | Tony Dorsett | 2.50 | 1.40 |
| 501 | Robin Earl | .10 | .06 |
| 502 | Theotis Brown (R) | .15 | .08 |
| 503 | Joe Ferguson | .20 | .12 |
| 504 | Beasley Reece | .07 | .04 |
| 505 | Lyle Alzado | .30 | .18 |
| 506 | Tony Nathan (R) | .40 | .22 |
| 507 | Eagles (TL) | .15 | .08 |
| 508 | Herb Orvis | .07 | .04 |
| 509 | Clarence Williams | .07 | .04 |
| 510 | Ray Guy | .25 | .15 |
| 511 | Jeff Komlo | .07 | .04 |
| 512 | Freddie Solomon (SA) | .10 | .06 |
| 513 | Tim Mazzetti | .07 | .04 |
| 514 | Elvis Peacock (R) | .15 | .08 |
| 515 | Russ Francis | .10 | .06 |
| 516 | Roland Harper | .10 | .06 |
| 517 | Checklist 397-528 | .40 | .05 |
| 518 | Billy Johnson | .15 | .08 |

| | | MINT | NR/MT |
|---|---|---|---|
| 519 | Dan Dierdorf | .30 | .18 |
| 520 | Fred Dean | .12 | .07 |
| 521 | Jerry Butler | .12 | .07 |
| 522 | Ron Saul | .07 | .04 |
| 523 | Charlie Smith | .07 | .04 |
| 524 | Kellen Winslow (SA) | 2.00 | 1.10 |
| 525 | Bert Jones | .30 | .18 |
| 526 | Steelers (TL) | .60 | .35 |
| 527 | Duriel Harris | .07 | .04 |
| 528 | William Andrews | .20 | .08 |

# 1982 Topps

This marks the tenth straight year Topps produced a 528-card football set. The card fronts feature full color photos. The player's name and position appear in a small pennant below the photograph. The team name is located under a picture of a team helmet in the bottom corner of the card. The horizontal card backs contain personal data, stats and brief highlights. Subsets include Record Breakers (RB) (1-6), Playoffs (7-9), League Leaders (257-262), In-Action (IA) and a new feature called Brothers (263-270). The set also includes Team Leaders (TL) which feature multi-photos on the front and a team checklist on the back. All cards measure 2-1/2" by 3-1/2".

| | | MINT | NR/MT |
|---|---|---|---|
| Complete Set (528) | | 100.00 | 60.00 |
| Commons | | .06 | .03 |
| 1 | Ken Anderson (RB) | .40 | .22 |
| 2 | Dan Fouts (RB) | .75 | .40 |

| | | MINT | NR/MT |
|---|---|---|---|
| 3 | LeRoy Irvin (RB) | .10 | .06 |
| 4 | Stump Mitchell (RB) | .12 | .07 |
| 5 | George Rogers (RB) | .15 | .08 |
| 6 | Dan Ross (RB) | .12 | .07 |
| 7 | AFC Championship | .15 | .08 |
| 8 | NFC Championship | .15 | .08 |
| 9 | Super Bowl XVI | .50 | .28 |
| 10 | Colts (TL) | .12 | .07 |
| 11 | Raymond Butler | .10 | .06 |
| 12 | Roger Carr | .06 | .03 |
| 13 | Curtis Dickey | .15 | .08 |
| 14 | Zachary Dixon | .06 | .03 |
| 15 | Nesby Glasgow | .06 | .03 |
| 16 | Bert Jones | .25 | .15 |
| 17 | Bruce Laird | .06 | .03 |
| 18 | Reese McCall | .06 | .03 |
| 19 | Randy McMillan | .06 | .03 |
| 20 | Ed Simonini | .06 | .03 |
| 21 | Bills (TL) | .15 | .08 |
| 22 | Mark Brammer | .06 | .03 |
| 23 | Curtis Brown | .06 | .03 |
| 24 | Jerry Butler | .15 | .08 |
| 25 | Mario Clark | .06 | .03 |
| 26 | Joe Cribbs | .25 | .15 |
| 27 | Joe Cribbs (IA) | .10 | .06 |
| 28 | Joe Ferguson | .20 | .12 |
| 29 | Jim Haslett | .06 | .03 |
| 30 | Frank Lewis | .10 | .06 |
| 31 | Frank Lewis (IA) | .07 | .04 |
| 32 | Shane Nelson | .06 | .03 |
| 33 | Charles Romes | .06 | .03 |
| 34 | Bill Simpson | .06 | .03 |
| 35 | Fred Smerlas | .15 | .08 |
| 36 | Bengals (TL) | .15 | .08 |
| 37 | Charles Alexander | .08 | .05 |
| 38 | Ken Anderson | .60 | .35 |
| 39 | Ken Anderson (IA) | .25 | .15 |
| 40 | Jim Breech | .06 | .03 |
| 41 | Jim Breech (IA) | .06 | .03 |
| 42 | Louis Breeden | .06 | .03 |
| 43 | Ross Browner | .12 | .07 |
| 44 | Cris Collinsworth(R) | 1.75 | 1.00 |
| 45 | Cris Collinsworth (IA) | .75 | .40 |
| 46 | Isaac Curtis | .15 | .08 |
| 47 | Pete Johnson | .12 | .07 |
| 48 | Pete Johnson (IA) | .07 | .04 |
| 49 | Steve Kreider | .06 | .03 |
| 50 | Pat McInally | .08 | .05 |
| 51 | Anthony Munoz (R) | 12.50 | 6.50 |
| 52 | Dan Ross | .10 | .06 |
| 53 | David Verser | .06 | .03 |
| 54 | Reggie Williams | .10 | .06 |
| 55 | Browns (TL) | .25 | .15 |
| 56 | Lyle Alzado | .25 | .15 |
| 57 | Dick Ambrose | .06 | .03 |
| 58 | Ron Bolton | .06 | .03 |
| 59 | Steve Cox | .06 | .03 |

| | | | |
|---|---|---|---|
| 60 | Joe DeLamielleure | .08 | .05 |
| 61 | Tom DeLeone | .06 | .03 |
| 62 | Doug Dieken | .06 | .03 |
| 63 | Ricky Feacher | .06 | .03 |
| 64 | Don Goode | .06 | .03 |
| 65 | Robert L. Jackson (R) | .25 | .15 |
| 66 | Dave Logan | .06 | .03 |
| 67 | Ozzie Newsome | 1.75 | 1.00 |
| 68 | Ozzie Newsome (IA) | .75 | .40 |
| 69 | Greg Pruitt | .20 | .12 |
| 70 | Mike Pruitt | .15 | .08 |
| 71 | Mike Pruitt (IA) | .08 | .05 |
| 72 | Reggie Rucker | .10 | .06 |
| 73 | Clarence Scott | .06 | .03 |
| 74 | Brian Sipe | .20 | .12 |
| 75 | Charles White | .25 | .15 |
| 76 | Broncos (TL) | .15 | .08 |
| 77 | Rubin Carter | .06 | .03 |
| 78 | Steve Foley | .06 | .03 |
| 79 | Randy Gradishar | .20 | .12 |
| 80 | Tom Jackson | .15 | .08 |
| 81 | Craig Morton | .25 | .15 |
| 82 | Craig Morton (IA) | .12 | .07 |
| 83 | Riley Odoms | .10 | .06 |
| 84 | Rick Parros | .06 | .03 |
| 85 | Dave Preston | .06 | .03 |
| 86 | Tony Reed | .06 | .03 |
| 87 | Bob Swenson (R) | .12 | .07 |
| 88 | Bill Thompson | .06 | .03 |
| 89 | Rick Upchurch | .10 | .06 |
| 90 | Steve Watson (R) | .35 | .20 |
| 91 | Steve Watson (IA) | .15 | .08 |
| 92 | Oilers (TL) | .15 | .08 |
| 93 | Mike Barber | .08 | .05 |
| 94 | Elvin Bethea | .10 | .06 |
| 95 | Gregg Bingham | .06 | .03 |
| 96 | Robert Brazile | .12 | .07 |
| 97 | Ken Burrough | .12 | .07 |
| 98 | Toni Fritsch | .06 | .03 |
| 99 | Leon Gray | .06 | .03 |
| 100 | Gifford Nielsen (R) | .25 | .15 |
| 101 | Vernon Perry | .06 | .03 |
| 102 | Mike Reinfeldt | .06 | .03 |
| 103 | Mike Renfro | .10 | .06 |
| 104 | Carl Roaches | .08 | .05 |
| 105 | Ken Stabler | .60 | .35 |
| 106 | Greg Stemrick | .06 | .03 |
| 107 | J.C. Wilson | .06 | .03 |
| 108 | Tim Wilson | .06 | .03 |
| 109 | Cheifs (TL) | .15 | .08 |
| 110 | Gary Barbaro | .08 | .05 |
| 111 | Brad Budde | .06 | .03 |
| 112 | Joe Delaney (R) | .35 | .20 |
| 113 | Joe Delaney (IA) | .15 | .08 |
| 114 | Steve Fuller | .12 | .07 |
| 115 | Gary Green | .06 | .03 |
| 116 | James Hadnot (R) | .12 | .07 |

| | | | |
|---|---|---|---|
| 117 | Eric Harris | .06 | .03 |
| 118 | Billy Jackson | .06 | .03 |
| 119 | Bill Kenney (R) | .25 | .15 |
| 120 | Nick Lowery | 1.00 | .60 |
| 121 | Nick Lowery (IA) | .35 | .20 |
| 122 | Henry Marshall | .06 | .03 |
| 123 | J.T. Smith | .30 | .18 |
| 124 | Art Still | .30 | .18 |
| 125 | Dolphins (TL) | .15 | .08 |
| 126 | Bob Baumhower | .08 | .05 |
| 127 | Glenn Blackwood | .08 | .05 |
| 128 | Jimmy Cefalo | .10 | .06 |
| 129 | A.J. Duhe | .12 | .07 |
| 130 | Andra Franklin (R) | .15 | .08 |
| 131 | Duriel Harris | .06 | .03 |
| 132 | Nat Moore | .15 | .08 |
| 133 | Tony Nathan | .10 | .06 |
| 134 | Ed Newman | .06 | .03 |
| 135 | Earnie Rhone | .06 | .03 |
| 136 | Don Strock | .12 | .07 |
| 137 | Tommy Vigorito | .06 | .03 |
| 138 | Uwe Von Schamann | .06 | .03 |
| 139 | Uwe Von Schamann (IA) | .06 | .03 |
| 140 | David Woodley | .15 | .08 |
| 141 | Patriots (TL) | .15 | .08 |
| 142 | Julius Adams | .06 | .03 |
| 143 | Richard Bishop | .06 | .03 |
| 144 | Matt Cavanaugh | .12 | .07 |
| 145 | Raymond Clayborn | .10 | .06 |
| 146 | Tony Collins (R) | .25 | .15 |
| 147 | Vagas Ferguson | .08 | .05 |
| 148 | Tim Fox | .06 | .03 |
| 149 | Steve Grogan | .25 | .15 |
| 150 | John Hannah | .50 | .28 |
| 151 | John Hannah (IA) | .20 | .12 |
| 152 | Don Hasselbeck | .06 | .03 |
| 153 | Mike Haynes | .15 | .08 |
| 154 | Harold Jackson | .15 | .08 |
| 155 | Andy Johnson | .06 | .03 |
| 156 | Stanley Morgan | .50 | .28 |
| 157 | Stanley Morgan (IA) | .20 | .12 |
| 158 | Steve Nelson | .06 | .03 |
| 159 | Rod Shoate | .06 | .03 |
| 160 | Jets (TL) | .35 | .20 |
| 161 | Dan Alexander | .06 | .03 |
| 162 | Mike Augustyniak | .06 | .03 |
| 163 | Jerome Barkum | .10 | .06 |
| 164 | Greg Buttle | .06 | .03 |
| 165 | Scott Dierking | .06 | .03 |
| 166 | Joe Fields | .10 | .06 |
| 167 | Mark Gastineau | .25 | .15 |
| 168 | Mark Gastineau (IA) | .10 | .06 |
| 169 | Bruce Harper | .06 | .03 |
| 170 | Johnny "Lam" Jones | .12 | .07 |
| 171 | Joe Kiecko | .15 | .08 |
| 172 | Joe Kiecko (IA) | .07 | .04 |

| | | | |
|---|---|---:|---:|
| 173 | Pat Leahy | .10 | .06 |
| 174 | Pat Leahy (IA) | .07 | .04 |
| 175 | Marty Lyons | .12 | .07 |
| 176 | Freeman McNeil (R) | 3.00 | 1.75 |
| 177 | Marvin Powell | .08 | .05 |
| 178 | Chuck Ramsey | .06 | .03 |
| 170 | Darrol Ray | .06 | .03 |
| 180 | Abdul Salaam | .06 | .03 |
| 181 | Richard Todd | .20 | .12 |
| 182 | Richard Todd (IA) | .08 | .05 |
| 183 | Wesley Walker | .20 | .12 |
| 184 | Chris Ward | .06 | .03 |
| 185 | Raiders (TL) | .15 | .08 |
| 186 | Cliff Branch | .30 | .18 |
| 187 | Bob Chandler | .06 | .03 |
| 188 | Ray Guy | .30 | .18 |
| 189 | Lester Hayes | .12 | .07 |
| 190 | Ted Hendricks | .40 | .22 |
| 191 | Monte Jackson | .06 | .03 |
| 192 | Derrick Jensen | .06 | .03 |
| 193 | Kenny King | .10 | .06 |
| 194 | Rod Martin | .10 | .06 |
| 195 | John Matuszak | .12 | .07 |
| 196 | Matt Millen (R) | 1.25 | .70 |
| 197 | Derrick Ramsey | .06 | .03 |
| 198 | Art Shell | .50 | .28 |
| 199 | Mark Van Eeghen | .12 | .07 |
| 200 | Arthur Whittington | .06 | .03 |
| 201 | Marc Wilson (R) | .30 | .18 |
| 202 | Steelers (TL) | .50 | .28 |
| 203 | Mel Blount | .50 | .28 |
| 204 | Terry Bradshaw | 1.75 | 1.00 |
| 205 | Terry Bradshaw (IA) | .75 | .40 |
| 206 | Craig Colquitt | .06 | .03 |
| 207 | Bennie Cunningham | .06 | .03 |
| 208 | Russell Davis | .06 | .03 |
| 209 | Gary Dunn | .06 | .03 |
| 210 | Jack Ham | .60 | .35 |
| 211 | Franco Harris | 1.00 | .60 |
| 212 | Franco Harris (IA) | .40 | .22 |
| 213 | Jack Lambert | .60 | .35 |
| 214 | Jack Lambert (IA) | .25 | .15 |
| 215 | Mark Malone (R) | .25 | .15 |
| 216 | Frank Pollard (R) | .20 | .12 |
| 217 | Donnie Shell | .20 | .12 |
| 219 | John Stallworth | .50 | .28 |
| 220 | John Stallworth (IA) | .20 | .12 |
| 221 | David Trout | .06 | .03 |
| 222 | Mike Webster | .30 | .18 |
| 223 | Chargers (TL) | .15 | .08 |
| 224 | Rolf Benirschke | .06 | .03 |
| 225 | Rolf Benirschke (IA) | .06 | .03 |
| 226 | James Brooks (R) | 4.00 | 2.25 |
| 227 | Willie Buchanon | .08 | .05 |
| 228 | Wes Chandler | .25 | .15 |
| 229 | Wes Chandler (IA) | .10 | .06 |
| 230 | Dan Fouts | 2.00 | 1.10 |

| | | | |
|---|---|---:|---:|
| 231 | Dan Fouts (IA) | .80 | .45 |
| 232 | Gary Johnson | .08 | .05 |
| 233 | Charlie Joiner | .60 | .35 |
| 234 | Charlie Joiner (IA) | .25 | .15 |
| 235 | Louie Kelcher | .08 | .05 |
| 236 | Chuck Muncie | .15 | .08 |
| 237 | Chuck Muncie (IA) | .07 | .04 |
| 238 | George Roberts | .06 | .03 |
| 239 | Ed White | .06 | .03 |
| 240 | Doug Wilkerson | .06 | .03 |
| 241 | Kellen Winslow | 1.75 | 1.00 |
| 242 | Kellen Winslow (IA) | .75 | .40 |
| 243 | Seahawks (TL) | .30 | .18 |
| 244 | Theotis Brown | .08 | .05 |
| 245 | Dan Doornink | .06 | .03 |
| 246 | John Harris | .06 | .03 |
| 247 | Efren Herrera | .06 | .03 |
| 248 | David Hughes | .06 | .03 |
| 249 | Steve Largent | 2.00 | 1.10 |
| 250 | Steve Largent (IA) | .80 | .45 |
| 251 | Sam McCullum | .06 | .03 |
| 252 | Sherman Smith | .06 | .03 |
| 253 | Manu Tuiasosopo | .06 | .03 |
| 254 | John Yarno | .06 | .03 |
| 255 | Jim Zorn | .20 | .12 |
| 256 | Jim Zorn (IA) | .08 | .05 |
| 257 | Passing Leaders | 1.75 | 1.00 |
| | Ken Anderson | | |
| | Joe Montana | | |
| 258 | Receiving Leaders | .30 | .18 |
| | Kellen Winslow | | |
| | Dwight Clark | | |
| 259 | QB Sack Leaders | .12 | .07 |
| | Joe Klecko | | |
| | Curtis Greer | | |
| 260 | Scoring Leaders | .15 | .08 |
| | Jim Breech | | |
| | Nick Lowery | | |
| | Ed Murray | | |
| | Rafael Septien | | |
| 261 | Interception Leaders | .15 | .08 |
| | John Harris | | |
| | Everson Walls | | |
| 262 | Punting Leaders | .08 | .05 |
| | Pat McInally | | |
| | Tom Skladany | | |
| 263 | Chris & Matt Bahr | .10 | .06 |
| 264 | Glen & Lyle Blackwood | .10 | .06 |
| 265 | Pete & Stan Brock | .10 | .06 |
| 266 | Archie & Ray Griffin | .12 | .07 |
| 267 | Charlie & John Hannah | .25 | .15 |
| 268 | Monte & Terry Jackson | .10 | .06 |
| 269 | Eddie & Walter Payton | 1.00 | .60 |
| 270 | Dewey & Lee Roy Selmon | .12 | .07 |
| 271 | Falcons (TL) | .15 | .08 |
| 272 | William Andrews | .15 | .08 |

| | | | |
|---|---|---|---|
| 273 | William Andrews (IA) | .07 | .04 |
| 274 | Steve Bartkowski | .30 | .18 |
| 275 | Steve Bartkowski (IA) | .12 | .07 |
| 276 | Bobby Butler | .06 | .03 |
| 277 | Lynn Cain | .08 | .05 |
| 278 | Wallace Francis | .06 | .03 |
| 279 | Alfred Jackson | .10 | .06 |
| 280 | John James | .06 | .03 |
| 281 | Alfred Jenkins | .10 | .06 |
| 282 | Alfred Jenkins (IA) | .06 | .03 |
| 283 | Kenny Johnson | .06 | .03 |
| 284 | Mike Kenn | .20 | .12 |
| 285 | Fulton Kuykendall | .06 | .03 |
| 286 | Mick Luckhurst (R) | .08 | .05 |
| 287 | Mick Luckhurst (IA) | .06 | .03 |
| 288 | Junior Miller | .10 | .06 |
| 289 | Al Richardson | .06 | .03 |
| 290 | R. C. Thielemann (R) | .10 | .06 |
| 291 | Jeff Van Note | .06 | .03 |
| 292 | Bears (TL) | .75 | .40 |
| 293 | Brian Baschnagel | .06 | .03 |
| 294 | Robin Earl | .06 | .03 |
| 295 | Vince Evans | .20 | .12 |
| 296 | Gary Fencik | .10 | .06 |
| 297 | Dan Hampton | 2.75 | 1.50 |
| 298 | Noah Jackson | .06 | .03 |
| 299 | Ken Margerum (R) | .12 | .07 |
| 300 | Jim Osborne | .06 | .03 |
| 301 | Bob Parsons | .06 | .03 |
| 302 | Walter Payton | 3.50 | 2.00 |
| 303 | Walter Payton (IA) | 2.00 | 1.10 |
| 304 | Revie Scorey | .06 | .03 |
| 305 | Matt Suhey (R) | .30 | .18 |
| 306 | Rickey Watts | .06 | .03 |
| 307 | Cowboys (TL) | .60 | .35 |
| 308 | Bob Breunig | .08 | .05 |
| 309 | Doug Cosbie (R) | .30 | .18 |
| 310 | Pat Donovan | .06 | .03 |
| 311 | Tony Dorsett | 1.75 | 1.00 |
| 312 | Tony Dorsett (IA) | .75 | .40 |
| 313 | Michael Downs (R) | .12 | .07 |
| 314 | Billy Joe DuPree | .12 | .07 |
| 315 | John Dutton | .10 | .06 |
| 316 | Tony Hill | .15 | .08 |
| 317 | Butch Johnson | .10 | .06 |
| 318 | Ed Too Tall Jones | .50 | .28 |
| 319 | James Jones | .06 | .03 |
| 320 | Harvey Martin | .25 | .15 |
| 321 | Drew Pearson | .35 | .20 |
| 322 | Herbert Scott | .06 | .03 |
| 323 | Rafael Septien | .06 | .03 |
| 324 | Rafael Septien (IA) | .06 | .03 |
| 325 | Ron Springs | .06 | .03 |
| 326 | Dennis Thurman (R) | .15 | .08 |
| 327 | Everson Walls (R) | 1.50 | .80 |
| 328 | Everson Walls (IA) | .50 | .28 |
| 329 | Danny White | .40 | .22 |
| 330 | Danny White (IA) | .15 | .08 |
| 331 | Randy White | .75 | .40 |
| 332 | Randy White (IA) | .30 | .18 |
| 333 | Lions (TL) | .15 | .08 |
| 334 | Jim Allen | .06 | .03 |
| 335 | Bubba Baker | .08 | .05 |
| 336 | Dexter Bussey | .06 | .03 |
| 337 | Doug English | .08 | .05 |
| 338 | Ken Fantetti | .06 | .03 |
| 339 | William Gay | .06 | .03 |
| 340 | David Hill | .06 | .03 |
| 341 | Eric Hipple (R) | .25 | .15 |
| 342 | Rick Kane | .06 | .03 |
| 343 | Ed Murray | .12 | .07 |
| 344 | Ed Murray (IA) | .06 | .03 |
| 345 | Ray Oldham | .06 | .03 |
| 346 | Dave Pureifory | .06 | .03 |
| 347 | Freddie Scott | .06 | .03 |
| 348 | Freddie Scott (IA) | .06 | .03 |
| 349 | Billy Sims | .40 | .22 |
| 350 | Billy Sims (IA) | .15 | .08 |
| 351 | Tom Skladany | .06 | .03 |
| 352 | Leonard Thompson | .06 | .03 |
| 353 | Stan White | .06 | .03 |
| 354 | Packers (TL) | .30 | .18 |
| 355 | Paul Coffman | .06 | .03 |
| 356 | George Cumby | .06 | .03 |
| 357 | Lynn Dickey | .20 | .12 |
| 358 | Lynn Dickey (IA) | .08 | .05 |
| 359 | Gerry Ellis | .06 | .03 |
| 360 | Maurice Harvey | .06 | .03 |
| 361 | Harlan Huckleby (R) | .10 | .06 |
| 362 | John Jefferson | .20 | .12 |
| 363 | Mark Lee (R) | .20 | .12 |
| 364 | James Lofton | 2.75 | 1.50 |
| 365 | James Lofton (IA) | 1.00 | .60 |
| 366 | Jan Stenerud | .25 | .15 |
| 367 | Jan Stenerud (IA) | .12 | .07 |
| 368 | Rich Wingo | .06 | .03 |
| 369 | Rams (TL) | .15 | .08 |
| 370 | Frank Corral | .06 | .03 |
| 371 | Nolan Cromwell | .15 | .08 |
| 372 | Nolan Cromwell (IA) | .07 | .04 |
| 373 | Preston Dennard | .06 | .03 |
| 374 | Mike Fanning | .06 | .03 |
| 375 | Doug France | .06 | .03 |
| 376 | Mike Guman | .06 | .03 |
| 377 | Pat Haden | .25 | .15 |
| 378 | Dennis Harrah | .06 | .03 |
| 379 | Drew Hill (R) | 4.00 | 2.25 |
| 380 | LeRoy Irvin (R) | .50 | .28 |
| 381 | Cody Jones | .06 | .03 |
| 382 | Rod Perry | .06 | .03 |
| 383 | Rich Saul | .06 | .03 |
| 384 | Pat Thomas | .06 | .03 |
| 385 | Wendell Tyler | .15 | .08 |
| 386 | Wendell Tyler (IA) | .07 | .04 |

| No. | Player | | |
|---|---|---|---|
| 387 | Billy Waddy | .06 | .03 |
| 388 | Jack Youngblood | .30 | .18 |
| 389 | Vikings (TL) | .15 | .08 |
| 390 | Matt Blair | .10 | .06 |
| 391 | Ted Brown | .08 | .05 |
| 392 | Ted Brown (IA) | .06 | .03 |
| 393 | Rick Danmeier | .06 | .03 |
| 394 | Tommy Kramer | .25 | .15 |
| 395 | Mark Mullaney | .06 | .03 |
| 396 | Eddie Payton | .08 | .05 |
| 397 | Ahmad Rashad | .30 | .18 |
| 398 | Joe Senser | .06 | .03 |
| 399 | Joe Senser (IA) | .06 | .03 |
| 400 | Sammie White | .10 | .06 |
| 401 | Sammie White (IA) | .06 | .03 |
| 402 | Ron Yary | .10 | .06 |
| 403 | Rickey Young | .06 | .03 |
| 404 | Saints (TL) | .20 | .12 |
| 405 | Russell Erxleben | .06 | .03 |
| 406 | Elois Grooms | .06 | .03 |
| 407 | Jack Holmes | .06 | .03 |
| 408 | Archie Manning | .30 | .18 |
| 409 | Derland Moore | .06 | .03 |
| 410 | George Rogers (R) | 1.00 | .60 |
| 411 | George Rogers (IA) | .40 | .22 |
| 412 | Toussaint Tyler | .06 | .03 |
| 413 | Dave Waymer (R) | .15 | .08 |
| 414 | Wayne Wilson | .06 | .03 |
| 415 | Giants (TL) | .15 | .08 |
| 416 | Scott Brunner (R) | .15 | .08 |
| 417 | Rob Carpenter | .08 | .05 |
| 418 | Harry Carson | .35 | .20 |
| 419 | Bill Currier | .06 | .03 |
| 420 | Joe Danelo | .06 | .03 |
| 421 | Joe Danelo (IA) | .06 | .03 |
| 422 | Mark Haynes (R) | .40 | .22 |
| 423 | Terry Jackson | .06 | .03 |
| 424 | Dave Jennings | .06 | .03 |
| 425 | Gary Jeter | .06 | .03 |
| 426 | Brian Kelley | .06 | .03 |
| 427 | George Martin | .08 | .05 |
| 428 | Curtis McGriff | .06 | .03 |
| 429 | Bill Neill | .06 | .03 |
| 430 | Johnny Perkins | .06 | .03 |
| 431 | Beasley Reece | .06 | .03 |
| 432 | Gary Shirk | .06 | .03 |
| 433 | Phil Simms | 1.75 | 1.00 |
| 434 | Lawrence Taylor (R) | 28.00 | 15.00 |
| 435 | Lawrence Taylor (IA) | 8.50 | 4.50 |
| 436 | Brad Van Pelt | .06 | .03 |
| 437 | Eagles (TL) | .15 | .08 |
| 438 | John Bunting | .06 | .03 |
| 439 | Billy Campfield | .06 | .03 |
| 440 | Harold Carmichael | .35 | .20 |
| 441 | Harold Carmichael (IA) | .15 | .08 |
| 442 | Herman Edwards | .06 | .03 |
| 443 | Tony Franklin | .06 | .03 |
| 444 | Tony Franklin (IA) | .06 | .03 |
| 445 | Carl Hairston | .06 | .03 |
| 446 | Dennis Harrison | .06 | .03 |
| 447 | Ron Jaworski | .20 | .12 |
| 448 | Charlie Johnson | .06 | .03 |
| 449 | Keith Krepfle | .06 | .03 |
| 450 | Frank LeMaster | .06 | .03 |
| 451 | Randy Logan | .06 | .03 |
| 452 | Wilbert Montgomery | .20 | .12 |
| 453 | Wilbert Montgomery (IA) | .08 | .05 |
| 454 | Hubert Oliver | .06 | .03 |
| 455 | Jerry Robinson | .15 | .08 |
| 456 | Jerry Robinson (IA) | .07 | .04 |
| 457 | Jerry Sisemore | .06 | .03 |
| 458 | Charlie Smith | .06 | .03 |
| 459 | Stan Walters | .06 | .03 |
| 460 | Brenard Wilson | .06 | .03 |
| 461 | Roynell Young | .10 | .06 |
| 462 | Cardinals (TL) | .25 | .15 |
| 463 | Ottis Anderson | .75 | .40 |
| 464 | Ottis Anderson (IA) | .30 | .18 |
| 465 | Carl Birdsong | .06 | .03 |
| 466 | Rush Brown | .06 | .03 |
| 467 | Mel Gray | .08 | .05 |
| 468 | Ken Greene | .06 | .03 |
| 469 | Jim Hart | .20 | .12 |
| 470 | E.J. Junior (R) | .50 | .28 |
| 471 | Neil Lomax (R) | 1.00 | .60 |
| 472 | Stump Mitchell (R) | .35 | .20 |
| 473 | Wayne Morris | .06 | .03 |
| 474 | Neil O'Donoghue | .06 | .03 |
| 475 | Pat Tilley | .06 | .03 |
| 476 | Pat Tilley (IA) | .06 | .03 |
| 477 | 49ers (TL) | .25 | .15 |
| 478 | Dwight Clark | .75 | .40 |
| 479 | Dwight Clark (IA) | .30 | .18 |
| 480 | Earl Cooper | .06 | .03 |
| 481 | Randy Cross | .08 | .05 |
| 482 | Johnny Davis | .06 | .03 |
| 483 | Fred Dean | .10 | .06 |
| 484 | Fred Dean (IA) | .06 | .03 |
| 485 | Dwight Hicks (R) | .40 | .22 |
| 486 | Ronnie Lott (R) | 25.00 | 15.00 |
| 487 | Ronnie Lott (IA) | 7.00 | 3.75 |
| 488 | Joe Montana | 28.50 | 15.50 |
| 489 | Joe Montana (IA) | 8.50 | 4.50 |
| 490 | Ricky Young | .06 | .03 |
| 491 | Jack Reynolds | .12 | .07 |
| 492 | Freddie Solomon | .08 | .05 |
| 493 | Ray Wersching | .06 | .03 |
| 494 | Charley Young | .06 | .03 |
| 495 | Buccaneers (TL) | .15 | .08 |
| 496 | Cedric Brown | .06 | .03 |
| 497 | Neal Colzie | .06 | .03 |
| 498 | Jerry Eckwood | .08 | .05 |
| 499 | Jimmie Giles | .12 | .07 |

| 500 | Hugh Green (R) | .60 | .35 |
| 501 | Kevin House | .10 | .06 |
| 502 | Kevin House (IA) | .06 | .03 |
| 503 | Cecil Johnson | .06 | .03 |
| 504 | James Owens | .06 | .03 |
| 505 | Lee Roy Selmon | .20 | .12 |
| 506 | Mike Washington | .06 | .03 |
| 507 | James Wilder (R) | .75 | .40 |
| 508 | Doug Williams | .25 | .15 |
| 509 | Redskins (TL) | .75 | .40 |
| 510 | Perry Brooks | .06 | .03 |
| 511 | Dave Butz | .12 | .07 |
| 512 | Wilbur Jackson | .10 | .06 |
| 513 | Joe Lavender | .06 | .03 |
| 514 | Terry Metcalf | .20 | .12 |
| 515 | Art Monk | 15.00 | 8.00 |
| 516 | Mark Moseley | .08 | .05 |
| 517 | Mark Murphy | .06 | .03 |
| 518 | Mike Nelms | .08 | .05 |
| 519 | Lemar Parrish | .08 | .05 |
| 520 | John Riggins | 1.25 | .70 |
| 521 | Joe Theismann | 1.00 | .60 |
| 522 | Ricky Thompson | .06 | .03 |
| 523 | Don Warren | .10 | .06 |
| 524 | Joe Washington | .15 | .08 |
| 525 | Checklist 1-132 | .20 | .05 |
| 526 | Checklist 133-264 | .20 | .05 |
| 527 | Checklist 265-396 | .20 | .05 |
| 528 | Checklist 397-528 | .20 | .05 |

# 1983 Topps

Topps cut the number of cards in their football set to 396 and one-third of the cards in the set were double printed (DP). The card fronts feature full color photos with the team name printed in block letters across the top. The player's name and position appear in a box at the bottom of the card. The card backs contain personal data and stats printed over a team helmet design. Subsets include Record Breakers (RB) (1-9), Playoffs (10-12) and League Leaders (202-207). Once again Topps produced a Team Leaders (TL) subset but changed the design. Only one photo appears on the card front and team stats have replaced the team checklist on the back. All cards measure 2-1/2" by 3-1/2".

| | | MINT | NR/MT |
| --- | --- | --- | --- |
| Complete Set (396) | | 55.00 | 30.00 |
| Commons | | .06 | .03 |
| Commons (DP) | | .04 | .02 |

| 1 | Ken Anderson (RB) | .35 | .15 |
| --- | --- | --- | --- |
| 2 | Tony Dorsett (RB) | .40 | .22 |
| 3 | Dan Fouts (RB) | .40 | .22 |
| 4 | Joe Montana (RB) | 1.75 | 1.00 |
| 5 | Mark Moseley (RB) | .08 | .05 |
| 6 | Mike Nelms (RB) | .08 | .05 |
| 7 | Darrol Ray (RB) | .08 | .05 |
| 8 | John Riggins (RB) | .35 | .20 |
| 9 | Fulton Walker (RB) | .10 | .06 |
| 10 | NFC Championship Game | .25 | .15 |
| 11 | AFC Championship Game | .12 | .07 |
| 12 | Super Bowl XVII | .35 | .20 |
| 13 | Falcons TL (Andrews) | .10 | .06 |
| 14 | William Andrews (DP) | .10 | .06 |
| 15 | Steve Bartkowski | .30 | .18 |
| 16 | Bobby Butler | .06 | .03 |
| 17 | Buddy Curry | .06 | .03 |
| 18 | Alfred Jackson (DP) | .06 | .03 |
| 19 | Alfred Jenkins | .10 | .06 |
| 20 | Kenny Johnson | .06 | .03 |
| 21 | Mike Kenn | .10 | .06 |
| 22 | Mick Luckhurst | .06 | .03 |
| 23 | Junior Miller | .08 | .05 |
| 24 | Al Richardson | .06 | .03 |
| 25 | Gerald Riggs (R) (DP) | 1.50 | .80 |
| 26 | R.C. Thielemann | .08 | .05 |
| 27 | Jeff Van Note | .08 | .05 |
| 28 | Bears TL (Payton) | .60 | .35 |
| 29 | Brian Baschnagel | .06 | .03 |
| 30 | Dan Hampton | 1.25 | .70 |
| 31 | Mike Hartenstine | .06 | .03 |
| 32 | Noah Jackson | .06 | .03 |
| 33 | Jim McMahon (R) | 3.00 | 1.75 |
| 34 | Emery Moorehead (DP) | .04 | .02 |
| 35 | Bob Parsons | .06 | .03 |

| # | Player | | |
|---|--------|---|---|
| 36 | Walter Payton | 3.00 | 1.75 |
| 37 | Terry Schmidt | .06 | .03 |
| 38 | Mike Singletary (R) | 14.00 | 7.50 |
| 39 | Matt Suhey (DP) | .04 | .02 |
| 40 | Rickey Watts (DP) | .04 | .02 |
| 41 | Otis Wilson (R) (DP) | .15 | .08 |
| 42 | Cowboys TL (Dorsett) | .40 | .22 |
| 43 | Bob Breunig | .08 | .05 |
| 44 | Doug Cosbie | .12 | .07 |
| 45 | Pat Donovan | .06 | .03 |
| 46 | Tony Dorsett (DP) | 1.00 | .60 |
| 47 | Tony Hill | .15 | .08 |
| 48 | Butch Johnson (DP) | .06 | .03 |
| 49 | Ed Too Tall Jones (DP) | .30 | .18 |
| 50 | Harvey Martin (DP) | .12 | .07 |
| 51 | Drew Pearson | .20 | .12 |
| 52 | Rafael Septien | .06 | .03 |
| 53 | Ron Springs (DP) | .04 | .02 |
| 54 | Dennis Thurman | .06 | .03 |
| 55 | Everson Walls | .40 | .22 |
| 56 | Danny White (DP) | .20 | .12 |
| 57 | Randy White | .50 | .28 |
| 58 | Lions TL (Sims) | .15 | .08 |
| 59 | Bubba Baker (DP) | .04 | .02 |
| 60 | Dexter Bussey (DP) | .04 | .02 |
| 61 | Gary Danielson (DP) | .08 | .05 |
| 62 | Keith Dorney (DP) | .04 | .02 |
| 63 | Doug English | .06 | .03 |
| 64 | Ken Fantetti (DP) | .04 | .02 |
| 65 | Alvin Hall (DP) | .04 | .02 |
| 66 | David Hill (DP) | .04 | .02 |
| 67 | Eric Hipple | .10 | .06 |
| 68 | Ed Murray (DP) | .08 | .05 |
| 69 | Freddie Scott | .06 | .03 |
| 70 | Billy Sims (DP) | .15 | .08 |
| 71 | Tom Skladany (DP) | .04 | .02 |
| 72 | Leonard Thompson (DP) | .04 | .02 |
| 73 | Bobby Watkins | .06 | .03 |
| 74 | Packers TL (Ivery) | .10 | .06 |
| 75 | John Anderson (R) | .10 | .06 |
| 76 | Paul Coffman | .06 | .03 |
| 77 | Lynn Dickey | .15 | .08 |
| 78 | Mike Douglass (DP) | .04 | .02 |
| 79 | Eddie Lee Ivery | .10 | .06 |
| 80 | John Jefferson (DP) | .15 | .08 |
| 81 | Ezra Johnson | .06 | .03 |
| 82 | Mark Lee | .06 | .03 |
| 83 | James Lofton | 1.50 | .80 |
| 84 | Larry McCarren | .06 | .03 |
| 85 | Jan Stenerud (DP) | .15 | .08 |
| 86 | Rams TL (Tyler) | .10 | .06 |
| 87 | Bill Bain (DP) | .04 | .02 |
| 88 | Nolan Cromwell | .08 | .05 |
| 89 | Preston Dennard | .06 | .03 |
| 90 | Vince Ferragamo (DP) | .12 | .07 |
| 91 | Mike Guman | .06 | .03 |
| 92 | Kent Hill | .06 | .03 |
| 93 | Mike Lansford (R)(DP) | .10 | .06 |
| 94 | Rod Perry | .06 | .03 |
| 95 | Pat Thomas (DP) | .04 | .02 |
| 96 | Jack Youngblood | .20 | .12 |
| 97 | Vikings TL (Brown) | .10 | .06 |
| 98 | Matt Blair | .08 | .05 |
| 99 | Ted Brown | .08 | .05 |
| 100 | Greg Coleman | .06 | .03 |
| 101 | Randy Holloway | .06 | .03 |
| 102 | Tommy Kramer | .20 | .12 |
| 103 | Doug Martin (DP) | .04 | .02 |
| 104 | Mark Mullaney | .06 | .03 |
| 105 | Joe Senser | .06 | .03 |
| 106 | Willie Teal (DP) | .04 | .02 |
| 107 | Sammie White | .08 | .05 |
| 108 | Rickey Young | .06 | .03 |
| 109 | Saints TL (Rogers) | .15 | .08 |
| 110 | Stan Brock (R) | .25 | .15 |
| 111 | Bruce Clark (R) | .10 | .06 |
| 112 | Russell Erxleben (DP) | .04 | .02 |
| 113 | Russell Gary | .06 | .03 |
| 114 | Jeff Groth (DP) | .04 | .02 |
| 115 | John Hill (DP) | .04 | .02 |
| 116 | Derland Moore | .06 | .03 |
| 117 | George Rogers | .25 | .15 |
| 118 | Ken Stabler | .50 | .28 |
| 119 | Wayne Wilson | .06 | .03 |
| 120 | Giants TL (Woolfolk) | .10 | .06 |
| 121 | Scott Brunner | .08 | .05 |
| 122 | Rob Carpenter | .08 | .05 |
| 123 | Harry Carson | .20 | .12 |
| 124 | Joe Danelo | .04 | .02 |
| 125 | Earnest Gray | .06 | .03 |
| 126 | Mark Haynes (DP) | .12 | .07 |
| 127 | Terry Jackson | .06 | .03 |
| 128 | Dave Jennings | .06 | .03 |
| 129 | Brian Kelley | .06 | .03 |
| 130 | George Martin | .08 | .05 |
| 131 | Tom Mullady | .06 | .03 |
| 132 | Johnny Perkins | .06 | .03 |
| 133 | Lawrence Taylor | 8.00 | 4.50 |
| 134 | Brad Van Pelt | .06 | .03 |
| 135 | Butch Woolfolk (DP) | .07 | .04 |
| 136 | Eagles TL (Montgomery) | .10 | .06 |
| 137 | Harold Carmichael | .20 | .12 |
| 138 | Herman Edwards | .06 | .03 |
| 139 | Tony Franklin (DP) | .04 | .02 |
| 140 | Carl Hairston (DP) | .04 | .02 |
| 141 | Dennis Harrison (DP) | .04 | .02 |
| 142 | Ron Jaworski (DP) | .12 | .07 |
| 143 | Frank LeMaster | .06 | .03 |
| 144 | Wilbert Montgomery | .12 | .07 |
| 145 | Guy Morriss | .06 | .03 |
| 146 | Jerry Robinson | .06 | .03 |

| | | | |
|---|---|---|---|
| 147 | Max Runager | .06 | .03 |
| 148 | Ron Smith (DP) | .04 | .02 |
| 149 | John Spagnola | .06 | .03 |
| 150 | Stan Walters (DP) | .04 | .02 |
| 151 | Roynell Young (DP) | .06 | .03 |
| 152 | Cardinals TL (Anderson) | .25 | .15 |
| 153 | Ottis Anderson | .35 | .20 |
| 154 | Carl Birdsong | .06 | .03 |
| 155 | Dan Dierdorf (DP) | .15 | .08 |
| 156 | Roy Green (R) | 1.75 | 1.00 |
| 157 | Elois Grooms | .06 | .03 |
| 158 | Neil Lomax (DP) | .20 | .12 |
| 159 | Wayne Morris | .06 | .03 |
| 160 | Tootie Robbins (R) | .10 | .06 |
| 161 | Luis Sharpe (R) | .30 | .18 |
| 162 | Pat Tilley | .06 | .03 |
| 163 | 49ers TL (Moore) | .10 | .06 |
| 164 | Dwight Clark | .30 | .18 |
| 165 | Randy Cross | .07 | .04 |
| 166 | Russ Francis | .08 | .05 |
| 167 | Dwight Hicks | .08 | .05 |
| 168 | Ronnie Lott | 6.50 | 3.50 |
| 169 | Joe Montana | 9.00 | 5.00 |
| 170 | Jeff Moore | .06 | .03 |
| 171 | Renaldo Nehemiah (R) | .20 | .12 |
| 172 | Freddie Solomon | .08 | .05 |
| 173 | Ray Wersching (DP) | .04 | .02 |
| 174 | Buccaneers TL (Wilder) | .10 | .06 |
| 175 | Cedric Brown | .06 | .03 |
| 176 | Bill Capece | .06 | .03 |
| 177 | Neal Colzie | .06 | .03 |
| 178 | Jimmie Giles | .10 | .06 |
| 179 | Hugh Green | .15 | .08 |
| 180 | Kevin House (DP) | .06 | .03 |
| 181 | James Owens | .08 | .05 |
| 182 | Lee Roy Selmon | .15 | .08 |
| 183 | Mike Washington | .06 | .03 |
| 184 | James Wilder | .15 | .08 |
| 185 | Doug Willaims (DP) | .15 | .08 |
| 186 | Redskins TL (Riggins) | .30 | .18 |
| 187 | Jeff Bostic (R) (DP) | .20 | .12 |
| 188 | Charlie Brown (R) | .12 | .07 |
| 189 | Vernon Dean (DP) | .04 | .02 |
| 190 | Joe Jacoby (R) | .80 | .45 |
| 191 | Dexter Manley (R) | .15 | .08 |
| 192 | Rich Milot | .06 | .03 |
| 193 | Art Monk (DP) | 4.50 | 2.50 |
| 194 | Mark Moseley (DP) | .06 | .03 |
| 195 | Mike Nelms | .06 | .03 |
| 196 | Neal Olkewicz (DP) | .04 | .02 |
| 197 | Tony Peters | .06 | .03 |
| 198 | John Riggins (DP) | .75 | .40 |
| 199 | Joe Theismann | .75 | .40 |
| 200 | Don Warren | .07 | .04 |
| 201 | Jeris White (DP) | .04 | .02 |
| 202 | Passing Leaders | .25 | .15 |
| | Joe Theismann | | |
| | Ken Anderson | | |
| 203 | Receiving Leaders | .15 | .08 |
| | Dwight Clark | | |
| | Kellen Winslow | | |
| 204 | Rushing Leaders | .35 | .20 |
| | Tony Dorsett | | |
| | Freeman McNeil | | |
| 205 | Scoring Leaders | .50 | .28 |
| | Wendell Tyler | | |
| | Marcus Allen | | |
| 206 | Interception Leaders | .08 | .05 |
| | Everson Walls | | |
| 207 | Punting Leaders | .08 | .05 |
| | Carl Birdsong | | |
| | Luke Prestridge | | |
| 208 | Colts TL (McMillan) | .10 | .06 |
| 209 | Matt Bouza | .06 | .03 |
| 210 | Johnie Cooks (R) (DP) | .10 | .06 |
| 211 | Curtis Dickey | .12 | .07 |
| 212 | Nesby Glasgow (DP) | .04 | .02 |
| 213 | Derrick Hatchett | .06 | .03 |
| 214 | Randy McMillan | .08 | .05 |
| 215 | Mike Pagel (R) | .25 | .15 |
| 216 | Rohn Stark (R) (DP) | .15 | .08 |
| 217 | Donnell Thompson (R) | .15 | .08 |
| 218 | Leo Wisniewski (DP) | .04 | .02 |
| 219 | Bills TL (Cribbs) | .10 | .06 |
| 220 | Curtis Brown | .06 | .03 |
| 221 | Jerry Butler | .10 | .06 |
| 222 | Greg Cater (DP) | .04 | .02 |
| 223 | Joe Cribbs | .20 | .12 |
| 224 | Joe Ferguson | .15 | .08 |
| 225 | Roosevelt Leaks | .08 | .05 |
| 226 | Frank Lewis | .08 | .05 |
| 227 | Eugene Marve (R) | .12 | .07 |
| 228 | Fred Smerlas (DP) | .08 | .05 |
| 229 | Ben Williams (DP) | .04 | .02 |
| 230 | Bengals TL (Johnson) | .10 | .06 |
| 231 | Charles Alexander | .08 | .05 |
| 232 | Ken Anderson (DP) | .25 | .15 |
| 233 | Jim Breech (DP) | .04 | .02 |
| 234 | Ross Browner | .12 | .07 |
| 235 | Cris Collinsworth (DP) | .40 | .22 |
| 236 | Isaac Curtis | .10 | .06 |
| 237 | Pete Johnson | .10 | .06 |
| 238 | Steve Kreider (DP) | .04 | .02 |
| 239 | Max Montoya (R) (DP) | .25 | .15 |
| 240 | Anthony Munoz | 3.00 | 1.75 |
| 241 | Ken Riley | .07 | .04 |
| 242 | Dan Ross | .08 | .05 |
| 243 | Reggie Williams | .10 | .06 |
| 244 | Browns TL (Pruitt) | .10 | .06 |
| 245 | Chip Banks (R) (DP) | .30 | .18 |
| 246 | Tom Cousineau (DP) | .10 | .06 |
| 247 | Joe DeLamielleure (DP) | .06 | .03 |

| | | | |
|---|---|---|---|
| 248 | Doug Dieken (DP) | .04 | .02 |
| 249 | Hanford Dixon (R) | .35 | .20 |
| 250 | Ricky Feacher (DP) | .04 | .02 |
| 251 | Lawrence Johnson (DP) | .04 | .02 |
| 252 | Dave Logan (DP) | .04 | .02 |
| 253 | Paul McDonald (R)(DP) | .07 | .04 |
| 254 | Ozzie Newsome (DP) | .60 | .35 |
| 255 | Mike Pruitt | .12 | .07 |
| 256 | Clarence Scott (DP) | .04 | .02 |
| 257 | Brian Sipe (DP) | .15 | .08 |
| 258 | Dwight Walker (DP) | .04 | .02 |
| 259 | Charles White | .15 | .08 |
| 260 | Broncos TL (Willhite) | .10 | .06 |
| 261 | Steve DeBerg (DP) | .40 | .22 |
| 262 | Randy Gradishar (DP) | .10 | .06 |
| 263 | Rulon Jones (R) (DP) | .12 | .07 |
| 264 | Rick Karlis | .04 | .02 |
| 265 | Don Latimer | .06 | .03 |
| 266 | Rick Parros (DP) | .04 | .02 |
| 267 | Luke Prestridge | .06 | .03 |
| 268 | Rick Upchurch | .10 | .06 |
| 269 | Steve Watson (R) (DP) | .10 | .06 |
| 270 | Gerald Willhite (DP) | .12 | .07 |
| 271 | Oilers TL (Nielsen) | .10 | .06 |
| 272 | Harold Bailey | .06 | .03 |
| 273 | Jesse Baker (DP) | .04 | .02 |
| 274 | Gregg Bingham (DP) | .04 | .02 |
| 275 | Robert Brazile (DP) | .06 | .03 |
| 276 | Donnie Craft | .06 | .03 |
| 277 | Daryl Hunt | .06 | .03 |
| 278 | Archie Manning (DP) | .20 | .12 |
| 279 | Gifford Nielsen | .10 | .06 |
| 280 | Mike Renfro | .08 | .05 |
| 281 | Carl Roaches (DP) | .04 | .02 |
| 282 | Chiefs TL (Delaney) | .10 | .06 |
| 283 | Gary Barbaro | .07 | .04 |
| 284 | Joe Delaney | .20 | .12 |
| 285 | Jeff Gossett (R) | .25 | .15 |
| 286 | Gary Green (DP) | .06 | .03 |
| 287 | Eric Harris (DP) | .04 | .02 |
| 288 | Billy Jackson (DP) | .04 | .02 |
| 289 | Bill Kenney (DP) | .10 | .06 |
| 290 | Nick Lowery | .50 | .28 |
| 291 | Henry Marshall | .06 | .03 |
| 292 | Art Still (DP) | .10 | .06 |
| 293 | Raiders TL (Allen) | .75 | .40 |
| 294 | Marcus Allen (R) (DP) | 10.00 | 6.00 |
| 295 | Lyle Alzado | .20 | .12 |
| 296 | Chris Bahr (DP) | .04 | .02 |
| 297 | Cliff Branch | .30 | .18 |
| 298 | Todd Christensen (R) | 1.75 | 1.00 |
| 299 | Ray Guy | .20 | .12 |
| 300 | Frank Hawkins (DP) | .04 | .02 |
| 301 | Lester Hayes (DP) | .10 | .06 |
| 302 | Ted Hendricks (DP) | .25 | .15 |
| 303 | Kenny King (DP) | .06 | .03 |
| 304 | Rod Martin | .08 | .05 |
| 305 | Matt Millen (DP) | .25 | .15 |
| 306 | Burgess Owens | .06 | .03 |
| 307 | Jim Plunkett | .35 | .20 |
| 308 | Dolphins TL (Franklin) | .10 | .06 |
| 309 | Bob Baumhower | .07 | .04 |
| 310 | Glenn Blackwood | .06 | .03 |
| 311 | Lyle Blackwood (DP) | .04 | .02 |
| 312 | A.J. Duhe | .12 | .07 |
| 313 | Andra Franklin | .10 | .06 |
| 314 | Duriel Harris | .07 | .04 |
| 315 | Bob Kuechenberg (DP) | .06 | .03 |
| 316 | Don McNeal | .06 | .03 |
| 317 | Tony Nathan | .10 | .06 |
| 318 | Ed Newman | .06 | .03 |
| 319 | Earnie Rhone (DP) | .04 | .02 |
| 320 | Joe Rose (R) (DP) | .06 | .03 |
| 321 | Don Strock (DP) | .08 | .05 |
| 322 | Uwe Von Schamann | .06 | .03 |
| 323 | David Woodley (DP) | .08 | .05 |
| 324 | Patriots TL (Collins) | .10 | .06 |
| 325 | Julius Adams | .06 | .03 |
| 326 | Pete Brock | .06 | .03 |
| 327 | Rich Camarillo (R)(DP) | .08 | .05 |
| 328 | Tony Collins | .10 | .06 |
| 329 | Steve Grogan | .15 | .08 |
| 330 | John Hannah | .30 | .18 |
| 331 | Don Hasselbeck | .06 | .03 |
| 332 | Mike Haynes | .10 | .06 |
| 333 | Roland James (R) | .12 | .07 |
| 334a | Stanley Morgan (ER) (Inside Linebacker on card back) | .60 | .35 |
| 334b | Stanley Morgan (Cor) | .30 | .18 |
| 335 | Steve Nelson | .06 | .03 |
| 336 | Kenneth Sims (R) (DP) | .10 | .06 |
| 337 | Mark Van Eeghen | .10 | .06 |
| 338 | Jets TL (McNeil) | .10 | .06 |
| 339 | Greg Buttle | .06 | .03 |
| 340 | Joe Fields | .08 | .05 |
| 341 | Mark Gastineau (DP) | .08 | .05 |
| 342 | Bruce Harper | .06 | .03 |
| 343 | Bobby Jackson | .06 | .03 |
| 344 | Bobby Jones | .06 | .03 |
| 345 | Johnny Lam Jones (DP) | .08 | .05 |
| 346 | Joe Klecko | .12 | .07 |
| 347 | Marty Lyons | .06 | .03 |
| 348 | Freeman McNeil | .75 | .40 |
| 349 | Lance Mehl (R) | .15 | .08 |
| 350 | Marvin Powell (DP) | .06 | .03 |
| 351 | Darrol Ray (DP) | .04 | .02 |
| 352 | Abdul Salaam | .06 | .03 |
| 353 | Richard Todd | .15 | .08 |
| 354 | Wesley Walker | .20 | .12 |
| 355 | Steelers TL (Harris) | .40 | .22 |
| 356 | Gary Anderson (R)(DP) | .25 | .15 |

| 357 | Mel Blount (DP) | .30 | .18 |
| 358 | Terry Bradshaw (DP) | .80 | .45 |
| 359 | Larry Brown | .06 | .03 |
| 360 | Bennie Cunningham | .06 | .03 |
| 361 | Gary Dunn | .06 | .03 |
| 362 | Franco Harris | .75 | .40 |
| 363 | Jack Lambert | .50 | .28 |
| 364 | Frank Pollard | .08 | .05 |
| 365 | Donnie Shell | .12 | .07 |
| 366 | John Stallworth | .25 | .15 |
| 367 | Loren Toews (R) | .08 | .05 |
| 368 | Mike Webster (DP) | .25 | .15 |
| 369 | Dwayne Woodruff (R) | .15 | .08 |
| 370 | Chargers TL (Muncie) | .10 | .06 |
| 371 | Rolf Benirschke (DP) | .04 | .02 |
| 372 | James Brooks | 1.00 | .60 |
| 373 | Wes Chandler PB | .12 | .07 |
| 374 | Dan Fouts (DP) | .75 | .40 |
| 375 | Tim Fox | .06 | .03 |
| 376 | Gary Johnson | .06 | .03 |
| 377 | Charlie Joiner (DP) | .30 | .18 |
| 378 | Louie Kelcher | .08 | .05 |
| 379 | Chuck Muncie | .12 | .07 |
| 380 | Cliff Thrift | .06 | .03 |
| 381 | Doug Wilkerson | .06 | .03 |
| 382 | Kellen Winslow | .50 | .28 |
| 383 | Seahawks TL (Smith) | .10 | .06 |
| 384 | Kenny Easley (R) | .75 | .40 |
| 385 | Jacob Green (R) | .80 | .45 |
| 386 | John Harris | .06 | .03 |
| 387 | Michael Jackson | .06 | .03 |
| 388 | Norm Johnson (R) | .25 | .15 |
| 389 | Steve Largent | 1.25 | .70 |
| 390 | Keith Simpson | .06 | .03 |
| 391 | Sherman Smith | .06 | .03 |
| 392 | Jeff West (DP) | .04 | .02 |
| 393 | Jim Zorn (DP) | .12 | .07 |
| 394 | Checklist 1-132 | .15 | .05 |
| 395 | Checklist 133-264 | .15 | .05 |
| 396 | Checklist 265-396 | .15 | .05 |

# 1984 Topps

The cards in this 396-card set feature full color photos on the fronts. The player's name is found in a diagonal box at the top of the card while his position and team name appear in a diagonal box below the photograph. A team helmet is located in the lower left corner. The card backs contain personal data, stats and highlights. Subsets include Record Breakers (RB) (1-6), Playoffs (7-9), League Leaders (202-207) and a new feature called Instant Replay (IR). Team Leaders (TL) consist of a single photo on the card fronts and team statistics on the backs. All cards measure 2-1/2" by 3-1/2".

|  | MINT | NR/MT |
|---|---|---|
| Complete Set (396) | 125.00 | 65.00 |
| Commons | .06 | .03 |

| 1 | Eric Dickerson (RB) | .90 | .25 |
|---|---|---|---|
| 2 | Ali Haji-Sheikh (RB) | .08 | .05 |
| 3 | Franco Harris (RB) | .35 | .20 |
| 4 | Mark Moseley (RB) | .08 | .05 |
| 5 | John Riggins (RB) | .30 | .18 |
| 6 | Jan Stenerud (RB) | .12 | .07 |
| 7 | AFC Championship | .15 | .08 |
| 8 | NFC Championship | .15 | .08 |
| 9 | Super Bowl XVIII | .30 | .18 |
| 10 | Colts TL (Dickey) | .10 | .06 |
| 11 | Raul Allegre (R) | .10 | .06 |
| 12 | Curtis Dickey | .10 | .06 |
| 13 | Ray Donaldson (R) | .15 | .08 |
| 14 | Nesby Glasgow | .06 | .03 |
| 15 | Chris Hinton (R) | 1.50 | .80 |
| 16 | Vernon Maxwell (R) | .25 | .15 |
| 17 | Randy McMillan | .08 | .05 |
| 18 | Mike Pagel | .10 | .06 |

| # | Player | | |
|---|--------|------|------|
| 19 | Rohn Stark | .06 | .03 |
| 20 | Leo Wisniewski | .06 | .03 |
| 21 | Bills TL (Cribbs) | .10 | .06 |
| 22 | Jerry Butler | .08 | .05 |
| 23 | Joe Danelo | .06 | .03 |
| 24 | Joe Ferguson | .15 | .08 |
| 25 | Steve Freeman | .06 | .03 |
| 26 | Roosevelt Leaks | .08 | .05 |
| 27 | Frank Lewis | .08 | .05 |
| 28 | Eugene Marve | .06 | .03 |
| 29 | Booker Moore | .06 | .03 |
| 30 | Fred Smerlas | .08 | .05 |
| 31 | Ben Williams | .06 | .03 |
| 32 | Bengals (Collinsworth) | .10 | .06 |
| 33 | Charles Alexander | .06 | .03 |
| 34 | Ken Anderson | .30 | .18 |
| 35 | Ken Anderson (IR) | .12 | .07 |
| 36 | Jim Breech | .06 | .03 |
| 37 | Cris Collinsworth | .20 | .12 |
| 38 | Cris Collinsworth (IR) | .08 | .05 |
| 39 | Issac Curtis | .12 | .07 |
| 40 | Eddie Edwards | .06 | .03 |
| 41 | Ray Horton (R) | .25 | .15 |
| 42 | Pete Johnson | .08 | .05 |
| 43 | Steve Kreider | .06 | .03 |
| 44 | Max Montoya | .08 | .05 |
| 45 | Anthony Munoz | .80 | .45 |
| 46 | Reggie Williams | .08 | .05 |
| 47 | Browns TL (Pruitt) | .10 | .06 |
| 48 | Matt Bahr | .06 | .03 |
| 49 | Chip Banks | .10 | .06 |
| 50 | Tom Cousineau | .06 | .03 |
| 51 | Joe DeLamielleure | .08 | .05 |
| 52 | Doug Dieken | .06 | .03 |
| 53 | Bob Golic (R) | .60 | .35 |
| 54 | Bobby Jones | .06 | .03 |
| 55 | Dave Logan | .06 | .03 |
| 56 | Clay Matthews | .20 | .12 |
| 57 | Paul McDonald | .10 | .06 |
| 58 | Ozzie Newsome | .60 | .35 |
| 59 | Ozzie Newsome (IR) | .25 | .15 |
| 60 | Mike Pruitt | .10 | .06 |
| 61 | Broncos TL (Watson) | .10 | .06 |
| 62 | Barney Chavous (R) | .12 | .07 |
| 63 | John Elway | 18.50 | 9.50 |
| 64 | Steve Foley | .06 | .03 |
| 65 | Tom Jackson | .12 | .07 |
| 66 | Rich Karlis | .06 | .03 |
| 67 | Luke Prestridge | .06 | .03 |
| 68 | Zack Thomas | .06 | .03 |
| 69 | Rick Upchurch | .08 | .05 |
| 70 | Steve Watson | .06 | .03 |
| 71 | Sammy Winder (R) | .30 | .18 |
| 72 | Louis Wright | .08 | .05 |
| 73 | Oilers TL (Smith) | .10 | .06 |
| 74 | Jesse Baker | .06 | .03 |
| 75 | Gregg Bingham | .06 | .03 |
| 76 | Robert Brazile | .08 | .05 |
| 77 | Steve Brown | .06 | .03 |
| 78 | Chris Dressel | .06 | .03 |
| 79 | Doug France | .06 | .03 |
| 80 | Florian Kempf | .06 | .03 |
| 81 | Carl Roaches | .06 | .03 |
| 82 | Tim Smith (R) | .12 | .07 |
| 83 | Willie Tullis | .06 | .03 |
| 84 | Chiefs TL (Carson) | .10 | .06 |
| 85 | Mike Bell | .06 | .03 |
| 86 | Theotis Brown | .06 | .03 |
| 87 | Carlos Carson | .15 | .08 |
| 88 | Carlos Carson (IR) | .07 | .04 |
| 89 | Deron Cherry (R) | 1.50 | .80 |
| 90 | Gary Green | .07 | .04 |
| 91 | Billy Jackson | .06 | .03 |
| 92 | Bill Kenney | .12 | .07 |
| 93 | Bill Kenney (IR) | .06 | .03 |
| 94 | Nick Lowery | .30 | .18 |
| 95 | Henry Marshall | .06 | .03 |
| 96 | Art Still | .10 | .06 |
| 97 | Raiders (Christensen) | .10 | .06 |
| 98 | Marcus Allen | 2.50 | 1.40 |
| 99 | Marcus Allen (IR) | 1.10 | .60 |
| 100 | Lyle Alzado | .15 | .08 |
| 101 | Lyle Alzado (IR) | .07 | .04 |
| 102 | Chris Bahr | .06 | .03 |
| 103 | Malcolm Barnwell (R) | .06 | .03 |
| 104 | Cliff Branch | .30 | .18 |
| 105 | Todd Christensen | .50 | .28 |
| 106 | Todd Christensen (IR) | .20 | .12 |
| 107 | Ray Guy | .15 | .08 |
| 108 | Frank Hawkins | .06 | .03 |
| 109 | Lester Hayes | .10 | .06 |
| 110 | Ted Hendricks | .25 | .15 |
| 111 | Howie Long (R) | 3.50 | 2.00 |
| 112 | Rod Martin | .08 | .05 |
| 113 | Vann McElroy (R) | .20 | .12 |
| 114 | Jim Plunkett | .25 | .15 |
| 115 | Greg Pruitt | .12 | .07 |
| 116 | Dolphins TL (Duper) | .40 | .22 |
| 117 | Bob Baumhower | .06 | .03 |
| 118 | Doug Betters (R) | .12 | .07 |
| 119 | A.J. Duhe | .12 | .07 |
| 120 | Mark Duper | 3.50 | 2.00 |
| 121 | Andra Franklin | .08 | .05 |
| 122 | William Judson | .06 | .03 |
| 123 | Dan Marino | 65.00 | 35.00 |
| 124 | Dan Marino (IR) | 8.50 | 4.50 |
| 125 | Nat Moore | .10 | .06 |
| 126 | Ed Newman | .06 | .03 |
| 127 | Reggie Roby (R) | .40 | .22 |
| 128 | Gerald Small | .06 | .03 |
| 129 | Dwight Stephenson (R) | .80 | .45 |
| 130 | Uwe Von Schamann | .06 | .03 |
| 131 | Patriots TL (Collins) | .10 | .06 |
| 132 | Rich Camarillo | .06 | .03 |

| 133 | Tony Collins | .10 | .06 |
| 134 | Tony Collins (IR) | .06 | .03 |
| 135 | Bob Cryder | .06 | .03 |
| 136 | Steve Grogan | .15 | .08 |
| 137 | John Hannah | .30 | .18 |
| 138 | Brian Holloway (R) | .12 | .07 |
| 139 | Roland James | .06 | .03 |
| 140 | Stanley Morgan | .30 | .18 |
| 141 | Rick Sanford | .06 | .03 |
| 142 | Mosi Tatupu (R) | .15 | .08 |
| 143 | Andre Tippett (R) | 1.75 | 1.00 |
| 144 | Jets TL (Walker) | .10 | .06 |
| 145 | Jerome Barkum | .06 | .03 |
| 146 | Mark Gastineau | .12 | .07 |
| 147 | Mark Gastineau (IR) | .06 | .03 |
| 148 | Bruce Harper | .06 | .03 |
| 149 | Johnny Lam Jones | .08 | .05 |
| 150 | Joe Klecko | .12 | .07 |
| 151 | Pat Leahy | .06 | .03 |
| 152 | Freeman McNeil | .30 | .18 |
| 153 | Lance Mehl | .06 | .03 |
| 154 | Marvin Powell | .08 | .05 |
| 155 | Darrol Ray | .06 | .03 |
| 156 | Pat Ryan (R) | .15 | .08 |
| 157 | Kirk Springs | .06 | .03 |
| 158 | Wesley Walker | .15 | .08 |
| 159 | Steelers TL (Harris) | .25 | .15 |
| 160 | Walter Abercrombie(R) | .15 | .08 |
| 161 | Gary Anderson | .07 | .04 |
| 162 | Terry Bradshaw | 1.00 | .60 |
| 163 | Craig Colquitt | .06 | .03 |
| 164 | Bennie Cunningham | .06 | .03 |
| 165 | Franco Harris | .75 | .40 |
| 166 | Franco Harris (IR) | .30 | .18 |
| 167 | Jack Lambert | .50 | .28 |
| 168 | Jack Lambert (IR) | .20 | .12 |
| 169 | Frank Pollard | .06 | .03 |
| 170 | Donnie Shell | .12 | .07 |
| 171 | Mike Webster | .30 | .18 |
| 172 | Keith Willis (R) | .15 | .08 |
| 173 | Rick Woods | .06 | .03 |
| 174 | Chargers TL (Winslow) | .12 | .07 |
| 175 | Rolf Benirschke | .06 | .03 |
| 176 | James Brooks | .50 | .28 |
| 177 | Maury Buford | .06 | .03 |
| 178 | Wes Chandler | .12 | .07 |
| 179 | Dan Fouts | 1.00 | .60 |
| 180 | Dan Fouts (IR) | .40 | .22 |
| 181 | Charlie Joiner | .35 | .20 |
| 182 | Linden King | .06 | .03 |
| 183 | Chuck Muncie | .10 | .06 |
| 184 | Billy Ray Smith (R) | .30 | .18 |
| 185 | Danny Walters (R) | .10 | .06 |
| 186 | Kellen Winslow | .35 | .20 |
| 187 | Kellen Winslow (IR) | .15 | .08 |
| 188 | Seahawks TL (Warner) | .12 | .07 |
| 189 | Steve August | .06 | .03 |
| 190 | Dave Brown | .08 | .05 |
| 191 | Zachary Dixon | .06 | .03 |
| 192 | Kenny Easley | .15 | .08 |
| 193 | Jacob Green | .15 | .08 |
| 194 | Norm Johnson | .06 | .03 |
| 195 | Dave Krieg (R) | 3.50 | 2.00 |
| 196 | Steve Largent | 1.50 | .80 |
| 197 | Steve Largent (IR) | .60 | .35 |
| 198 | Curt Warner (R) | .50 | .28 |
| 199 | Curt Warner (IR) | .20 | .12 |
| 200 | Jeff West | .06 | .03 |
| 201 | Charley Young | .06 | .03 |
| 202 | Passing Leaders | 2.50 | 1.40 |
|  | Dan Marino |  |  |
|  | Steve Bartkowski |  |  |
| 203 | Receiving Leaders | .15 | .08 |
|  | Todd Christensen |  |  |
|  | Charlie Brown |  |  |
|  | Earnest Gray |  |  |
|  | Roy Green |  |  |
| 204 | Rushing Leaders | .75 | .40 |
|  | Curt Warner |  |  |
|  | Eric Dickerson |  |  |
| 205 | Scoring Leaders | .08 | .05 |
|  | Gary Anderson |  |  |
|  | Mark Moseley |  |  |
| 206 | Interception Leaders | ..08 | .05 |
|  | Vann McElroy |  |  |
|  | Ken Riley |  |  |
|  | Mark Murphy |  |  |
| 207 | Punting Leaders | .08 | .05 |
|  | Rich Camarillo |  |  |
|  | Greg Coleman |  |  |
| 208 | Falcons TL (Andrews) | .10 | .06 |
| 209 | William Andrews | .10 | .06 |
| 210 | William Andrews (IR) | .06 | .03 |
| 211 | Stacey Bailey (R) | .15 | .08 |
| 212 | Steve Bartkowski | .25 | .15 |
| 213 | Steve Bartkowski (IR) | .10 | .06 |
| 214 | Ralph Giacomarro | .06 | .03 |
| 215 | Billy Johnson | .10 | .06 |
| 216 | Mike Kenn | .10 | .06 |
| 217 | Mick Luckhurst | .06 | .03 |
| 218 | Gerald Riggs | .30 | .18 |
| 219 | R.C. Thielemann | .08 | .05 |
| 220 | Jeff Van Note | .08 | .05 |
| 221 | Bears TL (Payton) | .75 | .40 |
| 222 | Jim Covert (R) | .80 | .45 |
| 223 | Leslie Frazier | .06 | .03 |
| 224 | Willie Gault (R) | 1.25 | .70 |
| 225 | Mike Hartenstine | .06 | .03 |
| 226 | Noah Jackson (ER) | .06 | .03 |
| 227 | Jim McMahon | 1.00 | .60 |
| 228 | Walter Payton | 2.75 | 1.50 |
| 229 | Walter Payton (IR) | 1.25 | .70 |
| 230 | Mike Richardson (R) | .15 | .08 |
| 231 | Terry Schmidt | .06 | .03 |

| | | | |
|---|---|---|---|
| 232 | Mike Singletary | 3.00 | 1.75 |
| 233 | Matt Suhey | .06 | .03 |
| 234 | Bob Thomas | .06 | .03 |
| 235 | Cowboys TL (Dorsett) | .25 | .15 |
| 236 | Bob Breunig | .07 | .04 |
| 237 | Doug Cosbie | .08 | .05 |
| 238 | Tony Dorsett | 1.00 | .60 |
| 239 | Tony Dorsett (IR) | .40 | .22 |
| 240 | John Dutton | .06 | .03 |
| 241 | Tony Hill | .12 | .07 |
| 242 | Ed Too Tall Jones | .25 | .15 |
| 243 | Drew Pearson | .25 | .15 |
| 244 | Rafael Septien | .06 | .03 |
| 245 | Ron Springs | .06 | .03 |
| 246 | Dennis Thurman | .06 | .03 |
| 247 | Everson Walls | .20 | .12 |
| 248 | Danny White | .25 | .15 |
| 249 | Randy White | .60 | .35 |
| 250 | Lions TL (Sims) | .15 | .08 |
| 251 | Jeff Chadwick (R) | .25 | .15 |
| 252 | Garry Cobb (R) | .08 | .05 |
| 253 | Doug English | .06 | .03 |
| 254 | William Gay | .06 | .03 |
| 255 | Eric Hipple | .08 | .05 |
| 256 | James Jones (R) | .15 | .08 |
| 257 | Bruce McNorton | .06 | .03 |
| 258 | Ed Murray | .06 | .03 |
| 259 | Ulysses Norris | .06 | .03 |
| 260 | Billy Sims | .20 | .12 |
| 261 | Billy Sims (IR) | .08 | .05 |
| 262 | Leonard Thompson | .06 | .03 |
| 263 | Packers TL (Lofton) | .25 | .15 |
| 264 | John Anderson | .06 | .03 |
| 265 | Paul Coffman | .06 | .03 |
| 266 | Lynn Dickey | .12 | .07 |
| 267 | Gerry Ellis | .06 | .03 |
| 268 | John Jefferson | .20 | .12 |
| 269 | John Jefferson (IR) | .08 | .05 |
| 270 | Ezra Johnson | .06 | .03 |
| 271 | Tim Lewis | .06 | .03 |
| 272 | James Lofton | 1.75 | 1.00 |
| 273 | James Lofton (IR) | .75 | .40 |
| 274 | Larry McCarren | .06 | .03 |
| 275 | Jan Stenerud | .25 | .15 |
| 276 | Rams TL (Dickerson) | .75 | .40 |
| 277 | Mike Barber | .06 | .03 |
| 278 | Jim Collins | .06 | .03 |
| 279 | Nolan Cromwell | .08 | .05 |
| 280 | Eric Dickerson (R) | 18.50 | 9.50 |
| 281 | Eric Dickerson (IR) | 4.00 | 2.25 |
| 282 | George Farmer | .06 | .03 |
| 283 | Vince Ferragamo | .15 | .08 |
| 284 | Kent Hill | .06 | .03 |
| 285 | John Misko | .06 | .03 |
| 286 | Jackie Slater (R) | 1.75 | 1.00 |
| 287 | Jack Youngblood | .20 | .12 |
| 288 | Vikings TL (Nelson) | .10 | .06 |
| 289 | Ted Brown | .08 | .05 |
| 290 | Greg Coleman | .06 | .03 |
| 291 | Steve Dils | .10 | .06 |
| 292 | Tony Galbreath | .08 | .05 |
| 293 | Tommy Kramer | .15 | .08 |
| 294 | Doug Martin | .06 | .03 |
| 295 | Darrin Nelson (R) | .40 | .22 |
| 296 | Benny Ricardo | .06 | .03 |
| 297 | John Swain | .06 | .03 |
| 298 | John Turner | .06 | .03 |
| 299 | Saints TL (Rogers) | .10 | .06 |
| 300 | Morten Andersen (R) | 3.00 | 1.75 |
| 301 | Russell Erxleben | .06 | .03 |
| 302 | Jeff Groth | .06 | .03 |
| 303 | Rickey Jackson (R) | 2.00 | 1.10 |
| 304 | Johnnie Poe | .06 | .03 |
| 305 | George Rogers | .15 | .08 |
| 306 | Richard Todd | .15 | .08 |
| 307 | Jim Wilks (R) | .10 | .06 |
| 308 | Dave Wilson (R) | .10 | .06 |
| 309 | Wayne Wilson | .06 | .03 |
| 310 | Giants TL (Gray) | .10 | .06 |
| 311 | Leon Bright | .06 | .03 |
| 312 | Scott Brunner | .08 | .05 |
| 313 | Rob Carpenter | .06 | .03 |
| 314 | Harry Carson | .25 | .15 |
| 315 | Earnest Gray | .10 | .06 |
| 316 | Ali Haji-Sheikh (R) | .08 | .05 |
| 317 | Mark Haynes | .10 | .06 |
| 318 | Dave Jennings | .06 | .03 |
| 319 | Brian Kelley | .06 | .03 |
| 320 | Phil Simms | .75 | .40 |
| 321 | Lawrence Taylor | 2.00 | 1.10 |
| 322 | Lawrence Taylor (IR) | .75 | .40 |
| 323 | Brad Van Pelt | .06 | .03 |
| 324 | Butch Woolfolk | .08 | .05 |
| 325 | Eagles TL (Quick) | .12 | .07 |
| 326 | Harold Carmichael | .25 | .15 |
| 327 | Herman Edwards | .06 | .03 |
| 328 | Michael Haddix (R) | .20 | .12 |
| 329 | Dennis Harrison | .06 | .03 |
| 330 | Ron Jaworski | .15 | .08 |
| 331 | Wilbert Montgomery | .12 | .07 |
| 332 | Hubert Oliver | .06 | .03 |
| 333 | Mike Quick (R) | .60 | .35 |
| 334 | Jerry Robinson | .06 | .03 |
| 335 | Max Runager | .06 | .03 |
| 336 | Michael Williams | .06 | .03 |
| 337 | Cardinals TL (Anderson) | .12 | .07 |
| 338 | Ottis Anderson | .30 | .18 |
| 339 | Bubba Baker | .06 | .03 |
| 340 | Carl Birdsong | .06 | .03 |
| 341 | David Galloway | .06 | .03 |
| 342 | Roy Green | .30 | .18 |
| 343 | Roy Green (IR) | .12 | .07 |
| 344 | Curtis Greer (R) | .15 | .08 |

| | | | |
|---|---|---|---|
| 345 | Neil Lomax | .15 | .08 |
| 346 | Doug Marsh | .06 | .03 |
| 347 | Stump Mitchell | .15 | .08 |
| 348 | Lionel Washington (R) | .35 | .20 |
| 349 | 49ers TL (Clark) | .12 | .07 |
| 350 | Dwaine Board | .06 | .03 |
| 351 | Dwight Clark | .20 | .12 |
| 352 | Dwight Clark (IR) | .08 | .05 |
| 353 | Roger Craig (R) | 5.00 | 2.75 |
| 354 | Fred Dean | .10 | .06 |
| 355 | Fred Dean (IR) | .06 | .03 |
| 356 | Dwight Hicks | .06 | .03 |
| 357 | Ronnie Lott | 2.00 | 1.10 |
| 358 | Joe Montana | 5.00 | 2.75 |
| 359 | Joe Montana (IR) | 2.00 | 1.10 |
| 360 | Freddie Solomon | .07 | .04 |
| 361 | Wendell Tyler | .10 | .06 |
| 362 | Ray Wersching | .06 | .03 |
| 363 | Eric Wright (R) | .20 | .12 |
| 364 | Buccaneers TL (House) | .10 | .06 |
| 365 | Gerald Carter | .06 | .03 |
| 366 | Hugh Green | .10 | .06 |
| 367 | Kevin House | .08 | .05 |
| 368 | Michael Morton | .06 | .03 |
| 369 | James Owens | .06 | .03 |
| 370 | Booker Reese | .06 | .03 |
| 371 | Lee Roy Selmon | .15 | .08 |
| 372 | Jack Thompson | .08 | .05 |
| 373 | James Wilder | .20 | .12 |
| 374 | Steve Wilson | .06 | .03 |
| 375 | Redskins TL (Riggins) | .25 | .15 |
| 376 | Jeff Bostic | .08 | .05 |
| 377 | Charlie Brown | .08 | .05 |
| 378 | Charlie Brown (IR) | .06 | .03 |
| 379 | Dave Butz | .10 | .06 |
| 380 | Darrell Green (R) | 6.00 | 3.25 |
| 381 | Russ Grimm (R) | .50 | .28 |
| 382 | Joe Jacoby | .15 | .08 |
| 383 | Dexter Manley | .08 | .05 |
| 384 | Art Monk | 1.75 | 1.00 |
| 385 | Mark Moseley | .08 | .05 |
| 386 | Mark Murphy | .06 | .03 |
| 387 | Mike Nelms | .06 | .03 |
| 388 | John Riggins | .60 | .35 |
| 389 | John Riggins (IR) | .25 | .15 |
| 390 | Joe Theismann | .50 | .28 |
| 391 | Joe Theismann (IR) | .20 | .12 |
| 392 | Don Warren | .08 | .05 |
| 393 | Joe Washington | .12 | .07 |
| 394 | Checklist 1-132 | .15 | .05 |
| 395 | Checklist 133-264 | .15 | .05 |
| 396 | Checklist 265-396 | .15 | .05 |

# 1984 Topps USFL

The cards in this 132-card set depict players from the United States Football League. The cards were originally sold as a complete set in a specially marked box. The card fronts feature full color photos with a USFL headline centered between the words "Premier Edition" at the top. The player's name, team and position appear in a box below the photograph and adjacent to a team helmet. The vertical card backs contain personal data, stats, a brief highlight and a USFL Fact. Due to limited production the cards are considered scarce. All cards measure 2-1/2" by 3-1/2".

| | | MINT | NR/MT |
|---|---|---|---|
| Complete Set (132) | | 475.00 | 260.00 |
| Commons | | .75 | .40 |

| | | | |
|---|---|---|---|
| 1 | Luther Bradley | 1.25 | .50 |
| 2 | Frank Corral | 1.00 | .60 |
| 3 | Trumaine Johnson (R) | 1.50 | .80 |
| 4 | Greg Landry | 1.00 | .60 |
| 5 | Kit Lathrop (R) | .75 | .40 |
| 6 | Kevin Long (R) | .75 | .40 |
| 7 | Tim Spencer (R) | 1.50 | .80 |
| 8 | Stan White | .75 | .40 |
| 9 | Buddy Aydelette (R) | .75 | .40 |
| 10 | Tom Banks | .75 | .40 |
| 11 | Fred Bohannon | .75 | .40 |
| 12 | Joe Cribbs | 1.25 | .70 |
| 13 | Joey Jones (R) | .75 | .40 |
| 14 | Scott Norwood (R) | 1.25 | .70 |
| 15 | Jim Smith | 1.00 | .60 |
| 16 | Cliff Stoudt (R) | 1.00 | .60 |
| 17 | Vince Evans | 1.25 | .70 |
| 18 | Vagas Ferguson | .75 | .40 |
| 19 | John Gillen | .75 | .40 |

| | | | |
|---|---|---|---|
| 20 | Kris Haines (R) | .75 | .40 |
| 21 | Glenn Hyde (R) | .75 | .40 |
| 22 | Mark Keel (R) | .75 | .40 |
| 23 | Gary Lewis (R) | .75 | .40 |
| 24 | Doug Plank | 1.00 | .60 |
| 25 | Neil Balholm (R) | .75 | .40 |
| 26 | David Dumars (R) | .75 | .40 |
| 27 | David Martin (R) | .75 | .40 |
| 28 | Craig Penrose (R) | .75 | .40 |
| 29 | Dave Stalls (R) | .75 | .40 |
| 30 | Harry Sydney (R) | 1.50 | .80 |
| 31 | Vincent White (R) | .75 | .40 |
| 32 | George Yarno | .75 | .40 |
| 33 | Kiki DeAyala (R) | .75 | .40 |
| 34 | Sam Harrell (R) | .75 | .40 |
| 35 | Mike Hawkins (R) | .75 | .40 |
| 36 | Jim Kelly (R) | 200.00 | 110.00 |
| 37 | Mark Rush (R) | .75 | .40 |
| 38 | Ricky Sanders (R) | 16.50 | 8.50 |
| 39 | Paul Bergmann (R) | .75 | .40 |
| 40 | Tom Dinkel (R) | .75 | .40 |
| 41 | Wyatt Henderson | .75 | .40 |
| 42 | Vaughan Johnson (R) | 12.00 | 6.50 |
| 43 | Willie McClendon (R) | .75 | .40 |
| 44 | Matt Robinson | 1.00 | .60 |
| 45 | George Achica (R) | 1.00 | .60 |
| 46 | Mark Adickes (R) | 1.25 | .70 |
| 47 | Howard Carson | .75 | .40 |
| 48 | Kevin Nelson (R) | .75 | .40 |
| 49 | Jeff Partridge (R) | .75 | .40 |
| 50 | Jo Jo Townsell (R) | 1.25 | .70 |
| 51 | Eddie Weaver | .75 | .40 |
| 52 | Steve Young (R) | 95.00 | 50.00 |
| 53 | Derrick Crawford | .75 | .40 |
| 54 | Walter Lewis (R) | .75 | .40 |
| 55 | Phil McKinnely (R) | .75 | .40 |
| 56 | Vic Minore (R) | .75 | .40 |
| 57 | Gary Shirk | .75 | .40 |
| 58 | Reggie White (R) | 60.00 | 35.00 |
| 59 | Anthony Carter (R) | 20.00 | 12.00 |
| 60 | John Corker (R) | 1.00 | .60 |
| 61 | David Greenwood (R) | 1.00 | .60 |
| 62 | Bobby Hebert (R) | 20.00 | 12.00 |
| 63 | Derek Holloway | .75 | .40 |
| 64 | Ken Lacy (R) | .75 | .40 |
| 65 | Tyrone McGriff (R) | .75 | .40 |
| 66 | Ray Pinney | .75 | .40 |
| 67 | Gary Barbaro | 1.00 | .60 |
| 68 | Sam Bowers | .75 | .40 |
| 69 | Clarence Collins (R) | .75 | .40 |
| 70 | Willie Harper | .75 | .40 |
| 71 | Jim LeClair | .75 | .40 |
| 72 | Bob Leopold | .75 | .40 |
| 73 | Brian Sipe | 1.25 | .70 |
| 74 | Herschel Walker (R) | 65.00 | 38.00 |
| 75 | Junior Ah You (R) | .75 | .40 |
| 76 | Marcus Dupree (R) | 2.00 | 1.10 |
| 77 | Marcus Marek (R) | 1.00 | .60 |
| 78 | Tim Mazzetti | 1.00 | .60 |
| 79 | Mike Robinson (R) | 1.00 | .60 |
| 80 | Dan Ross | 1.25 | .70 |
| 81 | Mark Schellen (R) | 1.00 | .60 |
| 82 | Johnnie Walton (R) | .75 | .40 |
| 83 | Gordon Banks (R) | 1.00 | .60 |
| 84 | Fred Besana (R) | .75 | .40 |
| 85 | Dave Browning (R) | .75 | .40 |
| 86 | Eric Jordan | .75 | .40 |
| 87 | Frank Manumaleuga (R) | .75 | .40 |
| 88 | Gary Plummer (R) | 2.50 | 1.40 |
| 89 | Stan Talley (R) | .75 | .40 |
| 90 | Arthur Whittington (R) | .75 | .40 |
| 91 | Terry Beeson | .75 | .40 |
| 92 | Mel Gray (R) | 1.75 | 1.00 |
| 93 | Mike Katolin (R) | .75 | .40 |
| 94 | Dewey McClain (R) | .75 | .40 |
| 95 | Sidney Thornton (R) | 1.25 | .70 |
| 96 | Doug Williams | 2.00 | 1.10 |
| 97 | Kelvin Bryant (R) | 2.50 | 1.40 |
| 98 | John Bunting | .75 | .40 |
| 99 | Irv Eatman (R) | 1.75 | 1.00 |
| 100 | Scott Fitzkee (R) | .75 | .40 |
| 101 | Chuck Fusina (R) | 1.25 | .70 |
| 102 | Sean Landeta (R) | 2.00 | 1.10 |
| 103 | David Trout (R) | .75 | .40 |
| 104 | Scott Woerner (R) | .75 | .40 |
| 105 | Glenn Carano (R) | .75 | .40 |
| 106 | Ron Crosby (R) | .75 | .40 |
| 107 | Jerry Holmes (R) | 1.50 | .70 |
| 108 | Bruce Huther (R) | .75 | .40 |
| 109 | Mike Rozier (R) | 6.00 | 3.25 |
| 110 | Larry Swider (R) | .75 | .40 |
| 111 | Danny Buggs | .75 | .40 |
| 112 | Putt Choate | .75 | .40 |
| 113 | Rich Garza (R) | .75 | .40 |
| 114 | Joey Hackett (R) | .75 | .40 |
| 115 | Rick Neuheisel (R) | 1.00 | .60 |
| 116 | Mike St. Clair (R) | .75 | .40 |
| 117 | Gary Anderson (R) | 7.50 | 4.00 |
| 118 | Zenon Andrusyshyn | .75 | .40 |
| 119 | Doug Beaudoin | .75 | .40 |
| 120 | Mike Butler | .75 | .40 |
| 121 | Willie Gillespie (R) | .75 | .40 |
| 122 | Fred Nrodgren (R) | .75 | .40 |
| 123 | John Reaves | 1.00 | .60 |
| 124 | Eric Truvillion (R) | .75 | .40 |
| 125 | Reggie Collier (R) | 1.00 | .60 |
| 126 | Mike Guess (R) | .75 | .40 |
| 127 | Mike Hohensee (R) | .75 | .40 |
| 128 | Craig James (R) | 2.00 | 1.10 |
| 129 | Eric Robinson (R) | .75 | .40 |
| 130 | Billy Taylor (R) | .75 | .40 |
| 131 | Joey Walters (R) | .75 | .40 |
| 132 | Checklist 1-132 | 2.00 | .50 |

# 1985 Topps

This 396-card set features players from the NFL. Card fronts consist of full color photographs that are horizontal while the player's last name is printed vertically in large block letters across the bottom of the card. The team name is in smaller type below the players last name. The vertical card backs include personal data, stats and highlights. Subsets consist of Record Breakers (RB) (1-6), Playoffs (7-9), League Leaders (192-197) and Team Leaders (TL). All cards measure 2-1/2" by 3-1/2".

|  |  | MINT | NR/MT |
|---|---|---|---|
| Complete Set (396) | | 90.00 | 55.00 |
| Commons | | .06 | .03 |
| 1 | Mark Clayton RB | .75 | .25 |
| 2 | Eric Dickerson RB | .75 | .40 |
| 3 | Charlie Joiner RB | .25 | .15 |
| 4 | Dan Marino RB | 4.00 | 2.25 |
| 5 | Art Monk RB | .40 | .22 |
| 6 | Walter Payton RB | .80 | .45 |
| 7 | NFC Championship | .10 | .06 |
| 8 | AFC Championship | .10 | .06 |
| 9 | Super Bowl XIX | .25 | .15 |
| 10 | Falcons TL (Riggs) | .12 | .07 |
| 11 | William Andrews | .10 | .06 |
| 12 | Stacey Bailey | .06 | .03 |
| 13 | Steve Bartkowski | .20 | .12 |
| 14 | Rick Bryan (R) | .25 | .15 |
| 15 | Alfred Jackson | .08 | .05 |
| 16 | Kenny Johnson | .06 | .03 |
| 17 | Mike Kenn | .08 | .05 |
| 18 | Mike Pitts (R) | .20 | .12 |
| 19 | Gerald Riggs | .15 | .08 |
| 20 | Sylvester Stamps | .06 | .03 |
| 21 | R.C. Thieleman | .06 | .03 |
| 22 | Bears TL (Payton) | .75 | .40 |
| 23 | Todd Bell | .15 | .08 |
| 24 | Richard Dent (R) | 5.00 | 2.75 |
| 25 | Gary Fencik | .08 | .05 |
| 26 | Dave Finzer | .06 | .03 |
| 27 | Leslie Frazier | .06 | .03 |
| 28 | Steve Fuller | .08 | .05 |
| 29 | Willie Gault | .25 | .15 |
| 30 | Dan Hampton | .75 | .40 |
| 31 | Jim McMahon | .50 | .28 |
| 32 | Steve McMichael (R) | 2.00 | 1.10 |
| 33 | Walter Payton | 2.00 | 1.10 |
| 34 | Mike Singletary | .90 | .50 |
| 35 | Matt Suhey | .06 | .03 |
| 36 | Bob Thomas | .06 | .03 |
| 37 | Cowboys TL (Dorsett) | .30 | .18 |
| 38 | Bill Bates (R) | .30 | .18 |
| 39 | Doug Cosbie | .08 | .05 |
| 40 | Tony Dorsett | .60 | .35 |
| 41 | Michael Downs | .06 | .03 |
| 42 | Mike Hegman (R) | .08 | .05 |
| 43 | Tony Hill | .10 | .06 |
| 44 | Gary Hogeboom (R) | .20 | .12 |
| 45 | Jeff Jeffcoat (R) | .50 | .28 |
| 46 | Ed Too Tall Jones | .30 | .18 |
| 47 | Mike Renfro | .06 | .03 |
| 48 | Rafael Septien | .06 | .03 |
| 49 | Dennis Thurman | .06 | .03 |
| 50 | Everson Walls | .06 | .03 |
| 51 | Danny White | .20 | .12 |
| 52 | Randy White | .40 | .22 |
| 53 | Lions TL (Defense) | .10 | .06 |
| 54 | Jeff Chadwick | .06 | .03 |
| 55 | Mike Cofer (R) | .35 | .20 |
| 56 | Gary Danielson | .08 | .05 |
| 57 | Keith Dorney | .06 | .03 |
| 58 | Doug English | .06 | .03 |
| 59 | William Gay | .06 | .03 |
| 60 | Ken Jenkins | .06 | .03 |
| 61 | James Jones | .06 | .03 |
| 62 | Ed Murray | .06 | .03 |
| 63 | Billy Sims | .15 | .08 |
| 64 | Leonard Thompson | .06 | .03 |
| 65 | Bobby Watkins | .06 | .03 |
| 66 | Packers TL (Dickey) | .10 | .06 |
| 67 | Paul Coffman | .06 | .03 |
| 68 | Lynn Dickey | .12 | .07 |
| 69 | Mike Douglass | .06 | .03 |
| 70 | Tom Flynn | .06 | .03 |
| 71 | Eddie Lee Ivery | .08 | .05 |
| 72 | Ezra Johnson | .06 | .03 |
| 73 | Mark Lee | .06 | .03 |
| 74 | Tim Lewis | .06 | .03 |
| 75 | James Lofton | 1.00 | .60 |
| 76 | Bucky Scribner | .06 | .03 |
| 77 | Rams TL (Dickerson) | .50 | .28 |
| 78 | Nolan Cromwell | .08 | .05 |

| 79 | Eric Dickerson | 4.50 | 2.50 |
| 80 | Henry Ellard (R) | 3.00 | 1.75 |
| 81 | Kent Hill | .06 | .03 |
| 82 | Leroy Irvin | .08 | .05 |
| 83 | Jeff Kemp (R) | .40 | .22 |
| 84 | Mike Lansford | .06 | .03 |
| 85 | Barry Redden | .06 | .03 |
| 86 | Jackie Slater | .30 | .18 |
| 87 | Doug Smith (R) | .20 | .12 |
| 88 | Jack Youngblood | .15 | .08 |
| 89 | Vikings TL (Defense) | .10 | .06 |
| 90 | Alfred Anderson (R) | .15 | .08 |
| 91 | Ted Brown | .08 | .05 |
| 92 | Greg Coleman | .06 | .03 |
| 93 | Tommy Hannon | .06 | .03 |
| 94 | Tommy Kramer | .15 | .08 |
| 95 | Leo Lewis (R) | .15 | .08 |
| 96 | Doug Martin | .06 | .03 |
| 97 | Darrin Nelson | .12 | .07 |
| 98 | Jan Stenerud | .20 | .12 |
| 99 | Sammie White | .08 | .05 |
| 100 | Saints TL (Line) | .10 | .06 |
| 101 | Morten Andersen | .60 | .35 |
| 102 | Hoby Brenner (R) | .15 | .08 |
| 103 | Bruce Clark | .06 | .03 |
| 104 | Hokie Gajan (R) | .10 | .06 |
| 105 | Brian Hansen (R) | .12 | .07 |
| 106 | Rickey Jackson | .75 | .40 |
| 107 | George Rogers | .15 | .08 |
| 108 | Dave Wilson | .08 | .05 |
| 109 | Tyrone Young (R) | .10 | .06 |
| 110 | Giants TL (Defense) | .10 | .06 |
| 111 | Carl Banks (R) | 4.50 | 2.50 |
| 112 | Jim Burt (R) | .35 | .20 |
| 113 | Rob Carpenter | .06 | .03 |
| 114 | Harry Carson | .25 | .15 |
| 115 | Earnest Gray | .06 | .03 |
| 116 | Ali Haji-Sheikh | .06 | .03 |
| 117 | Mark Haynes | .08 | .05 |
| 118 | Bobby Johnson | .06 | .03 |
| 119 | Lionel Manuel (R) | .20 | .12 |
| 120 | Joe Morris (R) | .80 | .45 |
| 121 | Zeke Mowatt (R) | .15 | .08 |
| 122 | Jeff Rutledge (R) | .25 | .15 |
| 123 | Phil Simms | .50 | .28 |
| 124 | Lawrence Taylor | 1.25 | .70 |
| 125 | Eagles TL (Montgomery) | .12 | .07 |
| 126 | Greg Brown | .06 | .03 |
| 127 | Ray Ellis | .06 | .03 |
| 128 | Dennis Harrison | .06 | .03 |
| 129 | Wes Hopkins (R) | .40 | .22 |
| 130 | Mike Horan | .06 | .03 |
| 131 | Kenny Jackson (R) | .15 | .08 |
| 132 | Ron Jaworski | .15 | .08 |
| 133 | Paul McFadden | .06 | .03 |
| 134 | Wilbert Montgomery | .12 | .07 |
| 135 | Mike Quick | .15 | .08 |
| 136 | John Spagnola | .06 | .03 |
| 137 | Cardinals TL (Lomax) | .12 | .07 |
| 138 | Ottis Anderson | .35 | .20 |
| 139 | Bubba Baker | .06 | .03 |
| 140 | Roy Green | .20 | .12 |
| 141 | Curtis Greer | .06 | .03 |
| 142 | E.J. Junior | .10 | .06 |
| 143 | Neil Lomax | .12 | .07 |
| 144 | Stump Mitchell | .10 | .06 |
| 145 | Neil O'Donoghue | .06 | .03 |
| 146 | Pat Tilley | .06 | .03 |
| 147 | Lionel Washington | .08 | .05 |
| 148 | 49ers TL (Montana) | .60 | .35 |
| 149 | Dwaine Board | .06 | .03 |
| 150 | Dwight Clark | .15 | .08 |
| 151 | Roger Craig | 1.25 | .70 |
| 152 | Randy Cross | .06 | .03 |
| 153 | Fred Dean | .08 | .05 |
| 154 | Keith Fahnhorst (R) | .10 | .06 |
| 155 | Dwight Hicks | .06 | .03 |
| 156 | Ronnie Lott | 1.50 | .80 |
| 157 | Joe Montana | 4.50 | 2.50 |
| 158 | Renaldo Nehemiah | .08 | .05 |
| 159 | Fred Quillan | .06 | .03 |
| 160 | Jack Reynolds | .08 | .05 |
| 161 | Freddie Solomon | .07 | .04 |
| 162 | Keena Turner (R) | .40 | .22 |
| 163 | Wendell Tyler | .10 | .06 |
| 164 | Ray Wersching | .06 | .03 |
| 165 | Carlton Williamson | .06 | .03 |
| 166 | Buccaneers TL (DeBerg) | .12 | .07 |
| 167 | Gerald Carter | .06 | .03 |
| 168 | Mark Cotney | .06 | .03 |
| 169 | Steve DeBerg | .40 | .22 |
| 170 | Sean Farrell (R) | .10 | .06 |
| 171 | Hugh Green | .08 | .05 |
| 172 | Kevin House | .06 | .03 |
| 173 | David Logan | .06 | .03 |
| 174 | Michael Morton | .06 | .03 |
| 175 | Lee Roy Selmon | .15 | .08 |
| 176 | James Wilder | .10 | .06 |
| 177 | Redskins TL (Riggins) | .25 | .15 |
| 178 | Charlie Brown | .06 | .03 |
| 179 | Monte Coleman (R) | .50 | .28 |
| 180 | Vernon Dean | .06 | .03 |
| 181 | Darrell Green | 1.75 | 1.00 |
| 182 | Russ Grimm | .10 | .06 |
| 183 | Joe Jacoby | .10 | .06 |
| 184 | Dexter Manley | .06 | .03 |
| 185 | Art Monk | 1.75 | 1.00 |
| 186 | Mark Moseley | .06 | .03 |
| 187 | Calvin Muhammad | .06 | .03 |
| 188 | Mike Nelms | .06 | .03 |
| 189 | John Riggins | .60 | .35 |
| 190 | Joe Theismann | .45 | .25 |

| 191 | Joe Washington | .10 | .06 |
|---|---|---|---|
| 192 | Passing Leaders | 4.00 | 2.25 |
| | Dan Marino | | |
| | Joe Montana | | |
| 193 | Receiving Leaders | .40 | .22 |
| | Ozzie Newsome | | |
| | Art Monk | | |
| 194 | Rushing Leaders | .50 | .28 |
| | Earnest Jackson | | |
| | Eric Dickerson | | |
| 195 | Scoring Leaders | .08 | .05 |
| | Gary Anderson | | |
| | Ray Wersching | | |
| 196 | Interception Leaders | .08 | .05 |
| | Kenny Easley | | |
| | Tom Flynn | | |
| 197 | Punting Leaders | .08 | .05 |
| | Jim Arnold | | |
| | Brian Hansen | | |
| 198 | Bills TL (Bell) | .12 | .07 |
| 199 | Greg Bell (R) | .75 | .40 |
| 200 | Preston Dennard | .06 | .03 |
| 201 | Joe Ferguson | .12 | .07 |
| 202 | Byron Franklin | .06 | .03 |
| 203 | Steve Freeman | .06 | .03 |
| 204 | Jim Haslett | .06 | .03 |
| 205 | Charles Romes | .06 | .03 |
| 206 | Fred Smerlas | .08 | .05 |
| 207 | Darryl Talley (R) | 2.50 | 1.40 |
| 208 | Van Williams | .06 | .03 |
| 209 | Bengals TL (Anderson) | .12 | .07 |
| 210 | Ken Anderson | .25 | .15 |
| 211 | Jim Breech | .06 | .03 |
| 212 | Louis Breeden | .06 | .03 |
| 213 | James Brooks | .25 | .15 |
| 214 | Ross Browner | .08 | .05 |
| 215 | Eddie Edwards | .06 | .03 |
| 216 | M.L.Harris | .06 | .03 |
| 217 | Bobby Kemp | .06 | .03 |
| 218 | Larry Kennebrew (R) | .12 | .07 |
| 219 | Anthony Munoz | .60 | .35 |
| 220 | Reggie Williams | .08 | .05 |
| 221 | Browns TL (Green) | .10 | .06 |
| 222 | Matt Bahr | .06 | .03 |
| 223 | Chip Banks | .08 | .05 |
| 224 | Reggie Camp | .06 | .03 |
| 225 | Tom Cousineau | .06 | .03 |
| 226 | Joe DeLamielleure | .08 | .05 |
| 227 | Ricky Feacher | .06 | .03 |
| 228 | Boyce Green (R) | .08 | .05 |
| 229 | Al Gross | .06 | .03 |
| 230 | Clay Matthews | .30 | .18 |
| 231 | Paul McDonald | .08 | .05 |
| 232 | Ozzie Newsome | .45 | .25 |
| 233 | Mike Pruitt | .08 | .05 |
| 234 | Don Rogers | .06 | .03 |
| 235 | Broncos TL (Elway) | .50 | .28 |

| 236 | Rubin Carter | .06 | .03 |
|---|---|---|---|
| 237 | Barney Chavous | .06 | .03 |
| 238 | John Elway | 4.50 | 2.50 |
| 239 | Steve Foley | .06 | .03 |
| 240 | Mike Harden (R) | .15 | .08 |
| 241 | Tom Jackson | .15 | .08 |
| 242 | Butch Johnson | .08 | .05 |
| 243 | Rulon Jones | .06 | .03 |
| 244 | Rich Karlis | .06 | .03 |
| 245 | Steve Watson | .06 | .03 |
| 246 | Gerald Willhite | .08 | .05 |
| 247 | Sammy Winder | .10 | .06 |
| 248 | Oilers TL (Moriarity) | .10 | .06 |
| 249 | Jesse Baker | .06 | .03 |
| 250 | Carter Hartwig | .06 | .03 |
| 251 | Warren Moon (R) | 28.00 | 15.00 |
| 252 | Larry Moriarty (R) | .15 | .08 |
| 253 | Mike Munchak (R) | 1.50 | .80 |
| 254 | Carl Roaches | .06 | .03 |
| 255 | Tim Smith | .06 | .03 |
| 256 | Willie Tullis | .06 | .03 |
| 257 | Jamie Williams (R) | .10 | .06 |
| 258 | Colts TL (Schlichter) | .10 | .06 |
| 259 | Raymond Butler | .08 | .05 |
| 260 | Johnnie Cooks | .06 | .03 |
| 261 | Eugene Daniel | .06 | .03 |
| 262 | Curtis Dickey | .10 | .06 |
| 263 | Chris Hinton | .25 | .15 |
| 264 | Vernon Maxwell | .06 | .03 |
| 265 | Randy McMillan | .06 | .03 |
| 266 | Art Schlichter (R) | .15 | .08 |
| 267 | Rohn Stark | .06 | .03 |
| 268 | Leo Wisniewski | .06 | .03 |
| 269 | Chiefs TL (Kenney) | .10 | .06 |
| 270 | Jim Arnold | .06 | .03 |
| 271 | Mike Bell | .06 | .03 |
| 272 | Todd Blackledge (R) | .15 | .08 |
| 273 | Carlos Carson | .08 | .05 |
| 274 | Deron Cherry | .25 | .15 |
| 275 | Herman Heard (R) | .10 | .06 |
| 276 | Bill Kenney | .08 | .05 |
| 277 | Nick Lowery | .25 | .15 |
| 278 | Bill Maas (R) | .30 | .18 |
| 279 | Henry Marshall | .06 | .03 |
| 280 | Art Still | .08 | .05 |
| 281 | Raiders TL (Allen) | .40 | .22 |
| 282 | Marcus Allen | 1.00 | .60 |
| 283 | Lyle Alzado | .12 | .07 |
| 284 | Chris Bahr | .06 | .03 |
| 285 | Malcolm Barnwell | .06 | .03 |
| 286 | Cliff Branch | .15 | .08 |
| 287 | Todd Christensen | .12 | .07 |
| 288 | Ray Guy | .12 | .07 |
| 289 | Lester Hayes | .08 | .05 |
| 290 | Mike Haynes | .10 | .06 |
| 291 | Henry Lawrence | .06 | .03 |
| 292 | Howie Long | .75 | .40 |

| | | | |
|---|---|---|---|
| 293 | Rod Martin | .08 | .05 |
| 294 | Vann McElroy | .06 | .03 |
| 295 | Matt Millen | .10 | .06 |
| 296 | Bill Pickel (R) | .12 | .07 |
| 297 | Jim Plunkett | .20 | .12 |
| 298 | Dokie Williams (R) | .12 | .07 |
| 299 | Marc Wilson | .10 | .06 |
| 300 | Dolphins TL (Duper) | .15 | .08 |
| 301 | Bob Baumhower | .06 | .03 |
| 302 | Doug Betters | .06 | .03 |
| 303 | Glenn Blackwood | .06 | .03 |
| 304 | Lyle Blackwood | .06 | .03 |
| 305 | Kim Bokamper | .06 | .03 |
| 306 | Charles Bowser | .06 | .03 |
| 307 | Jimmy Cefalo | .08 | .05 |
| 308 | Mark Clayton (R) | 7.50 | 4.00 |
| 309 | A.J. Duhe | .08 | .05 |
| 310 | Mark Duper | .80 | .45 |
| 311 | Andra Franklin | .08 | .05 |
| 312 | Bruce Hardy | .06 | .03 |
| 313 | Pete Johnson | .08 | .05 |
| 314 | Dan Marino | 20.00 | 12.00 |
| 315 | Tony Nathan | .08 | .05 |
| 316 | Ed Newman | .06 | .03 |
| 317 | Reggie Roby | .08 | .05 |
| 318 | Dwight Stephenson | .15 | .08 |
| 319 | Uwe Von Schamann | .06 | .03 |
| 320 | Patriots TL (Collins) | .10 | .06 |
| 321 | Raymond Clayborn | .06 | .03 |
| 322 | Tony Collins | .08 | .05 |
| 323 | Tony Eason (R) | .30 | .18 |
| 324 | Tony Franklin | .06 | .03 |
| 325 | Irving Fryar (R) | 1.50 | .80 |
| 326 | John Hannah | .20 | .12 |
| 327 | Brian Holloway | .06 | .03 |
| 328 | Craig James | .15 | .08 |
| 329 | Stanley Morgan | .20 | .12 |
| 330 | Steve Nelson | .06 | .03 |
| 331 | Derrick Ramsey | .06 | .03 |
| 332 | Stephen Starring | .06 | .03 |
| 333 | Mosi tatupu | .06 | .03 |
| 334 | Andre Tippett | .35 | .20 |
| 335 | Jets TL (Gastineau) | .10 | .06 |
| 336 | Russell Carter (R) | .12 | .07 |
| 337 | Mark Gastineau | .12 | .07 |
| 338 | Bruce Harper | .06 | .03 |
| 339 | Bobby Humphrey (R) | .12 | .07 |
| 340 | Johnny Lam Jones | .08 | .05 |
| 341 | Joe Klecko | .12 | .07 |
| 342 | Pat Leahy | .06 | .03 |
| 343 | Marty Lyons | .08 | .05 |
| 344 | Freeman McNeil | .25 | .15 |
| 345 | Lance Mehl | .06 | .03 |
| 346 | Ken O'Brien (R) | 1.25 | .70 |
| 347 | Marvin Powell | .07 | .04 |
| 348 | Pat Ryan | .10 | .06 |
| 349 | Mickey Shuler (R) | .35 | .20 |
| 350 | Wesley Walker | .12 | .07 |
| 351 | Steelers TL (Malone) | .10 | .06 |
| 352 | Walter Abercrombie | .08 | .05 |
| 353 | Gary Anderson | .06 | .03 |
| 354 | Robin Cole | .06 | .03 |
| 355 | Bennie Cunningham | .06 | .03 |
| 356 | Rich Erenberg (R) | .08 | .05 |
| 357 | Jack Lambert | .40 | .22 |
| 358 | Louis Lipps (R) | 1.25 | .70 |
| 359 | Mark Malone | .10 | .06 |
| 360 | Mike Merriweather (R) | .75 | .40 |
| 361 | Frank Pollard | .06 | .03 |
| 362 | Donnie Shell | .12 | .07 |
| 363 | John Stallworth | .20 | .12 |
| 364 | Sam Washington | .06 | .03 |
| 365 | Mike Webster | .25 | .15 |
| 366 | Dwayne Woodruff | .06 | .03 |
| 367 | Chargers TL (Defense) | .10 | .06 |
| 368 | Rolf Benirschke | .06 | .03 |
| 369 | Gill Byrd (R) | 2.00 | 1.10 |
| 370 | Wes Chandler | .08 | .05 |
| 371 | Bobby Duckworth | .06 | .03 |
| 372 | Dan Fouts | .90 | .50 |
| 373 | Mike Green | .06 | .03 |
| 374 | Pete Holohan (R) | .40 | .22 |
| 375 | Earnest Jackson (R) | .25 | .15 |
| 376 | Lionel James (R) | .25 | .15 |
| 377 | Charlie Joiner | .40 | .22 |
| 378 | Billy Ray Smith | .08 | .05 |
| 379 | Kellen Winslow | .25 | .15 |
| 380 | Seahawks TL (Krieg) | .10 | .06 |
| 381 | Dave Brown | .06 | .03 |
| 382 | Jeff Bryant | .06 | .03 |
| 383 | Dan Doornink | .06 | .03 |
| 384 | Kenny Easley | .08 | .05 |
| 385 | Jacob Green | .08 | .05 |
| 386 | David Hughes | .06 | .03 |
| 387 | Norm Johnson | .06 | .03 |
| 388 | Dave Krieg | .50 | .28 |
| 389 | Steve Largent | 1.25 | .70 |
| 390 | Joe Nash (R) | .15 | .08 |
| 391 | Daryl Turner (R) | .10 | .06 |
| 392 | Curt Warner | .20 | .12 |
| 393 | Fredd Young (R) | .20 | .12 |
| 394 | Checklist 1-132 | .15 | .05 |
| 395 | Checklist 133-264 | .15 | .05 |
| 396 | Checklist 265-396 | .15 | .05 |

# 1985 Topps USFL

For the second straight year Topps issued a set featuring players from the United States Football League. Available only as a complete 132-card boxed set the card fronts consist of full color photos framed by a red border with blue and white horizontal stripes in the center. The card backs contain personal data, stats and highlights. All cards measure 2-1/2" by 3-1/2".

|  | | MINT | NR/MT |
|---|---|---|---|
| Complete Set (132) | | 175.00 | 95.00 |
| Commons | | .20 | .12 |
| 1 | Case DeBruijn | .30 | .12 |
| 2 | Mike Katolin | .20 | .12 |
| 3 | Bruce Laird | .20 | .12 |
| 4 | Kit Lathrop | .20 | .12 |
| 5 | Kevin Long | .20 | .12 |
| 6 | Karl Lorch | .20 | .12 |
| 7 | Dave Tipton | .20 | .12 |
| 8 | Doug Williams | .75 | .40 |
| 9 | Luis Zendejas (R) | .25 | .15 |
| 10 | Kelvin Bryant | .75 | .40 |
| 11 | Willie Collier | .20 | .12 |
| 12 | Irv Eatman | .40 | .22 |
| 13 | Scott Fitzkee | .20 | .12 |
| 14 | William Fuller (R) | 2.50 | 1.40 |
| 15 | Chuck Fusina | .30 | .18 |
| 16 | Pete Kugler | .30 | .18 |
| 17 | Garcia Lane (R) | .25 | .15 |
| 18 | Mike Lush | .20 | .12 |
| 19 | Sam Mills (R) | 8.50 | 4.50 |
| 20 | Buddy Aydelette | .20 | .12 |
| 21 | Joe Cribbs | .50 | .28 |
| 22 | David Dumars | .20 | .12 |
| 23 | Robin Earl | .20 | .12 |
| 24 | Joey Jones | .20 | .12 |
| 25 | Leon Perry | .20 | .12 |
| 26 | Dave Pureifory | .20 | .12 |
| 27 | Bill Roe | .20 | .12 |
| 28 | Doug Smith (R) | 1.25 | .70 |
| 29 | Cliff Stoudt | .25 | .15 |
| 30 | Jeff Delaney | .20 | .12 |
| 31 | Vince Evans | .35 | .20 |
| 32 | Leonard Harris (R) | 1.25 | .70 |
| 33 | Bill Johnson | .20 | .12 |
| 34 | Marc Lewis | .20 | .12 |
| 35 | David Martin | .20 | .12 |
| 36 | Bruce Thornton | .20 | .12 |
| 37 | Craig Walls | .20 | .12 |
| 38 | Vincent White | .20 | .12 |
| 39 | Luther Bradley | .25 | .15 |
| 40 | Pete Catan | .20 | .12 |
| 41 | Kiki DeAyala | .20 | .12 |
| 42 | Toni Fritsch | .25 | .15 |
| 43 | Sam Harrell | .25 | .15 |
| 44 | Richard Johnson (R) | 1.50 | .80 |
| 45 | Jim Kelly | 65.00 | 35.00 |
| 46 | Gerald McNeil (R) | 1.50 | .80 |
| 47 | Clarence Verdin (R) | 2.50 | 1.40 |
| 48 | Dale Walters | .20 | .12 |
| 49 | Gary Clark (R) | 50.00 | 28.00 |
| 50 | Tom Dinkel | .20 | .12 |
| 51 | Mike Edwards | .20 | .12 |
| 52 | Brian Franco | .20 | .12 |
| 53 | Bob Gruber | .20 | .12 |
| 54 | Robbie Mahfouz | .20 | .12 |
| 55 | Mike Rozier | 1.75 | 1.00 |
| 56 | Brian Sipe | .60 | .35 |
| 57 | J.T. Turner | .20 | .12 |
| 58 | Howard Carson | .25 | .15 |
| 59 | Wymon Henderson (R) | .40 | .22 |
| 60 | Kevin Nelson | .20 | .12 |
| 61 | Jeff Partridge | .20 | .12 |
| 62 | Ben Rudolph | .20 | .12 |
| 63 | Jo Jo Townsell | .30 | .18 |
| 64 | Eddie Weaver | .20 | .12 |
| 65 | Steve Young | 35.00 | 20.00 |
| 66 | Tony Zendejas (R) | .30 | .18 |
| 67 | Mossy Cade | .20 | .12 |
| 68 | Leonard Coleman (R) | .35 | .20 |
| 69 | John Corker | .25 | .12 |
| 70 | Derrick Crawford | .20 | .12 |
| 71 | Art Kuehn | .20 | .12 |
| 72 | Walter Lewis | .20 | .12 |
| 73 | Tyrone McGriff | .20 | .12 |
| 74 | Tim Spencer | .40 | .22 |
| 75 | Reggie White | 25.00 | 14.00 |
| 76 | Gizmo Williams (R) | .60 | .35 |
| 77 | Sam Bowers | .20 | .12 |
| 78 | Maurice Carthon (R) | 1.50 | .80 |
| 79 | Clarence Collins | .20 | .12 |
| 80 | Doug Flutie (R) | 15.00 | 8.00 |
| 81 | Freddie Gilbert | .20 | .12 |

| | | | |
|---|---|---:|---:|
| 82 | Kerry Justin | .20 | .12 |
| 83 | Dave Lapham | .20 | .12 |
| 84 | Rick Partridge | .20 | .12 |
| 85 | Roger Ruzek (R) | .75 | .40 |
| 86 | Herschel Walker | 24.00 | 12.50 |
| 87 | Gordon Banks | .25 | .15 |
| 88 | Monte Bennette | .20 | .12 |
| 89 | Albert Bentley (R) | 3.50 | 2.00 |
| 90 | Novo Bojovic | .20 | .12 |
| 91 | Dave Browning | .20 | .12 |
| 92 | Anthony Carter | 4.00 | 2.25 |
| 93 | Bobby Hebert | 5.00 | 2.75 |
| 94 | Ray Pinney | .20 | .12 |
| 95 | Stan Talley | .20 | .12 |
| 96 | Ruben Vaughan | .20 | .12 |
| 97 | Curtis Bledsoe | .20 | .12 |
| 98 | Reggie Collier | .20 | .12 |
| 99 | Jerry Doerger | .20 | .12 |
| 100 | Jerry Golsteyn | .20 | .12 |
| 101 | Bob Niziolek | .20 | .12 |
| 102 | Joel Patten | .20 | .12 |
| 103 | Ricky Simmons | .20 | .12 |
| 104 | Joey Walters | .20 | .12 |
| 105 | Marcus Dupree | 1.00 | .60 |
| 106 | Jeff Gossett | .20 | .12 |
| 107 | Frank Lockett | .20 | .12 |
| 108 | Marcus Marek | .25 | .15 |
| 109 | Kenny Neil (R) | .25 | .15 |
| 110 | Robert Pennywell | .20 | .12 |
| 111 | Matt Robinson | .25 | .15 |
| 112 | Dan Ross | .35 | .20 |
| 113 | Doug Woodward | .20 | .12 |
| 114 | Danny Buggs | .20 | .12 |
| 115 | Putt Choate | .20 | .12 |
| 116 | Greg Fields | .20 | .12 |
| 117 | Ken Hartley | .20 | .12 |
| 118 | Nick Mike-Mayer | .20 | .12 |
| 119 | Rick Neuheisel | .25 | .15 |
| 120 | Peter Raeford | .20 | .12 |
| 121 | Gary Worthy | .20 | .12 |
| 122 | Gary Anderson | 2.00 | 1.25 |
| 123 | Zenon Andrusyshyn | .20 | .12 |
| 124 | Greg Boone | .20 | .12 |
| 125 | Mike Butler | .20 | .12 |
| 126 | Mike Clark | .20 | .12 |
| 127 | Willie Gillespie | .20 | .12 |
| 128 | James Harrell | .20 | .12 |
| 129 | Marvin Harvey | .20 | .12 |
| 130 | John Reaves | .30 | .18 |
| 131 | Eric Truvillion | .20 | .12 |
| 132 | Checklist | .50 | .10 |

# 1986 Topps

The cards in this 396-card set feature full color photos on the fronts framed by green borders with diagonal lines running across the borders. The player's name and position appear in a box below the photo while the team name appears in a diagonal stripe in the lower right corner of the card. Card backs are horizontal and contain personal data and stats. Key subsets include Record Breakers (RB) (1-7), League Leaders (225-229) and Team Leaders (TL). Team Leader cards are distinguished by their yellow borders. All cards measure 2-1/2" by 3-1/2".

| | MINT | NR/MT |
|---|---:|---:|
| **Complete Set (396)** | 115.00 | 65.00 |
| **Commons** | .05 | .02 |

| | | | |
|---|---|---:|---:|
| 1 | Marcus Allen (RB) | .30 | .18 |
| 2 | Eric Dickerson (RB) | .30 | .18 |
| 3 | Lionel James (RB) | .10 | .06 |
| 4 | Steve Largent (RB) | .30 | .18 |
| 5 | George Martin (RB) | .08 | .05 |
| 6 | Stephone Paige (RB) | .12 | .07 |
| 7 | Walter Payton (RB) | .70 | .40 |
| 8 | Super Bowl XX | .15 | .08 |
| 9 | Bears TL (Payton) | .50 | .28 |
| 10 | Jim McMahon | .30 | .18 |
| 11 | Walter Payton | 1.75 | 1.00 |
| 12 | Matt Suhey | .05 | .02 |
| 13 | Willie Gault | .25 | .15 |
| 14 | Dennis McKinnon (R) | .25 | .15 |
| 15 | Emery Moorehead | .05 | .02 |
| 16 | Jim Covert AP | .15 | .08 |
| 17 | Jay Hilgenberg (R) | 1.00 | .60 |
| 18 | Kevin Butler (R) | .30 | .18 |
| 19 | Richard Dent | .60 | .35 |

| No. | Player | | |
|---|---|---|---|
| 20 | William Perry (R) | .80 | .50 |
| 21 | Steve McMichael | .40 | .22 |
| 22 | Dan Hampton | .40 | .22 |
| 23 | Otis Wilson | .05 | .02 |
| 24 | Mike Singletary | .75 | .40 |
| 25 | Wilber Marshall (R) | 3.00 | 1.75 |
| 26 | Leslie Frazier | .05 | .02 |
| 27 | Dave Duerson (R) | .40 | .22 |
| 28 | Gary Fencik | .08 | .05 |
| 29 | Patriots TL (James) | .10 | .06 |
| 30 | Tony Eason | .15 | .08 |
| 31 | Steve Grogan | .15 | .08 |
| 32 | Craig James | .12 | .07 |
| 33 | Tony Collins | .08 | .05 |
| 34 | Irving Fryar | .25 | .15 |
| 35 | Brian Holloway | .05 | .02 |
| 36 | John Hannah | .20 | .12 |
| 37 | Tony Franklin | .05 | .02 |
| 38 | Garin Veris (R) | .10 | .06 |
| 39 | Andre Tippett | .15 | .08 |
| 40 | Steve Nelson | .05 | .02 |
| 41 | Raymond Clayborn | .05 | .02 |
| 42 | Fred Marion (R) | .15 | .08 |
| 43 | Rich Camarillo | .05 | .02 |
| 44 | Dolphins TL (Marino) | .50 | .28 |
| 45 | Dan Marino | 7.50 | 4.00 |
| 46 | Tony Nathan | .08 | .05 |
| 47 | Ron Davenport | .05 | .02 |
| 48 | Mark Duper | .30 | .18 |
| 49 | Mark Clayton | 1.75 | 1.00 |
| 50 | Nat Moore | .10 | .06 |
| 51 | Bruce Hardy | .05 | .02 |
| 52 | Roy Foster | .05 | .02 |
| 53 | Dwight Stephenson | .10 | .06 |
| 54 | Fuad Reveiz (R) | .07 | .04 |
| 55 | Bob Baumhower | .05 | .02 |
| 56 | Mike Charles | .05 | .02 |
| 57 | Hugh Green | .08 | .05 |
| 58 | Glenn Blackwood | .05 | .02 |
| 59 | Reggie Roby | .08 | .05 |
| 60 | Raiders TL (Allen) | .25 | .15 |
| 61 | Marc Wilson | .10 | .06 |
| 62 | Marcus Allen | .75 | .40 |
| 63 | Dokie Williams | .05 | .02 |
| 64 | Todd Christensen | .12 | .07 |
| 65 | Chris Bahr | .05 | .02 |
| 66 | Fulton Walker | .05 | .02 |
| 67 | Howie Long | .30 | .18 |
| 68 | Bill Pickel | .05 | .02 |
| 69 | Ray Guy | .15 | .08 |
| 70 | Greg Townsend (R) | 1.75 | 1.00 |
| 71 | Rod Martin | .08 | .05 |
| 72 | Matt Millen | .10 | .06 |
| 73 | Mike Haynes | .10 | .06 |
| 74 | Lester Hayes | .08 | .05 |
| 75 | Vann McElroy | .05 | .02 |
| 76 | Rams TL (Dickerson) | .35 | .20 |
| 77 | Dieter Brock | .12 | .07 |
| 78 | Eric Dickerson | 1.75 | 1.00 |
| 79 | Henry Ellard | .60 | .35 |
| 80 | Ron Brown (R) | .50 | .28 |
| 81 | Tony Hunter (R) | .10 | .06 |
| 82 | Kent Hill | .05 | .02 |
| 83 | Doug Smith | .05 | .02 |
| 84 | Dennis Harrah | .05 | .02 |
| 85 | Jackie Slater | .25 | .15 |
| 86 | Mike Lansford | .05 | .02 |
| 87 | Gary Jeter | .05 | .02 |
| 88 | Mike Wilcher | .05 | .02 |
| 89 | Jim Collins | .05 | .02 |
| 90 | LeRoy Irvin | .08 | .05 |
| 91 | Gary Green | .05 | .02 |
| 92 | Nolan Cromwell | .08 | .05 |
| 93 | Dale Hatcher (R) | .10 | .06 |
| 94 | Jets TL (McNeil) | .12 | .07 |
| 95 | Ken O'Brien | .40 | .22 |
| 96 | Freeman McNeil | .15 | .08 |
| 97 | Tony Paige (R) | .30 | .18 |
| 98 | Johnny Lam Jones | .07 | .04 |
| 99 | Wesley Walker | .10 | .06 |
| 100 | Kurt Sohn | .05 | .02 |
| 101 | Al Toon (R) | 5.00 | 2.75 |
| 102 | Mickey Shuler | .05 | .02 |
| 103 | Marvin Powell | .07 | .04 |
| 104 | Pat Leahy | .05 | .02 |
| 105 | Mark Gastineau | .10 | .06 |
| 106 | Joe Klecko | .10 | .06 |
| 107 | Marty Lyons | .05 | .02 |
| 108 | Lance Mehl | .05 | .02 |
| 109 | Boby Jackson | .05 | .02 |
| 110 | Dave Jennings | .05 | .02 |
| 111 | Broncos TL (Winder) | .10 | .06 |
| 112 | John Elway | 1.75 | 1.00 |
| 113 | Sammy Winder | .08 | .05 |
| 114 | Gerald Willhite | .08 | .05 |
| 115 | Steve Watson | .05 | .02 |
| 116 | Vance Johnson (R) | 1.00 | .60 |
| 117 | Rich Karlis | .05 | .02 |
| 118 | Rulon Jones | .05 | .02 |
| 119 | Karl Mecklenburg (R) | 3.00 | 1.75 |
| 120 | Louis Wright | .08 | .05 |
| 121 | Mike Harden | .05 | .02 |
| 122 | Dennis Smith (R) | 1.25 | .70 |
| 123 | Steve Foley | .05 | .02 |
| 124 | Cowboys TL (Hill) | .10 | .06 |
| 125 | Danny White | .15 | .08 |
| 126 | Tony Dorsett | .60 | .35 |
| 127 | Timmy Newsome | .05 | .02 |
| 128 | Mike Renfro | .05 | .02 |
| 129 | Tony Hill | .08 | .05 |
| 130 | Doug Cosbie | .07 | .04 |
| 131 | Rafael Septien | .05 | .02 |
| 132 | Ed Too Tall Jones | .20 | .12 |
| 133 | Randy White | .30 | .18 |

| | | | | | | | |
|---|---|---|---|---|---|---|---|
| 134 | Jim Jeffcoat | .12 | .07 | 191 | Ozzie Newsome | .35 | .20 |
| 135 | Everson Walls | .08 | .05 | 192 | Mike Baab | .05 | .02 |
| 136 | Dennis Thurman | .05 | .02 | 193 | Cody Risien | .07 | .04 |
| 137 | Giants TL (Morris) | .10 | .06 | 194 | Bob Golic | .15 | .08 |
| 138 | Phil Simms | .35 | .20 | 195 | Reggie Camp | .05 | .02 |
| 139 | Joe Morris | .20 | .12 | 196 | Chip Banks | .08 | .05 |
| 140 | George Adams (R) | .10 | .06 | 197 | Tom Cousineau | .05 | .02 |
| 141 | Lionel Manuel | .07 | .04 | 198 | Frank Minnifield (R) | .35 | .20 |
| 142 | Bobby Johnson | .05 | .02 | 199 | Al Gross | .05 | .02 |
| 143 | Phil McConkey (R) | .12 | .07 | 200 | Seahawks TL (Warner) | .10 | .06 |
| 144 | Mark Bavaro (R) | 1.00 | .60 | 201 | Dave Krieg | .35 | .20 |
| 145 | Zeke Mowatt | .05 | .02 | 202 | Curt Warner | .12 | .07 |
| 146 | Brad Benson (R) | .08 | .05 | 203 | Steve Largent | .80 | .45 |
| 147 | Bart Oates (R) | .50 | .28 | 204 | Norm Johnson | .05 | .02 |
| 148 | Leonard Marshall (R) | 1.50 | .80 | 205 | Daryl Turner | .05 | .02 |
| 149 | Jim Burt | .08 | .05 | 206 | Jacob Green | .08 | .05 |
| 150 | George Martin | .07 | .04 | 207 | Joe Nash | .08 | .05 |
| 151 | Lawrence Taylor | .90 | .50 | 208 | Jeff Bryant | .05 | .02 |
| 152 | Harry Carson | .20 | .12 | 209 | Randy Edwards | .05 | .02 |
| 153 | Elvis Patterson (R) | .10 | .06 | 210 | Fredd Young | .08 | .05 |
| 154 | Sean Landeta | .15 | .08 | 211 | Kenny Easley | .08 | .05 |
| 155 | 49ers TL (Craig) | .25 | .15 | 212 | John Harris | .05 | .02 |
| 156 | Joe Montana | 3.50 | 2.00 | 213 | Packers TL (Coffman) | .08 | .05 |
| 157 | Roger Craig | .80 | .45 | 214 | Lynn Dickey | .10 | .06 |
| 158 | Wendell Tyler | .08 | .05 | 215 | Gerry Ellis | .05 | .02 |
| 159 | Carl Monroe | .05 | .02 | 216 | Eddie Lee Ivery | .07 | .04 |
| 160 | Dwight Clark | .12 | .07 | 217 | Jessie Clark | .05 | .02 |
| 161 | Jerry Rice (R) | 55.00 | 30.00 | 218 | James Lofton | .75 | .40 |
| 162 | Randy Cross | .05 | .02 | 219 | Paul Coffman | .05 | .02 |
| 163 | Keith Fahnhorst | .05 | .02 | 220 | Alphonso Carreker | .05 | .02 |
| 164 | Jeff Stover | .05 | .02 | 221 | Ezra Johnson | .05 | .02 |
| 165 | Michael Carter (R) | .90 | .50 | 222 | Mike Douglass | .05 | .02 |
| 166 | Dwaine Board | .05 | .02 | 223 | Tim Lewis | .05 | .02 |
| 167 | Eric Wright | .05 | .02 | 224 | Mark Murphy (R) | .25 | .15 |
| 168 | Ronnie Lott | .80 | .45 | 225 | Passing Leaders: | .90 | .50 |
| 169 | Carlton Williamson | .05 | .02 | | Ken O'Brien | | |
| 170 | Redskins TL (Butz) | .08 | .05 | | Joe Montana | | |
| 171 | Joe Theismann | .30 | .18 | 226 | Receiving Leaders: | .15 | .08 |
| 172 | Jay Schroeder (R) | 1.00 | .60 | | Lionel James | | |
| 173 | George Rogers | .10 | .06 | | Roger Craig | | |
| 174 | Ken Jenkins | .05 | .02 | 227 | Rushing Leaders: | .25 | .15 |
| 175 | Art Monk | 1.25 | .80 | | Marcus Allen | | |
| 176 | Gary Clark (R) | 10.00 | 6.00 | | Gerry Riggs | | |
| 177 | Joe Jacoby | .08 | .05 | 228 | Scoring Leaders: | .08 | .05 |
| 178 | Russ Grimm | .08 | .05 | | Gary Anderson | | |
| 179 | Mark Moseley | .05 | .02 | | Kevin Butler | | |
| 180 | Dexter Manley | .05 | .02 | 229 | Interception Leaders: | .10 | .06 |
| 181 | Charles Mann (R) | 1.75 | 1.00 | | Eugene Daniel | | |
| 182 | Vernon Dean | .05 | .02 | | Albert Lewis | | |
| 183 | Raphel Cherry (R) | .15 | .08 | | Everson Walls | | |
| 184 | Curtis Jordan | .05 | .02 | 230 | Chargers TL (Fouts) | .25 | .15 |
| 185 | Browns TL (Kosar) | .25 | .15 | 231 | Dan Fouts | .75 | .40 |
| 186 | Gary Danielson | .08 | .05 | 232 | Lionel James | .08 | .05 |
| 187 | Bernie Kosar (R) | 6.00 | 3.25 | 233 | Gary Anderson (R) | 1.00 | .60 |
| 188 | Kevin Mack (R) | .60 | .35 | 234 | Tim Spencer (R) | .15 | .08 |
| 189 | Earnest Byner (R) | 3.50 | 2.00 | 235 | Wes Chandler | .08 | .05 |
| 190 | Glen Young | .05 | .02 | 236 | Charlie Joiner | .30 | .18 |

| | | | | | | | |
|---|---|---|---|---|---|---|---|
| 237 | Kellen Winslow | .25 | .15 | 293 | Tommy Kramer | .12 | .07 |
| 238 | Jim Lachey (R) | 1.75 | 1.00 | 294 | Darrin Nelson | .08 | .05 |
| 239 | Bob Thomas | .05 | .02 | 295 | Ted Brown | .07 | .04 |
| 240 | Jeffery Dale | .05 | .02 | 296 | Buster Rhymes (R) | .10 | .06 |
| 241 | Ralf Mojsiejenko | .05 | .02 | 297 | Anthony Carter (R) | 1.50 | .80 |
| 242 | Lions TL (Hipple) | .08 | .05 | 298 | Steve Jordan (R) | 1.00 | .60 |
| 243 | Eric Hipple | .08 | .05 | 299 | Keith Millard (R) | .90 | .50 |
| 244 | Billy Sims | .12 | .07 | 300 | Joey Browner (R) | 1.25 | .70 |
| 245 | James Jones | .07 | .04 | 301 | John Turner | .05 | .02 |
| 246 | Pete Mandley (R) | .08 | .05 | 302 | Greg Coleman | .05 | .02 |
| 247 | Leonard Thompson | .07 | .04 | 303 | Chiefs TL (Blackledge) | .08 | .05 |
| 248 | Lomas Brown (R) | .30 | .18 | 304 | Bill Kenney | .08 | .05 |
| 249 | Ed Murray | .07 | .04 | 305 | Herman Heard | .05 | .02 |
| 250 | Curtis Green | .05 | .02 | 306 | Stephone Paige (R) | 1.25 | .70 |
| 251 | William Gay | .05 | .02 | 307 | Carlos Carson | .08 | .05 |
| 252 | Jimmy Williams | .05 | .02 | 308 | Nick Lowery | .15 | .08 |
| 253 | Bobby Watkins | .05 | .02 | 309 | Mike Bell | .05 | .02 |
| 254 | Bengals TL (Esiason) | .40 | .22 | 310 | Bill Maas | .10 | .06 |
| 255 | Boomer Esiason (R) | 6.00 | 3.25 | 311 | Art Still | .08 | .05 |
| 256 | James Brooks | .20 | .12 | 312 | Albert Lewis (R) | 1.25 | .70 |
| 257 | Larry Kinnebrew | .05 | .02 | 313 | Deron Cherry | .15 | .08 |
| 258 | Cris Collinsworth | .12 | .07 | 314 | Colts TL (Stark) | .08 | .05 |
| 259 | Mike Martin | .05 | .02 | 315 | Mike Pagel | .08 | .05 |
| 260 | Eddie Brown (R) | 1.25 | .70 | 316 | Randy McMillan | .05 | .02 |
| 261 | Anthony Munoz | .35 | .20 | 317 | Albert Bentley (R) | .30 | .18 |
| 262 | Jim Breech | .05 | .02 | 318 | George Wonsley (R) | .08 | .05 |
| 263 | Ross Browner | .08 | .05 | 319 | Robbie Martin | .05 | .02 |
| 264 | Carl Zander | .05 | .02 | 320 | Pat Beach | .05 | .02 |
| 265 | James Griffin | .05 | .02 | 321 | Chris Hinton | .15 | .08 |
| 266 | Robert Jackson | .05 | .02 | 322 | Duane Bickett (R) | .40 | .22 |
| 267 | Pat McInally | .07 | .04 | 323 | Eugene Daniel | .05 | .02 |
| 268 | Eagles TL (Jaworski) | .10 | .06 | 324 | Cliff Odom (R) | .12 | .07 |
| 269 | Ron Jaworski | .10 | .06 | 325 | Rohn Stark | .05 | .02 |
| 270 | Earnest Jackson | .08 | .05 | 326 | Cardinals TL (Mitchell) | .08 | .05 |
| 271 | Mike Quick | .12 | .07 | 327 | Neil Lomax | .12 | .07 |
| 272 | John Spagnola | .05 | .02 | 328 | Stump Mitchell | .10 | .06 |
| 273 | Mark Dennard | .05 | .02 | 329 | Ottis Anderson | .30 | .18 |
| 274 | Paul McFadden | .05 | .02 | 330 | J.T. Smith | .08 | .05 |
| 275 | Reggie White (R) | 10.00 | 6.50 | 331 | Pat Tilley | .05 | .02 |
| 276 | Greg Brown | .05 | .02 | 332 | Roy Green | .20 | .12 |
| 277 | Herman Edwards | .05 | .02 | 333 | Lance Smith (R) | .08 | .05 |
| 278 | Roynell Young | .05 | .02 | 334 | Curtis Greer | .05 | .02 |
| 279 | Wes Hopkins | .08 | .05 | 335 | Freddie Joe Nunn (R) | .30 | .18 |
| 280 | Steelers (Abercrombie) | .08 | .05 | 336 | E.J. Junior | .08 | .05 |
| 281 | Mark Malone | .08 | .05 | 337 | Lonnie Young (R) | .12 | .07 |
| 282 | Frank Pollard | .05 | .02 | 338 | Saints TL (Wilson) | .08 | .05 |
| 283 | Walter Abercrombie | .08 | .05 | 339 | Bobby Hebert (R) | 2.00 | 1.25 |
| 284 | Louis Lipps | .40 | .22 | 340 | Dave Wilson | .08 | .05 |
| 285 | John Stallworth | .30 | .18 | 341 | Wayne Wilson | .05 | .02 |
| 286 | Mike Webster | .15 | .08 | 342 | Hoby Brenner | .05 | .02 |
| 287 | Gary Anderson | .05 | .02 | 343 | Stan Brock | .05 | .02 |
| 288 | Keith Willis | .05 | .02 | 344 | Morten Andersen | .15 | .08 |
| 289 | Mike Merriweather | .15 | .08 | 345 | Bruce Clark | .05 | .02 |
| 290 | Dwayne Woodruff | .05 | .02 | 346 | Rickey Jackson | .40 | .25 |
| 291 | Donnie Shell | .10 | .06 | 347 | Dave Waymer | .05 | .02 |
| 292 | Vikings TL (Kramer) | .10 | .06 | 348 | Brian Hansen | .05 | .02 |
| | | | | 349 | Oilers TL (Moon) | .50 | .28 |

| | | | |
|---|---|---|---|
| 350 | Warren Moon | 7.50 | 4.00 |
| 351 | Mike Rozier (R) | .40 | .22 |
| 352 | Butch Woolfolk | .05 | .02 |
| 353 | Drew Hill | .50 | .28 |
| 354 | Willie Drewrey (R) | .10 | .06 |
| 355 | Tim Smith | .05 | .02 |
| 356 | Mike Munchak | .15 | .08 |
| 357 | Ray Childress (R) | 2.00 | 1.25 |
| 358 | Frank Bush | .05 | .02 |
| 359 | Steve Brown | .05 | .02 |
| 360 | Falcons TL (Riggs) | .10 | .06 |
| 361 | Dave Archer (R) | .50 | .28 |
| 362 | Gerald Riggs | .12 | .07 |
| 363 | William Andrews | .08 | .05 |
| 364 | Billy Johnson | .08 | .05 |
| 365 | Arthur Cox | .05 | .02 |
| 366 | Mike Kenn | .08 | .05 |
| 367 | Bill Fralic (R) | .60 | .35 |
| 368 | Mick Luckhurst | .05 | .02 |
| 369 | Rick Bryan | .05 | .02 |
| 370 | Bobby Butler | .05 | .02 |
| 371 | Rick Donnelly (R) | .10 | .06 |
| 372 | Buccaneers TL (Wilder) | .08 | .05 |
| 373 | Steve DeBerg | .25 | .15 |
| 374 | Steve Young (R) | 15.00 | 10.00 |
| 375 | James Wilder | .08 | .05 |
| 376 | Kevin House | .05 | .02 |
| 377 | Gerald Carter | .05 | .02 |
| 378 | Jimmie Giles | .08 | .05 |
| 379 | Sean Farrell | .08 | .05 |
| 380 | Donald Igwebuike (R) | .08 | .05 |
| 381 | David Logan | .05 | .02 |
| 382 | Jeremiah Castille (R) | .10 | .06 |
| 383 | Bills TL (Bell) | .10 | .06 |
| 384 | Bruce Mathison (R) | .10 | .06 |
| 385 | Joe Cribbs | .12 | .07 |
| 386 | Greg Bell | .20 | .12 |
| 387 | Jerry Butler | .08 | .05 |
| 388 | Andre Reed (R) | 12.00 | 6.50 |
| 389 | Bruce Smith (R) | 7.50 | 4.00 |
| 390 | Fred Smerlas | .07 | .04 |
| 391 | Darryl Talley | .60 | .35 |
| 392 | Jim Haslett | .05 | .02 |
| 393 | Charles Romes | .05 | .02 |
| 394 | Checklist 1-132 | .12 | .02 |
| 395 | Checklist 133-264 | .12 | .02 |
| 396 | Checklist 265-396 | .12 | .02 |

# 1987 Topps

This 396-card set features full color photos on the fronts with the player's team and name printed in a pennant-type design at the top of the card. The horizontal card backs consist of personal data, stats and highlights. Subsets include Record Breakers (RB) (2-8), League Leaders (227-231) and Team Leaders (TL) which feature action photos on the fronts and team statistics on the backs. All cards measure 2-1/2" by 3-1/2".

| | | MINT | NR/MT |
|---|---|---|---|
| **Complete Set (396)** | | 55.00 | 32.00 |
| **Commons** | | .05 | .02 |
| | | | |
| 1 | Super Bowl XXI | .20 | .08 |
| 2 | Todd Christensen (RB) | .08 | .05 |
| 3 | Dave Jennings (RB) | .07 | .04 |
| 4 | Charlie Joiner (RB) | .12 | .07 |
| 5 | Steve Largent (RB) | .25 | .15 |
| 6 | Dan Marino (RB) | .80 | .50 |
| 7 | Donnie Shell (RB) | .08 | .05 |
| 8 | Phil Simms (RB) | .10 | .06 |
| 9 | Giants TL (Bavaro) | .10 | .06 |
| 10 | Phil Simms | .25 | .15 |
| 11 | Joe Morris | .12 | .07 |
| 12 | Maurice Carthon (R) | .15 | .08 |
| 13 | Lee Rouson | .05 | .02 |
| 14 | Bobby Johnson | .05 | .02 |
| 15 | Lionel Manuel | .08 | .05 |
| 16 | Phil McConkey | .08 | .05 |
| 17 | Mark Bavaro | .25 | .15 |
| 18 | Zeke Mowatt | .05 | .02 |
| 19 | Raul Allegre | .05 | .02 |
| 20 | Sean Landeta | .05 | .02 |
| 21 | Brad Benson | .05 | .02 |
| 22 | Jim Burt | .05 | .02 |
| 23 | Leonard Marshall | .25 | .15 |

| | | | |
|---|---|---|---|
| 24 | Carl Banks | .50 | .28 |
| 25 | Harry Carson | .15 | .08 |
| 26 | Lawrence Taylor | .60 | .35 |
| 27 | Terry Kinard (R) | .15 | .08 |
| 28 | Pepper Johnson (R) | 1.00 | .60 |
| 29 | Erik Howard (R) | .12 | .07 |
| 30 | Broncos TL (Willhite) | .08 | .05 |
| 31 | John Elway | 1.00 | .60 |
| 32 | Gerald Willhite | .08 | .05 |
| 33 | Sammy Winder | .08 | .05 |
| 34 | Ken Bell | .05 | .02 |
| 35 | Steve Watson | .05 | .02 |
| 36 | Rich Karlis | .05 | .02 |
| 37 | Keith Bishop | .05 | .02 |
| 38 | Rulon Jones | .05 | .02 |
| 39 | Karl Mecklenburg | .60 | .35 |
| 40 | Louis Wright | .08 | .05 |
| 41 | Mike Harden | .05 | .02 |
| 42 | Dennis Smith | .25 | .15 |
| 43 | Bears TL (Payton) | .40 | .22 |
| 44 | Jim McMahon | .20 | .12 |
| 45 | Doug Flutie (R) | 1.50 | .80 |
| 46 | Walter Payton | 1.75 | 1.00 |
| 47 | Matt Suhey | .05 | .02 |
| 48 | Willie Gault | .15 | .08 |
| 49 | Dennis Gentry (R) | .30 | .18 |
| 50 | Kevin Butler | .08 | .05 |
| 51 | Jim Covert | .08 | .05 |
| 52 | Jay Hilgenberg | .20 | .12 |
| 53 | Dan Hampton | .25 | .15 |
| 54 | Steve McMichael | .15 | .08 |
| 55 | William Perry | .15 | .08 |
| 56 | Richard Dent | .30 | .18 |
| 57 | Otis Wilson | .05 | .02 |
| 58 | Mike Singletary | .75 | .40 |
| 59 | Wilber Marshall | .60 | .35 |
| 60 | Mike Richardson | .05 | .02 |
| 61 | Dave Duerson | .10 | .06 |
| 62 | Gary Fencik | .08 | .05 |
| 63 | Redskins TL (Rogers) | .10 | .06 |
| 64 | Jay Schroeder | .30 | .18 |
| 65 | George Rogers | .10 | .06 |
| 66 | Kelvin Bryant | .20 | .12 |
| 67 | Ken Jenkins | .05 | .02 |
| 68 | Gary Clark | 1.50 | .80 |
| 69 | Art Monk | .90 | .50 |
| 70 | Clint Didier (R) | .15 | .08 |
| 71 | Steve Cox | .05 | .02 |
| 72 | Joe Jacoby | .07 | .04 |
| 73 | Russ Grimm | .07 | .04 |
| 74 | Charles Mann | .30 | .18 |
| 75 | Dave Butz | .07 | .04 |
| 76 | Dexter Manley | .07 | .04 |
| 77 | Darrell Green | .50 | .28 |
| 78 | Curtis Jordan | .05 | .02 |
| 79 | Browns TL (Holt) | .08 | .05 |
| 80 | Bernie Kosar | 1.00 | .60 |
| 81 | Curtis Dickey | .08 | .05 |
| 82 | Kevin Mack | .20 | .12 |
| 83 | Herman Fontenot | .05 | .02 |
| 84 | Brian Brennan (R) | .15 | .08 |
| 85 | Ozzie Newsome | .30 | .18 |
| 86 | Jeff Gossett | .05 | .02 |
| 87 | Cody Risien | .05 | .02 |
| 88 | Reggie Camp | .05 | .02 |
| 89 | Bob Golic | .07 | .04 |
| 90 | Carl Hairston | .05 | .02 |
| 91 | Chip Banks | .08 | .05 |
| 92 | Frank Minnifield | .08 | .05 |
| 93 | Hanford Dixon | .08 | .05 |
| 94 | Gerald McNeil | .15 | .08 |
| 95 | Dave Puzzuoli | .05 | .02 |
| 96 | Patriots TL (Tippett) | .10 | .06 |
| 97 | Tony Eason | .12 | .07 |
| 98 | Craig James | .10 | .06 |
| 99 | Tony Collins | .08 | .05 |
| 100 | Mosi Tatupu | .08 | .05 |
| 101 | Stanley Morgan | .20 | .12 |
| 102 | Irving Fryar | .20 | .12 |
| 103 | Stephen Starring | .05 | .02 |
| 104 | Tony Franklin | .05 | .02 |
| 105 | Rich Camarillo | .05 | .02 |
| 106 | Garin Veris | .05 | .02 |
| 107 | Andre Tippett | .10 | .06 |
| 108 | Don Blackmon | .05 | .02 |
| 109 | Ronnie Lippett (R) | .20 | .12 |
| 110 | Raymond Clayborn | .05 | .02 |
| 111 | 49ers TL (Craig) | .15 | .08 |
| 112 | Joe Montana | 2.50 | 1.40 |
| 113 | Roger Craig | .40 | .22 |
| 114 | Joe Cribbs | .08 | .05 |
| 115 | Jerry Rice | 12.00 | 6.50 |
| 116 | Dwight Clark | .12 | .07 |
| 117 | Ray Wersching | .05 | .02 |
| 118 | Max Runager | .05 | .02 |
| 119 | Jeff Stover | .05 | .02 |
| 120 | Dwaine Board | .05 | .02 |
| 121 | Tim McKyer (R) | .40 | .22 |
| 122 | Don Griffin (R) | .30 | .18 |
| 123 | Ronnie Lott | .50 | .28 |
| 124 | Tom Holmoe | .05 | .02 |
| 125 | Charles Haley (R) | 3.00 | 1.75 |
| 126 | Jets TL (Gastineau) | .10 | .06 |
| 127 | Ken O'Brien | .35 | .20 |
| 128 | Pat Ryan | .08 | .05 |
| 129 | Freeman McNeil | .20 | .12 |
| 130 | Johnny Hector (R) | .40 | .22 |
| 131 | Al Toon | 1.00 | .60 |
| 132 | Wesley Walker | .10 | .06 |
| 133 | Mickey Shuler | .05 | .02 |
| 134 | Pat Leahy | .05 | .02 |
| 135 | Mark Gastineau | .10 | .06 |
| 136 | Joe Klecko | .10 | .06 |
| 137 | Marty Lyons | .05 | .02 |

| # | Player | | |
|---|---|---|---|
| 138 | Bob Crable | .05 | .02 |
| 139 | Lance Mehl | .05 | .02 |
| 140 | Dave Jennings | .05 | .02 |
| 141 | Harry Hamilton (R) | .12 | .07 |
| 142 | Lester Lyles | .05 | .02 |
| 143 | Bobby Humphery | .05 | .02 |
| 144 | Rams TL (Dickerson) | .25 | .15 |
| 145 | Jim Everett (R) | 6.00 | 3.25 |
| 146 | Eric Dickerson | 1.50 | .80 |
| 147 | Barry Redden | .08 | .05 |
| 148 | Ron Brown | .20 | .12 |
| 149 | Kevin House | .05 | .02 |
| 150 | Henry Ellard | .30 | .18 |
| 151 | Doug Smith | .05 | .02 |
| 152 | Dennis Harrah | .05 | .02 |
| 153 | Jackie Slater | .15 | .08 |
| 154 | Gary Jeter | .05 | .02 |
| 155 | Carl Ekern | .05 | .02 |
| 156 | Mike Wilcher | .05 | .02 |
| 157 | Jerry Gray (R) | .35 | .20 |
| 158 | LeRoy Irvin | .10 | .06 |
| 159 | Nolan Cromwell | .08 | .05 |
| 160 | Chiefs TL (Blackledge) | .08 | .05 |
| 161 | Bill Kenney | .08 | .05 |
| 162 | Stephone Paige | .25 | .15 |
| 163 | Henry Marshall | .05 | .02 |
| 164 | Carlos Carson | .08 | .05 |
| 165 | Nick Lowery | .12 | .07 |
| 166 | Irv Eatman | .10 | .06 |
| 167 | Brad Budde | .05 | .02 |
| 168 | Art Still | .08 | .05 |
| 169 | Bill Maas | .08 | .05 |
| 170 | Lloyd Burruss (R) | .12 | .07 |
| 171 | Deron Cherry | .12 | .07 |
| 172 | Seahawks TL (Warner) | .10 | .06 |
| 173 | Dave Krieg | .25 | .15 |
| 174 | Curt Warner | .12 | .07 |
| 175 | John L. Williams (R) | 1.00 | .60 |
| 176 | Bobby Joe Edmonds (R) | .15 | .08 |
| 177 | Steve Largent | .75 | .40 |
| 178 | Bruce Scholtz | .05 | .02 |
| 179 | Norm Johnson | .05 | .02 |
| 180 | Jacob Green | .08 | .05 |
| 181 | Fredd Young | .08 | .05 |
| 182 | Dave Brown | .08 | .05 |
| 183 | Kenny Easley | .08 | .05 |
| 184 | Bengals TL (Brooks) | .10 | .06 |
| 185 | Boomer Esiason | 1.00 | .60 |
| 186 | James Brooks | .15 | .08 |
| 187 | Larry Kinnebrew | .05 | .02 |
| 188 | Cris Collinsworth | .10 | .06 |
| 189 | Eddie Brown | .30 | .18 |
| 190 | Tim McGee (R) | .60 | .35 |
| 191 | Jim Breech | .05 | .02 |
| 192 | Anthony Munoz | .25 | .15 |
| 193 | Max Montoya | .07 | .04 |
| 194 | Eddie Edwards | .05 | .02 |
| 195 | Ross Browner | .08 | .05 |
| 196 | Emanuel King | .05 | .02 |
| 197 | Louis Breeden | .05 | .02 |
| 198 | Vikings TL (Nelson) | .10 | .06 |
| 199 | Tommy Kramer | .12 | .07 |
| 200 | Darrin Nelson | .10 | .06 |
| 201 | Allen Rice (R) | .08 | .05 |
| 202 | Anthony Carter | .35 | .20 |
| 203 | Leo Lewis | .07 | .04 |
| 204 | Steve Jordan | .20 | .12 |
| 205 | Chuck Nelson (R) | .10 | .06 |
| 206 | Greg Coleman | .05 | .02 |
| 207 | Gary Zimmerman (R) | .25 | .15 |
| 208 | Doug Martin | .05 | .02 |
| 209 | Keith Millard | .20 | .12 |
| 210 | Issiac Holt (R) | .30 | .18 |
| 211 | Joey Browner | .25 | .15 |
| 212 | Rufus Bess | .05 | .02 |
| 213 | Raiders TL (Allen) | .20 | .12 |
| 214 | Jim Plunkett | .15 | .08 |
| 215 | Marcus Allen | .40 | .22 |
| 216 | Napoleon McCallum (R) | .10 | .06 |
| 217 | Dokie Williams | .05 | .02 |
| 218 | Todd Christensen | .12 | .07 |
| 219 | Chris Bahr | .05 | .02 |
| 220 | Howie Long | .20 | .12 |
| 221 | Bill Pickel | .05 | .02 |
| 222 | Sean Jones (R) | .25 | .15 |
| 223 | Lester Hayes | .08 | .05 |
| 224 | Mike Haynes | .10 | .06 |
| 225 | Vann McElroy | .05 | .02 |
| 226 | Fulton Walker | .05 | .02 |
| 227 | Passing Leaders Tommy Kramer Dan Marino | .75 | .40 |
| 228 | Receiving Leaders Jerry Rice Todd Christensen | .60 | .35 |
| 229 | Rushing Leaders Eric Dickerson Curt Warner | .25 | .15 |
| 230 | Scoring Leaders Kevin Butler Tony Franklin | .08 | .05 |
| 231 | Interception Leaders Ronnie Lott Deron Cherry | .20 | .12 |
| 232 | Dolphins TL (Roby) | .08 | .05 |
| 233 | Dan Marino | 5.00 | 2.75 |
| 234 | Lorenzo Hampton (R) | .15 | .08 |
| 235 | Tony Nathan | .08 | .05 |
| 236 | Mark Duper | .25 | .15 |
| 237 | Mark Clayton | .50 | .28 |
| 238 | Nat Moore | .10 | .06 |
| 239 | Bruce Hardy | .05 | .02 |

| | | | |
|---|---|---|---|
| 240 | Reggie Roby | .05 | .02 |
| 241 | Roy Foster | .05 | .02 |
| 242 | Dwight Stephenson | .10 | .06 |
| 243 | Hugh Green | .08 | .05 |
| 244 | John Offerdahl (R) | .80 | .45 |
| 245 | Mark Brown | .05 | .02 |
| 246 | Doug Betters | .05 | .02 |
| 247 | Bob Baumhower | .05 | .02 |
| 248 | Falcons TL (Riggs) | .10 | .06 |
| 249 | Dave Archer | .15 | .08 |
| 250 | Gerald Riggs | .10 | .06 |
| 251 | William Andrews | .08 | .05 |
| 252 | Charlie Brown | .05 | .02 |
| 253 | Arthur Cox | .05 | .02 |
| 254 | Rick Donnelly | .05 | .02 |
| 255 | Bill Fralic | .12 | .07 |
| 256 | Mike Gann (R) | .08 | .05 |
| 257 | Rick Bryan | .05 | .02 |
| 258 | Bret Clark | .05 | .02 |
| 259 | Mike Pitts | .05 | .02 |
| 260 | Cowboys TL (Dorsett) | .25 | .15 |
| 261 | Danny White | .15 | .08 |
| 262 | Steve Pelluer (R) | .20 | .12 |
| 263 | Tony Dorsett | .50 | .28 |
| 264 | Herschel Walker (R) | 4.00 | 2.50 |
| 265 | Timmy Newsome | .05 | .02 |
| 266 | Tony Hill | .10 | .06 |
| 267 | Mike Sherrard (R) | .80 | .45 |
| 268 | Jim Jeffcoat | .08 | .05 |
| 269 | Ron Fellows | .05 | .02 |
| 270 | Bill Bates | .08 | .05 |
| 271 | Michael Downs | .05 | .02 |
| 272 | Saints TL (Hebert) | .12 | .07 |
| 273 | Dave Wilson | .08 | .05 |
| 274 | Rueben Mayes (R) | .25 | .15 |
| 275 | Hoby Brenner | .05 | .02 |
| 276 | Eric Martin (R) | 1.00 | .60 |
| 277 | Morten Andersen | .20 | .12 |
| 278 | Brian Hansen | .05 | .02 |
| 279 | Rickey Jackson | .15 | .08 |
| 280 | Dave Waymer | .05 | .02 |
| 281 | Bruce Clark | .05 | .02 |
| 282 | James Geathers (R) | .12 | .07 |
| 283 | Steelers (Abercrombie) | .08 | .05 |
| 284 | Mark Malone | .08 | .05 |
| 285 | Earnest Jackson | .08 | .05 |
| 286 | Walter Abercrombie | .08 | .05 |
| 287 | Louis Lipps | .15 | .08 |
| 288 | John Stallworth | .20 | .12 |
| 289 | Gary Anderson | .05 | .02 |
| 290 | Keith Willis | .05 | .02 |
| 291 | Mike Merriweather | .08 | .05 |
| 292 | Lupe Sanchez | .05 | .02 |
| 293 | Donnie Shell | .10 | .06 |
| 294 | Eagles TL (Byars) | .10 | .06 |
| 295 | Mike Reichenbach | .05 | .02 |
| 296 | Randall Cunningham | 24.00 | 13.00 |

| | | | |
|---|---|---|---|
| | (R) | | |
| 297 | Keith Byars (R) | 1.75 | 1.00 |
| 298 | Mike Quick | .08 | .05 |
| 299 | Kenny Jackson | .05 | .02 |
| 300 | John Teltschik (R) | .12 | .07 |
| 301 | Reggie White | 2.00 | 1.10 |
| 302 | Ken Clarke | .05 | .02 |
| 303 | Greg Brown | .05 | .02 |
| 304 | Roynell Young | .07 | .04 |
| 305 | Andre Waters | .60 | .35 |
| 306 | Oilers TL (Moon) | .30 | .18 |
| 307 | Warren Moon | 3.50 | 2.00 |
| 308 | Mike Rozier | .12 | .07 |
| 309 | Drew Hill | .25 | .15 |
| 310 | Ernest Givins (R) | 3.50 | 2.00 |
| 311 | Lee Johnson (R) | .08 | .05 |
| 312 | Kent Hill | .05 | .02 |
| 313 | Dean Steinkuhler (R) | .25 | .15 |
| 314 | Ray Childress | .35 | .20 |
| 315 | John Grimsley (R) | .25 | .15 |
| 316 | Jesse Baker | .05 | .02 |
| 317 | Lions TL (Hipple) | .08 | .05 |
| 318 | Chuck Long (R) | .20 | .12 |
| 319 | James Jones | .05 | .02 |
| 320 | Gary James | .05 | .02 |
| 321 | Jeff Chadwick | .05 | .02 |
| 322 | Leonard Thompson | .05 | .02 |
| 323 | Pete Mandley | .05 | .02 |
| 324 | Jimmie Giles | .08 | .05 |
| 325 | Herman Hunter | .05 | .02 |
| 326 | Keith Ferguson (R) | .08 | .05 |
| 327 | Devon Mitchell | .05 | .02 |
| 328 | Cardinals TL (Lomax) | .10 | .06 |
| 329 | Neil Lomax | .12 | .07 |
| 330 | Stump Mitchell | .08 | .05 |
| 331 | Earl Ferrell | .08 | .05 |
| 332 | Vai Sikahema (R) | .40 | .22 |
| 333 | Ron Wolfley (R) | .12 | .07 |
| 334 | J.T. Smith | .08 | .05 |
| 335 | Roy Green | .15 | .08 |
| 336 | Bubba Baker | .05 | .02 |
| 337 | Freddie Joe Nunn | .05 | .02 |
| 338 | Cedric Mack | .05 | .02 |
| 339 | Chargers TL | .10 | .06 |
| | (Anderson) | | |
| 340 | Dan Fouts | .50 | .28 |
| 341 | Gary Anderson | .20 | .12 |
| 342 | Wes Chandler | .08 | .05 |
| 343 | Kellen Winslow | .20 | .12 |
| 344 | Ralf Mojsiejenko | .05 | .02 |
| 345 | Rolf Benirschke | .05 | .02 |
| 346 | Lee Williams (R) | .60 | .35 |
| 347 | Leslie O'Neal (R) | 1.50 | .80 |
| 348 | Billy Ray Smith | .07 | .04 |
| 349 | Gill Byrd | .35 | .20 |
| 350 | Packers TL (Carruth) | .08 | .05 |
| 351 | Randy Wright (R) | .10 | .06 |

| 352 | Kenneth Davis (R) | 1.50 | .90 |
|---|---|---|---|
| 353 | Gerry Ellis | .05 | .02 |
| 354 | James Lofton | .50 | .28 |
| 355 | Phillip Epps (R) | .15 | .08 |
| 356 | Walter Stanley (R) | .30 | .18 |
| 357 | Eddie Lee Ivery | .08 | .05 |
| 358 | Tim Harris (R) | 1.25 | .70 |
| 359 | Mark Lee | .05 | .02 |
| 360 | Mossy Cade | .05 | .02 |
| 361 | Bills TL (Kelly) | 1.25 | .70 |
| 362 | Jim Kelly (R) | 18.00 | 10.00 |
| 363 | Robb Riddick (R) | .10 | .06 |
| 364 | Greg Bell | .15 | .08 |
| 365 | Andre Reed | 2.50 | 1.40 |
| 366 | Pete Metzelaars (R) | .25 | .15 |
| 367 | Sean McNanie | .05 | .02 |
| 368 | Fred Smerlas | .07 | .04 |
| 369 | Bruce Smith | 1.50 | .80 |
| 370 | Darryl Talley | .25 | .15 |
| 371 | Charles Romes | .05 | .02 |
| 372 | Colts TL (Stark) | .08 | .05 |
| 373 | Jack Trudeau (R) | .35 | .20 |
| 374 | Gary Hogeboom | .08 | .05 |
| 375 | Randy McMillan | .05 | .02 |
| 376 | Albert Bentley | .15 | .08 |
| 377 | Matt Bouza | .05 | .02 |
| 378 | Bill Brooks (R) | .50 | .28 |
| 379 | Rohn Stark | .05 | .02 |
| 380 | Chris Hinton | .10 | .06 |
| 381 | Ray Donaldson | .05 | .02 |
| 382 | Jon Hand (R) | .25 | .15 |
| 383 | Buccaneers TL (Wilder) | .10 | .06 |
| 384 | Steve Young | 2.75 | 1.75 |
| 385 | James Wilder | .10 | .06 |
| 386 | Frank Garcia | .05 | .02 |
| 387 | Gerald Carter | .05 | .02 |
| 388 | Phil Freeman | .05 | .02 |
| 389 | Calvin Magee | .05 | .02 |
| 390 | Donald Igwebuike | .05 | .02 |
| 391 | David Logan | .05 | .02 |
| 392 | Jeff Davis | .05 | .02 |
| 393 | Chris Washington | .05 | .02 |
| 394 | Checklist 1-132 | .10 | .02 |
| 395 | Checklist 133-264 | .10 | .02 |
| 396 | Checklist 265-396 | .10 | .02 |

# 1988 Topps

The cards in this 396-card set feature full color photos on the front with the player's name and position printed within the bottom border. A team helmet also appears below the photograph. The flip side contains personal data, stats and a brief highlight. Subsets include Record Breakers (RB) (2-6), League Leaders (215-219) and Team Leaders (TL). Some cards carry the designation of Super Rookie in a diagonal stripe below the photograph. All cards measure 2-1/2" by 3-1/2".

|  |  | MINT | NR/MT |
|---|---|---|---|
| Complete Set (396) | | 22.00 | 12.00 |
| Commons | | .05 | .02 |

| 1 | Super Bowl XXII | .15 | .05 |
|---|---|---|---|
| 2 | Vencie Glenn (RB) | .05 | .02 |
| 3 | Steve Largent (RB) | .20 | .12 |
| 4 | Joe Montana (RB) | .35 | .20 |
| 5 | Walter Payton (RB) | .35 | .20 |
| 6 | Jerry Rice (RB) | .50 | .28 |
| 7 | Redskins TL (Bryant) | .08 | .05 |
| 8 | Doug Williams | .12 | .07 |
| 9 | George Rogers | .08 | .05 |
| 10 | Kelvin Bryant | .08 | .05 |
| 11 | Timmy Smith (R) | .12 | .07 |
| 12 | Art Monk | .75 | .04 |
| 13 | Gary Clark | .50 | .28 |
| 14 | Ricky Sanders (R) | .75 | .40 |
| 15 | Steve Cox | .05 | .02 |
| 16 | Joe Jacoby | .07 | .04 |
| 17 | Charles Mann | .10 | .06 |
| 18 | Dave Butz | .07 | .04 |
| 19 | Darrell Green | .25 | .15 |
| 20 | Dexter Manley | .05 | .02 |
| 21 | Barry Wilburn (R) | .08 | .05 |

| | | | |
|---|---|---|---|
| 22 | Broncos TL (Winder) | .08 | .05 |
| 23 | John Elway | .60 | .35 |
| 24 | Sammy Winder | .08 | .05 |
| 25 | Vance Johnson | .20 | .12 |
| 26 | Mark Jackson (R) | .30 | .18 |
| 27 | Ricky Nattiel (R) | .30 | .18 |
| 28 | Clarence Kay | .05 | .02 |
| 29 | Rich Karlis | .05 | .02 |
| 30 | Keith Bishop | .05 | .02 |
| 31 | Mike Horan | .05 | .02 |
| 32 | Rulon Jones | .05 | .02 |
| 33 | Karl Mecklenburg | .15 | .08 |
| 34 | Jim Ryan | .05 | .02 |
| 35 | Mark Haynes | .07 | .04 |
| 36 | Mike Harden | .05 | .02 |
| 37 | 49ers TL (Craig) | .12 | .07 |
| 38 | Joe Montana | 1.25 | .70 |
| 39 | Steve Young | 1.25 | .70 |
| 40 | Roger Craig | .25 | .15 |
| 41 | Tom Rathman (R) | .60 | .35 |
| 42 | Joe Cribbs | .08 | .05 |
| 43 | Jerry Rice | 2.50 | 1.40 |
| 44 | Mike Wilson (R) | .08 | .05 |
| 45 | Ron Heller (R) | .10 | .06 |
| 46 | Ray Wersching | .05 | .02 |
| 47 | Michael Carter | .10 | .06 |
| 48 | Dwaine Board | .05 | .02 |
| 49 | Michael Walter | .05 | .02 |
| 50 | Don Griffin | .08 | .05 |
| 51 | Ronnie Lott | .35 | .20 |
| 52 | Charles Haley | .30 | .18 |
| 53 | Dana McLemore | .05 | .02 |
| 54 | Saints TL (Hebert) | .10 | .06 |
| 55 | Bobby Hebert | .30 | .18 |
| 56 | Rueben Mayes | .10 | .06 |
| 57 | Dalton Hilliard (R) | .50 | .28 |
| 58 | Eric Martin | .25 | .15 |
| 59 | John Tice (R) | .10 | .06 |
| 60 | Brad Edelman | .05 | .02 |
| 61 | Morten Andersen | .12 | .07 |
| 62 | Brian Hansen | .05 | .02 |
| 63 | Mel Gray (R) | .40 | .22 |
| 64 | Rickey Jackson | .12 | .07 |
| 65 | Sam Mills (R) | .75 | .40 |
| 66 | Pat Swilling (R) | 2.50 | 1.40 |
| 67 | Dave Waymer | .05 | .02 |
| 68 | Bears TL (Gault) | .08 | .05 |
| 69 | Jim McMahon | .12 | .07 |
| 70 | Mike Tomczak (R) | .30 | .18 |
| 71 | Neal Anderson (R) | 2.50 | 1.40 |
| 72 | Willie Gault | .12 | .07 |
| 73 | Dennis Gentry | .08 | .05 |
| 74 | Dennis McKinnon | .05 | .02 |
| 75 | Kevin Butler | .05 | .02 |
| 76 | Jim Covert | .07 | .04 |
| 77 | Jay Hilgenberg | .08 | .05 |
| 78 | Steve McMichael | .10 | .06 |
| 79 | William Perry | .12 | .07 |
| 80 | Richard Dent | .20 | .12 |
| 81 | Ron Rivera (R) | .10 | .06 |
| 82 | Mike Singletary | .30 | .18 |
| 83 | Dan Hampton | .15 | .08 |
| 84 | Dave Duerson | .05 | .02 |
| 85 | Browns TL (Kosar) | .10 | .06 |
| 86 | Bernie Kosar | .40 | .22 |
| 87 | Earnest Byner | .30 | .18 |
| 88 | Kevin Mack | .15 | .08 |
| 89 | Webster Slaughter (R) | .75 | .40 |
| 90 | Gerald McNeil | .07 | .04 |
| 91 | Brian Brennan | .05 | .02 |
| 92 | Ozzie Newsome | .30 | .18 |
| 93 | Cody Risien | .05 | .02 |
| 94 | Bob Golic | .07 | .04 |
| 95 | Carl Hairston | .05 | .02 |
| 96 | Mike Johnson (R) | .25 | .15 |
| 97 | Clay Matthews | .07 | .04 |
| 98 | Frank Minnifield | .08 | .05 |
| 99 | Hanford Dixon | .07 | .04 |
| 100 | Dave Puzzuoli | .05 | .02 |
| 101 | Felix Wright | .08 | .05 |
| 102 | Oilers TL (Moon) | .25 | .15 |
| 103 | Warren Moon | 1.25 | .70 |
| 104 | Mike Rozier | .08 | .05 |
| 105 | Alonzo Highsmith (R) | .20 | .12 |
| 106 | Drew Hill | .30 | .18 |
| 107 | Ernest Givins | .75 | .40 |
| 108 | Curtis Duncan (R) | .75 | .40 |
| 109 | Tony Zendejas (R) | .08 | .05 |
| 110 | Mike Munchak | .10 | .06 |
| 111 | Kent Hill | .05 | .02 |
| 112 | Ray Childress | .12 | .07 |
| 113 | Al Smith (R) | .25 | .15 |
| 114 | Keith Bostic (R) | .10 | .06 |
| 115 | Jeff Donaldson | .05 | .02 |
| 116 | Colts TL (Dickerson) | .20 | .12 |
| 117 | Jack Trudeau | .15 | .08 |
| 118 | Eric Dickerson | .80 | .45 |
| 119 | Albert Bentley | .08 | .05 |
| 120 | Matt Bouza | .05 | .02 |
| 121 | Bill Brooks | .10 | .06 |
| 122 | Dean Biasucci (R) | .12 | .07 |
| 123 | Chris Hinton | .08 | .05 |
| 124 | Ray Donaldson | .05 | .02 |
| 125 | Ron Solt (R) | .08 | .05 |
| 126 | Donnell Thompson | .05 | .02 |
| 127 | Barry Krauss (R) | .10 | .06 |
| 128 | Duane Bickett | .07 | .04 |
| 129 | Mike Prior (R) | .20 | .12 |
| 130 | Seahawks TL (Warner) | .10 | .06 |
| 131 | Dave Krieg | .20 | .12 |
| 132 | Curt Warner | .12 | .07 |
| 133 | John L. Williams | .20 | .12 |
| 134 | Bobby Joe Edmonds | .05 | .02 |
| 135 | Steve Largent | .60 | .35 |

| # | Player | Value | Value |
|---|--------|-------|-------|
| 136 | Raymond Butler | .05 | .02 |
| 137 | Norm Johnson | .05 | .02 |
| 138 | Ruben Rodriguez (R) | .08 | .05 |
| 139 | Blair Bush | .05 | .02 |
| 140 | Jacob Green | .07 | .04 |
| 141 | Joe Nash | .07 | .04 |
| 142 | Jeff Bryant | .05 | .02 |
| 143 | Fredd Young | .07 | .04 |
| 144 | Brian Bosworth (R) | .15 | .08 |
| 145 | Kenny Easley | .08 | .05 |
| 146 | Vikings TL (Kramer) | .10 | .06 |
| 147 | Wade Wilson (R) | .40 | .22 |
| 148 | Tommy Kramer | .12 | .07 |
| 149 | Darrin Nelson | .08 | .05 |
| 150 | D.J. Dozier (R) | .50 | .28 |
| 151 | Anthony Carter | .25 | .15 |
| 152 | Leo Lewis | .07 | .04 |
| 153 | Steve Jordan | .15 | .08 |
| 154 | Gary Zimmerman | .07 | .04 |
| 155 | Chuck Nelson | .05 | .02 |
| 156 | Henry Thomas (R) | .25 | .15 |
| 157 | Chris Doleman (R) | 1.25 | .70 |
| 158 | Scott Studwell (R) | .15 | .08 |
| 159 | Jesse Solomon (R) | .15 | .08 |
| 160 | Joey Browner | .15 | .08 |
| 161 | Neal Guggemos | .05 | .02 |
| 162 | Steelers TL (Lipps) | .08 | .05 |
| 163 | Mark Malone | .08 | .05 |
| 164 | Walter Abercrombie | .07 | .04 |
| 165 | Earnest Jackson | .08 | .05 |
| 166 | Frank Pollard | .05 | .02 |
| 167 | Dwight Stone (R) | .15 | .08 |
| 168 | Gary Anderson | .05 | .02 |
| 169 | Harry Newsome (R) | .08 | .05 |
| 170 | Keith Willis | .05 | .02 |
| 171 | Keith Gary | .05 | .02 |
| 172 | David Little (R) | .15 | .08 |
| 173 | Mike Merriweather | .08 | .05 |
| 174 | Dwayne Woodruff | .05 | .02 |
| 175 | Patriots TL (Fryar) | .08 | .05 |
| 176 | Steve Grogan | .10 | .06 |
| 177 | Tony Eason | .10 | .06 |
| 178 | Tony Collins | .08 | .05 |
| 179 | Mosi Tatupu | .07 | .04 |
| 180 | Stanley Morgan | .12 | .07 |
| 181 | Irving Fryar | .08 | .05 |
| 182 | Stephen Starring | .05 | .02 |
| 183 | Tony Franklin | .05 | .02 |
| 184 | Rich Camarillo | .05 | .02 |
| 185 | Garin Veris | .05 | .02 |
| 186 | Andre Tippett | .10 | .06 |
| 187 | Ronnie Lippett | .07 | .04 |
| 188 | Fred Marion | .05 | .02 |
| 189 | Dolphins TL (Marino) | .40 | .22 |
| 190 | Dan Marino | 2.25 | 1.25 |
| 191 | Troy Stradford (R) | .10 | .06 |
| 192 | Lorenzo Hampton | .07 | .04 |
| 193 | Mark Duper | .15 | .08 |
| 194 | Mark Clayton | .25 | .15 |
| 195 | Reggie Roby | .05 | .02 |
| 196 | Dwight Stephenson | .10 | .06 |
| 197 | T.J. Turner | .05 | .02 |
| 198 | John Bosa (R) | .10 | .06 |
| 199 | Jackie Shipp | .05 | .02 |
| 200 | John Offerdahl | .12 | .07 |
| 201 | Mark Brown | .05 | .02 |
| 202 | Paul Lankford | .05 | .02 |
| 203 | Chargers TL (Winslow) | .10 | .06 |
| 204 | Tim Spencer | .05 | .02 |
| 205 | Gary Anderson | .10 | .06 |
| 206 | Curtis Adams | .05 | .02 |
| 207 | Lionel James | .08 | .05 |
| 208 | Chip Banks | .08 | .05 |
| 209 | Kellen Winslow | .15 | .08 |
| 210 | Ralf Mojsiejenko | .05 | .02 |
| 211 | Jim Lachey | .25 | .15 |
| 212 | Lee Williams | .12 | .07 |
| 213 | Billy Ray Smith | .07 | .04 |
| 214 | Vencie Glenn (R) | .12 | .07 |
| 215 | Passing Leaders<br>Bernie Kosar<br>Joe Montana | .35 | .20 |
| 216 | Receiving Leaders<br>Al Toon<br>J.T. Smith | .10 | .06 |
| 217 | Rushing Leaders<br>Charles White<br>Eric Dickerson | .25 | .15 |
| 218 | Scoring Leaders<br>Jim Breech<br>Jerry Rice | .25 | .15 |
| 219 | Interception Leaders<br>Keith Bostic<br>Mark Kelso<br>Mike Prior<br>Barry Wilburn | .08 | .05 |
| 220 | Bills TL (Kelly) | .25 | .15 |
| 221 | Jim Kelly | 2.00 | 1.10 |
| 222 | Ronnie Harmon (R) | .75 | .40 |
| 223 | Robb Riddick | .05 | .02 |
| 224 | Andre Reed | .80 | .45 |
| 225 | Chris Burkett (R) | .25 | .15 |
| 226 | Pete Metzelaars | .08 | .05 |
| 227 | Bruce Smith | .40 | .22 |
| 228 | Darryl Talley | .10 | .06 |
| 229 | Eugene Marve | .05 | .02 |
| 230 | Cornelius Bennett (R) | 2.50 | 1.40 |
| 231 | Mark Kelso (R) | .25 | .15 |
| 232 | Shane Conlan (R) | 1.00 | .60 |
| 233 | Eagles TL (Cunningham) | .20 | .12 |
| 234 | Randall Cunningham | 2.00 | 1.10 |
| 235 | Keith Byars | .25 | .15 |
| 236 | Anthony Toney (R) | .12 | .07 |

| | | | |
|---|---|---|---|
| 237 | Mike Quick | .08 | .05 |
| 238 | Kenny Jackson | .05 | .02 |
| 239 | John Spagnola | .05 | .02 |
| 240 | Paul McFadden | .05 | .02 |
| 241 | Reggie White | .40 | .22 |
| 242 | Ken Clarke | .05 | .02 |
| 243 | Mike Pitts | .05 | .02 |
| 244 | Clyde Simmons (R) | 1.25 | .70 |
| 245 | Seth Joyner (R) | .75 | .40 |
| 246 | Andre Waters | .08 | .05 |
| 247 | Jerome Brown (R) | .50 | .28 |
| 248 | Cardinals TL (Mitchell) | .08 | .05 |
| 249 | Neil Lomax | .10 | .06 |
| 250 | Stump Mitchell | .08 | .05 |
| 251 | Earl Ferrell | .05 | .02 |
| 252 | Vai Sikahema | .08 | .05 |
| 253 | J.T. Smith | .08 | .05 |
| 254 | Roy Green | .12 | .07 |
| 255 | Robert Awalt (R) | .12 | .07 |
| 256 | Freddie Joe Nunn | .05 | .02 |
| 257 | Leonard Smith (R) | .10 | .06 |
| 258 | Travis Curtis | .05 | .02 |
| 259 | Cowboys TL (Walker) | .15 | .08 |
| 260 | Danny White | .10 | .06 |
| 261 | Herschel Walker | .75 | .40 |
| 262 | Tony Dorsett | .50 | .28 |
| 263 | Doug Cosbie | .07 | .04 |
| 264 | Roger Ruzek (R) | .08 | .05 |
| 265 | Darryl Clack (R) | .08 | .05 |
| 266 | Ed Too Tall Jones | .20 | .12 |
| 267 | Jim Jeffcoat | .08 | .05 |
| 268 | Everson Walls | .07 | .04 |
| 269 | Bill Bates | .07 | .04 |
| 270 | Michael Downs | .05 | .02 |
| 271 | Giants TL (Bavaro) | .08 | .05 |
| 272 | Phil Simms | .25 | .15 |
| 273 | Joe Morris | .08 | .05 |
| 274 | Lee Rouson | .05 | .02 |
| 275 | George Adams | .05 | .02 |
| 276 | Lionel Manuel | .07 | .04 |
| 277 | Mark Bavaro | .12 | .07 |
| 278 | Raul Allegre | .05 | .02 |
| 279 | Sean Landeta | .05 | .02 |
| 280 | Erik Howard | .05 | .02 |
| 281 | Leonard Marshall | .10 | .06 |
| 282 | Carl Banks | .20 | .12 |
| 283 | Pepper Johnson | .15 | .08 |
| 284 | Harry Carson | .15 | .08 |
| 285 | Lawrence Taylor | .50 | .28 |
| 286 | Terry Kinard | .05 | .02 |
| 287 | Rams TL (Everett) | .12 | .07 |
| 288 | Jim Everett | .90 | .50 |
| 289 | Charles White | .08 | .05 |
| 290 | Ron Brown | .10 | .06 |
| 291 | Henry Ellard | .15 | .08 |
| 292 | Mike Lansford | .05 | .02 |
| 293 | Dale Hatcher | .05 | .02 |
| 294 | Doug Smith | .05 | .02 |
| 295 | Jackie Slater | .12 | .07 |
| 296 | Jim Collins | .05 | .02 |
| 297 | Jerry Gray | .08 | .05 |
| 298 | LeRoy Irvin | .08 | .05 |
| 299 | Nolan Cromwell | .07 | .04 |
| 300 | Kevin Greene (R) | .40 | .22 |
| 301 | Jets TL (O'Brien) | .10 | .06 |
| 302 | Ken O'Brien | .20 | .12 |
| 303 | Freeman McNeil | .12 | .07 |
| 304 | Johnny Hector | .08 | .05 |
| 305 | Al Toon | .30 | .18 |
| 306 | Jo Jo Townsell | .08 | .05 |
| 307 | Mickey Shuler | .05 | .02 |
| 308 | Pat Leahy | .05 | .02 |
| 309 | Roger Vick (R) | .10 | .06 |
| 310 | Alex Gordon (R) | .10 | .06 |
| 311 | Troy Benson | .05 | .02 |
| 312 | Bob Crable | .05 | .02 |
| 313 | Harry Hamilton | .05 | .02 |
| 314 | Packers TL (Epps) | .08 | .05 |
| 315 | Randy Wright | .07 | .04 |
| 316 | Kenneth Davis | .30 | .18 |
| 317 | Phillip Epps | .08 | .05 |
| 318 | Walter Stanley | .08 | .05 |
| 319 | Frankie Neal | .05 | .02 |
| 320 | Don Bracken | .05 | .02 |
| 321 | Brian Noble (R) | .15 | .08 |
| 322 | Johnny Holland (R) | .30 | .18 |
| 323 | Tim Harris | .25 | .15 |
| 324 | Mark Murphy | .05 | .02 |
| 325 | Raiders TL (Jackson) | .35 | .20 |
| 326 | Marc Wilson | .08 | .05 |
| 327 | Bo Jackson (R) | 3.00 | 1.75 |
| 328 | Marcus Allen | .25 | .15 |
| 329 | James Lofton | .25 | .15 |
| 330 | Todd Christensen | .08 | .05 |
| 331 | Chris Bahr | .05 | .02 |
| 332 | Stan Talley | .05 | .02 |
| 333 | Howie Long | .20 | .12 |
| 334 | Sean Jones | .05 | .02 |
| 335 | Matt Millen | .07 | .04 |
| 336 | Stacey Toran | .08 | .05 |
| 337 | Vann McElroy | .05 | .02 |
| 338 | Greg Townsend | .15 | .08 |
| 339 | Bengals TL (Esiason) | .12 | .07 |
| 340 | Boomer Esiason | .35 | .20 |
| 341 | Larry Kinnebrew | .05 | .02 |
| 342 | Stanford Jennings (R) | .10 | .06 |
| 343 | Eddie Brown | .12 | .07 |
| 344 | Jim Breech | .05 | .02 |
| 345 | Anthony Munoz | .25 | .15 |
| 346 | Scott Fulhage (R) | .08 | .05 |
| 347 | Tim Krumrie (R) | .25 | .15 |
| 348 | Reggie Williams | .07 | .04 |
| 349 | David Fulcher (R) | .25 | .15 |

| | | | |
|---|---|---|---|
| 350 | Buccaneers TL (Wilder) | .08 | .05 |
| 351 | Frank Garcia | .05 | .02 |
| 352 | Vinny Testaverde (R) | .80 | .45 |
| 353 | James Wilder | .08 | .05 |
| 354 | Jeff Smith | .05 | .02 |
| 355 | Gerald Carter | .05 | .02 |
| 356 | Calvin Magee | .05 | .02 |
| 357 | Donald Igwebuike | .05 | .02 |
| 358 | Ron Holmes (R) | .10 | .06 |
| 359 | Chris Washington | .05 | .02 |
| 360 | Ervin Randle | .05 | .02 |
| 361 | Chiefs TL (Kenney) | .08 | .05 |
| 362 | Bill Kenney | .08 | .05 |
| 363 | Christian Okoye (R) | 1.25 | .70 |
| 364 | Paul Palmer (R) | .10 | .06 |
| 365 | Stephone Paige | .12 | .07 |
| 366 | Carlos Carson | .07 | .04 |
| 367 | Kelly Goodburn (R) | .08 | .05 |
| 368 | Bill Maas | .08 | .05 |
| 369 | Mike Bell | .05 | .02 |
| 370 | Dino Hackett (R) | .20 | .12 |
| 371 | Deron Cherry | .08 | .05 |
| 372 | Lions TL (Jones) | .08 | .05 |
| 373 | Chuck Long | .10 | .06 |
| 374 | Garry James | .05 | .02 |
| 375 | James Jones | .08 | .05 |
| 376 | Pete Mandley | .05 | .02 |
| 377 | Gary Lee (R) | .08 | .05 |
| 378 | Ed Murray | .05 | .02 |
| 379 | Jim Arnold | .05 | .02 |
| 380 | Dennis Gibson (R) | .08 | .05 |
| 381 | Mike Cofer | .07 | .04 |
| 382 | James Griffin | .05 | .02 |
| 383 | Falcons TL (Riggs) | .10 | .06 |
| 384 | Scott Campbell | .08 | .05 |
| 385 | Gerald Riggs | .12 | .07 |
| 386 | Floyd Dixon (R) | .12 | .07 |
| 387 | Rick Donnelly | .05 | .02 |
| 388 | Bill Fralic | .07 | .04 |
| 389 | Major Everett | .05 | .02 |
| 390 | Mike Gann | .05 | .02 |
| 391 | Tony Casillas (R) | .40 | .22 |
| 392 | Rick Bryan | .05 | .02 |
| 393 | John Rade (R) | .08 | .05 |
| 394 | Checklist 1-132 | .10 | .02 |
| 395 | Checklist 133-264 | .10 | .02 |
| 396 | Checklist 265-396 | .10 | .02 |

# 1989 Topps

This 396-card set consists of full color photos on the card fronts with the player's name, team and position located in a small oval at the bottom of the ohotograph. A Topps logo appears in the top right corner of the card. The backs contain personal data, stats and highlights. Subsets include Record Breakers (RB) (2-5), League Leaders (217-221) and Team Leaders (TL). All cards measure 2-1/2" by 3-1/2".

| | | MINT | NR/MT |
|---|---|---|---|
| Complete Set (396) | | 16.00 | 9.50 |
| Commons | | .05 | .02 |

| | | | |
|---|---|---|---|
| 1 | Super Bowl XXIII | .25 | .10 |
| 2 | Tim Brown (RB) | .15 | .08 |
| 3 | Eric Dickerson RB | .20 | .12 |
| 4 | Steve Largent RB | .20 | .12 |
| 5 | Dan Marino RB | .25 | .15 |
| 6 | 49ers TL (Montana) | .25 | .15 |
| 7 | Jerry Rice | .80 | .45 |
| 8 | Roger Craig | .12 | .07 |
| 9 | Ronnie Lott | .20 | .12 |
| 10 | Michael Carter | .07 | .04 |
| 11 | Charles Haley | .10 | .06 |
| 12 | Joe Montana | .90 | .50 |
| 13 | John Taylor (R) | 1.25 | .70 |
| 14 | Michael Walter | .05 | .02 |
| 15 | Mike Cofer (R) | .08 | .05 |
| 16 | Tom Rathman | .12 | .07 |
| 17 | Danny Stubbs (R) | .08 | .05 |
| 18 | Keena Turner | .08 | .05 |
| 19 | Tim McKyer | .08 | .05 |
| 20 | Larry Roberts (R) | .08 | .05 |
| 21 | Jeff Fuller | .07 | .04 |
| 22 | Bubba Paris | .08 | .05 |
| 23 | Bengals TL (Esiason) | .08 | .05 |

| 24 | Eddie Brown | .08 | .05 |
| 25 | Boomer Esiason | .25 | .15 |
| 26 | Tim Krumrie | .07 | .04 |
| 27 | Ickey Woods (R) | .10 | .06 |
| 28 | Anthony Munoz | .15 | .08 |
| 29 | Tim McGee | .10 | .06 |
| 30 | Max Montoya | .07 | .04 |
| 31 | David Grant | .05 | .02 |
| 32 | Rodney Holman (R) | .25 | .15 |
| 33 | David Fulcher | .08 | .05 |
| 34 | Jim Skow (R) | .08 | .05 |
| 35 | James Brooks | .08 | .05 |
| 36 | Reggie Williams | .07 | .04 |
| 37 | Eric Thomas (R) | .12 | .07 |
| 38 | Stanford Jennings | .05 | .02 |
| 39 | Jim Breech | .05 | .02 |
| 40 | Bills TL (Kelly) | .20 | .12 |
| 41 | Shane Conlan | .15 | .08 |
| 42 | Scott Norwood (R) | .08 | .05 |
| 43 | Cornelius Bennett | .35 | .20 |
| 44 | Bruce Smith | .20 | .12 |
| 45 | Thurman Thomas (R) | 4.00 | 2.25 |
| 46 | Jim Kelly | .60 | .35 |
| 47 | John Kidd (R) | .08 | .05 |
| 48 | Kent Hull (R) | .15 | .08 |
| 49 | Art Still | .07 | .04 |
| 50 | Fred Smerlas | .07 | .04 |
| 51 | Derrick Burroughs | .05 | .02 |
| 52 | Andre Reed | .25 | .15 |
| 53 | Robb Riddick | .05 | .02 |
| 54 | Chris Burkett | .05 | .02 |
| 55 | Ronnie Harmon | .12 | .07 |
| 56 | Mark Kelso | .08 | .05 |
| 57 | Bears TL (Sanders) | .07 | .04 |
| 58 | Mike Singletary | .20 | .12 |
| 59 | Jay Hilgenberg | .07 | .04 |
| 60 | Richard Dent | .10 | .06 |
| 61 | Ron Rivera | .05 | .02 |
| 62 | Jim McMahon | .12 | .07 |
| 63 | Mike Tomczak | .10 | .06 |
| 64 | Neal Anderson | .30 | .18 |
| 65 | Dennis Gentry | .07 | .04 |
| 66 | Dan Hampton | .12 | .07 |
| 67 | David Tate (R) | .08 | .05 |
| 68 | Thomas Sanders (R) | .12 | .07 |
| 69 | Steve McMichael | .08 | .05 |
| 70 | Dennis McKinnon | .05 | .02 |
| 71 | Brad Muster (R) | .25 | .15 |
| 72 | Vestee Jackson (R) | .12 | .07 |
| 73 | Dave Duerson | .05 | .02 |
| 74 | Vikings TL (Millard) | .07 | .04 |
| 75 | Joey Browner | .07 | .04 |
| 76 | Carl Lee | .07 | .04 |
| 77 | Gary Zimmerman | .07 | .04 |
| 78 | Hassan Jones (R) | .20 | .12 |
| 79 | Anthony Carter | .12 | .07 |
| 80 | Ray Berry (R) | .08 | .05 |
| 81 | Steve Jordan | .08 | .05 |
| 82 | Issiac Holt | .07 | .04 |
| 83 | Wade Wilson | .12 | .07 |
| 84 | Chris Doleman | .12 | .07 |
| 85 | Alfred Anderson | .05 | .02 |
| 86 | Keith Millard | .08 | .05 |
| 87 | Darrin Nelson | .08 | .05 |
| 88 | D.J. Dozier | .08 | .05 |
| 89 | Scott Studwell | .05 | .02 |
| 90 | Oilers TL (Zendejas) | .07 | .04 |
| 91 | Bruce Matthews (R) | .20 | .12 |
| 92 | Curtis Duncan | .12 | .07 |
| 93 | Warren Moon | .50 | .28 |
| 94 | Johnny Meads (R) | .12 | .07 |
| 95 | Drew Hill | .12 | .07 |
| 96 | Alonzo Highsmith | .08 | .05 |
| 97 | Mike Munchak | .08 | .05 |
| 98 | Mike Rozier | .08 | .05 |
| 99 | Tony Zendejas | .05 | .02 |
| 100 | Jeff Donaldson | .05 | .02 |
| 101 | Ray Childress | .12 | .07 |
| 102 | Sean Jones | .05 | .02 |
| 103 | Ernest Givins | .25 | .15 |
| 104 | William Fuller (R) | .20 | .12 |
| 105 | Allen Pinkett (R) | .15 | .08 |
| 106 | Eagles TL (Cunningham) | .10 | .06 |
| 107 | Keith Jackson (R) | 1.00 | .60 |
| 108 | Reggie White | .20 | .12 |
| 109 | Clyde Simmons | .20 | .12 |
| 110 | John Teltschik | .05 | .02 |
| 111 | Wes Hopkins | .05 | .02 |
| 112 | Keith Byars | .10 | .06 |
| 113 | Jerome Brown | .08 | .05 |
| 114 | Mike Quick | .08 | .05 |
| 115 | Randall Cunningham | .50 | .28 |
| 116 | Anthony Toney | .05 | .02 |
| 117 | Ron Johnson | .05 | .02 |
| 118 | Terry Hoage | .05 | .02 |
| 119 | Seth Joyner | .12 | .07 |
| 120 | Eric Allen (R) | .20 | .12 |
| 121 | Cris Carter (R) | .80 | .45 |
| 122 | Rams TL (Bell) | .08 | .05 |
| 123 | Tom Newberry (R) | .10 | .06 |
| 124 | Pete Holohan | .05 | .02 |
| 125 | Robert Delpino | .25 | .15 |
| 126 | Carl Ekern | .05 | .02 |
| 127 | Greg Bell | .08 | .05 |
| 128 | Mike Lansford | .05 | .02 |
| 129 | Jim Everett | .20 | .12 |
| 130 | Mike Wilcher | .05 | .02 |
| 131 | Jerry Gray | .07 | .04 |
| 132 | Dale Hatcher | .05 | .02 |
| 133 | Doug Smith | .05 | .02 |
| 134 | Kevin Greene | .10 | .06 |
| 135 | Jackie Slater | .10 | .06 |
| 136 | Aaron Cox (R) | .12 | .07 |

| 137 | Henry Ellard | .10 | .06 |
|---|---|---|---|
| 138 | Browns TL (Kosar) | .10 | .06 |
| 139 | Frank Minnifield | .07 | .04 |
| 140 | Webster Slaughter | .15 | .08 |
| 141 | Bernie Kosar | .25 | .15 |
| 142 | Charles Buchanan (R) | .08 | .05 |
| 143 | Clay Matthews | .07 | .04 |
| 144 | Reggie Langhorne (R) | .15 | .08 |
| 145 | Hanford Dixon | .05 | .02 |
| 146 | Brian Brennan | .05 | .02 |
| 147 | Earnest Byner | .15 | .08 |
| 148 | Michael Dean Perry(R) | 1.50 | .80 |
| 149 | Kevin Mack | .08 | .05 |
| 150 | Matt Bahr | .05 | .02 |
| 151 | Ozzie Newsome | .20 | .12 |
| 152 | Saints TL (Heyward) | .08 | .05 |
| 153 | Morten Andersen | .08 | .05 |
| 154 | Pat Swilling | .25 | .15 |
| 155 | Sam Mills | .15 | .08 |
| 156 | Lonzell Hill (R) | .10 | .06 |
| 157 | Dalton Hilliard | .15 | .08 |
| 158 | Craig Heyward (R) | .20 | .12 |
| 159 | Vaughan Johnson (R) | .40 | .25 |
| 160 | Rueben Mayes | .07 | .04 |
| 161 | Gene Atkins (R) | .08 | .05 |
| 162 | Bobby Hebert | .15 | .08 |
| 163 | Rickey Jackson | .08 | .05 |
| 164 | Eric Martin | .08 | .05 |
| 165 | Giants TL (Morris) | .08 | .05 |
| 166 | Lawrence Taylor | .25 | .15 |
| 167 | Bart Oates | .05 | .02 |
| 168 | Carl Banks | .10 | .06 |
| 169 | Eric Moore (R) | .08 | .05 |
| 170 | Sheldon White (R) | .08 | .05 |
| 171 | Mark Collins (R) | .12 | .07 |
| 172 | Phil Simms | .20 | .12 |
| 173 | Jim Burt | .05 | .02 |
| 174 | Stephen Baker (R) | .25 | .15 |
| 175 | Mark Bavaro | .08 | .05 |
| 176 | Pepper Johnson | .07 | .04 |
| 177 | Lionel Manuel | .07 | .04 |
| 178 | Joe Morris | .08 | .05 |
| 179 | John Elliott (R) | .15 | .08 |
| 180 | Gary Reasons (R) | .12 | .07 |
| 181 | Seahawks TL (Krieg) | .08 | .05 |
| 182 | Brian Blades (R) | .80 | .45 |
| 183 | Steve Largent | .40 | .22 |
| 184 | Rufus Porter (R) | .20 | .12 |
| 185 | Ruben Rodriguez | .05 | .02 |
| 186 | Curt Warner | .10 | .06 |
| 187 | Paul Moyer (R) | .08 | .05 |
| 188 | Dave Krieg | .15 | .08 |
| 189 | Jacob Green | .07 | .04 |
| 190 | John L. Williams | .10 | .06 |
| 191 | Eugene Robinson (R) | .15 | .08 |
| 192 | Brian Bosworth | .08 | .05 |
| 193 | Patriots TL (Eason) | .08 | .05 |
| 194 | John Stephens (R) | .50 | .28 |
| 195 | Robert Perryman (R) | .10 | .06 |
| 196 | Andre Tippett | .08 | .05 |
| 197 | Fred Marion | .05 | .02 |
| 198 | Doug Flutie | .15 | .08 |
| 199 | Stanley Morgan | .12 | .07 |
| 200 | Johnny Rembert (R) | .12 | .07 |
| 201 | Tony Eason | .10 | .06 |
| 202 | Marvin Allen (R) | .08 | .05 |
| 203 | Raymond Clayborn | .05 | .02 |
| 204 | Irving Fryar | .08 | .05 |
| 205 | Colts TL (Chandler) | .10 | .06 |
| 206 | Eric Dickerson | .40 | .22 |
| 207 | Chris Hinton | .07 | .04 |
| 208 | Duane Bickett | .07 | .04 |
| 209 | Chris Chandler (R) | .40 | .22 |
| 210 | Jon Hand | .05 | .02 |
| 211 | Ray Donaldson | .05 | .02 |
| 212 | Dean Biasucci | .05 | .02 |
| 213 | Bill Brooks | .07 | .04 |
| 214 | Chris Goode (R) | .08 | .05 |
| 215 | Clarence Verdin (R) | .15 | .08 |
| 216 | Albert Bentley | .08 | .05 |
| 217 | Passing Leaders | .12 | .07 |
| | Wade Wilson | | |
| | Boomer Esiason | | |
| 218 | Receiving Leaders | .10 | .06 |
| | Henry Ellard | | |
| | Al Toon | | |
| 219 | Rushing Leaders | .25 | .15 |
| | Herschel Walker | | |
| | Eric Dickerson | | |
| 220 | Scoring Leaders | .07 | .04 |
| | Mike Cofer | | |
| | Scott Norwood | | |
| 221 | Interception Leaders | .07 | .04 |
| | Scott Case | | |
| | Erik McMillan | | |
| 222 | Jets TL (O'Brien) | .08 | .05 |
| 223 | Erik McMillan (R) | .20 | .12 |
| 224 | James Hasty (R) | .12 | .07 |
| 225 | Al Toon | .12 | .07 |
| 226 | John Booty (R) | .08 | .05 |
| 227 | Johnny Hector | .08 | .05 |
| 228 | Ken O'Brien | .12 | .07 |
| 229 | Marty Lyons | .05 | .02 |
| 230 | Mickey Shuler | .05 | .02 |
| 231 | Robin Cole | .05 | .02 |
| 232 | Freeman McNeil | .10 | .06 |
| 233 | Marion Barber | .05 | .02 |
| 234 | Jo Jo Townsell | .05 | .02 |
| 235 | Wesley Walker | .08 | .05 |
| 236 | Roger Vick | .05 | .02 |
| 237 | Pat Leahy | .05 | .02 |
| 238 | Broncos TL (Elway) | .10 | .06 |
| 239 | Mike Horan | .05 | .02 |
| 240 | Tony Dorsett | .25 | .15 |

| | | | |
|---|---|---|---|
| 241 | John Elway | .40 | .22 |
| 242 | Mark Jackson | .08 | .05 |
| 243 | Sammy Winder | .08 | .05 |
| 244 | Rich Karlis | .05 | .02 |
| 245 | Vance Johnson | .10 | .06 |
| 246 | Steve Sewell (R) | .12 | .07 |
| 247 | Karl Mecklenburg | .08 | .05 |
| 248 | Rulon Jones | .05 | .02 |
| 249 | Simon Fletcher (R) | .25 | .15 |
| 250 | Redskins TL (Williams) | .08 | .05 |
| 251 | Chip Lohmiller (R) | .25 | .15 |
| 252 | Jamie Morris (R) | .10 | .06 |
| 253 | Mark Rypien (R) | 2.50 | 1.40 |
| 254 | Barry Wilburn | .05 | .02 |
| 255 | Mark May (R) | .10 | .06 |
| 256 | Wilber Marshall | .20 | .12 |
| 257 | Charles Mann | .07 | .04 |
| 258 | Gary Clark | .25 | .15 |
| 259 | Doug Williams | .10 | .06 |
| 260 | Art Monk | .30 | .18 |
| 261 | Kelvin Bryant | .07 | .04 |
| 262 | Dexter Manley | .05 | .02 |
| 263 | Ricky Sanders | .10 | .06 |
| 264 | Raiders TL (Allen) | .10 | .06 |
| 265 | Tim Brown (R) | 1.00 | .60 |
| 266 | Jay Schroeder | .10 | .06 |
| 267 | Marcus Allen | .12 | .07 |
| 268 | Mike Haynes | .07 | .04 |
| 269 | Bo Jackson | .75 | .40 |
| 270 | Steve Beuerlein (R) | 1.25 | .70 |
| 271 | Vann McElroy | .05 | .02 |
| 272 | Willie Gault | .08 | .05 |
| 273 | Howie Long | .10 | .06 |
| 274 | Greg Townsend | .08 | .05 |
| 275 | Mike Wise (R) | .08 | .05 |
| 276 | Cardinals TL (Lomax) | .08 | .05 |
| 277 | Luis Sharpe | .05 | .02 |
| 278 | Scott Dill (R) | .07 | .04 |
| 279 | Vai Sikahema | .07 | .04 |
| 280 | Ron Wolfley | .05 | .02 |
| 281 | David Galloway | .05 | .02 |
| 282 | Jay Novacek (R) | 1.25 | .70 |
| 283 | Neil Lomax | .08 | .05 |
| 284 | Robert Awalt | .05 | .02 |
| 285 | Cedric Mack | .05 | .02 |
| 286 | Freddie Joe Nunn | .05 | .02 |
| 287 | J.T. Smith | .07 | .04 |
| 288 | Stump Mitchell | .08 | .05 |
| 289 | Roy Green | .10 | .06 |
| 290 | Dolphins TL (Marino) | .25 | .15 |
| 291 | Jarvis Williams (R) | .10 | .06 |
| 292 | Troy Stradford | .05 | .02 |
| 293 | Dan Marino | .75 | .40 |
| 294 | T.J. Turner | .07 | .04 |
| 295 | John Offerdahl | .10 | .06 |
| 296 | Ferrell Edmunds (R) | .15 | .08 |

| | | | |
|---|---|---|---|
| 297 | Scott Schwedes (R) | .10 | .06 |
| 298 | Lorenzo Hampton | .07 | .04 |
| 299 | Jim Jensen (R) | .12 | .07 |
| 300 | Brian Sochia (R) | .08 | .05 |
| 301 | Reggie Roby | .05 | .02 |
| 302 | Mark Clayton | .15 | .08 |
| 303 | Chargers TL (Spencer) | .07 | .04 |
| 304 | Lee Williams | .08 | .05 |
| 305 | Gary Plummer (R) | .12 | .07 |
| 306 | Gary Anderson | .08 | .05 |
| 307 | Gill Byrd | .10 | .06 |
| 308 | Jamie Holland (R) | .08 | .05 |
| 309 | Billy Ray Smith | .07 | .04 |
| 310 | Lionel James | .07 | .04 |
| 311 | Mark Vlasic (R) | .20 | .12 |
| 312 | Curtis Adams | .05 | .02 |
| 313 | Anthony Miller (R) | 1.50 | .90 |
| 314 | Steelers TL (Pollard) | .07 | .04 |
| 315 | Bubby Brister (R) | .30 | .18 |
| 316 | David Little | .05 | .02 |
| 317 | Tunch Ilkin (R) | .08 | .05 |
| 318 | Louis Lipps | .08 | .05 |
| 319 | Warren Williams (R) | .10 | .06 |
| 320 | Dwight Stone | .05 | .02 |
| 321 | Merril Hoge (R) | .25 | .15 |
| 322 | Thomas Everett (R) | .20 | .12 |
| 323 | Rod Woodson (R) | .50 | .28 |
| 324 | Gary Anderson | .05 | .02 |
| 325 | Buccaneers TL (Hall) | .07 | .04 |
| 326 | Donnie Elder (R) | .08 | .05 |
| 327 | Vinny Testaverde | .12 | .07 |
| 328 | Harry Hamilton | .05 | .02 |
| 329 | James Wilder | .08 | .05 |
| 330 | Lars Tate (R) | .10 | .06 |
| 331 | Mark Carrier (R)(TB) | .40 | .22 |
| 332 | Bruce Hill (R) | .10 | .06 |
| 333 | Paul Gruber (R) | .20 | .12 |
| 334 | Ricky Reynolds | .07 | .04 |
| 335 | Eugene Marve | .05 | .02 |
| 336 | Falcons TL (Williams) | .07 | .04 |
| 337 | Aundray Bruce (R) | .10 | .06 |
| 338 | John Rade | .05 | .02 |
| 339 | Scott Case (R) | .12 | .07 |
| 340 | Robert Moore | .05 | .02 |
| 341 | Chris Miller (R) | 1.50 | .80 |
| 342 | Gerald Riggs | .08 | .05 |
| 343 | Gene Lang (R) | .08 | .05 |
| 344 | Marcus Cotton (R) | .10 | .06 |
| 345 | Rick Donnelly | .05 | .02 |
| 346 | John Settle (R) | .12 | .07 |
| 347 | Bill Fralic | .07 | .04 |
| 348 | Chiefs TL (Hackett) | .07 | .04 |
| 349 | Steve DeBerg | .10 | .06 |
| 350 | Mike Stensrud (R) | .08 | .05 |
| 351 | Dino Hackett | .07 | .04 |
| 352 | Deron Cherry | .08 | .05 |
| 353 | Christian Okoye | .40 | .22 |

| | | | |
|---|---|---|---|
| 354 | Bill Maas | .07 | .04 |
| 355 | Carlos Carson | .07 | .04 |
| 356 | Albert Lewis | .08 | .05 |
| 357 | Paul Palmer | .05 | .02 |
| 358 | Nick Lowery | .08 | .05 |
| 359 | Stephone Paige | .08 | .05 |
| 360 | Lions TL (Long) | .07 | .04 |
| 361 | Chris Spielman (R) | .40 | .22 |
| 362 | Jim Arnold | .05 | .02 |
| 363 | Devon Mitchell | .05 | .02 |
| 364 | Mike Cofer | .05 | .02 |
| 365 | Bennie Blades (R) | .20 | .12 |
| 366 | James Jones | .05 | .02 |
| 367 | Garry James | .05 | .02 |
| 368 | Pete Mandley | .05 | .02 |
| 369 | Keith Ferguson | .05 | .02 |
| 370 | Dennis Gibson | .05 | .02 |
| 371 | Packers TL (Holland) | .07 | .04 |
| 372 | Brent Fullwood (R) | .10 | .06 |
| 373 | Don Majkowski (R) | .50 | .28 |
| 374 | Tim Harris | .08 | .05 |
| 375 | Keith Woodside (R) | .12 | .07 |
| 376 | Mark Murphy | .05 | .02 |
| 377 | Dave Brown | .05 | .02 |
| 378 | Perry Kemp (R) | .08 | .05 |
| 379 | Sterling Sharpe (R) | 4.00 | 2.25 |
| 380 | Chuck Cecil (R) | .20 | .12 |
| 381 | Walter Stanley | .05 | .02 |
| 382 | Cowboys TL (Pelluer) | .07 | .04 |
| 383 | Michael Irvin (R) | 4.00 | 2.25 |
| 384 | Bill Bates | .05 | .02 |
| 385 | Herschel Walker | .30 | .18 |
| 386 | Darryl Clack | .05 | .02 |
| 387 | Danny Noonan | .05 | .02 |
| 388 | Eugene Lockhart (R) | .10 | .06 |
| 389 | Ed Too Tall Jones | .12 | .07 |
| 390 | Steve Pelluer | .08 | .05 |
| 391 | Ray Alexander (R) | .08 | .05 |
| 392 | Nate Newton (R) | .12 | .07 |
| 393 | Garry Cobb | .05 | .02 |
| 394 | Checklist 1-132 | .08 | .02 |
| 395 | Checklist 133-264 | .08 | .02 |
| 396 | Checklist 265-396 | .08 | .02 |

# 1989 Topps Traded

This 132-card set is Topps first post-season update football set. The cards are printed on a white stock, otherwise the card design is identical to the 1989 Topps regular issue. The set consists primarily of rookies and players who changed teams during the year and the card numbers on the back carry the "T" designation. All cards measure 2-1/2" by 3-1/2".

| | | MINT | NR/MT |
|---|---|---|---|
| **Complete Set (132)** | | 9.50 | 5.75 |
| **Commons** | | .05 | .02 |
| 1T | Eric Ball (R) | .15 | .08 |
| 2T | Tony Mandarich (R) | .12 | .07 |
| 3T | Shawn Collins (R) | .12 | .07 |
| 4T | Ray Bentley (R) | .10 | .06 |
| 5T | Tony Casillas | .12 | .07 |
| 6T | Al Del Greco (R) | .07 | .04 |
| 7T | Dan Saleaumua (R) | .08 | .05 |
| 8T | Keith Bishop | .05 | .02 |
| 9T | Rodney Peete (R) | .60 | .35 |
| 10T | Lorenzo White (R) | .70 | .40 |
| 11T | Steve Smith | .12 | .07 |
| 12T | Pete Mandley | .05 | .02 |
| 13T | Mervyn Fernandez (R) | .20 | .12 |
| 14T | Flipper Anderson (R) | .40 | .22 |
| 15T | Louis Oliver (R) | .20 | .12 |
| 16T | Rick Fenney | .08 | .05 |
| 17T | Gary Jeter | .05 | .02 |
| 18T | Greg Cox | .05 | .02 |
| 19T | Bubba McDowell (R) | .12 | .07 |
| 20T | Ron Heller | .05 | .02 |
| 21T | Tim McDonald (R) | .20 | .12 |
| 22T | Jerrol Williams (R) | .12 | .07 |
| 23T | Marion Butts (R) | .80 | .50 |
| 24T | Steve Young | .60 | .35 |

| | | | |
|---|---|---|---|
| 25T | Mike Merriweather | .07 | .04 |
| 26T | Richard Johnson (R) | .08 | .05 |
| 27T | Gerald Riggs | .08 | .05 |
| 28T | Dave Waymer | .05 | .02 |
| 29T | Issiac Holt | .05 | .02 |
| 30T | Deion Sanders (R) | 1.00 | .60 |
| 31T | Todd Blackledge | .07 | .04 |
| 32T | Jeff Cross (R) | .10 | .06 |
| 33T | Steve Wisniewski (R) | .15 | .08 |
| 34T | Ron Brown | .10 | .06 |
| 35T | Rod Bernstine (R) | .30 | .18 |
| 36T | Jeff Uhlenhake (R) | .08 | .05 |
| 37T | Donnell Woolford (R) | .15 | .08 |
| 38T | Bob Gagliano (R) | .15 | .08 |
| 39T | Ezra Johnson | .05 | .02 |
| 40T | Ron Jaworski | .08 | .05 |
| 41T | Lawyer Tillman (R) | .10 | .06 |
| 42T | Lorenzo Lynch (R) | .08 | .05 |
| 43T | Mike Alexander | .05 | .02 |
| 44T | Tim Worley (R) | .15 | .08 |
| 45T | Guy Bingham (R) | .08 | .05 |
| 46T | Cleveland Gary (R) | .20 | .12 |
| 47T | Danny Peebles (R) | .05 | .02 |
| 48T | Clarence Weathers (R) | .08 | .05 |
| 49T | Jeff Lageman (R) | .15 | .08 |
| 50T | Eric Metcalf (R) | .40 | .22 |
| 51T | Myron Guyton (R) | .10 | .06 |
| 52T | Steve Atwater (R) | .50 | .28 |
| 53T | John Fourcade (R) | .10 | .06 |
| 54T | Randall McDaniel (R) | .15 | .08 |
| 55T | Al Noga (R) | .15 | .08 |
| 56T | Sammie Smith (R) | .25 | .15 |
| 57T | Jesse Solomon | .05 | .02 |
| 58T | Greg Kragen (R) | .10 | .06 |
| 59T | Don Beebe (R) | .40 | .22 |
| 60T | Hart Lee Dykes (R) | .20 | .12 |
| 61T | Trace Armstrong (R) | .15 | .08 |
| 62T | Steve Pelluer | .08 | .05 |
| 63T | Barry Krauss | .05 | .02 |
| 64T | Kevin Murphy (R) | .10 | .06 |
| 65T | Steve Tasker (R) | .20 | .12 |
| 66T | Jessie Small (R) | .10 | .06 |
| 67T | Dave Meggett (R) | .35 | .20 |
| 68T | Dean Hamel | .05 | .02 |
| 69T | Jim Covert | .08 | .05 |
| 70T | Troy Aikman (R) | 4.50 | 2.50 |
| 71T | Raul Allegre | .05 | .02 |
| 72T | Chris Jacke (R) | .08 | .05 |
| 73T | Leslie O'Neal | .08 | .05 |
| 74T | Keith Taylor (R) | .12 | .07 |
| 75T | Steve Walsh (R) | .25 | .15 |
| 76T | Tracy Rocker (R) | .12 | .07 |
| 77T | Robert Massey (R) | .15 | .08 |
| 78T | Bryan Wagner (R) | .08 | .05 |
| 79T | Steve DeOssie (R) | .10 | .06 |
| 80T | Carnell Lake (R) | .15 | .08 |
| 81T | Frank Reich (R) | .60 | .35 |
| 82T | Tyrone Braxton (R) | .15 | .08 |
| 83T | Barry Sanders (R) | 4.00 | 2.25 |
| 84T | Pete Stoyanovich (R) | .10 | .06 |
| 85T | Paul Palmer | .05 | .02 |
| 86T | Billy Joe Tolliver (R) | .25 | .15 |
| 87T | Eric Hill (R) | .10 | .06 |
| 88T | Gerald McNeil | .05 | .02 |
| 89T | Bill Hawkins (R) | .10 | .06 |
| 90T | Derrick Thomas (R) | 1.00 | .60 |
| 91T | Jim Harbaugh (R) | .50 | .28 |
| 92T | Brian Williams (R) | .10 | .06 |
| 93T | Jack Trudeau | .08 | .05 |
| 94T | Leonard Smith | .05 | .02 |
| 95T | Gary Hogeboom | .05 | .02 |
| 96T | A.J. Johnson (R) | .10 | .06 |
| 97T | Jim McMahon | .12 | .07 |
| 98T | David Williams | .07 | .04 |
| 99T | Rohn Stark | .05 | .02 |
| 100T | Sean Landeta | .05 | .02 |
| 101T | Tim Johnson (R) | .12 | .07 |
| 102T | Andre Rison (R) | 1.00 | .60 |
| 103T | Earnest Byner | .08 | .05 |
| 104T | Don McPherson (R) | .10 | .06 |
| 105T | Zefross Moss (R) | .08 | .05 |
| 106T | Frank Stams (R) | .12 | .07 |
| 107T | Courtney Hall (R) | .15 | .08 |
| 108T | Marc Logan (R) | .10 | .06 |
| 109T | James Lofton | .25 | .15 |
| 110T | Lewis Tillman (R) | .12 | .07 |
| 111T | Irv Pankey (R) | .12 | .07 |
| 112T | Ralf Mojsiejenko | .05 | .02 |
| 113T | Bobby Humphrey (R) | .30 | .18 |
| 114T | Chris Burkett | .05 | .02 |
| 115T | Greg Lloyd (R) | .12 | .07 |
| 116T | Matt Millen | .07 | .04 |
| 117T | Carl Zander | .05 | .02 |
| 118T | Wayne Martin (R) | .15 | .08 |
| 119T | Mike Saxon (R) | .08 | .05 |
| 120T | Herschel Walker | .25 | .15 |
| 121T | Andy Heck (R) | .12 | .07 |
| 122T | Mark Robinson (R) | .10 | .06 |
| 123T | Keith Van Horne (R) | .12 | .07 |
| 124T | Ricky Hunley (R) | .07 | .04 |
| 125T | Timm Rosenbach (R) | .50 | .28 |
| 126T | Steve Grogan | .08 | .05 |
| 127T | Stephen Braggs (R) | .10 | .06 |
| 128T | Terry Long (R) | .08 | .05 |
| 129T | Evan Cooper (R) | .08 | .05 |
| 130T | Robert Lyles (R) | .12 | .07 |
| 131T | Mike Webster | .08 | .05 |
| 132T | Checklist 1-132 | .07 | .02 |

# 1990 Topps

Topps increased the size of their football set to 528-cards for the first time since 1982. The card fronts consist of full color action photos with the player's name, team and position printed in a small horizontal box below the picture. A vertical lined stripe design appears in the upper and lower left corners while a horizontal stripe with small vertical lines is located across the bottom border. The Topps logo appears under a picture of a football in the bottom left corner. Card backs are vertical and contain personal data, stats and a brief highlight. Subsets include Record Breakers (RB) 91-4, League Leaders (28, 193, 229,431) and Team Leaders (TL) (501-528). All cards measure 2-1/2" by 3-1/2".

|  |  | MINT | NR/MT |
|---|---|---|---|
| **Complete Set (528)** | | 13.50 | 7.50 |
| **Commons** | | .04 | .02 |
| | | | |
| 1 | Joe Montana (RB) | .25 | .10 |
| 2 | Flipper Anderson (RB) | .08 | .05 |
| 3 | Troy Aikman (RB) | .50 | .28 |
| 4 | Kevin Butler (RB) | .06 | .03 |
| 5 | Super Bowl XXIV | .08 | .05 |
| 6 | Dexter Carter (R) | .25 | .15 |
| 7 | Matt Millen | .04 | .02 |
| 8 | Jerry Rice | .60 | .35 |
| 9 | Ronnie Lott | .12 | .07 |
| 10 | John Taylor | .12 | .07 |
| 11 | Guy McIntyre | .07 | .04 |
| 12 | Roger Criag | .10 | .06 |
| 13 | Joe Montana | .60 | .35 |
| 14 | Brent Jones (R) | .25 | .15 |
| 15 | Tom Rathman | .08 | .05 |
| 16 | Harris Barton | .04 | .02 |
| 17 | Charles Haley | .08 | .05 |
| 18 | Pierce Holt (R) | .10 | .06 |
| 19 | Michael Carter | .07 | .04 |
| 20 | Chet Brooks (R) | .08 | .05 |
| 21 | Eric Wright | .07 | .04 |
| 22 | Mike Cofer | .04 | .02 |
| 23 | Jim Fahnhorst | .04 | .02 |
| 24 | Keena Turner | .04 | .02 |
| 25 | Don Griffin | .04 | .02 |
| 26 | Kevin Fagen (R) | .08 | .05 |
| 27 | Bubba Paris | .04 | .02 |
| 28 | Rushing Leaders | .20 | .12 |
| | Barry Sanders | | |
| | Christian Okoye | | |
| 29 | Steve Atwater | .12 | .07 |
| 30 | Tyrone Braxton | .04 | .02 |
| 31 | Ron Holmes | .04 | .02 |
| 32 | Bobby Humphrey | .10 | .06 |
| 33 | Greg Kragen | .04 | .02 |
| 34 | David Treadwell | .04 | .02 |
| 35 | Karl Mecklenburg | .08 | .05 |
| 36 | Dennis Smith | .07 | .04 |
| 37 | John Elway | .25 | .15 |
| 38 | Vance Johnson | .08 | .05 |
| 39 | Simon Fletcher | .04 | .02 |
| 40 | Jim Juriga (R) | .07 | .04 |
| 41 | Mark Jackson | .08 | .05 |
| 42 | Melvin Bratton (R) | .10 | .06 |
| 43 | Wymon Henderson (R) | .08 | .05 |
| 44 | Ken Bell | .04 | .02 |
| 45 | Sammy Winder | .08 | .05 |
| 46 | Alphonso Carreker | .04 | .02 |
| 47 | Orson Mobley (R) | .08 | .05 |
| 48 | Rodney Hampton (R) | 1.00 | .60 |
| 49 | Dave Meggett | .15 | .08 |
| 50 | Myron Guyton | .04 | .02 |
| 51 | Phil Simms | .12 | .07 |
| 52 | Lawrence Taylor | .15 | .08 |
| 53 | Carl Banks | .08 | .05 |
| 54 | Pepper Johnson | .07 | .04 |
| 55 | Leonard Marshall | .07 | .04 |
| 56 | Mark Collins | .07 | .04 |
| 57 | Erik Howard | .04 | .02 |
| 58 | Eric Dorsey (R) | .10 | .06 |
| 59 | Ottis Anderson | .10 | .06 |
| 60 | Mark Bavaro | .07 | .04 |
| 61 | Odessa Turner (R) | .20 | .12 |
| 62 | Gary Reasons | .04 | .02 |
| 63 | Maurice Carthon | .04 | .02 |
| 64 | Lionel Manuel | .04 | .02 |
| 65 | Sean Landeta | .04 | .02 |
| 66 | Perry Williams | .04 | .02 |
| 67 | Pat Terrell (R) | .15 | .08 |
| 68 | Flipper Anderson | .10 | .06 |
| 69 | Jackie Slater | .08 | .05 |
| 70 | Tom Newberry | .04 | .02 |
| 71 | Jerry Gray | .04 | .02 |

| 72 | Henry Ellard | .08 | .05 |
|---|---|---|---|
| 73 | Doug Smith | .04 | .02 |
| 74 | Kevin Greene | .07 | .04 |
| 75 | Jim Everett | .15 | .08 |
| 76 | Mike Lansford | .04 | .02 |
| 77 | Greg Bell | .08 | .05 |
| 78 | Pete Holohan | .04 | .02 |
| 79 | Robert Delpino | .10 | .06 |
| 80 | Mike Witcher | .04 | .02 |
| 81 | Mike Piel (R) | .08 | .05 |
| 82 | Mel Owens | .04 | .02 |
| 83 | Michael Stewart (R) | .08 | .05 |
| 84 | Ben Smith (R) | .08 | .05 |
| 85 | Keith Jackson | .15 | .08 |
| 86 | Reggie White | .12 | .07 |
| 87 | Eric Allen | .07 | .04 |
| 88 | Jerome Brown | .07 | .04 |
| 89 | Robert Drummond | .04 | .02 |
| 90 | Anthony Toney | .04 | .02 |
| 91 | Keith Byars | .08 | .05 |
| 92 | Cris Carter | .15 | .08 |
| 93 | Randall Cunningham | .25 | .15 |
| 94 | Ron Johnson | .04 | .02 |
| 95 | Mike Quick | .08 | .05 |
| 96 | Clyde Simmons | .08 | .05 |
| 97 | Mike Pitts | .04 | .02 |
| 98 | Izel Jenkins (R) | .10 | .06 |
| 99 | Seth Joyner | .07 | .04 |
| 100 | Mike Schad (R) | .08 | .05 |
| 101 | Wes Hopkins | .04 | .02 |
| 102 | Kirk Lowdermilk | .04 | .02 |
| 103 | Rick Fenney | .04 | .02 |
| 104 | Randall McDaniel | .04 | .02 |
| 105 | Herschel Walker | .20 | .12 |
| 106 | Al Noga | .04 | .02 |
| 107 | Gary Zimmerman | .04 | .02 |
| 108 | Chris Doleman | .07 | .04 |
| 109 | Keith Millard | .07 | .04 |
| 110 | Carl Lee | .04 | .02 |
| 111 | Joey Browner | .07 | .04 |
| 112 | Steve Jordan | .04 | .02 |
| 113 | Reggie Rutland (R) | .08 | .05 |
| 114 | Wade Wilson | .08 | .05 |
| 115 | Anthony Carter | .08 | .05 |
| 116 | Rick Karlis | .04 | .02 |
| 117 | Hassan Jones | .08 | .05 |
| 118 | Henry Thomas | .04 | .02 |
| 119 | Scott Studwell | .04 | .02 |
| 120 | Ralf Mojsiejenko | .04 | .02 |
| 121 | Earnest Byner | .08 | .05 |
| 122 | Gerald Riggs | .08 | .05 |
| 123 | Tracy Rocker | .07 | .04 |
| 124 | A.J. Johnson | .04 | .02 |
| 125 | Charles Mann | .04 | .02 |
| 126 | Art Monk | .20 | .12 |
| 127 | Ricky Sanders | .08 | .05 |
| 128 | Gary Clark | .12 | .07 |
| 129 | Jim Lachey | .10 | .06 |
| 130 | Martin Mayhew (R) | .10 | .06 |
| 131 | Ravin Caldwell (R) | .08 | .05 |
| 132 | Don Warren | .04 | .02 |
| 133 | Mark Rypien | .30 | .18 |
| 134 | Ed Simmons (R) | .07 | .04 |
| 135 | Darryl Grant | .04 | .02 |
| 136 | Darrell Green | .15 | .08 |
| 137 | Chip Lohmiller | .04 | .02 |
| 138 | Tony Bennett (R) | .25 | .15 |
| 139 | Tony Mandarich | .07 | .04 |
| 140 | Sterling Sharpe | .60 | .35 |
| 141 | Tim Harris | .07 | .04 |
| 142 | Don Majkowski | .12 | .07 |
| 143 | Rich Moran (R) | .08 | .05 |
| 144 | Jeff Query (R) | .10 | .06 |
| 145 | Brent Fullwood | .07 | .04 |
| 146 | Chris Jacke | .04 | .02 |
| 147 | Keith Woodside | .04 | .02 |
| 148 | Perry Kemp | .04 | .02 |
| 149 | Herman Fontenot | .04 | .02 |
| 150 | Dave Brown | .04 | .02 |
| 151 | Brian Noble | .07 | .04 |
| 152 | Johnny Holland | .07 | .04 |
| 153 | Mark Murphy | .04 | .02 |
| 154 | Bob Nelson (R) | .08 | .05 |
| 155 | Darrell Thompson (R) | .25 | .15 |
| 156 | Lawyer Tillman | .04 | .02 |
| 157 | Eric Metcalf | .12 | .07 |
| 158 | Webster Slaughter | .10 | .06 |
| 159 | Frank Minnifield | .07 | .04 |
| 160 | Brian Brennan | .04 | .02 |
| 161 | Thane Gash (R) | .08 | .05 |
| 162 | Robert Banks (R) | .07 | .04 |
| 163 | Bernie Kosar | .15 | .08 |
| 164 | David Grayson | .04 | .02 |
| 165 | Kevin Mack | .08 | .05 |
| 166 | Mike Johnson | .04 | .02 |
| 167 | Tim Manoa (R) | .08 | .05 |
| 168 | Ozzie Newsome | .15 | .08 |
| 169 | Felix Wright | .04 | .02 |
| 170 | Bubba Baker | .04 | .02 |
| 171 | Reggie Langhorne | .04 | .02 |
| 172 | Clay Matthews | .04 | .02 |
| 173 | Andrew Stewart | .04 | .02 |
| 174 | Barry Foster (R) | 1.50 | .80 |
| 175 | Tim Worley | .08 | .05 |
| 176 | Tim Johnson | .04 | .02 |
| 177 | Carnell Lake | .07 | .04 |
| 178 | Greg Lloyd | .04 | .02 |
| 179 | Rod Woodson | .15 | .08 |
| 180 | Tunch Ilkin | .04 | .02 |
| 181 | Dermontti Dawson (R) | .08 | .05 |
| 182 | Gary Anderson | .04 | .02 |
| 183 | Bubby Brister | .12 | .07 |
| 184 | Louis Lipps | .08 | .05 |
| 185 | Merril Hoge | .08 | .05 |

| | | | |
|---|---|---|---|
| 186 Mike Mularkey (R) | .08 | .05 |
| 187 Derek Hill | .08 | .05 |
| 188 Rodney Carter | .04 | .02 |
| 189 Dwayne Woodruff | .04 | .02 |
| 190 Keith Willis | .04 | .02 |
| 191 Jerry Olsavsky (R) | .08 | .05 |
| 192 Mark Stock (R) | .07 | .04 |
| 193 Sacks Leaders | .07 | .04 |
|     Chris Doleman | | |
|     Lee Williams | | |
| 194 Leonard Smith | .04 | .02 |
| 195 Darryl Talley | .08 | .05 |
| 196 Mark Kelso | .04 | .02 |
| 197 Kent Hull | .04 | .02 |
| 198 Nate Odomes (R) | .12 | .07 |
| 199 Pete Metzelaars | .07 | .04 |
| 200 Don Beebe | .12 | .07 |
| 201 Ray Bentley | .04 | .02 |
| 202 Steve Tasker | .07 | .04 |
| 203 Scott Norwood | .04 | .02 |
| 204 Andre Reed | .15 | .08 |
| 205 Bruce Smith | .12 | .07 |
| 206 Thurman Thomas | .50 | .28 |
| 207 Jim Kelly | .35 | .20 |
| 208 Cornelius Bennett | .10 | .06 |
| 209 Shane Conlan | .08 | .05 |
| 210 Larry Kinnebrew | .04 | .02 |
| 211 Jeff Alm (R) | .08 | .05 |
| 212 Robert Lyles | .04 | .02 |
| 213 Bubba McDowell | .04 | .02 |
| 214 Mike Munchak | .07 | .04 |
| 215 Bruce Matthews | .07 | .04 |
| 216 Warren Moon | .25 | .15 |
| 217 Drew Hill | .08 | .05 |
| 218 Ray Childress | .08 | .05 |
| 219 Steve Brown | .04 | .02 |
| 220 Alonzo Highsmith | .07 | .04 |
| 221 Allen Pinkett | .08 | .05 |
| 222 Sean Jones | .04 | .02 |
| 223 Johnny Meads | .04 | .02 |
| 224 John Grimsley | .04 | .02 |
| 225 Haywood Jeffires (R) | 1.25 | .70 |
| 226 Curtis Duncan | .04 | .02 |
| 227 Greg Montgomery | .04 | .02 |
| 228 Ernest Givins | .12 | .07 |
| 229 Passsing Leaders | .25 | .15 |
|     Joe Montana | | |
|     Boomer Esiason | | |
| 230 Robert Massey | .04 | .02 |
| 231 John Fourcade | .07 | .04 |
| 232 Dalton Hilliard | .08 | .05 |
| 233 Vaughan Johnson | .07 | .04 |
| 234 Hoby Brenner | .04 | .02 |
| 235 Pat Swilling | .12 | .07 |
| 236 Kevin Haverdink (R) | .08 | .05 |
| 237 Bobby Hebert | .15 | .08 |
| 238 Sam Mills | .08 | .05 |
| 239 Eric Martin | .08 | .05 |
| 240 Lonzell Hill | .08 | .05 |
| 241 Steve Trapilo (R) | .08 | .05 |
| 242 Rickey Jackson | .08 | .05 |
| 243 Craig Heyward | .08 | .05 |
| 244 Rueben Mayes | .07 | .04 |
| 245 Morten Andersen | .08 | .05 |
| 246 Percy Snow (R) | .15 | .08 |
| 247 Pete Mandley | .04 | .02 |
| 248 Derrick Thomas | .30 | .18 |
| 249 Dan Saleaumua | .04 | .02 |
| 250 Todd McNair (R) | .10 | .06 |
| 251 Leonard Griffin (R) | .07 | .04 |
| 252 Jonathan Hayes | .04 | .02 |
| 253 Christian Okoye | .12 | .07 |
| 254 Albert Lewis | .07 | .04 |
| 255 Nick Lowery | .07 | .04 |
| 256 Kevin Ross | .04 | .02 |
| 257 Steve DeBerg | .10 | .06 |
| 258 Stephone Paige | .07 | .04 |
| 259 James Saxon (R) | .08 | .05 |
| 260 Herman Heard | .04 | .02 |
| 261 Deron Cherry | .07 | .04 |
| 262 Dino Hackett | .04 | .02 |
| 263 Neil Smith | .08 | .05 |
| 264 Steve Pelluer | .07 | .04 |
| 265 Eric Thomas | .04 | .02 |
| 266 Eric Ball | .07 | .04 |
| 267 Leon White | .04 | .02 |
| 268 Tim Krumrie | .07 | .04 |
| 269 Jason Buck | .07 | .04 |
| 270 Boomer Esiason | .15 | .08 |
| 271 Carl Zander | .04 | .02 |
| 272 Eddie Brown | .08 | .05 |
| 273 David Fulcher | .04 | .02 |
| 274 Tim McGee | .07 | .04 |
| 275 James Brooks | .08 | .05 |
| 276 Rickey Dixon (R) | .12 | .07 |
| 277 Ickey Woods | .07 | .04 |
| 278 Anthony Munoz | .10 | .06 |
| 279 Rodney Holman | .07 | .04 |
| 280 Mike Alexander | .04 | .02 |
| 281 Mervyn Fernandez | .08 | .05 |
| 282 Steve Wisniewski | .04 | .02 |
| 283 Steve Smith | .04 | .02 |
| 284 Howie Long | .08 | .05 |
| 285 Bo Jackson | .35 | .20 |
| 286 Mike Dyal (R) | .07 | .04 |
| 287 Thomas Benson | .04 | .02 |
| 288 Willie Gault | .07 | .04 |
| 289 Marcus Allen | .12 | .07 |
| 290 Greg Townsend | .07 | .04 |
| 291 Steve Beuerlein | .20 | .12 |
| 292 Scott Davis (R) | .07 | .04 |
| 293 Eddie Anderson (R) | .12 | .07 |
| 294 Terry McDaniel | .07 | .04 |
| 295 Tim Brown | .15 | .08 |

| | | | |
|---|---|---|---|
| 296 Bob Golic | .04 | .02 |
| 297 Jeff Jaeger (R) | .07 | .04 |
| 298 Jeff George (R) | 1.00 | .60 |
| 299 Chip Banks | .07 | .04 |
| 300 Andre Rison | .25 | .15 |
| 301 Rohn Stark | .04 | .02 |
| 302 Keith Taylor | .04 | .02 |
| 303 Jack Trudeau | .08 | .05 |
| 304 Chris Hinton | .07 | .04 |
| 305 Ray Donaldson (R) | .04 | .02 |
| 306 Jeff Herrod (R) | .08 | .05 |
| 307 Clarence Verdin | .08 | .05 |
| 308 Jon Hand | .04 | .02 |
| 309 Bill Brooks | .04 | .02 |
| 310 Albert Bentley | .07 | .04 |
| 311 Mike Prior | .04 | .02 |
| 312 Pat Beach | .04 | .02 |
| 313 Eugene Daniel | .04 | .02 |
| 314 Duane Beckett | .04 | .02 |
| 315 Dean Biasucci | .04 | .02 |
| 316 Richmond Webb (R) | .20 | .12 |
| 317 Jeff Cross | .04 | .02 |
| 318 Louis Oliver | .08 | .05 |
| 319 Sammie Smith | .08 | .05 |
| 320 Pete Stoyanovich | .04 | .02 |
| 321 John Offerdahl | .08 | .05 |
| 322 Ferrell Edmunds | .04 | .02 |
| 323 Dan Marino | .40 | .22 |
| 324 Andre Brown (R) | .07 | .04 |
| 325 Reggie Roby | .04 | .02 |
| 326 Jarvis Williams | .04 | .02 |
| 327 Roy Foster | .04 | .02 |
| 328 Mark Clayton | .12 | .07 |
| 329 Brian Sochia | .04 | .02 |
| 330 Mark Duper | .08 | .05 |
| 331 T.J. Turner | .04 | .02 |
| 332 Jeff Uhlenhake | .04 | .02 |
| 333 Jim Jensen | .04 | .02 |
| 334 Cortez Kennedy (R) | .80 | .50 |
| 335 Andy Heck | .04 | .02 |
| 336 Rufus Porter | .04 | .02 |
| 337 Brian Blades | .08 | .05 |
| 338 Dave Krieg | .10 | .06 |
| 339 John L. Williams | .08 | .05 |
| 340 David Wyman | .04 | .02 |
| 341 Paul Skansi (R) | .08 | .05 |
| 342 Eugene Robinson | .07 | .04 |
| 343 Joe Nash | .04 | .02 |
| 344 Jacob Green | .07 | .04 |
| 345 Jeff Bryant | .04 | .02 |
| 346 Ruben Rodriguez | .04 | .02 |
| 347 Norm Johnson | .04 | .02 |
| 348 Darren Comeaux (R) | .07 | .04 |
| 349 Andre Ware (R) | .45 | .25 |
| 350 Richard Johnson | .04 | .02 |
| 351 Rodney Peete | .20 | .12 |
| 352 Barry Sanders | 1.00 | .60 |
| 353 Chris Spielman | .10 | .06 |
| 354 Eddie Murray | .04 | .02 |
| 355 Jerry Ball | .07 | .04 |
| 356 Mel Gray | .08 | .05 |
| 357 Eric Williams (R) | .08 | .05 |
| 358 Robert Clark (R) | .15 | .08 |
| 359 Jason Phillips (R) | .08 | .05 |
| 360 Terry Taylor (R) | .08 | .05 |
| 361 Bennie Blades | .08 | .05 |
| 362 Michael Cofer | .04 | .02 |
| 363 Jim Arnold | .04 | .02 |
| 364 Marc Spindler (R) | .12 | .07 |
| 365 Jim Covert | .07 | .04 |
| 366 Jim Harbaugh | .15 | .08 |
| 367 Neal Anderson | .15 | .08 |
| 368 Mike Singletary | .15 | .08 |
| 369 John Roper (R) | .10 | .06 |
| 370 Steve McMichael | .07 | .04 |
| 371 Dennis Gentry | .04 | .02 |
| 372 Brad Muster | .07 | .04 |
| 373 Ron Morris | .04 | .02 |
| 374 James Thornton | .04 | .02 |
| 375 Kevin Butler | .04 | .02 |
| 376 Richard Dent | .08 | .05 |
| 377 Dan Hampton | .08 | .05 |
| 378 Jay Hilgenberg | .04 | .02 |
| 379 Donnell Woolford | .04 | .02 |
| 380 Trace Armstrong | .04 | .02 |
| 381 Junior Seau (R) | .80 | .50 |
| 382 Rod Bernstine | .10 | .06 |
| 383 Marion Butts | .12 | .07 |
| 384 Burt Grossman | .08 | .05 |
| 385 Darrin Nelson | .04 | .02 |
| 386 Leslie O'Neal | .08 | .05 |
| 387 Billy Joe Tolliver | .10 | .06 |
| 388 Courtney Hall | .04 | .02 |
| 389 Lee Williams | .04 | .02 |
| 390 Anthony Miller | .25 | .15 |
| 391 Gill Byrd | .07 | .04 |
| 392 Wayne Walker (R) | .08 | .05 |
| 393 Billy Ray Smith | .07 | .04 |
| 394 Vencie Glenn | .04 | .02 |
| 395 Tim Spencer | .04 | .02 |
| 396 Gary Plummer | .04 | .02 |
| 397 Arthur Cox | .07 | .04 |
| 398 Jamie Holland | .04 | .02 |
| 399 Keith McCants (R) | .25 | .15 |
| 400 Kevin Murphy | .04 | .02 |
| 401 Danny Peebles | .04 | .02 |
| 402 Mark Robinson | .04 | .02 |
| 403 Broderick Thomas (R) | .10 | .06 |
| 404 Ron Hall | .04 | .02 |
| 405 Mark Carrier (TB) | .10 | .06 |
| 406 Paul Gruber | .07 | .04 |
| 407 Vinny Testaverde | .12 | .07 |
| 408 Bruce Hill | .04 | .02 |
| 409 Lars Tate | .04 | .02 |

| | | | | | | |
|---|---|---|---|---|---|---|
| 410 | Harry Hamilton | .04 | .02 | 465 | Pat Leahy | .04 | .02 |
| 411 | Ricky Reynolds | .04 | .02 | 466 | Scott Case | .04 | .02 |
| 412 | Donald Igwebuike | .04 | .02 | 467 | Shawn Collins | .04 | .02 |
| 413 | Reuben Davis (R) | .08 | .05 | 468 | Floyd Dixon | .04 | .02 |
| 414 | William Howard (R) | .08 | .05 | 469 | Deion Sanders | .30 | .18 |
| 415 | Winston Moss (R) | .12 | .07 | 470 | Tony Casillas | .08 | .05 |
| 416 | Chris Singleton (R) | .15 | .08 | 471 | Michael Haynes (R) | .80 | .45 |
| 417 | Hart Lee Dykes | .08 | .05 | 472 | Chris Miller | .30 | .18 |
| 418 | Steve Grogan | .08 | .05 | 473 | John Settle | .07 | .04 |
| 419 | Bruce Armstrong | .04 | .02 | 474 | Aundray Bruce | .07 | .04 |
| 420 | Robert Perryman | .04 | .02 | 475 | Gene Lang | .04 | .02 |
| 421 | Andre Tippett | .08 | .05 | 476 | Tim Gordon (R) | .08 | .05 |
| 422 | Sammy Martin (R) | .10 | .06 | 477 | Scott Fulhage | .04 | .02 |
| 423 | Stanley Morgan | .10 | .06 | 478 | Bill Fralic | .07 | .04 |
| 424 | Cedric Jones | .07 | .04 | 479 | Jessie Tuggle (R) | .12 | .07 |
| 425 | Sean Farrell | .04 | .02 | 480 | Marcus Cotton | .04 | .02 |
| 426 | Marc Wilson | .07 | .04 | 481 | Steve Walsh | .10 | .06 |
| 427 | John Stephens | .10 | .06 | 482 | Troy Aikman | 1.50 | .80 |
| 428 | Eric Sievers (R) | .08 | .05 | 483 | Ray Horton | .04 | .02 |
| 429 | Maurice Hurst (R) | .12 | .07 | 484 | Tony Tolbert (R) | .10 | .06 |
| 430 | Johnny Rembert | .04 | .02 | 485 | Steve Folsom | .04 | .02 |
| 431 | Receiving Leaders | .25 | .15 | 486 | Ken Norton (R) | .20 | .12 |
| | Jerry Rice | | | 487 | Kelvin Martin (R) | .25 | .15 |
| | Andre Reed | | | 488 | Jack Del Rio | .07 | .04 |
| 432 | Eric Hill | .07 | .04 | 489 | Daryl Johnston (R) | .15 | .08 |
| 433 | Gary Hogeboom | .04 | .02 | 490 | Bill Bates | .07 | .04 |
| 434 | Timm Rosenbach | .15 | .08 | 491 | Jim Jeffcoat | .07 | .04 |
| 435 | Tim McDonald | .07 | .04 | 492 | Vince Albritton | .04 | .02 |
| 436 | Rich Camarillo | .04 | .02 | 493 | Eugene Lockhart | .04 | .02 |
| 437 | Luis Sharpe | .04 | .02 | 494 | Mike Saxon | .04 | .02 |
| 438 | J.T. Smith | .07 | .04 | 495 | James Dixon (R) | .08 | .05 |
| 439 | Roy Green | .08 | .05 | 496 | Willie Broughton (R) | .08 | .05 |
| 440 | Ernie Jones (R) | .20 | .12 | 497 | Checklist 1-132 | .06 | .02 |
| 441 | Robert Awalt | .04 | .02 | 498 | Checklist 133-264 | .06 | .02 |
| 442 | Vai Sikahema | .04 | .02 | 499 | Checklist 265-396 | .06 | .02 |
| 443 | Joe Wolf | .04 | .02 | 500 | Checklist 397-528 | .06 | .02 |
| 444 | Stump Mitchell | .07 | .04 | 501 | Bears TL (Harbaugh) | .07 | .04 |
| 445 | David Galloway | .04 | .02 | 502 | Bengals TL (Esiason) | .08 | .05 |
| 446 | Ron Wolfley | .04 | .02 | 503 | Bills TL (Conlan) | .07 | .04 |
| 447 | Freddie Joe Nunn | .04 | .02 | 504 | Broncos TL (Bratton) | .05 | .02 |
| 448 | Blair Thomas (R) | .45 | .25 | 505 | Browns TL (Kosar) | .08 | .05 |
| 449 | Jeff Lageman | .08 | .05 | 506 | Buccaneers TL (Moss) | .05 | .02 |
| 450 | Tony Eason | .08 | .05 | 507 | Cardinals TL (Zordich) | .05 | .02 |
| 451 | Erik McMillan | .04 | .02 | 508 | Chargers TL (Williams) | .05 | .02 |
| 452 | Jim Sweeney | .04 | .02 | 509 | Chiefs TL (Cherry) | .05 | .02 |
| 453 | Ken O'Brien | .10 | .06 | 510 | Colts TL (Trudeau) | .05 | .02 |
| 454 | Johnny Hector | .07 | .04 | 511 | Cowboys TL (Aikman) | .25 | .15 |
| 455 | Jo Jo Townsell | .04 | .02 | 512 | Dolphins TL (Oliver) | .07 | .04 |
| 456 | Roger Vick | .04 | .02 | 513 | Eagles TL (Toney) | .05 | .02 |
| 457 | James Hasty | .04 | .02 | 514 | Falcons TL (Tuggle) | .05 | .02 |
| 458 | Dennis Byrd (R) | .15 | .08 | 515 | 49ers TL (Montana) | .20 | .12 |
| 459 | Ron Stallworth (R) | .07 | .04 | 516 | Giants TL (Simms) | .08 | .05 |
| 460 | Mickey Shuler | .04 | .02 | 517 | Jets TL (Hasty) | .05 | .02 |
| 461 | Bobby Humphery | .04 | .02 | 518 | Lions TL (Gagliano) | .05 | .02 |
| 462 | Kyle Clifton | .04 | .02 | 519 | Oilers TL (Moon) | .10 | .06 |
| 463 | Al Toon | .10 | .06 | 520 | Packers TL(Majkowski) | .07 | .04 |
| 464 | Freeman McNeil | .08 | .05 | 521 | Patriots TL (Stephens) | .07 | .04 |

| | | | |
|---|---|---|---|
| 522 | Raiders TL (Bo Jackson) | .10 | .06 |
| 523 | Rams TL (Everett) | .08 | .05 |
| 524 | Redskins TL (Riggs) | .07 | .04 |
| 525 | Saints TL (Mills) | .05 | .02 |
| 526 | Seahawks TL (Feasel) | .05 | .02 |
| 527 | Steelers TL (Brister) | .07 | .04 |
| 528 | Vikings TL (Fenney) | .05 | .02 |

# 1990 Topps Traded

This 132-card update set consists of rookies and players who changed team during the year. The set was issued as a box set and the cards are nearly identical to Topps regular 1990 issue except for the "T" designation next to the card numbers on the card backs. All cards measure 2-1/2" by 3-1/2".

| | MINT | NR/MT |
|---|---|---|
| **Complete Set (132)** | 12.00 | 7.00 |
| **Commons** | .05 | .02 |

| | | | |
|---|---|---|---|
| 1T | Gerald McNeil | .06 | .03 |
| 2T | Andre Rison | .25 | .15 |
| 3T | Steve Walsh | .10 | .06 |
| 4T | Lorenzo White | .25 | .15 |
| 5T | Max Montoya | .05 | .02 |
| 6T | William Roberts (R) | .08 | .05 |
| 7T | Alonzo Highsmith | .07 | .04 |
| 8T | Chris Hinton | .08 | .05 |
| 9T | Stanley Morgan | .12 | .07 |
| 10T | Mickey Shuler | .05 | .02 |
| 11T | Bobby Humphery | .05 | .02 |
| 12T | Gary Anderson | .07 | .04 |
| 13T | Mike Tomczak | .08 | .05 |

| | | | |
|---|---|---|---|
| 14T | Anthony Pleasant (R) | .10 | .06 |
| 15T | Walter Stanley | .05 | .02 |
| 16T | Greg Bell | .08 | .05 |
| 17T | Tony Martin (R) | .08 | .05 |
| 18T | Terry Kinard | .05 | .02 |
| 19T | Cris Carter | .15 | .08 |
| 20T | James Wilder | .07 | .04 |
| 21T | Jerry Kauric (R) | .08 | .05 |
| 22T | Irving Fryar | .08 | .05 |
| 23T | Ken Harvey (R) | .15 | .08 |
| 24T | James Williams (R) | .10 | .06 |
| 25T | Ron Cox (R) | .10 | .06 |
| 26T | Andre Ware | .25 | .15 |
| 27T | Emmitt Smith (R) | 8.50 | 4.75 |
| 28T | Junior Seau | .35 | .20 |
| 29T | Mark Carrier (R) (Chi) | .35 | .20 |
| 30T | Rodney Hampton | 1.00 | .60 |
| 31T | Rob Moore (R) | .75 | .40 |
| 32T | Bern Brostek (R) | .10 | .06 |
| 33T | Dexter Carter | .15 | .08 |
| 34T | Blair Thomas | .30 | .18 |
| 35T | Harold Green (R) | .80 | .45 |
| 36T | Darrell Thompson | .15 | .08 |
| 37T | Eric Green (R) | .50 | .28 |
| 38T | Renaldo Turnbull (R) | .20 | .12 |
| 39T | Leroy Hoard (R) | .30 | .18 |
| 40T | Anthony Thompson (R) | .25 | .15 |
| 41T | Jeff George | 1.00 | .60 |
| 42T | Alexander Wright (R) | .25 | .15 |
| 43T | Richmond Webb | .20 | .12 |
| 44T | Cortez Kennedy | .35 | .20 |
| 45T | Ray Agnew (R) | .15 | .08 |
| 46T | Percy Snow | .12 | .07 |
| 47T | Chris Singleton | .10 | .06 |
| 48T | James Francis (R) | .30 | .18 |
| 49T | Tony Bennett | .12 | .07 |
| 50T | Reggie Cobb (R) | .80 | .45 |
| 51T | Barry Foster | 2.00 | 1.10 |
| 52T | Ben Smith | .07 | .04 |
| 53T | Anthony Smith (R) | .20 | .12 |
| 54T | Steve Christie (R) | .20 | .12 |
| 55T | Johnny Bailey (R) | .20 | .12 |
| 56T | Alan Grant (R) | .10 | .06 |
| 57T | Eric Floyd (R) | .10 | .06 |
| 58T | Robert Blackmon (R) | .12 | .07 |
| 59T | Brent Williams | .05 | .02 |
| 60T | Raymond Clayborn | .05 | .02 |
| 61T | Dave Duerson | .05 | .02 |
| 62T | Derrick Fenner (R) | .35 | .20 |
| 63T | Ken Willis (R) | .10 | .06 |
| 64T | Brad Baxter (R) | .40 | .22 |
| 65T | Tony Paige | .07 | .04 |
| 66T | Jay Schroeder | .10 | .06 |
| 67T | Jim Breech | .05 | .02 |
| 68T | Barry Word (R) | .60 | .35 |
| 69T | Anthony Dilweg | .12 | .07 |
| 70T | Rich Gannon (R) | .60 | .35 |

| | | | |
|---|---|---|---|
| 71T | Stan Humphries (R) | 1.75 | 1.00 |
| 72T | Jay Novacek | .40 | .25 |
| 73T | Tommy Kane (R) | .25 | .15 |
| 74T | Everson Walls | .05 | .02 |
| 75T | Mike Rozier | .07 | .04 |
| 76T | Robb Thomas (R) | .20 | .12 |
| 77T | Terance Mathis (R) | .35 | .20 |
| 78T | LeRoy Irvin | .07 | .04 |
| 79T | Jeff Donaldson | .05 | .02 |
| 80T | Ethan Horton (R) | .25 | .15 |
| 81T | J.B. Brown (R) | .10 | .06 |
| 82T | Joe Kelly | .05 | .02 |
| 83T | John Carney (R) | .08 | .05 |
| 84T | Dan Stryzinski (R) | .10 | .06 |
| 85T | John Kidd | .05 | .02 |
| 86T | Al Smith | .10 | .06 |
| 87T | Travis McNeal (R) | .10 | .06 |
| 88T | Reyna Thompson (R) | .12 | .07 |
| 89T | Rick Donnelly | .05 | .02 |
| 90T | Marv Cook (R) | .25 | .15 |
| 91T | Mike Farr (R) | .10 | .06 |
| 92T | Daniel Stubbs | .05 | .02 |
| 93T | Jeff Campbell (R) | .15 | .08 |
| 94T | Tim McKyer | .07 | .04 |
| 95T | Ian Beckles (R) | .10 | .06 |
| 96T | Lemuel Stinson | .07 | .04 |
| 97T | Frank Cornish (R) | .10 | .06 |
| 98T | Riki Ellison | .07 | .04 |
| 99T | Jamie Mueller (R) | .10 | .06 |
| 100T | Brian Hansen | .05 | .02 |
| 101T | Warren Powers (R) | .10 | .06 |
| 102T | Howard Cross (R) | .12 | .07 |
| 103T | Tim Grunhard (R) | .12 | .07 |
| 104T | Johnny Johnson (R) | .60 | .35 |
| 105T | Calvin Williams (R) | .50 | .28 |
| 106T | Keith McCants (R) | .12 | .07 |
| 107T | Lamar Lathon (R) | .20 | .12 |
| 108T | Steve Broussard (R) | .25 | .15 |
| 109T | Glenn Parker (R) | .10 | .06 |
| 110T | Alton Montgomery (R) | .12 | .07 |
| 111T | Jim McMahon | .12 | .07 |
| 112T | Aaron Wallace (R) | .25 | .15 |
| 113T | Keith Sims (R) | .12 | .07 |
| 114T | Ervin Randle | .05 | .02 |
| 115T | Walter Wilson | .07 | .04 |
| 116T | Terry Wooden (R) | .12 | .07 |
| 117T | Bernard Clark (R) | .10 | .06 |
| 118T | Tony Stargell (R) | .12 | .07 |
| 119T | Jimmie Jones (R) | .15 | .08 |
| 120T | Andre Collins (R) | .25 | .15 |
| 121T | Ricky Proehl (R) | .35 | .20 |
| 122T | Darion Conner (R) | .20 | .12 |
| 123T | Jeff Rutledge | .10 | .06 |
| 124T | Heath Sherman (R) | .30 | .18 |
| 125T | Tommie Agee (R) | .12 | .07 |
| 126T | Tory Epps (R) | .12 | .07 |
| 127T | Tommy Hodson (R) | .25 | .15 |
| 128T | Jessie Hester (R) | .20 | .12 |
| 129T | Alfred Oglesby (R) | .10 | .06 |
| 130T | Chris Chandler | .15 | .08 |
| 131T | Fred Barnett (R) | 1.00 | .60 |
| 132T | Checklist | .05 | .01 |

# 1991 Topps

At 660-cards this is Topps largest football set to date. Card fronts feature full color photos with the player's name and position located below the photograph. The team name is superimposed in the bottom corner of the photograph. Card backs contain personal data, stats and highlights. Key subsets include Highlights (HL) (2-7), League Leaders (8-12) and Team Leaders (TL) (628-655). All cards measure 2-1/2" by 3-1/2".

| | | MINT | NR/MT |
|---|---|---|---|
| Complete Set (660) | | 16.00 | 9.50 |
| Commons | | .04 | .02 |

| | | | |
|---|---|---|---|
| 1 | Super Bowl XXV | .10 | .06 |
| 2 | Roger Craig (HL) | .07 | .04 |
| 3 | Derrick Thomas (HL) | .10 | .06 |
| 4 | Pete Stoyanovich (HL) | .05 | .02 |
| 5 | Ottis Anderson (HL) | .07 | .04 |
| 6 | Jerry Rice (HL) | .20 | .12 |
| 7 | Warren Moon (HL) | .10 | .06 |
| 8 | Passing leaders | .10 | .06 |
| | Warren Moon | | |
| | Jim Everett | | |
| 9 | Rushing Leaders | .25 | .15 |
| | Barry Sanders | | |
| | Thurman Thomas | | |

| | | | |
|---|---|---|---|
| 10 | Receiving Leaders | .25 | .15 |
| | Jerry Rice | | |
| | Haywood Jeffires | | |
| 11 | Interception Leaders | .07 | .04 |
| | Mark Carrier | | |
| 12 | Sacks Leaders | .10 | .06 |
| | Derrick Thomas | | |
| | Charles Haley | | |
| 13 | Jumbo Elliott | .04 | .02 |
| 14 | Leoanrd Marshall | .07 | .04 |
| 15 | William Roberts | .04 | .02 |
| 16 | Lawrence Taylor | .15 | .08 |
| 17 | Mark Ingram | .07 | .04 |
| 18 | Rodney Hampton | .45 | .25 |
| 19 | Carl Banks | .08 | .05 |
| 20 | Ottis Anderson | .08 | .05 |
| 21 | Mark Collins | .04 | .02 |
| 22 | Pepper Johnson | .04 | .02 |
| 23 | Dave Meggett | .12 | .07 |
| 24 | Reyna Thompson | .07 | .04 |
| 25 | Stephen Baker | .07 | .04 |
| 26 | Mike Fox | .04 | .02 |
| 27 | Maurice Carthon | .04 | .02 |
| 28 | Jeff Hostetler (R) | .20 | .12 |
| 29 | Greg Jackson (R) | .08 | .05 |
| 30 | Sean Landeta | .04 | .02 |
| 31 | Bart Oates | .04 | .02 |
| 32 | Phil Simms | .12 | .07 |
| 33 | Erik Howard | .04 | .02 |
| 34 | Myron Guyton | .04 | .02 |
| 35 | Mark Bavaro | .07 | .04 |
| 36 | Jarrod Bunch (R) | .25 | .15 |
| 37 | Will Wolford | .04 | .02 |
| 38 | Ray Bentley | .04 | .02 |
| 39 | Nate Odomes | .04 | .02 |
| 40 | Scott Norwood | .04 | .02 |
| 41 | Darryl Talley | .08 | .05 |
| 42 | Carwell Gardner | .04 | .02 |
| 43 | James Lofton | .20 | .12 |
| 44 | Shane Conlan | .08 | .05 |
| 45 | Steve Tasker | .04 | .02 |
| 46 | James Williams | .04 | .02 |
| 47 | Kent Hull | .04 | .02 |
| 48 | Al Edwards (R) | .10 | .06 |
| 49 | Frank Reich | .10 | .06 |
| 50 | Leon Seals | .07 | .04 |
| 51 | Keith McKeller | .08 | .05 |
| 52 | Thurman Thomas | .60 | .35 |
| 53 | Leonard Smith | .04 | .02 |
| 54 | Andre Reed | .12 | .07 |
| 55 | Kenneth Davis | .10 | .06 |
| 56 | Jeff Wright (R) | .12 | .07 |
| 57 | Jamie Mueller | .04 | .02 |
| 58 | Jim Ritcher | .04 | .02 |
| 59 | Bruce Smith | .12 | .07 |
| 60 | Ted Washington (R) | .12 | .07 |
| 61 | Guy McIntyre | .04 | .02 |
| 62 | Michael Carter | .04 | .02 |
| 63 | Pierce Holt | .04 | .02 |
| 64 | Darryl Pollard | .04 | .02 |
| 65 | Mike Sherrard | .08 | .05 |
| 66 | Dexter Carter | .10 | .06 |
| 67 | Bubba Paris | .04 | .02 |
| 68 | Harry Sydney (R) | .08 | .05 |
| 69 | Tom Rathman | .08 | .05 |
| 70 | Jesse Sapolu | .04 | .02 |
| 71 | Mike Cofer | .04 | .02 |
| 72 | Keith DeLong | .07 | .04 |
| 73 | Joe Montana | .60 | .35 |
| 74 | Bill Romanowski | .04 | .02 |
| 75 | John Taylor | .15 | .08 |
| 76 | Brent Jones | .08 | .05 |
| 77 | Harris Barton | .04 | .02 |
| 78 | Charles Haley | .08 | .05 |
| 79 | Eric Davis | .04 | .02 |
| 80 | Kevin Fagan | .04 | .02 |
| 81 | Jerry Rice | .40 | .22 |
| 82 | Dave Waymer | .04 | .02 |
| 83 | Todd Marinovich (R) | .80 | .45 |
| 84 | Steve Smith | .07 | .04 |
| 85 | Tim Brown | .12 | .07 |
| 86 | Ethan Horton | .10 | .06 |
| 87 | Marcus Allen | .10 | .06 |
| 88 | Terry McDaniel | .04 | .02 |
| 89 | Thomas Benson | .04 | .02 |
| 90 | Roger Craig | .08 | .05 |
| 91 | Don Mosebar | .04 | .02 |
| 92 | Aaron Wallace | .08 | .05 |
| 93 | Eddie Anderson | .04 | .02 |
| 94 | Willie Gault | .07 | .04 |
| 95 | Howie Long | .08 | .05 |
| 96 | Jay Schroeder | .10 | .06 |
| 97 | Ronnie Lott | .10 | .06 |
| 98 | Bob Golic | .04 | .02 |
| 99 | Bo Jackson | .25 | .15 |
| 100 | Max Montoya | .04 | .02 |
| 101 | Scott Davis | .04 | .02 |
| 102 | Greg Townsend | .07 | .04 |
| 103 | Garry Lewis | .04 | .02 |
| 104 | Mervyn Fernandez | .08 | .05 |
| 105 | Steve Wisniewski | .04 | .02 |
| 106 | Jeff Jaeger | .04 | .02 |
| 107 | Nick Bell (R) | .60 | .35 |
| 108 | Mark Dennis (R) | .08 | .05 |
| 109 | Jarvis Williams | .04 | .02 |
| 110 | Mark Clayton | .12 | .07 |
| 111 | Harry Galbreath | .04 | .02 |
| 112 | Dan Marino | .35 | .20 |
| 113 | Louis Oliver | .07 | .04 |
| 114 | Pete Stoyanovich | .04 | .02 |
| 115 | Ferrell Edmunds | .04 | .02 |
| 116 | Jeff Cross | .04 | .02 |
| 117 | Ricmond Webb | .07 | .04 |
| 118 | Jim Jensen | .04 | .02 |

| # | Player | | | # | Player | | |
|---|--------|---|---|---|--------|---|---|
| 119 | Keith Sims | .04 | .02 | 176 | Mike Singletary | .12 | .07 |
| 120 | Mark Duper | .08 | .05 | 177 | Chris Zorich (R) | .20 | .12 |
| 121 | Shawn Lee (R) | .08 | .05 | 178 | Gerald Riggs | .08 | .05 |
| 122 | Reggie Roby | .04 | .02 | 179 | Jeff Bostic | .04 | .02 |
| 123 | Jeff Uhlenhake | .04 | .02 | 180 | Kurt Gouveia (R) | .10 | .06 |
| 124 | Sammie Smith | .08 | .05 | 181 | Stan Humphries | .60 | .35 |
| 125 | John Offerdahl | .07 | .04 | 182 | Chip Lohmiller | .04 | .02 |
| 126 | Hugh Green | .07 | .04 | 183 | Raleigh McKenzie (R) | .08 | .05 |
| 127 | Tony Paige | .07 | .04 | 184 | Alvin Walton | .07 | .04 |
| 128 | David Griggs | .04 | .02 | 185 | Earnest Byner | .08 | .05 |
| 129 | J.B. Brown | .04 | .02 | 186 | Markus Koch | .07 | .04 |
| 130 | Harvey Williams (R) | .60 | .35 | 187 | Art Monk | .15 | .08 |
| 131 | John Alt | .04 | .02 | 188 | Ed Simmons | .04 | .02 |
| 132 | Albert Lewis | .07 | .04 | 189 | Bobby Wilson (R) | .10 | .06 |
| 133 | Robb Thomas | .08 | .05 | 190 | Charles Mann | .04 | .02 |
| 134 | Neil Smith | .07 | .04 | 191 | Darrell Green | .12 | .07 |
| 135 | Stephone Paige | .08 | .05 | 192 | Mark Rypien | .20 | .12 |
| 136 | Nick Lowery | .08 | .05 | 193 | Ricky Sanders | .07 | .04 |
| 137 | Steve DeBerg | .08 | .05 | 194 | Jim Lachey | .07 | .04 |
| 138 | Rich Baldinger (R) | .08 | .05 | 195 | Martin Mayhew | .04 | .02 |
| 139 | Percy Snow | .08 | .05 | 196 | Gary Clark | .15 | .08 |
| 140 | Kevin Porter | .04 | .02 | 197 | Wilber Marshall | .07 | .04 |
| 141 | Chris Martin | .04 | .02 | 198 | Darryl Grant | .04 | .02 |
| 142 | Deron Cherry | .07 | .04 | 199 | Don Warren | .07 | .04 |
| 143 | Derrick Thomas | .25 | .15 | 200 | Ricky Ervins (R) | .75 | .40 |
| 144 | Tim Grunhard | .04 | .02 | 201 | Eric Allen | .04 | .02 |
| 145 | Todd McNair | .04 | .02 | 202 | Anthony Toney | .04 | .02 |
| 146 | David Szott (R) | .08 | .05 | 203 | Ben Smith | .04 | .02 |
| 147 | Dan Saleaumua | .04 | .02 | 204 | David Alexander | .04 | .02 |
| 148 | Johathan Hayes | .04 | .02 | 205 | Jerome Brown | .07 | .04 |
| 149 | Christian Okoye | .10 | .06 | 206 | Mike Golic | .04 | .02 |
| 150 | Dino Hackett | .04 | .02 | 207 | Roger Ruzek | .04 | .02 |
| 151 | Bryan Barker (R) | .08 | .05 | 208 | Andre Waters | .04 | .02 |
| 152 | Kevin Ross | .04 | .02 | 209 | Fred Barnett | .25 | .15 |
| 153 | Barry Word | .25 | .15 | 210 | Randall Cunningham | .20 | .12 |
| 154 | Stan Thomas (R) | .10 | .06 | 211 | Mike Schad | .04 | .02 |
| 155 | Brad Muster | .07 | .04 | 212 | Reggie White | .12 | .07 |
| 156 | Donnell Woolford | .04 | .02 | 213 | Mike Bellamy | .08 | .05 |
| 157 | Neal Anderson | .12 | .07 | 214 | Jeff Feagles (R) | .08 | .05 |
| 158 | Jim Covert | .07 | .04 | 215 | Wes Hopkins | .04 | .02 |
| 159 | Jim Harbaugh | .10 | .06 | 216 | Clyde Simmons | .07 | .04 |
| 160 | Shaun Gayle | .04 | .02 | 217 | Keith Byars | .08 | .05 |
| 161 | William Perry | .08 | .05 | 218 | Seth Joyner | .07 | .04 |
| 162 | Ron Morris | .04 | .02 | 219 | Byron Evans | .07 | .04 |
| 163 | Mark Bortz | .04 | .02 | 220 | Keith Jackson | .12 | .07 |
| 164 | James Thornton | .04 | .02 | 221 | Calvin Williams | .15 | .08 |
| 165 | Ron Rivera | .04 | .02 | 222 | Mike Dumas (R) | .10 | .06 |
| 166 | Kevin Butler | .04 | .02 | 223 | Ray Childress | .08 | .05 |
| 167 | Jay Hilgenberg | .04 | .02 | 224 | Ernest Givins | .15 | .08 |
| 168 | Peter Tom Willis (R) | .15 | .08 | 225 | Lamar Lathon | .08 | .05 |
| 169 | Johnny Bailey | .07 | .04 | 226 | Greg Montgomery | .04 | .02 |
| 170 | Ron Cox | .04 | .02 | 227 | Mike Munchak | .07 | .04 |
| 171 | Keith Van Horne | .04 | .02 | 228 | Al Smith | .07 | .04 |
| 172 | Mark Carrier | .08 | .05 | 229 | Bubba McDowell | .04 | .02 |
| 173 | Richard Dent | .08 | .05 | 230 | Haywood Jeffires | .25 | .15 |
| 174 | Wendell Davis (R) | .20 | .12 | 231 | Drew Hill | .08 | .05 |
| 175 | Trace Armstrong | .04 | .02 | 232 | William Fuller | .07 | .04 |

| 233 | Warren Moon | .25 | .15 |
|-----|-------------|-----|-----|
| 234 | Doug Smith (R) | .12 | .07 |
| 235 | Cris Dishman (R) | .12 | .07 |
| 236 | Teddy Garcia (R) | .08 | .05 |
| 237 | Richard Johnson (R) | .08 | .05 |
| 238 | Bruce Matthews | .04 | .02 |
| 239 | Gerald McNeil | .04 | .02 |
| 240 | Johnny Meads | .04 | .02 |
| 241 | Curtis Duncan | .07 | .04 |
| 242 | Sean Jones | .04 | .02 |
| 243 | Lorenzo White | .15 | .08 |
| 244 | Rob Carpenter (R) | .15 | .08 |
| 245 | Bruce Reimers | .04 | .02 |
| 246 | Ickey Woods | .07 | .04 |
| 247 | Lewis Billups | .04 | .02 |
| 248 | Boomer Esiason | .10 | .06 |
| 249 | Tim Krumrie | .04 | .02 |
| 250 | David Fulcher | .04 | .02 |
| 251 | Jim Breech | .04 | .02 |
| 252 | Mitchell Price (R) | .08 | .05 |
| 253 | Carl Zander | .04 | .02 |
| 254 | Barney Bussey (R) | .08 | .05 |
| 255 | Leon White | .04 | .02 |
| 256 | Eddie Brown | .08 | .05 |
| 257 | James Francis | .08 | .05 |
| 258 | Harold Green | .25 | .15 |
| 259 | Anthony Munoz | .10 | .06 |
| 260 | James Brooks | .07 | .04 |
| 261 | Kevin Walker (R) | .10 | .06 |
| 262 | Bruce Kozerski | .04 | .02 |
| 263 | David Grant | .04 | .02 |
| 264 | Tim McGee | .08 | .05 |
| 265 | Rodney Holman | .04 | .02 |
| 266 | Dan McGwire (R) | .60 | .35 |
| 267 | Andy Heck | .04 | .02 |
| 268 | Dave Krieg | .10 | .06 |
| 269 | David Wyman | .04 | .02 |
| 270 | Robert Blackmon | .04 | .02 |
| 271 | Grant Feasel | .04 | .02 |
| 272 | Patrick Hunter (R) | .10 | .06 |
| 273 | Travis McNeal | .07 | .04 |
| 274 | John L. Williams | .08 | .05 |
| 275 | Tony Woods | .07 | .04 |
| 276 | Derrick Fenner | .12 | .07 |
| 277 | Jacob Green | .07 | .04 |
| 278 | Brian Blades | .07 | .04 |
| 279 | Eugene Robinson | .07 | .04 |
| 280 | Terry Wooden | .07 | .04 |
| 281 | Jeff Bryant | .04 | .02 |
| 282 | Norm Johnson | .04 | .02 |
| 283 | Joe Nash | .04 | .02 |
| 284 | Rick Donnelly | .04 | .02 |
| 285 | Chris Warren (R) | .25 | .15 |
| 286 | Tommy Kane | .12 | .07 |
| 287 | Cortez Kennedy | .20 | .12 |
| 288 | Ernie Mills (R) | .25 | .15 |
| 289 | Dermontti Dawson | .04 | .02 |
| 290 | Tunch Ilkin | .04 | .02 |
| 291 | Tim Worley | .07 | .04 |
| 292 | David Little | .04 | .02 |
| 293 | Gary Anderson | .04 | .02 |
| 294 | Chris Calloway | .08 | .05 |
| 295 | Carnell Lake | .07 | .04 |
| 296 | Dan Stryzinski | .04 | .02 |
| 297 | Rod Woodson | .10 | .06 |
| 298 | John Jackson (R) | .08 | .05 |
| 299 | Bubby Brister | .10 | .06 |
| 300 | Thomas Everett | .07 | .04 |
| 301 | Merril Hoge | .07 | .04 |
| 302 | Eric Green | .20 | .12 |
| 303 | Greg Lloyd | .04 | .02 |
| 304 | Gerald Williams | .04 | .02 |
| 305 | Bryan Hinkle | .04 | .02 |
| 306 | Keith Willis | .04 | .02 |
| 307 | Louis Lipps | .07 | .04 |
| 308 | Donald Evans | .04 | .02 |
| 309 | David Johnson (R) | .08 | .05 |
| 310 | Wesley Carroll (R) | .30 | .18 |
| 311 | Eric Martin | .08 | .05 |
| 312 | Brett Maxie | .07 | .04 |
| 313 | Rickey Jackson | .08 | .05 |
| 314 | Robert Massey | .04 | .02 |
| 315 | Pat Swilling | .12 | .07 |
| 316 | Morten Andersen | .07 | .04 |
| 317 | Toi Cook (R) | .08 | .05 |
| 318 | Sam Mills | .08 | .05 |
| 319 | Steve Walsh | .08 | .05 |
| 320 | Tommy Barnhardt (R) | .07 | .04 |
| 321 | Vince Buck | .07 | .04 |
| 322 | Joel Hilgenberg | .04 | .02 |
| 323 | Rueben Mayes | .07 | .04 |
| 324 | Renaldo Turnbull | .07 | .04 |
| 325 | Brett Perriman | .08 | .05 |
| 326 | Vaughan Johnson | .07 | .04 |
| 327 | Gill Fenerty | .07 | .04 |
| 328 | Stan Brock | .04 | .02 |
| 329 | Dalton Hilliard | .08 | .05 |
| 330 | Hoby Brenner | .04 | .02 |
| 331 | Craig Heyward | .08 | .05 |
| 332 | Jon Hand | .04 | .02 |
| 333 | Duane Bickett | .04 | .02 |
| 334 | Jessie Hester | .08 | .05 |
| 335 | Rohn Stark | .04 | .02 |
| 336 | Zefross Moss | .04 | .02 |
| 337 | Bill Brooks | .04 | .02 |
| 338 | Clarence Verdin | .08 | .05 |
| 339 | Mike Prior | .04 | .02 |
| 340 | Chip Banks | .07 | .04 |
| 341 | Dean Biasucci | .04 | .02 |
| 342 | Ray Donaldson | .04 | .02 |
| 343 | Jeff Herrod | .04 | .02 |
| 344 | Donnell Thompson | .04 | .02 |
| 345 | Chris Goode | .04 | .02 |
| 346 | Eugene Daniel | .04 | .02 |

| | | | |
|---|---|---|---|
| 347 Pat Beach | .04 | .02 |
| 348 Keith Taylor | .04 | .02 |
| 349 Jeff George | .45 | .25 |
| 350 Tony Siragusa (R) | .08 | .05 |
| 351 Randy Dixon | .08 | .05 |
| 352 Albert Bentley | .07 | .04 |
| 353 Russell Maryland (R) | .50 | .28 |
| 354 Mike Saxon | .04 | .02 |
| 355 Godfrey Myles (R) | .08 | .05 |
| 356 Mark Stepnoski (R) | .15 | .08 |
| 357 James Washington (R) | .10 | .06 |
| 358 Jay Novacek | .12 | .07 |
| 359 Kelvin Martin | .08 | .05 |
| 360 Emmitt Smith | 1.75 | 1.00 |
| 361 Jim Jeffcoat | .07 | .04 |
| 362 Alexander Wright | .08 | .05 |
| 363 James Dixon | .04 | .02 |
| 364 Alonzo Highsmith | .07 | .04 |
| 365 Daniel Stubbs | .04 | .02 |
| 366 Jack Del Rio | .04 | .02 |
| 367 Mark Tuinei (R) | .08 | .05 |
| 368 Michael Irvin | .40 | .22 |
| 369 John Gesek (R) | .08 | .05 |
| 370 Ken Willis | .04 | .02 |
| 371 Troy Aikman | .90 | .55 |
| 372 Jimmie Jones | .07 | .04 |
| 373 Nate Newton | .04 | .02 |
| 374 Issiac Holt | .04 | .02 |
| 375 Alvin Harper (R) | .75 | .40 |
| 376 Todd Kalis | .04 | .02 |
| 377 Wade Wilson | .08 | .05 |
| 378 Joey Browner | .07 | .04 |
| 379 Chris Doleman | .07 | .04 |
| 380 Hassan Jones | .08 | .05 |
| 381 Henry Thomas | .04 | .02 |
| 382 Darrell Fullington | .04 | .02 |
| 383 Steve Jordan | .07 | .04 |
| 384 Gary Zimmerman | .04 | .02 |
| 385 Ray Berry | .04 | .02 |
| 386 Cris Carter | .12 | .07 |
| 387 Mike Merriweather | .04 | .02 |
| 388 Carl Lee | .04 | .02 |
| 389 Keith Millard | .07 | .04 |
| 390 Reggie Rutland | .04 | .02 |
| 391 Anthony Carter | .08 | .05 |
| 392 Mark Dusbabek (R) | .08 | .05 |
| 393 Kirk Lowdermilk | .04 | .02 |
| 394 Al Noga | .04 | .02 |
| 395 Herschel Walker | .12 | .07 |
| 396 Randall McDaniel | .04 | .02 |
| 397 Herman Moore (R) | .80 | .45 |
| 398 Eddie Murray | .04 | .02 |
| 399 Lomas Brown | .04 | .02 |
| 400 Marc Spindler | .07 | .04 |
| 401 Bennie Blades | .08 | .05 |
| 402 Kevin Glover | .04 | .02 |
| 403 Aubrey Matthews (R) | .08 | .05 |
| 404 Michael Cofer | .04 | .02 |
| 405 Robert Clark | .08 | .05 |
| 406 Eric Andolsek | .04 | .02 |
| 407 William White | .04 | .02 |
| 408 Rodney Peete | .12 | .07 |
| 409 Mel Gray | .04 | .02 |
| 410 Jim Arnold | .04 | .02 |
| 411 Jeff Campbell | .07 | .04 |
| 412 Chris Spielman | .07 | .04 |
| 413 Jerry Ball | .04 | .02 |
| 414 Dan Owens | .07 | .04 |
| 415 Barry Sanders | .75 | .40 |
| 416 Andre Ware | .15 | .08 |
| 417 Stanley Richard (R) | .20 | .12 |
| 418 Gill Byrd | .07 | .04 |
| 419 John Kidd | .04 | .02 |
| 420 Sam Seale (R) | .08 | .05 |
| 421 Gary Plummer | .04 | .02 |
| 422 Anthony Miller | .12 | .07 |
| 423 Ronnie Harmon | .07 | .04 |
| 424 Frank Cornish | .04 | .02 |
| 425 Marion Butts | .12 | .07 |
| 426 Leo Goeas (R) | .07 | .04 |
| 427 Junior Seau | .20 | .12 |
| 428 Courtney Hall | .04 | .02 |
| 429 Leslie O'Neal | .08 | .05 |
| 430 Martin Bayless | .04 | .02 |
| 431 John Carney | .04 | .02 |
| 432 Lee Williams | .07 | .04 |
| 433 Arthur Cox | .04 | .02 |
| 434 Burt Grossman | .07 | .04 |
| 435 Nate Lewis (R) | .25 | .15 |
| 436 Rod Bernstine | .08 | .05 |
| 437 Henry Rolling (R) | .10 | .06 |
| 438 Billy Joe Tolliver | .08 | .05 |
| 439 Vinnie Clark (R) | .10 | .06 |
| 440 Brian Noble | .04 | .02 |
| 441 Charles Wilson | .04 | .02 |
| 442 Don Majkowski | .10 | .06 |
| 443 Tim Harris | .07 | .04 |
| 444 Scott Stephen (R) | .08 | .05 |
| 445 Perry Kemp | .04 | .02 |
| 446 Darrell Thompson | .12 | .07 |
| 447 Chris Jacke | .04 | .02 |
| 448 Mark Murphy | .04 | .02 |
| 449 Ed West | .04 | .02 |
| 450 LeRoy Butler | .04 | .02 |
| 451 Keith Woodside | .07 | .04 |
| 452 Tony Bennett | .10 | .06 |
| 453 Mark Lee | .04 | .02 |
| 454 James Campen (R) | .08 | .05 |
| 455 Robert Brown | .04 | .02 |
| 456 Sterling Sharpe | .40 | .22 |
| 457 Tony Mandarich | .07 | .04 |
| 458 Johnny Holland | .07 | .04 |
| 459 Matt Brock (R) | .10 | .06 |
| 460 Esera Tuaolo (R) | .08 | .05 |

| | | | |
|---|---|---|---|
| 461 Freeman McNeil | .08 | .05 |
| 462 Terance Mathis | .08 | .05 |
| 463 Rob Moore | .30 | .18 |
| 464 Darrell Davis (R) | .10 | .06 |
| 465 Chris Burkett | .04 | .02 |
| 466 Jeff Criswell | .04 | .02 |
| 467 Tony Stargell | .04 | .02 |
| 468 Ken O'Brien | .10 | .06 |
| 469 Erik McMillan | .07 | .04 |
| 470 Jeff Lageman | .08 | .05 |
| 471 Pat Leahy | .04 | .02 |
| 472 Dennis Byrd | .07 | .04 |
| 473 Jim Sweeney | .04 | .02 |
| 474 Brad Baxter | .15 | .08 |
| 475 Joe Kelly | .04 | .02 |
| 476 Al Toon | .08 | .05 |
| 477 Joe Prokop | .07 | .04 |
| 478 Mark Boyer | .04 | .02 |
| 479 Kyle Clifton | .04 | .02 |
| 480 James Hasty | .04 | .02 |
| 481 Browning Nagle (R) | .80 | .45 |
| 482 Gary Anderson | .07 | .04 |
| 483 Mark Carrier | .07 | .04 |
| 484 Rickey Reynolds | .04 | .02 |
| 485 Bruce Hill | .04 | .02 |
| 486 Steve Christie | .04 | .02 |
| 487 Paul Gruber | .07 | .04 |
| 488 Jesse Anderson | .04 | .02 |
| 489 Reggie Cobb | .20 | .12 |
| 490 Harry Hamilton | .04 | .02 |
| 491 Vinny Testaverde | .10 | .06 |
| 492 Mark Royals (R) | .08 | .05 |
| 493 Keith McCants | .08 | .05 |
| 494 Ron Hall | .04 | .02 |
| 495 Ian Beckles | .04 | .02 |
| 496 Mark Robinson | .04 | .02 |
| 497 Reuben Davis | .04 | .02 |
| 498 Wayne Haddix | .07 | .04 |
| 499 Kevin Murphy | .04 | .02 |
| 500 Eugene Marve | .04 | .02 |
| 501 Broderick Thomas | .08 | .05 |
| 502 Eric Swann (R) | .15 | .08 |
| 503 Ernie Jones | .10 | .06 |
| 504 Rich Camarillo | .04 | .02 |
| 505 Tim McDonald | .07 | .04 |
| 506 Freddie Joe Nunn | .04 | .02 |
| 507 Tim Jorden (R) | .08 | .05 |
| 508 Johnny Johnson | .20 | .12 |
| 509 Eric Hill | .04 | .02 |
| 510 Derek Kennard | .04 | .02 |
| 511 Ricky Proehl | .12 | .07 |
| 512 Bill Lewis | .04 | .02 |
| 513 Roy Green | .08 | .05 |
| 514 Anthony Bell | .04 | .02 |
| 515 Timm Rosenbach | .10 | .06 |
| 516 Jim Wahler (R) | .08 | .05 |
| 517 Anthony Thompson | .10 | .06 |
| 518 Ken Harvey | .04 | .02 |
| 519 Luis Sharpe | .04 | .02 |
| 520 Walter Reeves | .04 | .02 |
| 521 Lonnie Young | .04 | .02 |
| 522 Rod Saddler (R) | .08 | .05 |
| 523 Todd Lyght (R) | .25 | .15 |
| 524 Alvin Wright | .07 | .04 |
| 525 Flipper Anderson | .08 | .05 |
| 526 Jackie Slater | .07 | .04 |
| 527 Damone Johnson (R) | .10 | .06 |
| 528 Cleveland Gary | .08 | .05 |
| 529 Mike Piel | .04 | .02 |
| 530 Buford McGee | .07 | .04 |
| 531 Michael Stewart | .04 | .02 |
| 532 Jim Everett | .12 | .07 |
| 533 Mike Wilcher | .04 | .02 |
| 534 Irv Pankey | .04 | .02 |
| 535 Bern Brostek | .04 | .02 |
| 536 Henry Ellard | .08 | .05 |
| 537 Doug Smith | .04 | .02 |
| 538 Larry Kelm | .04 | .02 |
| 539 Pat Terrell | .04 | .02 |
| 540 Tom Newberry | .04 | .02 |
| 541 Jerry Gray | .07 | .04 |
| 542 Kevin Greene | .07 | .04 |
| 543 Duval Love (R) | .08 | .05 |
| 544 Frank Stams | .04 | .02 |
| 545 Mike Croel (R) | .50 | .28 |
| 546 Mark Jackson | .07 | .04 |
| 547 Greg Kragen | .04 | .02 |
| 548 Karl Mecklenburg | .07 | .04 |
| 549 Simon Fletcher | .07 | .04 |
| 550 Bobby Humphrey | .10 | .06 |
| 551 Ken Lanier | .04 | .02 |
| 552 Vance Johnson | .08 | .05 |
| 533 Ron Holmes | .04 | .02 |
| 554 John Elway | .25 | .15 |
| 555 Melvin Bratton | .07 | .04 |
| 556 Dennis Smith | .04 | .02 |
| 557 Ricky Nattiel | .08 | .05 |
| 558 Clarence Kay | .04 | .02 |
| 559 Michael Brooks | .04 | .02 |
| 560 Mike Horan | .04 | .02 |
| 561 Warren Powers | .04 | .02 |
| 562 Keith Kartz (R) | .08 | .05 |
| 563 Shannon Sharpe (R) | .20 | .12 |
| 564 Wymon Henderson | .04 | .02 |
| 565 Steve Atwater | .08 | .05 |
| 566 David Treadwell | .04 | .02 |
| 567 Bruce Pickens (R) | .25 | .15 |
| 568 Jessie Tuggle | .04 | .02 |
| 569 Chris Hinton | .07 | .04 |
| 570 Keith Jones | .04 | .02 |
| 571 Bill Fralic | .07 | .04 |
| 572 Mike Rozier | .07 | .04 |
| 573 Scott Fulhage | .04 | .02 |

| 574 | Floyd Dixon | .04 | .02 |
|---|---|---|---|
| 575 | Andre Rison | .25 | .15 |
| 576 | Darion Conner | .07 | .04 |
| 577 | Brian Jordan (R) | .15 | .08 |
| 578 | Michael Haynes | .25 | .15 |
| 579 | Oliver Barnett | .07 | .04 |
| 580 | Shawn Collins | .07 | .04 |
| 581 | Tim Green | .07 | .04 |
| 582 | Deion Sanders | .25 | .15 |
| 583 | Mike Kenn | .04 | .02 |
| 584 | Mike Gann | .04 | .02 |
| 585 | Chris Miller | .25 | .15 |
| 586 | Tory Epps | .04 | .02 |
| 587 | Steve Broussard | .08 | .05 |
| 588 | Gary Wilkins (R) | .08 | .05 |
| 589 | Eric Turner (R) | .30 | .18 |
| 590 | Thane Gash | .04 | .02 |
| 591 | Clay Matthews | .04 | .02 |
| 592 | Mike Johnson | .04 | .02 |
| 593 | Raymond Clayborn | .04 | .02 |
| 594 | Leroy Hoard | .12 | .07 |
| 595 | Reggie Langhorne | .04 | .02 |
| 596 | Mike Baab | .04 | .02 |
| 597 | Anthony Pleasant | .04 | .02 |
| 598 | David Grayson | .04 | .02 |
| 599 | Rob Burnett (R) | .12 | .07 |
| 600 | Frank Minnifield | .04 | .02 |
| 601 | Gregg Rakoczy | .04 | .02 |
| 602 | Eric Metcalf | .10 | .06 |
| 603 | Paul Farren | .07 | .04 |
| 604 | Brian Brennan | .04 | .02 |
| 605 | Tony Jones | .07 | .04 |
| 606 | Stephen Braggs | .04 | .02 |
| 607 | Kevin Mack | .07 | .04 |
| 608 | Pat Harlow (R) | .15 | .08 |
| 609 | Marv Cook | .12 | .07 |
| 610 | John Stephens | .08 | .05 |
| 611 | Ed Reynolds | .04 | .02 |
| 612 | Tim Goad | .04 | .02 |
| 613 | Chris Singleton | .08 | .05 |
| 614 | Bruce Armstrong | .04 | .02 |
| 615 | Tommy Hodson | .10 | .06 |
| 616 | Sammy Martin | .07 | .04 |
| 617 | Andre Tippett | .08 | .05 |
| 618 | Johnny Rembert | .04 | .02 |
| 619 | Maurice Hurst | .04 | .02 |
| 620 | Vincent Brown | .04 | .02 |
| 621 | Ray Agnew | .04 | .02 |
| 622 | Ronnie Lippett | .04 | .02 |
| 623 | Greg McMurtry (R) | .15 | .08 |
| 624 | Brent Williams | .04 | .02 |
| 625 | Jason Staurovsky | .04 | .02 |
| 626 | Marvin Allen | .04 | .02 |
| 627 | Hart Lee Dykes | .07 | .04 |
| 628 | Falcons TL (Jones) | .05 | .02 |
| 629 | Bills TL (Wright) | .05 | .02 |
| 630 | Bears TL (Harbaugh) | .05 | .02 |
| 631 | Bengals TL (Jennings) | .05 | .02 |
| 632 | Browns TL (Metcalf) | .07 | .04 |
| 633 | Cowboys TL (Martin) | .07 | .04 |
| 634 | Broncos TL (Sharpe) | .07 | .04 |
| 635 | Lions TL (Peete) | .07 | .04 |
| 636 | Packers TL (Majkowski) | .07 | .04 |
| 637 | Oilers TL (Moon) | .10 | .06 |
| 638 | Colts TL (George) | .10 | .06 |
| 639 | Chiefs TL (Okoye) | .07 | .04 |
| 640 | Raiders TL (Allen) | .07 | .04 |
| 641 | Rams TL (Everett) | .07 | .04 |
| 642 | Dolphins (Stoyanovich) | .05 | .02 |
| 643 | Vikings TL (Gannon) | .07 | .04 |
| 644 | Patriots TL (Stephens) | .07 | .04 |
| 645 | Saints TL (Fenerty) | .05 | .02 |
| 646 | Giants TL (Carthon) | .05 | .02 |
| 647 | Jets TL (Leahy) | .05 | .02 |
| 648 | Eagles TL (Cunningham) | .10 | .06 |
| 649 | Cardinals TL (Lewis) | .05 | .02 |
| 650 | Steelers TL (Brister) | .07 | .04 |
| 651 | Chargers TL (Friesz) | .07 | .04 |
| 652 | 49ers TL (Carter) | .07 | .04 |
| 653 | Seahawks TL (Fenner) | .07 | .04 |
| 654 | Buccaneers TL (Cobb) | .07 | .04 |
| 655 | Redskins TL (Byner) | .07 | .04 |
| 656 | Checklist 1 | .04 | .01 |
| 657 | Checklist 2 | .04 | .01 |
| 658 | Checklist 3 | .04 | .01 |
| 659 | Checklist 4 | .04 | .01 |
| 660 | Checklist 5 | .04 | .01 |

# 1991 Topps Stadium Club

This 500-card set marks Topps first premium football product. The card fronts feature full-bleed, full color photographs while the player's name appears in a gold-bordered stripe at the bottom. The horizontal card backs contain personal data, a biography and a small photo of the player's rookie Topps card. All cards measure 2-1/2" by 3-1/2".

|  |  | MINT | NR/MT |
|---|---|---|---|
| | Complete Set (500) | 155.00 | 85.00 |
| | Commons | .15 | .10 |

| | | | |
|---|---|---|---|
| 1 | Pepper Johnson | .20 | .12 |
| 2 | Emmitt Smith | 26.00 | 16.00 |
| 3 | Deion Sanders | 3.00 | 1.75 |
| 4 | Andre Collins | .20 | .12 |
| 5 | Eric Metcalf | .30 | .18 |
| 6 | Richard Dent | .20 | .12 |
| 7 | Eric Martin | .20 | .12 |
| 8 | Marcus Allen | .40 | .25 |
| 9 | Gary Anderson | .15 | .10 |
| 10 | Joey Browner | .20 | .12 |
| 11 | Lorenzo White | .75 | .40 |
| 12 | Bruce Smith | .30 | .18 |
| 13 | Mark Boyer | .15 | .10 |
| 14 | Mike Piel | .15 | .10 |
| 15 | Albert Bentley | .20 | .12 |
| 16 | Bennie Blades | .25 | .15 |
| 17 | Jason Staurovsky | .15 | .10 |
| 18 | Anthony Toney | .15 | .10 |
| 19 | Dave Krieg | .30 | .18 |
| 20 | Harvey Williams (R) | 3.00 | 1.75 |
| 21 | Bubba Paris | .15 | .10 |
| 22 | Tim McGee | .20 | .12 |
| 23 | Brian Noble | .15 | .10 |
| 24 | Vinny Testaverde | .30 | .18 |
| 25 | Doug Widell | .15 | .10 |
| 26 | John Jackson (R) | .25 | .15 |
| 27 | Marion Butts | .60 | .35 |
| 28 | Deron Cherry | .25 | .15 |
| 29 | Don Warren | .15 | .10 |
| 30 | Rod Woodson | .30 | .18 |
| 31 | Mike Baab | .15 | .10 |
| 32 | Greg Jackson (R) | .25 | .15 |
| 33 | Jerry Robinson | .15 | .10 |
| 34 | Dalton Hilliard | .25 | .15 |
| 35 | Brian Jordan | .30 | .18 |
| 36 | James Thornton | .15 | .10 |
| 37 | Michael Irvin | 6.00 | 3.50 |
| 38 | Billy Joe Tolliver | .25 | .15 |
| 39 | Jeff Herrod | .15 | .10 |
| 40 | Scott Norwood | .15 | .10 |
| 41 | Ferrell Edmunds | .15 | .10 |
| 42 | Andre Waters | .15 | .10 |
| 43 | Kevin Glover | .15 | .10 |
| 44 | Ray Berry | .15 | .10 |
| 45 | Timm Rosenbach | .50 | .30 |
| 46 | Reuben Davis | .15 | .10 |
| 47 | Charles Wilson | .15 | .10 |
| 48 | Todd Marinovich (R) | 5.00 | 3.00 |
| 49 | Harris Barton | .15 | .10 |
| 50 | Jim Breech | .15 | .10 |
| 51 | Ron Holmes | .15 | .10 |
| 52 | Chris Singleton | .25 | .15 |
| 53 | Pat Leahy | .15 | .10 |
| 54 | Tom Newberry | .15 | .10 |
| 55 | Greg Montgomery | .15 | .10 |
| 56 | Robert Blackmon | .15 | .10 |
| 57 | Jay Hilgenberg | .15 | .10 |
| 58 | Rodney Hampton | 4.00 | 2.50 |
| 59 | Brett Perriman | .30 | .18 |
| 60 | Ricky Watters (R) | 15.00 | 10.00 |
| 61 | Howie Long | .30 | .18 |
| 62 | Frank Cornish | .15 | .10 |
| 63 | Chris Miller | 1.00 | .60 |
| 64 | Keith Taylor | .15 | .10 |
| 65 | Tony Paige | .15 | .10 |
| 66 | Gary Zimmerman | .15 | .10 |
| 67 | Mark Royals (R) | .25 | .15 |
| 68 | Ernie Jones | .30 | .18 |
| 69 | David Grant | .15 | .10 |
| 70 | Shane Conlan | .30 | .18 |
| 71 | Jerry Rice | 4.00 | 2.50 |
| 72 | Christian Okoye | .50 | .30 |
| 73 | Eddie Murray | .15 | .10 |
| 74 | Reggie White | .60 | .35 |
| 75 | Jeff Graham (R) | 1.50 | .90 |
| 76 | Mark Jackson | .25 | .15 |
| 77 | David Grayson | .15 | .10 |
| 78 | Dan Stryzinski | .15 | .10 |
| 79 | Sterling Sharpe | 4.50 | 2.75 |
| 80 | Cleveland Gary | .40 | .25 |
| 81 | Johnny Meads | .15 | .10 |
| 82 | Howard Cross | .15 | .10 |
| 83 | Ken O'Brien | .35 | .22 |
| 84 | Brian Blades | .30 | .18 |
| 85 | Ethan Horton | .20 | .12 |
| 86 | Bruce Armstrong | .15 | .10 |
| 87 | James Washington (R) | .35 | .22 |
| 88 | Eugene Daniel | .15 | .10 |
| 89 | James Lofton (R) | .90 | .50 |
| 90 | Louis Oliver | .30 | .18 |
| 91 | Boomer Esiason | .50 | .30 |
| 92 | Seth Joyner | .25 | .15 |
| 93 | Mark Carrier | .30 | .18 |
| 94 | Brett Favre (R) | 12.50 | 7.00 |
| 95 | Lee Williams | .20 | .12 |
| 96 | Neal Anderson | .50 | .30 |
| 97 | Brent Jones | .30 | .18 |
| 98 | John Alt | .15 | .10 |
| 99 | Rodney Peete | .35 | .22 |
| 100 | Steve Broussard | .35 | .22 |
| 101 | Cedric Mack | .15 | .10 |
| 102 | Pat Swilling | .35 | .22 |

| | | | |
|---|---|---|---|
| 103 Stan Humphries | 2.50 | 1.50 |
| 104 Darrell Thompson | .40 | .25 |
| 105 Reggie Langhorne | .15 | .10 |
| 106 Kenny Davidson | .15 | .10 |
| 107 Jim Everett | .75 | .40 |
| 108 Keith Millard | .25 | .15 |
| 109 Garry Lewis | .15 | .10 |
| 110 Jeff Hostetler | .60 | .35 |
| 111 Lamar Lathon | .30 | .18 |
| 112 Johnny Bailey | .30 | .18 |
| 113 Cornelius Bennett | .50 | .30 |
| 114 Travis McNeal | .15 | .10 |
| 115 Jeff Lageman | .25 | .15 |
| 116 Nick Bell (R) | 3.00 | 1.75 |
| 117 Calvin Williams | .75 | .40 |
| 118 Shawn Lee (R) | .30 | .18 |
| 119 Anthony Munoz | .35 | .22 |
| 120 Jay Novacek | .60 | .35 |
| 121 Kevin Fagan | .15 | .10 |
| 122 Leo Goeas | .15 | .10 |
| 123 Vance Johnson | .25 | .15 |
| 124 Brent Williams | .15 | .10 |
| 125 Clarence Verdin | .20 | .12 |
| 126 Luis Sharpe | .15 | .10 |
| 127 Darrell Green | .40 | .25 |
| 128 Barry Word | 1.25 | .70 |
| 129 Steve Walsh | .30 | .18 |
| 130 Bryan Hinkle | .15 | .10 |
| 131 Ed West | .15 | .10 |
| 132 Jeff Campbell | .15 | .10 |
| 133 Dennis Byrd | .20 | .12 |
| 134 Nate Odomes | .15 | .10 |
| 135 Trace Armstrong | .15 | .10 |
| 136 Jarvis Williams | .15 | .10 |
| 137 Warren Moon | 1.75 | 1.00 |
| 138 Eric Moten (R) | .20 | .12 |
| 139 Tony Woods | .15 | .10 |
| 140 Phil Simms | .40 | .25 |
| 141 Ricky Reynolds | .15 | .10 |
| 142 Frank Stams | .15 | .10 |
| 143 Kevin Mack | .25 | .15 |
| 144 Wade Wilson | .25 | .15 |
| 145 Shawn Collins | .25 | .15 |
| 146 Roger Craig | .35 | .22 |
| 147 Jeff Feagles (R) | .20 | .12 |
| 148 Norm Johnson | .15 | .10 |
| 149 Terance Mathis | .25 | .15 |
| 150 Reggie Cobb | 1.25 | .70 |
| 151 Chip Banks | .20 | .12 |
| 152 Darryl Pollard | .15 | .10 |
| 153 Karl Mecklenburg | .30 | .18 |
| 154 Ricky Proehl | .50 | .30 |
| 155 Pete Stoyanovich | .15 | .10 |
| 156 John Stephens | .30 | .18 |
| 157 Ron Morris | .15 | .10 |
| 158 Steve DeBerg | .30 | .18 |
| 159 Mike Munchak | .25 | .15 |
| 160 Brett Maxie | .15 | .10 |
| 161 Don Beebe | .50 | .30 |
| 162 Martin Mayhew | .15 | .10 |
| 163 Merril Hoge | .20 | .12 |
| 164 Kelvin Pritchett (R) | .50 | .30 |
| 165 Jim Jeffcoat | .20 | .12 |
| 166 Myron Guyton | .15 | .10 |
| 167 Ickey Woods | .20 | .12 |
| 168 Andre Ware | .50 | .30 |
| 169 Gary Plummer | .15 | .10 |
| 170 Henry Ellard | .30 | .18 |
| 171 Scott Davis | .15 | .10 |
| 172 Randall McDaniel | .15 | .10 |
| 173 Randal Hill (R) | 3.50 | 2.00 |
| 174 Anthony Bell | .15 | .10 |
| 175 Gary Anderson | .20 | .12 |
| 176 Byron Evans | .15 | .10 |
| 177 Tony Mandarich | .20 | .12 |
| 178 Jeff George | 3.00 | 1.75 |
| 179 Art Monk | 1.50 | .90 |
| 180 Mike Kenn | .15 | .10 |
| 181 Sean Landeta | .15 | .10 |
| 182 Shaun Gayle | .15 | .10 |
| 183 Michael Carter | .15 | .10 |
| 184 Robb Thomas | .30 | .18 |
| 185 Richmond Webb | .25 | .15 |
| 186 Carnell Lake | .20 | .12 |
| 187 Rueben Mayes | .20 | .12 |
| 188 Issiac Holt | .15 | .10 |
| 189 Leon Seals | .15 | .10 |
| 190 Al Smith | .15 | .10 |
| 191 Steve Atwater | .35 | .22 |
| 192 Greg McMurtry | .35 | .22 |
| 193 Al Toon | .30 | .18 |
| 194 Cortez Kennedy | 1.00 | .60 |
| 195 Gill Byrd | .20 | .12 |
| 196 Carl Zander | .15 | .10 |
| 197 Robert Brown | .15 | .10 |
| 198 Buford McGee | .20 | .12 |
| 199 Mervyn Fernandez | .30 | .18 |
| 200 Mike Dumas (R) | .40 | .25 |
| 201 Rob Burnett (R) | .50 | .30 |
| 202 Brian Mitchell | .50 | .30 |
| 203 Randall Cunningham | 1.25 | .70 |
| 204 Sammie Smith | .30 | .18 |
| 205 Ken Clarke | .15 | .10 |
| 206 Floyd Dixon | .15 | .10 |
| 207 Ken Norton | .25 | .15 |
| 208 Tony Siragusa (R) | .25 | .15 |
| 209 Louis Lipps | .25 | .15 |
| 210 Chris Martin | .15 | .10 |
| 211 Jamie Mueller | .15 | .10 |
| 212 Dave Waymer | .15 | .10 |
| 213 Donnell Woolford | .15 | .10 |
| 214 Paul Gruber | .25 | .15 |
| 215 Ken Harvey | .15 | .10 |
| 216 Henry Jones (R) | .75 | .40 |

| | | | |
|---|---|---|---|
| 217 | Tommy Barnahrdt (R) | .20 | .12 |
| 218 | Arthur Cox | .15 | .10 |
| 219 | Pat Terrell | .15 | .10 |
| 220 | Curtis Duncan | .25 | .15 |
| 221 | Jeff Jaeger | .15 | .10 |
| 222 | Scott Stephen (R) | .25 | .15 |
| 223 | Rob Moore | 1.50 | .90 |
| 224 | Chris Hinton | .25 | .15 |
| 225 | Marv Cook | .30 | .18 |
| 226 | Patrick Hunter (R) | .30 | .18 |
| 227 | Earnest Byner | .30 | .18 |
| 228 | Troy Aikman | 10.00 | 6.50 |
| 229 | Kevin Walker (R) | .30 | .18 |
| 230 | Keith Jackson | .50 | .30 |
| 231 | Russell Maryland (R) | 2.00 | 1.25 |
| 232 | Charles Haley | .30 | .18 |
| 233 | Nick Lowery | .25 | .15 |
| 234 | Erik Howard | .15 | .10 |
| 235 | Leonard Smith | .15 | .10 |
| 236 | Tim Irwin | .15 | .10 |
| 237 | Simon Fletcher | .20 | .12 |
| 238 | Thomas Everett | .20 | .12 |
| 239 | Reggie Roby | .15 | .10 |
| 240 | Leroy Hoard | .35 | .22 |
| 241 | Wayne Haddix | .20 | .12 |
| 242 | Gary Clark | .80 | .50 |
| 243 | Eric Andolsek | .15 | .10 |
| 244 | Jim Wahler (R) | .20 | .12 |
| 245 | Vaughan Johnson | .25 | .15 |
| 246 | Kevin Butler | .15 | .10 |
| 247 | Steve Tasker | .20 | .12 |
| 248 | LeRoy Butler | .15 | .10 |
| 249 | Darion Conner | .20 | .12 |
| 250 | Eric Turner (R) | 1.50 | .90 |
| 251 | Kevin Ross | .15 | .10 |
| 252 | Stephen Baker | .20 | .12 |
| 253 | Harold Green | 1.25 | .70 |
| 254 | Rohn Stark | .15 | .10 |
| 255 | Joe Nash | .15 | .10 |
| 256 | Jesse Sapolu | .15 | .10 |
| 257 | Willie Gault | .25 | .15 |
| 258 | Jerome Brown | .25 | .15 |
| 259 | Ken Willis | .15 | .10 |
| 260 | Courtney Hall | .15 | .10 |
| 261 | Hart Lee Dykes | .20 | .12 |
| 262 | William Fuller | .20 | .12 |
| 263 | Stan Thomas (R) | .25 | .15 |
| 264 | Dan Marino | 4.50 | 2.50 |
| 265 | Ron Cox | .15 | .10 |
| 266 | Eric Green | .50 | .30 |
| 267 | Anthony Carter | .30 | .18 |
| 268 | Jerry Ball | .15 | .10 |
| 269 | Ron Hall | .15 | .10 |
| 270 | Dennis Smith | .15 | .10 |
| 271 | Eric Hill | .20 | .12 |
| 272 | Dan McGwire (R) | 2.00 | 1.25 |
| 273 | Lewis Billups | .15 | .10 |
| 274 | Rickey Jackson | .25 | .15 |
| 275 | Jim Sweeney | .15 | .10 |
| 276 | Pat Beach | .15 | .10 |
| 277 | Kevin Porter | .15 | .10 |
| 278 | Mike Sherrard | .25 | .15 |
| 279 | Andy Heck | .15 | .10 |
| 280 | Ron Brown | .40 | .25 |
| 281 | Lawrence Taylor | .90 | .55 |
| 282 | Anthony Pleasant | .15 | .10 |
| 283 | Wes Hopkins | .15 | .10 |
| 284 | Jim Lachey | .30 | .18 |
| 285 | Tim Harris | .20 | .12 |
| 286 | Tory Epps | .15 | .10 |
| 287 | Wendell Davis | .80 | .50 |
| 288 | Bubba McDowell | .15 | .10 |
| 289 | Bubby Brister | .30 | .18 |
| 290 | Chris Zorich (R) | .50 | .30 |
| 291 | Mike Merriweather | .15 | .10 |
| 292 | Burt Grossman | .25 | .15 |
| 293 | Erik McMillan | .15 | .10 |
| 294 | John Elway | 1.75 | 1.00 |
| 295 | Toi Cook (R) | .25 | .15 |
| 296 | Tom Rathman | .25 | .15 |
| 297 | Matt Bahr | .15 | .10 |
| 298 | Chris Spielman | .25 | .15 |
| 299 | Freddie Joe Nunn | .15 | .10 |
| 300 | Jim Jensen | .15 | .10 |
| 301 | David Fulcher | .15 | .10 |
| 302 | Tommy Hodson | .30 | .18 |
| 303 | Stephone Paige | .25 | .15 |
| 304 | Greg Townsend | .20 | .12 |
| 305 | Dean Biasucci | .15 | .10 |
| 306 | Jimmie Jones | .15 | .10 |
| 307 | Eugene Marve | .15 | .10 |
| 308 | Flipper Anderson | .30 | .18 |
| 309 | Darryl Talley | .35 | .22 |
| 310 | Mike Croel (R) | 1.50 | .90 |
| 311 | Thane Gash | .15 | .10 |
| 312 | Perry Kemp | .15 | .10 |
| 313 | Heath Sherman | .25 | .15 |
| 314 | Mike Singletary | .40 | .25 |
| 315 | Chip Lohmiller | .15 | .10 |
| 316 | Tunch Ilkin | .15 | .10 |
| 317 | Junior Seau | 1.50 | .80 |
| 318 | Mike Gann | .15 | .10 |
| 319 | Tim McDonald | .20 | .12 |
| 320 | Kyle Clifton | .15 | .10 |
| 321 | Dan Owens | .20 | .12 |
| 322 | Tim Grunhard | .15 | .10 |
| 323 | Stan Brock | .15 | .10 |
| 324 | Rodney Holman | .15 | .10 |
| 325 | Mark Ingram | .20 | .12 |
| 326 | Browning Nagle (R) | 6.50 | 3.50 |
| 327 | Joe Montana | 3.00 | 1.75 |
| 328 | Carl Lee | .15 | .10 |
| 329 | John L. Williams | .25 | .15 |
| 330 | David Griggs | .15 | .10 |

| | | | | | | | |
|---|---|---|---|---|---|---|---|
| 331 | Clarence Kay | .15 | .10 | 388 | Mel Gray (ER) | .15 | .10 |
| 332 | Irving Fryar | .25 | .15 | 389 | Ernest Givins | .50 | .30 |
| 333 | Doug Smith (R) | .30 | .18 | 390 | Reyna Thompson | .15 | .10 |
| 334 | Kent Hull | .15 | .10 | 391 | Eric Bieniemy (R) | .75 | .40 |
| 335 | Mike Wilcher | .15 | .10 | 392 | Jon Hand | .15 | .10 |
| 336 | Ray Donaldson | .15 | .10 | 393 | Mark Rypien | 1.50 | .90 |
| 337 | Mark Carrier (Chi) | .40 | .25 | 394 | Bill Romanowski | .15 | .10 |
| 338 | Kelvin Martin | .40 | .25 | 395 | Thurman Thomas | 7.50 | 4.00 |
| 339 | Keith Byars | .30 | .18 | 396 | Jim Harbaugh | .40 | .25 |
| 340 | Wilber Marshall | .25 | .15 | 397 | Don Mosebar | .15 | .10 |
| 341 | Ronnie Lott | .60 | .35 | 398 | Andre Rison | 1.75 | 1.00 |
| 342 | Blair Thomas | .75 | .40 | 399 | Mike Johnson | .15 | .10 |
| 343 | Ronnie Harmon | .20 | .12 | 400 | Dermontti Dawson | .15 | .10 |
| 344 | Brian Brennan | .15 | .10 | 401 | Herschel Walker | .60 | .35 |
| 345 | Charles McRae (R) | .30 | .18 | 402 | Joe Prokop | .15 | .10 |
| 346 | Michael Cofer | .15 | .10 | 403 | Eddie Brown | .25 | .15 |
| 347 | Keith Willis | .15 | .10 | 404 | Nate Newton | .15 | .10 |
| 348 | Bruce Kozerski | .15 | .10 | 405 | Damone Johnson (R) | .25 | .15 |
| 349 | Dave Meggett | .50 | .30 | 406 | Jessie Hester | .25 | .15 |
| 350 | John Taylor | .60 | .35 | 407 | Jim Arnold | .15 | .10 |
| 351 | Johnny Holland | .15 | .10 | 408 | Ray Agnew | .15 | .10 |
| 352 | Steve Christie | .15 | .10 | 409 | Michael Brooks | .15 | .10 |
| 353 | Ricky Ervins (R) | 5.00 | 3.00 | 410 | Keith Sims | .15 | .10 |
| 354 | Robert Massey | .15 | .10 | 411 | Carl Banks | .30 | .18 |
| 355 | Derrick Thomas | 1.50 | .90 | 412 | Jonathan Hayes | .15 | .10 |
| 356 | Tommy Kane | .20 | .12 | 413 | Richard Johnson (R) | .20 | .12 |
| 357 | Melvin Bratton | .15 | .10 | 414 | Darryll Lewis (R) | .50 | .30 |
| 358 | Bruce Matthews | .20 | .12 | 415 | Jeff Bryant | .15 | .10 |
| 359 | Mark Duper | .30 | .18 | 416 | Leslie O'Neal | .25 | .15 |
| 360 | Jeff Wright (R) | .30 | .18 | 417 | Andre Reed | 1.25 | .70 |
| 361 | Barry Sanders | 8.50 | 5.50 | 418 | Charles Mann | .20 | .12 |
| 362 | Chuck Webb (R) | .50 | .30 | 419 | Keith DeLong | .15 | .10 |
| 363 | Darryl Grant | .15 | .10 | 420 | Bruce Hill | .15 | .10 |
| 364 | William Roberts | .15 | .10 | 421 | Matt Brock (R) | .30 | .18 |
| 365 | Reggie Rutland | .15 | .10 | 422 | Johnny Johnson | 1.00 | .60 |
| 366 | Clay Matthews | .15 | .10 | 423 | Mark Bortz | .15 | .10 |
| 367 | Anthony Miller | .80 | .50 | 424 | Ben Smith | .15 | .10 |
| 368 | Mike Prior | .15 | .10 | 425 | Jeff Cross | .15 | .10 |
| 369 | Jessie Tuggle | .15 | .10 | 426 | Irv Pankey | .15 | .10 |
| 370 | Brad Muster | .25 | .15 | 427 | Hassan Jones | .20 | .12 |
| 371 | Jay Schroeder | .30 | .18 | 428 | Andre Tippett | .25 | .15 |
| 372 | Greg Lloyd | .20 | .12 | 429 | Tim Worley | .25 | .15 |
| 373 | Mike Cofer | .15 | .10 | 430 | Daniel Stubbs | .15 | .10 |
| 374 | James Brooks | .25 | .15 | 431 | Max Montoya | .15 | .10 |
| 375 | Danny Noonan | .15 | .10 | 432 | Jumbo Elliott | .15 | .10 |
| 376 | Latin Berry (R) | .20 | .12 | 433 | Duane Bickett | .15 | .10 |
| 377 | Brad Baxter | .60 | .35 | 434 | Nate Lewis (R) | .50 | .30 |
| 378 | Godfrey Myles (R) | .30 | .18 | 435 | Leonard Russell (R) | 2.50 | 1.50 |
| 379 | Morten Andersen | .25 | .15 | 436 | Hoby Brenner | .15 | .10 |
| 380 | Keith Woodside | .20 | .12 | 437 | Ricky Sanders | .25 | .15 |
| 381 | Bobby Humphrey | .40 | .22 | 438 | Pierce Holt | .15 | .10 |
| 382 | Mike Golic | .15 | .10 | 439 | Derrick Fenner | .40 | .25 |
| 383 | Keith McCants | .25 | .15 | 440 | Drew Hill | .30 | .18 |
| 384 | Anthony Thompson | .40 | .25 | 441 | Will Wolford | .15 | .10 |
| 385 | Mark Clayton | .50 | .30 | 442 | Albert Lewis | .20 | .12 |
| 386 | Neil Smith | .25 | .15 | 443 | James Francis | .30 | .18 |
| 387 | Bryan Millard | .15 | .10 | 444 | Chris Jacke | .15 | .10 |

| | | | |
|---|---|---|---|
| 445 | Mike Farr | .15 | .10 |
| 446 | Stephen Braggs | .15 | .10 |
| 447 | Michael Haynes | 3.50 | 2.00 |
| 448 | Freeman McNeil | .25 | .15 |
| 449 | Kevin Donnalley (R) | .25 | .15 |
| 450 | John Offerdahl | .25 | .15 |
| 451 | Eric Allen | .15 | .10 |
| 452 | Keith McKeller | .20 | .12 |
| 453 | Kevin Greene | .20 | .12 |
| 454 | Ronnie Lippett | .15 | .10 |
| 455 | Ray Childress | .30 | .18 |
| 456 | Mike Saxon | .15 | .10 |
| 457 | Mark Robinson | .15 | .10 |
| 458 | Greg Kragen | .15 | .10 |
| 459 | Steve Jordan | .15 | .10 |
| 460 | John Johnson (R) | .25 | .15 |
| 461 | Sam Mills | .30 | .18 |
| 462 | Bo Jackson | 1.00 | .60 |
| 463 | Mark Collins | .20 | .12 |
| 464 | Percy Snow | .35 | .22 |
| 465 | Jeff Bostic | .15 | .10 |
| 466 | Jacob Green | .15 | .10 |
| 467 | Dexter Carter | .30 | .18 |
| 468 | Rich Camarillo | .15 | .10 |
| 469 | Bill Brooks | .15 | .10 |
| 470 | John Carney | .15 | .10 |
| 471 | Don Majkowski | .40 | .25 |
| 472 | Ralph Tamm (R) | .25 | .15 |
| 473 | Fred Barnett | 3.50 | 2.00 |
| 474 | Jim Covert | .20 | .12 |
| 475 | Kenneth Davis | .75 | .40 |
| 476 | Jerry Gray | .20 | .12 |
| 477 | Broderick Thomas | .25 | .15 |
| 478 | Chris Doleman | .25 | .15 |
| 479 | Haywood Jeffires | 4.50 | 2.50 |
| 480 | Craig Heyward | .25 | .15 |
| 481 | Markus Koch | .20 | .12 |
| 482 | Tim Krumrie | .15 | .10 |
| 483 | Robert Clark | .20 | .12 |
| 484 | Mike Rozier | .25 | .15 |
| 485 | Danny Villa | .15 | .10 |
| 486 | Gerald Williams | .15 | .10 |
| 487 | Steve Wisniewski | .20 | .12 |
| 488 | J.B. Brown | .15 | .10 |
| 489 | Eugene Robinson | .20 | .12 |
| 490 | Ottis Anderson | .30 | .18 |
| 491 | Tony Stargell | .15 | .10 |
| 492 | Jack Del Rio | .15 | .10 |
| 493 | Lamar Rogers (R) | .40 | .25 |
| 494 | Ricky Nattiel | .25 | .15 |
| 495 | Dan Saleaumua | .15 | .10 |
| 496 | Checklist | .15 | .05 |
| 497 | Checklist | .15 | .05 |
| 498 | Checklist | .15 | .05 |
| 499 | Checklist | .15 | .05 |
| 500 | Checklist | .15 | .05 |

# 1992 Topps

This 759-card set was issued in two 330-card series plus a 99-card High Number set (661-759). The cards feature full color action photos on the fronts with the player's name in a small box in the lower left corner while his team name appears in the lower right corner. Card backs contain personal data, stats, brief bio's and a shot of the player's home stadium. Topps also produced gold versions of each card. One gold card was inserted into each Topps pack. Those gold cards are valued at 8 to 10 times the price of the player's regular card listed below. The High Number Series (661-759) contained random inserts featuring four former number one draft picks. Those bonus cards (BC) are listed at the end of this checklist. All cards measure 2-1/2" by 3-1/2".

| | MINT | NR/MT |
|---|---|---|
| **Complete Set (759)** | 40.00 | 25.00 |
| **Complete Set (661-759)** | 15.00 | 9.00 |
| **Commons** | .04 | .02 |
| **Complete Set (Gold)** | 225.00 | 125.00 |
| **Commons (Gold)** | .50 | .28 |

| | | | |
|---|---|---|---|
| 1 | Tim McGee | .07 | .04 |
| 2 | Rich Camarillo | .04 | .02 |
| 3 | Anthony Johnson | .04 | .02 |
| 4 | Larry Kelm | .04 | .02 |
| 5 | Irving Fryar | .07 | .04 |
| 6 | Joey Browner | .06 | .03 |
| 7 | Michael Walter | .04 | .02 |
| 8 | Cortez Kennedy | .20 | .12 |
| 9 | Reyna Thompson | .04 | .02 |
| 10 | John Friesz | .12 | .07 |
| 11 | Leroy Hoard | .08 | .05 |

| | | | | | | | | |
|---|---|---|---|---|---|---|---|
| 12 | Steve McMichael | .07 | .04 | 69 | Simon Fletcher | .04 | .02 |
| 13 | Marvin Washington | .07 | .04 | 70 | Warren Moon | .25 | .15 |
| 14 | Clyde Simmons | .08 | .05 | 71 | Chris Jacke | .04 | .02 |
| 15 | Stephone Paige | .07 | .04 | 72 | Steve Wisniewski | .04 | .02 |
| 16 | Mike Utley | .12 | .07 | 73 | Mike Cofer | .04 | .02 |
| 17 | Tunch Ilkin | .04 | .02 | 74 | Tim Johnson | .04 | .02 |
| 18 | Lawrence Dawsey | .15 | .08 | 75 | T. J. Turner | .04 | .02 |
| 19 | Vance Johnson | .08 | .05 | 76 | Scott Case | .04 | .02 |
| 20 | Bryce Paup | .07 | .04 | 77 | Michael Jackson | .25 | .15 |
| 21 | Jeff Wright | .04 | .02 | 78 | Jon Hand | .04 | .02 |
| 22 | Gill Fenerty | .04 | .02 | 79 | Stan Brock | .04 | .02 |
| 23 | Lamar Lathon | .07 | .04 | 80 | Robert Blackmon | .04 | .02 |
| 24 | Danny Copeland | .04 | .02 | 81 | David Johnson | .04 | .02 |
| 25 | Marcus Allen | .10 | .06 | 82 | Damone Johnson | .04 | .02 |
| 26 | Tim Green | .04 | .02 | 83 | Marc Spindler | .04 | .02 |
| 27 | Pete Stoyanovich | .04 | .02 | 84 | Larry Brown | .04 | .02 |
| 28 | Alvin Harper | .40 | .25 | 85 | Ray Berry | .04 | .02 |
| 29 | Roy Foster | .04 | .02 | 86 | Andre Waters | .04 | .02 |
| 30 | Eugene Daniel | .04 | .02 | 87 | Carlos Huerta (R) | .08 | .05 |
| 31 | Luis Sharpe | .04 | .02 | 88 | Brad Muster | .08 | .05 |
| 32 | Terry Wooden | .04 | .02 | 89 | Chuck Cecil | .04 | .02 |
| 33 | Jim Breech | .04 | .02 | 90 | Nick Lowery | .07 | .04 |
| 34 | Randy Hilliard (R) | .08 | .05 | 91 | Cornelius Bennett | .10 | .06 |
| 35 | Roman Phifer | .04 | .02 | 92 | Jessie Tuggle | .04 | .02 |
| 36 | Erik Howard | .04 | .02 | 93 | Mark Schlereth (R) | .12 | .07 |
| 37 | Chris Singleton | .07 | .04 | 94 | Vestee Jackson | .04 | .02 |
| 38 | Matt Stover | .04 | .02 | 95 | Eric Bieniemy | .12 | .07 |
| 39 | Tim Irwin | .04 | .02 | 96 | Jeff Hostetler | .15 | .08 |
| 40 | Karl Mecklenburg | .07 | .04 | 97 | Ken Lanier | .04 | .02 |
| 41 | Joe Phillips | .04 | .02 | 98 | Wayne Haddix | .07 | .04 |
| 42 | Bill Jones (R) | .10 | .06 | 99 | Lorenzo White | .15 | .08 |
| 43 | Mark Carrier | .08 | .05 | 100 | Mervyn Fernandez | .08 | .05 |
| 44 | George Jamison | .04 | .02 | 101 | Brent Williams | .04 | .02 |
| 45 | Rob Taylor | .04 | .02 | 102 | Ian Beckles | .04 | .02 |
| 46 | Jeff Jaeger | .04 | .02 | 103 | Harris Barton | .04 | .02 |
| 47 | Don Majkowski | .10 | .06 | 104 | Edgar Bennett (R) | .40 | .25 |
| 48 | Al Edwards | .04 | .02 | 105 | Mike Pitts | .04 | .02 |
| 49 | Curtis Duncan | .08 | .05 | 106 | Fuad Reveiz | .04 | .02 |
| 50 | Sam Mills | .08 | .05 | 107 | Vernon Turner | .04 | .02 |
| 51 | Terance Mathis | .04 | .02 | 108 | Tracy Hayworth (R) | .10 | .06 |
| 52 | Brian Mitchell | .10 | .06 | 109 | Checklist 1-110 | .04 | .02 |
| 53 | Mike Pritchard | .35 | .20 | 110 | Tom Waddle | .12 | .07 |
| 54 | Calvin Williams | .10 | .06 | 111 | Fred Stokes | .04 | .02 |
| 55 | Hardy Nickerson | .04 | .02 | 112 | Howard Ballard | .04 | .02 |
| 56 | Nate Newton | .04 | .02 | 113 | David Szott | .04 | .02 |
| 57 | Steve Wallace | .04 | .02 | 114 | Tim McKyer | .04 | .02 |
| 58 | John Offerdahl | .07 | .04 | 115 | Kyle Clifton | .04 | .02 |
| 59 | Aeneas Williams | .12 | .07 | 116 | Tony Bennett | .12 | .07 |
| 60 | Lee Johnson | .04 | .02 | 117 | Joel Hilgenberg | .04 | .02 |
| 61 | Ricardo McDonald (R) | .10 | .06 | 118 | Dwayne Harper | .04 | .02 |
| 62 | David Richards | .04 | .02 | 119 | Mike Baab | .04 | .02 |
| 63 | Paul Gruber | .07 | .04 | 120 | Mark Clayton | .10 | .06 |
| 64 | Greg McMurtry | .10 | .06 | 121 | Eric Swann | .08 | .05 |
| 65 | Jay Hilgenberg | .04 | .02 | 122 | Neil O'Donnell | .50 | .28 |
| 66 | Tim Grunhard | .04 | .02 | 123 | Mike Munchak | .07 | .04 |
| 67 | Dwayne White (R) | .08 | .05 | 124 | Howie Long | .08 | .05 |
| 68 | Don Beebe | .12 | .07 | 125 | John Elway | .25 | .15 |

| | | | |
|---|---|---|---|
| 126 | Joe Prokop | .04 | .02 |
| 127 | Pepper Johnson | .04 | .02 |
| 128 | Richard Dent | .07 | .04 |
| 129 | Robert Porcher (R) | .20 | .12 |
| 130 | Earnest Byner | .08 | .05 |
| 131 | Kent Hull | .04 | .02 |
| 132 | Mike Merriweather | .04 | .02 |
| 133 | Scott Fulhage | .04 | .02 |
| 134 | Kevin Porter | .04 | .02 |
| 135 | Tony Casillas | .08 | .05 |
| 136 | Dean Biasucci | .04 | .02 |
| 137 | Ben Smith | .04 | .02 |
| 138 | Bruce Kozerski | .04 | .02 |
| 139 | Jeff Campbell | .04 | .02 |
| 140 | Kevin Greene | .07 | .04 |
| 141 | Gary Plummer | .04 | .02 |
| 142 | Vincent Brown | .04 | .02 |
| 143 | Ron Hall | .04 | .02 |
| 144 | Louie Aguiar (R) | .10 | .06 |
| 145 | Mark Duper | .08 | .05 |
| 146 | Jesse Sapolu | .04 | .02 |
| 147 | Jeff Gossett | .04 | .02 |
| 148 | Brian Noble | .04 | .02 |
| 149 | Derek Russell | .12 | .07 |
| 150 | Carlton Bailey (R) | .12 | .07 |
| 151 | Kelly Goodburn | .04 | .02 |
| 152 | Audrey McMilliam | .04 | .02 |
| 153 | Neal Anderson | .10 | .06 |
| 154 | Bill Maas | .04 | .02 |
| 155 | Rickey Jackson | .07 | .04 |
| 156 | Chris Miller | .20 | .12 |
| 157 | Darren Comeaux | .04 | .02 |
| 158 | David Williams | .04 | .02 |
| 159 | Rich Gannon | .20 | .12 |
| 160 | Kevin Mack | .08 | .05 |
| 161 | Jim Arnold | .04 | .02 |
| 162 | Reggie White | .12 | .07 |
| 163 | Leonard Russell | .35 | .20 |
| 164 | Doug Smith | .04 | .02 |
| 165 | Tony Mandarich | .07 | .04 |
| 166 | Greg Lloyd | .04 | .02 |
| 167 | Jumbo Elliott | .04 | .02 |
| 168 | Jonathan Hayes | .04 | .02 |
| 169 | Jim Ritcher | .04 | .02 |
| 170 | Mike Kenn | .07 | .04 |
| 171 | James Washington | .04 | .02 |
| 172 | Tim Harris | .07 | .04 |
| 173 | James Thornton | .04 | .02 |
| 174 | John Brandes (R) | .08 | .05 |
| 175 | Fred McAfee (R) | .20 | .12 |
| 176 | Henry Rolling | .04 | .02 |
| 177 | Tony Paige | .04 | .02 |
| 178 | Jay Schroeder | .12 | .07 |
| 179 | Jeff Herrod | .04 | .02 |
| 180 | Emmitt Smith | 1.75 | 1.00 |
| 181 | Wymon Henderson | .04 | .02 |
| 182 | Rob Moore | .20 | .12 |
| 183 | Robert Wilson | .08 | .05 |
| 184 | Michael Zordich (R) | .10 | .06 |
| 185 | Jim Harbaugh | .10 | .06 |
| 186 | Vince Workman | .10 | .06 |
| 187 | Ernest Givins | .12 | .07 |
| 188 | Herschel Walker | .15 | .08 |
| 189 | Dan Fike | .04 | .02 |
| 190 | Seth Joyner | .07 | .04 |
| 191 | Steve Young | .40 | .25 |
| 192 | Dennis Gibson | .04 | .02 |
| 193 | Darryl Talley | .08 | .05 |
| 194 | Emile Harry | .04 | .02 |
| 195 | Bill Fralic | .04 | .02 |
| 196 | Michael Stewart | .04 | .02 |
| 197 | James Francis | .08 | .05 |
| 198 | Jerome Henderson | .04 | .02 |
| 199 | John L. Williams | .08 | .05 |
| 200 | Rod Woodson | .10 | .06 |
| 201 | Mike Farr | .04 | .02 |
| 202 | Greg Montgomery | .04 | .02 |
| 203 | Andre Collins | .08 | .05 |
| 204 | Scott Miller | .04 | .02 |
| 205 | Clay Matthews | .04 | .02 |
| 206 | Ethan Horton | .07 | .04 |
| 207 | Rich Miano (R) | .08 | .05 |
| 208 | Chris Mims (R) | .35 | .20 |
| 209 | Anthony Morgan | .12 | .07 |
| 210 | Rodney Hampton | .30 | .18 |
| 211 | Chris Hinton | .07 | .04 |
| 212 | Esera Tuaolo | .04 | .02 |
| 213 | Shane Conlan | .08 | .05 |
| 214 | John Carney | .04 | .02 |
| 215 | Kenny Walker | .10 | .06 |
| 216 | Scott Radecic | .04 | .02 |
| 217 | Chris Martin | .04 | .02 |
| 218 | Checklist 111-220 | .04 | .02 |
| 219 | Wesley Carroll | .15 | .08 |
| 220 | Bill Romanowski | .04 | .02 |
| 221 | Reggie Cobb | .20 | .12 |
| 222 | Alfred Anderson | .04 | .02 |
| 223 | Cleveland Gary | .07 | .04 |
| 224 | Eddie Blake (R) | .12 | .07 |
| 225 | Chris Spielman | .07 | .04 |
| 226 | John Roper | .04 | .02 |
| 227 | George Thomas (R) | .10 | .06 |
| 228 | Jeff Faulkner | .04 | .02 |
| 229 | Chip Lohmiller | .04 | .02 |
| 230 | Hugh Millen | .20 | .12 |
| 231 | Ray Horton | .04 | .02 |
| 232 | James Campen | .04 | .02 |
| 233 | Howard Cross | .04 | .02 |
| 234 | Keith McKeller | .07 | .04 |
| 235 | Dino Hackett | .04 | .02 |
| 236 | Jerome Brown | .07 | .04 |
| 237 | Andy Heck | .04 | .02 |
| 238 | Rodney Holman | .04 | .02 |
| 239 | Bruce Matthews | .07 | .04 |

| | | | | | | | |
|---|---|---|---|---|---|---|---|
| 240 | Jeff Lageman | .07 | .04 | 297 | Broderick Thompson | .04 | .02 |
| 241 | Bobby Hebert | .15 | .08 | 298 | Doug Widell | .04 | .02 |
| 242 | Gary Anderson | .04 | .02 | 299 | Carwell Gardner | .04 | .02 |
| 243 | Mark Bortz | .04 | .02 | 300 | Barry Sanders | .75 | .40 |
| 244 | Rich Moran | .04 | .02 | 301 | Eric Metcalf | .10 | .06 |
| 245 | Jeff Uhlenhake | .04 | .02 | 302 | Erick Thomas | .04 | .02 |
| 246 | Ricky Sanders | .07 | .04 | 303 | Terrell Buckley (R) | .75 | .40 |
| 247 | Clarence Kay | .04 | .02 | 304 | Byron Evans | .04 | .02 |
| 248 | Ed King | .07 | .04 | 305 | Johnny Hector | .07 | .04 |
| 249 | Eddie Anderson | .04 | .02 | 306 | Steve Broussard | .08 | .05 |
| 250 | Amp Lee (R) | .40 | .25 | 307 | Gene Atkins | .04 | .02 |
| 251 | Norm Johnson | .04 | .02 | 308 | Terry McDaniel | .04 | .02 |
| 252 | Michael Carter | .04 | .02 | 309 | Charles McRae | .04 | .02 |
| 253 | Felix Wright | .04 | .02 | 310 | Jim Lachey | .08 | .05 |
| 254 | Leon Seals | .04 | .02 | 311 | Pat Harlow | .07 | .04 |
| 255 | Nate Lewis | .12 | .07 | 312 | Kevin Butler | .04 | .02 |
| 256 | Kevin Call | .04 | .02 | 313 | Scott Stephen | .04 | .02 |
| 257 | Darryl Henley | .04 | .02 | 314 | Dermontti Dawson | .04 | .02 |
| 258 | Jon Vaughn | .15 | .08 | 315 | Johnny Meads | .04 | .02 |
| 259 | Matt Bahr | .04 | .02 | 316 | Checklist 221-330 | .04 | .02 |
| 260 | Johnny Johnson | .15 | .08 | 317 | Aaron Craver | .10 | .06 |
| 261 | Ken Norton | .08 | .05 | 318 | Michael Brooks | .04 | .02 |
| 262 | Wendell Davis | .12 | .07 | 319 | Guy McIntyre | .04 | .02 |
| 263 | Eugene Robinson | .07 | .04 | 320 | Thurman Thomas | .60 | .35 |
| 264 | David Treadwell | .04 | .02 | 321 | Courtney Hall | .04 | .02 |
| 265 | Michael Haynes | .25 | .15 | 322 | Dan Saleaumua | .04 | .02 |
| 266 | Robb Thomas | .08 | .05 | 323 | Vinson Smith (R) | .10 | .06 |
| 267 | Nate Odomes | .04 | .02 | 324 | Steve Jordan | .04 | .02 |
| 268 | Martin Mayhew | .04 | .02 | 325 | Walter Reeves | .04 | .02 |
| 269 | Perry Kemp | .04 | .02 | 326 | Erik Kramer | .20 | .12 |
| 270 | Jerry Ball | .04 | .02 | 327 | Duane Bickett | .04 | .02 |
| 271 | Tommy Vardell (R) | .75 | .40 | 328 | Tom Newberry | .04 | .02 |
| 272 | Ernie Mills | .10 | .06 | 329 | John Kasay | .04 | .02 |
| 273 | Mo Lewis | .04 | .02 | 330 | Dave Meggett | .12 | .07 |
| 274 | Roger Ruzek | .04 | .02 | 331 | Kevin Ross | .04 | .02 |
| 275 | Steve Smith | .04 | .02 | 332 | Keith Hamilton (R) | .12 | .07 |
| 276 | Bo Orlando (R) | .12 | .07 | 333 | Dwight Stone | .04 | .02 |
| 277 | Louis Oliver | .07 | .04 | 334 | Mel Gray | .07 | .04 |
| 278 | Toi Cook | .04 | .02 | 335 | Harry Galbreath | .04 | .02 |
| 279 | Eddie Brown | .07 | .04 | 336 | William Perry | .07 | .04 |
| 280 | Keith McCants | .08 | .05 | 337 | Brian Blades | .07 | .04 |
| 281 | Rob Burnett | .08 | .05 | 338 | Randall McDaniel | .04 | .02 |
| 282 | Keith DeLong | .04 | .02 | 339 | Pat Coleman (R) | .10 | .06 |
| 283 | Stan Thomas | .04 | .02 | 340 | Michael Irvin | .35 | .20 |
| 284 | Robert Brown | .04 | .02 | 341 | Checklist 331-340 | .04 | .02 |
| 285 | John Alt | .04 | .02 | 342 | Chris Mohr | .04 | .02 |
| 286 | Randy Dixon | .04 | .02 | 343 | Greg Davis | .04 | .02 |
| 287 | Siran Stacy (R) | .30 | .18 | 344 | Dave Cadigan | .04 | .02 |
| 288 | Ray Agnew | .07 | .04 | 345 | Art Monk | .20 | .12 |
| 289 | Darion Conner | .04 | .02 | 346 | Tim Goad | .04 | .02 |
| 290 | Kirk Lowdermilk | .04 | .02 | 347 | Vinnie Clark | .04 | .02 |
| 291 | Greg Jackson | .04 | .02 | 348 | David Fulcher | .04 | .02 |
| 292 | Ken Harvey | .04 | .02 | 349 | Craig Heyward | .07 | .04 |
| 293 | Jacob Green | .04 | .02 | 350 | Ronnie Lott | .10 | .06 |
| 294 | Mark Tuinei | .04 | .02 | 351 | Dexter Carter | .10 | .06 |
| 295 | Mark Rypien | .20 | .12 | 352 | Mark Jackson | .07 | .04 |
| 296 | Gerald Robinson (R) | .10 | .06 | 353 | Brian Jordan | .10 | .06 |

| # | Name | | |
|---|------|---|---|
| 354 | Ray Donaldson | .04 | .02 |
| 355 | Jim Price | .04 | .02 |
| 356 | Rod Bernstine | .07 | .04 |
| 357 | Tony Mayberry (R) | .10 | .06 |
| 358 | Richard Brown | .04 | .02 |
| 359 | David Alexander | .04 | .02 |
| 360 | Haywood Jeffires | .20 | .12 |
| 361 | Henry Thomas | .04 | .02 |
| 362 | Jeff Graham | .25 | .15 |
| 363 | Don Warren | .04 | .02 |
| 364 | Scott Davis | .04 | .02 |
| 365 | Harlon Barnett | .04 | .02 |
| 366 | Mark Collins | .07 | .04 |
| 367 | Rick Tuten | .04 | .02 |
| 368 | Lonnie Marts (R) | .10 | .06 |
| 369 | Dennis Smith | .04 | .02 |
| 370 | Steve Tasker | .04 | .02 |
| 371 | Robert Massey | .04 | .02 |
| 372 | Ricky Reynolds | .04 | .02 |
| 373 | Alvin Wright | .04 | .02 |
| 374 | Kelvin Martin | .10 | .06 |
| 375 | Vince Buck | .04 | .02 |
| 376 | John Kidd | .04 | .02 |
| 377 | William White | .04 | .02 |
| 378 | Bryan Cox | .15 | .08 |
| 379 | Jamie Dukes (R) | .10 | .06 |
| 380 | Anthony Munoz | .10 | .06 |
| 381 | Mark Gunn (R) | .10 | .06 |
| 382 | Keith Henderson | .04 | .02 |
| 383 | Charles Wilson | .04 | .02 |
| 384 | Shawn McCarthy (R) | .10 | .06 |
| 385 | Ernie Jones | .10 | .06 |
| 386 | Nick Bell | .30 | .18 |
| 387 | Derrick Walker | .07 | .04 |
| 388 | Mark Strepnoski | .04 | .02 |
| 389 | Broderick Thomas | .07 | .04 |
| 390 | Reggie Roby | .04 | .02 |
| 391 | Bubba McDowell | .04 | .02 |
| 392 | Eric Martin | .07 | .04 |
| 393 | Toby Caston (R) | .08 | .05 |
| 394 | Bern Brostek | .04 | .02 |
| 395 | Christian Okoye | .12 | .07 |
| 396 | Frank Minnifield | .04 | .02 |
| 397 | Mike Golic | .04 | .02 |
| 398 | Grant Feasel | .04 | .02 |
| 399 | Michael Ball | .04 | .02 |
| 400 | Mike Croel | .25 | .15 |
| 401 | Maury Buford | .04 | .02 |
| 402 | Jeff Bostic | .04 | .02 |
| 403 | Sean Landeta | .04 | .02 |
| 404 | Terry Allen | .60 | .35 |
| 405 | Donald Evans | .04 | .02 |
| 406 | Don Mosebar | .04 | .02 |
| 407 | D.J. Dozier | .08 | .05 |
| 408 | Bruce Pickens | .20 | .12 |
| 409 | Jim Dombrowski | .04 | .02 |
| 410 | Deron Cherry | .04 | .02 |
| 411 | Richard Johnson | .04 | .02 |
| 412 | Alexander Wright | .08 | .05 |
| 413 | Tom Rathman | .08 | .05 |
| 414 | Mark Dennis | .04 | .02 |
| 415 | Phil Hansen | .04 | .02 |
| 416 | Lonnie Young | .04 | .02 |
| 417 | Burt Grossman | .07 | .04 |
| 418 | Tony Covington | .04 | .02 |
| 419 | John Stephens | .10 | .06 |
| 420 | Jim Everett | .15 | .08 |
| 421 | Johnny Holland | .04 | .02 |
| 422 | Mike Barber (R) | .12 | .07 |
| 423 | Carl Lee | .04 | .02 |
| 424 | Craig Patterson (R) | .10 | .06 |
| 425 | Greg Townsend | .07 | .04 |
| 426 | Brett Perriman | .07 | .04 |
| 427 | Morton Andersen | .07 | .04 |
| 428 | John Gesek | .04 | .02 |
| 429 | Bryan Barker | .04 | .02 |
| 430 | John Taylor | .12 | .07 |
| 431 | Donnell Woolford | .04 | .02 |
| 432 | Ron Holmes | .04 | .02 |
| 433 | Lee Williams | .07 | .04 |
| 434 | Alfred Oglesby | .04 | .02 |
| 435 | Jarrod Bunch | .15 | .08 |
| 436 | Carlton Haselrig | .04 | .02 |
| 437 | Rufus Porter | .04 | .02 |
| 438 | Rohn Stark | .04 | .02 |
| 439 | Tony Jones | .04 | .02 |
| 440 | Andre Rison | .25 | .15 |
| 441 | Eric Hill | .04 | .02 |
| 442 | Jesse Solomon | .04 | .02 |
| 443 | Jackie Slater | .07 | .04 |
| 444 | Donnie Elder | .04 | .02 |
| 445 | Brett Maxie | .04 | .02 |
| 446 | Max Montoya | .04 | .02 |
| 447 | Will Wolford | .04 | .02 |
| 448 | Craig Taylor | .04 | .02 |
| 449 | Jimmy Jones | .04 | .02 |
| 450 | Anthony Carter | .08 | .05 |
| 451 | Brian Bollinger (R) | .10 | .06 |
| 452 | Checklist 441-550 | .04 | .02 |
| 453 | Brad Edwards | .04 | .02 |
| 454 | Gene Chilton (R) | .10 | .06 |
| 455 | Eric Allen | .04 | .02 |
| 456 | William Roberts | .04 | .02 |
| 457 | Eric Green | .12 | .07 |
| 458 | Irv Eatman | .04 | .02 |
| 459 | Derrick Thomas | .20 | .12 |
| 460 | Tommy Kane | .08 | .05 |
| 461 | LeRoy Butler | .04 | .02 |
| 462 | Oliver Barnett | .07 | .04 |
| 463 | Anthony Smith | .07 | .04 |
| 464 | Chris Dishman | .07 | .04 |
| 465 | Pat Terrell | .04 | .02 |
| 466 | Greg Kragen | .04 | .02 |
| 467 | Rodney Peete | .12 | .07 |

| | | | |
|---|---|---|---|
| 468 Willie Drewrey | .04 | .02 |
| 469 Jim Wilks | .04 | .02 |
| 470 Vince Newsome | .04 | .02 |
| 471 Chris Gardocki | .04 | .02 |
| 472 Chris Chandler | .10 | .06 |
| 473 George Thornton | .04 | .02 |
| 474 Albert Lewis | .04 | .02 |
| 475 Kevin Glover | .04 | .02 |
| 476 Joe Bowden (R) | .12 | .07 |
| 477 Harry Sydney | .04 | .02 |
| 478 Bob Golic | .04 | .02 |
| 479 Tony Zendejas | .04 | .02 |
| 480 Brad Baxter | .08 | .05 |
| 481 Steve Beuerlein | .20 | .12 |
| 482 Mark Higgs | .20 | .12 |
| 483 Drew Hill | .08 | .05 |
| 484 Bryan Millard | .04 | .02 |
| 485 Mark Kelso | .04 | .02 |
| 486 David Grant | .04 | .02 |
| 487 Gary Zimmerman | .04 | .02 |
| 488 Leonard Marshall | .08 | .05 |
| 489 Keith Jackson | .15 | .08 |
| 490 Sterling Sharpe | .30 | .18 |
| 491 Ferrell Edmunds | .04 | .02 |
| 492 Wilber Marshall | .07 | .04 |
| 493 Charles Haley | .08 | .05 |
| 494 Riki Ellison | .04 | .02 |
| 495 Bill Brooks | .04 | .02 |
| 496 Bill Hawkins | .04 | .02 |
| 497 Erik Williams | .04 | .02 |
| 498 Leon Searcy (R) | .15 | .08 |
| 499 Mike Horan | .04 | .02 |
| 500 Pat Swilling | .12 | .07 |
| 501 Maurice Hurst | .04 | .02 |
| 502 William Fuller | .07 | .04 |
| 503 Tim Newton | .04 | .02 |
| 504 Lorenzo Lynch | .04 | .02 |
| 505 Tim Barnett | .20 | .12 |
| 506 Tom Thayer | .04 | .02 |
| 507 Chris Burkett | .04 | .02 |
| 508 Ronnie Harmon | .08 | .05 |
| 509 James Brooks | .08 | .05 |
| 510 Bennie Blades | .07 | .04 |
| 511 Roger Craig | .08 | .05 |
| 512 Tony Woods | .04 | .02 |
| 513 Greg Lewis | .12 | .07 |
| 514 Eric Pegram | .10 | .06 |
| 515 Elvis Patterson | .04 | .02 |
| 516 Jeff Cross | .04 | .02 |
| 517 Myron Guyton | .04 | .02 |
| 518 Jay Novacek | .12 | .07 |
| 519 Leo Barker (R) | .12 | .07 |
| 520 Keith Byars | .08 | .05 |
| 521 Dalton Hilliard | .08 | .05 |
| 522 Ted Washington | .10 | .06 |
| 523 Dexter McNabb (R) | .20 | .12 |
| 524 Frank Reich | .10 | .06 |
| 525 Henry Ellard | .08 | .05 |
| 526 Barry Foster | .60 | .35 |
| 527 Barry Word | .20 | .12 |
| 528 Gary Anderson | .04 | .02 |
| 529 Reggie Rutland | .04 | .02 |
| 530 Stephen Baker | .07 | .04 |
| 531 John Flannery | .04 | .02 |
| 532 Steve Wright | .04 | .02 |
| 533 Eric Sanders | .04 | .02 |
| 534 Bob Whitfield (R) | .15 | .08 |
| 535 Gaston Green | .12 | .07 |
| 536 Anthony Pleasant | .04 | .02 |
| 537 Jeff Bryant | .04 | .02 |
| 538 Jarvis Williams | .04 | .02 |
| 539 Jim Morrissey | .04 | .02 |
| 540 Andre Tippett | .07 | .04 |
| 541 Gill Byrd | .07 | .04 |
| 542 Raleigh McKenzie | .04 | .02 |
| 543 Jim Sweeney | .04 | .02 |
| 544 Dave Lutz | .04 | .02 |
| 545 Wayne Martin | .07 | .04 |
| 546 Karl Wilson | .04 | .02 |
| 547 Pierce Holt | .04 | .02 |
| 548 Doug Smith | .07 | .04 |
| 549 Nolan Harrison (R) | .12 | .07 |
| 550 Freddie Joe Nunn | .04 | .02 |
| 551 Eric Moore | .04 | .02 |
| 552 Chris Carter | .15 | .08 |
| 553 Kevin Gogan | .04 | .02 |
| 554 Harold Green | .25 | .15 |
| 555 Kenneth Davis | .15 | .08 |
| 556 Travis McNeal | .04 | .02 |
| 557 Jim Jensen | .04 | .02 |
| 558 Willie Green | .20 | .12 |
| 559 Scott Galbraith (R) | .12 | .07 |
| 560 Luis Lipps | .07 | .04 |
| 561 Matt Brock | .04 | .02 |
| 562 Mike Prior | .04 | .02 |
| 563 Checklist 551-560 | .04 | .02 |
| 564 Robert Delpino | .07 | .04 |
| 565 Vinny Testaverde | .10 | .06 |
| 566 Willie Gault | .07 | .04 |
| 567 Quinn Early | .04 | .02 |
| 568 Eric Moten | .04 | .02 |
| 569 Lance Smith | .04 | .02 |
| 570 Darrell Green | .10 | .06 |
| 571 Moe Gardner | .07 | .04 |
| 572 Steve Atwater | .08 | .05 |
| 573 Ray Childress | .08 | .05 |
| 574 Dave Krieg | .10 | .06 |
| 575 Bruce Armstrong | .04 | .02 |
| 576 Fred Barnett | .15 | .08 |
| 577 Don Griffin | .04 | .02 |
| 578 David Brandon (R) | .12 | .07 |
| 579 Robert Young | .04 | .02 |
| 580 Keith Van Horne | .04 | .02 |
| 581 Jeff Criswell | .04 | .02 |

| | | | |
|---|---|---|---|
| 582 Lewis Tillman | .04 | .02 |
| 583 Bubby Brister | .10 | .06 |
| 584 Aaron Wallace | .07 | .04 |
| 585 Chris Doleman | .07 | .04 |
| 586 Marty Carter (R) | .10 | .06 |
| 587 Chris Warren | .10 | .06 |
| 588 David Griggs | .04 | .02 |
| 589 Darrell Thompson | .08 | .05 |
| 590 Marion Butts | .12 | .07 |
| 591 Scott Norwood | .04 | .02 |
| 592 Lomas Brown | .07 | .04 |
| 593 Daryl Johnston | .12 | .07 |
| 594 Alonzo Mitz (R) | .10 | .06 |
| 595 Tommy Barnhardt | .04 | .02 |
| 596 Tim Jorden | .04 | .02 |
| 597 Neil Smith | .07 | .04 |
| 598 Todd Marinovich | .60 | .35 |
| 599 Sean Jones | .04 | .02 |
| 600 Clarence Verdin | .07 | .04 |
| 601 Trace Armstrong | .04 | .02 |
| 602 Steve Bono | .50 | .28 |
| 603 Mark Ingram | .08 | .05 |
| 604 Flipper Anderson | .08 | .05 |
| 605 James Jones | .04 | .02 |
| 606 Al Noga | .04 | .02 |
| 607 Rick Bryan | .04 | .02 |
| 608 Eugene Lockhart | .04 | .02 |
| 609 Charles Mann | .07 | .04 |
| 610 James Hasty | .04 | .02 |
| 611 Jeff Feagles | .04 | .02 |
| 612 Tim Brown | .12 | .07 |
| 613 David Little | .04 | .02 |
| 614 Keith Sims | .04 | .02 |
| 615 Kevin Murphy | .04 | .02 |
| 616 Ray Crockett | .04 | .02 |
| 617 Jim Jeffcoat | .07 | .04 |
| 618 Patrick Hunter | .04 | .02 |
| 619 Keith Kartz | .04 | .02 |
| 620 Peter Tom Willis | .10 | .06 |
| 621 Vaughn Johnson | .07 | .04 |
| 622 Shawn Jefferson | .15 | .08 |
| 623 Anthony Thompson | .08 | .05 |
| 624 John Rienstra | .04 | .02 |
| 625 Don Maggs | .04 | .02 |
| 626 Todd Lyght | .15 | .08 |
| 627 Brent Jones | .08 | .05 |
| 628 Todd McNair | .04 | .02 |
| 629 Winston Moss | .04 | .02 |
| 630 Mark Carrier | .08 | .05 |
| 631 Dan Owens | .04 | .02 |
| 632 Sammy Smith | .08 | .05 |
| 633 James Lofton | .20 | .12 |
| 634 Paul McJulien (R) | .10 | .06 |
| 635 Tony Tolbert | .04 | .02 |
| 636 Carnell Lake | .07 | .04 |
| 637 Gary Clark | .15 | .08 |
| 638 Brian Washington | .04 | .02 |

| | | | |
|---|---|---|---|
| 639 Jessie Hester | .04 | .02 |
| 640 Doug Riesenburg | .04 | .02 |
| 641 Joe Walter (R) | .10 | .06 |
| 642 John Rade | .04 | .02 |
| 643 Wes Hopkins | .04 | .02 |
| 644 Kelly Stouffer | .12 | .07 |
| 645 Marv Cook | .08 | .05 |
| 646 Ken Clarke | .04 | .02 |
| 647 Bobby Humphrey | .12 | .07 |
| 648 Tim McDonald | .04 | .02 |
| 649 Donald Frank (R) | .08 | .05 |
| 650 Richmond Webb | .07 | .04 |
| 651 Lemuel Stinson | .04 | .02 |
| 652 Merton Hanks | .04 | .02 |
| 653 Frank Warren | .04 | .02 |
| 654 Thomas Benson | .04 | .02 |
| 655 Al Smith | .07 | .04 |
| 656 Steve DeBerg | .10 | .06 |
| 657 Jayice Pearson (R) | .10 | .06 |
| 658 Joe Morris | .04 | .02 |
| 659 Fred Strickland | .04 | .02 |
| 660 Kelvin Pritchett | .12 | .07 |
| 661 Lewis Billups | .04 | .02 |
| 662 Todd Collins (R) | .10 | .06 |
| 663 Corey Miller (R) | .12 | .07 |
| 664 Levon Kirkland (R) | .15 | .08 |
| 665 Jerry Rice | .40 | .25 |
| 666 Mike Lodish (R) | .10 | .06 |
| 667 Chuck Smith (R) | .10 | .06 |
| 668 Lance Olberding (R) | .08 | .05 |
| 669 Kevin Smith (R) | .20 | .12 |
| 670 Dale Carter (R) | .40 | .25 |
| 671 Sean Gilbert (R) | .30 | .18 |
| 672 Ken O'Brien | .10 | .06 |
| 673 Ricky Proehl | .10 | .06 |
| 674 Junior Seau | .15 | .08 |
| 675 Courtney Hawkins (R) | .35 | .20 |
| 676 Eddie Robinson (R) | .15 | .08 |
| 677 Tommy Jeter (R) | .12 | .07 |
| 678 Jeff George | .25 | .15 |
| 679 Cary Conklin | .10 | .06 |
| 680 Ruben Mayes | .04 | .02 |
| 681 Sean Lumpkin (R) | .12 | .07 |
| 682 Dan Marino | .35 | .20 |
| 683 Ed McDaniel (R) | .10 | .06 |
| 684 Greg Skrepenak (R) | .15 | .08 |
| 685 Tracy Scroggins (R) | .20 | .12 |
| 686 Tommy Maddox (R) | 1.50 | .90 |
| 687 Mike Singletary | .10 | .06 |
| 688 Patrick Rowe (R) | .25 | .15 |
| 689 Phillippi Sparks (R) | .12 | .07 |
| 690 Joel Steed (R) | .12 | .07 |
| 691 Kevin Fagan | .04 | .02 |
| 692 Deion Sanders | .20 | .12 |
| 693 Bruce Smith | .10 | .06 |
| 694 David Klingler (R) | 2.00 | 1.25 |
| 695 Clayton Holmes (R) | .15 | .08 |

| | | | |
|---|---|---|---|
| 696 | Brett Favre | 1.00 | .60 |
| 697 | Marc Boutte (R) | .12 | .07 |
| 698 | Dwayne Sabb (R) | .10 | .06 |
| 699 | Ed McCaffrey (R) | .08 | .05 |
| 700 | Randall Cunningham | .20 | .12 |
| 701 | Quentin Coryatt (R) | .75 | .40 |
| 702 | Bernie Kosar | .12 | .07 |
| 703 | Vaughn Dunbar (R) | .60 | .35 |
| 704 | Browning Nagle | .50 | .28 |
| 705 | Mark Wheeler (R) | .12 | .07 |
| 706 | Paul Siever (R) | .10 | .06 |
| 707 | Anthony Miller | .20 | .12 |
| 708 | Corey Widmer (R) | .12 | .07 |
| 709 | Eric Dickerson | .25 | .15 |
| 710 | Martin Bayless | .04 | .02 |
| 711 | Jason Hanson (R) | .10 | .06 |
| 712 | Michael Dean Perry | .15 | .08 |
| 713 | Billy Joe Tolliver | .10 | .06 |
| 714 | Chad Hennings (R) | .20 | .12 |
| 715 | Bucky Richardson (R) | .25 | .15 |
| 716 | Steve Israel (R) | .12 | .07 |
| 717 | Robert Harris (R) | .12 | .07 |
| 718 | Timm Rosenbach | .10 | .06 |
| 719 | Joe Montana | .60 | .35 |
| 720 | Derek Brown (R) | .40 | .25 |
| 721 | Robert Brooks (R) | .20 | .12 |
| 722 | Boomer Esiason | .12 | .07 |
| 723 | Troy Auzenne (R) | .15 | .08 |
| 724 | John Fina (R) | .12 | .07 |
| 725 | Chris Crooms (R) | .12 | .07 |
| 726 | Eugene Chung (R) | .12 | .07 |
| 727 | Darren Woodson (R) | .10 | .06 |
| 728 | Leslie O'Neal | .08 | .05 |
| 729 | Dan McGwire | .35 | .20 |
| 730 | Al Toon | .08 | .05 |
| 731 | Michael Brandon (R) | .10 | .06 |
| 732 | Steve DeOssie | .04 | .02 |
| 733 | Jim Kelly | .50 | .28 |
| 734 | Webster Slaughter | .10 | .06 |
| 735 | Tony Smith (R) | .60 | .35 |
| 736 | Shane Collins (R) | .15 | .08 |
| 737 | Randal Hill | .20 | .12 |
| 738 | Chris Holder (R) | .15 | .08 |
| 739 | Russell Maryland | .20 | .12 |
| 740 | Carl Pickens (R) | .80 | .45 |
| 741 | Andre Reed | .10 | .06 |
| 742 | Steve Emtman (R) | 1.25 | .70 |
| 743 | Carl Banks | .08 | .05 |
| 744 | Troy Aikman | .75 | .40 |
| 745 | Mark Royals | .04 | .02 |
| 746 | J. J. Burden | .04 | .02 |
| 747 | Michael Cofer | .04 | .02 |
| 748 | Darryl Ashmore (R) | .10 | .06 |
| 749 | Dion Lambert (R) | .12 | .07 |
| 750 | Phil Simms | .10 | .06 |
| 751 | Reggie White (R) | .10 | .06 |
| 752 | Harvey Williams | .30 | .18 |

| | | | |
|---|---|---|---|
| 753 | Ty Detmer | .15 | .08 |
| 754 | Tony Brooks (R) | .25 | .15 |
| 755 | Steve Christie | .04 | .02 |
| 756 | Lawrence Taylor | .15 | .08 |
| 757 | Merrill Hoge | .07 | .04 |
| 758 | Robert Jones (R) | .25 | .15 |
| 759 | Checklist (661-759) | .04 | .02 |
| BC1 | Jeff George (#1 Pick) | 1.25 | .70 |
| BC2 | Russell Maryland (#1 Pick) | .75 | .40 |
| BC3 | Steve Emtman (#1 Pick) | 1.25 | .70 |
| BC4 | Rocket Ismail (#1 Pick) | 1.50 | .90 |

# 1992 Topps 1000 Yard Club

The cards in this 20-card insert set were randomly distributed in 1992 Topps football jumbo packs. The cards measure 2-1/2" by 3-1/2" and feature players who gained more than 1,000 yards the previous season.

| | | MINT | NR/MT |
|---|---|---|---|
| Complete Set (20) | | 20.00 | 12.50 |
| Commons | | .40 | .25 |
| 1 | Emmitt Smith | 7.50 | 4.50 |
| 2 | Barry Sanders | 4.50 | 2.50 |
| 3 | Michael Irvin | 2.50 | 1.40 |
| 4 | Thurman Thomas | 3.50 | 2.00 |
| 5 | Gary Clark | 1.00 | .60 |
| 6 | Haywood Jeffires | 1.25 | .70 |
| 7 | Michael Haynes | 1.25 | .70 |
| 8 | Drew Hill | .40 | .25 |
| 9 | Mark Duper | .40 | .25 |
| 10 | James Lofton | 1.00 | .60 |
| 11 | Rodney Hampton | 1.25 | .70 |
| 12 | Mark Clayton | .60 | .35 |
| 13 | Henry Ellard | .40 | .25 |
| 14 | Art Monk | 1.25 | .70 |
| 15 | Earnest Byner | .40 | .25 |
| 16 | Gaston Green | .60 | .35 |
| 17 | Christian Okoye | .50 | .28 |
| 18 | Irving Fryar | .40 | .25 |

| | | | |
|---|---|---|---|
| 19 | John Taylor | .75 | .40 |
| 20 | Brian Blades | .40 | .25 |

# 1992 Topps Stadium Club

This 600-card premium set was issued in two 300-card series. A 100-card High Number series (601-700) is listed separately. The design is similar to the 1991 Stadium Club set with full bleed, full-color photos on the fronts with a Stadium Club logo in the lower corner just above the player's name. The team name appears to the right of the player's name. The set includes a 20-card Members Choice subset (MC). All Cards measure 2-1/2" by 3-1/2".

| | | MINT | NR/MT |
|---|---|---|---|
| | Complete Set (600) | 50.00 | 35.00 |
| | Commons | .15 | .10 |
| | | | |
| 1 | Mark Rypien | .50 | .30 |
| 2 | Carlton Bailey (R) | .25 | .15 |
| 3 | Kevin Glover | .15 | .10 |
| 4 | Vance Johnson | .20 | .12 |
| 5 | Jim Jeffcoat | .20 | .12 |
| 6 | Dan Saleaumua | .15 | .10 |
| 7 | Darion Conner | .15 | .10 |
| 8 | Don Maggs | .15 | .10 |
| 9 | Richard Dent | .20 | .12 |
| 10 | Mark Murphy | .15 | .10 |
| 11 | Wesley Carroll | .25 | .15 |
| 12 | Chris Burkett | .15 | .10 |
| 13 | Steve Wallace | .15 | .10 |

| | | | |
|---|---|---|---|
| 14 | Jacob Green | .15 | .10 |
| 15 | Roger Ruzek | .15 | .10 |
| 16 | J.B. Brown | .15 | .10 |
| 17 | Dave Meggett | .25 | .15 |
| 18 | David Johnson | .15 | .10 |
| 19 | Rich Gannon | .25 | .15 |
| 20 | Kevin Mack | .20 | .12 |
| 21 | Reggie Cobb | .40 | .25 |
| 22 | Nate Lewis | .25 | .15 |
| 23 | Doug Smith | .15 | .10 |
| 24 | Irving Fryar | .20 | .12 |
| 25 | Anthony Thompson | .20 | .12 |
| 26 | Duane Bickett | .15 | .10 |
| 27 | Don Majkowski | .20 | .12 |
| 28 | Mark Schlereth (R) | .20 | .12 |
| 29 | Melvin Jenkins | .15 | .10 |
| 30 | Michael Haynes | .75 | .40 |
| 31 | Greg Lewis | .25 | .15 |
| 32 | Kenneth Davis | .40 | .25 |
| 33 | Derrick Thomas | .60 | .35 |
| 34 | David Williams | .15 | .10 |
| 35 | Neal Anderson | .25 | .15 |
| 36 | Andre Collins | .20 | .12 |
| 37 | Jesse Solomon | .15 | .10 |
| 38 | Barry Sanders | 2.00 | 1.25 |
| 39 | Jeff Gossett | .15 | .10 |
| 40 | Rickey Jackson | .20 | .12 |
| 41 | Ray Berry | .15 | .10 |
| 42 | Leroy Hoard | .20 | .12 |
| 43 | Eric Thomas | .15 | .10 |
| 44 | Brian Washington | .15 | .10 |
| 45 | Pat Terrell | .15 | .10 |
| 46 | Eugene Robinson | .15 | .10 |
| 47 | Luis Sharpe | .15 | .10 |
| 48 | Jerome Brown | .15 | .10 |
| 49 | Mark Collins | .20 | .12 |
| 50 | Johnny Holland | .15 | .10 |
| 51 | Tony Paige | .15 | .10 |
| 52 | Willie Green | .50 | .30 |
| 53 | Steve Atwater | .25 | .15 |
| 54 | Brad Muster | .20 | .12 |
| 55 | Chris Dishman | .15 | .10 |
| 56 | Eddie Anderson | .15 | .10 |
| 57 | Sam Mills | .20 | .12 |
| 58 | Donald Evans | .15 | .10 |
| 59 | John Vaughn | .40 | .25 |
| 60 | Marion Butts | .25 | .15 |
| 61 | Rodney Holman | .15 | .10 |
| 62 | Dwayne White (R) | .20 | .12 |
| 63 | Martin Mayhew | .15 | .10 |
| 64 | Jonathan Hayes | .15 | .10 |
| 65 | Andre Rison | .75 | .40 |
| 66 | Calvin Williams | .20 | .12 |
| 67 | James Washington | .15 | .10 |
| 68 | Tim Harris | .20 | .12 |
| 69 | Jim Ritcher | .15 | .10 |
| 70 | Johnny Johnson | .40 | .25 |

| | | | |
|---|---|---|---|
| 71 John Offerdahl | .20 | .12 |
| 72 Herschel Walker | .30 | .18 |
| 73 Perry Kemp | .15 | .10 |
| 74 Erik Howard | .15 | .10 |
| 75 Lamar Lathon | .20 | .12 |
| 76 Greg Kragen | .15 | .10 |
| 77 Jay Schroeder | .20 | .12 |
| 78 Jim Arnold | .15 | .10 |
| 79 Chris Miller | .40 | .25 |
| 80 Deron Cherry | .15 | .10 |
| 81 Jim Harbaugh | .20 | .12 |
| 82 Gill Fenerty | .15 | .10 |
| 83 Fred Stokes | .15 | .10 |
| 84 Roman Phifer | .15 | .10 |
| 85 Clyde Simmons | .20 | .12 |
| 86 Vince Newsome | .15 | .10 |
| 87 Lawrence Dawsey | .25 | .15 |
| 88 Eddie Brown | .20 | .12 |
| 89 Greg Montgomery | .15 | .10 |
| 90 Jeff Lageman | .20 | .12 |
| 91 Terry Wooden | .15 | .10 |
| 92 Nate Newton | .15 | .10 |
| 93 David Richards | .15 | .10 |
| 94 Derek Russell | .25 | .15 |
| 95 Steve Jordan | .15 | .10 |
| 96 Hugh Millen | .35 | .20 |
| 97 Mark Duper | .20 | .12 |
| 98 Sean Landeta | .15 | .10 |
| 99 James Thornton | .15 | .10 |
| 100 Darrell Green | .25 | .15 |
| 101 Harris Barton | .15 | .10 |
| 102 John Alt | .15 | .10 |
| 103 Mike Farr | .15 | .10 |
| 104 Bob Golic | .15 | .10 |
| 105 Gene Atkins | .15 | .10 |
| 106 Gary Anderson | .15 | .10 |
| 107 Norm Johnson | .15 | .10 |
| 108 Eugene Daniel | .15 | .10 |
| 109 Kent Hull | .15 | .10 |
| 110 John Elway | .50 | .30 |
| 111 Rich Camarillo | .15 | .10 |
| 112 Charles Wilson | .15 | .10 |
| 113 Matt Bahr | .15 | .10 |
| 114 Mark Carrier | .20 | .12 |
| 115 Richmond Webb | .20 | .12 |
| 116 Charles Mann | .15 | .10 |
| 117 Tim McGee | .20 | .12 |
| 118 Wes Hopkins | .15 | .10 |
| 119 Mo Lewis | .15 | .10 |
| 120 Warren Moon | .50 | .30 |
| 121 Damone Johnson | .15 | .10 |
| 122 Kevin Gogan | .15 | .10 |
| 123 Joey Browner | .15 | .10 |
| 124 Tommy Kane | .20 | .12 |
| 125 Vincent Brown | .15 | .10 |
| 126 Barry Word | .35 | .20 |
| 127 Michael Brooks | .15 | .10 |
| 128 Jumbo Elliott | .15 | .10 |
| 129 Marcus Allen | .25 | .15 |
| 130 Tom Waddle | .35 | .20 |
| 131 Jim Dombrowski | .15 | .10 |
| 132 Aeneas Williams | .15 | .10 |
| 133 Clay Matthews | .15 | .10 |
| 134 Thurman Thomas | 1.25 | .80 |
| 135 Dean Biasucci | .15 | .10 |
| 136 Moe Gardner | .20 | .12 |
| 137 James Campen | .15 | .10 |
| 138 Tim Johnson | .15 | .10 |
| 139 Erik Kramer | .35 | .20 |
| 140 Keith McCants | .20 | .12 |
| 141 John Carney | .15 | .10 |
| 142 Tunch Ilkin | .15 | .10 |
| 143 Louis Oliver | .20 | .12 |
| 144 Bill Maas | .15 | .10 |
| 145 Wendell Davis | .30 | .18 |
| 146 Pepper Johnson | .20 | .12 |
| 147 Howie Long | .20 | .12 |
| 148 Brett Maxie | .15 | .10 |
| 149 Tony Casillas | .20 | .12 |
| 150 Michael Carter | .15 | .10 |
| 151 Bryon Evans | .15 | .10 |
| 152 Lorenzo White | .25 | .15 |
| 153 Larry Kelm | .15 | .10 |
| 154 Andy Heck | .15 | .10 |
| 155 Harry Newsome | .15 | .10 |
| 156 Chris Singleton | .20 | .12 |
| 157 Mike Kenn | .15 | .10 |
| 158 Jeff Faulkner | .15 | .10 |
| 159 Ken Lanier | .15 | .10 |
| 160 Darryl Talley | .20 | .12 |
| 161 Louie Aguiar (R) | .20 | .12 |
| 162 Danny Copeland | .15 | .10 |
| 163 Kevin Porter | .15 | .10 |
| 164 Trace Armstrong | .15 | .10 |
| 165 Dermontti Dawson | .15 | .10 |
| 166 Fred McAfee (R) | .30 | .18 |
| 167 Ronnie Lott | .25 | .15 |
| 168 Tony Mandarich | .15 | .10 |
| 169 Howard Cross | .15 | .10 |
| 170 Vestee Jackson | .15 | .10 |
| 171 Jeff Herrod | .15 | .10 |
| 172 Randy Hilliard (R) | .20 | .12 |
| 173 Robert Wilson | .20 | .12 |
| 174 Joe Walter (R) | .20 | .12 |
| 175 Chris Spielman | .20 | .12 |
| 176 Darryl Henley | .15 | .10 |
| 177 Jay Hilgenberg | .15 | .10 |
| 178 John Kidd | .15 | .10 |
| 179 Doug Widell | .15 | .10 |
| 180 Seth Joyner | .20 | .12 |
| 181 Nick Bell | .50 | .30 |
| 182 Don Griffin | .15 | .10 |
| 183 Johnny Meads | .15 | .10 |
| 184 Jeff Bostic | .15 | .10 |

| | | | |
|---|---|---|---|
| 185 | Johnny Hector | .20 | .12 |
| 186 | Jessie Tuggle | .15 | .10 |
| 187 | Robb Thomas | .20 | .12 |
| 188 | Shane Conlan | .20 | .12 |
| 189 | Michael Zordich (R) | .25 | .15 |
| 190 | Emmitt Smith | 4.50 | 2.50 |
| 191 | Robert Blackmon | .15 | .10 |
| 192 | Carl Lee | .15 | .10 |
| 193 | Harry Galbreath | .15 | .10 |
| 194 | Ed King | .15 | .10 |
| 195 | Stan Thomas | .15 | .10 |
| 196 | Andre Waters | .15 | .10 |
| 197 | Pat Harlow | .20 | .12 |
| 198 | Zefross Moss | .15 | .10 |
| 199 | Bobby Hebert | .25 | .15 |
| 200 | Doug Riesenberg | .15 | .10 |
| 201 | Mike Croel | .30 | .18 |
| 202 | Jeff Jaeger | .15 | .10 |
| 203 | Gary Plummer | .15 | .10 |
| 204 | Chris Jacke | .15 | .10 |
| 205 | Neil O'Donnell | .80 | .50 |
| 206 | Mark Bortz | .15 | .10 |
| 207 | Tim Barnett | .35 | .20 |
| 208 | Jerry Ball | .15 | .10 |
| 209 | Chip Lohmiller | .15 | .10 |
| 210 | Jim Everett | .30 | .18 |
| 211 | Tim McKyer | .15 | .10 |
| 212 | Aaron Craver | .25 | .15 |
| 213 | John L. Williams | .20 | .12 |
| 214 | Simon Fletcher | .15 | .10 |
| 215 | Walter Reeves | .15 | .10 |
| 216 | Terance Mathis | .15 | .10 |
| 217 | Mike Pitts | .15 | .10 |
| 218 | Bruce Matthews | .15 | .10 |
| 219 | Howard Ballard | .15 | .10 |
| 220 | Leonard Russell | .50 | .30 |
| 221 | Michael Stewart | .15 | .10 |
| 222 | Mike Merriweather | .15 | .10 |
| 223 | Ricky Sanders | .20 | .12 |
| 224 | Ray Horton | .15 | .10 |
| 225 | Michael Jackson | .50 | .30 |
| 226 | Bill Romanowski | .15 | .10 |
| 227 | Steve McMichael | .20 | .12 |
| 228 | Chris Martin | .15 | .10 |
| 229 | Tim Green | .15 | .10 |
| 230 | Karl Mecklenburg | .20 | .12 |
| 231 | Felix Wright | .15 | .10 |
| 232 | Charles McRae | .15 | .10 |
| 233 | Pete Stoyanovich | .15 | .10 |
| 234 | Stephen Baker | .20 | .12 |
| 235 | Herman Moore | .80 | .50 |
| 236 | Terry McDaniel | .15 | .10 |
| 237 | Dalton Hilliard | .20 | .12 |
| 238 | Gill Byrd | .20 | .12 |
| 239 | Leon Seals | .15 | .10 |
| 240 | Rod Woodson | .25 | .15 |
| 241 | Curtis Duncan | .20 | .12 |
| 242 | Keith Jackson | .30 | .18 |
| 243 | Mark Strepnoski | .15 | .10 |
| 244 | Art Monk | .40 | .25 |
| 245 | Matt Stover | .15 | .10 |
| 246 | John Roper | .15 | .10 |
| 247 | Rodney Hampton | .75 | .40 |
| 248 | Steve Wisniewski | .15 | .10 |
| 249 | Bryan Millard | .15 | .10 |
| 250 | Todd Lyght | .30 | .18 |
| 251 | Marvin Washington | .20 | .12 |
| 252 | Eric Swann | .20 | .12 |
| 253 | Bruce Kozerski | .15 | .10 |
| 254 | Jon Hand | .15 | .10 |
| 255 | Scott Fulhage | .15 | .10 |
| 256 | Chuck Cecil | .15 | .10 |
| 257 | Eric Martin | .20 | .12 |
| 258 | Eric Metcalf | .25 | .15 |
| 259 | T.J. Turner | .15 | .10 |
| 260 | Kirk Lowdermilk | .15 | .10 |
| 261 | Keith McKeller | .20 | .12 |
| 262 | Wymon Henderson | .15 | .10 |
| 263 | David Alexander | .15 | .10 |
| 264 | George Jamison | .15 | .10 |
| 265 | Ken Norton | .20 | .12 |
| 266 | Jim Lachey | .20 | .12 |
| 267 | Bo Orlando (R) | .30 | .18 |
| 268 | Nick Lowery | .20 | .12 |
| 269 | Keith Van Horne | .15 | .10 |
| 270 | Dwight Stone | .15 | .10 |
| 271 | Keith DeLong | .15 | .10 |
| 272 | James Francis | .20 | .12 |
| 273 | Greg McMurtry | .20 | .12 |
| 274 | Ethan Horton | .20 | .12 |
| 275 | Stan Brock | .15 | .10 |
| 276 | Ken Harvey | .15 | .10 |
| 277 | Ronnie Harmon | .25 | .15 |
| 278 | Mike Pritchard | .50 | .30 |
| 279 | Kyle Clifton | .15 | .10 |
| 280 | Anthony Johnson | .15 | .10 |
| 281 | Esera Tuaolo | .15 | .10 |
| 282 | Vernon Turner | .15 | .10 |
| 283 | David Griggs | .15 | .10 |
| 284 | Dino Hackett | .15 | .10 |
| 285 | Carwell Gardner | .15 | .10 |
| 286 | Ron Hall | .15 | .10 |
| 287 | Reggie White | .25 | .15 |
| 288 | Checklist 1-100 | .15 | .05 |
| 289 | Checklist 101-200 | .15 | .05 |
| 290 | Checklist 201-300 | .15 | .05 |
| 291 | Mark Clayton (MC) | .20 | .12 |
| 292 | Pat Swilling (MC) | .20 | .12 |
| 293 | Ernest Givens (MC) | .20 | .12 |
| 294 | Broderick Thomas (MC) | .20 | .12 |
| 295 | John Friesz (MC) | .20 | .12 |
| 296 | Cornelius Bennett (MC) | .20 | .12 |
| 297 | Anthony Carter (MC) | .20 | .12 |

| 298 | Earnest Byner (MC) | .20 | .12 |
| 299 | Michael Irvin (MC) | .50 | .30 |
| 300 | Cortez Kennedy (MC) | .25 | .15 |
| 301 | Barry Sanders (MC) | 2.25 | 1.25 |
| 302 | Mike Croel (MC) | .30 | .18 |
| 303 | Emmitt Smith (MC) | 5.00 | 3.00 |
| 304 | Leonard Russell (MC) | .50 | .30 |
| 305 | Neal Anderson (MC) | .20 | .12 |
| 306 | Derrick Thomas (MC) | .30 | .18 |
| 307 | Mark Rypien (MC) | .25 | .15 |
| 308 | Reggie White (MC) | .20 | .12 |
| 309 | Rod Woodson (MC) | .20 | .12 |
| 310 | Rodney Hampton (MC) | .50 | .30 |
| 311 | Carnell Lake | .15 | .10 |
| 312 | Robert Delpino | .20 | .12 |
| 313 | Brian Blades | .20 | .12 |
| 314 | Marc Spindler | .15 | .10 |
| 315 | Scott Norwood | .15 | .10 |
| 316 | Frank Warren | .15 | .10 |
| 317 | David Treadwell | .15 | .10 |
| 318 | Steve Broussard | .25 | .15 |
| 319 | Lorenzo Lynch | .15 | .10 |
| 320 | Ray Agnew | .15 | .10 |
| 321 | Derrick Walker | .20 | .12 |
| 322 | Vinson Smith (R) | .20 | .12 |
| 323 | Gary Clark | .30 | .18 |
| 324 | Charles Haley | .20 | .12 |
| 325 | Keith Byars | .20 | .12 |
| 326 | Winston Moss | .15 | .10 |
| 327 | Paul McJulien (R) | .20 | .12 |
| 328 | Tony Covington | .15 | .10 |
| 329 | Mark Carrier | .20 | .12 |
| 330 | Mark Tuinei | .15 | .10 |
| 331 | Tracy Simien (R) | .25 | .15 |
| 332 | Jeff Wright | .15 | .10 |
| 333 | Bryan Cox | .25 | .15 |
| 334 | Lonnie Young | .15 | .10 |
| 335 | Clarence Verdin | .20 | .12 |
| 336 | Dan Fike | .15 | .10 |
| 337 | Steve Sewell | .15 | .10 |
| 338 | Gary Zimmerman | .15 | .10 |
| 339 | Barney Bussey | .15 | .10 |
| 340 | William Perry | .20 | .12 |
| 341 | Jeff Hostetler | .25 | .15 |
| 342 | Doug Smith | .15 | .10 |
| 343 | Cleveland Gary | .20 | .12 |
| 344 | Todd Marinovich | .50 | .30 |
| 345 | Rich Moran | .15 | .10 |
| 346 | Tony Woods | .15 | .10 |
| 347 | Vaughn Johnson | .20 | .12 |
| 348 | Marv Cook | .25 | .15 |
| 349 | Pierce Holt | .15 | .10 |
| 350 | Gerald Williams | .15 | .10 |
| 351 | Kevin Butler | .15 | .10 |
| 352 | William White | .15 | .10 |
| 353 | Henry Rolling | .15 | .10 |
| 354 | James Joseph | .25 | .15 |
| 355 | Vinny Testaverde | .25 | .15 |
| 356 | Scott Radecic | .15 | .10 |
| 357 | Lee Johnson | .15 | .10 |
| 358 | Steve Tasker | .15 | .10 |
| 359 | David Lutz | .15 | .10 |
| 360 | Audrey McMillian | .15 | .10 |
| 361 | Brad Baxter | .20 | .12 |
| 362 | Mark Dennis | .15 | .10 |
| 363 | Erric Pegram | .25 | .15 |
| 364 | Sean Jones | .15 | .10 |
| 365 | William Roberts | .15 | .10 |
| 366 | Steve Young | .75 | .40 |
| 367 | Joe Jacoby | .15 | .10 |
| 368 | Richard Brown (R) | .20 | .12 |
| 369 | Keith Kartz | .15 | .10 |
| 370 | Freddie Joe Nunn | .15 | .10 |
| 371 | Darren Comeaux | .15 | .10 |
| 372 | Larry Brown | .15 | .10 |
| 373 | Haywood Jeffires | .45 | .28 |
| 374 | Tom Newberry | .15 | .10 |
| 375 | Steve Bono | .80 | .50 |
| 376 | Kevin Ross | .15 | .10 |
| 377 | Kelvin Pritchett | .25 | .15 |
| 378 | Jessie Hester | .20 | .12 |
| 379 | Mitchell Price | .15 | .10 |
| 380 | Barry Foster | 1.50 | .90 |
| 381 | Reyna Thompson | .15 | .10 |
| 382 | Cris Carter | .25 | .15 |
| 383 | Lemuel Stinson | .15 | .10 |
| 384 | Rod Bernstine | .20 | .12 |
| 385 | James Lofton | .35 | .20 |
| 386 | Kevin Murphy | .15 | .10 |
| 387 | Greg Townsend | .20 | .12 |
| 388 | Edgar Bennett (R) | .60 | .35 |
| 389 | Rob Moore | .30 | .18 |
| 390 | Eugene Lockhart | .15 | .10 |
| 391 | Bern Brostek | .15 | .10 |
| 392 | Craig Heyward | .20 | .12 |
| 393 | Ferrell Edmunds | .15 | .10 |
| 394 | John Kasay | .15 | .10 |
| 395 | Jesse Sapolu | .15 | .10 |
| 396 | Jim Breech | .15 | .10 |
| 397 | Neil Smith | .20 | .12 |
| 398 | Bryce Paup | .15 | .10 |
| 399 | Tony Tolbert | .15 | .10 |
| 400 | Bubby Brister | .25 | .15 |
| 401 | Dennis Smith | .15 | .10 |
| 402 | Dan Owens | .15 | .10 |
| 403 | Steve Beuerlein | .40 | .25 |
| 404 | Rick Tuten | .15 | .10 |
| 405 | Eric Allen | .15 | .10 |
| 406 | Eric Hill | .15 | .10 |
| 407 | Don Warren | .15 | .10 |
| 408 | Greg Jackson | .15 | .10 |
| 409 | Chris Doleman | .20 | .12 |
| 410 | Anthony Munoz | .25 | .15 |
| 411 | Michael Young | .15 | .10 |

| | | | |
|---|---|---|---|
| 412 Cornelius Bennett | .25 | .15 |
| 413 Ray Childress | .20 | .12 |
| 414 Kevin Call | .15 | .10 |
| 415 Burt Grossman | .20 | .12 |
| 416 Scott Miller | .15 | .10 |
| 417 Tim Newton | .15 | .10 |
| 418 Robert Young | .15 | .10 |
| 419 Tommy Vardell (R) | 1.00 | .60 |
| 420 Michael Walter | .15 | .10 |
| 421 Chris Port (R) | .20 | .12 |
| 422 Carlton Haselrig | .15 | .10 |
| 423 Rodney Peete | .25 | .15 |
| 424 Scott Stephen | .15 | .10 |
| 425 Chris Warren | .20 | .12 |
| 426 Scott Galbraith | .15 | .10 |
| 427 Fuad Reveiz | .15 | .10 |
| 428 Irv Eatman | .15 | .10 |
| 429 David Szott | .15 | .10 |
| 430 Brent Williams | .15 | .10 |
| 431 Mike Horan | .15 | .10 |
| 432 Brent Jones | .20 | .12 |
| 433 Paul Gruber | .20 | .12 |
| 434 Carlos Huerta (R) | .20 | .12 |
| 435 Scott Case | .15 | .10 |
| 436 Greg Davis | .15 | .10 |
| 437 Ken Clarke | .15 | .10 |
| 438 Alfred Williams | .15 | .10 |
| 439 Jim Jensen | .15 | .10 |
| 440 Louis Lipps | .20 | .12 |
| 441 Larry Roberts | .15 | .10 |
| 442 James Jones | .15 | .10 |
| 443 Don Mosebar | .15 | .10 |
| 444 Quinn Early | .15 | .10 |
| 445 Robert Brown | .15 | .10 |
| 446 Tom Thayer | .15 | .10 |
| 447 Michael Irvin | 1.00 | .60 |
| 448 Jarrod Bunch | .30 | .18 |
| 449 Riki Ellison | .15 | .10 |
| 450 Joe Phillips | .15 | .10 |
| 451 Ernest Givens | .30 | .18 |
| 452 Glenn Parker | .15 | .10 |
| 453 Brett Perriman | .20 | .12 |
| 454 Jayice Pearson (R) | .20 | .12 |
| 455 Mark Jackson | .20 | .12 |
| 456 Siran Stacy (R) | .50 | .30 |
| 457 Rufus Porter | .15 | .10 |
| 458 Michael Ball | .15 | .10 |
| 459 Craig Taylor | .15 | .10 |
| 460 George Thomas (R) | .25 | .15 |
| 461 Alvin Wright | .15 | .10 |
| 462 Ron Hallstrom | .15 | .10 |
| 463 Mike Mooney (R) | .20 | .12 |
| 464 Dexter Carter | .25 | .15 |
| 465 Marty Carter (R) | .25 | .15 |
| 466 Pat Swilling | .25 | .15 |
| 467 Mike Golic | .15 | .10 |
| 468 Reggie Roby | .15 | .10 |

| | | | |
|---|---|---|---|
| 469 Randall McDaniel | .15 | .10 |
| 470 John Stephens | .25 | .15 |
| 471 Ricardo McDonald (R) | .20 | .12 |
| 472 Wilber Marshall | .20 | .12 |
| 473 Jim Sweeney | .15 | .10 |
| 474 Ernie Jones | .20 | .12 |
| 475 Bennie Blades | .20 | .12 |
| 476 Don Beebe | .25 | .15 |
| 477 Grant Feasel | .15 | .10 |
| 478 Ernie Mills | .25 | .15 |
| 479 Tony Jones | .15 | .10 |
| 480 Jeff Uhlenhake | .15 | .10 |
| 481 Gaston Green | .25 | .15 |
| 482 John Taylor | .30 | .18 |
| 483 Anthony Smith | .15 | .10 |
| 484 Tony Bennett | .25 | .15 |
| 485 David Brandon (R) | .25 | .15 |
| 486 Shawn Jefferson | .25 | .15 |
| 487 Christian Okoye | .25 | .15 |
| 488 Leonard Marshall | .20 | .12 |
| 489 Jay Novacek | .25 | .15 |
| 490 Harold Green | .30 | .18 |
| 491 Bubba McDowell | .15 | .10 |
| 492 Gary Anderson | .15 | .10 |
| 493 Terrell Buckley (R) | 1.00 | .60 |
| 494 Jamie Dukes (R) | .20 | .12 |
| 495 Morten Andersen | .20 | .12 |
| 496 Henry Thomas | .15 | .10 |
| 497 Bill Lewis | .15 | .10 |
| 498 Jeff Cross | .15 | .10 |
| 499 Hardy Nickerson | .15 | .10 |
| 500 Henry Ellard | .20 | .12 |
| 501 Joe Bowden (R) | .25 | .15 |
| 502 Brian Noble | .15 | .10 |
| 503 Mike Cofer | .15 | .10 |
| 504 Jeff Bryant | .15 | .10 |
| 505 Lomas Brown | .20 | .12 |
| 506 Chip Banks | .15 | .10 |
| 507 Keith Traylor | .15 | .10 |
| 508 Mark Kelso | .15 | .10 |
| 509 Dexter McNabb (R) | .25 | .15 |
| 510 Gene Chilton (R) | .20 | .12 |
| 511 George Thornton | .15 | .10 |
| 512 Jeff Criswell | .15 | .10 |
| 513 Brad Edwards | .15 | .10 |
| 514 Ron Heller | .15 | .10 |
| 515 Tim Brown | .25 | .15 |
| 516 Keith Hamilton (R) | .25 | .15 |
| 517 Mark Higgs | .35 | .20 |
| 518 Tommy Barnhardt | .15 | .10 |
| 519 Brian Jordan | .25 | .15 |
| 520 Ray Crockett | .15 | .10 |
| 521 Karl Wilson | .15 | .10 |
| 522 Ricky Reynolds | .15 | .10 |
| 523 Max Montoya | .15 | .10 |
| 524 David Little | .15 | .10 |
| 525 Alonzo Mitz (R) | .20 | .12 |

| 526 | Darryll Lewis | .20 | .12 |
|-----|---------------|-----|-----|
| 527 | Keith Henderson | .15 | .10 |
| 528 | LeRoy Butler | .15 | .10 |
| 529 | Rob Burnett | .20 | .12 |
| 530 | Chris Chandler | .25 | .15 |
| 531 | Maury Buford | .15 | .10 |
| 532 | Mark Ingram | .20 | .12 |
| 533 | Mike Saxon | .15 | .10 |
| 534 | Bill Fralic | .15 | .10 |
| 535 | Craig Patterson (R) | .20 | .12 |
| 536 | John Randle | .15 | .10 |
| 537 | Dwayne Harper | .15 | .10 |
| 538 | Chris Hakel (R) | .35 | .20 |
| 539 | Maurice Hurst | .15 | .10 |
| 540 | Warren Powers | .15 | .10 |
| 541 | Will Wolford | .15 | .10 |
| 542 | Dennis Gibson | .15 | .10 |
| 543 | Jackie Slater | .20 | .12 |
| 544 | Floyd Turner | .15 | .10 |
| 545 | Guy McIntyre | .15 | .10 |
| 546 | Eric Green | .25 | .15 |
| 547 | Rohn Stark | .15 | .10 |
| 548 | William Fuller | .15 | .10 |
| 549 | Alvin Harper | .75 | .40 |
| 550 | Mark Clayton | .25 | .15 |
| 551 | Natu Tuatagaloa (R) | .20 | .12 |
| 552 | Fred Barnett | .50 | .30 |
| 553 | Bob Whitfield (R) | .25 | .15 |
| 554 | Courtney Hall | .15 | .10 |
| 555 | Brian Mitchell | .25 | .15 |
| 556 | Patrick Hunter | .15 | .10 |
| 557 | Rick Bryan | .15 | .10 |
| 558 | Anthony Carter | .25 | .15 |
| 559 | Jim Wahler | .15 | .10 |
| 560 | Joe Morris | .15 | .10 |
| 561 | Tony Zendejas | .15 | .10 |
| 562 | Mervyn Fernandez | .20 | .12 |
| 563 | Jamie Williams | .15 | .10 |
| 564 | Darrell Thompson | .25 | .15 |
| 565 | Adrian Cooper | .15 | .10 |
| 566 | Chris Goode | .15 | .10 |
| 567 | Jeff Davidson (R) | .20 | .12 |
| 568 | James Hasty | .20 | .12 |
| 569 | Chris Mims (R) | .40 | .25 |
| 570 | Ray Seals (R) | .25 | .15 |
| 571 | Myron Guyton | .15 | .10 |
| 572 | Todd McNair | .15 | .10 |
| 573 | Andre Tippett | .20 | .12 |
| 574 | Kirby Jackson | .15 | .10 |
| 575 | Mel Gray | .20 | .12 |
| 576 | Stephone Paige | .20 | .12 |
| 577 | Scott Davis | .15 | .10 |
| 578 | John Gesek | .15 | .10 |
| 579 | Earnest Byner | .20 | .12 |
| 580 | John Friesz | .25 | .15 |
| 581 | Al Smith | .20 | .12 |
| 582 | Flipper Anderson | .25 | .15 |

| 583 | Amp Lee (R) | 1.00 | .60 |
|-----|-------------|------|-----|
| 584 | Greg Lloyd | .15 | .10 |
| 585 | Cortez Kennedy | .30 | .18 |
| 586 | Keith Sims | .15 | .10 |
| 587 | Terry Allen | 1.00 | .60 |
| 588 | David Fulcher | .15 | .10 |
| 589 | Chris Hinton | .20 | .12 |
| 590 | Tim McDonald | .15 | .10 |
| 591 | Bruce Armstrong | .15 | .10 |
| 592 | Sterling Sharpe | .75 | .40 |
| 593 | Tom Rathman | .20 | .12 |
| 594 | Bill Brooks | .15 | .10 |
| 595 | Broderick Thomas | .20 | .12 |
| 596 | Jim Wilks | .15 | .10 |
| 597 | Tyrone Braxton | .15 | .10 |
| 598 | Checklist 301-400 | .15 | .05 |
| 599 | Checklist 401-500 | .15 | .05 |
| 600 | Checklist 501-600 | .15 | .05 |

# 1992 Topps
# Stadium Club
# High Number Series

This 100-card update set was supposedly limited to just 300 total cases. The cards are identical to the 1992 Stadium Club regular edition and sequentially numbered from 601-700. The set includes rookies and players excluded from the regular edition. 10 additional Members Choice (MC) cards are included in this series. Four bonus cards (BC) depicting former number NFL draft picks were randomly distributed in High Series packs. Those cards are listed at the end of this checklist. All cards measure 2-1/2" by 3-1/2".

|  |  | MINT | NR/MT |
|--|--|------|-------|
| Complete Set (100) | | 140.00 | 85.00 |
| Commons | | .50 | .30 |

| 601 | Andre Reed (MC) | 1.00 | .70 |
|-----|-----------------|------|-----|
| 602 | Troy Aikman (MC) | 10.00 | 6.00 |
| 603 | Dan Marino (MC) | 2.00 | 1.25 |
| 604 | R. Cunningham(MC) | 1.50 | .90 |

| | | | |
|---|---|---|---|
| 605 Jim Kelly (MC) | 3.00 | 1.75 | |
| 606 Deion Sanders (MC) | 1.50 | .90 | |
| 607 Junior Seau (MC) | 1.00 | .70 | |
| 608 Jerry Rice (MC) | 4.50 | 2.50 | |
| 609 Bruce Smith (MC) | .90 | .60 | |
| 610 Lawrence Taylor (MC) | 1.25 | .80 | |
| 611 Todd Collins (R) | .75 | .45 | |
| 612 Ty Detmer | .75 | .45 | |
| 613 Browning Nagle | 2.00 | 1.25 | |
| 614 Tony Sacca (R) | 1.75 | 1.00 | |
| 615 Boomer Esiason | .80 | .50 | |
| 616 Leslie O'Neal | .60 | .35 | |
| 617 Mark Wheeler (R) | .60 | .35 | |
| 618 Eric Dickerson | 2.00 | 1.25 | |
| 619 Phil Simms | .25 | .15 | |
| 620 Troy Vincent (R) | 1.50 | .90 | |
| 621 Jason Hanson (R) | .75 | .45 | |
| 622 Andre Reed | .90 | .60 | |
| 623 Russell Maryland | 1.25 | .80 | |
| 624 Steve Emtman (R) | 7.00 | 4.00 | |
| 625 Sean Gilbert (R) | 2.50 | 1.50 | |
| 626 Dana Hall (R) | 1.00 | .70 | |
| 627 Dan McGwire | .80 | .50 | |
| 628 Lewis Billups | .50 | .30 | |
| 629 Darryl Williams (R) | 1.25 | .80 | |
| 630 Dwayne Sabb (R) | .75 | .45 | |
| 631 Mark Royals | .50 | .30 | |
| 632 Cary Conklin | .50 | .30 | |
| 633 Al Toon | .50 | .30 | |
| 634 Junior Seau | 1.00 | .70 | |
| 635 Billy Joe Toliver | .50 | .30 | |
| 636 Greg Skrepenak (R) | 1.00 | .70 | |
| 637 Deion Sanders | 1.25 | .80 | |
| 638 Steve DeOssie | .50 | .30 | |
| 639 Randall Cunningham | 1.50 | .90 | |
| 640 Jim Kelly | 3.00 | 1.75 | |
| 641 Michael Brandon (R) | .60 | .35 | |
| 642 Clayton Holmes (R) | .75 | .45 | |
| 643 Webster Slaughter | .60 | .35 | |
| 644 Ricky Proehl | .60 | .35 | |
| 645 Jerry Rice | 6.00 | 3.75 | |
| 646 Carl Banks | .60 | .35 | |
| 647 J.J. Burden | .50 | .30 | |
| 648 Tracy Scroggins (R) | 1.00 | .70 | |
| 649 Alonzo Spellman (R) | 1.25 | .80 | |
| 650 Joe Montana | 5.00 | 3.00 | |
| 651 Courtney Hawkins (R) | 1.75 | 1.00 | |
| 652 Corey Widmer (R) | .75 | .45 | |
| 653 Robert Brooks (R) | .75 | .45 | |
| 654 Darren Woodson (R) | .75 | .45 | |
| 655 Derrick Fenner | .60 | .35 | |
| 656 Steve Christie | .50 | .30 | |
| 657 Chester McGlockton (R) | 1.25 | .80 | |
| 658 Steve Israel (R) | .80 | .50 | |
| 659 Robert Harris (R) | .75 | .45 | |
| 660 Dan Marino | 3.50 | 2.25 | |
| 661 Ed McCaffrey | .50 | .30 | |
| 662 Johnny Mitchell (R) | 1.50 | .90 | |
| 663 Timm Rosenbach | .90 | .60 | |
| 664 Anthony Miller | 1.25 | .80 | |
| 665 Merril Hoge | .60 | .35 | |
| 666 Eugene Chung (R) | .80 | .50 | |
| 667 Rueben Mayes | .50 | .30 | |
| 668 Martin Bayliss | .50 | .30 | |
| 669 Ashley Ambrose (R) | 1.00 | .70 | |
| 670 Michael Cofer | .50 | .30 | |
| 671 Shane Dronett (R) | 1.25 | .80 | |
| 672 Bernie Kosar | 1.00 | .70 | |
| 673 Mike Singletary | 1.00 | .70 | |
| 674 Mike Lodish (R) | .60 | .35 | |
| 675 Phillippi Sparks (R) | .75 | .45 | |
| 676 Joel Steed (R) | .75 | .45 | |
| 677 Kevin Fagan | .50 | .30 | |
| 678 Randal Hill | 1.25 | .80 | |
| 679 Ken O'Brien | .80 | .50 | |
| 680 Lawrence Taylor | 1.00 | .70 | |
| 681 Harvey Williams | 1.00 | .70 | |
| 682 Quentin Coryatt (R) | 5.00 | 3.00 | |
| 683 Brett Favre | 7.00 | 4.00 | |
| 684 Robert Jones (R) | 1.75 | 1.00 | |
| 685 Michael Dean Perry | .90 | .60 | |
| 686 Bruce Smith | .90 | .60 | |
| 687 Troy Auzenne (R) | .75 | .45 | |
| 688 Thomas McLemore (R) | .60 | .35 | |
| 689 Dale Carter (R) | 2.50 | 1.50 | |
| 690 Marc Boutte (R) | .80 | .50 | |
| 691 Jeff George | 2.00 | 1.25 | |
| 692 Dion Lambert (R) | .60 | .35 | |
| 693 Vaughn Dunbar (R) | 2.50 | 1.50 | |
| 694 Derek Brown (R) | 1.25 | .80 | |
| 695 Troy Aikman | 10.00 | 6.00 | |
| 696 John Fina (R) | .75 | .45 | |
| 697 Kevin Smith (R) | 1.25 | .80 | |
| 698 Corey Miller (R) | .75 | .45 | |
| 699 Lance Olberding (R) | .60 | .35 | |
| 700 Checklist 601-700 | .50 | .15 | |
| BC1 Jeff George (#1 Pick) | 20.00 | 14.00 | |
| BC2 Russell Maryland (#1 Pick) | 15.00 | 10.00 | |
| BC3 Steve Emtman (#1 Pick) | 28.00 | 20.00 | |
| BC4 Rocket Ismail (#1 Pick) | 32.00 | 25.00 | |

## 1992 Topps Stadium Club Quarterback Legends

These six insert cards were randomly distributed in 1992 Stadium Club football foil packs. The cards measure 2-1/2" by 3-1/2" and depict six Hall of Famers.

|  | MINT | NR/MT |
|---|---|---|
| Complete Set (6) | 30.00 | 18.00 |
| Commons | 3.00 | 2.00 |

| | | MINT | NR/MT |
|---|---|---|---|
| 1 | Y.A. Tittle | 3.00 | 2.00 |
| 2 | Bart Starr | 7.50 | 4.50 |
| 3 | Johnny Unitas | 8.50 | 5.00 |
| 4 | George Blanda | 3.00 | 2.00 |
| 5 | Roger Staubach | 12.00 | 8.00 |
| 6 | Terry Bradshaw | 12.00 | 8.00 |

## 1993 Topps Series I

For the second straight year Topps issued their football set in two 330-card series. The cards in Series I feature full color action photographs on the front with a smaller photo on the back along with personal data, stats and a brief biography. All cards measure 2-1/2" by 3-1/2".

|  | MINT | NR/MT |
|---|---|---|
| Complete Set (330) | 22.00 | 14.00 |
| Commons | .05 | .02 |

| | | MINT | NR/MT |
|---|---|---|---|
| 1 | Art Monk | .12 | .07 |
| 2 | Jerry Rice | .50 | .28 |
| 3 | Stanley Richard | .08 | .05 |
| 4 | Ron Hall | .05 | .02 |
| 5 | Daryl Johnson | .10 | .06 |
| 6 | Wendell Davis | .12 | .07 |
| 7 | Vaughn Dunbar | .40 | .25 |
| 8 | Mike Jones | .05 | .02 |
| 9 | Anthony Johnson | .07 | .04 |
| 10 | Chris Miller | .15 | .10 |
| 11 | Kyle Clifton | .05 | .02 |
| 12 | Curtis Conway (R) | 1.00 | .60 |
| 13 | Lionel Washington | .05 | .02 |
| 14 | Reggie Johnson | .05 | .02 |
| 15 | David Little | .05 | .02 |
| 16 | Nick Lowery | .07 | .04 |
| 17 | Darryl Williams | .10 | .06 |
| 18 | Brent Jones | .08 | .05 |
| 19 | Bruce Matthews | .07 | .04 |
| 20 | Heath Sherman | .08 | .05 |
| 21 | John Kasay | .05 | .02 |
| 22 | Troy Drayton (R) | .40 | .25 |
| 23 | Eric Metcalf | .12 | .07 |
| 24 | Andre Tippett | .07 | .04 |
| 25 | Rodney Hampton | .25 | .15 |
| 26 | Henry Jones | .05 | .02 |
| 27 | Jim Everett | .15 | .10 |
| 28 | Steve Jordan | .05 | .02 |
| 29 | LeRoy Butler | .05 | .02 |
| 30 | Troy Vincent | .10 | .06 |
| 31 | Nate Lewis | .12 | .07 |
| 32 | Rickey Jackson | .07 | .04 |
| 33 | Darion Conner | .05 | .02 |
| 34 | Tom Carter (R) | .50 | .2835 |

| 35 | Jeff George | .30 | .18 |
|---|---|---|---|
| 36 | Larry Centers | .05 | .02 |
| 37 | Reggie Cobb | .20 | .12 |
| 38 | Mike Saxon | .05 | .02 |
| 39 | Brad Baxter | .08 | .05 |
| 40 | Reggie White | .15 | .10 |
| 41 | Haywood Jeffires | .20 | .12 |
| 42 | Alfred Williams | .05 | .02 |
| 43 | Aaron Wallace | .05 | .02 |
| 44 | Tracy Simien | .05 | .02 |
| 45 | Pat Harlow | .05 | .02 |
| 46 | D.J. Johnson | .05 | .02 |
| 47 | Don Griffin | .05 | .02 |
| 48 | Flipper Anderson | .08 | .05 |
| 49 | Keith Kartz | .05 | .02 |
| 50 | Bernie Kosar | .15 | .10 |
| 51 | Kent Hull | .05 | .02 |
| 52 | Erik Howard | .05 | .02 |
| 53 | Pierce Holt | .05 | .02 |
| 54 | Dwayne Harper | .05 | .02 |
| 55 | Bennie Blades | .07 | .04 |
| 56 | Mark Duper | .10 | .06 |
| 57 | Brian Noble | .05 | .02 |
| 58 | Jeff Feagles | .05 | .02 |
| 59 | Michael Haynes | .25 | .15 |
| 60 | Junior Seau | .20 | .12 |
| 61 | Gary Anderson | .05 | .02 |
| 62 | Jon Hand | .05 | .02 |
| 63 | Lin Elliott | .05 | .02 |
| 64 | Dana Stubblefield (R) | .40 | .25 |
| 65 | Vaughn Johnson | .07 | .04 |
| 66 | Mo Lewis | .05 | .02 |
| 67 | Aeneas Williams | .08 | .05 |
| 68 | David Fulcher | .05 | .02 |
| 69 | Chip Lohmiller | .05 | .02 |
| 70 | Greg Townsend | .05 | .02 |
| 71 | Simon Fletcher | .05 | .02 |
| 72 | Sean Salisbury | .12 | .07 |
| 73 | Christian Okoye | .12 | .07 |
| 74 | Jim Arnold | .05 | .02 |
| 75 | Bruce Smith | .12 | .07 |
| 76 | Fred Barnett | .20 | .12 |
| 77 | Bill Romanowski | .05 | .02 |
| 78 | Dermontti Dawson | .05 | .02 |
| 79 | Bern Brostek | .05 | .02 |
| 80 | Warren Moon | .25 | .15 |
| 81 | Bill Fralic | .05 | .02 |
| 82 | Lomas Brown | .05 | .02 |
| 83 | Duane Bickett | .05 | .02 |
| 84 | Neil Smith | .07 | .04 |
| 85 | Reggie White | .15 | .10 |
| 86 | Tim McDonald | .05 | .02 |
| 87 | Leslie O'Neal | .08 | .05 |
| 88 | Steve Young | .30 | .18 |
| 89 | Paul Gruber | .05 | .02 |
| 90 | Wilber Marshall | .05 | .02 |
| 91 | Trace Armstrong | .05 | .02 |
| 92 | Bobby Houston | .05 | .02 |
| 93 | George Thornton | .05 | .02 |
| 94 | Keith McCants | .05 | .02 |
| 95 | Ricky Sanders | .08 | .05 |
| 96 | Jackie Harris | .05 | .02 |
| 97 | Todd Marinovich | .30 | .18 |
| 98 | Henry Thomas | .05 | .02 |
| 99 | Jeff Wright | .05 | .02 |
| 100 | John Elway | .25 | .15 |
| 101 | Garrison Hearst (R) | 1.75 | 1.00 |
| 102 | Roy Foster | .05 | .02 |
| 103 | David Lang | .05 | .02 |
| 104 | Matt Stover | .05 | .02 |
| 105 | Lawrence Taylor | .12 | .07 |
| 106 | Pete Stoyanovich | .05 | .02 |
| 107 | Jessie Tuggle | .05 | .02 |
| 108 | William White | .05 | .02 |
| 109 | Andy Harmon | .05 | .02 |
| 110 | John L. Williams | .08 | .05 |
| 111 | Jon Vaughn | .20 | .12 |
| 112 | John Alt | .05 | .02 |
| 113 | Chris Jacke | .05 | .02 |
| 114 | Jim Breech | .05 | .02 |
| 115 | Eric Martin | .05 | .02 |
| 116 | Derrick Walker | .07 | .04 |
| 117 | Ricky Ervins | .25 | .15 |
| 118 | Roger Craig | .08 | .05 |
| 119 | Jeff Gossett | .05 | .02 |
| 120 | Emmitt Smith | 1.50 | .90 |
| 121 | Bob Whitfield | .05 | .02 |
| 122 | Alonzo Spellman | .05 | .02 |
| 123 | David Klingler | 1.25 | .70 |
| 124 | Tommy Maddox | .90 | .60 |
| 125 | Robert Porcher | .08 | .05 |
| 126 | Edgar Bennett | .05 | .02 |
| 127 | Harvey Williams | .20 | .12 |
| 128 | Dave Brown | .05 | .02 |
| 129 | Johnny Mitchell | .20 | .12 |
| 130 | Drew Bledsoe (R) | 3.00 | 1.75 |
| 131 | Zefross Moss | .05 | .02 |
| 132 | Nate Odomes | .05 | .02 |
| 133 | Rufus Porter | .05 | .02 |
| 134 | Jackie Slater | .07 | .04 |
| 135 | Steve Young | .30 | .18 |
| 136 | Chris Calloway | .10 | .06 |
| 137 | Steve Atwater | .08 | .05 |
| 138 | Mark Carrier | .08 | .05 |
| 139 | Marvin Washington | .05 | .02 |
| 140 | Barry Foster | .60 | .35 |
| 141 | Ricky Reynolds | .05 | .02 |
| 142 | Bubba McDowell | .05 | .02 |
| 143 | Dan Footman (R) | .35 | .20 |
| 144 | Richmond Webb | .07 | .04 |
| 145 | Mike Pritchard | .25 | .15 |
| 146 | Chris Spielman | .05 | .02 |
| 147 | Dave Krieg | .10 | .06 |
| 148 | Nick Bell | .25 | .15 |

| | | | |
|---|---|---|---|
| 149 | Vincent Brown | .05 | .02 |
| 150 | Seth Joyner | .07 | .04 |
| 151 | Tommy Kane | .10 | .06 |
| 152 | Carlton Gray (R) | .40 | .25 |
| 153 | Harry Newsome | .05 | .02 |
| 154 | Rohn Stark | .05 | .02 |
| 155 | Shannon Sharpe | .08 | .05 |
| 156 | Charles Haley | .08 | .05 |
| 157 | Cornelius Bennett | .10 | .06 |
| 158 | Doug Riesenberg | .05 | .02 |
| 159 | Amp Lee | .50 | .28 |
| 160 | Sterling Sharpe | .35 | .20 |
| 161 | Alonzo Mitz | .08 | .05 |
| 162 | Pat Terrell | .05 | .02 |
| 163 | Mark Schlereth | .05 | .02 |
| 164 | Gary Anderson | .05 | .02 |
| 165 | Quinn Early | .08 | .05 |
| 166 | Jerome Bettis (R) | 1.00 | .60 |
| 167 | Lawrency Dawsey | .15 | .10 |
| 168 | Derrick Thomas | .20 | .12 |
| 169 | Rodney Peete | .12 | .07 |
| 170 | Jim Kelly | .50 | .28 |
| 171 | Deion Sanders | .20 | .12 |
| 172 | Richard Dent | .07 | .04 |
| 173 | Emmitt Smith | 1.50 | .90 |
| 174 | Barry Sanders | .75 | .45 |
| 175 | Sterling Sharpe | .35 | .20 |
| 176 | Cleveland Gary | .12 | .07 |
| 177 | Terry Allen | .40 | .25 |
| 178 | Vaughn Johnson | .07 | .04 |
| 179 | Rodney Hampton | .25 | .15 |
| 180 | Randall Cunningham | .15 | .10 |
| 181 | Ricky Proehl | .12 | .07 |
| 182 | Jerry Rice | .50 | .28 |
| 183 | Reggie Cobb | .20 | .12 |
| 184 | Earnest Byner | .07 | .04 |
| 185 | Jeff Lageman | .07 | .04 |
| 186 | Carlos Jenkins | .05 | .02 |
| 187 | Cardinals Draft Picks (R) | .75 | .45 |
| 188 | Todd Lyght | .05 | .02 |
| 189 | Carl Simpson | .05 | .02 |
| 190 | Barry Sanders | .75 | .45 |
| 191 | Jim Harbaugh | .12 | .07 |
| 192 | Roger Ruzek | .05 | .02 |
| 193 | Brent Williams | .05 | .02 |
| 194 | Chip Banks | .05 | .02 |
| 195 | Mike Croel | .12 | .07 |
| 196 | Marion Butts | .12 | .07 |
| 197 | James Washington | .05 | .02 |
| 198 | John Offerdahl | .07 | .04 |
| 199 | Tom Rathman | .08 | .05 |
| 200 | Joe Montana | .75 | .45 |
| 201 | Pepper Johnson | .05 | .02 |
| 202 | Cris Dishman | .05 | .02 |
| 203 | Adrian White | .05 | .02 |
| 204 | Reggie Brooks (R) | .60 | .35 |
| 205 | Cortez Kennedy | .25 | .15 |
| 206 | Robert Massey | .05 | .02 |
| 207 | Toi Cook | .05 | .02 |
| 208 | Harry Sydney | .05 | .02 |
| 209 | Lincoln Kennedy (R) | .40 | .25 |
| 210 | Randall McDaniel | .05 | .02 |
| 211 | Eugene Daniel | .05 | .02 |
| 212 | Rob Burnett | .12 | .07 |
| 213 | Steve Broussard | .08 | .05 |
| 214 | Brian Washington | .05 | .02 |
| 215 | Leonard Renfro (R) | .35 | .20 |
| 216 | A.McMillian/H.Jones | .08 | .05 |
| 217 | S. Sharpe/A.Miller | .35 | .20 |
| 218 | C. Simmons/L. O'Neal | .08 | .05 |
| 219 | E. Smith/B. Foster | 1.75 | 1.00 |
| 220 | S. Young/W. Moon | .50 | .35 |
| 221 | Mel Gray | .05 | .02 |
| 222 | Luis Sharpe | .05 | .02 |
| 223 | Eric Moten | .05 | .02 |
| 224 | Albert Lewis | .05 | .02 |
| 225 | Alvin Harper | .30 | .18 |
| 226 | Steve Wallace | .05 | .02 |
| 227 | Mark Higgs | .25 | .15 |
| 228 | Eugene Lockhart | .05 | .02 |
| 229 | Sean Jones | .05 | .02 |
| 230 | Bucs Draft Picks | .40 | .25 |
| 231 | Jimmy Williams | .05 | .02 |
| 232 | Demetrius DuBose (R) | .50 | .28 |
| 233 | John Roper | .05 | .02 |
| 234 | Keith Hamilton | .07 | .04 |
| 235 | Donald Evans | .05 | .02 |
| 236 | Kenneth Davis | .12 | .07 |
| 237 | John Copeland (R) | .50 | .28 |
| 238 | Leonard Russell | .25 | .15 |
| 239 | Ken Harvey | .05 | .02 |
| 240 | Dale Carter | .40 | .25 |
| 241 | Anthony Pleasant | .05 | .02 |
| 242 | Darrell Green | .10 | .06 |
| 244 | Rob Moore | .12 | .07 |
| 245 | Chris Doleman | .07 | .04 |
| 246 | J.B. Brown | .05 | .02 |
| 247 | Ray Crockett | .05 | .02 |
| 248 | John Taylor | .15 | .10 |
| 249 | Russell Maryland | .15 | .10 |
| 250 | Brett Favre | 1.50 | .90 |
| 251 | Carl Pickens | .75 | .45 |
| 252 | Andy Heck | .05 | .02 |
| 253 | Jerome Henderson | .05 | .02 |
| 254 | Deion Sanders | .20 | .12 |
| 255 | Steve Emtman | 1.00 | .60 |
| 256 | Calvin Williams | .10 | .06 |
| 257 | Sean Gilbert | .20 | .12 |
| 258 | Don Beebe | .12 | .07 |
| 259 | Robert Smith (R) | .80 | .50 |
| 260 | Robert Blackmon | .05 | .02 |
| 261 | Jim Kelly | .50 | .28 |
| 262 | Harold Green | .25 | .15 |

| | | | |
|---|---|---|---|
| 263 | Clay Matthews | .05 | .02 |
| 264 | John Elway | .25 | .15 |
| 265 | Warren Moon | .25 | .15 |
| 266 | Jeff George | .30 | .18 |
| 267 | Derrick Thomas | .20 | .12 |
| 268 | Howie Long | .08 | .05 |
| 269 | Dan Marino | .50 | .28 |
| 270 | Jon Vaughn | .20 | .12 |
| 271 | Chris Burkett | .05 | .02 |
| 272 | Barry Foster | .60 | .35 |
| 273 | Marion Butts | .12 | .07 |
| 274 | Chris Warren | .12 | .07 |
| 275 | Giants Draft Picks | .60 | .35 |
| 276 | Tony Casillas | .07 | .04 |
| 277 | Jarrod Bunch | .12 | .07 |
| 278 | Eric Green | .12 | .07 |
| 279 | Stan Brock | .05 | .02 |
| 280 | Chester McGlockton | .05 | .02 |
| 281 | Ricky Watters | .60 | .35 |
| 282 | Dan Saleaumus | .05 | .02 |
| 283 | Rich Camarillo | .05 | .02 |
| 284 | Cris Carter | .15 | .10 |
| 285 | Rick Mirer (R) | 2.50 | 1.50 |
| 286 | Matt Brock | .05 | .02 |
| 287 | Burt Grossman | .07 | .04 |
| 288 | Andre Collins | .05 | .02 |
| 289 | Mark Jackson | .08 | .05 |
| 290 | Dan Marino | .50 | .28 |
| 291 | Cornelius Bennett | .10 | .06 |
| 292 | Steve Atwater | .08 | .05 |
| 293 | Bryan Cox | .08 | .05 |
| 294 | Sam Mills | .07 | .04 |
| 295 | Pepper Johnson | .05 | .02 |
| 296 | Seth Joyner | .07 | .04 |
| 297 | Chris Spielman | .05 | .02 |
| 298 | Junior Seau | .20 | .12 |
| 299 | Cortez Kennedy | .20 | .12 |
| 300 | Broderick Thomas | .05 | .02 |
| 301 | Todd McNair | .05 | .02 |
| 302 | Nate Newton | .05 | .02 |
| 303 | Mike Walter | .05 | .02 |
| 304 | Clyde Simmons | .07 | .04 |
| 305 | Ernie Mills | .15 | .10 |
| 306 | Steve Wisniewski | .05 | .02 |
| 307 | Coleman Rudolph (R) | .30 | .18 |
| 308 | Thurman Thomas | .40 | .25 |
| 309 | Reggie Roby | .05 | .02 |
| 310 | Eric Swann | .08 | .05 |
| 311 | Mark Wheeler | .05 | .02 |
| 312 | Jeff Herrod | .05 | .02 |
| 313 | Leroy Hoard | .12 | .07 |
| 314 | Patrick Bates (R) | .60 | .35 |
| 315 | Earnest Byner | .08 | .05 |
| 316 | Dave Meggett | .12 | .07 |
| 317 | George Teague (R) | .40 | .25 |
| 318 | Ray Childress | .08 | .05 |
| 319 | Mike Kenn | .05 | .02 |

| | | | |
|---|---|---|---|
| 320 | Jason Hanson | .05 | .02 |
| 321 | Gary Clark | .15 | .10 |
| 322 | Chris Gardocki | .05 | .02 |
| 323 | Ken Norton | .07 | .04 |
| 324 | Eric Curry (R) | .60 | .35 |
| 325 | Byron Evans | .05 | .02 |
| 326 | O.J. McDuffie (R) | .75 | .45 |
| 327 | Dwight Stone | .05 | .02 |
| 328 | Tommy Barnhardt | .05 | .02 |
| 329 | Checklist 1 | .05 | .02 |
| 330 | Checklist 2 | .05 | .02 |

# UPPER DECK

## 1991 Upper Deck

This 700-card set marked Upper Deck's entry into the football card market. The set was released in two series including a low series (1-500) and a high series (501-700). Card fronts feature full color action photos framed by inner border stripes that reflect the player's team colors and white borders. The player's name and position appear at the bottom of the card while the team name is printed inside a small football design. Card backs include a full color action shot, stats and brief bio's. Key subsets include Star Rookies, Aerial Threats (AT), Season Leaders (LL), Team MVP's (MVP), Rookie Force (RF), and Arch Rivals (AR). The set also includes two limited 10-card Football Hero insert sets featuring Joe Montana and Joe Namath. Those cards were randomly inserted into

Upper Deck foil packs. The set also includes two special cards honoring Darrell Green as the NFL's fastest man and Don Shula's 300th NFL win. Those inserts are listed at the end of this checklist but are not included in the complete set price. All cards measure 2-1/2" by 3-1/2".

|  |  | MINT | NR/MT |
|---|---|---|---|
| | Complete Set (700) | 27.00 | 17.00 |
| | Commons | .05 | .02 |
| 1 | Dan McGwire (CL) | .35 | .20 |
| 2 | Eric Bieniemy (R) | .25 | .15 |
| 3 | Mike Dumas (R) | .10 | .06 |
| 4 | Mike Croel (R) | .40 | .25 |
| 5 | Russell Maryland (R) | .25 | .15 |
| 6 | Charles McRae (R) | .08 | .05 |
| 7 | Dan McGwire (R) | .60 | .35 |
| 8 | Mike Pritchard (R) | .60 | .35 |
| 9 | Ricky Watters (R) | 2.00 | 1.25 |
| 10 | Chris Zorich (R) | .10 | .06 |
| 11 | Browning Nagle (R) | 1.25 | .80 |
| 12 | Wesley Carroll (R) | .35 | .20 |
| 13 | Brett Favre (R) | 2.00 | 1.25 |
| 14 | Rob Carpenter (R) | .15 | .10 |
| 15 | Eric Swann (R) | .12 | .07 |
| 16 | Stanley Richard (R) | .15 | .10 |
| 17 | Herman Moore (R) | .50 | .30 |
| 18 | Todd Marinovich (R) | 1.25 | .80 |
| 19 | Aaron Craver (R) | .10 | .06 |
| 20 | Chuck Webb (R) | .12 | .07 |
| 21 | Todd Lyght (R) | .15 | .10 |
| 22 | Greg Lewis (R) | .25 | .15 |
| 23 | Eric Turner (R) | .30 | .18 |
| 24 | Alvin Harper (R) | .80 | .50 |
| 25 | Jarrod Bunch (R) | .25 | .15 |
| 26 | Bruce Pickens (R) | .15 | .10 |
| 27 | Harvey Williams (R) | .60 | .35 |
| 28 | Randal Hill (R) | .40 | .25 |
| 29 | Nick Bell (R) | .60 | .35 |
| 30 | Jim Everett (AT) | .08 | .05 |
| 31 | Randall Cunningham(AT) | .10 | .06 |
| 32 | Steve DeBerg (AT) | .07 | .04 |
| 33 | Warren Moon (AT) | .10 | .06 |
| 34 | Dan Marino (AT) | .20 | .12 |
| 35 | Joe Montana (AT) | .25 | .15 |
| 36 | Percy Snow | .08 | .05 |
| 37 | Kelvin Martin | .07 | .04 |
| 38 | Scott Case | .05 | .02 |
| 39 | John Gesek (R) | .07 | .04 |
| 40 | Barry Word | .25 | .15 |
| 41 | Cornelius Bennett | .10 | .06 |
| 42 | Mike Kenn | .05 | .02 |
| 43 | Andre Reed | .12 | .07 |
| 44 | Bobby Hebert | .12 | .07 |
| 45 | William Perry | .07 | .04 |
| 46 | Dennis Byrd | .05 | .02 |
| 47 | Martin Mayhew | .05 | .02 |
| 48 | Issaic Holt | .05 | .02 |
| 49 | William White | .05 | .02 |
| 50 | JoJo Townsell | .05 | .02 |
| 51 | Jarvis Williams | .05 | .02 |
| 52 | Joey Browner | .07 | .04 |
| 53 | Pat Terrell | .05 | .02 |
| 54 | Joe Montana | .60 | .35 |
| 55 | Jeff Herrod | .05 | .02 |
| 56 | Cris Carter | .20 | .12 |
| 57 | Jerry Rice | .40 | .25 |
| 58 | Brett Perriman | .07 | .04 |
| 59 | Kevin Fagen | .05 | .02 |
| 60 | Wayne Haddix | .05 | .02 |
| 61 | Tommy Kane | .07 | .04 |
| 62 | Pat Beach | .05 | .02 |
| 63 | Jeff Lageman | .07 | .04 |
| 64 | Hassan Jones | .08 | .05 |
| 65 | Bennie Blades | .07 | .04 |
| 66 | Tim McGee | .08 | .05 |
| 67 | Robert Blackmon | .05 | .02 |
| 68 | Fred Stokes (R) | .08 | .05 |
| 69 | Barney Bussey (R) | .08 | .05 |
| 70 | Eric Metcalf | .10 | .06 |
| 71 | Mark Kelso | .05 | .02 |
| 72 | Neal Anderson (CL) | .08 | .05 |
| 73 | Boomer Esiason (CL) | .08 | .05 |
| 74 | Thurman Thomas (CL) | .20 | .12 |
| 75 | John Elway (CL) | .12 | .07 |
| 76 | Eric Metcalf (CL) | .07 | .04 |
| 77 | Vinny Testaverde (CL) | .08 | .05 |
| 78 | Johnny Johnson (CL) | .08 | .05 |
| 79 | Anthony Miller (CL) | .08 | .05 |
| 80 | Derrick Thomas (CL) | .12 | .07 |
| 81 | Jeff George (CL) | .15 | .10 |
| 82 | Troy Aikman (CL) | .35 | .20 |
| 83 | Dan Marino (CL) | .20 | .12 |
| 84 | Randall Cunningham(CL) | .10 | .06 |
| 85 | Deion Sanders (CL) | .10 | .06 |
| 86 | Jerry Rice (CL) | .15 | .10 |
| 87 | Lawrence Taylor (CL) | .10 | .06 |
| 88 | Al Toon (CL) | .07 | .04 |
| 89 | Barry Sanders (CL) | .20 | .12 |
| 90 | Warren Moon (CL) | .10 | .06 |
| 91 | Sterling Sharpe (CL) | .10 | .06 |
| 92 | Andre Tippett (CL) | .07 | .04 |
| 93 | Bo Jackson (CL) | .15 | .10 |
| 94 | Jim Everett (CL) | .08 | .05 |
| 95 | Art Monk (CL) | .10 | .06 |
| 96 | Morten Andersen (CL) | .07 | .04 |
| 97 | John L. Williams (CL) | .07 | .04 |
| 98 | Rod Woodson (CL) | .07 | .04 |
| 99 | Herschel Walker (CL) | .08 | .05 |
| 100 | Checklist | .05 | .02 |

| | | | |
|---|---|---|---|
| 101 | Steve Young | .30 | .18 |
| 102 | Jim Lachey | .07 | .04 |
| 103 | Tom Rathman | .08 | .05 |
| 104 | Earnest Byner | .07 | .04 |
| 105 | Karl Mecklenburg | .07 | .04 |
| 106 | Wes Hopkins | .05 | .02 |
| 107 | Michael Irvin | .35 | .20 |
| 108 | Burt Grossman | .07 | .04 |
| 109 | Jay Novacek | .12 | .07 |
| 110 | Ben Smith | .05 | .02 |
| 111 | Rod Woodson | .08 | .05 |
| 112 | Ernie Jones | .05 | .02 |
| 113 | Bryan Hinkle | .05 | .02 |
| 114 | Vai Sikahema | .05 | .02 |
| 115 | Bubby Brister | .10 | .06 |
| 116 | Brian Blades | .08 | .05 |
| 117 | Don Majkowski | .10 | .06 |
| 118 | Rod Bernstine | .07 | .04 |
| 119 | Brian Noble | .05 | .02 |
| 120 | Eugene Robinson | .05 | .02 |
| 121 | John Taylor | .15 | .10 |
| 122 | Vance Johnson | .08 | .05 |
| 123 | Art Monk | .20 | .12 |
| 124 | John Elway | .20 | .12 |
| 125 | Dexter Carter | .10 | .06 |
| 126 | Anthony Miller | .10 | .06 |
| 127 | Keith Jackson | .12 | .07 |
| 128 | Albert Lewis | .05 | .02 |
| 129 | Billy Ray Smith | .05 | .02 |
| 130 | Clyde Simmons | .07 | .04 |
| 131 | Merril Hoge | .07 | .04 |
| 132 | Ricky Proehl | .10 | .06 |
| 133 | Tim McDonald | .05 | .02 |
| 134 | Louis Lipps | .07 | .04 |
| 135 | Ken Harvey | .05 | .02 |
| 136 | Sterling Sharpe | .15 | .10 |
| 137 | Gill Byrd | .05 | .02 |
| 138 | Tim Harris | .05 | .02 |
| 139 | Derrick Fenner | .10 | .06 |
| 140 | Johnny Holland | .05 | .02 |
| 141 | Ricky Sanders | .07 | .04 |
| 142 | Bobby Humphrey | .10 | .06 |
| 143 | Roger Craig | .08 | .05 |
| 144 | Steve Atwater | .08 | .05 |
| 145 | Ickey Woods | .05 | .02 |
| 146 | Randall Cunningham | .15 | .10 |
| 147 | Marion Butts | .10 | .06 |
| 148 | Reggie White | .10 | .06 |
| 149 | Ronnie Harmon | .05 | .02 |
| 150 | Mike Saxon | .05 | .02 |
| 151 | Greg Townsend | .05 | .02 |
| 152 | Troy Aikman | .90 | .60 |
| 153 | Shane Conlan | .08 | .05 |
| 154 | Deion Sanders | .25 | .15 |
| 155 | Bo Jackson | .25 | .15 |
| 156 | Jeff Hostetler | .12 | .07 |
| 157 | Albert Bentley | .05 | .02 |
| 158 | James Williams | .05 | .02 |
| 159 | Bill Brooks | .05 | .02 |
| 160 | Nick Lowery | .07 | .04 |
| 161 | Ottis Anderson | .07 | .04 |
| 162 | Kevin Greene | .05 | .02 |
| 163 | Neil Smith | .05 | .02 |
| 164 | Jim Everett | .12 | .07 |
| 165 | Derrick Thomas | .20 | .12 |
| 166 | John L. Williams | .07 | .04 |
| 167 | Timm Rosenbach | .12 | .07 |
| 168 | Leslie O'Neal | .07 | .04 |
| 169 | Clarence Verdin | .07 | .04 |
| 170 | Dave Krieg | .10 | .06 |
| 171 | Steve Broussard | .08 | .05 |
| 172 | Emmitt Smith | 2.00 | 1.25 |
| 173 | Andre Rison | .20 | .12 |
| 174 | Bruce Smith | .08 | .05 |
| 175 | Mark Clayton | .10 | .06 |
| 176 | Christian Okoye | .10 | .06 |
| 177 | Duane Bickett | .05 | .02 |
| 178 | Stephone Paige | .07 | .04 |
| 179 | Fredd Young | .05 | .02 |
| 180 | Mervyn Fernandez | .07 | .04 |
| 181 | Phil Simms | .10 | .06 |
| 182 | Pete Holohan | .05 | .02 |
| 183 | Pepper Johnson | .05 | .02 |
| 184 | Jackie Slater | .05 | .02 |
| 185 | Stephen Baker | .05 | .02 |
| 186 | Frank Cornish | .05 | .02 |
| 187 | Dave Waymer | .05 | .02 |
| 188 | Terance Mathis | .08 | .05 |
| 189 | Darryl Talley | .07 | .04 |
| 190 | James Hasty | .05 | .02 |
| 191 | Jay Schroeder | .10 | .06 |
| 192 | Kenneth Davis | .08 | .05 |
| 193 | Chris Miller | .25 | .15 |
| 194 | Scott Davis | .05 | .02 |
| 195 | Tim Green | .05 | .02 |
| 196 | Dan Saleaumua | .05 | .02 |
| 197 | Rohn Stark | .05 | .02 |
| 198 | John Alt | .05 | .02 |
| 199 | Steve Tasker | .05 | .02 |
| 200 | Checklist 101-200 | .05 | .02 |
| 201 | Freddie Joe Nunn | .05 | .02 |
| 202 | Jim Breech | .05 | .02 |
| 203 | Roy Green | .07 | .04 |
| 204 | Gary Anderson | .05 | .02 |
| 205 | Rich Camarillo | .05 | .02 |
| 206 | Mark Bortz | .05 | .02 |
| 207 | Eddie Brown | .08 | .05 |
| 208 | Brad Muster | .08 | .05 |
| 209 | Anthony Munoz | .08 | .05 |
| 210 | Dalton Hilliard | .08 | .05 |
| 211 | Erik McMillan | .05 | .02 |
| 212 | Perry Kemp | .05 | .02 |
| 213 | Jim Thornton | .05 | .02 |
| 214 | Anthony Dilweg | .08 | .05 |

| | | | |
|---|---|---|---|
| 215 Cleveland Gary | .08 | .05 |
| 216 Leo Goeas | .05 | .02 |
| 217 Mike Merriweather | .05 | .02 |
| 218 Courtney Hall | .05 | .02 |
| 219 Wade Wilson | .08 | .05 |
| 220 Billy Joe Tolliver | .08 | .05 |
| 221 Harold Green | .20 | .12 |
| 222 Bubba Baker | .05 | .02 |
| 223 Carl Zander | .05 | .02 |
| 224 Thane Gash | .05 | .02 |
| 225 Kevin Mack | .07 | .04 |
| 226 Morten Andersen | .07 | .04 |
| 227 Dennis Gentry | .05 | .02 |
| 228 Vince Buck | .05 | .02 |
| 229 Mike Singletary | .10 | .06 |
| 230 Rueben Mayes | .05 | .02 |
| 231 Mark Carrier (TB) | .07 | .04 |
| 232 Tony Mandarich | .05 | .02 |
| 233 Al Toon | .08 | .05 |
| 234 Renaldo Turnbull | .05 | .02 |
| 235 Broderick Thomas | .08 | .05 |
| 236 Anthony Carter | .08 | .05 |
| 237 Flipper Anderson | .08 | .05 |
| 238 Jerry Robinson | .05 | .02 |
| 239 Vince Newsome | .05 | .02 |
| 240 Keith Millard | .07 | .04 |
| 241 Reggie Langhorne | .05 | .02 |
| 242 James Francis | .08 | .05 |
| 243 Felix Wright | .05 | .02 |
| 244 Neal Anderson | .12 | .07 |
| 245 Boomer Esiason | .12 | .07 |
| 246 Pat Swilling | .10 | .06 |
| 247 Richard Dent | .07 | .04 |
| 248 Craig Heyward | .07 | .04 |
| 249 Ron Morris | .05 | .02 |
| 250 Eric Martin | .08 | .05 |
| 251 Jim Jensen | .05 | .02 |
| 252 Anthony Toney | .05 | .02 |
| 253 Sammie Smith | .10 | .06 |
| 254 Calvin Williams | .10 | .06 |
| 255 Dan Marino | .35 | .20 |
| 256 Warren Moon | .20 | .12 |
| 257 Tommie Agee | .05 | .02 |
| 258 Haywood Jeffires | .20 | .12 |
| 259 Eugene Lockhart | .05 | .02 |
| 260 Drew Hill | .08 | .05 |
| 261 Vinny Testaverde | .10 | .06 |
| 262 Jim Arnold | .05 | .02 |
| 263 Steve Christie | .05 | .02 |
| 264 Chris Spielman | .05 | .02 |
| 265 Reggie Cobb | .20 | .12 |
| 266 John Stephens | .08 | .05 |
| 267 Jay Hilgenberg | .05 | .02 |
| 268 Brent Williams | .05 | .02 |
| 269 Rodney Hampton | .60 | .35 |
| 270 Irving Fryar | .07 | .04 |
| 271 Terry McDaniel | .05 | .02 |
| 272 Reggie Roby | .05 | .02 |
| 273 Allen Pinkett | .05 | .02 |
| 274 Tim McKyer | .05 | .02 |
| 275 Bob Golic | .05 | .02 |
| 276 Wilber Marshall | .07 | .04 |
| 277 Ray Childress | .07 | .04 |
| 278 Charles Mann | .05 | .02 |
| 279 Cris Dishman (R) | .15 | .10 |
| 280 Mark Rypien | .20 | .12 |
| 281 Michael Cofer | .05 | .02 |
| 282 Keith Byars | .07 | .04 |
| 283 Mike Rozier | .07 | .04 |
| 284 Seth Joyner | .07 | .04 |
| 285 Jessie Tuggle | .05 | .02 |
| 286 Mark Bavaro | .05 | .02 |
| 287 Eddie Anderson | .05 | .02 |
| 288 Sean Landeta | .05 | .02 |
| 289 Howie Long (W/Brett) | .15 | .10 |
| 290 Reyna Thompson | .05 | .02 |
| 291 Ferrell Edmunds | .05 | .02 |
| 292 Willie Gault | .07 | .04 |
| 293 John Offerdahl | .08 | .05 |
| 294 Tim Brown | .10 | .06 |
| 295 Bruce Matthews | .05 | .02 |
| 296 Kevin Ross | .05 | .02 |
| 297 Lorenzo White | .15 | .10 |
| 298 Dino Hackett | .05 | .02 |
| 299 Curtis Duncan | .05 | .02 |
| 300 Checklist 201-300 | .05 | .02 |
| 301 Andre Ware | .15 | .10 |
| 302 David Little | .05 | .02 |
| 303 Jerry Ball | .05 | .02 |
| 304 Dwight Stone | .05 | .02 |
| 305 Rodney Peete | .10 | .06 |
| 306 Mike Baab | .05 | .02 |
| 307 Tim Worley | .08 | .05 |
| 308 Paul Farren | .05 | .02 |
| 309 Carnell Lake | .05 | .02 |
| 310 Clay Matthews | .05 | .02 |
| 311 Alton Montgomery | .05 | .02 |
| 312 Ernest Givins | .12 | .07 |
| 313 Mike Horan | .05 | .02 |
| 314 Sean Jones | .05 | .02 |
| 315 Leonard Smith | .05 | .02 |
| 316 Carl Banks | .07 | .04 |
| 317 Jerome Brown | .07 | .04 |
| 318 Everson Walls | .05 | .02 |
| 319 Ron Heller | .05 | .02 |
| 320 Mark Collins | .05 | .02 |
| 321 Eddie Murray | .05 | .02 |
| 322 Jim Harbaugh | .15 | .10 |
| 323 Mel Gray | .05 | .02 |
| 324 Keith Van Horne | .05 | .02 |
| 325 Lomas Brown | .05 | .02 |
| 326 Carl Lee | .05 | .02 |
| 327 Ken O'Brien | .10 | .06 |
| 328 Dermontti Dawson | .05 | .02 |

| | | | |
|---|---|---|---|
| 329 | Brad Baxter | .15 | .10 |
| 330 | Chris Doleman | .08 | .05 |
| 331 | Louis Oliver | .07 | .04 |
| 332 | Frank Stams | .05 | .02 |
| 333 | Mike Munchak | .05 | .02 |
| 334 | Fred Strickland | .05 | .02 |
| 335 | Mark Duper | .07 | .04 |
| 336 | Jacob Green | .05 | .02 |
| 337 | Tony Paige | .05 | .02 |
| 338 | Jeff Bryant | .05 | .02 |
| 339 | Lemuel Stinson | .05 | .02 |
| 340 | David Wyman | .05 | .02 |
| 341 | Lee Williams | .05 | .02 |
| 342 | Trace Armstrong | .05 | .02 |
| 343 | Junior Seau | .25 | .15 |
| 344 | John Roper | .05 | .02 |
| 345 | Jeff George | .35 | .20 |
| 346 | Herschel Walker | .12 | .07 |
| 347 | Sam Clancy | .05 | .02 |
| 348 | Steve Jordan | .05 | .02 |
| 349 | Nate Odomes | .05 | .02 |
| 350 | Martin Bayless | .05 | .02 |
| 351 | Brent Jones | .07 | .04 |
| 352 | Ray Agnew | .05 | .02 |
| 353 | Charles Haley | .07 | .04 |
| 354 | Andre Tippett | .07 | .04 |
| 355 | Ronnie Lott | .10 | .06 |
| 356 | Thurman Thomas | .60 | .35 |
| 357 | Fred Barnett | .20 | .12 |
| 358 | James Lofton | .15 | .10 |
| 359 | William Frizzell (R) | .08 | .05 |
| 360 | Keith McKeller | .05 | .02 |
| 361 | Rodney Holman | .05 | .02 |
| 362 | Henry Ellard | .07 | .04 |
| 363 | David Fulcher | .05 | .02 |
| 364 | Jerry Gray | .05 | .02 |
| 365 | James Brooks | .07 | .04 |
| 366 | Tony Stargell | .05 | .02 |
| 367 | Keith McCants | .08 | .05 |
| 368 | Lewis Billups | .05 | .02 |
| 369 | Ervin Randle | .05 | .02 |
| 370 | Pat Leahy | .05 | .02 |
| 371 | Bruce Armstrong | .05 | .02 |
| 372 | Steve DeBerg | .10 | .06 |
| 373 | Guy McIntyre | .05 | .02 |
| 374 | Deron Cherry | .05 | .02 |
| 375 | Fred Marion | .05 | .02 |
| 376 | Michael Haddix | .05 | .02 |
| 377 | Kent Hull | .05 | .02 |
| 378 | Jerry Holmes | .05 | .02 |
| 379 | Jim Richter | .05 | .02 |
| 380 | Ed West | .05 | .02 |
| 381 | Richmond Webb | .07 | .04 |
| 382 | Mark Jackson | .07 | .04 |
| 383 | Tom Newberry | .05 | .02 |
| 384 | Ricky Nattiel | .08 | .05 |
| 385 | Keith Sims | .05 | .02 |
| 386 | Ron Hall | .05 | .02 |
| 387 | Ken Norton | .05 | .02 |
| 388 | Paul Gruber | .05 | .02 |
| 389 | Danny Stubbs | .05 | .02 |
| 390 | Ian Beckles | .05 | .02 |
| 391 | Hoby Brenner | .05 | .02 |
| 392 | Tory Epps | .05 | .02 |
| 393 | Sam Mills | .07 | .04 |
| 394 | Chris Hinton | .05 | .02 |
| 395 | Steve Walsh | .10 | .06 |
| 396 | Simon Fletcher | .05 | .02 |
| 397 | Tony Bennett | .07 | .04 |
| 398 | Aundray Bruce | .05 | .02 |
| 399 | Mark Murphy | .05 | .02 |
| 400 | Checklist 301-400 | .05 | .02 |
| 401 | Barry Sanders LL | .25 | .15 |
| 402 | Jerry Rice LL | .20 | .12 |
| 403 | Warren Moon LL | .10 | .06 |
| 404 | Derrick Thomas LL | .10 | .06 |
| 405 | Nick Lowery LL | .05 | .02 |
| 406 | Mark Carrier LL | .07 | .04 |
| 407 | Michael Carter | .05 | .02 |
| 408 | Chris Singleton | .07 | .04 |
| 409 | Matt Millen | .05 | .02 |
| 410 | Ronnie Lippett | .05 | .02 |
| 411 | E.J. Junior | .05 | .02 |
| 412 | Ray Donaldson | .05 | .02 |
| 413 | Keith Willis | .05 | .02 |
| 414 | Jessie Hester | .07 | .04 |
| 415 | Jeff Cross | .05 | .02 |
| 416 | Greg Jackson (R) | .07 | .04 |
| 417 | Alvin Walton | .05 | .02 |
| 418 | Bart Oates | .05 | .02 |
| 419 | Chip Lohmiller | .05 | .02 |
| 420 | John Elliott | .05 | .02 |
| 421 | Randall McDaniel | .05 | .02 |
| 422 | Richard Johnson (R) | .08 | .05 |
| 423 | Al Noga | .05 | .02 |
| 424 | Lamar Lathon | .07 | .04 |
| 425 | Rick Fenney | .05 | .02 |
| 426 | Jack Del Rio | .05 | .02 |
| 427 | Don Mosebar | .05 | .02 |
| 428 | Luis Sharpe | .05 | .02 |
| 429 | Steve Wisniewski | .05 | .02 |
| 430 | Jimmie Jones | .05 | .02 |
| 431 | Freeman McNeil | .08 | .05 |
| 432 | Ron Rivera | .05 | .02 |
| 433 | Hart Lee Dykes | .07 | .04 |
| 434 | Mark Carrier (Chi) | .08 | .05 |
| 435 | Rob Moore | .25 | .15 |
| 436 | Gary Clark | .15 | .10 |
| 437 | Heath Sherman | .07 | .04 |
| 438 | Darrell Green | .10 | .06 |
| 439 | Jessie Small | .05 | .02 |
| 440 | Monte Coleman | .05 | .02 |
| 441 | Leonard Marshall | .07 | .04 |
| 442 | Richard Johnson | .05 | .02 |

| | | | |
|---|---|---|---|
| 443 Dave Meggett | .12 | .07 |
| 444 Barry Sanders | 1.00 | .70 |
| 445 Lawrence Taylor | .15 | .10 |
| 446 Marcus Allen | .10 | .06 |
| 447 Johnny Johnson | .15 | .10 |
| 448 Aaron Wallace | .07 | .04 |
| 449 Anthony Thompson | .08 | .05 |
| 450 Marino/DeBerg (CL) | .15 | .10 |
| 451 Andre Rison (MVP) | .10 | .06 |
| 452 Thurman Thomas (MVP) | .25 | .15 |
| 453 Neal Anderson (MVP) | .07 | .04 |
| 454 Boomer Esiason (MVP) | .08 | .05 |
| 455 Eric Metcalf (MVP) | .07 | .04 |
| 456 Emmitt Smith (MVP) | .80 | .50 |
| 457 Bobby Humphrey (MVP) | .08 | .05 |
| 458 Barry Sanders (MVP) | .30 | .18 |
| 459 Sterling Sharpe (MVP) | .10 | .06 |
| 460 Warren Moon (MVP) | .10 | .06 |
| 461 Albert Bentley (MVP) | .05 | .02 |
| 462 Steve DeBerg (MVP) | .07 | .04 |
| 463 Greg Townsend (MVP) | .05 | .02 |
| 464 Henry Ellard (MVP) | .07 | .04 |
| 465 Dan Marino (MVP) | .20 | .12 |
| 466 Anthony Carter (MVP) | .07 | .04 |
| 467 John Stephens (MVP) | .07 | .04 |
| 468 Pat Swilling (MVP) | .08 | .05 |
| 469 Ottis Anderson (MVP) | .07 | .04 |
| 470 Dennis Byrd (MVP) | .07 | .04 |
| 471 Randall Cunningham (MVP) | .10 | .06 |
| 472 Johnny Johnson (MVP) | .08 | .05 |
| 473 Rod Woodson (MVP) | .08 | .05 |
| 474 Anthony Miller (MVP) | .07 | .04 |
| 475 Jerry Rice (MVP) | .20 | .12 |
| 476 John L. Williams (MVP) | .05 | .02 |
| 477 Wayne Haddix (MVP) | .05 | .02 |
| 478 Earnest Byner (MVP) | .07 | .04 |
| 479 Doug Widell | .05 | .02 |
| 480 Tommy Hodson | .08 | .05 |
| 481 Shawn Collins | .05 | .02 |
| 482 Rickey Jackson | .07 | .04 |
| 483 Tony Casillas | .05 | .02 |
| 484 Vaughan Johnson | .07 | .04 |
| 485 Floyd Dixon | .05 | .02 |
| 486 Eric Green | .12 | .07 |
| 487 Harry Hamilton | .05 | .02 |
| 488 Gary Anderson | .05 | .02 |
| 489 Bruce Hill | .05 | .02 |
| 490 Gerald Williams | .05 | .02 |
| 491 Cortez Kennedy | .25 | .15 |
| 492 Chet Brooks | .05 | .02 |
| 493 Dwayne Harper | .05 | .02 |
| 494 Don Griffin | .05 | .02 |
| 495 Andy Heck | .05 | .02 |
| 496 David Treadwell | .05 | .02 |
| 497 Irv Pankey | .05 | .02 |
| 498 Dennis Smith | .05 | .02 |
| 499 Marcus Dupree | .07 | .04 |
| 500 Checklist 401-500 | .05 | .02 |
| 501 Wendell Davis | .10 | .06 |
| 502 Matt Bahr | .05 | .02 |
| 503 Rob Burnett (R) | .08 | .05 |
| 504 Maurice Carthon | .05 | .02 |
| 505 Donnell Woolford | .05 | .02 |
| 506 Howard Ballard | .05 | .02 |
| 507 Mark Boyer | .05 | .02 |
| 508 Eugene Marve | .05 | .02 |
| 509 Joe Kelly | .05 | .02 |
| 510 Will Wolford | .05 | .02 |
| 511 Robert Clark | .05 | .02 |
| 512 Matt Brock (R) | .08 | .05 |
| 513 Chris Warren | .05 | .02 |
| 514 Ken Willis | .05 | .02 |
| 515 George Jamison (R) | .08 | .05 |
| 516 Rufus Porter | .05 | .02 |
| 517 Mark Higgs (R) | .60 | .35 |
| 518 Thomas Everett | .05 | .02 |
| 519 Robert Brown | .05 | .02 |
| 520 Gene Atkins | .05 | .02 |
| 521 Hardy Nickerson | .05 | .02 |
| 522 Johnny Bailey | .05 | .02 |
| 523 William Frizzell | .05 | .02 |
| 524 Steve McMichael | .07 | .04 |
| 525 Kevin Porter | .05 | .02 |
| 526 Carwell Gardner | .05 | .02 |
| 527 Eugene Daniel | .05 | .02 |
| 528 Vestee Jackson | .05 | .02 |
| 529 Chris Goode | .05 | .02 |
| 530 Leon Seals | .05 | .02 |
| 531 Darion Conner | .05 | .02 |
| 532 Stan Brock | .05 | .02 |
| 533 Kirby Jackson (R) | .08 | .05 |
| 534 Marv Cook | .08 | .05 |
| 535 Bill Fralic | .05 | .02 |
| 536 Keith Woodside | .05 | .02 |
| 537 Hugh Green | .05 | .02 |
| 538 Grant Feasel | .05 | .02 |
| 539 Bubba McDowell | .05 | .02 |
| 540 Via Sikahema | .05 | .02 |
| 541 Aaron Cox | .05 | .02 |
| 542 Roger Craig | .08 | .05 |
| 543 Robb Thomas | .05 | .02 |
| 544 Ronnie Lott | .10 | .06 |
| 545 Robert Delpino | .07 | .04 |
| 546 Greg McMurtry | .10 | .06 |
| 547 Jim Morrissey (R) | .08 | .05 |
| 548 Johnny Rembert | .05 | .02 |
| 549 Markus Paul (R) | .10 | .06 |
| 550 Karl Wilson (R) | .08 | .05 |
| 551 Gaston Green | .15 | .10 |
| 552 Willie Drewrey | .05 | .02 |
| 553 Michael Young | .05 | .02 |

| | | | |
|---|---|---|---|
| 554 | Tom Tupa | .10 | .06 |
| 555 | John Friesz | .12 | .07 |
| 556 | Cody Carlson (R) | .20 | .12 |
| 557 | Eric Allen | .05 | .02 |
| 558 | Tom Bensen | .05 | .02 |
| 559 | Scott Mersereau (R) | .08 | .05 |
| 560 | Lionel Washington | .05 | .02 |
| 561 | Brian Brennan | .05 | .02 |
| 562 | Jim Jeffcoat | .05 | .02 |
| 563 | Jeff Jaeger | .05 | .02 |
| 564 | David Johnson (R) | .08 | .05 |
| 565 | Danny Villa | .05 | .02 |
| 566 | Don Beebe | .08 | .05 |
| 567 | Michael Haynes | .25 | .15 |
| 568 | Brett Faryniarz (R) | .07 | .04 |
| 569 | Mike Prior | .05 | .02 |
| 570 | John Davis (R) | .08 | .05 |
| 571 | Vernon Turner (R) | .10 | .06 |
| 572 | Michael Brooks | .05 | .02 |
| 573 | Mike Gann | .05 | .02 |
| 574 | Ron Holmes | .05 | .02 |
| 575 | Gary Plummer | .05 | .02 |
| 576 | Bill Romanowski | .05 | .02 |
| 577 | Chris Jacke | .05 | .02 |
| 578 | Gary Reasons | .05 | .02 |
| 579 | Tim Jorden (R) | .08 | .05 |
| 580 | Tim McKyer | .05 | .02 |
| 581 | Johnny Jackson (R) | .10 | .06 |
| 582 | Ethan Horton | .07 | .04 |
| 583 | Pete Stoyanovich | .05 | .02 |
| 584 | Jeff Query | .10 | .06 |
| 585 | Frank Reich | .07 | .04 |
| 586 | Riki Ellison | .05 | .02 |
| 587 | Eric Hill | .05 | .02 |
| 588 | Anthony Shelton (R) | .08 | .05 |
| 589 | Steve Smith | .05 | .02 |
| 590 | Garth Jax (R) | .08 | .05 |
| 591 | Greg Davis (R) | .08 | .05 |
| 592 | Bill Maas | .05 | .02 |
| 593 | Henry Rolling (R) | .08 | .05 |
| 594 | Keith Jones | .05 | .02 |
| 595 | Tootie Robbins | .05 | .02 |
| 596 | Brian Jordan | .12 | .07 |
| 597 | Derrick Walker (R) | .10 | .06 |
| 598 | Jonathan Hayes | .05 | .02 |
| 599 | Nate Lewis (R) | .15 | .10 |
| 600 | Checklist 501-600 | .05 | .02 |
| 601 | Rookie Force (CL) (AFC) | .12 | .07 |
| 602 | James Jones (R) | .10 | .06 |
| 603 | Tim Barnett (R) | .25 | .15 |
| 604 | Ed King (R) | .08 | .05 |
| 605 | Shane Curry (R) | .08 | .05 |
| 606 | Mike Croel | .25 | .15 |
| 607 | Bryan Cox (R) | .35 | .20 |
| 608 | Shawn Jefferson (R) | .20 | .12 |
| 609 | Kenny Walker (R) | .30 | .18 |
| 610 | Michael Jackson (R) | .25 | .15 |
| 611 | Jon Vaughn (R) | .25 | .15 |
| 612 | Greg Lewis | .15 | .10 |
| 613 | Joe Valerio (R) | .08 | .05 |
| 614 | Pat Harlow (R) | .08 | .05 |
| 615 | Henry Jones (R) | .30 | .18 |
| 616 | Jeff Graham (R) | .30 | .18 |
| 617 | Darryll Lewis (R) | .12 | .07 |
| 618 | Keith Traylor (R) | .10 | .06 |
| 619 | Scott Miller (R) | .08 | .05 |
| 620 | Nick Bell | .30 | .18 |
| 621 | John Flannery (R) | .08 | .05 |
| 622 | Leonard Russell (R) | .70 | .40 |
| 623 | Alfred Williams (R) | .20 | .12 |
| 624 | Browning Nagle | .60 | .35 |
| 625 | Harvey Williams | .25 | .15 |
| 626 | Dan McGwire | .30 | .18 |
| 627 | Rookie Force (CL) (NFC) | .30 | .18 |
| 628 | William Thomas (R) | .08 | .05 |
| 629 | Lawrence Dawsey (R) | .50 | .30 |
| 630 | Aeneas Williams (R) | .15 | .10 |
| 631 | Stan Thomas (R) | .08 | .05 |
| 632 | Randal Hill | .20 | .12 |
| 633 | Moe Gardner (R) | .15 | .10 |
| 634 | Alvin Harper | .35 | .20 |
| 635 | Esera Tuaolo (R) | .08 | .05 |
| 636 | Russell Maryland | .20 | .12 |
| 637 | Anthony Morgan (R) | .25 | .15 |
| 638 | Erric Pegram (R) | .20 | .12 |
| 639 | Herman Moore | .25 | .15 |
| 640 | Ricky Ervins (R) | 1.00 | .70 |
| 641 | Kelvin Pritchett (R) | .15 | .10 |
| 642 | Roman Phifer (R) | .08 | .05 |
| 643 | Antone Davis (R) | .08 | .05 |
| 644 | Mike Pritchard | .20 | .12 |
| 645 | Vinnie Clark (R) | .10 | .06 |
| 646 | Jake Reed (R) | .08 | .05 |
| 647 | Brett Favre | 1.00 | .70 |
| 648 | Todd Lyght | .15 | .10 |
| 649 | Bruce Pickens | .08 | .05 |
| 650 | Darren Lewis (R) | .35 | .20 |
| 651 | Wesley Carroll | .15 | .10 |
| 652 | James Joseph (R) | .25 | .15 |
| 653 | Robert Delpino (AR) | .05 | .02 |
| 654 | Deion Sanders (AR) | .10 | .06 |
| 655 | Jerry Rice (AR) | .20 | .12 |
| 656 | Barry Sanders (AR) | .25 | .15 |
| 657 | Ken Tippins (AR) | .07 | .04 |
| 658 | Christian Okoye (AR) | .08 | .05 |
| 659 | Rich Gannon | .20 | .12 |
| 660 | Johnny Meads | .05 | .02 |
| 661 | J.J. Birden (R) | .15 | .10 |
| 662 | Bruce Kozerski | .05 | .02 |
| 663 | Felix Wright | .05 | .02 |

| | | | |
|---|---|---|---|
| 664 | Al Smith | .05 | .02 |
| 665 | Stan Humphries | .75 | .45 |
| 666 | Alfred Anderson | .05 | .02 |
| 667 | Nate Newton | .05 | .02 |
| 668 | Vince Workman (R) | .30 | .18 |
| 669 | Ricky Reynolds | .05 | .02 |
| 670 | Bryce Paup (R) | .08 | .05 |
| 671 | Gill Fenerty | .08 | .05 |
| 672 | Darrell Thompson | .08 | .05 |
| 673 | Anthony Smith (R) | .08 | .05 |
| 674 | Darryl Henley (R) | .08 | .05 |
| 675 | Brett Maxie (R) | .07 | .04 |
| 676 | Craig Taylor (R) | .08 | .05 |
| 677 | Steve Wallace (R) | .07 | .04 |
| 678 | Jeff Feagles (R) | .07 | .04 |
| 679 | James Washington (R) | .10 | .06 |
| 680 | Tim Harris | .05 | .02 |
| 681 | Dennis Gibson | .05 | .02 |
| 682 | Toi Cook (R) | .07 | .04 |
| 683 | Lorenzo Lynch (R) | .07 | .04 |
| 684 | Brad Edwards (R) | .08 | .05 |
| 685 | Ray Crockett (R) | .08 | .05 |
| 686 | Harris Barton | .05 | .02 |
| 687 | Byron Evans | .05 | .02 |
| 688 | Eric Thomas | .05 | .02 |
| 689 | Jeff Criswell | .05 | .02 |
| 690 | Eric Ball | .05 | .02 |
| 691 | Brian Mitchell | .15 | .10 |
| 692 | Quinn Early | .05 | .02 |
| 693 | Aaron Jones | .05 | .02 |
| 694 | Jim Dombrowski | .05 | .02 |
| 695 | Jeff Bostic | .05 | .02 |
| 696 | Tony Casillas | .07 | .04 |
| 697 | Ken Lanier | .05 | .02 |
| 698 | Henry Thomas | .05 | .02 |
| 699 | Steve Beuerlein | .15 | .10 |
| 700 | Checklist 601-700 | .05 | .02 |
| SP1 | Darrell Green | 5.00 | 3.50 |
| SP2 | Don Shula | 6.50 | 4.50 |
| H1-9 | Joe Montana Heroes (ea) | .80 | .50 |
| ___ | Joe Montana Cover | 8.50 | 3.50 |
| 10-18 | Joe Namath ) Heroes (ea) | .80 | .50 |
| ___ | Joe Namath Cover | 8.50 | 3.50 |

# 1991 Upper Deck Holograms Game Breakers

The cards in this 9-card hologram set were randomly inserted into Upper Deck foil packs. The cards honor the NFL's best running backs. Card fronts feature a full color action shot in the foreground with a play diagram in the background. The player's name appears across the bottom. The card backs contain career highlights of the player. The cards measure 2-1/2" by 3-1/2".

| | | MINT | NR/MT |
|---|---|---|---|
| Complete Set (9) | | 15.00 | 9.00 |
| Commons | | .80 | .50 |
| 1 | Barry Sanders | 4.00 | 2.75 |
| 2 | Thurman Thomas | 3.50 | 2.25 |
| 3 | Bobby Humphrey | 1.00 | .65 |
| 4 | Earnest Byner | .80 | .50 |
| 5 | Emmitt Smith | 6.50 | 4.50 |
| 6 | Neal Anderson | 1.25 | .80 |
| 7 | Marion Butts | 1.00 | .65 |
| 8 | James Brooks | .80 | .50 |
| 9 | Marcus Allen | 1.25 | .80 |

# 1992 Upper Deck

This 620-card set was issued in two series and has become known as the Silver Series. Card fronts feature full color game action photos with the player's name and position printed in a small bar at the bottom of the card. The team logo is located in the lower right corner. Card backs contain a full color photo, stats and highlights. Key subsets include Star Rookies (1-29), All-Rookie Team (AR)(30-55), Team Checklists (CL), League Leaders (LL)(301-311), Team MVP's (350-378), Rookie Force (401-425) and NFL Scrapbook (S) (511-520). The set is also noted for a number of limited insert subsets including two 9-card Football Heroes sets featurings Walter Payton and Dan Marino. These inserts are listed at the end of this checklist but are not included in the complete set price below. All cards measure 2-1/2" by 3-1/2".

|  |  | MINT | NR/MT |
|---|---|---|---|
| Complete Set (620) | | 35.00 | 23.00 |
| Commons | | .05 | .02 |
| | | | |
| 1 | Star Rookie (CL) | .20 | .12 |
| 2 | Edgar Bennett (R) | .35 | .20 |
| 3 | Eddie Blake (R) | .10 | .06 |
| 4 | Brian Bollinger (R) | .08 | .05 |
| 5 | Joe Bowden (R) | .08 | .05 |
| 6 | Terrell Buckley (R) | .80 | .50 |
| 7 | Willie Clay (R) | .10 | .06 |
| 8 | Ed Cunningham (R) | .08 | .05 |
| 9 | Matt Darby (R) | .08 | .05 |
| 10 | Will Furrer (R) | .30 | .18 |
| 11 | Chris Hakel (R) | .12 | .07 |
| 12 | Carlos Huerta (R) | .07 | .04 |
| 13 | Amp Lee (R) | .60 | .35 |
| 14 | Ricardo McDonald (R) | .08 | .05 |
| 15 | Dexter McNabb (R) | .12 | .07 |
| 16 | Chris Mims (R) | .25 | .15 |
| 17 | Derrick Moore (R) | .08 | .05 |
| 18 | Robert Porcher (R) | .12 | .07 |
| 19 | Patrick Rowe (R) | .20 | .12 |
| 20 | Leon Searcy (R) | .08 | .05 |
| 21 | Torrance Small (R) | .10 | .06 |
| 22 | Jimmy Smith (R) | .12 | .07 |
| 23 | Tony Smith (R) | .60 | .35 |
| 24 | Siran Stacy (R) | .25 | .15 |
| 25 | Kevin Turner (R) | .15 | .10 |
| 26 | Tommy Vardell (R) | .75 | .45 |
| 27 | Bob Whitfield (R) | .08 | .05 |
| 28 | Darryl Williams (R) | .15 | .10 |
| 29 | Jeff Sydner (R) | .20 | .12 |
| 30 | All-Rookie Checklist | .12 | .07 |
| 31 | Todd Marinovich (AR) | .35 | .20 |
| 32 | Leonard Russell (AR) | .25 | .15 |
| 33 | Nick Bell (AR) | .20 | .12 |
| 34 | Alvin Harper (AR) | .20 | .12 |
| 35 | Mike Pritchard (AR) | .20 | .12 |
| 36 | Lawrence Dawsey (AR) | .15 | .10 |
| 37 | Tim Barnett (AR) | .15 | .10 |
| 38 | John Flannery (AR) | .07 | .04 |
| 39 | Stan Thomas (AR) | .07 | .04 |
| 40 | Ed King (AR) | .08 | .05 |
| 41 | Charles McRae (AR) | .08 | .05 |
| 42 | Eric Moten (AR) | .05 | .02 |
| 43 | Moe Gardner (AR) | .08 | .05 |
| 44 | Kenny Walker (AR) | .10 | .06 |
| 45 | Esera Tuaolo (AR) | .05 | .02 |
| 46 | Alfred Williams (AR) | .08 | .05 |
| 47 | Bryan Cox (AR) | .07 | .04 |
| 48 | Mo Lewis (AR) | .07 | .04 |
| 49 | Mike Croel (AR) | .15 | .10 |
| 50 | Stanley Richard (AR) | .08 | .05 |
| 51 | Tony Covington (AR) | .05 | .02 |
| 52 | Larry Brown (AR) | .05 | .02 |
| 53 | Aeneas Williams (AR) | .07 | .04 |
| 54 | John Kasay (AR) | .05 | .02 |
| 55 | Jon Vaughn (AR) | .10 | .06 |
| 56 | David Fulcher | .05 | .02 |
| 57 | Barry Foster | .35 | .20 |
| 58 | Terry Wooden | .05 | .02 |
| 59 | Gary Anderson | .05 | .02 |
| 60 | Alfred Williams | .08 | .05 |
| 61 | Robert Blackmon | .05 | .02 |
| 62 | Brian Noble | .05 | .02 |
| 63 | Terry Allen | .60 | .35 |
| 64 | Darrell Green | .10 | .06 |
| 65 | Darren Comeaux | .05 | .02 |
| 66 | Rob Burnett | .08 | .05 |
| 67 | Jarrod Bunch | .12 | .07 |
| 68 | Michael Jackson | .20 | .12 |
| 69 | Greg Lloyd | .05 | .02 |

| | | | | | | | |
|---|---|---|---|---|---|---|---|
| 70 | Richard Brown (R) | .08 | .05 | 127 | Leonard Marshall | .07 | .04 |
| 71 | Harold Green | .15 | .10 | 128 | Jim Price | .05 | .02 |
| 72 | William Fuller | .05 | .02 | 129 | Jessie Hester | .07 | .04 |
| 73 | Mark Carrier (CL) | .07 | .04 | 130 | Mark Carrier | .07 | .04 |
| 74 | David Fulcher (CL) | .05 | .02 | 131 | Bubba McDowell | .05 | .02 |
| 75 | Cornelius Bennett (CL) | .08 | .05 | 132 | Andre Tippett | .07 | .04 |
| 76 | Steve Atwater (CL) | .07 | .04 | 133 | James Hasty | .05 | .02 |
| 77 | Kevin Mack (CL) | .07 | .04 | 134 | Mel Gray | .05 | .02 |
| 78 | Mark Carrier (CL) | .07 | .04 | 135 | Christian Okoye | .10 | .06 |
| 79 | Tim McDonald (CL) | .05 | .02 | 136 | Earnest Byner | .08 | .05 |
| 80 | Marion Butts (CL) | .08 | .05 | 137 | Ferrell Edmunds | .05 | .02 |
| 81 | Christian Okoye (CL) | .08 | .05 | 138 | Henry Ellard | .07 | .04 |
| 82 | Jeff Herrod (CL) | .05 | .02 | 139 | Rob Moore | .15 | .10 |
| 83 | Emmitt Smith (CL) | .75 | .45 | 140 | Brian Jordan | .10 | .06 |
| 84 | Mark Duper (CL) | .07 | .04 | 141 | Clarence Verdin | .07 | .04 |
| 85 | Keith Jackson (CL) | .08 | .05 | 142 | Cornelius Bennett | .10 | .06 |
| 86 | Andre Rison (CL) | .10 | .06 | 143 | John Taylor | .12 | .07 |
| 87 | John Taylor (CL) | .08 | .05 | 144 | Derrick Thomas | .20 | .12 |
| 88 | Rodney Hampton (CL) | .15 | .10 | 145 | Thurman Thomas | .40 | .25 |
| 89 | Rob Moore (CL) | .12 | .07 | 146 | Warren Moon | .20 | .12 |
| 90 | Chris Spielman (CL) | .05 | .02 | 147 | Vinny Testaverde | .10 | .06 |
| 91 | Haywood Jeffires (CL) | .10 | .06 | 148 | Steve Bono | .25 | .15 |
| 92 | Sterling Sharpe (CL) | .10 | .06 | 149 | Robb Thomas | .05 | .02 |
| 93 | Irving Fryar (CL) | .07 | .04 | 150 | John Friesz | .10 | .06 |
| 94 | Marcus Allen (CL) | .08 | .05 | 151 | Richard Dent | .07 | .04 |
| 95 | Henry Ellard (CL) | .07 | .04 | 152 | Eddie Anderson | .05 | .02 |
| 96 | Mark Rypien (CL) | .12 | .07 | 153 | Kevin Greene | .05 | .02 |
| 97 | Pat Swilling (CL) | .08 | .05 | 154 | Marion Butts | .10 | .06 |
| 98 | Brian Blades (CL) | .07 | .04 | 155 | Barry Sanders | .75 | .45 |
| 99 | Eric Green (CL) | .08 | .05 | 156 | Andre Rison | .20 | .12 |
| 100 | Anthony Carter (CL) | .07 | .04 | 157 | Ronnie Lott | .10 | .06 |
| 101 | Burt Grossman | .07 | .04 | 158 | Eric Allen | .05 | .02 |
| 102 | Gary Anderson | .05 | .02 | 159 | Mark Clayton | .10 | .06 |
| 103 | Neil Smith | .05 | .02 | 160 | Terance Mathis | .08 | .05 |
| 104 | Jeff Feagles | .05 | .02 | 161 | Darryl Talley | .07 | .04 |
| 105 | Shane Conlan | .08 | .05 | 162 | Eric Metcalf | .10 | .06 |
| 106 | Jay Novacek | .10 | .06 | 163 | Reggie Cobb | .15 | .10 |
| 107 | Billy Brooks | .05 | .02 | 164 | Ernie Jones | .05 | .02 |
| 108 | Mark Ingram | .05 | .02 | 165 | David Griggs | .05 | .02 |
| 109 | Anthony Munoz | .08 | .05 | 166 | Tom Rathman | .07 | .04 |
| 110 | Wendell Davis | .12 | .07 | 167 | Bubby Brister | .10 | .06 |
| 111 | Jim Everett | .12 | .07 | 168 | Broderick Thomas | .08 | .05 |
| 112 | Bruce Matthews | .05 | .02 | 169 | Chris Doleman | .08 | .05 |
| 113 | Mark Higgs | .30 | .18 | 170 | Charles Haley | .07 | .04 |
| 114 | Chris Warren | .10 | .06 | 171 | Michael Haynes | .20 | .12 |
| 115 | Brad Baxter | .12 | .07 | 172 | Rodney Hampton | .35 | .20 |
| 116 | Greg Townsend | .05 | .02 | 173 | Nick Bell | .20 | .12 |
| 117 | Al Smith | .05 | .02 | 174 | Gene Atkins | .05 | .02 |
| 118 | Jeff Cross | .05 | .02 | 175 | Mike Merriweather | .05 | .02 |
| 119 | Terry McDaniel | .05 | .02 | 176 | Reggie Roby | .05 | .02 |
| 120 | Ernest Givins | .10 | .06 | 177 | Bennie Blades | .07 | .04 |
| 121 | Fred Barnett | .15 | .10 | 178 | John L. Williams | .07 | .04 |
| 122 | Flipper Anderson | .08 | .05 | 179 | Rodney Peete | .10 | .06 |
| 123 | Floyd Turner | .05 | .02 | 180 | Greg Montgomery | .05 | .02 |
| 124 | Stephen Baker | .05 | .02 | 181 | Vince Newsome | .05 | .02 |
| 125 | Tim Johnson | .05 | .02 | 182 | Andre Collins | .07 | .04 |
| 126 | Brent Jones | .07 | .04 | 183 | Erik Kramer | .20 | .12 |

| | | | |
|---|---|---|---|
| 184 | Bryan Hinkle | .05 | .02 |
| 185 | Reggie White | .10 | .06 |
| 186 | Bruce Armstrong | .05 | .02 |
| 187 | Anthony Carter | .08 | .05 |
| 188 | Pat Swilling | .10 | .06 |
| 189 | Robert Delpino | .07 | .04 |
| 190 | Brent Williams | .05 | .02 |
| 191 | Johnny Johnson | .15 | .10 |
| 192 | Aaron Craver | .10 | .06 |
| 193 | Vincent Brown | .05 | .02 |
| 194 | Herschel Walker | .12 | .07 |
| 195 | Tim McDonald | .05 | .02 |
| 196 | Gaston Green | .12 | .07 |
| 197 | Brian Blades | .07 | .04 |
| 198 | Rod Bernstine | .07 | .04 |
| 199 | Brett Perriman | .07 | .04 |
| 200 | John Elway | .20 | .12 |
| 201 | Michael Carter | .05 | .02 |
| 202 | Mark Carrier | .07 | .04 |
| 203 | Cris Carter | .20 | .12 |
| 204 | Kyle Clifton | .05 | .02 |
| 205 | Alvin Wright | .05 | .02 |
| 206 | Andre Ware | .12 | .07 |
| 207 | Dave Waymer | .05 | .02 |
| 208 | Darren Lewis | .15 | .10 |
| 209 | Joey Browner | .07 | .04 |
| 210 | Rich Miano | .05 | .02 |
| 211 | Marcus Allen | .10 | .06 |
| 212 | Steve Broussard | .08 | .05 |
| 213 | Joel Hilgenberg | .05 | .02 |
| 214 | Bo Orlando (R) | .08 | .05 |
| 215 | Clay Matthews | .05 | .02 |
| 216 | Chris Hinton | .05 | .02 |
| 217 | Al Edwards | .05 | .02 |
| 218 | Tim Brown | .10 | .06 |
| 219 | Sam Mills | .07 | .04 |
| 220 | Don Majkowski | .12 | .07 |
| 221 | James Francis | .08 | .05 |
| 222 | Steve Hendrickson (R) | .08 | .05 |
| 223 | James Thornton | .05 | .02 |
| 224 | Byron Evans | .05 | .02 |
| 225 | Pepper Johnson | .05 | .02 |
| 226 | Darryl Henley | .05 | .02 |
| 227 | Simon Fletcher | .05 | .02 |
| 228 | Hugh Millen | .20 | .12 |
| 229 | Tim McGee | .08 | .05 |
| 230 | Richmond Webb | .07 | .04 |
| 231 | Tony Bennett | .08 | .05 |
| 232 | Nate Odomes | .05 | .02 |
| 233 | Scott Case | .05 | .02 |
| 234 | Dalton Hilliard | .08 | .05 |
| 235 | Paul Gruber | .05 | .02 |
| 236 | Jeff Lageman | .07 | .04 |
| 237 | Tony Mandarich | .05 | .02 |
| 238 | Cris Dishman | .08 | .05 |
| 239 | Steve Walsh | .10 | .06 |
| 240 | Moe Gardner | .08 | .05 |
| 241 | Bill Romanowski | .05 | .02 |
| 242 | Chris Zorich | .07 | .04 |
| 243 | Stephone Paige | .07 | .04 |
| 244 | Mike Croel | .20 | .12 |
| 245 | Leonard Russell | .35 | .20 |
| 246 | Mark Rypien | .20 | .12 |
| 247 | Aeneas Williams | .08 | .05 |
| 248 | Steve Atwater | .08 | .05 |
| 249 | Michael Stewart | .05 | .02 |
| 250 | Pierce Holt | .05 | .02 |
| 251 | Kevin Mack | .07 | .04 |
| 252 | Sterling Sharpe | .25 | .15 |
| 253 | Lawrence Dawsey | .15 | .10 |
| 254 | Emmitt Smith | 1.75 | 1.00 |
| 255 | Todd Marinovich | .60 | .35 |
| 256 | Neal Anderson | .10 | .06 |
| 257 | Mo Lewis | .07 | .04 |
| 258 | Vance Johnson | .08 | .05 |
| 259 | Rickey Jackson | .07 | .04 |
| 260 | Esera Tuaolo | .05 | .02 |
| 261 | Wilber Marshall | .07 | .04 |
| 262 | Keith Henderson | .08 | .05 |
| 263 | William Thomas | .05 | .02 |
| 264 | Rickey Dixon | .05 | .02 |
| 265 | Dave Meggett | .10 | .06 |
| 266 | Gerald Riggs | .07 | .04 |
| 267 | Tim Harris | .05 | .02 |
| 268 | Ken Harvey | .05 | .02 |
| 269 | Clyde Simmons | .07 | .04 |
| 270 | Irving Fryar | .07 | .04 |
| 271 | Darion Conner | .05 | .02 |
| 272 | Vince Workman | .12 | .07 |
| 273 | Jim Harbaugh | .15 | .10 |
| 274 | Lorenzo White | .15 | .10 |
| 275 | Bobby Hebert | .12 | .07 |
| 276 | Duane Bickett | .05 | .02 |
| 277 | Jeff Bryant | .05 | .02 |
| 278 | Scott Stephen | .05 | .02 |
| 279 | Bob Golic | .05 | .02 |
| 280 | Steve McMichael | .07 | .04 |
| 281 | Jeff Graham | .15 | .10 |
| 282 | Keith Jackson | .15 | .10 |
| 283 | Howard Ballard | .05 | .02 |
| 284 | Michael Brooks | .05 | .02 |
| 285 | Freeman McNeil | .08 | .05 |
| 286 | Rodney Holman | .05 | .02 |
| 287 | Eric Bieniemy | .12 | .07 |
| 288 | Seth Joyner | .07 | .04 |
| 289 | Carwell Gardner | .05 | .02 |
| 290 | Brian Mitchell | .07 | .04 |
| 291 | Chris Miller | .25 | .15 |
| 292 | Ray Berry | .05 | .02 |
| 293 | Matt Brock | .05 | .02 |
| 294 | Eric Thomas | .05 | .02 |
| 295 | John Kasay | .05 | .02 |
| 296 | Jay Hilgenberg | .05 | .02 |
| 297 | Darrell Thompson | .07 | .04 |

| # | Player | | |
|---|--------|---|---|
| 298 | Rich Gannon | .20 | .12 |
| 299 | Steve Young | .35 | .20 |
| 300 | Mike Kenn | .05 | .02 |
| 301 | Emmitt Smith (LL) | .80 | .50 |
| 302 | Haywood Jeffires (LL) | .10 | .06 |
| 303 | Michael Irvin (LL) | .15 | .10 |
| 304 | Warren Moon (LL) | .10 | .06 |
| 305 | Chip Lohmiller (LL) | .05 | .02 |
| 306 | Barry Sanders (LL) | .30 | .18 |
| 307 | Ronnie Lott (LL) | .08 | .05 |
| 308 | Pat Swilling (LL) | .08 | .05 |
| 309 | Thurman Thomas (LL) | .20 | .12 |
| 310 | Reggie Roby (LL) | .05 | .02 |
| 311 | Checklist (LL) | .15 | .10 |
| 312 | Jacob Green | .05 | .02 |
| 313 | Stephen Braggs | .05 | .02 |
| 314 | Haywood Jeffires | .20 | .12 |
| 315 | Freddie Joe Nunn | .05 | .02 |
| 316 | Gary Clark | .12 | .07 |
| 317 | Tim Barnett | .12 | .07 |
| 318 | Mark Duper | .07 | .04 |
| 319 | Eric Green | .10 | .06 |
| 320 | Robert Wilson | .08 | .05 |
| 321 | Michael Ball | .05 | .02 |
| 322 | Eric Martin | .08 | .05 |
| 323 | Alexander Wright | .08 | .05 |
| 324 | Jessie Tuggle | .05 | .02 |
| 325 | Ronnie Harmon | .05 | .02 |
| 326 | Jeff Hostetler | .15 | .10 |
| 327 | Eugene Daniel | .05 | .02 |
| 328 | Ken Norton | .05 | .02 |
| 329 | Reyna Thompson | .05 | .02 |
| 330 | Jerry Ball | .05 | .02 |
| 331 | Leroy Hoard | .12 | .07 |
| 332 | Chris Martin | .05 | .02 |
| 333 | Keith McKeller | .05 | .02 |
| 334 | Brian Washington | .05 | .02 |
| 335 | Eugene Robinson | .05 | .02 |
| 336 | Maurice Hurst | .05 | .02 |
| 337 | Dan Saleaumua | .05 | .02 |
| 338 | Neil O'Donnell | .60 | .35 |
| 339 | Dexter Davis | .05 | .02 |
| 340 | Keith McCants | .08 | .05 |
| 341 | Steve Beuerlein | .15 | .10 |
| 342 | Roman Phifer | .05 | .02 |
| 343 | Bryan Cox | .08 | .05 |
| 344 | Art Monk | .20 | .12 |
| 345 | Michael Irvin | .35 | .20 |
| 346 | Vaughn Johnson | .07 | .04 |
| 347 | Jeff Herrod | .05 | .02 |
| 348 | Stanley Richard | .08 | .05 |
| 349 | Michael Young | .05 | .02 |
| 350 | Team MVP (CL) | .15 | .10 |
| 351 | Jim Harbaugh (MVP) | .08 | .05 |
| 352 | David Fulcher (MVP) | .05 | .02 |
| 353 | Thurman Thomas (MVP) | .20 | .12 |
| 354 | Gaston Green (MVP) | .08 | .05 |
| 355 | Leroy Hoard (MVP) | .07 | .04 |
| 356 | Reggie Cobb (MVP) | .08 | .05 |
| 357 | Tim McDonald (MVP) | .05 | .02 |
| 358 | Ronnie Harmon (MVP) | .05 | .02 |
| 359 | Derrick Thomas (MVP) | .10 | .06 |
| 360 | Jeff Herrod (MVP) | .05 | .02 |
| 361 | Michael Irvin (MVP) | .15 | .10 |
| 362 | Mark Higgs (MVP) | .10 | .06 |
| 363 | Reggie White (MVP) | .08 | .05 |
| 364 | Chris Miller (MVP) | .10 | .06 |
| 365 | Steve Young (MVP) | .12 | .07 |
| 366 | Rodney Hampton (MVP) | .12 | .07 |
| 367 | Jeff Lageman (MVP) | .05 | .02 |
| 368 | Barry Sanders (MVP) | .25 | .15 |
| 369 | Haywood Jeffires (MVP) | .10 | .06 |
| 370 | Tony Bennett (MVP) | .07 | .04 |
| 371 | Leonard Russell (MVP) | .10 | .06 |
| 372 | Jeff Jaeger (MVP) | .05 | .02 |
| 373 | Robert Delpino (MVP) | .05 | .02 |
| 374 | Mark Rypien (MVP) | .12 | .07 |
| 375 | Pat Swilling (MVP) | .08 | .05 |
| 376 | Cortez Kennedy (MVP) | .10 | .06 |
| 377 | Eric Green (MVP) | .08 | .05 |
| 378 | Cris Carter (MVP) | .10 | .06 |
| 379 | John Roper | .05 | .02 |
| 380 | Barry Word | .15 | .10 |
| 381 | Shawn Jefferson | .12 | .07 |
| 382 | Tony Casillas | .07 | .04 |
| 383 | John Baylor (R) | .08 | .05 |
| 384 | Al Noga | .05 | .02 |
| 385 | Charles Mann | .05 | .02 |
| 386 | Gil Byrd | .05 | .02 |
| 387 | Chris Singleton | .07 | .04 |
| 388 | James Joseph | .12 | .07 |
| 389 | Larry Brown | .05 | .02 |
| 390 | Chris Spielman | .05 | .02 |
| 391 | Anthony Thompson | .08 | .05 |
| 392 | Karl Mecklenburg | .07 | .04 |
| 393 | Joe Kelly | .05 | .02 |
| 394 | Kanavis McGhee | .07 | .04 |
| 395 | Bill Maas | .05 | .02 |
| 396 | Marv Cook | .07 | .04 |
| 397 | Louis Lipps | .07 | .04 |
| 398 | Marty Carter (R) | .10 | .06 |
| 399 | Louis Oliver | .07 | .04 |
| 400 | Eric Swann | .08 | .05 |
| 401 | Troy Auzenne (R) | .08 | .05 |
| 402 | Kurt Barber | .05 | .02 |
| 403 | Mark Boutte (R) | .08 | .05 |
| 404 | Dale Carter | .30 | .18 |
| 405 | Marco Coleman | .40 | .25 |
| 406 | Quentin Coryatt | .80 | .50 |
| 407 | Shane Dronett (R) | .12 | .07 |
| 408 | Vaughn Dunbar | .60 | .35 |

| | | | |
|---|---|---|---|
| 409 Steve Emtman | 1.00 | .70 |
| 410 Dana Hall (R) | .20 | .12 |
| 411 Jason Hansen (R) | .08 | .05 |
| 412 Courtney Hawkins (R) | .35 | .20 |
| 413 Terrell Buckley | .40 | .25 |
| 414 Robert Jones (R) | .25 | .15 |
| 415 David Klingler | 1.25 | .80 |
| 416 Tommy Maddox | 1.00 | .70 |
| 417 Johnny Mitchell (R) | .40 | .25 |
| 418 Carl Pickens | .80 | .50 |
| 419 Tracy Scroggins | .10 | .06 |
| 420 Tony Sacca (R) | .25 | .15 |
| 421 Kevin Smith | .12 | .07 |
| 422 Alonzo Spellman (R) | .20 | .12 |
| 423 Troy Vincent (R) | .25 | .15 |
| 424 Sean Gilbert (R) | .25 | .15 |
| 425 Larry Webster (R) | .08 | .05 |
| 426 Rookie Force Checklist | .60 | .35 |
| 427 Bill Fralic | .05 | .02 |
| 428 Kevin Murphy | .05 | .02 |
| 429 Lemuel Stinson | .05 | .02 |
| 430 Harris Barton | .05 | .02 |
| 431 Dino Hackett | .05 | .02 |
| 432 John Stephens | .10 | .06 |
| 433 Keith Jennings (R) | .08 | .05 |
| 434 Derrick Fenner | .15 | .10 |
| 435 Kenneth Gant (R) | .08 | .05 |
| 436 Willie Gault | .08 | .05 |
| 437 Steve Jordan | .07 | .04 |
| 438 Charles Haley | .07 | .04 |
| 439 Keith Kartz | .05 | .02 |
| 440 Nate Lewis | .10 | .06 |
| 441 Doug Widell | .05 | .02 |
| 442 William White | .05 | .02 |
| 443 Eric Hill | .05 | .02 |
| 444 Melvin Jenkins | .05 | .02 |
| 445 David Wyman | .05 | .02 |
| 446 Ed West | .05 | .02 |
| 447 Brad Muster | .08 | .05 |
| 448 Ray Childress | .08 | .05 |
| 449 Kevin Ross | .05 | .02 |
| 450 Johnnie Jackson | .07 | .04 |
| 451 Tracy Simien (R) | .12 | .07 |
| 452 Don Mosebar | .05 | .02 |
| 453 Jay Hilgenberg | .05 | .02 |
| 454 Wes Hopkins | .05 | .02 |
| 455 Jay Schroeder | .10 | .06 |
| 456 Jeff Bostic | .05 | .02 |
| 457 Bryce Paup | .05 | .02 |
| 458 Dave Waymer | .05 | .02 |
| 459 Toi Cook | .05 | .02 |
| 460 Anthony Smith | .05 | .02 |
| 461 Don Griffin | .05 | .02 |
| 462 Bill Hawkins | .05 | .02 |
| 463 Courtney Hall | .05 | .02 |
| 464 Jeff Ulenhake | .05 | .02 |
| 465 Mike Sherrard | .08 | .05 |

| | | | |
|---|---|---|---|
| 466 James Jones | .05 | .02 |
| 467 Jerrol Williams | .05 | .02 |
| 468 Eric Ball | .05 | .02 |
| 469 Randall McDaniel | .05 | .02 |
| 470 Alvin Harper | .35 | .20 |
| 471 Tom Waddle | .12 | .07 |
| 472 Tony Woods | .05 | .02 |
| 473 Kelvin Martin | .08 | .05 |
| 474 Jon Vaughn | .20 | .12 |
| 475 Gil Fenerty | .05 | .02 |
| 476 Aundray Bruce | .05 | .02 |
| 477 Morton Anderson | .07 | .04 |
| 478 Lamar Lathon | .08 | .05 |
| 479 Steve DeOssie | .05 | .02 |
| 480 Marvin Washington | .05 | .02 |
| 481 Herschel Walker | .15 | .10 |
| 482 Howie Long | .08 | .05 |
| 483 Calvin Williams | .15 | .10 |
| 484 Brett Favre | 1.25 | .80 |
| 485 Johnny Bailey | .05 | .02 |
| 486 Jeff Gossett | .05 | .02 |
| 487 Carnell Lake | .05 | .02 |
| 488 Michael Zordich (R) | .08 | .05 |
| 489 Henry Rolling | .07 | .04 |
| 490 Steve Smith | .05 | .02 |
| 491 Vestee Jackson | .05 | .02 |
| 492 Ray Crockett | .05 | .02 |
| 493 Dexter Carter | .08 | .05 |
| 494 Nick Lowery | .07 | .04 |
| 495 Cortez Kennedy | .12 | .07 |
| 496 Cleveland Gary | .08 | .05 |
| 497 Kelly Stouffer | .15 | .10 |
| 498 Carl Carter | .05 | .02 |
| 499 Shannon Sharpe | .07 | .04 |
| 500 Roger Craig | .08 | .05 |
| 501 Willie Drewrey | .05 | .02 |
| 502 Mark Schlereth (R) | .08 | .05 |
| 503 Tony Martin | .05 | .02 |
| 504 Tom Newberry | .05 | .02 |
| 505 Ron Hall | .05 | .02 |
| 506 Scott Miller | .05 | .02 |
| 507 Donnell Woolford | .05 | .02 |
| 508 Dave Krieg | .10 | .06 |
| 509 Erric Pegram | .05 | .02 |
| 510 Checklist | .05 | .02 |
| 511 Barry Sanders (S) | .50 | .30 |
| 512 Thurman Thomas (S) | .50 | .30 |
| 513 Warren Moon (S) | .15 | .10 |
| 514 John Elway (S) | .15 | .10 |
| 515 Ronnie Lott (S) | .10 | .06 |
| 516 Emmitt Smith (S) | .80 | .50 |
| 517 Andre Rison (S) | .12 | .07 |
| 518 Steve Atwater (S) | .08 | .05 |
| 519 Steve Young (S) | .20 | .12 |
| 520 Mark Rypien (S) | .15 | .10 |
| 521 Rich Camarillo | .05 | .02 |
| 522 Mark Bavaro | .07 | .04 |

| | | | |
|---|---|---|---|
| 523 Brad Edwards | .05 | .02 |
| 524 Chad Hennings (R) | .25 | .15 |
| 525 Tony Paige | .05 | .02 |
| 526 Shawn Moore | .20 | .12 |
| 527 Sidney Johnson (R) | .08 | .05 |
| 528 Sanjay Beach (R) | .15 | .10 |
| 529 Kelvin Pritchett | .12 | .07 |
| 530 Jerry Holmes | .05 | .02 |
| 531 Al Del Greco | .05 | .02 |
| 532 Bob Gagliano | .10 | .06 |
| 533 Drew Hill | .08 | .05 |
| 534 Donald Frank (R) | .08 | .05 |
| 535 Pio Sagapolutele (R) | .08 | .05 |
| 536 Donald Hollas (R) | .20 | .12 |
| 537 Vernon Turner | .05 | .02 |
| 538 Bobby Humphrey | .10 | .06 |
| 539 Audray McMillen | .07 | .04 |
| 540 Gary Brown (R) | .08 | .05 |
| 541 Wesley Carroll | .15 | .10 |
| 542 Nate Newton | .05 | .02 |
| 543 Vai Sikahema | .05 | .02 |
| 544 Chris Chandler | .10 | .06 |
| 545 Nolan Harrison (R) | .10 | .06 |
| 546 Mark Green | .05 | .02 |
| 547 Rickey Watters | 1.25 | .80 |
| 548 J.J. Birden | .05 | .02 |
| 549 Cody Carlson | .30 | .18 |
| 550 Tim Green | .05 | .02 |
| 551 Mark Jackson | .08 | .05 |
| 552 Vince Buck | .05 | .02 |
| 553 George Jamison | .05 | .02 |
| 554 Anthony Pleasant | .05 | .02 |
| 555 Reggie Johnson | .05 | .02 |
| 556 John Jackson | .05 | .02 |
| 557 Ian Beckles | .05 | .02 |
| 558 Buford McGee | .05 | .02 |
| 559 Fraud Reveiz | .05 | .02 |
| 560 Joe Montana | .60 | .35 |
| 561 Phil Simms | .10 | .06 |
| 562 Greg McMurtry | .12 | .07 |
| 563 Gerald Williams | .05 | .02 |
| 564 Dave Cadigan | .05 | .02 |
| 565 Rufus Porter | .05 | .02 |
| 566 Jim Kelly | .50 | .30 |
| 567 Deion Sanders | .25 | .15 |
| 568 Mike Singletary | .12 | .07 |
| 569 Boomer Esiason | .12 | .07 |
| 570 Andre Reed | .15 | .10 |
| 571 James Washington | .05 | .02 |
| 572 Jack Del Rio | .05 | .02 |
| 573 Gerald Perry | .05 | .02 |
| 574 Vinnie Clark | .05 | .02 |
| 575 Mike Piel | .05 | .02 |
| 576 Michael Dean Perry | .10 | .06 |
| 577 Rickey Proel | .10 | .06 |
| 578 Leslie O'Neal | .07 | .04 |
| 579 Russell Maryland | .15 | .10 |

| | | |
|---|---|---|
| 580 Eric Dickerson | .25 | .15 |
| 581 Fred Strickland | .05 | .02 |
| 582 Nick Lowery | .07 | .04 |
| 583 Joe Milinichik (R) | .08 | .05 |
| 584 Mark Vlasic | .07 | .04 |
| 585 James Lofton | .15 | .10 |
| 586 Bruce Smith | .10 | .06 |
| 587 Harvey Williams | .25 | .15 |
| 588 Bernie Kosar | .12 | .07 |
| 589 Carl Banks | .07 | .04 |
| 590 Jeff George | .30 | .18 |
| 591 Fred Jones (R) | .12 | .07 |
| 592 Todd Scott | .05 | .02 |
| 593 Keith Jones | .05 | .02 |
| 594 Tootie Robbins | .05 | .02 |
| 595 Todd Philcox (R) | .30 | .18 |
| 596 Browning Nagle | .60 | .35 |
| 597 Troy Aikman | .75 | .45 |
| 598 Dan Marino | .40 | .25 |
| 599 Lawrence Taylor | .15 | .10 |
| 600 Webster Slaughter | .08 | .05 |
| 601 Aaron Cox | .05 | .02 |
| 602 Matt Stover | .05 | .02 |
| 603 Keith Sims | .05 | .02 |
| 604 Dennis Smith | .05 | .02 |
| 605 Kevin Porter | .05 | .02 |
| 606 Anthony Miller | .15 | .10 |
| 607 Ken O'Brien | .10 | .06 |
| 608 Randall Cunningham | .20 | .12 |
| 609 Timm Rosenbach | .12 | .07 |
| 610 Junior Seau | .12 | .07 |
| 611 Johnny Rembert | .05 | .02 |
| 612 Rick Tuten | .05 | .02 |
| 613 Willie Green | .15 | .10 |
| 614 Sean Salisbury (R) | .50 | .30 |
| 615 Martin Bayless | .05 | .02 |
| 616 Jerry Rice | .40 | .25 |
| 617 Randal Hill | .20 | .12 |
| 618 Dan McGwire | .30 | .18 |
| 619 Merrill Hoge | .07 | .04 |
| 620 Checklist | .05 | .02 |
| SP1 James Lofton (Yards) | 8.50 | 5.50 |
| SP2 Art Monk (TD's) | 10.00 | 7.00 |
| H19-Walter Payton (ea) | 4.50 | 2.75 |
| H27 (Football Heroes) | | |
| ___ Walter Payton Cover | 15.00 | 10.00 |
| H28-Dan Marino (ea) | 4.50 | 2.75 |
| H36 (Football Heroes) | | |
| ___ Dan Marino Cover | 15.00 | 10.00 |

# 1992 Upper Deck Gold

This 50-card set was produced in limited quantities and is identical to the regular Upper Deck set except for the gold hologram on the card back. The cards also carry a "G" prefix next to the card number. The set contains rookies and stars licensed by NFL Properties. The cards were distributed in foil packs identical to the regular issue. The odds of finding a pack of gold cards was 1 in 30. The cards measure 2-1/2" by 3-1/2".

|                    | MINT  | NR/MT |
|--------------------|-------|-------|
| Complete Set (50)  | 34.00 | 23.00 |
| Commons            | .35   | .20   |
|                    |       |       |
| G1 Steve Emtman (R)       | 3.00 | 1.75 |
| G2 Carl Pickens (R)       | 2.00 | 1.25 |
| G3 Dale Carter (R)        | 1.50 | .90  |
| G4 Greg Skrepenak (R)     | .40  | .25  |
| G5 Kevin Smith (R)        | .90  | .60  |
| G6 Marco Coleman (R)      | .75  | .45  |
| G7 David Klingler (R)     | 4.00 | 2.75 |
| G8 Phillippi Sparks (R)   | .50  | .30  |
| G9 Tommy Maddox (R)       | 3.00 | 2.00 |
| G10 Quinten Coryatt (R)   | 2.50 | 1.50 |
| G11 Ty Detmer             | .80  | .50  |
| G12 Vaughn Dunbar (R)     | 1.75 | 1.00 |
| G13 Ashley Ambrose (R)    | .75  | .45  |
| G14 Kurt Barber (R)       | .50  | .30  |
| G15 Chester McGlockton (R)| .50  | .30  |
| G16 Todd Collins (R)      | .75  | .45  |
| G17 Steve Israel (R)      | .40  | .25  |
| G18 Marquez Pope (R)      | .35  | .20  |
| G19 Alonzo Spellman (R)   | .75  | .45  |
| G20 Tracy Scroggins (R)   | .75  | .45  |
| G21 Jim Kelly             | 1.25 | .80  |
| G22 Troy Aikman           | 3.00 | 1.75 |
| G23 Randall Cunningham    | .80  | .50  |
| G24 Bernie Kosar          | .40  | .25  |
| G25 Dan Marino            | 2.00 | 1.25 |
| G26 Andre Reed            | .50  | .30  |
| G27 Deion Sanders         | .50  | .30  |
| G28 Randall Hill          | .60  | .35  |
| G29 Eric Dickerson        | .80  | .50  |
| G30 Jim Kelly             | 1.75 | 1.00 |
| G31 Bernie Kosar          | .50  | .30  |
| G32 Mike Singletary       | .40  | .25  |
| G33 Anthony Miller        | .50  | .30  |
| G34 Harvey Williams       | .75  | .45  |
| G35 Randall Cunningham    | 1.00 | .70  |
| G36 Joe Montana           | 1.75 | 1.00 |
| G37 Dan McGwire           | .70  | .40  |
| G38 Al Toon               | .35  | .20  |
| G39 Carl Banks            | .35  | .20  |
| G40 Troy Aikman           | 3.50 | 2.00 |
| G41 Junior Seau           | .80  | .50  |
| G42 Jeff George           | 1.25 | .80  |
| G43 Michael Dean Perry    | .60  | .35  |
| G44 Lawrence Taylor       | .75  | .45  |
| G45 Dan Marino            | 2.50 | 1.50 |
| G46 Jerry Rice            | 2.50 | 1.50 |
| G47 Boomer Esiason        | .40  | .25  |
| G48 Bruce Smith           | .50  | .30  |
| G49 Leslie O'Neal         | .35  | .20  |
| G50 Checklist             | .50  | .30  |

# 1992 Upper Deck Holograms Game Breakers

This 9-card hologram set features the top receivers in the NFL. The cards, which measure 2-1/2" by 3-1/2", were randomly distributed in Upper Deck foil packs.

|                   | MINT  | NR/MT |
|-------------------|-------|-------|
| Complete Set (9)  | 18.00 | 12.50 |
| Commons           | 1.75  | 1.00  |
|                   |       |       |
| GB1 Art Monk           | 3.00 | 1.75 |
| GB2 Drew Hill          | 1.75 | 1.00 |
| GB3 Haywood Jeffires   | 3.50 | 2.00 |
| GB4 Andre Rison        | 3.00 | 1.75 |
| GB5 Mark Clayton       | 2.50 | 1.50 |
| GB6 Jerry Rice         | 6.00 | 3.50 |
| GB7 Michael Haynes     | 3.00 | 1.75 |
| GB8 Andre Reed         | 3.00 | 1.75 |
| GB9 Michael Irvin      | 4.50 | 2.75 |

# 1992 Upper Deck Pro Bowl Inserts

The cards in this limited insert set were randomly distributed in Upper Deck's low series foil packs. The horizontal card fronts feature two players separated by a colorful rainbow with the words "Pro Bowl" printed on the rainbow. Cards measure 3-1/2" by 2-1/2".

|  | MINT | NR/MT |
|---|---|---|
| Complete Set (15) | 140.00 | 80.00 |
| Commons | 4.50 | 2.75 |
| | | |
| PB1 Haywood Jeffires/ Michael Irvin | 20.00 | 12.50 |
| PB2 Mark Clayton/ Gary Clark | 10.00 | 6.00 |
| PB3 Anthony Munoz/ Jim Lachey | 6.00 | 3.75 |
| PB4 Warren Moon/ Mark Rypien | 12.00 | 7.00 |
| PB5 Thurman Thomas/ Barry Sanders | 25.00 | 18.00 |
| PB6 Marion Butts/ Emmitt Smith | 28.00 | 20.00 |
| PB7 Greg Townsend/ Reggie White | 7.00 | 4.50 |
| PB8 Cornelius Bennett/ Seth Joyner | 6.00 | 3.75 |
| PB9 Derrick Thomas/ Pat Swilling | 10.00 | 6.50 |
| PB10 Darryl Talley/ Chris Spielman | 5.00 | 3.00 |
| PB11 Ronnie Lott/ Mark Carrier | 8.50 | 5.00 |
| PB12 Steve Atwater/ Shaun Gayle | 5.00 | 3.00 |
| PB13 Rod Woodson/ Darrell Green | 8.00 | 4.50 |
| PB14 Jeff Gossett/ Chip Lohmiller | 4.50 | 2.75 |
| PB15 Tim Brown/ Mel Gray | 5.00 | 3.00 |

# 1992 Upper Deck Fanimation

The cards in this 10-card insert set were randomly distributed in Upper Deck Series II foil packs. The cards depict some top NFL players as comic book heroes. Cards measure 2-1/2" by 3-1/2".

|  |  | MINT | NR/MT |
|---|---|---|---|
| Complete Set (10) | | 38.00 | 24.00 |
| Commons | | 3.00 | 1.75 |
| | | | |
| 1 | Jim Kelly | 6.00 | 3.75 |
| 2 | Dan Marino | 5.00 | 3.00 |
| 3 | Lawrence Taylor | 3.00 | 1.75 |
| 4 | Deion Sanders | 4.50 | 2.75 |
| 5 | Troy Aikman | 12.00 | 8.00 |
| 6 | Junior Seau | 3.00 | 1.75 |
| 7 | Mike SIngletary | 3.00 | 1.75 |
| 8 | Eric Dickerson | 5.00 | 3.00 |
| 9 | Jerry Rice | 8.00 | 5.00 |
| 10 | Checklist (Kelly, Marino) | 4.50 | 2.75 |

# 1992 Upper Deck Coaches Report

This 20-card insert set features full color action photos on the front with a "Coaches Report" logo printed in a shield in the top right corner of the card. The player's name and position are printed on a horizontal pencil directly beneath the photograph. The card backs carry a "CR" prefix on the number and feature an analysis of the player by former Steelers Head Coach Chuck Noll. The cards measure 2-1/2" by 3-1/2" and were distributed randomly only in Upper Deck Series II hobby packs.

| | | MINT | NR/MT |
|---|---|---|---|
| | Complete Set (20) | 60.00 | 35.00 |
| | Commons | 2.00 | 1.25 |
| | | | |
| 1 | Mike Pritchard | 3.50 | 2.00 |
| 2 | Will Furrer | 3.00 | 1.75 |
| 3 | Alfred Williams | 2.00 | 1.25 |
| 4 | Tommy Vardell | 5.00 | 3.00 |
| 5 | Brett Favre | 10.00 | 7.00 |
| 6 | Alvin Harper | 6.00 | 3.75 |
| 7 | Mike Croel | 3.00 | 1.75 |
| 8 | Herman Moore | 4.00 | 2.75 |
| 9 | Edgar Bennett | 3.50 | 2.00 |
| 10 | Todd Marinovich | 6.00 | 3.75 |
| 11 | Aeneas Williams | 2.00 | 1.25 |
| 12 | Ricky Watters | 10.00 | 7.00 |
| 13 | Amp Lee | 6.00 | 3.75 |
| 14 | Terrell Buckley | 5.00 | 3.00 |
| 15 | Tim Barnett | 4.00 | 2.75 |
| 16 | Nick Bell | 4.00 | 2.75 |
| 17 | Leonard Russell | 5.00 | 3.00 |
| 18 | Lawrence Dawsey | 3.50 | 2.00 |
| 19 | Robert Porcher | 2.00 | 1.25 |
| 20 | Checklist | 5.00 | 3.00 |

# WILD CARD

## 1991 Wild Card Draft Picks

This 160-card set is made up of mostly NFL draft prospects pictured in their college uniforms. Card fronts feature full color action shots framed by a thin orange line and a black border with numbers printed in the top and right border. A smal circle in the lower left corner contains the words "1st Edition. The player's name and position are printed in the lower right corner. The vertical card backs contain a small head shot, a brief biography and college stats. Limited edition "wild" cards were inserted randomly in the company's foil packs. These cards feature stripes in denominations of 5, 10, 20, 50, 100, and 1,000. The cards are redeemable for single cards of that player equal to the amount shown in the wild card stripe. The checklist below contains values for the regular Wild Card Set. The striped versions are valued at the regular book price times the amount on the stripe less 25%. All cards measure 2-1/2" by 3-1/2".

| | | MINT | NR/MT |
|---|---|---|---|
| | Complete Set (160) | 10.50 | 6.50 |
| | Commons | .05 | .02 |
| | | | |
| 1 | Wild Card (Lyght) | .40 | .25 |
| 2 | Kelvin Pritchett | .25 | .15 |
| 3 | Robert Young | .05 | .02 |

| # | Name | | | # | Name | | |
|---|------|---|---|---|------|---|---|
| 4 | Reggie Johnson | .05 | .02 | 62 | Mike Pritchard | .60 | .35 |
| 5 | Eric Turner | .25 | .15 | 63 | Craig Erickson | .30 | .18 |
| 6 | Pat Tyrance | .08 | .05 | 64 | Browning Nagle | .80 | .50 |
| 7 | Curvin Richards | .15 | .10 | 65 | Mike Dumas | .12 | .07 |
| 8 | Calvin Stephens | .07 | .04 | 66 | Andre Jones | .05 | .02 |
| 9 | Corey Miller | .05 | .02 | 67 | Herman Moore | .80 | .50 |
| 10 | Michael Jackson | .75 | .45 | 68 | Greg Lewis | .25 | .15 |
| 11 | Simmie Carter | .05 | .02 | 69 | James Goode | .05 | .02 |
| 12 | Roland Smith | .07 | .04 | 70 | Stan Thomas | .08 | .05 |
| 13 | Pat O'Hara | .15 | .10 | 71 | Jerome Henderson | .08 | .05 |
| 14 | Scott Conover | .05 | .02 | 72 | Doug Thomas | .05 | .02 |
| 15 | Wild Card (Maryland) | .75 | .45 | 73 | Tony Covington | .08 | .05 |
| 16 | Greg Amsler | .05 | .02 | 74 | Charles Mincy | .05 | .02 |
| 17 | Moe Gardner | .12 | .07 | 75 | Kanavis McGhee | .15 | .10 |
| 18 | Howard Griffith | .10 | .06 | 76 | Tom Backes | .05 | .02 |
| 19 | David Daniels | .05 | .02 | 77 | Fernandus Vinson | .05 | .02 |
| 20 | Henry Jones | .08 | .05 | 78 | Marcus Robertson | .05 | .02 |
| 21 | Don Davey | .05 | .02 | 79 | Eric Harmon | .05 | .02 |
| 22 | Wild Card (Ismail) | .80 | .50 | 80 | Rob Selby | .05 | .02 |
| 23 | Richie Andrews | .05 | .02 | 81 | Ed King | .10 | .06 |
| 24 | Shawn Moore | .25 | .15 | 82 | William Thomas | .05 | .02 |
| 25 | Anthony Moss | .07 | .04 | 83 | Mike Jones | .07 | .04 |
| 26 | Vince Moore | .05 | .02 | 84 | Paul Justin | .12 | .07 |
| 27 | Leroy Thompson | .10 | .06 | 85 | Robert Wilson | .20 | .12 |
| 28 | Darrick Brownlow | .12 | .07 | 86 | Jesse Campbell | .08 | .05 |
| 29 | Mel Agee | .10 | .06 | 87 | Hayward Haynes | .05 | .02 |
| 30 | Darryl Lewis | .15 | .10 | 88 | Mike Croel | .60 | .35 |
| 31 | Hyland Hickson | .05 | .02 | 89 | Jeff Graham | .40 | .25 |
| 32 | Leonard Russell | .80 | .50 | 90 | Vinnie Clark | .15 | .10 |
| 33 | Floyd Fields | .05 | .02 | 91 | Keith Cash | .10 | .06 |
| 34 | Esera Tuaolo | .08 | .05 | 92 | Tim Ryan | .08 | .05 |
| 35 | Todd Marinovich | 1.25 | .80 | 93 | Jarrod Bunch | .35 | .20 |
| 36 | Gary Wellman | .07 | .04 | 94 | Stanley Richard | .20 | .12 |
| 37 | Ricky Ervins | 1.50 | .90 | 95 | Alvin Harper | .70 | .40 |
| 38 | Pat Harlow | .08 | .05 | 96 | Bob Dahl | .07 | .04 |
| 39 | Mo Lewis | .10 | .06 | 97 | Mark Gunn | .05 | .02 |
| 40 | John Kasay | .05 | .02 | 98 | Frank Blevins | .05 | .02 |
| 41 | Phil Hansen | .08 | .05 | 99 | Harvey Williams | .60 | .35 |
| 42 | Kevin Donnalley | .05 | .02 | 100 | Dixon Edwards | .12 | .07 |
| 43 | Dexter Davis | .08 | .05 | 101 | Blake Miller | .05 | .02 |
| 44 | Vance Hammond | .05 | .02 | 102 | Bobby Wilson | .15 | .10 |
| 45 | Chris Gardocki | .10 | .06 | 103 | Chuck Webb | .15 | .10 |
| 46 | Bruce Pickens | .25 | .15 | 104 | Randal Hill | .50 | .30 |
| 47 | Ernie Mills | .12 | .07 | 105 | Shane Curry | .05 | .02 |
| 49 | Derek Russell | .15 | .10 | 106 | Barry Sanders | 1.25 | .80 |
| 50 | Chris Zorich | .12 | .07 | 107 | Richard Fain | .10 | .06 |
| 51 | Alfred Williams | .20 | .12 | 108 | Joe Garten | .07 | .04 |
| 52 | Jon Vaughn | .30 | .18 | 109 | Dean Dingman | .05 | .02 |
| 53 | Adrian Cooper | .10 | .06 | 110 | Mark Tucker | .05 | .02 |
| 54 | Eric Bieniemy | .20 | .12 | 111 | Dan McGwire | .70 | .40 |
| 55 | Robert Bailey | .05 | .02 | 112 | Paul Glonek | .05 | .02 |
| 56 | Ricky Watters | .80 | .50 | 113 | Tom Dohring | .05 | .02 |
| 57 | Mark Vander Poel | .08 | .05 | 114 | Joe Sims | .05 | .02 |
| 58 | James Joseph | .15 | .10 | 115 | Bryan Cox | .20 | .12 |
| 59 | Darren Lewis | .25 | .15 | 116 | Bobby Olive | .05 | .02 |
| 60 | Wesley Carroll | .40 | .25 | 117 | Blaise Bryant | .10 | .06 |
| 61 | Dave Key | .05 | .02 | 118 | Charles Johnson | .08 | .05 |

| 119 | Brett Favre | 1.50 | .90 |
| 120 | Luis Cristobal | .05 | .02 |
| 121 | Don Gibson | .05 | .02 |
| 122 | Scott Ross | .05 | .02 |
| 123 | Huey Richardson | .08 | .05 |
| 124 | Chris Smith | .10 | .06 |
| 125 | Duane Young | .05 | .02 |
| 126 | Eric Swann | .15 | .10 |
| 127 | Jeff Fite | .05 | .02 |
| 128 | Eugene Williams | .05 | .02 |
| 129 | Harlan Davis | .05 | .02 |
| 130 | James Bradley | .05 | .02 |
| 131 | Rob Carpenter | .20 | .12 |
| 132 | Dennis Ransom | .05 | .02 |
| 133 | Mike Arthur | .05 | .02 |
| 134 | Chuck Weatherspoon | .08 | .05 |
| 135 | Darrell Malone | .05 | .02 |
| 136 | George Thornton | .08 | .05 |
| 137 | Lamar McGriggs | .05 | .02 |
| 138 | Alex Johnson | .05 | .02 |
| 139 | Eric Moten | .05 | .02 |
| 140 | Joe Valerio | .07 | .04 |
| 141 | Jake Reed | .12 | .07 |
| 142 | Ernie Thompson | .07 | .04 |
| 143 | Roland Poles | .05 | .02 |
| 144 | Randy Bethel | .05 | .02 |
| 145 | Terry Bagsby | .05 | .02 |
| 146 | Tim James | .05 | .02 |
| 147 | Kenny Walker | .25 | .15 |
| 148 | Nolan Harrison | .07 | .04 |
| 149 | Keith Traylor | .12 | .07 |
| 150 | Mick Subis | .05 | .02 |
| 151 | Scott Zolak | .25 | .15 |
| 152 | Pio Sagapolutele | .10 | .06 |
| 153 | James Jones | .12 | .07 |
| 154 | Mike Sullivan | .05 | .02 |
| 155 | Joe Johnson | .05 | .02 |
| 156 | Todd Scott | .05 | .02 |
| 157 | Checklist 1 | .05 | .02 |
| 158 | Checklist 2 | .05 | .02 |
| 159 | Checklist 3 | .05 | .02 |
| 160 | Checklist 4 | .05 | .02 |

# 1991 Wild Card NFL

The cards in this 160-card set feature NFL players and are similar in design to the College Draft Pick edition. Card fronts feature full color action photos framed by black borders. Multi-colored numbers appear in the border at the top and right side. The player's name and position are printed in the bottom right corner while the words "NFL Prremier Edition" appear in a small football design in the lower left corner. The vertical card backs contain a small head shot along with the player's bio and stats. Limited edition striped or "wild cards" were randomly inserted throughout the company's foil packs. Those wild cards in denominations of 5, 10, 20, 50, 100 and 1,000 are redeemable for the player's regular card in an amount equal the number on the stripe. The checklist below contains values for the regular Wild Card Set. The striped versions are valued at regular book value times the amount on the stripe less 25%. A special Wild Card (#126) was redeemable for a limited 10-card NFL Experience subset that featured players from the Washington Redskins and Buffalo Bills. All cards measure 2-1/2" by 3-1/2".

| | | MINT | NR/MT |
|---|---|---|---|
| **Complete Set (160)** | | 12.00 | 7.50 |
| **Commons** | | .05 | .02 |
| | | | |
| 1 | Jeff George | .25 | .15 |
| 2 | Sean Jones | .05 | .02 |

| 3 | Duane Bickett | .05 | .02 |
|---|---|---|---|
| 4 | John Elway | .20 | .12 |
| 5 | Christian Okoye | .12 | .07 |
| 6 | Steve Atwater | .08 | .05 |
| 7 | Anthony Munoz | .08 | .05 |
| 8 | Dave Krieg | .10 | .06 |
| 9 | Nick Lowery | .07 | .04 |
| 10 | Albert Bentley | .05 | .02 |
| 11 | Mark Jackson | .07 | .04 |
| 12 | Jeff Bryant | .05 | .02 |
| 13 | Johnny Hector | .05 | .02 |
| 14 | John L. Williams | .07 | .04 |
| 15 | Jim Everett | .12 | .07 |
| 16 | Mark Duper | .07 | .04 |
| 17 | Drew Hill | .08 | .05 |
| 18 | Randall Hill (R) | .50 | .30 |
| 19 | Ernest Givins | .10 | .06 |
| 20 | Ken O'Brien | .10 | .06 |
| 21 | Blair Thomas | .20 | .12 |
| 22 | Derrick Thomas | .20 | .12 |
| 23 | Harvey Williams (R) | .50 | .30 |
| 24 | Simon Fletcher | .05 | .02 |
| 25 | Stephone Paige | .07 | .04 |
| 26 | Barry Word | .20 | .12 |
| 27 | Warren Moon | .20 | .12 |
| 28 | Derrick Fenner | .12 | .07 |
| 29 | Shane Conlan | .07 | .04 |
| 30 | Karl Mecklenburg | .07 | .04 |
| 31 | Gary Anderson | .05 | .02 |
| 32 | Sammie Smith | .10 | .06 |
| 33 | Steve DeBerg | .10 | .06 |
| 34 | Dan McGwire (R) | .60 | .35 |
| 35 | Roger Craig | .10 | .06 |
| 36 | Tom Tupa | .07 | .04 |
| 37 | Rod Woodson | .08 | .05 |
| 38 | Junior Seau | .20 | .12 |
| 39 | Bruce Pickens (R) | .20 | .12 |
| 40 | Greg Townsend | .05 | .02 |
| 41 | Gary Clark | .12 | .07 |
| 42 | Broderick Thomas | .08 | .05 |
| 43 | Charles Mann | .05 | .02 |
| 44 | Browning Nagle (R) | 1.00 | .70 |
| 45 | James Joseph (R) | .25 | .15 |
| 46 | Emmitt Smith | 1.75 | 1.00 |
| 47 | Cornelius Bennett | .08 | .05 |
| 48 | Maurice Hurst | .05 | .02 |
| 49 | Art Monk | .20 | .12 |
| 50 | Louis Lipps | .07 | .04 |
| 51 | Mark Rypien | .20 | .12 |
| 52 | Bubby Brister | .10 | .06 |
| 53 | John Stephens | .08 | .05 |
| 54 | Merril Hoge | .07 | .04 |
| 55 | Kevin Mack | .07 | .04 |
| 56 | Al Toon | .08 | .05 |
| 57 | Ronnie Lott | .10 | .06 |
| 58 | Eric Metcalf | .08 | .05 |
| 59 | Vinny Testaverde | .10 | .06 |

| 60 | Darrell Green | .10 | .06 |
|---|---|---|---|
| 61 | Randall Cunningham | .15 | .10 |
| 62 | Charles Haley | .07 | .04 |
| 63 | Mark Carrier (Chi) | .08 | .05 |
| 64 | Jim Harbaugh | .12 | .07 |
| 65 | Richard Dent | .07 | .04 |
| 66 | Stan Thomas (R) | .08 | .05 |
| 67 | Neal Anderson | .12 | .07 |
| 68 | Troy Aikman | 1.00 | .70 |
| 69 | Mike Pritchard (R) | .75 | .45 |
| 70 | Deion Sanders | .25 | .15 |
| 71 | Andre Rison | .20 | .12 |
| 72 | Keith Millard | .07 | .04 |
| 73 | Jerry Rice | .40 | .25 |
| 74 | Johnny Johnson | .15 | .10 |
| 75 | Tim McDonald | .05 | .02 |
| 76 | Leonard Russell (R) | .75 | .45 |
| 77 | Keith Jackson | .12 | .07 |
| 78 | Keith Byars | .07 | .04 |
| 79 | Ricky Proehl | .08 | .05 |
| 80 | Dexter Carter (R) | .08 | .05 |
| 81 | Alvin Harper (R) | .75 | .45 |
| 82 | Irving Fryar | .07 | .04 |
| 83 | Marion Butts | .12 | .07 |
| 84 | Alfred Williams (R) | .20 | .12 |
| 85 | Tim Rosenbach | .12 | .07 |
| 86 | Steve Young | .35 | .20 |
| 87 | Albert Lewis | .05 | .02 |
| 88 | Rodney Peete | .10 | .06 |
| 89 | Barry Sanders | 1.00 | .70 |
| 90 | Bennie Blades | .07 | .04 |
| 91 | Chris Spielman | .05 | .02 |
| 92 | John Friesz | .10 | .06 |
| 93 | Jerome Brown | .07 | .04 |
| 94 | Reggie White | .10 | .06 |
| 95 | Michael Irvin | .35 | .20 |
| 96 | Keith McCants | .08 | .05 |
| 97 | Vinnie Clark (R) | .12 | .07 |
| 98 | Louis Oliver | .07 | .04 |
| 99 | Mark Clayton | .12 | .07 |
| 100 | John Offerdahl | .07 | .04 |
| 101 | Michael Carter | .05 | .02 |
| 102 | John Taylor | .12 | .07 |
| 103 | William Perry | .07 | .04 |
| 104 | Gill Byrd | .05 | .02 |
| 105 | Burt Grossman | .05 | .02 |
| 106 | Herman Moore (R) | .75 | .45 |
| 107 | Howie Long | .07 | .04 |
| 108 | Bo Jackson | .25 | .15 |
| 109 | Kelvin Pritchett (R) | .20 | .12 |
| 110 | Jacob Green | .05 | .02 |
| 111 | Chris Doleman | .08 | .05 |
| 112 | Herschel Walker | .12 | .07 |
| 113 | Russell Maryland (R) | .35 | .20 |
| 114 | Anthony Carter | .08 | .05 |
| 115 | Joey Browner | .07 | .04 |
| 116 | Tony Mandarich | .05 | .02 |

| | | | |
|---|---|---|---|
| 117 | Don Majkowski | .10 | .06 |
| 118 | Ricky Ervins (R) | 1.00 | .70 |
| 119 | Sterling Sharpe | .20 | .12 |
| 120 | Tim Harris | .05 | .02 |
| 121 | Hugh Millen | .25 | .15 |
| 122 | Mike Rozier | .05 | .02 |
| 123 | Chris Miller | .25 | .15 |
| 124 | Morten Andersen | .07 | .04 |
| 125 | Neil O'Donnell (R) | 1.50 | .90 |
| 126 | Surprise Wild Card | 3.00 | 1.75 |
| 127 | Eddie Brown | .08 | .05 |
| 128 | James Francis | .08 | .05 |
| 129 | James Brooks | .07 | .04 |
| 130 | David Fulcher | .05 | .02 |
| 131 | Michael Jackson (R) | .50 | .30 |
| 132 | Clay Matthews | .05 | .02 |
| 133 | Scott Norwood | .05 | .02 |
| 134 | Wesley Carroll (R) | .25 | .15 |
| 135 | Thurman Thomas | .60 | .35 |
| 136 | Mark Ingram | .05 | .02 |
| 137 | Bobby Hebert | .12 | .07 |
| 138 | Bobby Wilson (R) | .12 | .07 |
| 139 | Craig Heyward | .07 | .04 |
| 140 | Dalton Hilliard | .08 | .05 |
| 141 | Jeff Hostetler | .15 | .10 |
| 142 | Dave Meggett | .15 | .10 |
| 143 | Cris Dishman (R) | .12 | .07 |
| 144 | Lawrence Taylor | .12 | .07 |
| 145 | Leonard Marshall | .05 | .02 |
| 146 | Pepper Johnson | .05 | .02 |
| 147 | Todd Marinovich (R) | 1.00 | .70 |
| 148 | Mike Croel (R) | .40 | .25 |
| 149 | Erik McMillan | .05 | .02 |
| 150 | Flipper Anderson | .08 | .05 |
| 151 | Cleveland Gary | .08 | .05 |
| 152 | Henry Ellard | .07 | .04 |
| 153 | Kevin Greene | .05 | .02 |
| 154 | Michael Cofer | .05 | .02 |
| 155 | Todd Lyght (R) | .20 | .12 |
| 156 | Bruce Smith | .08 | .05 |
| 157 | Checklist 1 | .05 | .02 |
| 158 | Checklist 2 | .05 | .02 |
| 159 | Checklist 3 | .05 | .02 |
| 160 | Checklist 4 | .05 | .02 |

# 1992 Wild Card NFL

This 460-card set was issued in two series (1-250) and (251-460). Card fronts feature full color action photos framed by multi-colored borders with numbers printed across the top and right borders. Card backs consist of a small head shot inside a football shaped design along with the player's personal data and stats. Limited inserts include Wild Card's striped subset containing denominations of 5, 10, 20, 50, 100 or 1,000 printed on the stripes. The checklist below contains values for the regular edition. The striped versions are valued at regular book value times the amount on the stripe less 25%. All cards meausre 2-1/2" by 3-1/2".

| | | MINT | NR/MT |
|---|---|---|---|
| Complete Set (460) | | 27.00 | 18.00 |
| Commons | | .05 | .02 |
| 1 | Surprise Card | 3.00 | 2.00 |
| 2 | Marcus Dupree | .07 | .04 |
| 3 | Jackie Slater | .07 | .04 |
| 4 | Robert Delpino | .07 | .04 |
| 5 | Jerry Gray | .05 | .02 |
| 6 | Jim Everett | .12 | .07 |
| 7 | Roman Phifer | .05 | .02 |
| 8 | Alvin Wright | .05 | .02 |
| 9 | Todd Lyght | .12 | .07 |
| 10 | Reggie White | .12 | .07 |
| 11 | Randal Hill | .15 | .10 |
| 12 | Keith Byars | .07 | .04 |
| 13 | Clyde Simmons | .07 | .04 |
| 14 | Keith Jackson | .15 | .10 |
| 15 | Seth Joyner | .07 | .04 |
| 16 | James Joseph | .10 | .06 |
| 17 | Eric Allen | .05 | .02 |
| 18 | Sammie Smith | .08 | .05 |

| # | Player | | |
|---|--------|------|------|
| 19 | Mark Clayton | .15 | .10 |
| 20 | Aaron Craver | .07 | .04 |
| 21 | Hugh Green | .05 | .02 |
| 22 | John Offerdahl | .07 | .04 |
| 23 | Jeff Cross | .05 | .02 |
| 24 | Ferrell Edmunds | .05 | .02 |
| 25 | Mark Duper | .08 | .05 |
| 26 | Ronnie Harmon | .07 | .04 |
| 27 | Derrick Walker | .07 | .04 |
| 28 | Gary Plummer | .05 | .02 |
| 29 | Rod Bernstine | .07 | .04 |
| 30 | Burt Grossman | .07 | .04 |
| 31 | Donnie Elder | .05 | .02 |
| 32 | John Friesz | .10 | .06 |
| 33 | Billy Ray Smith | .05 | .02 |
| 34 | Luis Sharpe | .05 | .02 |
| 35 | Aeneas Williams | .08 | .05 |
| 36 | Ken Harvey | .05 | .02 |
| 37 | Johnny Johnson | .15 | .10 |
| 38 | Eric Swann | .07 | .04 |
| 39 | Tom Tupa | .07 | .04 |
| 40 | Anthony Thompson | .08 | .05 |
| 41 | Broderick Thomas | .08 | .05 |
| 42 | Vinny Testaverde | .10 | .06 |
| 43 | Mark Carrier (TB) | .07 | .04 |
| 44 | Gary Anderson | .05 | .02 |
| 45 | Keith McCants | .07 | .04 |
| 46 | Reggie Cobb | .20 | .12 |
| 47 | Lawrence Dawsey | .15 | .10 |
| 48 | Kevin Murphy | .05 | .02 |
| 49 | Keith Woodside | .05 | .02 |
| 50 | Darrell Thompson | .08 | .05 |
| 51 | Vinnie Clark | .05 | .02 |
| 52 | Sterling Sharpe | .30 | .18 |
| 53 | Mike Tomczak | .08 | .05 |
| 54 | Don Majkowski | .12 | .07 |
| 55 | Tony Mandarich | .05 | .02 |
| 56 | Mark Murphy | .05 | .02 |
| 57 | Dexter McNabb (R) | .15 | .10 |
| 58 | Rick Fenney | .05 | .02 |
| 59 | Cris Carter | .15 | .10 |
| 60 | Wade Wilson | .07 | .04 |
| 61 | Mike Merriweather | .05 | .02 |
| 62 | Rich Gannon | .15 | .10 |
| 63 | Herschel Walker | .12 | .07 |
| 64 | Chris Doleman | .08 | .05 |
| 65 | Al Noga | .05 | .02 |
| 66 | Chris Mims (R) | .25 | .15 |
| 67 | Ed Cunningham (R) | .08 | .05 |
| 68 | Marcus Allen | .10 | .06 |
| 69 | Kevin Turner (R) | .15 | .10 |
| 70 | Howie Long | .07 | .04 |
| 71 | Tim Brown | .08 | .05 |
| 72 | Nick Bell | .25 | .15 |
| 73 | Todd Marinovich | .40 | .25 |
| 74 | Jay Schroeder | .10 | .06 |
| 75 | Mervyn Fernandez | .08 | .05 |
| 76 | Tony Smith | .08 | .05 |
| 77 | John Alt | .05 | .02 |
| 78 | Christian Okoye | .12 | .07 |
| 79 | Nick Lowery | .07 | .04 |
| 80 | Derrick Thomas | .20 | .12 |
| 81 | Bill Maas | .05 | .02 |
| 82 | Dino Hackett | .05 | .02 |
| 83 | Deron Cherry | .05 | .02 |
| 84 | Barry Word | .20 | .12 |
| 85 | Mike Mooney (R) | .08 | .05 |
| 86 | Cris Dishman | .07 | .04 |
| 87 | Bruce Matthews | .05 | .02 |
| 88 | Tony Jones | .05 | .02 |
| 89 | William Fuller | .05 | .02 |
| 90 | Ray Childress | .07 | .04 |
| 91 | Warren Moon | .20 | .12 |
| 92 | Lorenzo White | .15 | .10 |
| 93 | Joe Bowden (R) | .08 | .05 |
| 94 | Tom Rathman | .08 | .05 |
| 95 | Keith Henderson | .08 | .05 |
| 96 | Jesse Sapolu | .05 | .02 |
| 97 | Charles Haley | .07 | .04 |
| 98 | Steve Young | .35 | .20 |
| 99 | John Taylor | .15 | .10 |
| 100 | Tim Harris | .05 | .02 |
| 101 | Scott Davis | .05 | .02 |
| 102 | Steve Bono (R) | .40 | .25 |
| 103 | Mike Kenn | .05 | .02 |
| 104 | Mike Farr | .05 | .02 |
| 105 | Rodney Peete | .12 | .07 |
| 106 | Jerry Ball | .05 | .02 |
| 107 | Chris Spielman | .05 | .02 |
| 108 | Barry Sanders | .75 | .45 |
| 109 | Bennie Blades | .07 | .04 |
| 110 | Herman Moore | .25 | .15 |
| 111 | Erik Kramer | .15 | .10 |
| 112 | Vance Johnson | .08 | .05 |
| 113 | Mike Croel | .20 | .12 |
| 114 | Mark Jackson | .07 | .04 |
| 115 | Steve Atwater | .08 | .05 |
| 116 | Gaston Green | .15 | .10 |
| 117 | John Elway | .20 | .12 |
| 118 | Simon Fletcher | .05 | .02 |
| 119 | Karl Mecklenberg | .07 | .04 |
| 120 | Hart Lee Dykes | .07 | .04 |
| 121 | Jerome Henderson | .05 | .02 |
| 122 | Chris Singleton | .07 | .04 |
| 123 | Marv Cook | .08 | .05 |
| 124 | Leonard Russell | .35 | .20 |
| 125 | Hugh Millen | .15 | .10 |
| 126 | Pat Harlow | .05 | .02 |
| 127 | Andre Tippett | .07 | .04 |
| 128 | Bruce Armstrong | .05 | .02 |
| 129 | Gary Clark | .15 | .10 |
| 130 | Art Monk | .20 | .12 |
| 131 | Darrell Green | .10 | .06 |
| 132 | Wilbur Marshall | .07 | .04 |

| | | | |
|---|---|---|---|
| 133 | Jim Lachey | .07 | .04 |
| 134 | Ernest Byner | .07 | .04 |
| 135 | Chip Lohmiller | .05 | .02 |
| 136 | Mark Rypien | .20 | .12 |
| 137 | Ricky Sanders | .08 | .05 |
| 138 | Stan Thomas | .05 | .02 |
| 139 | Neal Anderson | .12 | .07 |
| 140 | Trace Armstrong | .05 | .02 |
| 141 | Kevin Butler | .05 | .02 |
| 142 | Mark Carrier (Chi) | .08 | .05 |
| 143 | Dennis Gentry | .05 | .02 |
| 144 | Jim Harbaugh | .12 | .07 |
| 145 | Richard Dent | .07 | .04 |
| 146 | Andre Rison | .20 | .12 |
| 147 | Bruce Pickens | .08 | .05 |
| 148 | Chris Hinton | .05 | .02 |
| 149 | Brian Jordan | .08 | .05 |
| 150 | Chris Miller | .20 | .12 |
| 151 | Moe Gardner | .07 | .04 |
| 152 | Bill Fralic | .05 | .02 |
| 153 | Michael Haynes | .20 | .12 |
| 154 | Mike Pritchard | .20 | .12 |
| 155 | Dean Biasucci | .05 | .02 |
| 156 | Clarence Verdin | .07 | .04 |
| 157 | Donnell Thompson | .05 | .02 |
| 158 | Duane Bickett | .05 | .02 |
| 159 | Jon Hand | .05 | .02 |
| 160 | Sam Graddy | .08 | .05 |
| 161 | Emmitt Smith | 1.75 | 1.00 |
| 162 | Michael Irvin | .35 | .20 |
| 163 | Danny Noonan | .05 | .02 |
| 164 | Jack Del Rio | .05 | .02 |
| 165 | Jim Jeffcoat | .05 | .02 |
| 166 | Alexander Wright | .08 | .05 |
| 167 | Frank Minnifield | .05 | .02 |
| 168 | Ed King | .05 | .02 |
| 169 | Reggie Langhorne | .05 | .02 |
| 170 | Mike Baab | .05 | .02 |
| 171 | Eric Metcalf | .10 | .06 |
| 172 | Clay Matthews | .05 | .02 |
| 173 | Kevin Mack | .07 | .04 |
| 174 | Mike Johnson | .05 | .02 |
| 175 | Jeff Lageman | .07 | .04 |
| 176 | Freeman McNeil | .07 | .04 |
| 177 | Eric McMillian | .05 | .02 |
| 178 | James Hasty | .05 | .02 |
| 179 | Klye Clifton | .05 | .02 |
| 180 | Joe Kelly | .05 | .02 |
| 181 | Phil Simms | .10 | .06 |
| 182 | Everson Walls | .05 | .02 |
| 183 | Jeff Hostetler | .15 | .10 |
| 184 | Dave Meggett | .08 | .05 |
| 185 | Matt Bahr | .05 | .02 |
| 186 | Mark Ingram | .05 | .02 |
| 187 | Rodney Hampton | .35 | .20 |
| 188 | Kanavis McGee | .07 | .04 |
| 189 | Tim McGee | .07 | .04 |
| 190 | Eddie Brown | .08 | .05 |
| 191 | Rodney Holman | .05 | .02 |
| 192 | Harold Green | .25 | .15 |
| 193 | James Francis | .08 | .05 |
| 194 | Anthony Munoz | .10 | .06 |
| 195 | David Fulcher | .05 | .02 |
| 196 | Tim Krumrie | .05 | .02 |
| 197 | Bubby Brister | .10 | .06 |
| 198 | Rod Woodson | .10 | .06 |
| 199 | Louis Lipps | .07 | .04 |
| 200 | Carnell Lake | .05 | .02 |
| 201 | Don Beebe | .08 | .05 |
| 202 | Thurman Thomas | .60 | .35 |
| 203 | Cornelius Bennett | .10 | .06 |
| 204 | Mark Kelso | .05 | .02 |
| 205 | James Lofton | .15 | .10 |
| 206 | Darryl Talley | .07 | .04 |
| 207 | Morten Anderson | .07 | .04 |
| 208 | Vince Buck | .05 | .02 |
| 209 | Wesley Carroll | .15 | .10 |
| 210 | Bobby Hebert | .12 | .07 |
| 211 | Craig Heyward | .07 | .04 |
| 212 | Dalton Hilliard | .08 | .05 |
| 213 | Rickey Jackson | .07 | .04 |
| 214 | Eric Martin | .08 | .05 |
| 215 | Pat Swilling | .12 | .07 |
| 216 | Steve Walsh | .10 | .06 |
| 217 | Torrance Small (R) | .08 | .05 |
| 218 | Jacob Green | .05 | .02 |
| 219 | Cortez Kennedy | .15 | .10 |
| 220 | John L. Williams | .07 | .04 |
| 221 | Terry Wooden | .05 | .02 |
| 222 | Grant Feasel | .05 | .02 |
| 223 | Siran Stacey (R) | .20 | .12 |
| 224 | Chris Hakel (R) | .15 | .10 |
| 225 | Todd Harrison (R) | .10 | .06 |
| 226 | Bob Whitfield (R) | .08 | .05 |
| 227 | Eddie Blake (R) | .12 | .07 |
| 228 | Keith Hamilton (R) | .12 | .07 |
| 229 | Darryl Williams (R) | .20 | .12 |
| 230 | Ricardo McDonald (R) | .12 | .07 |
| 231 | Alan Haller (R) | .08 | .05 |
| 232 | Leon Searcy (R) | .10 | .06 |
| 233 | Patrick Rowe (R) | .25 | .15 |
| 234 | Edgar Bennett (R) | .30 | .18 |
| 235 | Terrell Buckley (R) | .60 | .35 |
| 236 | Will Furrer (R) | .20 | .12 |
| 237 | Amp Lee (R) | .75 | .45 |
| 238 | Jimmy Smith (R) | .12 | .07 |
| 239 | Tommy Vardell (R) | .70 | .40 |
| 240 | Leonard Russell (ROY) | .25 | .15 |
| 241 | Mike Croel (ROY) | .15 | .10 |
| 242 | Warren Moon (LL) | .12 | .07 |
| 243 | Mark Rypien (LL) | .12 | .07 |
| 244 | Thurman Thomas (LL) | .25 | .15 |
| 245 | Emmitt Smith (LL) | .80 | .50 |
| 246 | Checklist | .05 | .02 |

| | | | |
|---|---|---|---|
| 247 Checklist | .05 | .02 |
| 248 Checklist | .05 | .02 |
| 249 Checklist | .05 | .02 |
| 250 Checklist | .05 | .02 |
| 251 Surprise Card | 2.00 | 1.25 |
| 252 Erric Pegram | .08 | .05 |
| 253 Anthony Carter | .08 | .05 |
| 254 Roger Craig | .08 | .05 |
| 255 Hassan Jones | .08 | .05 |
| 256 Steve Jordan | .05 | .02 |
| 257 Randall McDaniel | .05 | .02 |
| 258 Henry Thomas | .05 | .02 |
| 259 Carl Lee | .05 | .02 |
| 260 Ray Agnew | .05 | .02 |
| 261 Irving Fryar | .07 | .04 |
| 262 Tom Waddle | .15 | .10 |
| 263 Greg McMurtry | .15 | .10 |
| 264 Stephen Baker | .05 | .02 |
| 265 Mark Collins | .05 | .02 |
| 266 Howard Cross | .05 | .02 |
| 267 Pepper Johnson | .05 | .02 |
| 268 Fred Barnett | .15 | .10 |
| 269 Heath Sherman | .08 | .05 |
| 270 William Thomas | .05 | .02 |
| 271 Bill Bates | .05 | .02 |
| 272 Issiac Holt | .05 | .02 |
| 273 Emmitt Smith | 1.75 | 1.00 |
| 274 Eric Bieniemy | .10 | .06 |
| 275 Marion Butts | .10 | .06 |
| 276 Gill Byrd | .05 | .02 |
| 277 Robert Blackmon | .05 | .02 |
| 278 Brian Blades | .07 | .04 |
| 279 Joe Nash | .05 | .02 |
| 280 Bill Brooks | .05 | .02 |
| 281 Mel Gray | .05 | .02 |
| 282 Andre Ware | .15 | .10 |
| 283 Steve McMichael | .07 | .04 |
| 284 Brad Muster | .08 | .05 |
| 285 Ron Rivera | .05 | .02 |
| 286 Chris Zorich | .07 | .04 |
| 287 Chris Burkett | .05 | .02 |
| 288 Irv Eatman | .05 | .02 |
| 289 Rob Moore | .20 | .12 |
| 290 Joe Mott | .05 | .02 |
| 291 Brian Washington | .05 | .02 |
| 292 Michael Carter | .05 | .02 |
| 293 Dexter Carter | .10 | .06 |
| 294 Don Griffin | .05 | .02 |
| 295 John Taylor | .15 | .10 |
| 296 Ted Washington | .07 | .04 |
| 297 Monte Coleman | .05 | .02 |
| 298 Andre Collins | .07 | .04 |
| 299 Charles Mann | .05 | .02 |
| 300 Shane Conlon | .07 | .04 |
| 301 Keith McKeller | .07 | .04 |
| 302 Nate Odomes | .05 | .02 |
| 303 Riki Ellison | .05 | .02 |

| | | | |
|---|---|---|---|
| 304 Willie Gault | .07 | .04 |
| 305 Bob Golic | .05 | .02 |
| 306 Ethan Horton | .07 | .04 |
| 307 Ronnie Lott | .10 | .06 |
| 308 Don Mosebar | .05 | .02 |
| 309 Aaron Wallace | .07 | .04 |
| 310 Wymon Henderson | .05 | .02 |
| 311 Vance Johnson | .08 | .05 |
| 312 Ken Lanier | .05 | .02 |
| 313 Steve Sewell | .05 | .02 |
| 314 Dennis Smith | .05 | .02 |
| 315 Kenny Walker | .10 | .06 |
| 316 Chris Martin | .05 | .02 |
| 317 Albert Lewis | .05 | .02 |
| 318 Todd McNair | .05 | .02 |
| 319 Tracy Simien (R) | .10 | .06 |
| 320 Percy Snow | .07 | .04 |
| 321 Mark Rypien | .20 | .12 |
| 322 Bryan Hinkle | .05 | .02 |
| 323 David Little | .05 | .02 |
| 324 Dwight Stone | .05 | .02 |
| 325 Van Waiters (R) | .08 | .05 |
| 326 Pio Sagapolutele (R) | .08 | .05 |
| 327 Michael Jackson | .15 | .10 |
| 328 Vestee Jackson | .05 | .02 |
| 329 Tony Paige | .05 | .02 |
| 330 Reggie Roby | .05 | .02 |
| 331 Haywood Jeffires | .20 | .12 |
| 332 Lamar Lathon | .07 | .04 |
| 333 Bubba McDowell | .05 | .02 |
| 334 Doug Smith | .05 | .02 |
| 335 Dean Steinkuhler | .05 | .02 |
| 336 Jessie Tuggle | .05 | .02 |
| 337 Freddie Joe Nunn | .05 | .02 |
| 338 Pat Terrell | .05 | .02 |
| 339 Tom McHale (R) | .08 | .05 |
| 340 Sam Mills | .07 | .04 |
| 341 John Tice | .05 | .02 |
| 342 Brent Jones | .07 | .04 |
| 343 Robert Porcher (R) | .15 | .10 |
| 344 Mark D'Onofrio (R) | .12 | .07 |
| 345 David Tate | .05 | .02 |
| 346 Courtney Hawkins (R) | .25 | .15 |
| 347 Ricky Watters | .80 | .50 |
| 348 Amp Lee | .25 | .15 |
| 349 Steve Young | .25 | .15 |
| 350 Natu Tuatagaloa (R) | .08 | .05 |
| 351 Alfred Williams | .08 | .05 |
| 352 Derek Brown (R) | .25 | .15 |
| 353 Marco Coleman (R) | .30 | .18 |
| 354 Tommy Maddox (R) | 1.25 | .80 |
| 355 Siran Stacy | .15 | .10 |
| 356 Greg Lewis | .12 | .07 |
| 357 Paul Gruber | .05 | .02 |
| 358 Troy Vincent (R) | .20 | .12 |
| 359 Robert Wilson | .07 | .04 |
| 360 Jessie Hester | .05 | .02 |

| | | | |
|---|---|---|---|
| 361 | Shaun Gayle | .05 | .02 |
| 362 | Deron Cherry | .05 | .02 |
| 363 | Wendell Davis | .10 | .06 |
| 364 | David Klingler (R) | 1.50 | .90 |
| 365 | Jason Hanson (R) | .08 | .05 |
| 366 | Marquez Pope (R) | .10 | .06 |
| 367 | Robert Williams (R) | .08 | .05 |
| 368 | Kelvin Pritchett | .10 | .06 |
| 369 | Dana Hall (R) | .20 | .12 |
| 370 | David Brandon (R) | .12 | .07 |
| 371 | Tim McKyer | .05 | .02 |
| 372 | Darion Conner | .05 | .02 |
| 373 | Derrick Fenner | .10 | .06 |
| 374 | Hugh Millen | .10 | .06 |
| 375 | Bill Jones (R) | .08 | .05 |
| 376 | J.J. Birden | .05 | .02 |
| 377 | Ty Detmer | .20 | .12 |
| 378 | Alonzo Spellman | .20 | .12 |
| 379 | Sammie Smith | .08 | .05 |
| 380 | Al Smith | .05 | .02 |
| 381 | Louis Clark (R) | .08 | .05 |
| 382 | Vernice Smith (R) | .08 | .05 |
| 383 | Tony Martin | .05 | .02 |
| 384 | Willie Green | .15 | .10 |
| 385 | Sean Gilbert (R) | .25 | .15 |
| 386 | Eugene Chung (R) | .08 | .05 |
| 387 | Toi Cook | .05 | .02 |
| 388 | Brett Maxie | .05 | .02 |
| 389 | Steve Israel (R) | .12 | .07 |
| 390 | Mike Mularkey | .05 | .02 |
| 391 | Barry Foster | 1.00 | .70 |
| 392 | Hardy Nickerson | .05 | .02 |
| 393 | Johnny Mitchell (R) | .25 | .15 |
| 394 | Thurman Thomas | .50 | .30 |
| 395 | Tony Smith (R) | .75 | .45 |
| 396 | Keith Goganious | .05 | .02 |
| 397 | Matt Darby (R) | .08 | .05 |
| 398 | Nate Turner (R) | .10 | .06 |
| 399 | Keith Jennings (R) | .10 | .06 |
| 400 | Mitchell Benson (R) | .10 | .06 |
| 401 | Kurt Barber (R) | .12 | .07 |
| 402 | Tony Sacca (R) | .25 | .15 |
| 403 | Steve Hendrickson (R) | .10 | .06 |
| 404 | Johnny Johnson | .15 | .10 |
| 405 | Lorenzo Lynch | .05 | .02 |
| 406 | Luis Sharpe | .05 | .02 |
| 407 | Jim Everett | .15 | .10 |
| 408 | Neal Anderson | .12 | .07 |
| 409 | Ashley Ambrose (R) | .20 | .12 |
| 410 | George Williams (R) | .08 | .05 |
| 411 | Clarence Kay | .05 | .02 |
| 412 | Dave Krieg | .10 | .06 |
| 413 | Terrell Buckley | .30 | .18 |
| 414 | Ricardo McDonald | .08 | .05 |
| 415 | Kelly Stouffer | .12 | .07 |
| 416 | Barney Bussey | .05 | .02 |
| 417 | Ray Roberts (R) | .08 | .05 |
| 418 | Fred McAfee (R) | .25 | .15 |
| 419 | Fred Banks | .05 | .02 |
| 420 | Tim McDonald | .05 | .02 |
| 421 | Darryl Williams | .10 | .06 |
| 422 | Bobby Abrams (R) | .08 | .05 |
| 423 | Tommy Vardell | .30 | .18 |
| 424 | William White | .05 | .02 |
| 425 | Billy Ray Smith | .05 | .02 |
| 426 | Lemuel Stinson | .05 | .02 |
| 427 | Brad Johnson (R) | .12 | .07 |
| 428 | Herschel Walker | .12 | .07 |
| 429 | Eric Thomas | .05 | .02 |
| 430 | Anthony Thompson | .08 | .05 |
| 431 | Ed West | .05 | .02 |
| 432 | Edgar Bennett | .15 | .10 |
| 433 | Warren Powers | .05 | .02 |
| 434 | Byron Evans | .05 | .02 |
| 435 | Rodney Culver (R) | .15 | .10 |
| 436 | Ray Horton | .05 | .02 |
| 437 | Richmond Webb | .07 | .04 |
| 438 | Mark McMillian (R) | .08 | .05 |
| 439 | Checklist | .05 | .02 |
| 440 | Lawrence Pete (R) | .08 | .05 |
| 441 | Rodney Smith (R) | .10 | .06 |
| 442 | Mark Rodenhauser (R) | .08 | .05 |
| 443 | Scott Lockwood (R) | .10 | .06 |
| 444 | Charles Davenport (R) | .20 | .12 |
| 445 | Terry McDaniel | .05 | .02 |
| 446 | Darren Perry (R) | .12 | .07 |
| 447 | Darrick Owens (R) | .10 | .06 |
| 448 | Alvin Wright | .05 | .02 |
| 449 | Frank Stams | .05 | .02 |
| 450 | Santana Dotson (R) | .35 | .20 |
| 451 | Mark Carrier | .08 | .05 |
| 452 | Kevin Murphy | .05 | .02 |
| 453 | Jeff Bryant | .05 | .02 |
| 454 | Eric Allen | .05 | .02 |
| 455 | Brian Bollinger (R) | .08 | .05 |
| 456 | Elston Ridgle (R) | .08 | .05 |
| 457 | Jim Riggs (R) | .08 | .05 |
| 458 | Checklist | .05 | .02 |
| 459 | Checklist | .05 | .02 |
| 460 | Checklist | .05 | .02 |

# 1992 Wild Card Field Force

| | | MINT | NR/MT |
|---|---|---|---|
| | | | |

The cards in this 30-card subset were randomly distributed in Wild Card Series II foil boxes. Each box contain approximately six Field Force cards. The card fronts feature full color action photos with a small Field Force logo in the lower left corner. The player's name and position are located in the lower right corner. The subset also contains limited silver and gold stamped versions of the cards. The checklist below includes values for the regular subset. The silver version is valued at 2 times the regular book value below. The gold version is valued at 5 times the regular book value. All cards measure 2-1/2" by 3-1/2"

| | | MINT | NR/MT |
|---|---|---|---|
| Complete Set (30) | | 32.00 | 20.00 |
| Commons | | .75 | .45 |
| 1 | Joe Montana | 3.50 | 2.50 |
| 2 | Quentin Coryatt | 2.00 | 1.25 |
| 3 | Tommy Vardell | 2.00 | 1.25 |
| 4 | Jim Kelly | 2.50 | 1.50 |
| 5 | John Elway | 2.00 | 1.25 |
| 6 | Ricky Watters | 5.00 | 3.00 |
| 7 | Vinny Testaverde | .75 | .45 |
| 8 | Randal Hill | 1.25 | .80 |
| 9 | Amp Lee | 3.00 | 2.00 |
| 10 | Vaughn Dunbar | 2.50 | 1.50 |
| 11 | Troy Aikman | 5.00 | 3.00 |
| 12 | Deion Sanders | 1.50 | .90 |
| 13 | Rodney Hampton | 2.50 | 1.50 |
| 14 | Brett Favre | 7.00 | 4.50 |
| 15 | Warren Moon | 2.00 | 1.25 |
| 16 | Browning Nagle | 2.50 | 1.50 |
| 17 | Terrell Buckley | 1.75 | 1.00 |
| 18 | Barry Sanders | 4.50 | 3.00 |
| 19 | Dan Marino | 3.50 | 2.50 |
| 20 | Carl Pickens | 2.00 | 1.25 |
| 21 | Herschel Walker | 1.00 | .70 |
| 22 | Ronnie Lott | 1.25 | .80 |
| 23 | Steve Emtman | 3.00 | 2.00 |
| 24 | Mark Rypien | 1.50 | .90 |
| 25 | Bobby Hebert | .75 | .45 |
| 26 | Dan McGwire | 1.25 | .80 |
| 27 | Neil O'Donnell | 2.00 | 1.25 |
| 28 | Cris Carter | 1.00 | .70 |
| 29 | Randall Cunningham | 1.75 | 1.00 |
| 30 | Jerry Rice | 4.00 | 2.75 |

# 1992 Wild Card Stat Smashers

This 52-card subset was randomly distributed in Wild Card Series II foil boxes and Jumbo Packs. The cards are embossed on a foil stock giving them a a 3-D effect. The fronts feature full color action shots with a Stat Smashers logo in the top right corner. The player's name, team and position appear in small horizontal stripes across the bottom of the card. The striped versions are valued at regular book value times the pvalue of the stripe less 25%. Card numbers contain the prefix SS and the cards measure 2-1/2" by 3-1/2".

| | MINT | NR/MT |
|---|---|---|
| Complete Set (52) | 110.00 | 65.00 |
| Commons (1-16) | 3.50 | 2.00 |
| Commons (17-52) | .80 | .50 |

| | | | |
|---|---|---|---|
| SS1 | Barry Sanders | 10.00 | 6.00 |
| SS2 | Leonard Russell | 3.50 | 2.00 |
| SS3 | Thurman Thomas | 8.00 | 5.00 |
| SS4 | John Elway | 3.50 | 2.00 |
| SS5 | Steve Young | 6.00 | 3.75 |
| SS6 | Warren Moon | 3.50 | 2.00 |
| SS7 | Terrell Buckley | 3.50 | 2.00 |
| SS8 | Randall Cunningham | 3.50 | 2.00 |
| SS9 | Steve Emtman | 6.00 | 3.75 |
| SS10 | Dan Marino | 7.50 | 4.50 |
| SS11 | Joe Montana | 7.50 | 4.50 |
| SS12 | Carl Pickens | 5.00 | 3.00 |
| SS13 | Jerry Rice | 8.00 | 5.00 |
| SS14 | Deion Sanders | 3.50 | 2.00 |
| SS15 | Tommy Vardell | 4.50 | 2.75 |
| SS16 | Ricky Watters | 10.00 | 6.00 |
| SS17 | Troy Aikman | 8.50 | 5.50 |
| SS18 | Dale Carter | 1.75 | 1.00 |
| SS19 | Quentin Coryatt | 2.50 | 1.50 |
| SS20 | Vaughn Dunbar | 2.50 | 1.50 |
| SS21 | Mark Duper | .80 | .50 |
| SS22 | Eric Metcalf | 1.00 | .70 |
| SS23 | Brett Favre | 4.50 | 2.75 |
| SS24 | Barry Foster | 4.00 | 2.50 |
| SS25 | Jeff George | 1.75 | 1.00 |
| SS26 | Sean Gilbert | 1.25 | .80 |
| SS27 | Jim Harbaugh | 1.00 | .70 |
| SS28 | Courtney Hawkins | 1.75 | 1.00 |
| SS29 | Charles Haley | .80 | .50 |
| SS30 | Bobby Hebert | 1.00 | .70 |
| SS31 | Stan Humphries | 2.50 | 1.50 |
| SS32 | Michael Irvin | 3.50 | 2.00 |
| SS33 | Jim Kelly | 3.50 | 2.00 |
| SS34 | David Klingler | 5.00 | 3.00 |
| SS35 | Ronnie Lott | 1.75 | 1.00 |
| SS36 | Tommy Maddux | 3.50 | 2.00 |
| SS37 | Todd Marinovich | 1.75 | 1.00 |
| SS38 | Hugh Millen | .80 | .50 |
| SS39 | Art Monk | 2.00 | 1.25 |
| SS40 | Browning Nagle | 2.00 | 1.25 |
| SS41 | Neil O'Donnell | 2.50 | 1.50 |
| SS42 | Tom Rathman | .80 | .50 |
| SS43 | Andre Rison | 1.75 | 1.00 |
| SS44 | Mike Singletary | 1.50 | .90 |
| SS45 | Tony Smith | 1.50 | .90 |
| SS46 | Emmitt Smith | 12.00 | 8.00 |
| SS47 | Pete Stoyanovich | .80 | .50 |
| SS48 | John Taylor | 1.25 | .80 |
| SS49 | Troy Vincent | 1.25 | .80 |
| SS50 | Herschel Walker | 1.00 | .70 |
| SS51 | Lorenzo White | 1.25 | .80 |
| SS52 | Rodney Culver | 1.25 | .80 |

# 1992 Wild Card Red Hot Rookies

The cards in this limited 30-card subset were packed randomly in Wild Card's Series I and Series II foil packs. Card fronts feature full color action photos surrounded by multi-colored borders with numbers printed inside the borders. A Red Hot Rookie logo appears in a football in the lower left corner. The player's name and position are located in the lower right corner. Striped versions are valued at the regular book value below times the amount on the stripe less 25%. All cards measure 2-1/2" by 3-1/2".

| | | MINT | NR/MT |
|---|---|---|---|
| Complete Set (30) | | 40.00 | 25.00 |
| Commons | | .80 | .50 |
| | | | |
| 1 | Darryl Williams | 1.25 | .80 |
| 2 | Amp Lee | 4.00 | 2.50 |
| 3 | Will Furrer | 3.00 | 2.00 |
| 4 | Edgar Bennett | 3.00 | 2.00 |
| 5 | Terrell Buckley | 3.50 | 2.25 |
| 6 | Bob Whitfield | .80 | .50 |
| 7 | Siran Stacy | 2.00 | 1.25 |
| 8 | Jimmy Smith | 1.25 | .80 |
| 9 | Kevin Turner | .80 | .50 |
| 10 | Tommy Vardell | 4.50 | 2.75 |
| 11 | Surprise Card | 3.00 | 2.00 |
| 12 | Derek Brown | 2.50 | 1.50 |
| 13 | Marco Coleman | 3.00 | 2.00 |
| 14 | Quentin Coryatt | 4.50 | 2.75 |
| 15 | Rodney Culver | 2.00 | 1.25 |
| 16 | Ty Detmer | 3.00 | 2.00 |
| 17 | Vaughn Dunbar | 4.50 | 2.75 |
| 18 | Steve Emtman | 5.00 | 3.00 |
| 19 | Sean Gilbert | 1.25 | .80 |

| 20 | Courtney Hawkins | 2.50 | 1.50 |
|----|------------------|------|------|
| 21 | David Klingler | 6.00 | 3.75 |
| 22 | Amp Lee | 3.00 | 2.00 |
| 23 | Tommy Maddox | 4.50 | 2.75 |
| 24 | Johnny Mitchell | 2.50 | 1.50 |
| 25 | Darren Perry | .80 | .50 |
| 26 | Carl Pickens | 4.00 | 2.50 |
| 27 | Robert Porcher | 1.00 | .70 |
| 28 | Tony Smith | 2.50 | 1.50 |
| 29 | Alonzo Spellman | 1.50 | .90 |
| 30 | Troy Vincent | 2.50 | 1.50 |

| 15 | Harold Green | 2.00 | 1.25 |
|----|--------------|------|------|
| 16 | Gaston Green | 1.25 | .80 |
| 17 | Rodney Hampton | 3.00 | 1.75 |
| 18 | Mark Higgs | 2.00 | 1.25 |
| 19 | Dalton Hilliard | 1.25 | .80 |
| 20 | Bobby Humphries | 1.25 | .80 |
| 21 | Amp Lee | 2.50 | 1.50 |
| 22 | Kevin Mack | 1.25 | .80 |
| 23 | Eric Metcalf | 1.50 | .90 |
| 24 | Brad Muster | 1.25 | .80 |
| 25 | Christian Okoye | 1.50 | .90 |
| 26 | Tom Rathman | 1.25 | .80 |
| 27 | Leonard Russell | 2.50 | 1.50 |
| 28 | Barry Sanders | 8.50 | 5.50 |
| 29 | Heath Sherman | 1.25 | .80 |
| 30 | Emmitt Smith | 12.00 | 8.00 |
| 31 | Blair Thomas | 1.50 | .90 |
| 32 | Thurman Thomas | 6.50 | 3.75 |
| 33 | Tommy Vardell | 2.50 | 1.50 |
| 34 | Herschel Walker | 1.75 | 1.00 |
| 35 | Chris Warren | 1.25 | .80 |
| 36 | Ricky Watters | 6.50 | 3.75 |
| 37 | Lorenzo White | 1.50 | .90 |
| 38 | John L. Williams | 1.25 | .80 |
| 39 | Barry Word | 2.00 | 1.25 |
| 40 | Vince Workman | 1.50 | .90 |

# 1992 Wild Card Running Wild Gold

The cards in this 40-card insert set were randomly distributed in Wild Card Jumbo Packs. Gold and silver versions of each card were issued. The silver versions are valued at half the book price for the gold set listed below. Striped versions are valued at regular book value times the amount on the stripe less 25%. All cards measure 2-1/2" by 3-1/2".

| | MINT | NR/MT |
|--|------|-------|
| Complete Set Gold (40) | 75.00 | 50.00 |
| Commons (Gold) | 1.25 | .80 |
| Complete Set Silver(40) | 38.00 | 22.00 |
| Commons (Silver) | .70 | .40 |

| 1 | Terry Allen | 5.00 | 3.00 |
|---|-------------|------|------|
| 2 | Neal Anderson | 1.75 | 1.00 |
| 3 | Eric Ball | 1.25 | .80 |
| 4 | Nick Bell | 2.00 | 1.25 |
| 5 | Edgar Bennett | 1.75 | 1.00 |
| 6 | Rod Bernstine | 1.25 | .80 |
| 7 | Marion Butts | 1.50 | .90 |
| 8 | Keith Byars | 1.25 | .80 |
| 9 | Earnest Byner | 1.25 | .80 |
| 10 | Reggie Cobb | 1.75 | 1.00 |
| 11 | Roger Craig | 1.25 | .80 |
| 12 | Rodney Culver | 1.25 | .80 |
| 13 | Barry Foster | 6.50 | 3.75 |
| 14 | Cleveland Gary | 1.25 | .80 |